$$F = \frac{9}{5}C + 32$$

$$c = \frac{5}{9}(F - 32)$$

$$k = c + 273°$$

Modern

College

Physics

———————————————————————

Nuclear Ramjet Engine "TORY II A," developed under Project Pluto by the University of California's Lawrence Radiation Laboratory. This is an experimental nuclear reactor designed for the propulsion of aircraft at supersonic speeds, and is under study by the U.S. Airforce at the Atomic Energy Commission's test site near Las Vegas, Nevada.

MODERN
COLLEGE
PHYSICS

HARVEY E. WHITE, Ph.D., Sc.D.

*Professor of Physics and
Director of the Lawrence Hall of Science
University of California*

**FOURTH
EDITION**

D. VAN NOSTRAND COMPANY, INC.

PRINCETON, NEW JERSEY

TORONTO · LONDON · NEW YORK

To my son
DON

D. VAN NOSTRAND COMPANY, INC.
120 Alexander St., Princeton, New Jersey (*Principal office*)
24 West 40 Street, New York 18, New York

D. VAN NOSTRAND COMPANY, LTD.
358, Kensington High Street, London, W.14, England

D. VAN NOSTRAND COMPANY (Canada), LTD.
25 Hollinger Road, Toronto 16, Canada

COPYRIGHT © 1948, 1953, 1956, 1962, BY
D. VAN NOSTRAND COMPANY, INC.

Published simultaneously in Canada by
D. VAN NOSTRAND COMPANY (Canada), LTD.

First Published February 1948
Second Edition March 1953
Third Edition January 1956
Fourth Edition May 1962
Reprinted October 1962

PRINTED IN THE UNITED STATES OF AMERICA

Preface

This book is designed to be used as a text in the standard one-year college physics course required by most colleges and universities as part of the basic training of students who plan to major in one of the physical or life sciences.

Originally published in 1947, the book has been revised twice prior to this, its 4th edition. Here, for the first time, a double-column text page is used and accents of red color appear in most of the line diagrams to clarify the basic principles illustrated.

The main objective in originally preparing the manuscript was to unite under one cover the elementary principles of classical physics and that branch of modern science called atomic and nuclear physics. The ever-increasing importance of satellites and space ships, of electronics, atomic structure, and nuclear physics has led to the extensive revision of many chapters and to the addition of new ones. Included in the new material are discussions of the basic principles of planetary motion, gravitational fields, space flight, Einstein's theory of relativity, and elementary atomic particles.

The mathematics of this text is confined to elementary algebra, plane geometry, and trigonometry. Although the cgs and English system of units are often used in sample calculations, the mks system is emphasized throughout the book.

Even though a large number of students who plan to major in one of the life sciences are enrolled in physics courses, the illustrations in many physics texts are almost entirely selected from the fields of engineering. It is for this reason that the author has introduced, wherever it has been convenient, illustrations of basic principles of physics from the biological and medical sciences as well as engineering.

Since instructors differ widely in their decisions as to which subjects to include or to emphasize in an introductory physics course, the book has been divided into many chapters, thus making it possible to eliminate a subject by omitting an entire chapter.

The answers to even-numbered problems have been determined and checked by the author. Yet whenever a human being is involved mistakes can be made and a recorded answer may be in error. The author would, therefore, greatly appreciate his being notified of any errors, as they can be corrected in succeeding printings of this edition.

The author wishes to thank his colleagues, Messrs. L. Alvarez, R. T. Birge,

R. B. Brode, R. R. Brown, O. Chamberlain, D. Cooksey, W. B. Fretter, E. W. Friesen, V. F. Lenzen, L. B. Loeb, E. M. McMillan, W. M. Powell, G. T. Seaborg, E. Segre, C. D. Shane, H. Shugart, L. L. Skolil, H. Snodgrass, and E. Teller, for their valuable contributions to this text through discussions with the author of various special subjects. The author also wishes to thank the many teachers and students whose written comments have been most helpful throughout the years, and also the various publishers and research laboratories whose permission to reproduce certain illustrations has been so kindly granted.

Sincere thanks are also extended to my wife for the proofreading of the entire book, and to Mrs. Polly Thomas for the typing of all the new material.

Berkeley, California   HARVEY E. WHITE
March, 1962

Contents

NUCLEAR PHYSICS

Chapter 1

Optical Illusions

In the early dawn on the morning of July 16, 1945, there occurred in a remote spot on the desert sands of Almagordo, New Mexico, a man-made explosion of enormous magnitude. This, the explosion of the first atomic bomb, marked the culmination of a five-year coordinated research program, the size of which in terms of manpower and material is best expressed by its total cost to the United States government of approximately two billion dollars. With the ending of World War II and the subsequent dissemination of many of the scientific and technical developments made during that war, the civilized world awakened to the realization that we stand today on the threshold of a scientific era. This is the beginning of an era in which the wonders of television, radar, electronics, atomic energy, jet propulsion, and rocket ships are already a commonplace reality.

In all of these developments in the physical sciences, as well as many others in the field of medicine and the life sciences in general, the subject we call physics has played a most important role. So important is this role that many authorities in other fields of knowledge and endeavor consider physics to be the most basic of all the sciences. Certainly, a knowledge of the fundamental principles of physics is today an essential part of the education of all who desire to become proficient in the physical and medical professions.

One of the reasons physics is called an exact science is that reproducible experiments are performed and observations are made with high-precision measuring instruments. Laws and theories are formulated from the measured results of these experiments and then used to predict the results of new experiments. If these new experimental results do not agree with theory, the theory is either modified and brought into agreement or it is discarded for a new and better theory. Physics may be defined as that branch of knowledge treating the inanimate world and its phenomena and includes the subjects of:

Mechanics	Electricity
Properties of matter	Magnetism
Heat	Atomic physics
Sound	Nuclear physics
Light	Quantum theory

1.1. Physics as an Objective Method. It has long been known that when experiments are to be performed one cannot rely too much upon the human senses of touch, sight, hearing, etc., to make accurate observations. Methods of measurement that rely upon the senses entirely are called *subjective methods*. Methods that make use of scientific instruments are generally called *objective methods*.

In the early history of science, laws were frequently discovered by the use of subjective methods. Progress was slow, however, until such methods were replaced by objective methods using measuring instruments devised to give greater and greater precision.

It is true that many scientific discoveries have been made in the past with what we now would call the crudest of apparatus and equipment. It is the development of precision instruments and apparatus, however, that has led, particularly within the last several decades, to discoveries that are far-reaching in their theoretical implications and are of extreme practical importance to the advancement of civilization.

1

As an introduction to the subject of physics, we will first consider a number of experiments illustrating the false impressions so easily arrived at from the use of subjective methods of observation. Although these experiments are of the nature of an entertainment, they do have more serious aspects, for they demonstrate the necessity for using objective methods in advancing science.

1.2. Subjective Methods. If someone asks you to determine the temperature of a pan of water, your first impulse, if the water is not too hot, is to use your hand or your finger-tips and not to bother looking for a thermometer. To illustrate the gross inaccuracy of the touch in determining temperature, consider the three pans of water as shown in Fig. 1A. If the hand is first held

cold   warm   hot

Fig. 1A *Experiment illustrating the uncertainty of subjective methods of measurement.*

for some little time in the pan containing *cold* water and then plunged into the *warm* water, the senses tell you it is hot. If, however, the hand is first held in the *hot* water and then plunged into the *warm* water, your senses tell you it is cold. Your conclusion in either case is thus influenced by your experiences immediately preceding your determination of the temperature of the middle pan. When a thermometer is used in this experiment the same temperature will be indicated in either case. Although this latter would be called an objective method of measurement, one still relies upon the senses to obtain a reading of the thermometer scale.

If the length and breadth of a table top are to be measured, a *foot rule*, a *yardstick*, or a *meter stick* should be used and not the *span of a hand*. In a similar way the time that it takes a sprinter to run the *"one-hundred yard dash"* is measured by a *clock,*

a *watch,* or a *chronometer* and not by the *heart beat* or *pulse.*

1.3. The Eye. In making many scientific measurements the eye is considered as the most useful of all recording instruments. In some instances, however, the eye is not and should not be used directly in making observations, since it cannot be relied upon to observe what is really there. To illustrate how unreliable the sense of vision can be in some cases, we will consider in the next section a number of examples commonly referred to as "optical illusions."

Despite its many and sometimes serious imperfections and limitations, the human eye is a marvelous optical instrument. It is nature's priceless gift to man, enabling him to enjoy the beauties of form, color, and motion made possible by light. Optically the eye is like an exceptionally fine camera with an elaborate lens system on the one side and a sensitive screen or photographic film, called the *retina,* on the other. See Fig. 1B. The refracting media of the eye consists of the *cornea,* the *aqueous humor,* the *crystalline lens,* and *vitreous humor,* and its function is to focus an image of the objects to be seen on the retina. Like a camera, the eye contains an *iris diaphragm* which opens wider for faint light and closes down to a bare pinhole opening for very bright sunlight. It is this iris that contains the pigment determining the color of the eye.

In the retina of the eye the light pulses are received by tiny *cones* and *rods* whose function it seems to be to change the light into electricity. Each cone and rod is connected with an individual nerve which conducts the electricity through the nerve canal to the brain. Just how these electrical impulses are produced by the cell-like structures, the cones and rods, and how they are interpreted by the brain as vision, is still but vaguely understood by scientists. Experiments seem to indicate that the cones respond only to bright light and are particularly responsible for the detection and distinction of color, whereas the rods are sensitive to very feeble light, to motion, and to slight variations in intensity.

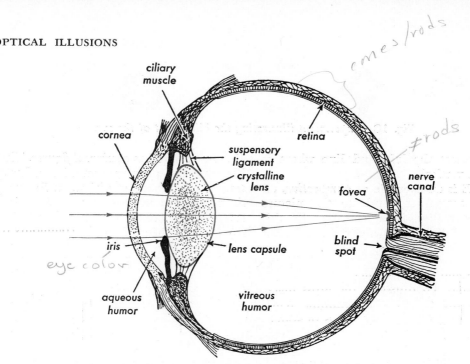

Fig. 1B *Cross-section diagram of the human eye.*

At the very center of the retina is a small yellowish-looking spot called the *fovea*. This small region contains a large number of cones, but no rods. It is on this spot in each eye that the words and letters of this page are focused one after the other when reading. Note when scrutinizing one word or particularly a single letter in a word that the rest of the page and even the words and letters close by appear indistinct.

It is customary to divide into two parts all sensory data that contribute to sight perception of any object: first, the formation of the retinal image by the light coming from the object; and second, the integrative property of the brain to interpret this image.

1.4. The Blind Spot. Not far from the fovea on the retina of the eye is a small region called the *blind spot*. This spot, which is insensitive to light, is where the nerve canal joins the eyeball. The existence of the blind spot can be demonstrated by closing the right eye, and holding the book at arm's length, looking continuously at the center of the circle of Fig. 1C with the left eye. Both the circle and square will be

seen from this distance. If the book is now moved slowly toward the eye, still fixing the eye upon the circle, a position (about 8 to 10 inches from the eye) will be reached where the square disappears. When both eyes are open, no position will be found where either the cross or the square disappears. One eye always sees that part of an object to which the other eye is blind. A similar experiment with the right eye focused on the square will cause the circle to disappear. A further discussion of the human eye and how it functions as an optical instrument is given in Chap. 41.

1.5. Optical Illusions. Of the hundreds of well-known optical illusions, only a few of the most interesting ones will be presented here. In Fig. 1D is a group of six figures classified as illusions due to *lines* and *angles*. In (a), the first figure, the brim of the hat is as long as the hat is high; in (b) the diagonal lines of each parallelogram are of the same length; and in (c) the perfect circle appears to be distorted. In figure (d) the two horizontal lines are parallel and straight and in (f) they are of equal length. In (e) the lower right-hand line if extended

Fig. 1C *Experiment illustrating the blind spot of the eye.*

will intersect the left-hand line where it joins the vertical.

Fig. 1E is an example of *perspective,* an illusion suggesting depth to the picture when, in reality, it is flat. Actually this figure is a building showing three figures of

1F, are classified as *equivocal figures.* These illustrate the phenomenon of the *fluctuation* of the process of vision. In Figure (a) six cubes may be seen stacked 3, 2, 1; or seven cubes may be seen stacked 2, 3, 2. In (b) a folded sheet of paper is seen opening

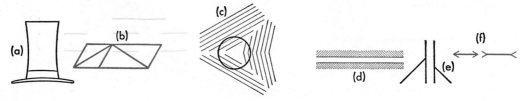

Fig. 1D *Optical illusions with lines and angles.*

equal height. By means of slanting lines these figures are made to appear to have different heights. Experiences from early childhood have trained us to interpret the slanting lines as depth.

The next set of illusions, shown in Fig.

either toward or away from the reader. In (c) is a flight of steps seen from above looking down, or from below looking up.

Fig. 1F(d) is one of the most interesting of all illusions. To appreciate the effect fully, one must himself perform the experiment

Fig. 1E *Which figure is tallest? Measure them.*

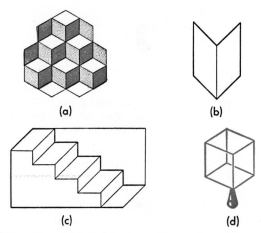

(a)   (b)

(c)   (d)

Fig. 1F   *Optical illusions illustrating fluctuation of the attention.*

with a small wire cube about 1 in. in size. The cube is held by a small handle at one corner and viewed with one eye at a distance of from 1 to 2 ft. By the principle of fluctuation, the observer next tries to make the farthest corner of the cube appear as the nearest corner. When this condition is attained, the cube upon being turned about a horizontal or vertical axis will appear to turn in the opposite direction. A little practice in the fluctuation of the visual senses is required in this experiment, and it is well worth performing.

In Fig. 1G are two pairs of similar figures

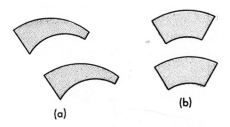

(a)   (b)

Fig. 1G   *Optical illusions of area.*

of equal area. The slanting lines at the ends make the lower figure in each case appear to be larger than the one immediately above. Such figures should be cut from white cardboard and held one above the other. When the upper figure is interchanged with the corresponding lower figure, one figure seems to grow and the other to shrink before your eyes.

In Fig. 1H(a) are two small squares of equal size, a white square on a black background, and a black square on a white background. When an image of this is formed on the retina of the eye, the cones and rods just beyond the white edges are stimulated by those nearby, thus causing the white square to be larger than the black one. This phenomenon is called *irradiation* or *brightness contrast*. A similar phenomenon is illustrated in Fig. 1H(b) where gray spots are seen at the intersections of the white lines.

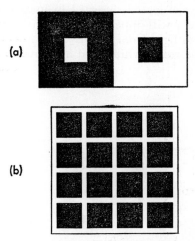

(a)

(b)

Fig. 1H   *Illustrations of irradiation.*

1.6. Fatigue and Color Illusions. There exists a large number of illusions that are classified as *color illusions*. Two of these are diagramed in Fig. 1I. A disk painted black and white as shown in (a) will appear to be colored when set rotating at a relatively low speed. The colors to be seen are rather faint pastel shades of violet, blue, green, yellow, and pink. The speed of the wheel should be from about 4 to 15 revolutions per sec. The explanation usually given for the phenomenon is that the retina of the eye responds more quickly to some colors than to others. Since the white image of the disk moves around on the retina and since white light contains all the colors of the rainbow, some colors are perceived at each given spot on the retina sooner than others, and the effect of color is produced.

The second diagram (b) in Fig. 1I illustrates the appearance of color by virtue of contrast. If a white patch of light, for example, is seen on a background of red, it will appear to be pale green. If, on the other hand, a white patch is seen on a background of green, it will appear to be pink. The experiment may be performed with two similar arc lights producing white light. Each of these is made to cast a shadow of the same rod R on a white screen. If a piece of red glass is placed in front of light L_2 as shown in the figure, the white patch of light at A will appear to be pale green. If a green glass is inserted in its place, the region A will appear pink. In each case, A receives light from L_1 only and must therefore be really white. Red and green of the

Fig. 1J and keep it there for about 15 to 20 sec. Then turn the eyes toward a white wall of the room, or toward the open sky, and in one or two seconds the American flag will appear in all of its true colors. Similar effects can be observed with other color photographs.

Delayed images of this kind are always complementary in color to the original pictures, black becomes white, yellow becomes blue, green becomes magenta, magenta becomes green, etc. (For an explanation of complementary colors, see Chap. 42.)

1.8. The Stroboscopic Effect. In moving pictures, when a wagon with spoked wheels is coming to a stop, the wheels are often noticed to stand still, then turn backward,

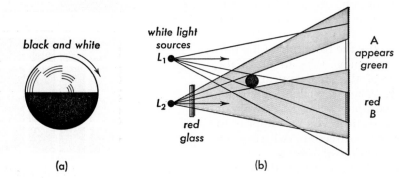

Fig. 1I *Diagrams of experiments demonstrating color illusions.*

proper shades are complementary colors and when they are added together produce white light. The subject of the mixing of colors will be taken up in detail in Chap. 42.

1.7. Complementary Images. When the eyes are subjected to bright light for some little time, the retina seems to show tiring or *fatigue*. Furthermore, continued subjection of any part of the retina to one particular color causes only those cones sensitive to that color to tire. When the same retinal area is subsequently subjected to white light, the previously inactive cones respond more strongly than those originally stimulated and a complementary color is seen.

To observe these colored images, fix the attention on the black star in the lower right-hand corner of the field of the flag in

stop, turn forward, and then stop again. This phenomenon, known as the "stroboscopic effect," is due to interrupted illumination of the moving-picture screen and can be illustrated in many ways. An interesting experiment illustrating the phenomenon is shown in Fig. 1K. Two disks are mounted on the shafts of two separate motors. The smaller disk A with a narrow slot is used to interrupt the light beam illuminating the larger disk. The disk B is white with black circles and dots arranged exactly as shown. Suppose now that disk A makes 16 revolutions per second, thus illuminating disk B with 16 short flashes of light per second. Suppose also that B makes only one revolution per second, and that one flash of light comes when the disk has the position shown in the figure.

Fig. 1J *Fatigue images enable the above objects to appear in their natural colors.*

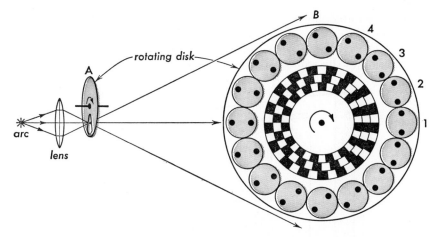

Fig. 1K *Experimental arrangement for demonstrating the stroboscopic effect.*

If the attention is confined to the circle at position (1), the two enclosed dots are one above the other. When the second flash of light appears, the circle (2) will be in position (1) and the two dots will appear to have shifted slightly clockwise. When the next flash of light comes, the circle (3) will be in position (1) and the two dots will have shifted still farther. This process continued shows that the circles will appear to stand still and the dots to rotate within them.

If the light flashes in any such experiment as the one described above are slower than 16 per sec, the illuminated object will appear to flicker badly. If, however, the flashes come at an increasingly higher rate, the flicker will soon disappear entirely and the illumination will seem to be steady. The reason for this is that each retinal image is somehow retained by the vision mechanism for about $\frac{1}{16}$ of a second. This is called the *persistence of vision*.

1.9. Circles and Spirals. If this page of the book is held about 1 ft in front of the observer's eyes and the book moved rapidly in a circle about 2 to 3 in. in diameter, the spiral in Fig. 1L will appear to rotate in the direction of motion. A set of alternately dark and light concentric circles will show the same effect, the apparent rotation being due to the persistence of vision.

We have seen in the previous illustrations how some optical illusions break down or diminish under critical inspection. There are others, however, that persist. No amount of staring or thought will teach you to see the circles of Fig. 1M as anything other than spirals.

Fig. 1L *Illusion of rotation.*

1.10. The Trapezoidal Window. One of the most striking optical illusions in perspective is that of a slowly rotating window having the design shown in Fig. 1N. This device is cut from a single sheet of $\frac{1}{4}$-inch plywood, painted white, grey, and black on

Fig. 1M *Circles appear to be spirals.*

both sides,* and mounted on a slowly rotating motor-driven shaft.

Viewed in a darkened room, with front and side illumination of the window by two

of the small end. The ball appears to continue around in the same direction while the window appears to oscillate back and forth.

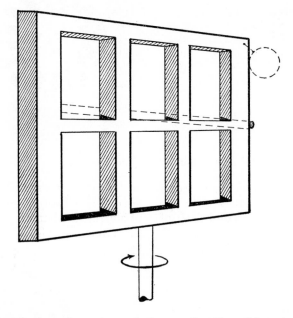

Fig. 1N   *Rotating slowly and continuously in one direction, this trapezoidal-shaped window appears to oscillate back and forth.*

lights shielded from the audience, the window appears to rotate first one direction, then the other.

An added effect is obtained by hanging a brightly colored ball at the upper corner

* In constructing such a window make all dimensions proportional to the reproduction in Fig. 1N.

Another striking effect is to place a colored rod through the upper center window pane, as shown dotted in the figure. The rod's apparent behavior must be observed to be appreciated.

For supplementary reading on optical illusions, see *Am. J. of Physics,* Vol. 14, p. 104 (1946).

SUMMARY

Physics is an exact science. It is a science in which objective measurements are made, using precision instruments. Repetition of an experiment produces the same results. Although the eye is a remarkable instrument for observing different phenomena, optical illusions often arise, thereby demonstrating that our vision is not always reliable. Measuring instruments are more reliable than the human senses.

EXERCISE

1. Using 13 match sticks and some quick drying glue, make a small cube as shown in Fig. 1F(d) and carry out the experiment described at the top of page 5. One stick is for the handle.

QUESTIONS

1. Briefly explain what is meant by the subjective method of measurement.

2. How would you measure the length of a table, using the subjective method of measurement?

3. How would you measure the temperature of a pan of water, using an objective method of measurement?

4. Briefly explain how the subjective method enters into the measurement of temperature with a thermometer.

5. What is the stroboscopic effect? Briefly explain.

6. Explain why the wheels of a wagon may appear to turn backward on a motion picture screen when the wagon is moving forward.

7. Briefly explain why motion pictures flicker when the projector runs too slowly, but do not flicker when it runs fast.

8. In what ways are any of the principles developed in this lesson involved in things happening in the world around us?

1. Subjective = by means of entirely the senses.

2. By a ruler or yardstick, etc.

3. By employing the use of a thermometer

4. The thermometer measures the temperature but our senses (eyes) measure the amount shown on the thermometer.

5. In wagon wheels where the spokes stand still turn backwards; turn forward and stop again. Stroboscopic

6. Due to interrupted illumination of the moving-picture screen

7. The persistence of vision (1/16) of a second is marred. Slower than 16/sec will cause flickering. If kept above the persistence of vision it remains smooth.

8. In our everyday lives there are signs, advertising, etc which play on our senses to promote their ideas and sell us on something.

Chapter 2

Units of Measurement

Since physics is a science based upon exact measurement, it is essential that the student first become familiar with several of the more commonly used measuring devices and the units into which each is usually divided. Every measurement, whether it be a distance, a weight, an interval of time, or anything else, requires *two* things: first, a *number;* and second, a *unit.* One might, for example, obtain as the result of the measurement of different distances, *20 feet, 5 miles, 3 rods,* or as the result of the measurement of different weights, *6 pounds, 25 tons, 4½ ounces,* or as the result of the measurement of different time intervals, *7 hours, 26 seconds,* etc. As the result of some experiment or the reading of certain instruments, one might obtain the measurements, *10.7 calories, 90 horsepower, 6 volts, 12 kilowatts,* etc. In each case, the *unit* is just as essential as the *number* expressing the amount.

Although there are numerous different units, each one can be expressed in terms of not more than three special units. These three, called *fundamental units,* are the units of *length, mass,* and *time.* All other units are called *derived units* since, as we shall see later, they can always be written as some combination of the three fundamental units.

There are in general two widely used sets of fundamental units: (a) the *metric,* and (b) the *English.* Throughout the civilized world, scientific observations are nearly always expressed in terms of metric units. This set employs the *standard meter* as the unit of length, the *standard kilogram* as the unit of mass, and the *second* as the unit of time.

2.1. The Standard Meter and Yard. The standard meter is a platinum-iridium bar about 40 inches long which is kept in the vaults of the International Bureau of Weights and Measures near Paris, France. Three facsimiles of this bar are to be found at the United States Bureau of Standards in Washington, D. C. Each of these duplicate copies may be called an *International Prototype Meter* and is now the standard of length in the United States. From these prototypes, all other measuring rods and tapes are standardized.

When the standard meter was first devised, it was intended that it have a length equal to one ten-millionth part of the distance from one of the earth's poles to the equator. Although more recent measurements of the earth's dimensions have shown that the distance from pole to equator is about 10,000,880 *standard meters,* the two groove marks, one on either end of the original platinum-iridium bar, are now taken to be exactly one meter apart.

The standard meter is usually divided into 100 equal parts. Each of these parts is called the *centimeter.*

$$1 \text{ meter} = 100 \text{ centimeters}$$

or, abbreviated, $1 \text{ m} = 100 \text{ cm}$

The centimeter is further divided into ten equal parts. Each of these parts is called the *millimeter.* (See Fig. 2A.)

$$1 \text{ centimeter} = 10 \text{ millimeters}$$
$$1 \text{cm} = 10 \text{ mm}$$
$$1 \text{m} = 1000 \text{ mm}$$

The millimeter is further divided into 1000 equal parts. Each of these parts is called a *micron.*

$$1 \text{ millimeter} = 1000 \text{ microns}$$
$$1 \text{ mm} = 1000 \text{ } \mu$$

10

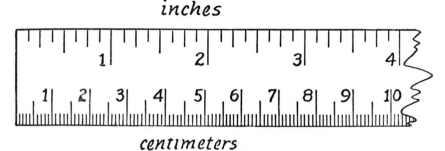

Fig. 2A Diagram comparing the centimeter scale with the inch scale.

In civil life in the United States the *yard* is used as the standard unit of length. By an act of Congress in 1866 the standard yard to be used legally in the United States was defined as 3600/3937 part of a standard meter. Since the yard is divided into 36 inches,

$$1 \text{ meter} = 39.37 \text{ inches}$$
$$1 \text{ m} = 39.37 \text{ in.}$$

With 12 in. to 1 ft,

in the English system. One kilometer is equivalent to 1000 meters, and one mile is equivalent to 5280 ft.

$$1000 \text{ meters} = 1 \text{ kilometer}$$
$$1000 \text{ m} = 1 \text{ Km}$$
$$1 \text{ mile} = 5280 \text{ feet}$$
$$1 \text{ mi} = 5280 \text{ ft}$$

The relations between units of length in the metric system and those in the English system are given in the following table:

TABLE 2A. CONVERSION FACTORS FOR UNITS OF LENGTH

	Km	m	cm	in.	ft	mi
1 kilometer =	1	1000	100,000	39370	3280.83	0.62137
1 meter =	0.00100	1	100	39.370	3.28083	6.21×10^{-4}
1 centimeter =	1.0×10^{-5}	0.0100	1	0.39370	0.032808	6.21×10^{-6}
1 inch =	2.54×10^{-5}	0.02540	2.5400	1	0.08333	1.58×10^{-5}
1 foot =	3.05×10^{-4}	0.30480	30.480	12	1	1.89×10^{-4}
1 mile =	1.60935	1609.35	160935	63360	5280	1

$$3 \text{ ft} = 1 \text{ yd}$$
$$1 \text{ ft} = 30.48 \text{ cm}$$
and $\qquad 1 \text{ in.} = 2.54 \text{ cm}$

The sizes of the inch, fractions of an inch relative to the centimeter, and millimeter, are illustrated in Fig. 2A.

When large distances are to be measured, it is convenient as well as customary to use large units of length. Such units are the *kilometer* in the metric system and the *mile*

2.2. The Standard Kilogram and Pound. The standard unit of mass is the *kilogram,* a block of platinum also preserved at the International Bureau of Weights and Measures near Paris. Two copies of this kilogram (which may be called International Prototype Kilograms) are kept in the vaults of the U. S. Bureau of Standards. The kilogram is divided into one thousand equal parts called *grams.*

1000 grams = 1 kilogram

1000 gm = 1 Kg

The original intent was to base the standard kilogram upon the gram, the gram being the mass of one cubic centimeter of pure water taken at a temperature of four degrees centigrade.

The standard pound is defined in terms of the standard kilogram by the relation that its mass shall equal 0.4536 kilogram.

453.6 gm weigh 1 lb

Following this we have the relations

28.35 gm weigh 1 oz

1 lb = 16 oz

and   1 ton = 2000 lb

The relative sizes of the kilogram, gram, and pound may be seen in Fig. 2B.

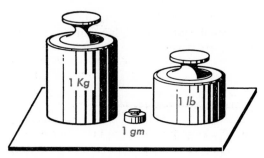

Fig. 2B *The mass of a standard kilogram is 2.2 times the mass of a standard pound weight.*

2.3. Historical Timepieces.
Instruments for the measurement of time go back historically to the Babylonians, at least, and probably to the time of the Greeks five centuries B.C. The earliest timepieces on record were chiefly water clocks, some of very simple design and others of more elaborate design. These clocks were based upon the very elementary principle that it takes the same time for equal amounts of water to flow through a small opening. The *hourglass,* employing the same principle and using sand instead of water, is an outgrowth of the water clock and dates back to medieval times.

A water clock of moderately simple design is shown in Fig. 2C. Small holes at the

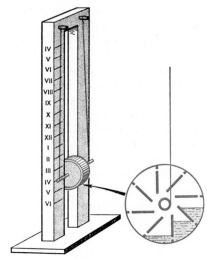

Fig. 2C *Diagram of an early form of water clock.*

edge of the vanes (shown in the detail diagram) allow the water to flow from one compartment to the other. This permits the cylinder to turn slowly, thus unwinding the suspending cords.

The *sundial* dates back to the Chaldean astronomer Berosus who lived about the time of Alexander the Great, 300 B.C. Today, similar instruments serve as ornaments in many of our public parks. A sundial of common design, as shown in Fig. 2D, consists essentially of a *pin* called a *gnomon* mounted at an angle on a circular plate

Fig. 2D *Diagram of a sundial.*

called the *dial*. The gnomon is mounted in the vertical North and South plane. The edge of the gnomon is parallel to the earth's rotational axis and its purpose is to cast a shadow on the dial which is marked with the hours of the day. Due to the apparent yearly precessional motion of the earth's axis, small corrections must be made to the time as shown by the shadow. These corrections, amounting to several minutes, are usually engraved upon every sundial. The sundial on the University of California campus, for example, has the following corrections:

Jan. 10, + 17 min	July 19, + 15 "
Feb. 9, + 23 "	Aug. 18, + 18 "
Mar. 11, + 19 "	Sept. 17, + 4 "
Apr. 10, + 8 "	Oct. 17, − 5 "
May 20, + 5 "	Nov. 16, − 6 "
June 19, + 10 "	Dec. 16, + 5 "

Modern clocks depend for their regulation upon the swinging of a pendulum or the oscillation of a balance wheel. Examples of these are the grandfather clock and the modern wrist watch. Such devices will be discussed later, under the heading of vibrations and waves, Chap. 31. Electric clocks commonly found in the city homes of today are run by tiny electric motors. The speed of these motors is controlled at the city's electric power plant by controlling the frequency of the alternating current supplied to the power lines leading to the house. The master clock at the power house is frequently a pendulum clock.

2.4. Time and the Mean Solar Day. Three kinds of time are always recognized by astronomers: first, *sidereal time;* second, *apparent solar time;* and third, *mean solar time.* The last is the time used in civil life. If at any given point on the earth's surface we adjust the gnomon of a sundial to lie in the North and South vertical plane, the time interval between two successive transits of the sun's shadow over the 12 o'clock mark is called the apparent solar day. For several reasons, one being that the earth's orbit around the sun is elliptical, this interval of time varies slightly from day to day. An apparent solar day in December is

about one minute longer than an apparent solar day in September. It is clear, therefore, why in this day of accurate timepieces we do not regulate our clocks to apparent solar time.

The *average* length of all apparent solar days throughout a solar year is called the *mean solar day.* Since there are 3600 sec in one hr, 24 hr in one day, and 365.241 days in one tropical year, there are approximately $3600 \times 24 \times 365.241$, or 31,556,822 sec in one year. The *tropical year* is defined as the time between two successive passages of the vernal equinox by the sun. Since tropical years vary slightly, the *second* is defined as,[*]

$$\frac{1}{31{,}556{,}825.9747} \text{ part of tropical year 1900}$$

For astronomical purposes, a different time scale known as sidereal time is used. There is one more sidereal day in one solar year than there are mean solar days. One solar year equals 366.241 sidereal days. The reason for the additional day is that in making one complete turn around the sun in its orbit the earth has actually made 366.241 rotations with respect to the fixed stars. The sidereal second as ticked off by an astronomical clock is therefore slightly shorter than the second given by an ordinary clock keeping mean solar time.

2.5. Metric Units. Nearly all scientific experiments, in the United States as well as abroad, are performed using metric units. In these units distance is usually measured in millimeters, centimeters, meters, or kilometers; mass is measured in grams or kilograms; and time is measured in seconds, minutes, or hours. In metric units the abbreviation *cgs* means *centimeter, gram, second;* and *mks* means *meter, kilogram, second.*

The English system, as already referred to, uses the foot, yard, and mile as units of length; the ounce, pound, and ton as units of force; and the second as the unit of time. We Americans inherited the English system

[*] International standard adopted on October 14, 1960, by the General Conference on Weights and Measures, at Paris, France.

with all of its cumbersome fractions, and because it is so firmly ingrained in our civil life it will be a difficult task ever to change over completely to the simpler metric system. There is a strong movement today, however, advocating such a change.

The chief advantage of metric units over English units is that all units are divided into 10 or 100 parts. This enables fractional distances and masses to be expressed as decimals. Decimals, it is well known, are easier to manipulate in the addition, subtraction, multiplication, and division of two or more quantities.

2.6. Abbreviated System of Numbers. In speaking of the size and shape of an object or the time interval between the occurrence of two events, it is convenient to express very large numbers and very small decimals in an abbreviated form. This is done principally to conserve time and space. It is convenient for the astronomer in the study of stars, on the one hand, and the physicist and chemist in the study of atoms on the other. The abbreviations in common use are based upon powers of tens as follows:

$$10 = 10^1 \qquad\qquad 1 = 10^0$$
$$100 = 10^2 \qquad\qquad 0.1 = 10^{-1}$$
$$1000 = 10^3 \qquad\qquad 0.01 = 10^{-2}$$
$$10,000 = 10^4 \qquad\qquad 0.001 = 10^{-3}$$
$$100,000 = 10^5 \qquad\qquad 0.0001 = 10^{-4}$$
$$1,000,000 = 10^6 \qquad\qquad 0.00001 = 10^{-5}$$

The abbreviated form on the right side of each equation is mathematically correct. For example,

$$10^3 = 10 \times 10 \times 10 = 1000$$

and

$$10^{-3} = \frac{1}{10^3} = \frac{1}{1000} = 0.001$$

In every case, *the exponent is seen to give directly the number of digits the decimal point is moved from unity*, positive integers specifying the number of places the decimal point is moved to the right to make large numbers, and negative integers specifying the number of places it is moved to the left to make small fractions. To illustrate the use of this system, suppose we say that a truck weighs three million grams. This can be written

$$3,000,000 \text{ gm} = 3 \times 1,000,000 \text{ gm}$$
$$= 3 \times 10^6 \text{ gm}$$

In the abbreviated notation the mass is therefore written 3×10^6 gm. If more than one numeral occurs, any one of several abbreviations might be written. For example, in the case of large numbers,

$$840,000,000 = 84 \times 10,000,000 = 84 \times 10^7$$

or

$$840,000,000 = 8.4 \times 100,000,000 = 8.4 \times 10^8$$

In the case of small numbers, on the other hand,

$$0.0024 = 2.4 \times 10^{-3}, \text{ or } 24 \times 10^{-4}$$

To illustrate the advantages of this abbreviated notation, the mass of the *earth* and the mass of an *electron* are found by experiment to be as follows:

mass of the earth, $\quad m = 5.97 \times 10^{24}$ Kg

mass of an electron, $\quad m = 9.11 \times 10^{-31}$ Kg

If these are written down in complete decimal form they would appear as follows:

mass of the earth
$$= 5,970,000,000,000,000,000,000,000 \text{ Kg}$$
mass of the electron $= 0.000,000,000,$
$$000,000,000,000,000,000,911 \text{ Kg}$$

At a meeting held by the International Union for Pure and Applied Physics a few years ago, the following symbolism was adopted for general use:[*]

10^3	Kilo	K		10^{-3}	milli	m
10^6	Mega	M		10^{-6}	micro	μ
10^9	Giga	G		10^{-9}	nana	n
10^{12}	Terra	T		10^{-12}	pica	p

One of the reasons for adopting these notations was that B, for billion, stands for 10^9 in the United States, and for 10^{12} in Great Britain. Because the term "billion" is so thoroughly entrenched in the minds of scientists in the United States, only a few have adopted G and T, while the change from k

[*] See *Physics Today*, Vol. 9, p. 23, 1956; Vol. 10, p. 30, 1957.

to K for *one thousand* is becoming more common.

2.7. Multiplication and Division of Large and Small Numbers. The multiplication and division of large and small numbers in the abbreviated notation involves the addition and subtraction of exponents.

Rule 1. When a power number is changed from numerator to denominator, or vice versa, the sign of the exponent is changed. For example,

$$\frac{5}{2 \times 10^{-6}} \text{ equals } \frac{5 \times 10^6}{2}$$

Rule 2. When two power numbers are multiplied, their exponents are added. For example,

$$3 \times 10^5 \times 2 \times 10^4 = 3 \times 2 \times 10^{5+4} = 6 \times 10^9$$

Again,

$$3 \times 10^{17} \times 2 \times 10^{-12}$$
$$= 3 \times 2 \times 10^{17-12} = 6 \times 10^5$$

Rule 3. When one power number is divided by another, their exponents are subtracted. For example,

$$\frac{8 \times 10^9}{2 \times 10^4} = \frac{8 \times 10^{9-4}}{2} = 4 \times 10^5$$

Again,

$$\frac{6 \times 10^{-7}}{3 \times 10^{-2}} = \frac{6 \times 10^{-7+2}}{3} = 2 \times 10^{-5}$$

2.8. Algebra. Although you have studied algebra, you may feel that you have forgotten most of it. For this reason it is well to review certain principles, even though only the very simplest manipulation of symbols will be used in the lessons that follow.

As the various subjects in physics are developed, we will see that an algebraic equation is nothing more than an abbreviated, but formal, way of expressing a principle or law and that the equation is derived from a series of experimental measurements.

Example 1. As a simple illustration of the experimental process, suppose that we have a simple platform balance of the type shown schematically in Fig. 2E. On one pan we place a 2-lb weight, and on the other pan we add weights until balance is re-

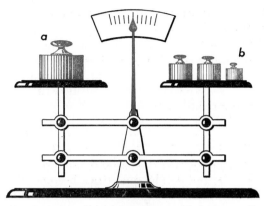

Fig. 2E *Equal weights only will balance the scales.*

stored. Experimentally we then find that b must have a total of 2 lb. If a is increased to 5 lb, b must be 5 lb, and if a is changed to 21.5 lb, b must be 21.5 lb. In other words, we find experimentally that, whatever may be the magnitude of the weight a, the total magnitude of b must be the same.

Hence we bring mathematics into the problem and write

$$a = b \qquad (2a)$$

Having established this relation from many measurements, we now have confidence in this equation. We feel that if we put an unknown weight a on one pan and balance it with known weights on the other, Eq.(2a) can be applied and we know that a weighs the same as b. The known or measured quantity b is on the right, and the unknown quantity a is on the left.

Example 2. Let us imagine that we have performed an experiment in which we repeatedly measured three quantities $x, y,$ and z; we have established the relation

$$x = yz \qquad (2b)$$

This equation says that the measurable quantity x is always equal to the product of two other measurable quantities, y and z. It follows, therefore, that if we do the experiment again and measure y and z, we need not measure x to find its value.

Our experimentally established Eq.(2b) tells us that the unmeasured quantity x, which we call the *unknown,* is always equal to the product $y \times z$.

Example 3. Suppose we have repeatedly performed a third experiment in which four quantities a, b, c, and d have been measured and we have established the following relation.

$$\frac{a}{b} = \frac{c}{d} \qquad (2c)$$

Now we repeat the experiment and measure b, c, and d. The quantity a becomes the unknown, and we can find its value by substituting the known quantities and carrying out the required arithmetic.

Before substituting quantities in any equation, it is customary to put all known quantities on the right side of the equation and the unknown quantities on the left. For Eq.(2c) this means putting b on the right side of the equation. To do this we can multiply both sides of Eq.(2c) by b. We obtain

$$\frac{ab}{b} = \frac{cb}{d}$$

then

$$\frac{a}{1} = \frac{cb}{d}$$

and the desired relation becomes

$$a = \frac{cb}{d}$$

If the quantity c in Eq.(2c) is the unknown, we would solve for c as follows:

Multiply both sides of the equation by d and simplify.

$$\frac{ad}{b} = \frac{cd}{d}; \quad \frac{ad}{b} = \frac{c}{1}; \quad \frac{ad}{b} = c$$

Turn this last equation around, and we obtain

$$c = \frac{ad}{b}$$

as the desired relation.

In similar ways we may solve Eq.(2c) for b as the unknown quantity and find

$$b = \frac{ad}{c}$$

Or we can solve for d as the unknown quantity and find

$$d = \frac{bc}{a}$$

A re-examination of Eq.(2c) will now show that, to move any one of the four factors a, b, c, or d across the equal sign to the other side, it obeys the following rule: *When any factor is moved from the denominator on one side of an equation, it goes into the numerator on the other side, and vice versa.* This last rule is a good one to memorize, for it is a short cut to any one of the four equations just derived.

These examples involve the algebraic principles of much of the mathematics we shall encounter in this book, and it would be well worthwhile to practice carrying out these same operations using different letters for the symbols.

PROBLEMS

1. Write each of the following in powers of ten notation, and then express the answers in powers of ten notation: (a) $6000 \times 30{,}000$, (b) $58{,}000 \times 0.002$, (c) $345 \times 0.0004 \div 0.00002$, and (d) $0.00042 \times 0.00000007 \div 0.006$.

2. Solve each of the following problems and find the answers in powers of ten notation: (a) $5 \times 10^3 \times 4 \times 10^8$, (b) $3.2 \times 10^7 \times 7 \times 10^{-4}$, (c) $6.5 \times 10^3 \times 5 \times 10^4 \div 2 \times 10^{-5}$, and (d) $1.8 \times 10^{-6} \times 4 \times 10^{-15} \div 9 \times 10^{-28}$. (*Ans.* (a) 2×10^{12}, (b) 2.24×10^4, (c) 1.625×10^{13}, (d) 8×10^6.)

3. Solve each of the following problems and express the answers in powers of ten notation: (a) $2.6 \times 10^6 \times 5.0 \times 10^2$, (b) $4 \times 10^{18} \times 3.5 \times 10^{-8}$, (c) $3 \times 10^5 \times 8 \times 10^7 \div 4 \times 10^4$, and (d) $5 \times 10^{-3} \times 6 \times 10^{11} \div 3 \times 10^{-4}$.

4. Write each of the following in powers of ten notation; express the answers in powers of ten: (a) $30{,}000 \times 2500$, (b) 3800×0.00004, (c) $5{,}200{,}000 \times 20{,}000 \div 0.0004$, and (d) $0.00081 \times 7000 \div 0.003$. (*Ans.* (a) 7.5×10^7, (b) 15.2×10^{-2}, (c) 2.6×10^{14}, (d) 1.89×10^3.)

5. If a 1-lb weight were made only of particles

having the mass of an electron, of how many particles would it be composed?

6. The sun's mass is 1.98×10^{33} gm. To how many earth masses is this equivalent? (*Ans.* 3.32×10^5.)

7. Calculate the number of seconds in one week, and express the answer in powers of ten.

8. Calculate the number of seconds in a life span of 50 years, and express the answer in powers of ten. (*Ans.* 1.58×10^9 sec.)

9. Find the sum of 5 yd and 3 m in (a) yards, (b) meters, and (c) centimeters.

10. Find the sum of 150 in. and 325 cm in (a) yards, (b) meters, and (c) centimeters. (*Ans.* (a) 7.62 yd, (b) 7.06 m, (c) 706 cm.)

11. Find the difference between 10 mi and 20 Km in (a) miles, and (b) kilometers.

12. Find the difference between 25 Km and 15 mi in (a) miles, and (b) kilometers. (*Ans.* (a) 0.534 mi (b) .860 Km.)

13. Calculate the distance to the moon in meters if the distance is 239,000 mi. Express your answer in powers of ten.

14. Calculate the distance to the sun in kilometers if the distance is 90,000,000 miles. (*Ans.* 1.448×10^8 Km.)

15. Solve each of the following and give each answer in powers of ten: (a) $3 \times 10^5 \times 10^6$, (b) $2.5 \times 10^4 \div 5 \times 10^{-2}$, (c) $3.9 \times 10^8 \times 5 \times 10^{-3}$, (d) $4.2 \times 10^{-6} \div 7 \times 10^{-2}$, and (e) $6 \times 10^{-2} \div 1.5 \times 10^4$.

16. Solve each of the following and give each answer in powers of ten: (a) $3.2 \times 10^5 \times 6.0 \times 10^2$, (b) $4.2 \times 10^3 \div 2.0 \times 10^{-2}$, (c) $8.6 \times 10^6 \times 5 \times 10^{-2}$, (d) $6 \times 10^{-6} \div 1.2 \times 10^{-2}$, and (e) $12 \times 10^{-3} \div 3 \times 10^4$. (*Ans.* (a) 1.92×10^8, (b) 2.1×10^5, (c) 4.3×10^5, (d) 5×10^{-4}, (e) 4×10^{-7}.)

17. Solve each of the following and give each answer in powers of ten: (a) $4 \times 10^{-2} \times 3.2 \times$ $10^6 \div 8 \times 10^4$, (b) $2.2 \times 10^{-3} \times 5 \times 10^{-2} \div (4 \times 10^2 \times 5 \times 10^{-4})$, (c) $9.2 \times 10^6 \times 3 \times 10^7 \div 6 \times 10^{-8}$, and (d) $3.4 \times 10^{-5} \times 2.8 \times 10^{-2} \div 8 \times 10^7$.

18. The following measurements were made in the laboratory: $m = 2$ Kg, $v = 4.8$ m/sec, and $r = 1.6$ m. If the known physical law concerning this experiment is expressed by the algebraic equation $F = mv^2/r$, find the value of F. (*Ans.* 28.8 Kg m/sec².)

19. The following measurements were made in the performance of an experiment: $v_0 = 5$ m/sec, $t = 4$ sec, and $a = 8$ m/sec². If the physical law relating these observations is known to have the form of $a = (v - v_0)/t$, what is the value of the unknown quantity v?

20. In performing a certain laboratory experiment, the following measurements were made: $W = 60$ lb, $h = 48$ ft, and $t = 18$ sec. If the known physical law concerning this experiment is expressed by the algebraic equation $P = Wh/t$, find the value of P. (*Ans.* $P = 160$ ft-lb/sec.)

21. The following measurements were made in a laboratory experiment: $m = 8$ Kg, $s = 6$ m, and $t = 4$ sec. If the known physical law concerning this experiment is expressed by the algebraic equation $F = ms/t^2$, find the value of F.

22. Solve each of the following equations for v:

(a) $\dfrac{v}{w} = \dfrac{5s}{r}$, (b) $\dfrac{v}{s} = \dfrac{2w + 6}{5r}$, (c) $\dfrac{2v}{p} = \dfrac{s + r}{2w}$,

(d) $\dfrac{p}{2v} = \dfrac{q}{s + w}$, and (e) $\dfrac{s}{r} = \dfrac{w}{x + v}$.

Ans. (a) $5sw/r$, (b) $s(2w + 6)/5r$, (c) $p(s + r)/4w$, (d) $p(s + w)/2q$, (e) $(rw - sx/s.)$

23. Solve each of the following equations for x: (a) $\dfrac{x}{a} = \dfrac{2y}{b}$, (b) $\dfrac{x}{a} = \dfrac{2y + 2}{b}$, (c) $\dfrac{5x}{y} = \dfrac{2a}{b}$,

(d) $\dfrac{y}{x} = \dfrac{a}{b}$, and (e) $\dfrac{a + b}{2} = \dfrac{y}{x}$.

Chapter 3

Velocity and Speed

Mechanics is defined as that branch of physics dealing with the *motions* or *states* of material bodies. It is generally divided into two parts: the first called *kinematics,* dealing with various kinds of motion, and the second called *dynamics,* dealing with the causes for changes in motion. Dynamics is further divided into two parts, *statics* and *kinetics.*

While statics deals with bodies in a state of equilibrium, a condition brought about by balanced forces, kinetics deals with changes in motion brought about by one or more unbalanced forces. As an introduction to the kinematics of motion, the elementary concepts of *velocity* and *speed* will first be taken up.

3.1. Velocity. *Velocity is defined as the rate of change of position.* Since by *change in position* of a body is meant the distance traveled, this definition of velocity can be written

$$\text{velocity} = \frac{\text{distance traveled}}{\text{time}} \quad (3a)$$

As an algebraic equation,

$$v = \frac{s}{t} \quad (3b)$$

where v is the velocity, and s the distance traveled, and t the elapsed time.

Change of position is illustrated in Fig. 3A. A car traveling with uniform velocity

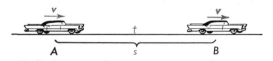

Fig. 3A   *Diagram of a body moving with constant velocity.*

along a straight line passes the point A at one instant and the point B at some later instant of time. In substituting in Eq.(3b), the distance traveled is AB, and the time interval between A and B is time t.

Example 1. A man takes 2 hr to drive his car to a distant city 120 mi due East. What is his velocity?

Solution. Here the distance traveled $s = 120$ mi, and the time interval $t = 2$ hr. The velocity therefore is

$$v = \frac{120 \text{ mi}}{2 \text{ hr}} = 60 \frac{\text{mi}}{\text{hr}} \quad (3c)$$

The answer is *60 mi/hr due East.* The units are just as important as the numbers and must be included in the answer.

If, in the answer to the above example, the time 1 hr in the denominator is replaced by its equivalent of 3600 sec, a velocity of 60 mi/hr becomes

$$v = 60 \frac{\text{mi}}{\text{hr}} = 60 \frac{\text{mi}}{3600 \text{ sec}} = 0.0167 \frac{\text{mi}}{\text{sec}} \quad (3d)$$

If at the same time the distance 1 mi in the numerator is replaced by its equivalent of 5280 ft,

$$v = 60 \frac{\text{mi}}{\text{hr}} = 60 \frac{5280 \text{ ft}}{3600 \text{ sec}} = 88 \frac{\text{ft}}{\text{sec}} \quad (3e)$$

All three of the answers above, 60 mi/hr, 0.0167 mi/sec, and 88 ft/sec, are exactly equal; they are only expressed in different units. This last derived result that 60 mi/hr is equivalent to 88 ft/sec should be memorized, as it is very useful in the solving of many practical problems. A velocity of 120 mi/hr, for example, is equivalent to 2×88 or 176 ft/sec, while a velocity of 30 mi/hr is equivalent to $\frac{1}{2} \times 88$ or 44 ft/sec.

60 mph = 88 ft/sec.

Example 2. A toy train running along a straight track at constant velocity requires 8 sec to travel a distance of 20 m. Find the velocity.

Solution. Since $s = 20$ m and $t = 8$ sec, the velocity

$$v = \frac{20 \text{ m}}{8 \text{ sec}} = 2.5 \frac{\text{m}}{\text{sec}}$$

The answer is read *two point five meters per second.* To change this answer to centimeters per second, the unit 1 m in the numerator is changed to 100 cm, and the answer becomes

$$v = 2.5 \frac{\text{m}}{\text{sec}} = 2.5 \frac{100 \text{ cm}}{\text{sec}} = 250 \frac{\text{cm}}{\text{sec}}$$

3.2. Constant (or Uniform) Velocity. *A body moving along the same straight line, traveling equal distances in equal intervals of time, is moving with constant velocity.* Suppose, as a demonstration of the scientific method, we perform an experiment of the kind shown in Fig. 3B. A toy automobile is

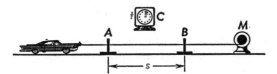

Fig. 3B *Experimental arrangement for measuring the velocity of a car.*

pulled across the table top by means of a cord wrapped around a drum, and a stop-clock is used to measure the time. A small synchronous motor M, with a geared down shaft making one revolution per sec, and a drum about 1 in. in diameter makes a suitable power unit.

Markers A and B are located a short distance apart, and the distance s between them is measured with a meter stick. The car is started, and, as it passes marker A, the clock is started; as it passes marker B, the clock is stopped. The time t in sec, as read on the clock, is then recorded. This procedure should be repeated with the markers farther and farther apart, and the data recorded in a table. Suppose this experiment has now been performed at five different distances and the data recorded are those shown in Table 3A.

To find how s and t are related to each

TABLE 3A. RECORDED DATA FOR CAR

Trial	Distance s (cm)	Time t (sec)
1	39.8	5.3
2	86.2	11.5
3	108.8	14.5
4	141.6	18.9
5	174.2	23.2

other, it is most informative to plot a graph of the two measured quantities. If we plot s vertically and t horizontally, as shown in Fig. 3C, we obtain the points shown as X's.

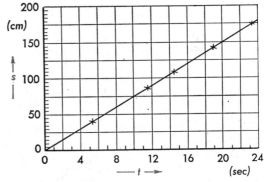

Fig. 3C *Graph of the data recorded in the car experiment.*

When a smooth line is drawn through these points, it is observed to be a straight line. Furthermore, this straight line passes through the origin $s = 0$ and $t = 0$. From the fact that the graph is a straight line, one concludes that the two quantities s and t are directly proportional to each other.

$$s \propto t$$

To make an equation of this, the proportionality sign is replaced by an equal sign, and a proportionality constant inserted on the right. Calling this constant v, we obtain

$$\boxed{s = vt}$$

To find the value of this constant which we call the velocity, transpose t to the other side of the equation and obtain

$$\frac{s}{t} = v$$

$$s = 45 \frac{cm}{sec} \times 120 \ sec = 5400 \ cm$$

The next step is to take each value of s in Table 3A and divide by the corresponding value of t. When this is done for each of the five trials, the value 7.5 cm/sec is obtained in all cases. (Note that the units are divided one by the other to obtain cm/sec.) This then is the velocity of the car, and, since all trials give the same result, we say that the velocity is constant, or uniform.

That the motion of the car follows the definition of constant velocity, as stated at the beginning of this section, may be seen from the graph. In 10 sec the distance traveled is 75 cm. During the next 10 sec the distance traveled is 75 cm, making the total distance 150 cm. *In equal time intervals, the car travels equal distances.* Although this is a simple experiment illustrating a simple principle in mechanics, its purpose is that of illustrating the scientific method, namely, of making measurements of a given phenomenon and, from the recorded observations, of finding the simplest relations between them.

3.3. Distance Traveled. If the velocity of a body is known, the distance traveled can be calculated for any given interval of time. For such problems Eq.(3b) is conveniently changed by solving for s. Multiplying both sides of the equation by t does not alter the equality.

$$vt = \frac{st}{t}$$

Canceling t's on the right-hand side gives $vt = s$, or

$$s = vt \qquad (3f)$$

Example 3. If a body moves with a velocity of 45 cm/sec, how far will it travel in 2 min?

Solution. The distance traveled can be determined by Eq.(3f).

$$s = 45 \frac{cm}{sec} \times 2 \ min = 90 \frac{cm \ min}{sec}$$

In order to eliminate *time* units in this answer, they must both be expressed in the same units. To do this, the minutes may be changed to seconds as follows:

Note that *sec* in the numerator cancels *sec* in the denominator, leaving *cm* in the answer as the unit of length. This illustrates a common practice that should be followed in the solving of all problems. Always express like quantities in the same units.

Dividing both sides of Eq.(3f) by v and canceling the v's on the right-hand side, we obtain

$$t = \frac{s}{v} \qquad (3g)$$

an equation for the time of travel in terms of s and v.

Example 4. If a car travels with an average velocity of 30 mi/hr, how long will it take to go 175 mi?

Solution. Using Eq.(3g), we find

$$t = \frac{s}{v} = \frac{175 \ mi}{30 \ mi/hr} = 5.83 \ hr$$

3.4. Vectors and Scalars. Nearly all physical measurements, whether they are made with the simplest of instruments or with the most complex of apparatus, may be classified as *vector* or *scalar* quantities. *Measurable quantities that have magnitude and direction are called vectors.* Examples of vector quantities are *displacement, velocity, acceleration,* and *force. Measurable quantities that have magnitude only are called scalars.* Examples of scalar quantities are *volume, area,* and *mass.*

The importance of this seemingly trivial distinction between quantities that have direction and those that do not, is realized when in solving certain problems the simple process of the addition of two or more like quantities becomes necessary.

No difficulty is generally encountered with scalars since such quantities are added algebraically. For example, in the addition of volumes, the sum of 2 gal and 3 gal is 5 gal. The addition of two vectors, on the other hand, is more complicated and requires a special process called *vector addition.* (This process will be treated in detail in Chap. 7.)

scalars = magnitude
vectors = magnitude + direction

3.5. Speed and Velocity. The terms *speed* and *velocity* are often used synonymously. Strictly speaking, however, *speed is a scalar quantity* and *velocity is a vector quantity*. In the last section it was explained that vector quantities have magnitude and direction, while scalars have magnitude only.

Speed is a term applied only to the magnitude of velocity and does not specify the direction of motion. In moving along a straight line, *speed* and *velocity* are numerically equal to each other. If, however, the speed along a curved path is constant, the velocity is not considered to be constant because of its changing direction.

When a body moves with constant speed along a straight line whose direction is specified, it is customary to speak of its *velocity*. Movement along a straight or curved path, with no reference being made to direction, is properly referred to as *speed*.

Speed and velocity always have the *dimensions* of *length divided by time*, i.e., *L/T*.

about 15% greater than speed in miles per hour. It is *not* correct to say the speed of a ship is 10 knots/hr; it is correct to say the speed is 10 knots.

3.6. Constant and Variable Velocity. In mechanics, it is often convenient to neglect the size and shape of a body and to consider its motion as that of a small *particle* of negligible size. For example, in describing the motion of an airplane flying between two cities, it is not necessary to give a detailed description of the plane in order to give its position and progress. Hence, it is customary to speak of the motion of a body as the motion of a particle.

If the statement is made that a particle travels 30 mi in 1 hr, it does not necessarily mean that its speed or velocity is constant. Moving due East in a straight line, the particle either moved with a *constant velocity* or with a *variable velocity*. A constant velocity is defined as one in which equal displacements are traversed in equal intervals of time and the direction is at all times that

TABLE 3B. CONVERSION FACTORS FOR SPEED AND VELOCITY

Velocity	m/sec	ft/sec	Km/hr	mi/hr	knots
1 m/sec =	1	3.281	3.600	2.240	1.940
1 ft/sec =	0.30480	1	1.0973	0.6818	0.5921
1 Km/hr =	0.27778	0.9113	1	0.6214	0.5396
1 mi/hr =	0.44704	1.4667	1.6093	1	0.8684
1 knot =	0.51480	1.689	1.853	1.152	1

Example 5. Change 30 mi/hr to kilometers per hour.

Solution. From Table 3B, 1 mi/hr in the left-hand column is (read across to the fourth column) equal to 1.6093 Km/hr. Therefore,

$$30 \times 1.6093 = 48.279 \frac{Km}{hr}$$

Upon dropping off the last two figures, we find the answer, to three significant figures:

$$30 \frac{mi}{hr} = 48.3 \frac{Km}{hr}$$

The *knot* is a nautical unit of speed,

of the same straight line. In other words, the distance traveled in any 1 sec is equal to that traveled in any other second.

A particle has a *variable velocity* when, in equal intervals of time, its displacements are unequal. In such cases it is customary to speak of the *average velocity*. Average velocity, $\bar{v}$, is defined by

$$\bar{v} = \frac{s}{t} \qquad (3h)$$

where t is the total time required to travel the total distance s.

3.7. *Curvilinear Motion.* Motion along a curved path is called curvilinear motion. When a particle moves along a curved path as shown in Fig. 3D, it may have a constant

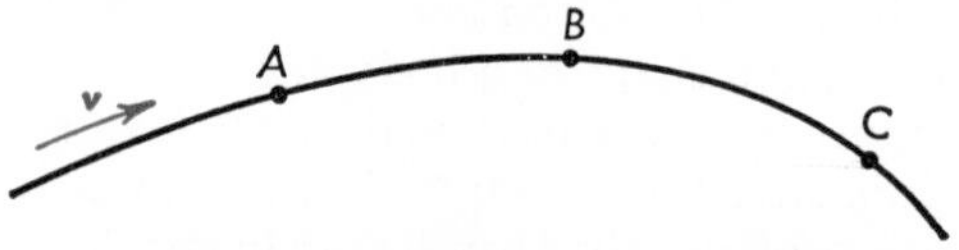

Fig. 3D *Motion along a curved path.*

or variable speed. The term *speed* is used here in place of velocity since the path is not straight. A *constant speed* is defined as one in which the distances traveled in equal intervals of time are equal, the distances being measured along the curved path.

A *variable speed* means that the distances traveled in equal intervals of time are different. It follows from these definitions, by comparison with those for linear motion in the preceding section, that all of the equations in this chapter apply equally well to constant and average speed.

3.8. *Instantaneous Velocity.* In describing the curvilinear motion of a particle, it sometimes becomes necessary to specify its *instantaneous velocity*. As shown in Fig. 3E,

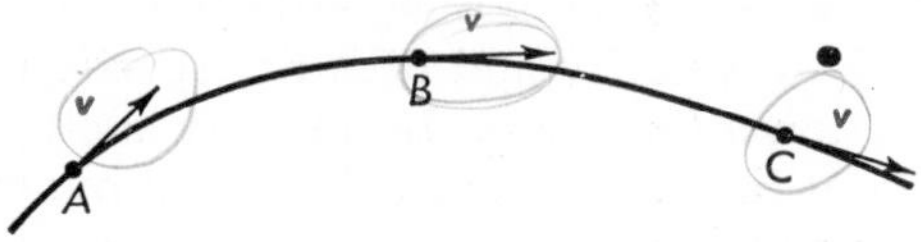

Fig. 3E *Arrows indicate instantaneous velocity.*

the instantaneous velocity of a particle at any given point in its path is obtained by drawing a tangent to the curve at the point in question. The magnitude of the instantaneous velocity is equal to the speed of the particle as it passes that point, and the direction is that of the tangent to the curve at that point.

PROBLEMS

1. In the Olympic Games of 1936, the marathon, covering a course of 26 mi and 385 yd, was won by Kitei, a Japanese boy of 21 years, in the time of 2 hr, 29 min, 19.2 sec. What was his average speed in mi/hr?

2. An automobile, leaving an airport, averages 45 mi/hr along a straight highway. If a plane leaves the same airport 1 hr later and travels at a rate of 120 mi/hr, (a) how much time will be required for it to overtake the automobile? (b) What will be the distance traveled? (*Ans.* (a) 36 min, (b) 72 mi.)

3. A person drives a car 200 mi at an average speed of 44 mi/hr. What must be his average speed for the next 220 mi if he is to cover the total distance in 9 hr?

4. How much longer would it take to travel a distance of 500 mi at a speed of 40 mi/hr than it would at a speed of 50 mi/hr? (*Ans.* 2 hr and 30 min.)

5. A world record in the 10,000-m run was set in 1924 by P. Nurmi of Finland in the time of 30 min $6\frac{1}{2}$ sec. Calculate his average speed in (a) mi/hr, and (b) ft/sec.

6. In the Olympic games of 1928, the following races were run in the respective times: (a) 100 m in $10\frac{3}{5}$ sec; (b) 200 m in $21\frac{3}{5}$ sec; (c) 400 m in $47\frac{3}{5}$ sec; (d) 800 m in 1 min, $51\frac{4}{5}$ sec; (e) 1500 m in 3 min, $53\frac{1}{5}$ sec; (f) 5000 m in 14 min, $31\frac{1}{5}$ sec; (g) 10,000 m in 30 min, $18\frac{4}{5}$ sec; and (h) 15,000 m in 46 min, $49\frac{3}{5}$ sec. Calculate the average speed of each in mi/hr. (*Ans.* (a) 21.1 mi/hr, (b) 20.7 mi/hr, (c) 18.8 mi/hr, (d) 16.0 mi/hr, (e) 14.4 mi/hr, (f) 12.9 mi/hr, (g) 12.3 mi/hr, (h) 12.0 mi/hr.

7. Make a graph of the answers in Prob. 10, plotting average speeds horizontally and the logarithms of the distances vertically.

8. Find the cruising range of a plane if its fuel tank contains 45 gal of gasoline. Assume that at a cruising speed of 175 mi/hr the fuel consumption is 12 gal/hr. (*Ans.* 656 mi.)

9. In a track-meet the 100-yd dash was won in the time of 9.4 sec. Calculate the average speed in (a) ft/sec. and (b) mi/hr.

10. In the Olympic games the 100-m dash was won in the time of 10.0 sec. Calculate the average speed in (a) ft/sec, and (b) mi/hr. (*Ans.* (a) 32.81 ft/sec, (b) 22.4 mi/hr.)

11. How long will it take a ship traveling at 20 knots to go 525 mi?

12. How long will it take a ship traveling at 28 knots to go 5400 mi? (*Ans.* 167.4 hr.)

13. An airplane in a steep dive moves with a speed of 570 mi/hr. Compute its speed in (a) ft/sec, (b) Km/hr, and (c) knots.

14. A ship sailing from San Francisco to Hawaii makes the trip of 2300 mi in $4\frac{1}{2}$ days. What is its average speed in (a) mi/hr, (b) Km/hr, and (c) knots? (*Ans.* (a) 21.3 mi/hr, (b) 34.3 Km/hr, (c) 18.5 knots.)

15. It takes a farmer 3 hr to walk the full length of the fence surrounding his farm one mile square. Calculate his average speed in (a) mi/hr, (b) ft/sec, and (c) cm/sec.

16. A circular racetrack is 1500 ft in diameter. A car makes 100 laps around the track in 56 min. Calculate the average speed in (a) mi/hr, (b) ft/sec, and (c) Km/hr. (*Ans.* (a) 95.6 mi/hr, (b) 140.25 ft/sec, (c) 153.9 Km/hr.)

17. The 100-m, free-style event in a swimming meet was won in 1 min, 5.9 sec. Calculate the average speed in (a) m/sec, (b) ft/sec, and (c) mi/hr.

18. The 5-mile, cross-country run in a track-meet was won in 26 min, 26 sec. Calculate the average speed in (a) ft/sec, and (b) m/sec. (*Ans.* (a) 16.6 ft/sec, (b) 5.06 m/sec.

19. A jet passenger plane crosses the country, a distance of 2800 mi, in 4 hr, 28 min. Calculate its average speed in (a) mi/hr, (b) ft/sec, and (c) m/sec.

20. A satellite circles the earth 140 mi above the surface in 1 hr, 30 min. Calculate its average speed in mi/hr. Assume the earth's radius to be 3960 mi. (*Ans.* 17,200 mi/hr.)

Chapter 4

Acceleration

4.1. Constant (or Uniform) Acceleration. Whenever the speed or velocity of a body changes, the body is said to be accelerated. Acceleration is defined as *the rate of change of velocity.* A car "picking up speed" has a *positive acceleration,* while another slowing down has a *negative acceleration.* Standing still or moving with constant velocity a car has no acceleration.

Consider as an illustration of accelerated motion the car shown in Fig. 4A. Due to a

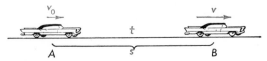

Fig. 4A *A car is accelerated for a period of t seconds.*

constantly acting force, exerted by the motor through the drive wheels, this car is continually accelerated as it moves along the straight line *AB.* As it passes *A* it has a relatively low velocity v_0, while farther along its path at a point *B* it is moving faster and has a velocity *v.* The *initial velocity* is called v_0 and the *final velocity* is called *v.*

If the time required to go from *A* to *B* is *t,* the acceleration, by the definition given above, is schematically written.

acceleration
$$= \frac{\text{final velocity} - \text{initial velocity}}{\text{time}}$$

or algebraically as

$$a = \frac{v - v_0}{t} \qquad (4a)$$

Example 1. Suppose at *A,* in Fig. 4A, that the velocity of the car is 20 ft/sec, that at *B* it has increased to 40 ft/sec, and that it takes 4 sec to go from *A* to *B.* What is the acceleration?

Solution. By direct substitution in Eq.(4a), we obtain

$$a = \frac{40 \text{ ft/sec} - 20 \text{ ft/sec}}{4 \text{ sec}} = \frac{20 \text{ ft/sec}}{4 \text{ sec}} = 5 \frac{\text{ft}}{\text{sec sec}}$$

The answer is read *five feet per second per second* and means that the velocity increases 5 ft/sec every second of time. Initially the velocity, as shown in Fig. 4B, is 20 ft/sec. An increase of 5 ft/sec every second means that at the end of 1 sec the velocity is 25 ft/sec, at the end of 2 sec it is 30 ft/sec, at the end of 3 sec it is 35 ft/sec, and at the end of 4 sec it is 40 ft/sec. Uniform or constant acceleration is, therefore, one in which *the velocity changes by equal amounts in equal intervals of time.*

4.2. Negative Acceleration. When a body is slowing down, the initial velocity is greater than the final velocity, and the acceleration as given by Eq.(4a) is negative.

Example 2. In going up a long steep hill a car slows down from 60 mi/hr to 30 mi/hr in 2 min. Find the acceleration.

Solution. Substitute the foregoing values in Eq.(4a); then

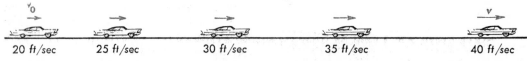

| 20 ft/sec | 25 ft/sec | 30 ft/sec | 35 ft/sec | 40 ft/sec |

Fig. 4B *Diagram showing instantaneous velocity at end of each second for uniformly accelerated car (see Example 1).*

$$a = \frac{30 \text{ mi/hr} - 60 \text{ mi/hr}}{2 \text{ min}} = -15 \frac{\text{mi}}{\text{hr min}}$$

The velocity thus decreases by 15 mi/hr each minute of time. During the first minute it drops from 60 mi/hr to 45 mi/hr, and during the next minute from 45 mi/hr to 30 mi/hr.

The above answer, as written, has two different units of time in the denominator. It can be left this way or changed to the same units as follows: replace 1 hr in the denominator by its equality, 60 min, so that

$$a = -15 \frac{\text{mi}}{60 \text{ min min}} = -0.25 \frac{\text{mi}}{\text{min}^2}$$

To express this answer in feet and seconds, 1 mi in the numerator is replaced by its equivalent, 5280 ft, and (1 min)² in the denominator by (60 sec)², to give

$$a = -0.25 \frac{5280 \text{ ft}}{3600 \text{ sec}^2} = -0.367 \frac{\text{ft}}{\text{sec}^2}$$

This answer is read *minus zero point three six seven feet per second per second,* or *per second squared.*

4.3. Distance Traveled during Uniform Acceleration. As a demonstration of the scientific method we may perform an experiment of the kind shown in Fig. 4C.

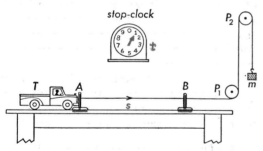

Fig. 4C *Demonstration experiment with a toy truck.*

Here a toy truck *T* with ball-bearing, steel-rimmed wheels is shown free to roll with a minimum amount of friction along a level glass plate.

Uniform acceleration is brought about by a thin cord passing over two pulleys P_1 and P_2 to a small mass *m*. We now wish to accelerate the truck and find the relation between the *distance traveled* and the *time*

of travel. Markers *A* and *B* are located a short distance apart, and the distance *s* between them is measured with a meter stick. With the front bumper at marker *A*, the truck is released and the clock is started. As the truck reaches marker *B*, the clock is stopped and the time is recorded. This procedure should be repeated with the markers farther and farther apart, and the data recorded in a table. Suppose this experiment has been performed at five different distances and the data recorded are as shown in Table 4A.

TABLE 4A. RECORDED DATA FOR TRUCK

Trial	Distance s (cm)	Time t (sec)
1	17.5	1.6
2	39.2	2.4
3	98.1	3.8
4	163.4	4.9
5	213.3	5.6

To find how *s* and *t* are related to each other, we can follow the procedure used in Chap. 3, namely, that of plotting a graph of the measured quantities. If we plot *s* vertically and *t* horizontally as shown at the left in Fig. 4D, we obtain the points marked X. When a smooth line is drawn through these points, it is definitely not a straight line. The curve must be drawn through the origin $s = 0$ and $t = 0$, since this is an observed point. In zero time, the distance traveled is zero.

Since the graph does not yield a straight line, *s* is not proportional to *t*. The problem then becomes one of seeing if either or both of the measured quantities can be modified to produce a straight-line graph. A few trials of plotting such quantities as $2s$, s^2, $\sqrt{s}$, $2t$, t^2, $\sqrt{t}$, etc., will show that if *s* is plotted against t^2, a straight line like that shown in Fig. 4E will be the result. From this graph we can conclude that *s* is proportional to t^2.

$$s \propto t^2$$

To make an equation of this relation, the

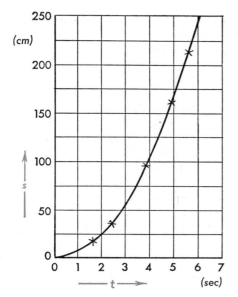

Fig. 4D *Graph of measurements made with a toy truck.*

proportionality sign is replaced by an equal sign, and a proprotionality constant inserted on the right. Calling this constant k, we can write

$$s = kt^2 \qquad (4b)$$

To find the value of k in this particular

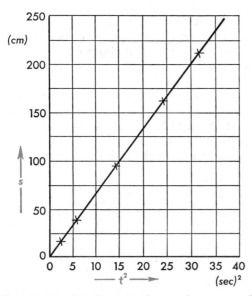

Fig. 4E *Straight-line graph for the toy truck experiment.*

experiment, transpose t^2 to the other side of the equation, and obtain

$$\frac{s}{t^2} = k \qquad (4c)$$

If we divide each of the measured values of s in Table 4A, with the corresponding value of t^2, we find in all cases,

$$k = 6.8 \frac{cm}{sec^2}$$

This result we will see in Sec. 4.7 is just one half the quantity called the acceleration a.

$$a = 2k = 13.6 \frac{cm}{sec^2}$$

One who is familiar with analytical geometry will recognize the curve at the left in Fig. 4D, as a parabola, and that an equation of the form given by Eq.(4b) is its algebraic counterpart.

If this experiment were to be repeated with a different mass m, the graph shown in Fig. 4D could well be expected to change. It will be left for the student to determine by experiment, or by reasoning, what the new graph might look like, and whether the value of k would be different.

4.4. Final Velocity. Return now to the definition of acceleration introduced at the beginning of this chapter. By transposing Eq.(4a), the formula for acceleration is made to take on a different aspect. If both sides of the equation are multiplied by t, the two t's on the right side cancel, and there results

$$v - v_0 = at$$

Transposing v_0 to the other side of the equation, we obtain

$$\boxed{v = v_0 + at} \qquad (4d)$$

Here the final velocity v of a body is given as the sum of two terms, the initial velocity v_0 plus the increase in velocity at.

Example 3. A particle with an initial velocity of 50 cm/sec is subject to an acceleration of 8 cm/sec² for 5 sec. What is its final velocity?
Solution. Use Eq.(4d). The known quantities

for direct substitution are: $v_0 = 50$ cm/sec, $a = 8$ cm/sec^2, and $t = 5$ sec.

$$v = 50 \frac{cm}{sec} + 8 \frac{cm}{sec^2} \times 5 \, sec$$

$$= 50 \frac{cm}{sec} + 40 \frac{cm}{sec} = 90 \frac{cm}{sec}$$

Note that the product at has the dimensions of a velocity; *length* divided by *time*. It can therefore be added to v_0 because it is expressed in the same units (*cm* divided by *sec*). It is a rule well worth remembering when solving a problem by the substitution of known quantities in an equation, that quantities can be added or subtracted only when they are like quantities; that is, they have the same dimensions and the same units.

4.5. Average Velocity. While the velocity of an accelerated body is continually changing, the distance traveled in any given time t may be described in terms of its *average velocity*. The average velocity of a particle moving with uniform acceleration is given by

$$\bar{v} = \frac{v + v_0}{2} \tag{4e}$$

The bar over the v indicates an average value. The equation $s = vt$ already given in Chap. 3 to hold for constant velocity also holds for uniform acceleration if v is replaced by $\bar{v}$. Thus

$$s = \bar{v}t$$

or

$$s = \frac{v + v_0}{2} t \tag{4f}$$

Example 4. If 5 sec are required to increase the velocity of a particle from 2 m/sec to 5 m/sec, what are (a) the average velocity, and (b) the distance traveled?

Solution. The given quantities are $t = 5$ sec, $v_0 = 2$ m/sec, and $v = 5$ m/sec. By direct substitution in Eq.(4e),

$$\bar{v} = \frac{5 \, m/sec + 2 \, m/sec}{2} = \frac{7 \, m/sec}{2} = 3.5 \frac{m}{sec}$$

Substitute this answer in Eq.(4f). Then

$$s = \bar{v}t = 3.5 \frac{m}{sec} \times 5 \, sec = 17.5 \, m$$

For the special case of a body starting from rest, $v_0 = 0$; and Eq.(4e) for the average velocity becomes

$$\bar{v} = \frac{v}{2} \tag{4g}$$

4.6. Derived Equations. By combining Eq.(4a) with Eq.(4f), a new and useful equation is obtained. To do this each of the two equations is solved for t and then set equal to each other as follows:

Eq.(4a) is first transposed and then Eq.(4f) to give respectively,

$$t = \frac{v - v_0}{a} \quad \text{and} \quad t = \frac{2s}{v + v_0}$$

Since the left-hand sides are both equal to t, the right-hand sides must be equal to each other. By setting them equal and then cross-multiplying, we obtain

$$\frac{v - v_0}{a} = \frac{2s}{v + v_0}, \quad (v - v_0)(v + v_0) = 2as$$

By multiplying out and transposing, we get

$$v^2 - v_0^2 = 2as$$

$$v^2 = v_0^2 + 2as \tag{4h}$$

Another useful equation is obtained by eliminating v from the same two original equations. From Eqs.(4a) and (4f), we get separately

$$v = v_0 + at \quad \text{and} \quad v = \frac{2s}{t} - v_0$$

If the right-hand sides of these two equations are set equal to each other, and if v_0 is transposed to the right-hand side,

$$\frac{2s}{t} - v_0 = v_0 + at \quad \frac{2s}{t} = 2v_0 + at$$

Multiplying through by $t/2$, we obtain

$$s = v_0 t + \tfrac{1}{2}at^2 \tag{4i}$$

These equations, (4h) and (4i), are called *derived equations.* They give no additional information to that given by Eqs.(4a) and

(4f); they are only rearrangements of the same quantities. In their new form, however, they are more readily applied to certain types of problems.

Example 5. A train is traveling 15 mi/hr when the throttle is suddenly opened full and kept open for a distance of 1 mi. If the acceleration is 0.5 ft/sec², what is the final velocity?

Solution. Since a velocity of 60 mi/hr is equivalent to 88 ft/sec, the given velocity of 15 mi/hr is equivalent to 22 ft/sec. By direct substitution in Eq.(4h), we obtain

$$v^2 = (22 \text{ ft/sec})^2 + 2 \times 0.5 \text{ ft/sec}^2 \times 5280 \text{ ft}$$
$$v^2 = 484 \text{ ft}^2/\text{sec}^2 + 5280 \text{ ft}^2/\text{sec}^2 = 5764 \text{ ft}^2/\text{sec}^2$$
$$v = 75.9 \text{ ft/sec}^2$$

4.7. Starting from Rest. When a body starts from rest and undergoes uniform acceleration, the initial velocity v_0 is zero. The acceleration a as defined by Eq.(4a) can therefore be simplified by placing $v_0 = 0$. Making this substitution, we obtain

$$a = \frac{v}{t} \tag{4j}$$

Transposed, this equation takes the form

$$v = at \tag{4k}$$

Example 6. An airplane starting from rest at one end of a runway acquires its take-off speed of 60 mi/hr in 8 sec. What is its acceleration?

Solution. The acceleration is obtained from Eq.(4j).

$$a = \frac{60 \text{ mi/hr}}{8 \text{ sec}} = 7.5 \frac{\text{mi}}{\text{hr sec}}$$

The answer is read *seven point five miles per hour per second.*

Remembering that 60 mi/hr is equivalent to 88 ft/sec, we can express this same acceleration as

$$a = \frac{88 \text{ ft/sec}}{8 \text{ sec}} = 11 \frac{\text{ft}}{\text{sec}^2}$$

read *eleven feet per second squared.*

The other equations involving uniformly accelerated motion, and derived in the preceding sections of this chapter, are also simplified if a body starts from rest. With $v_0 = 0$, Eq.(4f) becomes

$$s = \frac{v}{2}t \tag{4l}$$

Eq. (4h) becomes

$$v^2 = 2as \tag{4m}$$

and Eq.(4i) becomes

$$s = \tfrac{1}{2}at^2 \tag{4n}$$

Compare this last equation with the conclusions reached with the toy truck experiment in Sec. 4.3. The constant k derived from experiment, and equal to 6.8 cm/sec² is just $\tfrac{1}{2}$ the acceleration, $\tfrac{1}{2}a$.

Because of the importance of the equations developed in this chapter, the student would do well to memorize the four general equations for uniformly accelerated motion, Eqs.(4d),(4f),(4h), and (4i). The special equations need not be memorized, since they are just special cases for starting from rest and are obtained by placing $v_0 = 0$.

TABLE 4B. FORMULAS FOR UNIFORMLY ACCELERATED MOTION

General Equations	Special Equations
$v = v_0 + at$	$v = at$
$s = \dfrac{v + v_0}{2}t$	$s = \dfrac{v}{2}t$
$v^2 = v_0^2 + 2as$	$v^2 = 2as$
$s = v_0t + \tfrac{1}{2}at^2$	$s = \tfrac{1}{2}at^2$

PROBLEMS

1. A car starting from rest acquires a speed of 30 m/sec in 12 sec. Find (a) the acceleration in m/sec², (b) the total distance traveled in meters, and (c) the speed in m/sec at the end of 7 sec.

2. A jet airliner starting from rest at the end of a runway acquires a take-off speed of 180 mi/hr in a distance of 6600 ft. Calculate (a) the time to reach take-off, (b) the acceleration in ft/sec², and (c) the speed acquired 20 sec after starting. (*Ans.* (a) 50 sec, (b) 5.28 ft/sec², (c) 105.6 ft/sec.)

3. Starting from rest, a car acquires a speed of 60 mi/hr in 11 sec. Find (a) the acceleration in ft/sec², (b) the total distance traveled in ft, and

(c) the speed in ft/sec at the end of 5 sec. (Show units in your answers.)

4. A car starting from rest acquires a speed of 45 mi/hr in 11 sec, after which it maintains a constant speed for 5 sec. Find (a) the acceleration in ft/sec^2, (b) the distance traveled while accelerating, (c) the total distance traveled, and (d) the speed 5 sec after starting. (*Ans.* (a) 6 ft/sec^2, (b) 363 ft, (c) 693 ft, (d) 30 ft/sec.)

5. A racing car starting from rest acquires a speed of 100 mi/hr in 8 sec. What is its acceleration and how far did it travel during this time?

6. A train starts from rest and after a constant acceleration for 60 sec acquires a speed of 45 mi/hr. (a) What is the acceleration in ft/sec^2, and (b) how far does it travel during this time? (*Ans.* (a) 1.10 ft/sec^2, (b) 1980 ft.)

7. An airplane with a speed of 200 mi/hr goes into a power glide and acquires a speed of 350 mi/hr in 6 sec. Find (a) the acceleration in mi/hr sec, and (b) the distance traveled during this time.

8. A truck with a speed of 30 mi/hr at the top of a long grade starts coasting down and acquires a speed of 60 mi/hr in 45 sec. Assuming constant acceleration find (a) the acceleration in mi/hr sec, and (b) the distance traveled in mi during this time. (*Ans.* (a) 0.667 mi/hr sec, (b) 0.562 mi.)

9. A bullet from an army rifle with a barrel 30 in. long has a muzzle velocity of 2600 ft/sec. Find (a) the average speed of the bullet while being accelerated in the gun barrel, (b) the time taken to travel the length of the barrel, and (c) the average acceleration.

10. A passenger car starting from rest has an acceleration of 5 ft/sec^2 for 12 sec, after which time it continues at constant speed. After 8 sec at this constant speed the brakes are applied, bringing the car to rest in 6 sec. Find (a) the constant speed acquired, in mi/hr, and (b) the total distance traveled in feet. (*Ans.* (a) 40.9 mi/hr, (b) 1020 ft.)

11. A switch engine starting from rest travels with an acceleration of 4 ft/sec^2 for 6 sec. After traveling with the acquired speed for 13 sec, the brakes are applied, stopping the engine in 4 sec. Find (a) the speed acquired due to the acceleration, (b) the acceleration while the brakes are applied, and (c) the total distance traveled.

12. A rifle bullet with a speed of 800 m/sec

strikes the ground and penetrates to a depth of 0.5 m. Find (a) the average speed while being stopped, (b) the time of stopping, and (c) the acceleration. (*Ans.* (a) 400 m/sec, (b) 0.00125 sec, (c) — 640,000 m/sec^2.)

13. The engine of a train 1000 ft long stands at a road crossing. If the train starts up with an acceleration of 0.25 ft/sec^2, how long must the motorist wait for the end of the train to cross the intersection?

14. A truck starting from rest maintains a constant acceleration of 0.35 ft/sec^2. How long will it take the truck to go 1 mi? (*Ans.* 174 sec.)

15. A man, driving a car with an initial speed of 60 mi/hr, suddenly applies the brakes bringing the car to a stop in 5 sec. Find (a) the acceleration, (b) the total distance traveled, (c) the speed at the end of 3 sec, and (d) the distance traveled during the first 3 sec.

16. A train, moving 45 mi/hr, is brought to a stop in 24 sec by the sudden application of the brakes. Calculate (a) the acceleration, (b) the total distance traveled after the brakes are applied, (c) the velocity at the end of 8 sec, and (d) the distance traveled during the first 8 sec. (*Ans.* (a) —2.75 ft/sec^2, (b) 792 ft, (c) 44 ft/sec, (d) 440 ft.)

17. A plane starting from rest at the end of a runway maintains a constant acceleration, taking it a distance of 2 ft during the first second. If the plane becomes airborne at 60 mi/hr, (a) what distance is required for take-off, and (b) what is the total time?

18. In starting from rest, a large ship requires 5 min to acquire its cruising speed of 20 knots. Assuming constant acceleration, calculate (a) the acceleration in knots/hr, and (b) the distance in nautical mi required to reach cruising speed. (*Ans.* (a) 240 knots/hr, (b) 0.833 nautical mi, or 5067 ft.

19. A jet fighter plane initially at rest is catapulted forward from an aircraft carrier to a speed of 90 mi/hr in 3 sec. Calculate the acceleration in ft/sec^2.

20. Starting from rest an object A undergoes an acceleration of 2 m/sec^2. Starting from the same point 4 sec later, object B undergoes an acceleration of 8 m/sec^2. Find (a) the time required for B to overtake A, and (b) the distance both have traveled. (*Ans.* (a) 4 sec, (b) 64 m.)

21. Starting from rest a locomotive undergoes

an acceleration of 2 ft/sec^2 for 40 sec, then continues with constant velocity. Some time later the brakes are applied, bringing the locomotive to a stop. If the total distance traveled is exactly $\frac{1}{2}$ mi and the total time is exactly 1 min, what was the average acceleration during the time the brakes were applied?

22. A marble rolls down an inclined plane acquiring at the end of 5 sec a speed of 0.22 m/sec. Find (a) the acceleration, (b) the total distance traveled, and (c) the distance traveled during the third second. (*Ans.* (a) 0.044 m/sec^2, (b) 0.55 m, (c) 0.11 m.)

23. Starting from rest a plane takes off after traveling 3000 ft along a runway. If the plane becomes airborne at speed of 80 mi/hr, find (a) the acceleration, (b) the total time of take-off, and (c) the distance traveled during the last second on the ground.

24. A plane coming in for a landing travels a distance of 3500 ft along the runway before coming to rest. Assuming constant acceleration and a landing speed of 75 mi/hr, find (a) the acceleration, (b) the total time for stopping, and (c) the distance traveled during the first 10 sec. (*Ans.* (a) −1.73 ft/sec^2, (b) 63.6 sec. (c) 1013.6 ft.)

25. A box accidentally drops from a truck traveling 30 mi/hr and slides along the ground for a distance of 100 ft. Find (a) the acceleration, (b) the time to come to rest, and (c) the distance traveled the first second.

Chapter 5

Gravity and Falling Bodies

Neglecting friction, all bodies, large and small, fall with the same acceleration. This, the law of falling bodies, is a physical paradox for it contradicts the conclusion the average person might derive *a priori*. This is not to be wondered at, for centuries ago the great philosopher Aristotle* (384-322 B.C.) taught that heavy bodies fall proportionately faster than lighter ones.

It took the world nearly two thousand years to produce a challenger of Aristotle's scientific teachings. In the year 1590, Galileo† was pondering over the question of falling bodies and found apparent inconsistencies in Aristotle's teachings. As tests, he is said to have dropped various kinds of objects from different levels of the leaning tower of Pisa and to have timed their fall and measured their velocities.

* Aristotle (384-322 B.C.), famous Greek philosopher, logician, moralist, political thinker, biologist, and founder of literary criticism, spent his early years as a student and fellow worker with Plato. While practically all of Aristotle's teachings concerning physical principles are now known to be erroneous, his contributions to other fields of knowledge have placed him high among the great men of ancient Greece.

† Galileo Galilei (1564-1642), Italian mathematician, astronomer, and experimental physicist, who at the early age of twenty-four wrote a treatise on the center of gravity of solids. This led the following year to his appointment as professor of mathematics at the University of Pisa. A rumor that a Dutch lens grinder had observed that two lenses used together make distant objects appear close at hand led Galileo to construct the first telescope. Successful telescopes of greater and greater magnification enabled him eventually to observe, for the first time, the mountains on the moon, the major satellites of Jupiter, and sunspots. While at Pisa, Galileo carried out many experiments and public demonstrations of principles which laid the foundations of mechanics and the laws of projectiles and falling bodies.

On one occasion, Galileo is alleged to have attracted a large crowd to the leaning tower, where he climbed the spiral staircase to the bell chamber at the top and there through an open archway dropped two stones, one large and one small. These two bodies fell side by side and struck the ground together, thus sounding the death knell of an old hypothesis and the birth of a new era in science.

Whether this particular incident is true or not, the importance of Galileo's many authentic experiments lies not in the fact that they demonstrated the fallacy of Aristotle's reasoning, but that they presented to the world a new and more reliable scientific method, the method of experimentation.

5.1. Gravitation. The principle that all objects fall with the same acceleration can be demonstrated in various ways. One of these is illustrated in Fig. 5A where two steel balls, one large and one small, are supported in the groove of a wooden block 10 or 20 ft above the ground. When the block is tipped by pulling the cord, both balls fall together and strike the ground together. Dropped from a height of 16 ft, the time of fall is just 1 sec. The shaded circles in the figure show the position of the two bodies at the end of each quarter second.

If the balls in the experiment are replaced by two marbles of the same size, one steel and the other wood, they too will fall side by side and strike the ground together. In this case, the steel marble weighs fifteen times as much as the wood. (Density of steel 7.8 gm/cm^3: density of wood, 0.5 gm/cm^3.)

The question of air friction usually arises in this latter experiment, for careful observation will show that the wooden ball lags

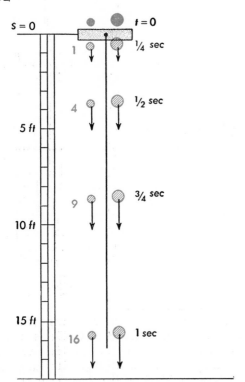

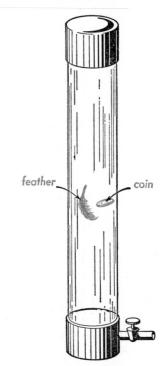

Fig. 5A *All bodies falling freely under the constant pull of gravity fall a distance of 16 ft in the first second.*

Fig. 5B *In a vacuum, a feather and coin fall with the same acceleration and strike the bottom together.*

ever so slightly behind the steel ball. **This** lagging due to air friction increases the farther they fall, and is even more pronounced when a still lighter object, like a feather or leaf, is allowed to fall at the same time. Due to its large surface area, a feather or leaf flutters to the ground, being held back by the large amount of air that must be pushed aside to let it by.

In the absence of air, even a feather will fall with the acceleration of a solid steel ball. An experiment illustrating just this is shown in Fig. 5B. A long glass cylinder containing a feather and silver coin is connected by a flexible tube to a vacuum pump. If after evacuation the tube is turned upside down, the feather and the coin will be observed to fall together. When the air is once more admitted to the cylinder, the feather will again flutter slowly to the bottom. *In the absence of air friction, all bodies fall with the same acceleration.*

In the treatment of falling bodies given in the remainder of this chapter, air friction is entirely neglected. The formulas presented and used in working problems are known to hold only approximately. In most practical cases, however, the calculated results are so nearly realized experimentally that corrections for air friction need only be made where the distances and velocities involved are large. A detailed discussion of the effects of air friction on falling bodies is given in Chap. 11.

5.2. Free Fall. Let us perform an experiment on free fall and, by making quantitative measurements, apply the graphical method of analysis to determine a relation between *distance* and *time of fall*. The experimental arrangement to be used is shown in Fig. 5C. A small steel ball is dropped from different fixed positions, and its time of fall is determined for each distance. Because the time of fall is less than a second, for the heights to be used, an electrically

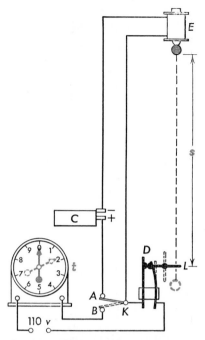

Fig. 5C *Falling body experiment.*

the electromagnet higher and higher, and the measurements of distance and time recorded in a table. Suppose this experiment has been performed at five different heights and the data recorded as shown in Table 5A.

TABLE 5A. RECORDED DATA FOR THE FREELY FALLING STEEL BALL

Trial	Distance *s* (m)	Time *t* (sec)
1	0.356	0.270
2	0.824	0.410
3	1.262	0.508
4	1.867	0.616
5	2.350	0.694

To see how *s* and *t* are related to each other, we shall follow the analytical method described in the preceding chapter. First we plot *s* vertically and *t* horizontally, as shown at the left in Fig. 5D. When a smooth line is drawn through these points (dots with circles), the curve obtained has the general appearance of a parabola. Taking the same steps described in detail in Sec. 4.3, we next try plotting *s* against t^2, as shown at the

operated stop-clock with one-hundredth of a second divisions around its dial is used. To reduce the subjective errors introduced by the observers' having to start and stop the clock, electric switching is employed. Repeated falls from the same height will then show that interpolations between marks on the clock dial are significant, and the time averages can be given to thousandths of a second.

When the switch *K* is in position *A*, an electric current supplied by the battery *C* energizes the electromagnet *E* and holds the steel ball suspended ready for dropping. When switch *K* is snapped to position *B*, the electromagnet circuit is opened, releasing the ball, and the clock circuit is closed, starting the clock. When the ball strikes the lower switch *L*, contacts *D* are instantly opened, stopping the clock. The time *t* is then recorded, along with the distance of fall *s*. By dropping the ball a number of times, the slight differences will not only demonstrate the reliability of the timing mechanism but enable good average values to be obtained.

This procedure should be repeated with

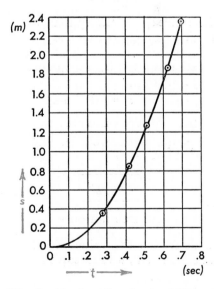

Fig. 5D *Graph for the freely falling body experiment.*

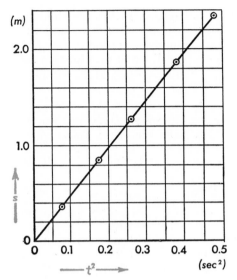

Fig. 5E *Straight-line graph for free fall experiment.*

right in Fig. 5E. The fact that this graph yields a straight line shows that s is proportional to t^2.

$$s \propto t^2 \qquad (5a)$$

Replacing the proportionality sign by an equal sign, and putting in a constant, we obtain

$$s = kt^2 \qquad (5b)$$

This result shows clearly that, with little or no air friction, a falling body has a uniform downward acceleration, and that this acceleration is given by an equation of the form of Eq.(4n).

$$s = \tfrac{1}{2}at^2 \qquad (5c)$$

For free fall it is customary to represent the acceleration due to gravity by the letter g. Starting from rest,

$$\boxed{s = \tfrac{1}{2}gt^2} \qquad (5d)$$

for free fall only

To determine the value of g from the above experiment, we first solve Eq.(5d) for g.

$$g = \frac{2s}{t^2} \qquad (5e)$$

The result of substituting values of s and t from Table 5A, in Eq.(5e), is shown in Table 5B.

TABLE 5B. CALCULATED RESULTS OF FREE FALL EXPERIMENT

Trial	Acceleration g (m/sec^2)
1	9.77
2	9.80
3	9.78
4	9.84
5	9.76

The average value of these five determinations of the acceleration due to gravity is

$$g = 9.79 \,\frac{\text{m}}{\text{sec}^2}$$

When different-sized masses are used in an experiment of this kind, the final result, within the limits of experimental error, is the same. It is for this reason that the special letter g is often used in formulas to represent free fall acceleration.

5.3. The Acceleration Due to Gravity. Experiments carried on at many points over the earth show that the acceleration due to gravity is not everywhere the same; there are slight variations. Although these variations are small and are not of any consequence in most practical problems, they do exist and should be mentioned.

In general, the values of g lie between a minimum of 32.09 ft/sec^2 or 9.7804 m/sec^2 at the equator and a maximum of 32.26 ft/sec^2 or 9.8321 m/sec^2 at the North and South poles. Referring here to the equator and the poles is only a generalization, for not all points on the equator have the same values as quoted above, nor do all points on any one latitude have the same value. Irregularities of the earth's structure give rise to minute random differences.

The International Committee on Weights and Measures has adopted as a standard or accepted value, 9.80665 m/sec^2 or 32.174 ft/sec^2. For practical purposes, however, it is customary to use the even-numbered values 9.80 m/sec² and 32 ft/sec². For freely falling bodies, then, we shall assume that

$$g = 9.80 \frac{m}{sec^2}$$

$$g = 980 \frac{cm}{sec^2}$$

$$g = 32 \frac{ft}{sec^2}$$

The formulas developed for accelerated motion, given at the end of Chap. 4, are customarily rewritten as follows:

TABLE 5C. EQUATIONS FOR FREE FALL ONLY

General Equations	Special Equations	
$v = v_0 + gt$	$v = gt$	(5f)
$s = \dfrac{v + v_0}{2} t$	$s = \dfrac{v}{2} t$	(5g)
$v^2 = v_0^2 + 2gs$	$v^2 = 2gs$	(5h)
$s = v_0 t + \frac{1}{2} gt^2$	$s = \frac{1}{2} gt^2$	(5i)

Example 1. A boy standing on a bridge 200 ft above a river throws a stone straight downward with a velocity of 50 ft/sec. (a) With what speed will the stone strike the water, and (b) how long will it take to descend?

Solution. To find the answer to (a), use the general Eq.(5h). The known quantities are $v_0 = 50$ ft/sec, $s = 200$ ft, and $g = 32$ ft/sec². Direct substitution gives

$$v^2 = \left(50 \frac{ft}{sec}\right)^2 + 2 \times 32 \frac{ft}{sec^2} \times 200 \text{ ft}$$

$$v^2 = 2500 + 12,800 = 15,300 \text{ ft}^2/\text{sec}^2$$

If the square root of both sides of the equation is taken, we obtain

$$v = 123.7 \text{ ft/sec}$$

For the answer to (b) use Eq.(5f). The known quantities are $v = 123.7$ ft/sec, $v_0 = 50$ ft/sec, and $g = 32$ ft/sec². By transposing the general Eq.(5f), we obtain

$$t = \frac{v - v_0}{g}$$

Then substitute known values in this equation.

$$t = \frac{123.7 \text{ ft/sec} - 50 \text{ ft/sec}}{32 \text{ ft/sec}^2} = \frac{73.7 \text{ ft/sec}}{32 \text{ ft/sec}^2} = 2.3 \text{ sec}$$

The stone, therefore, hits the water with a speed of 123.7 ft/sec, 2.3 sec after it leaves the boy's hand.

5.4. Projection Straight Upward. When a body is projected straight upward, its speed will rapidly diminish until at some point it comes momentarily to rest and then falls back toward the earth, acquiring again at the ground the same speed it had upon projection. Experiment shows that the time taken to rise to the highest point of its trajectory is equal to the time taken to fall from there to the ground. This implies that the upward motions are just the same as the downward motions, but in reverse, and that the time and speed for any point along the path are given by the same equations for free fall, Eqs.(5f), (5g), (5h), and (5i).

In Fig. 5F, a particle is shown projected upward with a velocity of 128 ft/sec. After each second's time, its speed on the way up is shown to be the same as its speed at the same level on the way down.

To treat the motion mathematically, it is convenient to use Eqs.(5f), (5g), (5h), and (5i), taking the point of projection as the *origin,* and adopting the following convention of signs, for projection upward:

(1) Distances above the origin are positive.
(2) Distances below the origin are negative.
(3) Velocities upward are positive.
(4) Velocities downward are negative.
(5) Acceleration downward (gravity) is negative.

Whether a body is moving up or down, the acceleration g is always downward. Using the above sign conventions, g is given by

$$g = -9.8 \text{ m/sec}^2$$

or $$g = -32 \text{ ft/sec}^2 \qquad (5j)$$

Example 2. A stone is projected upward with a speed of 128 ft/sec. Calculate the time required to reach the highest point.

Solution. The known quantities in this problem are $v_0 = 128$ ft/sec, $g = -32$ ft/sec², and at the highest point $v = 0$. Since t is the unknown,

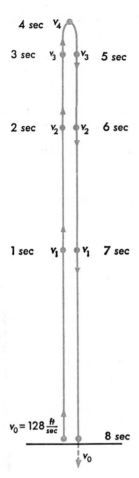

Fig. 5F *The upward motion of a body is just the same as the downward motion, but in reverse. A stone thrown upward returns to the ground with the same speed.*

the ground as shown in Fig. 5G. Find (a) the maximum height to which the ball rises, (b) the total time required to reach the point of projection again, (c) the time required to reach a height of 64 ft, (d) the velocity upon arrival at the ground, and (e) the total time in the air.

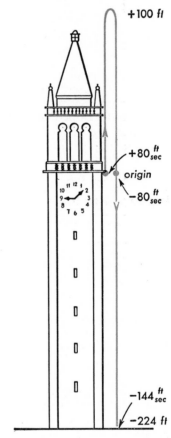

Fig. 5G *A body projected upward rises to a predetermined height, then falls with increasing speed.*

general Eq.(5f) may be used.

$$v = v_0 + gt$$

Direct substitution gives

$$0 = 128 \text{ ft/sec} + (-32 \text{ ft/sec}^2)t$$

Transposing, we obtain

$$t = \frac{128 \text{ ft/sec}}{32 \text{ ft/sec}^2} = 4 \text{ sec}$$

In 4 sec, therefore, the stone will reach its highest point. In another 4 sec it will fall to the ground, as shown in Fig. 5F.

Example 3. A baseball is thrown upward with a speed of 80 ft/sec from a point 224 ft above

Solution. (a) The given quantities for part (a) are $v_0 = 80$ ft/sec, and $g = -32$ ft/sec². At the highest point of the path $v = 0$. Since s is the unknown, general Eq.(5h) may be used. By direct substitution,

$$v^2 = v_0^2 + 2gs$$
$$0 = (80 \text{ ft/sec})^2 + 2(-32 \text{ ft/sec}^2)s$$

Transposing, we find

$$s = \frac{(80 \text{ ft/sec})^2}{2 \times 32 \text{ ft/sec}^2} = \frac{6400 \text{ ft}^2/\text{sec}^2}{64 \text{ ft/sec}^2} = 100 \text{ ft}$$

(b) Upon returning to its starting point, *the*

origin, the ball is at $s = 0$. Since t is the unknown, general Eq.(5i) may be used.

$$s = v_0 t + \tfrac{1}{2} g t^2$$

$$0 = (80 \text{ ft/sec})t + \tfrac{1}{2}(-32 \text{ ft/sec}^2)t^2$$

Transposing, we get

$$(16 \text{ ft/sec}^2)t^2 = (80 \text{ ft/sec})t$$

Dividing both sides by $16t$, we find that

$$t \text{ ft/sec}^2 = 5 \text{ ft/sec} \qquad \text{or} \qquad t = 5 \text{ sec}$$

(c) Here the given quantities are $s = 64$ ft, $v_0 = 80$ ft/sec, $g = -32$ ft/sec^2, and the unknown is t. Inspection of equations shows that general Eq.(5i) may be used. Direct substitution gives

$$64 \text{ ft} = (80 \text{ ft/sec})t + \tfrac{1}{2}(-32 \text{ ft/sec}^2)t^2$$

Transposing, we obtain

$$(16 \text{ ft/sec}^2)t^2 - (80 \text{ ft/sec})t + 64 \text{ ft} = 0$$

and dividing through by 16 ft/sec^2,

$$t^2 - 5 \text{ sec} + 4 \text{ sec}^2 = 0$$

Upon factoring, we get

$$(t - 1 \text{ sec})(t - 4 \text{ sec}) = 0$$

from which, we obtain

$$t = 1 \text{ sec} \qquad \text{and} \qquad t = 4 \text{ sec}$$

Both of these answers are correct. The first answer, 1 sec, is the time required for the ball to reach the 64-ft level on its way up, whereas the second answer, 4 sec, is the time required to reach the 64-ft level on the way down.

(d) Upon reaching the ground, the ball is below the origin making $s = -224$ ft. Since v is the unknown, general Eq.(5h) may be used. Substituting directly, we get

$$v^2 = (80 \text{ ft/sec})^2 + 2(-32 \text{ ft/sec}^2)(-224 \text{ ft})$$
$$v^2 = 20{,}736 \text{ ft}^2/\text{sec}^2$$
$$v = \pm 144 \text{ ft/sec}$$

Of these two answers only the one $v = -144$ ft/sec is correct; the ball is moving downward. The answer $+144$ ft/sec means that the baseball could have been thrown upward from the ground level with this velocity, to acquire the same height.

(e) To find the total flight time we may use general Eq.(5f). The known quantities are $v_0 = 80$ ft/sec, $g = -32$ ft/sec^2, and $v = -144$ ft/sec.

$$-144 \text{ ft/sec} = 80 \text{ ft/sec} + (-32 \text{ ft/sec}^2)t$$

from which $v = v_0 + gt$

$$t = \frac{224 \text{ ft/sec}}{32 \text{ ft/sec}^2} = 7 \text{ sec}$$

Or we may use general Eq.(5i), and obtain

$$-224 \text{ ft} = (80 \text{ ft/sec})t + \tfrac{1}{2}(-32 \text{ ft/sec}^2)t^2$$

from which

$$(16 \text{ ft/sec}^2)t^2 - (80 \text{ ft/sec})t - 224 \text{ ft} = 0$$

Dividing by 16 ft/sec^2, we find

$$t^2 - 5 \text{ sec} - 14 \text{ sec}^2 = 0$$

Factoring, we obtain

$$(t - 7 \text{ sec})(t + 2 \text{ sec}) = 0$$

which gives

$$t = 7 \text{ sec} \qquad \text{and} \qquad t = -2 \text{ sec}$$

Only the answer $t = 7$ sec is a real answer for this problem. The question of what the answer $t = -2$ sec means is left to be answered by the student.

PROBLEMS

1. A sandbag dropped from a balloon hits the ground with a speed of 180 mi/hr. (a) How high is the balloon, and (b) how long is the sandbag in falling?

2. An object falls from a bridge 180 ft above the water. (a) With what speed does it hit the water, and (b) how long is it in the air? (*Ans.* (a) 107.2 ft/sec, (b) 3.35 sec.)

3. A workman accidentally drops a hammer while working on a tall building. If it requires 8 sec to reach the ground, (a) how high is the

building, and (b) with what speed does the hammer strike the ground?

4. A stone dropped into a well hits the water in 2.6 sec. (a) How deep is the well, and (b) with what speed does the stone hit the water? (*Ans.* (a) 108.2 ft, (b) 83.2 ft/sec.)

5. An arrow is shot upward with a velocity of 144 ft/sec. Find (a) the time taken to reach the highest point, (b) the maximum height reached, (c) the total time of flight, and (d) the velocity at the end of 6 sec.

6. An arrow shot straight upward reaches a maximum height of 490 m. Calculate (a) the time to reach its highest point, (b) its velocity upon arrival at the ground, and (c) its velocity at the end of 5 sec. (*Ans.* (a) 10 sec, (b) 98 m/sec, (c) 49 m/sec.)

7. A batter knocks a baseball straight upward. The ball is caught 10 sec later. Find (a) the initial upward velocity, (b) the maximum height reached, and (c) the velocity of the ball 7 sec after it is struck.

8. A stone thrown straight upward by a boy reaches a maximum height of 36 ft. Find (a) the time to reach its highest point, (b) its velocity upon arrival at the ground, and (c) its position at the end of 1 sec. (*Ans.* (a) 1.5 sec, (b) 48 ft/sec, (c) 32 ft high.)

9. An arrow shot straight upward returns to the ground again in 10.5 sec. Calculate (a) the maximum height reached, and (b) the speed of projection. Use mks units.

10. A baseball hit straight upward is caught 9.0 sec later by the catcher. Find (a) the maximum height reached, and (b) the speed it acquired upon leaving the bat. (*Ans.* (a) 324 ft, (b) 144 ft/sec.)

11. A stone thrown straight upward by a catapult reaches a height of 96 ft in 1 sec. Find (a) the maximum height reached, (b) the total time of flight, and (c) the speed of projection.

12. An arrow shot straight upward reaches a height of 256 ft in 2 sec. Find (a) the maximum height reached, (b) the total time of flight, and (c) the speed of projection. (*Ans.* (a) 400 ft, (b) 10 sec, (c) 160 ft/sec.)

13. An arrow is shot straight upward with a speed of 34.3 m/sec. Find (a) the height to which it rises, and (b) the time required to return to the ground.

14. A stone is thrown vertically upward with speed of 90 mi/hr. Find (a) the height to which it rises, and (b) the total time to reach the ground. (*Ans.* (a) 272 ft, (b) 8.25 sec.)

15. A baseball is hit straight upward with a speed of 39.2 m/sec. Find (a) the maximum height reached, (b) its height at the end of 3 sec, (c) its velocity at the end of 7 sec, and (d) the total time it is in the air.

16. An arrow is shot upward with a speed of 256 ft/sec. Find (a) the maximum height reached, (b) its height at the end of 5.5 sec, (c) its velocity at the end of 10 sec, and (d) the total time in flight. (*Ans.* (a) 1024 ft, (b) 924 ft, (c) −64 ft/sec, (d) 16 sec.)

17. A stone is thrown upward from the edge of a cliff with a speed of 104 ft/sec. Find (a) the maximum height reached, (b) its velocity at the end of 2 sec, (c) its height at the end of 6 sec, and (d) its height at the end of 8 sec.

18. A boy standing on a bridge 200 ft above the water throws a stone straight upward with a speed of 100 ft/sec. Find (a) the maximum height reached, (b) the time required to reach the bridge level again, and (c) the speed with which it hits the water. (*Ans.* (a) 156 ft, (b) 6.25 sec, (c) 151 ft/sec.)

19. Two arrows are shot upward simultaneously, one with a speed of 39.2 m/sec and the other with a speed of 49.0 m/sec. At what time will they be 20 m apart?

20. Arrows are shot upward at 2-sec intervals with an initial speed of 34.3 m/sec. (a) After several arrows have been shot, how long will each arrow be in the air before another passes it, and (b) at what distances above the origin will arrows be passing each other? (*Ans.* (a) Each arrow passes three others on the way up and three on the way down. $t = 0.5$, 1.5, 2.5, 4.5, 5.5, and 6.5 sec, (b) 15.9 m, 40.4 m, and 55.1 m.)

21. A dart thrown straight upward travels a distance of 19.6 m during the second second. Calculate (a) the maximum height reached, (b) the speed of projection, and (c) the total time of flight.

22. An anti-aircraft shell when shot straight upward travels a distance of 543.9 m during the third second. Neglecting air friction find (a) the total time of flight, (b) the speed of projection, (c) the maximum height reached. (*Ans.* (a) 116 sec, (b) 568.4 m/sec, (c) 16,484 m.)

23. A ball is thrown upward with an initial speed of 120 ft/sec. At the end of 6.5 sec, (a) how far will it be from its starting point, and (b) in what direction will it be moving?

Chapter 6

Newton's First and Second Laws of Motion

In the preceding chapters the motions of bodies have been described in terms of *speed, velocity, acceleration,* and *time.* The definitions of these quantities, and the laws and formulas relating to them, are classified as belonging to that branch of mechanics called "kinematics." Here, and in later chapters, the cause of motion is to be treated. Such a treatment involves the introduction of *mass* and *force* into the equations already presented.

To Isaac Newton,* goes the credit of having been the first to systematically introduce

* Sir Isaac Newton (1642-1727), English physicist and mathematician, was born in England on Christmas day, 1642. He obtained his education at Trinity College, Cambridge, where in 1665 he was awarded the Master of Arts degree. At just this time, the prevalence of the black plague forced him into retirement at his old home in Woolsthorpe where, in the two years 1665 and 1666, his genius developed. In this period he invented the calculus, discovered the composition of white light, and conceived the idea of universal gravitation. In the years that followed, he published much of his work on optics and developed his ideas on gravitation which were published in 1687 in his *Principia.* At the age of fifty he suffered a nervous breakdown, and never again did any extensive scientific work, but devoted his time to theology. He became very absent-minded and slovenly in his personal appearance. He never married. His *Principia* is considered to be one of the greatest monuments of the human intellect. In it, Newton lays the foundations of mechanics which are broad enough to include all future developments, and these he applies to the motions of heavenly bodies under the law of gravitation. He was elected to Parliament, was president of the Royal Society for twenty-years, and was knighted by Queen Anne in 1705. The greatness of this modest man is illustrated by a remark of his made on his deathbed, "If I have seen farther than others, it is by standing on the shoulders of giants."

these concepts into mechanics and to formulate the fundamental laws governing all motion. These laws constitute the fundamental principles of that branch of mechanics called "dynamics" and resolve themselves into three laws commonly referred to as "Newton's laws of motion."

6.1. Newton's First Law. A body at rest or in uniform motion will remain at rest or in uniform motion unless some external force is applied to it.† This law can be demonstrated by many simple experiments. In Fig. 6A a tablecloth is shown in the process of being removed from under the dishes and silverware on a table without disturbing their original setting. In Fig. 6B a small car is shown free to move on a smooth hard track. If the track is jerked quickly to right or left, the wheels of the car will turn, but the car itself will tend to remain at rest.

In both of these experiments the dishes and the car are at rest. They tend to remain at rest because the sudden motion of the objects on which they are resting exerts no large force for any appreciable length of time. Actually, the dishes and the car do move slightly because of frictional forces between the moving parts in contact. The tendency for each body to remain at rest is due to that property, common to all material bodies, called *inertia.*

The inertia of a body may be defined as that property of a body which tends to resist a change in its state of rest or motion.

† Newton's first law of motion is given in Latin in his famous book *Principia.* Lex. I. Corpus omne perseverare in statu suo quiesendi vel movendi uniformiter in directum, nisi quatenus illud a viribus impressis cogitur statum suum mutare.

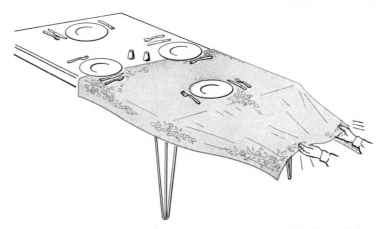

Fig. 6A *A tablecloth can be pulled from a table without dislodging the dishes.*

Mass *is defined as a quantitative measure of inertia.*

Inertia and mass are both measured in the same units, in grams, or kilograms.

A third experiment illustrating inertia, and Newton's first law, is illustrated in Fig. 6C. A mass M of 1000 gm is suspended by a piece of thread A, then pulled downward by another piece of the same thread B. If the force F is a slow steady pull, the thread will always break at A; whereas if it is a

ceding demonstrations are concerned with bodies at rest. The second part of Newton's first law of motion is concerned with moving bodies, and a restatement of the law confined to this aspect would change the law to read:

A body in uniform motion will remain in uniform motion unless some external force is applied to it.

This aspect of Newton's first law was first recognized by Galileo. In order to study the

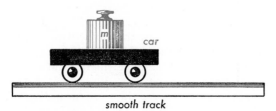

Fig. 6B *The smooth track can quickly be moved so as not to set the car in motion.*

sudden jerk, it will always break at B. In the first case, the tension in the upper thread is greater and is equivalent to the force F plus the weight of the mass M. In the second case, the force F is momentarily very large, causing the thread to break before the mass M has had time to move down far enough to stretch and break the upper thread. It is the inertia of M that permits the very large force F to be momentarily applied to the lower thread only.

6.2. Inertia and Motion. The three pre-

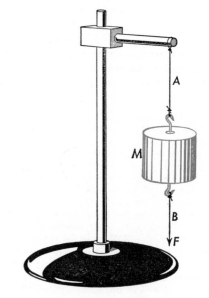

Fig. 6C *A slow, steady pull at F breaks the thread at A, while a quick pull at F breaks the thread at B.*

acceleration due to gravity, he used an inclined plane to reduce the acceleration due to gravity, thereby permitting better measurements. He observed that a ball rolling down one incline would roll up another to approximately the same height regardless of the inclination of the second plane. Furthermore, if the ball were allowed to roll out on a level plane when it reached the bottom of the incline, it could never achieve its original height but tended to roll on and on. Due to friction it would eventually stop.

A most striking demonstration of this property of inertia is provided by a "dry ice disk" as shown in Fig. 6D. Here, friction

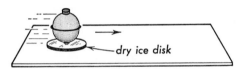

Fig. 6D *Demonstration of the inertia of a body moving with uniform velocity.*

is reduced to practically zero by a metal disk that rides over a glass plate and literally floats on a thin layer of carbon dioxide gas. When this body is given a very slight push, it rides across the plate and seems to keep going on and on, with constant velocity, as if by magic. What keeps the body moving in the same straight line is its inertia.* The above law, of course, neglects friction, for we know that, left to itself, friction will eventually bring the body to rest. The greater the friction, the sooner it

---

* A cross-section diagram of this dry ice disk is shown in Fig. 6E. A thin-walled, brass or copper ball about 10 cm in diameter is soldered to a flat, circular brass disk about 2 cm thick and 15 cm in diameter. Thin-walled vessels of this kind are used as a float in certain plumbing utilities and may be purchased in most hardware stores. Dry ice is available in almost every drugstore soda fountain, and one loading will last a couple of hours. The bottom surface of the disk is undercut several thousandths of a centimeter, and a hole about 0.5 cm in diameter is drilled through the center. A short section of metal tubing is mounted directly above this center and prevents the dry ice from clogging the hole. A larger hole in the top is provided for the insertion of dry ice, and a tight-fitting cork closes the opening.

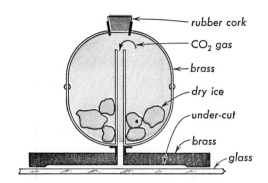

Fig. 6E *Cross-section diagram of "dry ice disk."*

will stop. The smaller the friction, the longer it will move. If friction could be entirely eliminated, the *inertia* of the body would keep it moving indefinitely with constant velocity.

6.3. Inertia and Mass. Mass is a measure of inertia. In the metric system, inertia and mass are measured in grams and kilograms. In the English system they are both measured in slugs. Fig. 6F is a diagram illustrat-

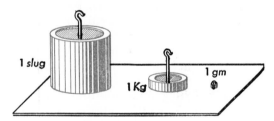

Fig. 6F *Units of mass are also units of inertia.*

ing the relative sizes of these three units. They are shown in a hooked weight form convenient for use in experiments. If one were to weigh these three fundamental units of mass, 1 slug would weigh 32 lb, 1 Kg would weigh 9.8 newtons, and 1 gm would weigh 980 dynes. The difference between mass and weight will be taken up in detail in Sec. 6.6.

6.4. An Experiment on Accelerated Motion. Newton's first law of motion, concerning bodies at rest or in uniform motion, assumes that no forces are acting to change them. Newton's second law of motion, however, assumes that some force is acting, and the law describes exactly how the motion changes. To learn just how the motion of a body changes and how this change is related to its mass and to the force acting upon it, we may perform an experiment like that shown in Fig. 6G.

adjusted so that $m_1 + m_2$ remains constant. If done correctly, the first set of measurements can be used to determine how acceleration changes with increasing mass, and the second set to determine how acceleration changes with increasing force.

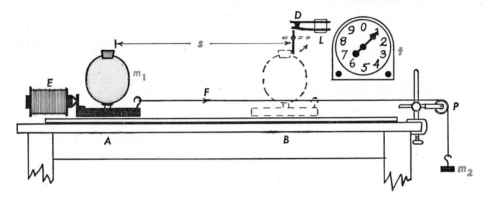

Fig. 6G   *Diagram of apparatus for acceleration experiment.*

A "dry ice disk" of the kind described in the preceding section is accelerated along a level plane (a long glass plate) by means of a thread, a pulley, and a small mass m_2. A switching circuit, like that shown in Fig. 5C is used to time the moving mass m_1 as it starts from position A and passes position B.

After weighing and recording its mass m_1, the body is held in position A by the small electromagnet E. With the snap of a switch the electromagnet circuit is opened releasing the disk, and the clock circuit is closed starting the clock. When the top edge of the body m_1 strikes the switch L, contacts D are instantly opened, stopping the clock. The time t is then recorded, along with the distance s. By repeating this procedure several times, a good average of the time is obtained.

A number of different trials should be performed with this experiment, first by adding masses to the moving body, and then by increasing the accelerating mass m_2. The mass m_1 should be reweighed with each trial since the loss of CO_2 will change the value. Furthermore, for trials 4, 5, 6, and 7, the mass m_2 added to m_1 should be

Suppose we have performed this experiment and have recorded the data shown in Table 6A.

TABLE 6A. RECORDED DATA FOR ACCELERATION EXPERIMENT

Trial	Mass m_1 (Kg)	Mass m_2 (Kg)	Distance s (m)	Time t (sec)
1	0.560	0.020	1.00	2.45
2	0.965	0.020	1.00	3.18
3	1.460	0.020	1.00	3.91
4	1.980	0.020	1.00	4.51
5	1.960	0.040	1.00	3.20
6	1.940	0.060	1.00	2.61
7	1.920	0.080	1.00	2.27

To find the acceleration for each of the seven trials we make use of the kinematic Eq.(4n).

$$s = \tfrac{1}{2}at^2$$

Upon solving for the unknown, we get

$$a = \frac{2s}{t^2} \qquad (6a)$$

Substituting the recorded values of s and t

in this relation, we obtain the values of a shown in the first column of Table 6B. Since m_1 and m_2 both undergo the same acceleration, the total mass being accelerated is $m_1 + m_2$. This sum is shown as m in the third column of the table. (Here we have assumed that the mass of the thread and the effective mass of the pulley are negligibly small.)

TABLE 6B. CALCULATIONS FOR ACCELERATION EXPERIMENT

Trial	Acceleration a (m/sec²)	Mass m (Kg)	Reciprocal $1/m$ (1/Kg)
1	0.333	0.580	1.72
2	0.198	0.985	1.02
3	0.131	1.480	0.676
4	0.098	2.000	0.500
5	0.195	2.000	0.500
6	0.294	2.000	0.500
7	0.388	2.000	0.500

To see how the acceleration a is related to the mass of the acclerated body, we use the first four trials, for which the applied force is constant, and plot a graph. Plotting m vertically and a horizontally, we obtain the graph in Fig. 6H. Since this is not a straight line, we should try modifying a and m to see if a straight-line plot can be obtained.

With the graph for a guide, we note that as the mass increases the acceleration decreases. This suggests the possibility that an inverse ratio exists between the two quantities, that is, that one of the quantities might be proportional to the reciprocal of the other. Assuming this as a possibility, the values of $1/m$ are given in Table 6B. When these reciprocal values are plotted against a, as shown at the right in Fig. 6I, a straight line is the result.

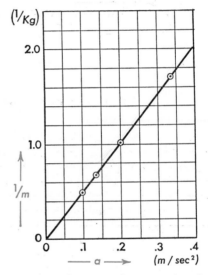

Fig. 6I *Straight-line graph for acceleration experiment.*

The conclusion to be drawn from this straight-line graph is that a is proportional to $1/m$.

$$a \propto \frac{1}{m} \qquad (6b)$$

Replacing the proportionality sign by an equal sign and a constant, we can write

$$a = F\frac{1}{m} \qquad (6c)$$

from which

$$F = ma$$

The constant F is called the *force* and has the units of *mass times acceleration*.

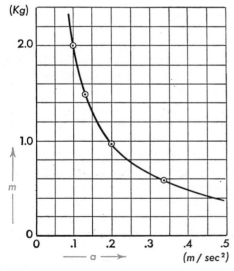

Fig. 6H *Graph for the acceleration experiment.*

To find how the acceleration changes with the applied force, the value of a given in Table 6B can be plotted against m_2 from Table 6A. The plotting of this graph, and the conclusions to be drawn from it, are left as an exercise for the student.

6.5. Newton's Second Law of Motion. *When a body is acted upon by a constant force, its resulting acceleration is proportional to the force and inversely proportional to the mass.* The experiment described in the preceding section verifies this statement and leads us to the so-called force equation.

$$F = ma \qquad (6d)$$

force = mass × acceleration

Example 1. If we neglect friction, what constant force will give a mass of 50 gm an acceleration of 5 cm/sec²?

Solution. Substitute the foregoing values into the force equation, Eq.(6d).

$$F = 50 \text{ gm} \times 5 \frac{\text{cm}}{\text{sec}^2} = 250 \frac{\text{gm cm}}{\text{sec}^2}$$

The answer is a force of 250 gm cm/sec². Thus force is not as simple a concept as it might seem at first hand; it involves all three of the fundamental units, *length, mass,* and *time.*

By definition, 1 gm cm/sec² is a unit of force called the *dyne.* According to this definition, the answer to the above problem could have been written *250 dynes. The dyne is a force which, acting on a 1-gm mass, will give it an acceleration of 1 cm/ sec².*

1 dyne = 1 gm × 1 cm/sec²

In the cgs system (centimeter-gram-second), the units of Eq.(6d) become: dynes, grams, and centimeters/seconds².

There is a growing movement among scientists and teachers of physics to use the kilogram and meter in place of the gram and centimeter as units of mass and length. According to the meter, kilogram, second system (*abbr.* mks system), unit force is called the "newton" in honor of Sir Isaac Newton.

The newton *is defined as that force which, applied to a mass of 1 Kg, will give it an acceleration of 1 m/sec².*

In the mks system the units of Eq.(6d) become

1 newton = 1 kilogram × 1 $\frac{\text{meter}}{\text{second}^2}$

Example 2. Neglecting friction, what constant force in newtons will give a mass of 4 Kg an acceleration of 3.8 m/sec²?

Solution. Apply the force equation, Eq.(6d).

$$F = 4 \text{ Kg} \times 3.8 \frac{\text{m}}{\text{sec}^2} = 15.2 \frac{\text{Kg m}}{\text{sec}^2} = 15.2 \text{ newtons}$$

The answer is a constant force of 15.2 newtons.

Dynes and newtons are absolute units of force. They arise from the force equation when the absolute units of *mass* and *time* are used.

Since 1 Kg = 1000 gm, and 1 m = 100 cm, 1 newton = 100,000 dynes.

1 newton = 10⁵ dynes

To the above statement of Newton's second law of motion should be added the statement that *the acceleration takes place in the direction of the applied force.*

6.6. Weight and Mass. When a mass m is allowed to fall freely, it is the constant downward force of gravity on the mass that gives rise to its constant acceleration. If Newton's second law is applied to this motion, the force F is none other than the weight W of the body, and the acceleration a is the acceleration due to gravity g. For falling bodies, the force equation, $F = ma$, is written in different symbols.

$$W = mg \qquad (6e)$$

weight = mass × acceleration

In absolute units, the weight of a body is expressed in dynes or newtons.

Weight and *force* have both magnitude and direction and are therefore vector quantities. Mass, on the other hand, is a scalar quantity since it has only magnitude. The distinction between *weight* and *mass* is illustrated by imagining a given body to be carried out into free space far removed from other bodies and their gravitational attraction. There, a body at rest will still have its mass but it will have no weight. That such a body has its mass would be demonstrated if another mass were to bump into it. The smaller the mass of the incoming body, the less would be the recoil of the first mass from the impact.

Weight here on the earth is due to the gravitational attraction of the earth upon a mass at its surface and will be treated in detail in the next chapter. In the equation $W = mg$ we may define g as the *weight per unit mass*. W is equal to the *mass* times the *weight per unit mass*.

Example 3. Calculate the weight of a body having a mass of 1 Kg.
Solution. By Eq.(6e),

$$W = 1 \text{ Kg} \times 9.80 \frac{\text{m}}{\text{sec}^2} =$$

$$9.80 \frac{\text{Kg m}}{\text{sec}^2} = 9.80 \text{ newtons} \quad (6f)$$

This answer shows that to lift a mass of 1 Kg requires an upward force of 9.80 newtons and that the weight and mass differ from each other numerically by a ratio equal to the acceleration due to gravity. By similar calculations to the above, the weight of a 1-gm mass is found to be 980 dynes. See Fig. 6J.

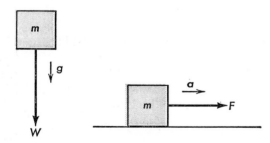

Fig. 6J *A mass m falling freely has an acceleration g; pulled by a force F it has an acceleration a.*

6.7. The Engineering System of Units.

The engineer seldom uses metric units as described above. He finds it more convenient to measure forces in *pounds* or *tons*. In the construction of buildings,

bridges, airplanes, and all kinds of machines, the loads to be carried are usually specified in pounds. To apply Newton's second law of motion, as expressed by the force equation $F = ma$, it is necessary to modify one of the two factors, *mass* or *acceleration*.

It is general engineering practice to modify *mass* by defining it not in pounds but in *slugs*. To see how these units are derived from the "force equation," Eqs.(6d) and (6e) are both solved for m, and then set equal to each other.

$$\frac{F}{a} = \frac{W}{g} \quad (6g)$$

The justification for this is that Newton's second law of motion applied to a given mass holds for any force, whether it be its own weight W due to the earth's downward pull or any other applied force F. If the force is F the acceleration is a; if the force is W the acceleration is g. See Fig. 6J. The engineer's form of the force equation evolves from Eq.(6g). By transposing a,

$$F = \frac{W}{g} a \quad (6h)$$

$\frac{W}{g} = \text{slug}$

In this relation F and W are to be considered as forces, both measured in pounds, while the accelerations g and a are both measured in the customary units ft/sec². $g = 32$ ft/sec².

Example 4. A small wagon weighing 80 lb stands at rest on a level road. What force is required to give it an acceleration of 3 ft/sec²?
Solution. By direct substitution in the force equation, Eq.(6h),

$$F = \frac{80 \text{ lb}}{32 \text{ ft/sec}^2} \times 3 \text{ ft/sec}^2 = 7.5 \text{ lb}$$

The answer is a force of 7.5 lb.

The term W/g represents mass in the engineering or British system of units. Such units are called *slugs*. *Mass in slugs is always obtained by dividing the weight in pounds by the acceleration due to gravity, 32 ft/sec².*

In turning this around, we may *define*

unit force (the pound) as that force which, applied to a mass of one slug, will give it an acceleration of one foot per second per second. Consider now a mass of one slug falling freely under the pull of gravity with an acceleration of 32 ft/sec.[2] By the above definition of unit force, such an acceleration of unit mass (1 slug) could be caused

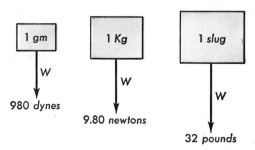

Fig. 6K *Weight is a force equal in magnitude to the mass multiplied by the acceleration of gravity.* $W = mg$.

only by a force of 32 lb. In other words, one slug weighs 32 lb. See Fig. 6K.

$$1 \text{ newton} = 0.225 \text{ lb}$$
$$1 \text{ dyne} = 2.25 \times 10^{-6} \text{ lb}$$
$$1 \text{ slug} = 14.6 \text{ Kg}$$

6.8. Change in Velocity. In Chap. 4, acceleration was defined as the rate of change of velocity and written algebraically as

$$a = \frac{v - v_0}{t}$$

If the acceleration a, in the force equation $F = ma$, is replaced by $(v - v_0)/t$, Newton's second low of motion takes on a new form.

$$F = m \frac{v - v_0}{t} \qquad (6i)$$

This equation is used in solving problems where the initial and final velocities are involved.

Example 5. A 3000-lb automobile is moving with a velocity of 15 mi/hr. What constant force, applied for a period of 12 sec, will increase its velocity to 60 mi/hr?

Solution. In solving this problem, it is convenient to express all quantities in the same

units. With the time given in seconds, the velocity is better expressed in feet per second. Since 60 mi/hr is equivalent to 88 ft/sec, 15 mi/hr = 22 ft/sec. Then, by substitution in Eq.(6i), we obtain

$$F = \frac{3000 \text{ lb}}{32 \text{ ft/sec}^2} \times \frac{88 \text{ ft/sec} - 22 \text{ ft/sec}}{12 \text{ sec}} = 515.6 \text{ lb}$$

6.9. Momentum. When Eq.(6i) is multiplied out, there results an equation involving a new concept; namely, that of *momentum.*

$$F = \frac{mv - mv_0}{t} \qquad (6j)$$

mass × velocity

Momentum is defined as the product *mass times velocity.* According to this definition, all moving bodies have momentum. In Fig. 6G, the dry ice disk m_1 at the left has momentum $m_1 v_0$. Under the action of a force F, it gains in momentum, acquiring, after a time of t seconds, a greater momentum $m_1 v$. Two masses, one large and one small, moving with the same velocity, have quite different momenta: the larger mass has a proportionately larger momentum.

Newton's second law of motion was originally stated in terms of momentum.[*]

The rate at which the momentum of a body changes is proportional to the impressed force and takes place in the direction of the straight line in which the force acts.

As an equation in words,

$$\text{force} = \frac{\text{change in momentum}}{\text{time}}$$

In algebraic symbols, this is Eq.(6j) above.

6.10. Impulse. Transferring t to the left side in Eq.(6j), we find

$$Ft = mv - mv_0 \qquad (6k)$$

This is called the "impulse equation." $F \times t$ is the *impulse* and $mv - mv_0$ is the *change in momentum.* Its meaning is illustrated in Fig. 6L where a hammer is shown

[*] Newton's second law of motion is stated in Latin in his *Principia.* Lex. II. Mutationem motus, proportionalem esse vi motrici impressae, et fieri secundum lineam rectam qua vis illa imprimitur.

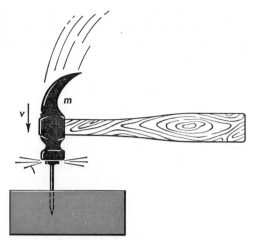

Fig. 6L   *The impulse of a hammer drives a nail into a block of wood.*

driving a nail into a block of wood. Moving with a velocity v, the hammer head of mass m strikes the nail a blow of force F. Lasting for only a fraction of a second, this force has by an impulse driven the nail a short distance into the wood. If F represents the average force, and t the time interval during which the force acts,

$$\text{impulse} = F \times t \qquad (6l)$$

When a body starts from rest, the initial velocity v_0 of Eq.(6k) is zero, and

$$Ft = mv \qquad (6m)$$

As the result of an impulse Ft, a body initially at rest acquires a momentum mv. Conversely, a body moving with a momen-tum mv can be brought to rest by an impulse $-Ft$. The minus sign indicates that the force is opposite in direction to the velocity.

Example 6. A hammer weighing 2 lb, moving with a velocity of 20 ft/sec, strikes the head of a spike and drives it into a block of hard wood. If the hammer comes to rest in 0.001 sec, find (a) the impulse, (b) the average force, and (c) the distance the nail is driven into the wood.

Solution. By direct substitution in Eq.(6m),

(a) $\quad Ft = -\dfrac{2\text{ lb}}{32\text{ ft/sec}^2} \times 20\text{ ft/sec} = -1.25\text{ lb sec}$

The average force is

(b) $\quad F = -\dfrac{1.25\text{ lb sec}}{0.001\text{ sec}} = -1250\text{ lb}$

That such a large force as this is really ex-erted is due in part to the very short time in which the force acts and its reality can be dem-onstrated by trying to push a nail into a block of wood by piling weights on top of it. The minus sign indicates that the force stopping the hammer is opposite in direction to the motion. The hammer velocity is down and the stopping force is up.

To find the distance the nail is driven into the wood in the above example, the equations for accelerated motion may be used. From Eq. (4l),

$$s = \frac{v}{2}t$$

substitution of the known quantities gives

(c) $\quad s = 10\text{ ft/sec} \times 0.001\text{ sec} = 0.01\text{ ft}$

which is about $\frac{1}{8}$ in.

PROBLEMS

1. A force of 25 newtons acts on a mass of 80 Kg. Find the acceleration.

2. A force of 8.4 newtons acts on a mass of 6.8 Kg. Find the acceleration. (*Ans.* 124 m/sec².)

3. A mass of 5 Kg is acted on by a force of 15,000 dynes. Find the acceleration.

4. A car weighing 4000 lb and traveling 30 mi/hr is accelerated for 6 sec to obtain a speed of 60 mi/hr. Find the force in pounds. (*Ans.* 917 lb.)

5. A mass of 2 Kg is given a constant accel-eration of 0.5 m/sec². Calculate the force re-quired in (a) dynes, and (b) newtons.

6. A mass of 890 gm is given an acceleration of 160 cm/sec². Find the force in (a) newtons, and (b) dynes. (*Ans.* (a) 1.42 newtons, (b) 142,-400 dynes.)

7. A motorcycle weighing 350 lb can acceler-ate at 2.5 ft/sec². Find the force in pounds.

8. A midget car weighing 750 lb can acceler-ate at 3.6 ft/sec². Find the force in pounds. (*Ans.* 84.4 lb.)

9. A 5-Kg shell traveling 900 m/sec strikes a hillside where it penetrates the ground to a depth of 2 m. Find (a) the time of stopping, and (b) the average force in newtons.

10. Starting from rest a 3200-lb car acquires a speed of 60 ft/sec in a distance of 500 ft. Assuming the acceleration to be uniform, find (a) the acceleration, (b) the time, (c) the force, and (d) the final momentum of the car. (*Ans.* (a) 3.6 ft/sec^2, (b) 16.67 sec, (c) 360 lb, (d) 6000 slug ft/sec.)

11. A sledge hammer of mass 5 Kg moving downward with a speed of 4 m/sec strikes the head of a railroad spike driving it 1 cm into a wooden railroad tie. Assuming constant acceleration, find (a) the acceleration, (b) the time of impact, (c) the force, and (d) the impulse during impact (neglect the mass of the spike). (Use the mks system.)

12. A 200-gm bullet is fired from a gun with a muzzle velocity of 800 m/sec. If the gun barrel is 1 m long, find (a) the acceleration, (b) the time, (c) the force, and (d) the impulse. (Assume constant acceleration throughout the gun barrel.) (Use the mks system.) (*Ans.* (a) 320,000 m/sec^2, (b) 0.0025 sec, (c) 64,000 newtons, (d) 160 Kg m/sec.)

13. A golf ball of 50-gm mass and moving with a speed of 30 m/sec lands on muddy ground where it becomes embedded a distance of 5 cm. Assuming constant acceleration during impact, find (a) the acceleration, (b) the time of impact, (c) the force, and (d) the momentum just before impact. (Use the mks system.)

14. A 65-ton passenger plane requires a runway 4000 ft long to acquire its take-off speed of 90 mi/hr. Calculate the total average thrust of its propellers. (*Ans.* 8848 lb.)

15. A 2-Kg shell is fired from a 3.2-m gun barrel with a speed of 840 m/sec. Calculate the average force involved.

16. A mortar shell weighing 3.8 lb is fired from a mortar 2.75 ft long. If the muzzle speed is 320 ft/sec, find the average force. (*Ans.* 2211 lb.)

17. A 1.1-oz golf ball lying on the fairway is driven by a golf club with a speed of 140 ft/sec. If the time of impact is 0.012 sec, find (a) the average force in pounds, (b) the distance over which the force acts, and (c) the impulse.

18. A body moving with a speed of 4.5 ft/sec has a momentum of 54 slugs ft/sec. Find its mass. (*Ans.* 12 slugs.)

19. A 3000-lb car traveling 30 mi/hr crashes into a stone wall smashing in the front end of the car for 2 ft. Find (a) the momentum, (b) the acceleration, (c) the average force, and (d) the impulse.

20. A hammer of mass 1 Kg moving with a speed of 8 m/sec strikes the head of a nail driving it 2 cm into a large block of wood. Neglecting the mass of the nail, calculate (a) the momentum of the hammer before impact, (b) the acceleration during impact, and (c) the time interval during impact. (*Ans.* (a) 8 Kg m/sec, (b) −1600 m/sec^2, (c) 0.005 sec.)

21. A constant horizontal force of 20 lb acts on a body on a smooth horizontal plane. The body starts from rest and is observed to move 180 ft in 12 sec. Assuming constant acceleration, what is the mass of the body?

22. A 22-rifle fires a 1.8-gm bullet at 400 m/sec into a block of wood. If the bullet penetrates to a depth of 10 cm, find (a) the average acceleration, and (b) the average force exerted on the bullet. (c) What is the time required in stopping? (*Ans.* (a) −800,000 m/sec^2, (b) −1440 newtons, (c) 0.0005 sec.)

23. A locomotive is capable of exerting a maximum pull of 4 tons. What speed can it give to a passenger train weighing 200 tons in a distance of ½ mile? Assume the train starts from rest.

24. A freight train with a mass of 8×10^5 Kg is traveling along a straight and level track at a speed of 90 Km/hr. (a) What force applied by the brakes will stop it in a distance of 1 Km? (b) Find the time of stopping. (*Ans.* (a) -2.5×10^5 newtons, (b) 80 sec.)

25. (a) How large a force is required to move a 6-Kg mass 2 m along a smooth level surface in 1 sec? (b) How large a force will move this same mass 2 m vertically in 1 sec? Assume the mass initially at rest and no friction.

26. A fireman's hose delivers 240 Kg/sec of water at a speed of 12 m/sec. If this stream, moving horizontally, strikes a vertical wall, thereby stopping its forward motion, (a) what is the momentum destroyed per second, and (b) what is the force against the wall? (*Ans.* (a) 2880 Kg m/sec^2, (b) 2880 newtons.)

Chapter 7

Vector Addition and Composition of Forces

7.1. Vector Addition. The process of vector addition will first be illustrated by an example involving two displacements. Suppose that a ship starts from a point A and sails due north for a distance of 6 mi to a point B where it changes course and sails due east for a distance of 4 mi to a point C. Although the ship has sailed a total distance of $6 + 4$ (or 10) mi, it is obvious that its distance from the starting point is not given by this arithmetic sum.

To find the actual displacement, that is, the distance from the starting point, a scale diagram like that shown in Fig. 7A may be

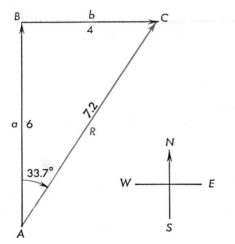

Fig. 7A *Diagram illustrating vector addition as applied to displacements.*

drawn. With a pencil and a ruler (a centimeter scale) a vertical line AB, 6 cm long, is drawn to represent the displacement 6

miles north. The line BC is next drawn to the right from B and 4 cm long to represent the *4 miles east.* The triangle is finally completed by joining A and C. With an arrowhead at C, the hypotenuse R, measuring 7.2 cm, represents the resultant displacement of 7.2 mi.

Vectorially, we write

$$\overrightarrow{AB} + \overrightarrow{BC} = \overrightarrow{AC} \qquad \text{or} \qquad \boxed{\overrightarrow{R} = \overrightarrow{a} + \overrightarrow{b}}$$

Using a protractor, the angle A is measured to be 33.7°. The direction of the resultant vector R is therefore 33.7° east of north.

It is customary in any vector diagram to represent all vector quantities by arrows, each arrow being drawn in the proper direction and to the proper length. A little practice in drawing will show that, regardless of what scale is used to make the diagram, the resultant must be the same in magnitude and direction, and that the more carefully the diagram is drawn, the more accurate will be the measured result.

To calculate the magnitude of the resultant R in Fig. 7A, use is made of the Pythagorean theorem in geometry that, for any right triangle, *the square of the hypotenuse is equal to the sum of the squares of the other two sides.*

$$R^2 = a^2 + b^2$$

Substitute the two values of a and b.

$$R^2 = (6)^2 + (4)^2 = 52$$

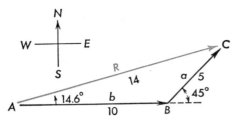

Fig. 7B   *Vector diagram for Example 1.*

By taking the square root* of 52, we obtain

$$R = 7.21 \text{ mi}$$

Example 1. A man walks east for a distance of 10 mi, then turns and walks north-east for a distance of 5 mi. Find the resultant displacement.

Solution. Following the procedure outlined above, a horizontal line AB is first drawn 10 units long and labeled as shown in Fig. 7B. The second vector, BC, is next drawn NE in direction, i.e., at 45°, and 5 units long. The resultant R is then drawn and measured; its length is found to be 14 units which represents a displacement of 14 mi. The angle at A measured with a protractor is found to be 14.6°. The answer, therefore, is 14 mi in direction 14.6° north of east.

To calculate the magnitude of R, it is seen that a right triangle can be formed as shown in Fig. 7C. The right triangle theorem is then applied to the triangle BCD

$$(BC)^2 = (BD)^2 + (CD)^2$$

Since two angles of BCD are equal to each other, the triangle is isosceles and the sides BD and CD are equal. $BD = CD$. Therefore,

$$(BC)^2 = 2(BD)^2 = 25$$

from which $(BD)^2 = 25/2$

and $BD = \sqrt{12.5} = 3.54$

---

* A simplified method for finding the square root of a number to an accuracy of three figures is the following. By inspection, a guess of the square root is made to two figures. For example, if the number is 685, inspection shows that it lies between $(20)^2 = 400$ and $(30)^2 = 900$, and that a reasonable guess might be 25. The original number is then divided by 25 and gives 27.4. The average of these two numbers, 26.2, is then the square root to three figures. If greater accuracy is desired, the averaged number may be assumed to be an original guess and the process repeated.

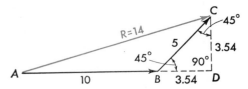

Fig. 7C   *Vector diagram for Example 1.*

Applying the same theorem to the right triangle ADC, we get

$$R^2 = (3.54)^2 + (13.54)^2 = 195.8$$

from which $R = 14.0 \text{ mi}$

7.2. The Parallelogram Method of Vector Addition. There are two generally accepted methods of vector addition; namely, the triangle method described in the preceding section and shown in Figs. 7A and 7B, and the parallelogram method described below. Consider, as an illustration of the latter, the addition of the same two vectors given in Fig. 7B, $b = 10$ mi and $a = 5$ mi, the two making an angle of 45° with each other.

As shown at the left in Fig. 7D, the vectors are first drawn outward from the same origin A. From D a dotted line is next drawn parallel to vector b, and from B a dotted line is drawn parallel to vector a, as in the middle diagram. From the point C, where these two lines cross, the diagonal line AC is drawn in and labeled with an arrowhead as the resultant R.

A comparison of the parallelogram with the triangle in Fig. 7B shows that the triangle ABC in both diagrams is identical. Both methods, therefore, lead to the same result. In solving certain problems, the triangle method will be found more convenient, while in solving others, the parallelogram is more readily applicable.

There are two common systems by which the directions of vector quantities are designated: one is to refer all angles to the points of the compass as in Figs. 7A and 7B; and the other is to specify all angles with reference to the *x axis*, as in Fig. 7D and 7E. In navigation the *true bearing* of a ship is measured from the *north* clockwise around the compass. To sail east is to have a true bearing of 90°, and to sail south-west is to have a true bearing of 225°.

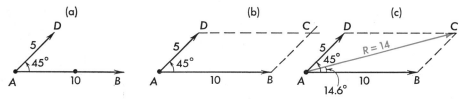

Fig. 7D *Diagram illustrating the parallelogram method of vector addition.*

When directions are referred to the *x axis,* angles measured in a counterclockwise direction from the +*x* axis are called +; those measured clockwise from the same line are called −. For example, the direction-angle for the second vector in Fig. 7E is +60°, or −300°.

body upon another. For example, in towing an automobile as shown in Fig. 7H, there are two forces acting: (1) a downward force *W* due to gravity, and (2) a horizontal force *F* due to a pull on the towline. The latter force is supplied by some external object or machine. In pushing a lawnmower there

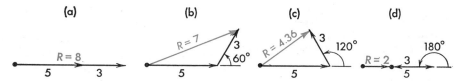

Fig. 7E *Diagram illustrating the triangle method of vector addition.*

7.3. Weight Is a Vector. Everyone knows that, when he weighs himself as illustrated in Fig. 7F, he is measuring the downward force he exerts on the foot board of the scales, and that this force causes some mechanism within the scales to indicate his weight. The greater the downward force, the greater is the indicated weight. We are not interested here in the system of levers, weights, or springs within the scales, but rather with the downward force we call our *weight.*

Weight, as explained in the last chapter, is due to the gravitational attraction of the earth for all bodies and is given by the formula,

$$W = mg$$

As illustrated in Fig. 7G, gravitational forces always act in the direction of a line joining the body and the center of the earth and they are, therefore, perpendicular to the earth's surface at the body.

The term "force" is not confined to weight alone but to the action of any one

are also two forces: (1) the downward force *W* due to gravity and (2) a diagonal force *F* due to some person pushing on the lawnmower handle.

Regardless of the direction in which a

Fig. 7F *Weight is a downward force. The earth attracts all bodies toward its center.*

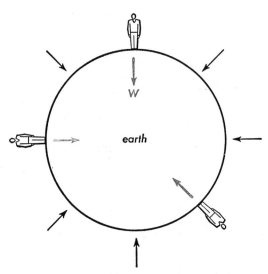

Fig. 7G *Weight is a force due to gravitational attraction, and gravitational force acts in the direction of a line joining the body and the center of the earth.*

force may act, its magnitude may be expressed in *dynes, newtons,* or *pounds.* The justification for this is illustrated in Fig. 7I where spring scales are used to measure forces. In diagram (a), the 3-lb weight exerts a downward force of 3 lb. A horizontal force of the same magnitude is produced by running the cord over a pulley as in diagram (b).

sider the diagram in Fig. 7J, illustrating a heavy trunk being pulled along the floor by two ropes. With steady pulls of 25 lb and 25 lb exerted in directions at 90° from each other, the trunk moves in a direction indicated by the dotted arrow. By vector addition, a *resultant* force can now be found which, upon taking the place of the two forces shown, will produce the same motion.

The addition of the two force vectors of Fig. 7J is illustrated in Fig. 7K. Starting at *O,* the two vectors *a* and *b* are first drawn to scale and in their proper directions. The dotted lines *QS* and *PS* are next drawn in to complete the parallelogram, and then followed by the diagonal *R.* With an arrowhead at *S,* the diagonal represents the resultant whose magnitude *R* and direction θ is to be calculated by trigonometry.

Since *a* and *b* make an angle of 90° with each other, *OQS* is a right triangle with the sides, *a, b,* and *R.* By definition from trigonometry,

$$\frac{a}{b} = \tan \theta$$

In this equation, substitute known values, as follows:

$$\frac{25}{40} = 0.6250 = \tan \theta$$

(a)   (b)

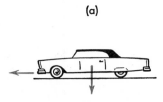
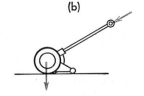

Fig. 7H *Illustration of two independent forces acting on the same body.*

This is not to imply that gravitational attraction is responsible for all forces, for it is not; it is only to indicate that all forces, whatever their origin or direction, may be expressed in terms of weight.

7.4. Forces Are Added Vectorially. Since forces have both magnitude and direction, they are vector quantities and, therefore, subject to the rules of *vector addition.* Con-

Look up 0.6250 in the tangent column of the table of trigonometric functions, Appendix III. We find that $\theta = 32°$.

Again, by definition,

$$\frac{b}{R} = \cos \theta$$

Since *R* is the unknown to be calculated, upon transposing we obtain

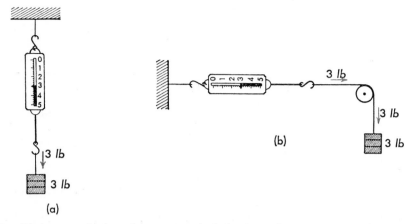

Fig. 7I   *All forces, whether they are vertical, horizontal, or at any angle, may be expressed in terms of weight.*

$$\frac{b}{\cos \theta} = R$$

Look up the natural cosine of 32° in Appendix III; then, by substitution,

$$\frac{40}{0.8480} = 47.2 \text{ lb}$$

The resultant force is, therefore, equal to 47.2 lb at an angle of 32° with OQ.

Example 2. A boat is being towed through a canal by two ropes, one on either side of the canal, as shown at the left in Fig. 7L. If the ap-

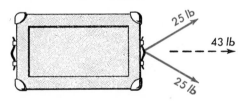

Fig. 7J   *Two forces acting at an angle to each other are equivalent to a single force acting in a direction between them.*

plied forces are 400 and 600 newtons, respectively, and the angle between the ropes is 60°, find the magnitude of the resultant force on the boat and the angles the ropes make with the canal. Assume the resultant force to be parallel to the canal.

Solution. The triangle method is applied to the solution of this problem at the right in Fig. 7L. First a vector b, 6 cm long, is drawn down and to the right to represent the one force of 600 newtons. From the end of this vector, and at an angle of 60°, the second vector a, 4 cm long, is drawn to represent the other force of 400 newtons. The line R is then drawn in with an arrowhead to represent the resultant force on the boat.

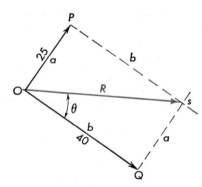

Fig. 7K   *Diagram illustrating the addition of two forces acting at an angle of 90° with each other.*

By trigonometry the unknown quantities, (1) the magnitude of R, (2) the angle θ, and (3) the angle ϕ, can be calculated as follows.

Use the law of cosines for an oblique triangle. (See Appendix II.)

$$\boxed{R^2 = a^2 + b^2 + 2ab \cos 60°}$$

Look up the cosine of 60° in tables and substitute the value in this equation.

$$R^2 = (400)^2 + (600)^2 + 2(400)(600) \times 0.500$$

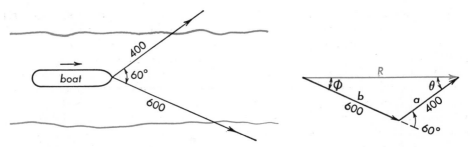

Fig. 7L *The pull of two ropes at an angle on a canal boat is equivalent to a single force straight along the canal.*

from which

$$R^2 = 160,000 + 360,000 + 240,000$$

so that

$$R^2 = 760,000 \quad \text{and} \quad R = 872$$

The resultant force $R = 872$ newtons.

To find angles ϕ, and θ, either the law of sines or the law of cosines may be used. (See Appendix II.) Using the law of cosines to find angle ϕ,

$$\cos \phi = \frac{b^2 + R^2 - a^2}{2bR} = \frac{(600)^2 + (872)^2 - (400)^2}{2 \times 600 \times 872}$$

Thus

$$\cos \phi = 0.9178$$

which from the tables of cosines is

$$\phi = 23.4°$$

Use the law of sines to find the angle θ.

$$\boxed{\frac{a}{\sin \phi} = \frac{b}{\sin \theta}}$$

By transposing and substituting, we find

$$\sin \theta = \frac{b \sin \phi}{a} = \frac{600 \times 0.3971}{400} = 0.5957$$

From the tables of natural sines,

$$\theta = 36.6°$$

7.5. Force Polygon. When three or more forces act simultaneously upon a body, a single force, called their resultant, can be found which acting alone upon that body will produce the same result. To find such a resultant force, the *polygon method* of vector addition is often employed. In principle, this is an extension of the triangle method and consists of placing the tail of one vector at the head of the one preceding it, and continuing this process until all vectors have been added.

An illustration of the polygon method applied to five forces is given in Fig. 7M. The space diagram at the left shows the

(a)

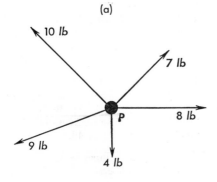

space diagram

(b)

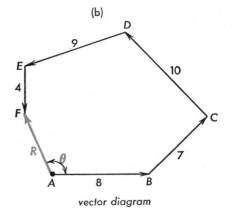

vector diagram

Fig. 7M *Diagrams illustrating the graphical addition of five forces to find their resultant. (The polygon method.)*

forces acting on a body at P, while the *vector diagram* at the right shows the vector addition and the resultant force R. Starting at A as the origin, vector AB is drawn 8 cm long, parallel to the 8-lb vector in diagram (a). Vector BC is next drawn 7 cm long and parallel to the 7-lb vector. These are followed in succession by vectors CD, DE, and EF, respectively. With all five vectors added, the resultant R is found by joining the last arrowhead F with the origin A.

Drawn to scale, the measured length of R will give the magnitude of the resultant force, and the measured angle θ will give the direction in which it acts.

To calculate the resultant force R in such a problem, the polygon may either be divided up into triangles and all sides and angles of the triangles calculated in their turn, or each force can be resolved into components and the components added arithmetically. The latter method is generally the easier of the two, and will be treated in detail in Sec. 8.3.

PROBLEMS

1. Two forces of 6 newtons and 8 newtons, respectively, are exerted simultaneously on the same object. If the angle between them is 60°, find by graphical construction their resultant.

2. Two forces of 60 newtons each make an angle of 50° with each other. Find by graphical construction their resultant. (*Ans.* 108.7 newtons.)

3. Two forces of 20 newtons and 30 newtons act on the same body at right angles to each other. Find, by calculation, the magnitude of their resultant.

4. Two forces of 5 lb and 7 lb act on the same body. If the angle between them is 120°, calculate the magnitude of the resultant. (*Ans.* 10.44 lb.)

5. A canal boat is being pulled by two ropes making an angle of 45° with each other. If the forces are 150 lb and 175 lb, respectively, what is the magnitude of the resultant force?

6. A ship sails south a distance of 320 mi, then turns and sails northwest for 190 mi. Apply the triangle method to find the ship's distance from home port. (*Ans.* 229 mi at 36.0° south of west.)

7. An airplane flies due east for a distance of 250 Km, then turns and flies 60° south of east for 180 Km. How far, and in what direction, is the plane from its starting point?

8. A girl riding a bicycle at the rate of 8 mi/hr rides south for 2 hr, then turns and rides east for 1.5 hr. Determine the displacement graphically, and by calculation. (*Ans.* 20 mi at 36.9° east of south.)

9. Find the resultant of two forces, (a) 5 dynes at 65°, and (b) 8 dynes at 155°.

10. Calculate the magnitude and direction of the resultant of the two following forces: (a) 15 newtons at 80°, and (b) 21 newtons at 230°. (*Ans.* 11.0 newtons at 186.9°.)

11. A plane flies southwest for a distance of 200 Km, then turns and flies east for a distance of 200 Km when he is forced down. How far, and in what direction, is the plane from its base?

12. A taxi driver averages 30 mi/hr. After traveling east for 15 min, he turns and drives north for 20 min, then east again for 30 min. How far, and in what direction, is he from his starting point? (*Ans.* 24.6 mi at 24° north of east.)

13. Cruising at 300 Km/hr, a pilot flies southwest for 45 min, then turns and flies north for 1 hr and 15 min. He finally turns toward home port and flies for 30 min when he is forced down. How far, and in what direction, is he from home port?

14. A pilot cruising at 240 mi/hr flies northeast for 1 hr and 20 min, then turns and flies south for 2 hr. Turning then for home base, he flies for 50 min before being forced down at sea. How far, and in what direction, is he from home base? (*Ans.* 140 mi at 48.3° south of east.)

15. Combine the following forces and find their resultant: 50 lb east and 40 lb northeast.

16. Determine the resultant of two forces: (a) 16 lb toward the south, and (b) 20 lb toward the southwest. (*Ans.* 33.3 lb at 25.1° west of south.)

17. Calculate the magnitude and direction of the resultant of two forces: (a) 15 newtons at 205°, and (b) 10 newtons at 255°.

18. Find the resultant of two forces, one of 450 newtons vertically upward and the other of 270 newtons making an angle of 35° with the vertical. (*Ans.* 689 newtons making 13° with the vertical.)

19. An airplane flying 300 mi/hr travels northeast for 10 min, then turns southeast for 20 min, then turns for home. Forced down at sea after a total elapsed time of 40 min, the pilot sends out an SOS signal giving his position. How long will it take another plane capable of flying 150 mi/hr to reach the downed ship?

20. A car speeding along the highway at 70 mi/hr travels for 1 hr and 40 min in a direction 32° north of east. Determine graphically and by calculation how far north and how far east the car is from its starting point. (*Ans.* 61.8 mi north and 99.0 mi east.)

21. Two forces, 6 newtons and 8 newtons, are exerted simultaneously on the same body. If these two forces make an angle of 30° with each other, what equivalent force would produce the same result?

22. A car is being towed by two ropes making an angle of 70° with each other. If the forces on the ropes are 150 lb and 240 lb, what is the magnitude and direction of the resultant force? (*Ans.* 324 lb at 25.8° with the 240 lb.)

23. A horizontal force of 50 newtons is combined with a vertically upward force. If their resultant has a direction of 32°, find the magnitude of (a) the vertical force, and (b) the resultant force.

24. A vertically upward force of 12 newtons is combined with a second force directed at 30°. If their resultant has a direction of 45°, find the magnitude of (a) the second force, and (b) the resultant. (*Ans.* (a) 32.8 newtons, (b) 40.1 newtons.)

25. Find the resultant of the following three forces: (a) 8 lb at 0°, (b) 6 lb at 90°, and (c) 4 lb at 135°.

26. Find the resultant of the following forces: (a) 40 newtons at 30°, (b) 26 newtons at 120°, and (c) 30 newtons at 180°. (*Ans.* 43.3 newtons at 101.2°.)

27. The following four forces are applied to the same body. Graphically determine their resultant. (a) 5 newtons at 20°, (b) 6 newtons at 80°, (c) 3 newtons at 180°, and (d) 4 newtons at 225°.

28. Graphically determine the resultant of the following five coplaner forces: (a) 6.8 newtons at 0°, (b) 40 newtons at 30°, (c) 27 newtons at 90°, (d) 16 newtons at 135°, and (e) 24 newtons at 240°. (*Ans.* 41.7 newtons at 64.2°.)

29. The following five forces act on the same body. Graphically determine their resultant. (a) 4 lb at 120°, (b) 6 lb at 240°, (c) 3 lb at 300°, (d) 7 lb at 30°, and (e) 5 lb at 90°.

30. Graphically determine the resultant of the following coplanar forces: (a) 4 newtons at 0°, (b) 4 newtons at 45°, (c) 6 newtons at 90°, (d) 5 newtons at 180°, (e) 3 newtons at 210°, and (f) 2 newtons at 270°. (*Ans.* 5.38 newtons at 98.3°.)

Chapter 8

Vector Resolution and
the Method of Components

8.1. Resolution of a Force into Components. Many of the problems in mechanics are most easily solved by the so-called "*method of components.*" To apply this method to typical problems, it is necessary that we first see how a single vector may be resolved into two components. Consider as an illustration the known force F, making an angle of θ degrees with the x axis as shown in Fig. 8A.

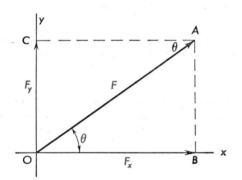

Fig. 8A *The resolution of a vector into two rectangular components.*

By dropping lines from A, perpendicular to the x and y axes, the component forces F_x and F_y are equivalent to the original force F, since by adding them vectorially they give F as a resultant.

With F_x and F_y perpendicular to each other, triangles OAB and OAC are equivalent right triangles with corresponding sides equal. $F_y = AB$ and $F_x = AC$.

By trigonometry, then,

$$\frac{F_x}{F} = \cos \theta, \qquad \frac{F_y}{F} = \sin \theta, \text{ and}$$

$$\frac{F_y}{F_x} = \tan \theta \quad (8a)$$

Since F and θ are usually the known quantities, the first two equations are the most useful in finding the magnitudes of force components. Upon transposing, they become

$$\boxed{\begin{array}{l} F_x = F \cos \theta \\[2mm] F_y = F \sin \theta \end{array}} \quad (8b)$$

Example 1. A force of 50 lb is applied to the handle of a 150-lb lawn roller. See Fig. 8B. Cal-

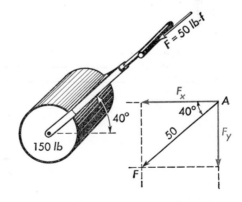

Fig. 8B *The force on the handle of a lawn roller is resolved into two components.*

culate (a) the horizontal and vertical components of this force if the handle makes an angle of 40° with the horizontal, and (b) the force exerted by the roller on the ground.

57

Solution. The graphical solution to (a) is shown at the right in Fig. 8B. The magnitudes of the two components F_x and F_y are calculated by direct substitutions in Eq.(8b).

$$F_x = 50 \text{ lb} \times \cos 40°$$
$$F_y = 50 \text{ lb} \times \sin 40°$$

From the tables of natural sines and cosines, substitution gives

$$F_x = 50 \times 0.766 = 38.3 \text{ lb}$$
$$F_y = 50 \times 0.643 = 32.1 \text{ lb}$$

The horizontal component, $F_x = 38.3$ lb, is the force causing the roller to move, while the vertical component, $F_y = 32.1$ lb, acting straight downward must be added to the weight of the roller to find the total force exerted by the roller on the ground.

Total downward force = $150 + 32.1 = 182.1$ lb

8.2. The Sailboat. A problem that puzzles many people, particularly those more or less familiar with sailboats, is that of sailing across the water into the wind. This phenomenon, commonly known as *tacking,* is another illustration of the resolution of a force into rectangular components.

As shown in Fig. 8C, the wind is from the east and the boat is headed NE. When the

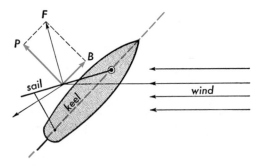

Fig. 8C *A boat sailing into the wind. An example of the resolution of a force F into two rectangular components, P and B.*

sail is properly set, the wind, in blowing across the canvas, is deflected away in such a way that it exerts a force F normal to the surface as shown. By resolving this force into two rectangular components, one parallel and the other perpendicular to the

keel, the force B, responsible for the boat's motion, is found.

The other component, P, has little effect upon the boat since it is perpendicular to the motion. It is a useless force which tends to tip the boat and move it to leeward. To reduce tipping or being pushed sideways, sailboats are equipped with a deep heavy keel. By increasing the angle between the sail and the wind, the force F will increase but the forward component will decrease. If the boat is headed more directly into the wind, without changing the relative position of the sail and the keel, the useful component B will again decrease. Most rapid progress upwind is attained when the wind and keel make an angle of 45° and the sails are so rigged that the rudder is parallel to the keel.

8.3. Vector Addition by the Method of Components. When several forces act upon a body simultaneously, their resultant force may be determined by any one of a number of different methods. Some methods involve long and tedious processes of calculation, while others involve a minimum number of simple operations. Of the graphical solutions of force problems, the polygon method described in Sec. 7.5 is undoubtedly the simplest. Of the analytical solutions, however, "the method of components" is generally the shortest and is preferred because of its simplicity.

As an illustration of the method of components, consider the example of the four forces shown graphically at the left in Fig. 8D; $F_1 = 5$ lb at 30°, $F_2 = 4$ lb at 90°, $F_3 = 7$ lb at 135°, and $F_4 = 6$ lb at 240°. The problem here is to find the resultant force equivalent to all four together.

The right-hand figure shows the graphical solution with all given angles measured from the x axis. The analytical solution consists of performing the following operations:

(1) Each force is resolved into x- and y-components.

(2) The x-components are added to give a resultant X-component.

(3) The y-components are added to give a resultant Y-component.

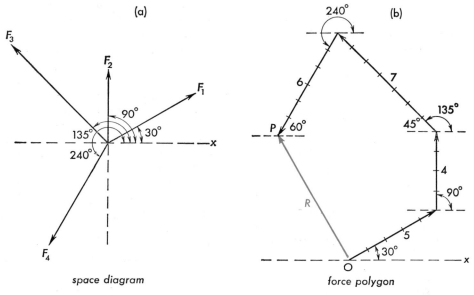

Fig. 8D *The polygon method of vector addition for four forces.*

(4) The resultant X- and Y-components are combined at right angles to obtain their resultant R.

The first of these steps is shown graphically in Fig. 8E. Each vector is drawn in its proper direction and the x- and y-components found separately by using Eq.(8b). For F_1 the x-component is 5 cos 30° = 4.33 lb, and the y-component is 5 sin 30° = 2.5 lb. For F_2, the x-component is zero and the y-component 4 lb. For F_3 the x-component is 7 cos 45° = 4.95 lb and the y-component is 7 sin 45° = 4.95 lb. Finally, for F_4 the x-component is 6 cos 60° = 3.0 lb and the y-component is 6 sin 60° = 5.20 lb.

Components to the right or up are positive in sign; components to the left or down are negative in sign.

The second and third steps of adding x- and y-components separately are tabulated below, and the fourth step of combining the X- and Y-components is shown graphically in Fig. 8F.

x-components	y-components
+4.33 lb	+2.50 lb
+0.00	+4.00
−4.95	+4.95
−3.00	−5.20
$X = -3.62$ lb	$Y = +6.25$ lb

From the tabulated x-components, X has the magnitude −3.62 lb; and from the

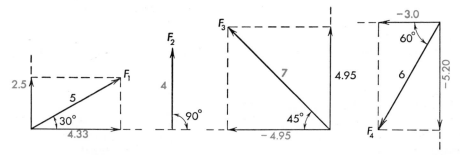

Fig. 8E *Resolution of all forces into x- and y-components.*

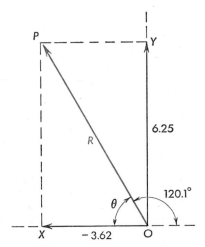

Fig. 8F   *Resultant X- and Y-components added vectorially to give the resultant R.*

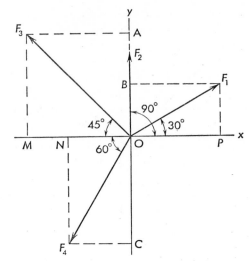

Fig. 8G   *Vector diagram showing all forces and the x- and y-components.*

y-components, Y has the magnitude $+6.25$ lb.

Since X and Y are at right angles to each other, the triangle OPX is a right triangle and the hypotenuse R is given by

$$R = \sqrt{(3.62)^2 + (6.25)^2} = 7.23 \text{ lb}$$

The angle θ is obtained from the tangent relation in Eq.(8a),

$$\tan \theta = \frac{6.25}{3.62} = 1.726$$

giving $\theta = 59.9°$. The direction angle of R from the $+x$ direction is $180 - 59.9$, or $120.1°$.

The graphs accompanying the solution above may be combined into one diagram as shown in Fig. 8G. In this figure, the original space diagram of forces, as well as all the components, are indicated. The

x-components are OP, OM, and ON, while the y-components are OA, OB, OC, and OF_2.

A general formula that can be used for solving problems involving many forces by the method of components is the following:

$$X = F_1 \cos \theta_1 + F_2 \cos \theta_2 + F_3 \cos \theta_3 + \cdots + F_n \cos \theta_n \qquad (8c)$$
$$Y = F_1 \sin \theta_1 + F_2 \sin \theta_2 + F_3 \sin \theta_3 + \cdots + F_n \sin \theta_n \qquad (8d)$$
$$\text{and } R^2 = X^2 + Y^2 \quad \text{and } \tan \theta = Y/X \quad (8e)$$

In abbreviated notation,

$$X = \Sigma F \cos \theta \qquad (8f)$$
$$Y = \Sigma F \sin \theta \qquad (8g)$$

The Greek letter Σ indicates a summation.

PROBLEMS

1. Find the x- and y-components of a 16-lb force acting in a direction making an angle of $28°$ with the x axis.

2. Find the x- and y-components of a 25-newton force acting in a direction making an angle of $42°$ with the x axis. (*Ans.* 18.6 and 16.7 newtons.)

3. The car on a 30° incline weighs 5000 lb.

Calculate the tension in the cable required to keep it moving with constant speed up or down the incline.

4. A force of 10 lb is resolved into two forces at right angles to each other. What are the magnitudes of the two forces if one is three times the other? (*Ans.* 9.48 lb and 3.16 lb.)

5. An upward force of 16 newtons makes an

angle of 35 with the vertical. Calculate its vertical and horizontal components.

6. A force of 75 dynes makes an angle of 62° with the x axis. Calculate the x- and y-components. (*Ans.* 35.2 dynes and 66.2 dynes.)

7. A heavy box weighing 100 lb is being pulled across the floor by a 65-lb force inclined at an angle of 40° with the horizontal. Find (a) the vertical and horizontal components of the applied force, and (b) the resultant vertically downward force on the floor.

8. A lawn roller weighing 280 lb is pushed along the ground by a force of 65 lb making an angle of 35° with the horizontal. Find the x- and y-components of the applied force. (*Ans.* 35.1 lb and 53.2 lb.)

9. A 60-lb force makes an angle of 35° with the x axis. Find the two components of this force acting in directions of 15° and 65°, respectively.

10. A single force of 320 lb at 27° is to be resolved into two components whose direction angles are 5° and 76°, respectively. Determine their magnitude. (*Ans.* 255 lb and 127 lb.)

11. Apply the method of components to the following pair of forces: (1) 10 lb at 30° with the $+x$ axis, and (2) 6 lb at 135° with the $+x$ axis. Find (a) the resultant X-component, (b) the resultant Y-component, and (c) the resultant magnitude. Make a diagram to scale and graphically find the direction of the resultant with respect to the $+x$ axis.

12. Apply the method of components to the following pair of forces: (1) 6 lb at 150° with the $+x$ axis, and (2) 10 lb at 315° with the $+x$ axis. Find (a) the resultant X-component, (b) the resultant Y-component, and (c) the resultant magnitude. (d) Make a diagram to scale and graphically find the direction of the resultant with respect to the $+x$ axis. (*Ans.* (a) 1.87 lb, (b) −4.07 lb, (c) 4.47 lb, (d) 294.6°.)

13. Apply the method of components to the following pair of forces: (1) 10 lb at 45° with the $+x$ axis, and (2) 6 lb at 300° with the $+x$ axis. Find (a) the resultant X-component, (b) the resultant Y-component, and (c) the resultant magnitude. (d) Make a diagram to scale and graphically find the direction of the resultant with respect to the $+x$ axis.

14. Apply the method of components to the following pair of forces: (1) 10 lb at 30° with

the $+x$ axis, and (2) 6 lb at 315° with the $+x$ axis. Find (a) the resultant X-component, (b) the resultant Y-component, and (c) the resultant magnitude. (d) Make a diagram to scale and graphically find the direction of the resultant with respect to the $+x$ axis. (*Ans.* (a) 12.9 lb, (b) 0.76 lb, (c) 12.9 lb, (d) 3.3°.)

15. Apply the method of components to the following three forces, and find their resultant: (1) 8 dynes at 35°, (2) 3 dynes at 125°, and (3) 2 dynes at 165°.

16. Apply the method of components to the following three forces and find their resultant: (1) 4 newtons at 120°, (2) 6 newtons at 30°, and (3) 5 newtons at 340°. (*Ans.* 9.2 newtons at 31.1°.)

17. The following four forces act on the same body, (a) 20 newtons at 245°, (b) 12 newtons at 340°, (c) 15 newtons at 25°, and (d) 10 newtons at 135°. Apply the method of components to find the resultant.

18. Four forces act on the same body: (a) 40 lb at 315°, (b) 50 lb at 200°, (c) 60 lb at 35°, and (d) 35 lb at 100°. Find their resultant by the method of components. (*Ans.* 33.8 lb at 44°.)

19. A man exerts a force of 250 newtons along the handle of a 150-Kg roller. The handle makes an angle of 35° with the ground. Find (a) the horizontal and vertical components of this force, and (b) the force exerted by the roller on the ground.

20. A sailboat is tacking at 45° into the wind. If the resultant force exerted by the wind on the sail is 180 lb and the boom makes an angle of 30° with the keel, find the forward thrust on the boat. (*Ans.* 90 lb.)

21. The wind exerts a resultant force of 500 newtons on the sail of a small boat. If the angle between the wind and keel is 45° and the angle between the boom and keel is 20°, find the forward thrust on the boat.

22. Apply the method of components to find the resultant of the following four forces: (a) 10 newtons at 120°, (b) 5 newtons at 270°, (c) 4 newtons at 45°, and (d) 12.5 newtons at 0°. (*Ans.* 12.2 newtons at 32.1°.)

23. A ball weighing 3.5 lb on a 30° inclined plane rests against a brick lying on the plane. Find the force exerted on the brick by the ball.

24. Four forces act on the same body. Find

their resultant. (a) 10 lb at 20°, (b) 6 lb at 90°, (c) 12 lb at 220°, and (d) 2 lb at 0°. (*Ans.* 2.78 lb at 37.7°.)

25. A 50-Kg wagon on a 20° inclined plane is kept from rolling down hill by a rope tied to a tree. If the rope is parallel to the incline, what is the tension in the rope?

26. A long rope, making an angle of 30° with the horizontal, has the upper end tied to the top of a tree. (a) If the tension in the rope is 100 lb, what are the components of this force parallel and perpendicular to the ground? (b) Which component tends to pull the tree over? (*Ans.* (a) 86.6 lb and 50 lb, (b) 86.6 lb.)

27. A force of 50 lb is exerted in the handle of a 300-lb lawn roller. If the handles make an angle of 30° with the horizontal, what is the total downward force on the ground?

28. One end of a rope is tied to a log and the other end to an elephant. If the rope makes an angle of 55° with the ground and a tension of 420 lb exists in the rope, what horizontal force is applied to drag the log? (*Ans.* 241 lb.)

Chapter 9

Newton's Law of Gravitation and Third Law of Motion

9.1. Newton's Law of Gravitation. Nearly everyone has heard the story of how young Isaac Newton, while sitting under an apple tree one day, was struck on the head by a falling apple. This incident set Newton to thinking about falling bodies and led him at the early age of twenty-three to the discovery of the law of gravity.

It has often been said incorrectly that Newton discovered gravity. What Newton discovered was the *universal law of gravitation. Any two bodies attract each other with a force proportional to the product of their masses and inversely proportional to the square of the distance between them.* Written in algebraic symbols,

$$F \propto \frac{m_1 m_2}{d^2}$$

As illustrated in Fig. 9A, F is the force of attraction, m_1 and m_2 are the two masses,

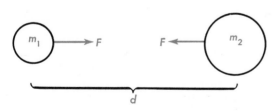

Fig. 9A *The gravitational attraction of one body of mass m_1 for another of mass m_2.*

and d is the distance between them. Mass m_1 pulls on m_2 with a force F to the left and m_2 pulls on m_1 with an equal force F to the right. To make an equation of this symbolism it is only necessary to replace the proportionality constant above by an equal sign and insert a constant on either side of the equality.

$$F = G \frac{m_1 m_2}{d^2} \qquad (9a)$$

Experiment shows that, if F is measured in newtons, m_1 and m_2 in kilograms, and d in meters, the "Newtonian constant of gravitation" G has the value

$$G = 6.66 \times 10^{-11} \frac{m^3}{\text{Kg sec}^2} \qquad (9b)$$

If F is in dynes, m_1 and m_2 in grams, and d in centimeters,

$$G = 6.66 \times 10^{-8} \frac{\text{cm}^3}{\text{gm sec}^2}$$

If F is in pounds, m_1 and m_2 in slugs, and d in feet,

$$G = 3.41 \times 10^{-8} \frac{\text{ft}^3}{\text{slug sec}^2} \qquad (9c)$$

To obtain some idea of the magnitude of gravitational forces, consider the following example.

Example 1. Calculate the force of attraction between two weights of 1 lb each, held in the hands 1 ft apart.

Solution. By substitution in Eq.(9a),

$$F = 3.41 \times 10^{-8} \frac{\text{ft}^3}{\text{slug sec}^2} \cdot \frac{1/32 \text{ slug} \times 1/32 \text{ slug}}{1 \text{ ft}^2}$$

$$= 3.33 \times 10^{-11} \frac{\text{slug ft}}{\text{sec}^2} = 3.33 \times 10^{-11} \text{ lb}$$

This force is far too small to be detected by the muscle senses of the hands or arms.

9.2. The Cavendish Experiment. This famous experiment was performed by

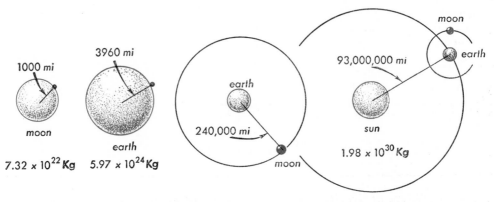

3960 mi

1000 mi

moon

earth

93,000,000 mi

moon

earth

240,000 mi

sun

moon

7.32 × 10²² Kg   5.97 × 10²⁴ Kg

1.98 × 10³⁰ Kg

Fig. 9B   Gravitational attraction keeps the moon in its orbit around the earth, and the earth in its orbit around the sun.

Henry Cavendish* in the year 1797 to 1798, and is frequently referred to as "weighing the earth." The principal features of the experiment consisted in determining the attracting forces between two pairs of lead spheres by means of a torsion balance and from these measurements determining the value of G. A diagram of the apparatus is shown in Fig. 9C. A rod 6 ft long was supported at its center by a long wire P. At the ends of the rod were two lead balls, m_1 and m_2, each 2 in. in diameter. Two lead spheres, M_1 and M_2, each 12 in. in diameter, were then placed on either side as shown. Gravitational attraction between m_1 and M_1 and between m_2 and M_2 caused the rod C to turn through a small angle and come to rest in some position like that shown by the solid line.

The shifting of M_1 and M_2 to the opposite sides of m_1 and m_2 caused the rod C to turn to a new position indicated by the dotted line. The angle through which the

* Henry Cavendish (1731-1810), English chemist and physicist, elder son of Lord Charles Cavendish, brother of the third duke of Devonshire, and Lady Anne Grey, daughter of the duke of Kent, was born at Nice on October 10, 1731. Although one of the richest men of his time through inheritance, he devoted his life to scientific work. He had little interest in society, always avoided the attention of his fellows, and never married. He was a member of the Royal Society and is best known for his experiments on gravitational attraction. He is also noted for his contributions to the chemistry of gases, and for his work on electrical capacitors and the inverse square law of force between electrical charges.

rod turned was measured by a small telescope or by reflection of a beam of light from a small mirror R onto a distant scale. From previous measurements of the stiffness of the supporting wire P, and a measure of the angle turned through, the force of attraction between the masses could be calculated.

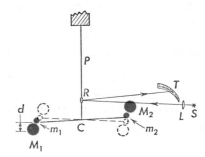

Fig. 9C   The Cavendish experiment. Weighing the earth.

If we neglect cross attractions of the right sphere on the left ball and the left sphere on the right ball, this angle between the two positions is assumed to be four times as great as that caused by the deflection of the rod, due to the attraction force of only one sphere on one ball.

It will now be shown how this measured force F in such an experiment makes it possible to calculate the earth's mass. If we know the masses of m_1 and M_1 by weighing, and the distance between them, d, from measurement, these known values can be substituted in Eq.(9a) and the only unknown quantity, G, calculated. The value which will be found is that given in Eqs.(9b) and (9c).

Consider now the attraction between the earth, of unknown mass M, and a 1-gm mass on its surface, as shown in Fig. 9D. In this

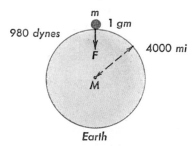

980 dynes m 1 gm

4000 mi

F

M

Fig. 9D *The earth exerts a downward force of 980 dynes on each gram of mass on its surface.*

instance, the force on the 1-gm mass is known. The force is just 980 dynes, for it can be calculated from Newton's second law, Eq.(6e), using the measured acceleration due to gravity $g = 980$ cm/sec². (See Fig. 6K.)

From experimental measurements and calculation, the following quantities are therefore known.

$m = 1$ gm $G = 6.66 \times 10^{-8}$ cm³/gm sec²
$F = 980$ dynes $d = 3960$ mi $= 6.37 \times 10^8$ cm

Substituting these values in Eq.(9a), the only unknown quantity, the mass of the earth M, can be calculated. Letting $m_1 = m$ and $m_2 = M$,

$$F = G \frac{m \times M}{d^2}$$

Transposition and substitution of known values give

$$M = \frac{F \times d^2}{m \times G} = \frac{980 \times (6.37 \times 10^8)^2}{1 \times 6.66 \times 10^{-8}}$$
$$= 5.97 \times 10^{27} \text{ gm}$$

This is a reasonable value for the earth's mass, for if it is divided by the earth's volume, $\frac{4}{3}\pi r^3$, the average density of *5.4 gm/ cm³* is obtained. The average density of the rocks found at and near the earth's surface is 2.7 gm/cm³. This means, therefore, that deep within the earth's body the average density must rise to 8 or 10 gm/cm³. Such values are entirely reasonable since most metals have just such densities.

The above experiment is assumed, therefore, to be correct in principle and to be a means for determining the mass of the earth.

Earth's mass $M = 5.97 \times 10^{27}$ gm

9.3. Newton's Third Law of Motion. Of Newton's three laws of motion the third is perhaps the least understood. This is probably due to the fact that it is seldom used in solving problems, and often when it is used it is incorrectly applied. The law states:

*To every action force there is an equal and opposite reaction force.**

The principle of action and reaction may be illustrated by a bat striking a ball, Fig. 9E. During impact the bat exerts a force F on the ball, and the ball exerts an equal but opposite force B on the bat. The force F being exerted on the ball gives it an acceleration to the right, while the force B being exerted on the bat gives it an acceleration to the left. The ball speeds up during the impact and acquires a high velocity, while the bat in the same time interval slows down to a lower velocity. The impulse Ft from the bat gives the ball a momentum mv. See Eq.(6m). The impulse Bt from the ball decreases the momentum of the bat from a higher value to one of lower value.

Consider the second example of a block hanging by a cord as illustrated in Fig. 9F. The weight of the block W is the force with which the earth pulls downward on the block, while the equal and opposite force X is the upward force exerted by the block on the earth.

In addition to this pair of forces, the block exerts a downward force B on the

---

* Newton's third law, as published in Latin in his "Principia" is, Lex. III. Actioni contrariam semper et aequalem esse reactionem; sive corporum duorum actiones in se mutuo semper esse aequales et in partes contrarias dirigi.

Fig. 9E   *A bat at all times exerts a force on the ball equal in magnitude to the force that the ball exerts on the bat.*

the state of that body depends upon the forces acting on it and not upon the forces it exerts on something else. So far as the body is concerned, the latter do not determine its motion.

9.4. Isolating a Body. Forces are vector quantities and must be added by the principles of vector addition. To illustrate, the block in Fig. 9F remains at rest because two equal and opposite forces are acting upon it. To see what these forces are, the body is isolated by drawing a dotted line around it as shown in Fig. 9G. Only those forces

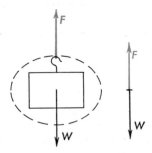

Fig. 9G   *Balanced forces produce equilibrium.*

cord, while the cord pulls upward with the reaction force *F*. Although to many people these forces may seem confusing, it should be pointed out that Newton himself had some difficulty in applying his third law to certain problems. The difficulty arises from trying to apply action and reaction forces to the same body when in reality they apply to different ones.

It is important to note that the action force and the reaction force in Newton's third law of motion act on different bodies.

Whether a body is at rest or in motion,

acting on the body from outside this boundary determine its state or motion. The earth is pulling down on the block with a force *W* while the cord is pulling up on the block with an equal but opposite force *F*. By vector addition shown at the right, the resultant force must be zero. (It should be noted that *F* and *W* are not an action and reaction pair, even though they happen here to be equal.)

Suppose in Fig. 9F that the force *F* is increased to a value greater than *W*. The block will then have an unbalanced force acting and it will be accelerated upward. By vector addition, as shown in Fig. 9H, the resultant upward force is equal to $F - W$. The acceleration can be calculated by applying Newton's second law, $F = ma$, the force here being $F - W$.

$$F - W = ma \qquad (9d)$$

resultant force = mass $\times$ acceleration

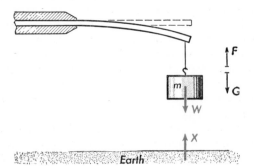

Fig. 9F   *Diagram illustrating Newton's third law of motion. Forces always exist in pairs.*

If, on the other hand, the force *F* is smaller than the weight *W*, the body will be accelerated downward and $W - F$ is the

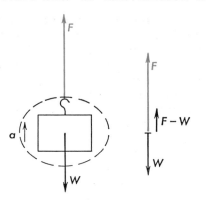

Fig. 9H *Because of a resultant force, F — W, the body is accelerated upward.*

resultant force acting. Again applying Newton's second law,

$$W - F = ma \qquad (9e)$$
resultant force = mass × acceleration

In each case, the smaller force is subtracted from the larger to make the acceleration come out with a positive sign in the direction of motion.

Example 3. An elevator weighing 1000 lb is raised and lowered by a cable fastened at the top. Calculate the upward force exerted by the cable when the elevator (a) starts up with an acceleration of 2.4 ft/sec²; (b) is rising with constant velocity; (c) starts down with an acceleration of 2.4 ft/sec²; and (d) goes down with constant velocity.

Solution. (a) For acceleration upward, Eq.(9d) is applied. By direct substitution,

$$F - 1000 \text{ lb} = \frac{1000 \text{ slugs}}{32} \times 2.4 \text{ ft/sec}^2$$

Hence

$$F = 1000 \text{ lb} + 75 \text{ lb} = 1075 \text{ lb}$$

(b) Moving upward with constant velocity, the elevator has no acceleration. With $a = 0$, Eq.(9d) becomes

$$F - W = 0 \qquad \text{or} \qquad F = W$$

The upward force, or tension, in the cable equals the weight of the elevator, 1000 lb.

(c) For acceleration downward, Eq.(9e) is used. By direct substitution,

$$1000 \text{ lb} - F = \frac{1000 \text{ slugs}}{32} \times 2.4 \text{ ft/sec}^3$$

so that

$$F = 1000 \text{ lb} - 75 \text{ lb} = 925 \text{ lb}$$

(d) Moving downward with constant velocity, the elevator has no acceleration, and the tension in the cable is 1000 lb.

9.5. The Train-and-Track Experiment.
Another illustration of Newton's third law is that of a train on a track, both of which, the track as well as the train, are free to move. The drive wheels push back on the track with a force B, and the track pushes forward on the wheels with an equal and opposite force F. These two form an action and reaction pair.

In Fig. 9I, the track is mounted on a large wheel with its axis of rotation vertical.

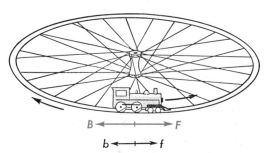

Fig. 9I *Demonstration of Newton's third law of motion. The train moves forward, and the track, if free to move, moves backward.*

With the track free to move, both forces of the pair are seen to be real; the track moves backward and the train moves forward. The track moves backward because the wheels exert a force B upon it in that direction, and the train goes forward because the track exerts a force F upon it in that direction. If, when the train acquires a certain velocity, the power is shut off, the force F *vanishes*— so also does B—and by Newton's first law of motion the train and track would be expected to continue to move with constant speed.

In a practical case, however, the track is not only fastened down, but there is some frictional resistance to motion. Because of this friction the track pushes backward on the wheels with a force b, and the wheels push forward on the track with an equal but opposite force f.

In order to keep a train moving with constant speed, a minimum force B great enough to overcome friction must continually be supplied to the locomotive drive wheels. The two forces acting on the train, then, are F and b, and if these are equal and opposite they have a zero resultant.

There being no resultant force, there is no acceleration, and the train continues to move with constant velocity.

To start the train moving, and to maintain an acceleration, F must be greater than b. Under these conditions the acceleration, by Newton's second law, is

$$F - b = ma$$
resultant force = mass $\times$ acceleration

PROBLEMS

1. Two metal spheres, each having a mass of 3 million Kg, are located with their centers 4 m apart. Calculate the force of attraction between them in newtons.

2. The moon has a mass of 7.3×10^{22} Kg, and the earth a mass of 6.0×10^{24} Kg. Find the attractive force between these two bodies in newtons if their centers are 3.9×10^8 m apart. (*Ans.* 1.92×10^{20} newtons.)

3. Two army tanks, weighing 15 tons each, pass each other. If the distance between their centers of mass at closest approach is 14 ft, what is the gravitational attraction between them in pounds?

4. A 20-lb stone is dropped from a bridge. What is the direction and magnitude of the force exerted by the stone on the earth? (*Ans.* 20 lb up.)

5. A man weighing 200 lb sits in a chair. What are the directions and magnitudes of the two forces acting on him?

6. An elephant weighing 3000 lb is being lifted at constant velocity by an elevator. What are the directions and magnitudes of the two forces acting on the elephant? (*Ans.* Earth pulling down 3000 lb; floor pushing up 3000 lb.)

7. An elevator car weighing 1200 lb is pulled upward with an acceleration of 1.4 ft/sec. Calculate the total tension in the cables.

8. The hopper in a coal hoist has a mass of 1200 Kg when fully loaded. If, starting from rest at the bottom of a mine shaft, it is given an upward acceleration of 0.7 m/sec², what is the tension in the cable in newtons? (*Ans.* 12,-600 newtons.)

9. An elevator weighing 900 lb. contains 6 persons averaging 140 lb each. Find the tension in the cable supporting the car if the car is (a) standing still, (b) moving upward with an acceleration of 1.5 ft/sec², and (c) moving downward with the same acceleration.

10. Two masses of 325 and 375 gm, respectively, are fastened to opposite ends of a string and the string hung over a pulley. Calculate (a) the acceleration of the system, and (b) the tension in the string. Neglect friction and the weight of the string and pulley. (*Ans.* (a) 70 cm/sec², (b) 341,000 dynes.)

11. A 15-lb weight and a 6-lb weight are fastened to opposite ends of a cord and the cord hung over a pulley. What is (a) the acceleration of the system, and (b) the tension in the cord? Neglect friction and the weight of the string and pulley.

12. If the frictional force offered to the acceleration of a 80-ton locomotive is 480 lb, what force is required to give it an acceleration of 1.2 ft/sec.²? (*Ans.* 6480 lb.)

13. If the frictional force acting against the acceleration, along the runway, of a 40,000 Kg transport plane is 1500 newtons, what force will be required to give it an acceleration of 0.6 m/sec²?

14. A boy weighing 120 lb stands on a spring scale on the floor of an elevator. What will the scale read when (a) the elevator starts up with an acceleration of 3.8 ft/sec², (b) when it starts down with the same acceleration? (*Ans.* (a) 134 lb, (b) 106 lb.)

15. A man weighing 150 lb slides down a rope. By wrapping the rope once around his leg he maintains a downward acceleration of 2 ft/sec². What is the tension in the rope in pounds?

16. An elevator car having a mass of 420 Kg

is descending with a speed of 5 m/sec. If the maximum load permitted on the cables is 6000 newtons, what is the shortest distance in which the car can be stopped? (*Ans.* 2.79 m.)

17. Driving along a level road at 60 mi/hr in a car weighing 3600 lb, a driver suddenly applies the brakes. If the car comes to rest in 3 sec, find the average force.

18. A large box weighing 90 lb falls from a truck traveling with a speed of 60 mi/hr along the highway. If the box slides for a total distance of 180 ft, what is the average force slowing it down? (*Ans.* 60.5 lb.)

19. A man weighs 160 lb on the earth. Calculate his weight if he were on the moon. Assume the earth's mass to be 81 times that of the moon and the respective radii to be 4000 mi and 1000 mi.

20. Two masses of 5 Kg and 7 Kg, respectively, are fastened to opposite ends of a string and the string hung over the end of a pulley. Calculate (a) the acceleration of the system, and (b) the tension in the string. Neglect friction and the weight of the string and pulley. (*Ans.* (a) 1.63 m/sec², (b) 57.2 newtons.)

21. Two masses of 10 Kg and 12 Kg, respectively, are fastened to opposite ends of a string and the string hung over the end of a pulley. Calculate (a) the acceleration of the system, and (b) the tension in the string. Neglect friction and the weight of the string and pulley.

22. Two masses of 60 gm and 50 gm, respectively, are fastened to the opposite ends of a light flexible string which passes over a pulley assumed to be frictionless. Neglecting the mass of the string and pulley, find (a) the acceleration, and (b) the tension in the string. (*Ans.* (a) 89.1 cm/sec², (b) 53,500 dynes.)

23. A 200-lb. man stands in an elevator car. What force does the floor exert on him when the elevator (a) rises at a constant speed of 4 ft/sec, and (b) accelerates upward at 4 ft/sec²?

24. A locomotive capable of exerting a force of 5 tons is connected to a train of cars. If the total weight of the train is 240 tons, and the resistance to motion amounts to 1500 lb, find the maximum possible acceleration. (*Ans.* 0.567 ft/sec².)

25. A 120-Kg trunk falls from a truck traveling with a speed of 24 Km/hr along the highway. If the trunk slides for a total distance of 20 m before coming to rest, what is the average force slowing it down?

26. (a) What is the least acceleration with which a man weighing 170 lb can slide down a rope that can sustain a tension of 100 lb? (b) What will his speed be after sliding 20 ft? (*Ans.* (a) 13.2 ft/sec², (b) 23 ft/sec.)

27. (a) State Newton's law of gravitation, as given in the text, or in your own words. (b) Since this law shows that the earth would exert a ten-times-larger force on a 10-lb weight than on a 1-lb weight, explain why two such bodies would fall with the same acceleration of $g = 32$ ft/sec.²

Chapter 10

Balanced and Unbalanced Forces

10.1. Conditions for Equilibrium. When one or more forces act upon a body at rest, and their resultant sum is not zero, the body will be set into motion. Under such conditions there is an *unbalanced force* acting, and this force alone accounts for the motion. If, however, the vector sum of all the forces acting is zero, the body is in equilibrium and the body will either remain at rest or, if moving, maintain constant velocity. To turn this statement around is to say that

"Any object remaining at rest, or moving with uniform motion, is in equilibrium and the resultant of all forces acting upon it is zero."

If two and only two forces act upon a body in equilibrium, a little study will show that they must be equal in magnitude and opposite in direction. A book lying on the table or a lamp hanging from the ceiling are good examples of dual forces in equilibrium. See Figs. 10A and 10B.

The two forces acting on the book are W,

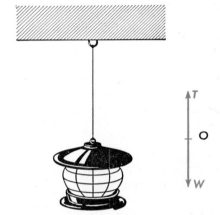

Fig. 10B *A lamp hanging from the ceiling is in equilibrium.*

the downward pull of the earth, called the *weight*, and F, the upward thrust of the table. Since the book is in equilibrium, the force F is equal in magnitude to the weight W. For the lamp at the left, the downward force or weight is counterbalanced by the upward tension in the cord. Here again, the forces are equal in magnitude and opposite in direction. A body moving with constant velocity is in equilibrium: since there is no acceleration, there is no unbalanced force.

In the game of tug-of-war, when two opposing teams are pulling with equal but opposite forces at the ends of a rope, a condition of equilibrium exists. As illustrated in Fig. 10C, the force F of 1000 lb acting to

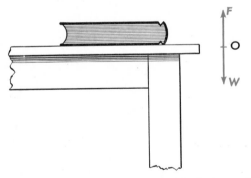

Fig. 10A *A book lying on a table is in equilibrium.*

Fig. 10C *The tension in the rope is 1000 lb.*

pull the knot K to the right is counter-balanced by an equal but opposite force $-F$ of 1000 lb pulling it to the left. If the two forces become unequal, equilibrium will no longer exist and the knot K will move in the direction of the greater force. It should be noted in the equilibrium case that the tension in the rope is 1000 lb and not 2000 lb. This apparent paradox can be explained away by supposing that one team ties its end of the rope to a post. The other team, still pulling with its 1000 lb, maintains the same equilibrium conditions as before and in so doing maintains the tension of 1000 lb. One team can be looked upon as holding the rope so the other team can pull.

10.2. Three Forces in Equilibrium. When, as the result of the action of three forces, a body is in equilibrium, the *resultant* of all three forces must be zero. In other words, *to be in equilibrium, the force polygon must close.* With three forces, such a polygon would have only three sides, that is, it would be a triangle. As an illustration, consider the street light suspended from two poles as shown in Fig. 10D.

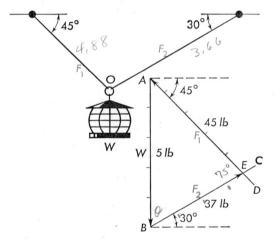

Fig. 10D *Three forces produce equilibrium if their vector sum is zero.*

The three forces acting through the common point O are W, the weight of the lamp (5 lb) acting straight downward; F_1, the pull of one rope at 45° up and to the left; and F_2, the pull of the other rope at 30° up

and to the right. The force polygon is shown in diagram (b), where vectorially

$$\overrightarrow{W} + \overrightarrow{F_2} + \overrightarrow{F_1} = 0 \qquad (10a)$$

In constructing this diagram, the conditions of equilibrium are imposed as a means of determining the magnitude of the forces F_1 and F_2. The graphical procedure is as follows: a vector of length 5 units is first drawn straight downward to represent W, the weight of the light. To the head of this vector at B, a dotted line BC is drawn parallel to the rope exerting the force F_2. From A, another dotted line AD is drawn parallel to the rope exerting the force F_1. At E, where these two lines intersect, the vectors F_1 and F_2 are terminated and arrowheads inserted in the directions shown. The solid lines AE and BE, when measured, are found to have lengths of 4.48 and 3.66 units and represent the forces $F_1 = 4.48$ lb and $F_2 = 3.66$ lb, respectively.

To solve the same problem analytically, the internal angles of the triangle ABE are first determined and then the law of sines is applied to find the lengths of the sides AE and BE. Using the angles given in diagram (b), subtraction gives angle $\phi = 45°$, angle $\theta = 60°$, and angle $\psi = 75°$. By the law of sines,

$$\frac{AE}{\sin \theta} = \frac{W}{\sin \psi} \quad \text{or}$$

$$AE = \frac{W \sin 60°}{\sin 75°} = \frac{5 \times 0.866}{0.966} = 4.48 \, \text{lb}$$

and

$$\frac{BE}{\sin \phi} = \frac{W}{\sin \psi} \quad \text{or}$$

$$BE = \frac{W \sin 45°}{\sin 75°} = \frac{5 \times 0.707}{0.966} = 3.66 \, \text{lb}$$

The magnitudes of the forces are therefore $F_1 = 4.48$ lb, and $F_2 = 3.66$ lb.

10.3. Resultant and Equilibrant. When, as the result of the action of three forces, a body is in equilibrium, the *resultant* of any two of the forces is always equal and opposite to the remaining force. This is but another statement of the conditions of equilibrium already treated and is in reality the reduction of a three-force problem to a two-force problem. Consider as an illustration the experiment shown in Fig. 10E.

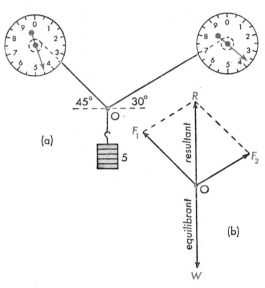

(a)

(b)

Fig. 10E   *Experiment illustrating three forces in equilibrium.*

A weight of 5 lb is supported by two cords at the same angles given in Fig. 10D. The spring scales in diagram (a) show the tensions in the cords, $F_1 = 4.48$ lb and $F_2 = 3.66$ lb. The downward force W in the *force diagram* (b) is the *equilibrant* of the forces F_1 and F_2. The *resultant* R of the upward two forces, found by the parallelogram method, is equal and opposite to W. By another diagram similar to (b), it may be

shown that the resultant of F_1 and W is a force equal and opposite to F_2, and that the resultant of F_2 and W is a force equal and opposite to F_1. The latter will be left as an exercise for the student.

10.4. The Inclined Plane. As an illustration of the resolution of a force into rectangular components and the principle of equilibrium, consider the following problem. A boy wishes to pull a small 100-lb wagon up a 50% grade. Such a grade, as shown in Fig. 10F, is one in which for every 100 ft measured along the horizontal there is a vertical rise of 50 ft. The angle θ of such an incline is given by

$$\tan \theta = \frac{50}{100} = 0.500$$

from which $\theta = 26.5°$

To find how hard the boy must pull on the wagon, the downward force W, called the weight, is resolved into two components, one a force Q parallel to the inclined plane and the other N perpendicular to it. Resolution is shown graphically in diagram (b). The component N, being perpendicular to the inclined plane, neither aids nor hinders the motion up or down. The component Q represents the force which, in the absence of a counterbalancing force, would accelerate the wagon down the incline. To pull the wagon the boy must, therefore, exert a force P up the incline equal to or greater than Q. Once the wagon is started, a force P, equal to Q, will keep it moving with constant velocity.

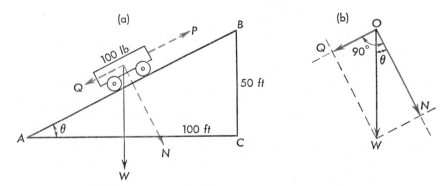

Fig. 10F   *The resolution of a force into components.*

To find the magnitudes of Q and N, it will be noted that the triangle NOW at the right and the triangle CAB at the left are similar triangles. The side ON is perpendicular to AB, and OW is perpendicular to AC. This relation makes angles θ equal. Since both triangles are right triangles, corresponding sides are proportional and we can write

$$\sin \theta = \frac{Q}{W}, \quad \text{and} \quad \cos \theta = \frac{N}{W}$$

By trigonometry,

$$Q = W \sin \theta \qquad (10b)$$
$$N = W \cos \theta \qquad (10c)$$

Substitute known values of W and θ.

$$Q = 100 \times 0.446 = 44.6 \text{ lb}$$
$$N = 100 \times 0.895 = 89.5 \text{ lb}$$

An experiment illustrating the above example and its solution is shown in Fig. 10G.

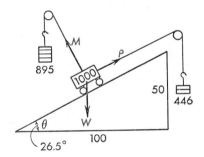

Fig. 10G   *Experiment illustrating equilibrium conditions for a car on an inclined plane.*

A car weighing 1000 lb is held in equilibrium on a 26.5° inclined plane by two cords passing over pulleys to weights of 446 lb and 895 lb. One cord runs parallel and the other perpendicular to the incline. If P is increased or decreased slightly the car will move up or down the plane, whereas if M is increased slightly the car will be lifted from the plane. The removal of the inclined plane entirely does not alter the equilibrium of the suspended mass, and the experimental arrangement is similar to that of Fig. 10E. The three forces acting to maintain equilibrium are P, M, and W.

10.5. Acceleration Down an Inclined Plane. Neglecting friction, a body placed on an incline is accelerated down the plane by an unbalanced force. The active force causing the acceleration is Q, calculated in the preceding section as one of the components of the weight W.

$$Q = W \sin \theta$$

It is shown in Fig. 10H that Q is in reality the resultant of two forces, one W, the

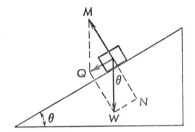

Fig. 10H   *A block on an inclined plane has an unbalanced force Q acting upon it.*

downward pull of the earth; and the other M, the upward thrust of the incline. In the absence of any friction, M is equal in magnitude and opposite in direction to N, the normal component of W.

$$N = W \cos \theta \qquad (10d)$$

By Newton's third law of motion, if N is taken to represent the force exerted by the block on the incline, M is the equal and opposite force of the incline on the block. The adding of M and W by the parallelogram method gives Q as a resultant. (Note that M and W are the forces acting *on the block*.)

The acceleration down the incline is given by Newton's second law of motion. By the force equation, $F = ma$,

$$Q = ma \qquad (10e)$$

where m is the mass of the body and a is its acceleration. See Fig. 10I. Remembering that $W = mg$, we substitute in Eq.(10b) to get

$$Q = mg \sin \theta \qquad (10f)$$

which, substituted in Eq.(10e), gives

$$ma = mg \sin \theta$$

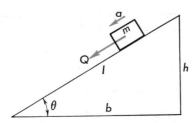

Fig. 10I   *A body is accelerated down an inclined plane, because of the unbalanced force acting upon it.*

Dividing each side of the equation by m, we obtain

$$a = g \sin \theta \qquad (10g)$$

Because the mass does not appear in the final equation, the acceleration is independent of mass. In other words, all bodies moving without friction down the same inclined plane should have the same acceleration. Starting from rest, all the bodies should acquire the same velocity at the bottom. For an inclined plane tilted up until it is straight up and down, the angle θ is increased to 90°, $\sin \theta = 1$, and Eq.(10g) becomes $a = g$, as it should for free fall. The acceleration a then equals the acceleration due to gravity g.

Since acceleration is a vector quantity, Eq.(10g) can be derived directly from the inclined plane. If we replace W in Fig. 10F by g, component Q becomes a, and Eq.(10b) becomes Eq.(10g).

PROBLEMS

1. Two forces acting on a body are 6 lb at 20° and 8 lb at 150°. What additional single force will produce equilibrium?

2. What single force will balance the following forces: (a) 8.4 newtons at 60°, and (b) 12.5 newtons at 180°. (*Ans.* 11.1 newtons at 318.8°.)

3. A force of 6 newtons has a direction angle of 30°. What two forces having direction angles of 150° and 250° will produce equilibrium?

4. A force of 80 dynes has a direction angle of 0°. What two forces having direction angles of 135° and 215° will produce equilibrium? (*Ans.* 56.6 dynes and 65.5 dynes.)

5. The two ends of a chain 10 ft long are fastened to hooks 6 ft apart in the ceiling. An airplane motor weighing 240 lb is suspended from the midpoint of the chain. Find the tension in the chain.

6. The ends of a rope 4 m long are fastened to hooks 2.5 m apart in the ceiling. A 75-Kg trunk is hanging from the center of the rope. Find the tension in the rope. (*Ans.* 481 newtons.)

7. A farmer wishing to pull a small tree stump out of the ground, fastens one end of a 40-ft cable to the stump and the other end to the trunk of a large tree. By exerting a sideward force of 100 lb, he moves the center point of the cable 18 in. Find the pull produced on the stump.

8. Two ends of a picture wire 32 in. long are fastened to two screw eyes 24 in. apart on the back of the frame. If the entire picture and frame weighs 16 lb, find the tension in the wire when the picture is hung from a hook on the wall. (*Ans.* 12.1 lb.)

9. An automobile with a mass of 2000 Kg is towed up a 4% grade. Neglecting friction, what force is required to keep the car moving at constant speed?

10. A loaded boxcar weighs 30 tons. What force in lb is required from the engine to pull this car up a 1.2% grade? (*Ans.* 720 lb.)

11. A man uses a small hand truck to transport a 250-lb crate up a plank onto a station platform. If the truck weighs 70 lb, the platform is 4 ft high, and the plank is 15 ft long, what force parallel to the plank must the man exert?

12. A car on an inclined plane weighs 4200 lb when loaded with passengers. What tension is required in the cable pulling the car up if the incline has a 32% grade? (*Ans.* 1280 lb.)

13. A car weighing 3200 lb is coasting down a 10% grade. What total force applied by the brakes will keep it moving at 20 mi/hr?

14. A 10-ton truck coasts down a 5% grade. What total force applied by the brakes will keep it moving at a constant speed of 30 mi/hr? (*Ans.* 1000 lb.)

15. A boy in a small wagon starts from rest and coasts down a hill. If the grade is 4%, find (a) his acceleration, and (b) his speed after traveling 300 ft. Neglect friction.

16. A toboggan sled starts from rest at the top of a slide 560 ft long. If the grade is 9%, find (a) the acceleration, and (b) the speed at the bottom, in mi/hr. Neglect friction. (*Ans.* (a) 2.87 ft/sec², (b) 38.7 mi/hr.)

17. A car weighing 2000 lb coasts down a 4% grade. What total force applied by the brakes will hold the car to a downhill acceleration of 0.32 ft/sec²?

18. A train weighing 1000 tons starts down a 1.5% grade. What total force applied by the brakes will hold the train to a downhill acceleration of 0.20 ft/sec²? (*Ans.* 17,500 lb.)

19. A stone weighing 250 lb is attached to the upper end of a light pole which makes an angle of 45° with the horizontal. A horizontal rope attached to this same end of the pole holds it at this angle. Find (a) the pull of the rope, and (b) the compressional force in the pole.

20. A stone weighing 60 lb is suspended from one end of a lightweight horizontal rod 3 ft long, the other end of which rests against a vertical wall. The rod is supported at the stone end by a lightweight rope 5 ft long attached to a point higher up on the wall. Find (a) the ten-

sion in the rope, and (b) the compressional force in the rod. (*Ans.* (a) 75 lb, (b) 45 lb.)

21. A boy weighing 80 lb sits in a swing capable of supporting a load of 140 lb. With what force would he have to pull on a horizontal rope to break the swing?

22. A boy weighing 100 lb sits in a swing. (a) with what force should he pull on a horizontal rope to keep the swing at 25° with the vertical? (b) Find the tension in the rope. (*Ans.* (a) 46.6 lb, (b) 110 lb.)

23. Four forces act on a body in equilibrium. Three of the forces are: 50 dynes at 0°, 70 dynes at 70°, and 60 dynes at 230°. Find the remaining force.

24. Four forces act on a body in equilibrium. Three of the forces are: 25 lb at 50°, 40 lb at 110°, and 30 lb at 210°. Find the remaining force. (*Ans.* 47.9 lb at 299.5°.)

25. Five forces act on a body in equilibrium. Four of the forces are: 4 newtons at 30°, 6 newtons at 70°, 5 newtons at 160°, and 7 newtons at 310°. Find (a) the x- and y-components of the remaining force, and (b) the remaining force.

26. A boy coasts down a hill on a sled. Neglecting friction, what force accelerates the boy and sled if they weigh 120 lb and the hill has a slope of 10°? (*Ans.* 20.9 lb.)

Chapter 11

Friction and Streamlining

In the preceding chapters on mechanics, the formulas presented, the experiments described, and the problems solved were idealized to the extent that all friction was neglected. Since friction does exist, and in some cases is not negligibly small, a quantitative treatment of friction becomes a necessity in the solving of many problems.

11.1. Friction. Whenever one body slides over another, frictional forces opposing the motion are developed between them. Such forces are due largely to the atomic and molecular attractive forces at the small *contact areas*. (See Fig. 11A.) Within limits, the

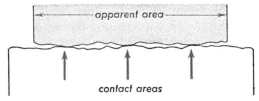

Fig. 11A *The relatively small contact areas between two bodies have a much larger apparent contact area.*

smoothness of the surfaces does not greatly affect *f*, the force of sliding friction. If the surfaces are smooth there will be many small areas in contact, while if they are rough there may be fewer but larger ones. It is well known that surfaces of the same material show greater friction than do surfaces of different materials. This is one of the reasons why machine bearings are often made of one metal like bronze while their rotating shafts are made of another like steel.

Experiments show that to start a body sliding requires a greater force than that needed to keep it moving. In other words

static friction, or *starting friction*, is greater than *kinetic friction*. Once a body is moving, however, the force of sliding friction increases only slightly with increasing speed and then remains nearly constant over a moderate range of speeds.

Recent experiments,* particularly with metals in contact, show that, when one surface is pressed against another and sliding is brought about, the enormous pressures existing at the tiny contact areas cause a kind of welding of the two materials. With all materials in general, the atoms and molecules are so close together at the contact areas that strong mutual attractive forces often pull microscopic bits of material from one body to the other as they move along. To start a body moving is to break these bonds simultaneously, while to keep it moving is to break them smoothly and continuously.

The general statement can be made that wherever there is motion there is friction. All forms of friction may be classified as one of three kinds—

> *sliding friction*
> *rolling friction*
> *fluid friction*

Sliding and rolling friction are usually confined to solids while fluid friction applies to liquids and gases. Generally speaking, sliding friction is greater than fluid friction at low speeds, while the reverse is true at high speeds.

11.2. Sliding Friction. A quantitative treatment of sliding friction will here be given as the result of a simple laboratory experiment illustrated in Fig. 11B. In dia-

* Review by Frederic Palmer, American Journal of Physics, Vol. 17, p. 327 (1949).

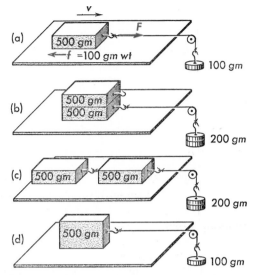

Fig. 11B *Sliding friction is proportional to the normal force pushing the surfaces together and is independent of the apparent area of contact.*

gram (a), a block of wood of mass 500 gm is shown being pulled with uniform speed across a table top by the force of a 100 gm-wt. The latter force has been arrived at by trying different loads on the hook at the right. A load greater than 100 gm will accelerate the block, while a load smaller than 100 gm will allow it to stop. Moving with constant speed, the applied force F is just counterbalanced by f, the force of sliding friction.

In diagram (b), a second block of mass 500 gm is added to make the sliding mass 1000 gm. By experiment, the force required to pull the two with constant velocity is now found to be a 200 gm-wt. Should a third and then a fourth block be added successively, 300 and 400 gm-weights, respectively, will be found necessary to pull them. From these results we can draw the following conclusions:

The force of sliding friction f is directly proportional to the total downward or normal force N.

$$f \propto N \qquad (11a)$$

When the two blocks in diagram (b) are connected in tandem, one behind the other

as in diagram (c), the force of friction is still that of a 200 gm-wt.

Again, if the single block in diagram (a) is turned on edge as in diagram (d), the force of a 100 gm-wt is just enough to slide it with constant speed. These observations, along with the results of other similar experiments, may be explained largely in terms of molecular attractive forces. In general, the total contact area where molecular attraction is effective (see Fig. 11A) is small compared with the total apparent area. When a greater force is applied normal to the surfaces, the contact areas increase in size and number, and the following relations are found to hold reasonably true.

(1) The total contact area is proportional to the total normal force.

(2) The total contact area is independent of the total apparent area.

(3) The force of sliding friction is proportional to the total contact area.

(4) The force of sliding friction is proportional to the total normal force.*

Introducing the Greek letter μ as a constant of proportionality, Eq.(11a) becomes

$$f = \mu N \qquad (11b)$$

μ is called the *coefficient of friction,* and is defined as the ratio

$$\boxed{\mu = \frac{f}{N}} \qquad (11c)$$

By knowing the value of μ for a given pair of surfaces, one is able to calculate the force of friction f in terms of the normal force N. Average values of μ for a number of surfaces are given in Table 11A.

As an illustration of the general use of the coefficient of friction, consider the following problem, diagramed in Fig. 11C.

Example 1. What force is required to pull an iron box weighing 60 lb across a smooth oak floor?

* Curiously enough, an increased normal force increases the pressure over the apparent area but not over the contact area. The proportionate increase in total contact area with increased force means that the force of friction on unit contact area is independent of apparent pressure.

TABLE 11A. COEFFICIENTS OF SLIDING FRICTION
FOR A FEW COMMON MATERIALS
(AVERAGE VALUES FOR DRY SURFACES)

Material	μ
Oak on oak	0.25
Rubber on concrete	0.70
Metals on oak	0.55
Metals on elm	0.20
Hemp on oak	0.53
Pine on pine	0.35
Steel on steel	0.18
Greased surfaces	0.05
Iron on concrete	0.30
Leather on metals	0.56
Steel on babbit	0.14
Rubber on oak	0.46

$$\boxed{F - f = ma} \qquad (11d)$$

resultant force = mass × acceleration

Upon transposing,

$$F = f + ma$$

or,

$$F = \mu N + ma$$

Speed (cm/sec)	μ
1.88	0.150
3.87	0.163
6.21	0.171
8.54	0.177
10.00	0.179
11.50	0.181
12.81	0.183

Solution. From Table 11A, μ for metals on oak is 0.55. The normal force N is the weight of the box, or 60 lb. Substituting in Eq.(11b), the force of friction is found to be

$$f = 0.55 \times 60 \text{ lb} = 33 \text{ lb}$$

The general observation that sliding fric-

11.3. Angle of Uniform Slip. One method of measuring the coefficient of sliding friction is to place a block on an inclined plane and then tilt the plane until the block

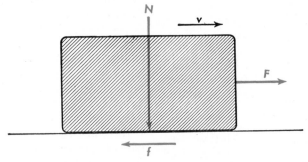

Fig. 11C *Sliding friction f is proportional to the normal force N pushing the surfaces together.*

tion increases only slightly at low speeds and levels off to become practically constant at higher speeds is illustrated by the following experimental values of pine on walnut wood, measured by C. A. Maney.

If the force F applied to a body is greater than that required to overcome friction f, the resultant force $(F - f)$ is effective in producing acceleration. As an equation of motion, Newton's force equation takes the form,

slides down with constant velocity. See Fig. 11D. When this condition exists, Eq.(11b) can be imposed directly upon the components of the weight W. The component F is equal in magnitude to f, the sliding friction, and the component N is the normal force pushing the two surfaces together. If θ is the angle of the incline, then

$$\mu = \frac{f}{N} = \frac{F}{N} = \frac{W \sin \theta}{W \cos \theta} = \tan \theta$$

which gives

$$\mu = \tan \theta \qquad (11e)$$

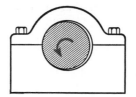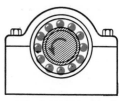

Fig. 11E *Sleeve bearings and ball bearings illustrate the two kinds of friction: (a) sliding friction, and (b) rolling friction. (Note: the clearance in the sleeve bearing is exaggerated.)*

The coefficient of friction μ equals the tangent of the angle of uniform slip. The angle of uniform slip is defined as that angle of an incline that will keep a body slid-

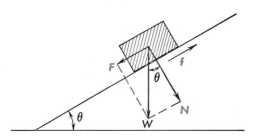

Fig. 11D *The angle of uniform slip for a block on an inclined plane.*

ing down it with constant velocity. At a steeper angle the force component F down the plane is greater than that required to overcome friction f, and the difference between them produces an acceleration as given by Eq.(11d).

11.4. Rolling Friction. A comparison of the force required to slide a heavy box along the ground with the force required to move it on rollers shows that sliding friction is many times greater than rolling friction. It is for this reason that wheels are used on vehicles instead of runners, and that ball-bearings are employed in some machines in place of sleeve-bearings.

A comparison of the sleeve type of bear-

ing with a ball-bearing is made in Fig. 11E. The rotating axle, as shown at the left, slides on the bottom of the sleeve at low speeds and climbs part way up the side as the speed increases. The purpose of lubricating such bearings with oils and greases is to keep the two metal surfaces from coming into direct contact. Properly lubricated, the axle rides on a thin film of oil. In diagram (b) it may be seen how the axle rolls around on the balls with little or no possibility for sliding. The balls themselves roll in a groove called a "race."

The harder a rolling wheel or ball, and the harder the surface over which it rolls, the less is the force of rolling friction. A better understanding of the origin of rolling friction is to be had by a comparison of the different kinds of wheels shown in Fig. 11F. For a hard wheel on a soft dirt road, as shown in (a), the applied force is continually pulling the wheel over a mound developed in the ground. For a soft wheel on a hard paved road, as in (b), the road is continually pushing the wheel out of shape.

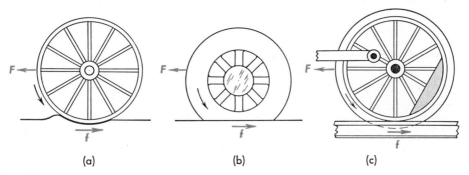

(a)   (b)   (c)

Fig. 11F *Rolling friction between soft and hard surfaces: (a) wagon wheel, (b) soft automobile tire, and (c) locomotive drive wheel.*

For a hard wheel on a hard road, both wheel and road are distorted ever so little, so that the force of friction is exceedingly small.

The same equations that hold for sliding friction also hold for rolling friction, the only difference being that the coefficients for rolling friction are exceedingly small.

$$f = \mu N \qquad (11f)$$

TABLE 11B. COEFFICIENTS OF ROLLING FRICTION

Cast iron on rails................	$\mu = 0.004$
Rubber tires on concrete..........	$\mu = 0.030$
Ball-bearing on steel.............	$\mu = 0.002$

11.5. Fluid Friction. Friction in a gas or liquid manifests itself when the fluid is made to flow around a stationary obstacle or an object is made to move through a previously stationary fluid. Such friction is involved in the propulsion of ships through the water, and automobiles, trains, and airplanes through the air. In any discussion or treatment of fluid friction, it makes no difference whether the fluid is considered as moving and the object as standing still, or vice versa. It is only necessary to specify that there is a relative motion between the two.

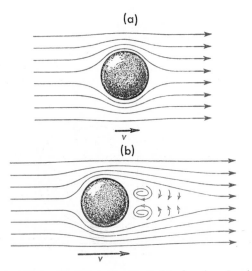

Fig. 11G (a) *Low-velocity fluid showing laminar flow.* (b) *High-velocity fluid showing turbulent flow.*

Experiments show that, at relatively low speeds, the flow of fluid around an object is smooth and regular and that fluid friction is proportional to the velocity. See Fig. 11G(a).

$$f \propto v \qquad \text{or} \qquad f = Kv \qquad (11g)$$

where K is a constant of proportionality.

If, initially, $v = 0$, frictional resistance to motion is zero and an applied force is entirely effective in producing acceleration. As the speed increases, however, friction increases proportionally so that less and less force is available for acceleration. Newton's second law, applied to motion through a fluid, therefore takes the same form as Eq. (11d) where f is given by Eq.(11g).

$$F = Kv + ma \qquad (11h)$$

The above equations hold only for "laminar flow," that is, for relatively low velocities. As the speed increases, a point is reached where "turbulence" sets in and the force of friction increases rapidly and becomes proportional to the square of the velocity.

$$f \propto v^2 \qquad \text{or} \qquad f = Tv^2 \qquad (11i)$$

Turbulent flow is characterized by small eddy currents that form behind the object as shown in Fig. 11G(b). Not only does the fluid have to move out and around the obstacle quickly, but considerable energy is taken up by the eddies. This, of course, results in greater loss of energy and therefore greater friction. When the velocity is increased still further, the eddies, instead of forming symmetrical pairs, form alternately on one side and then on the other, leaving a long trail of vortex motions like those shown in Fig. 11H. These strings of whirlwinds or whirlpools are commonly referred to as *Kármán trails*. The existence of such trails is illustrated by the flapping of the rope on a flagpole. The waving of the flag at the top of the pole is direct evidence of the whirlwinds that follow each other alternately along the sides. As the velocity of a streamlined body approaches the velocity of sound, friction again increases rapidly, becoming proportional to the cube of the velocity: $f \propto v^3$.

11.6. Terminal Velocity. It is well known that raindrops fall with a speed that depends upon their size and not upon the height from which they fall. Starting from rest, a particle falling in a gas or a liquid increases in velocity until the retarding force of friction becomes as great as the downward force of gravity. When this condition is reached, the body is in equilibrium and falls with a constant velocity called its *terminal velocity*.

The terminal velocity for small particles like fog drops is so low that the air stream around them is one of *laminar flow*. It was Stokes who first discovered that the terminal velocity of small particles is proportional to their weight. This relation is known as *Stokes' law.**

For increasingly larger bodies, terminal velocity increases and turbulent flow sets in, to eventually be the predominating part of frictional resistance. Under these conditions, both the resistance to laminar flow and the resistance to turbulent flow exist, so that, equating downward forces to upward forces of friction,

$$W = Kv + Tv^2 \qquad (11j)$$

This equation applies not only to falling bodies but to airplanes in the air and ships in the water. Their speed remains constant where the resistance is just equalized by the forward thrust of the propellers.

If a parachutist delays the opening of his chute long enough, he will attain a terminal velocity of from 130 to 150 mi/hr. At such speeds wind resistance pushes upward with a total force equal to his weight, with the result that he is no longer accelerated.

11.7. Streamlining. By shaping a body to the streamlines of the fluid through which it is moving, the retarding force of friction may be greatly reduced. This is particularly effective at high velocities where the condi-

* Sir George G. Stokes (1819-1903), British mathematician and physicist, is well known for his fundamental contribution to hydrodynamics, diffraction, double refraction, and the polarization of light. He received the Rumford Medal in 1852 and the Copley Medal in 1893, and was one time president of the Royal Society.

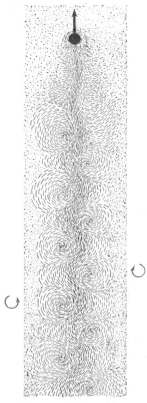

Fig. 11H *Eddies set up by drawing an obstacle through still water form a Kármán trail.*

tions of turbulent flow would otherwise predominate.

Referring to Fig. 11G(b) it may be seen that by adding a tail to an object, so that its cross-section has the form shown in Fig. 11I, the tendency to form eddy currents can be reduced and the body made to slip through the fluid with a minimum disturbance.

The experiment diagramed in Fig. 11J shows that a long pointed tail and a rounded or pointed nose are both effective

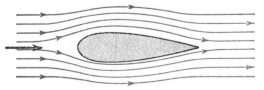

Fig. 11I *The flow of air or water around a properly shaped body may be smooth and steady.*

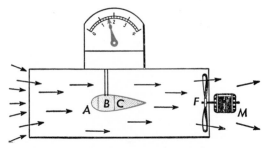

Fig. 11J *Diagram of a wind tunnel for testing the air friction of an airfoil or streamlined body.*

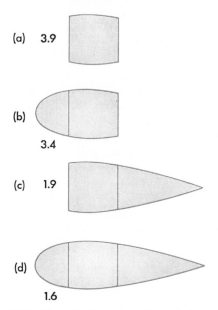

(a) 3.9

(b) 3.4

(c) 1.9

(d) 1.6

Fig. 11K *Test bodies for the wind tunnel shown in Fig. 11J.*

in cutting down resistance. The diagrams picture a small wind tunnel through which a stream of air is drawn by a fan *F*. Objects for which wind resistance is to be measured are suspended from a support connected at the center to a spring balance. Parts of a streamlined body are tested in the order shown in Fig. 11K. Their wind resistance changes in the order indicated. Note that it is greatest for the top figure and smallest for the bottom one.

The bodies of airplanes, torpedoes, and ships are streamlined to cut down resistance and hence permit higher speed with the same forward thrust of the propellers. Bombs are streamlined to enable them to acquire higher terminal velocities. Automobiles, if they are to travel at high speeds, should be streamlined to make more efficient use of gasoline.

and by cars on the speedway or open road.

11.8. Airplanes. The necessity for streamlinging all outside structures of an airplane where high speeds must be maintained is quite clear. For land planes, *solid friction* is of importance only during take-off. Once a plane is in the air, friction is almost entirely due to turbulent flow and is approximately proportional to the square of the velocity.

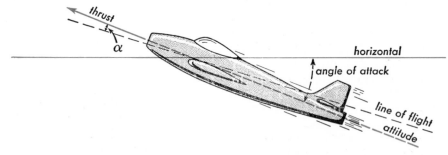

Fig. 11L *Diagram of a plane in a climb.*

Experiments with airplane and automobile models in wind tunnels show the importance of streamlining for speeds as low as 30 mi/hr. The findings from such tests are confirmed by full-sized planes in the air

In Fig. 11L a streamlined plane is shown in a climb. If the plane rises with constant velocity, the conditions of equilibrium exist and all forces acting form a closed polygon. The external forces acting on an airplane may be reduced to three: *weight, thrust,* and *friction.* (See Fig. 11M.)

The weight W may be assumed to act vertically downward through the center of gravity of the plane. The thrust T is the result of the push of the exhaust gases leaving the jet engine and acts in the direction of the plane axis. The friction F is the resultant force of air friction on the plane and acts in a direction upward and back as shown in Fig. 11M. The angle between the

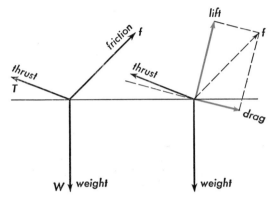

Fig. 11M *Force diagrams for an airplane, showing the origin of lift and drag.*

plane's *attitude* and the horizontal is called the *angle* of *attack.* Note that the line of flight, the path along which the plane is flying, is not quite the same as the plane's attitude.

It is customary to resolve the frictional force into two components: one, a useful component perpendicular to the line of flight and called *lift,* and the other a detrimental component parallel to the line of flight called the *drag.* The conditions of equilibrium require that these combined forces form a closed polygon as shown in Fig. 11N. The latter polygon is often used to determine certain factors in the performance of a plane. For example, if the forward thrust and weight are known, and the line of flight determined, the force polygon may be used to find the lift L and the drag D.

When a plane is in level flight and has constant velocity, T and D are practically horizontal, equal in magnitude, and opposite in direction, while W and L are verti-

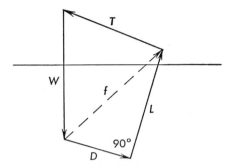

Fig. 11N *Force polygon for plane flying at constant velocity, in a climb, as shown in Fig. 11L.*

cal, equal in magnitude, and opposite in direction. With the motor throttled down and the plane in a dive at constant velocity, equilibrium conditions exist again and the forces form a closed polygon.

11.9. Supersonic Velocities. The rapid development of rockets and jet propelled planes, all capable of acquiring and maintaining speeds greater than the velocity of sound, has increased the importance of studying high-speed air flow around bodies of different size and shape. The flow of air around missiles moving with *supersonic velocity,* that is, a velocity greater than the velocity of sound, is characterized by the existence in the air of discontinuities known as *shock waves.*

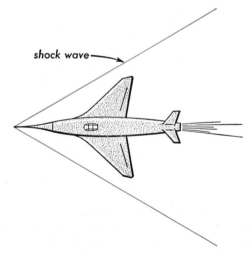

Fig. 11O *Shock wave produced by jet or rocket plane at supersonic velocity.*

These sudden discontinuities, shown in Fig. 11O, are the result of sudden encounters of the air with an impenetrable body. At subsonic velocities the fluid seems to be forewarned and begins its outward flow in advance of the arrival of the leading edge. With supersonic velocity, however, the fluid in front of the missile is undisturbed, while immediately behind the missile it is moving sideways. The sudden impulse at the nose creates a high pressure region which travel-

ing outward with the velocity of sound creates the conical-shaped shock wave that changes the direction of air flow.

It is customary in supersonic studies to specify the velocity of a body relative to the velocity of sound. The ratio between these two velocities is called the *Mach number*.

$$\text{Mach number} = \frac{\text{velocity of body}}{\text{velocity of sound}} \quad (11\text{k})$$

PROBLEMS

1. An oak box is to slide with uniform speed down an inclined oak plank. At what angle should the plank be supported?

2. A steel safe is to be lowered from one floor of a building to another by sliding it down an oak plank. At what angle should the plank be supported to make it slide with uniform speed? (*Ans.* 28.8 degrees.)

3. The angle of uniform slip for a rubber-soled shoe on a wooden plank is 24.5 degrees. Find the coefficient of sliding friction.

4. The angle of uniform slip for a 20-Kg trunk on a pine board is 26°. (a) What is the coefficient of sliding friction? (b) If the plank is inclined at an angle of 30° to the horizontal, what will be the box's acceleration down the board? (*Ans.* (a) 0.488, (b) 0.76 m/sec².)

5. A horizontal force of 24 lb is required to pull a trunk weighing 120 lb across the floor. Find the coefficient of sliding friction.

6. What force acting at an angle of 18° with the horizontal is required to move an oak box weighing 200 lb across an oak floor? (*Ans.* 48.6 lb.)

7. The angle of uniform slip for a sled weighing 40 lb is 8°. What force is required to pull the sled up the same slope?

8. A horse-drawn sleigh weighing 628 lb requires a force of 22.4 lb to keep it moving over the snow at constant speed. Find the coefficient of sliding friction. (*Ans.* 0.0357.)

9. A man, driving a car weighing 3300 lb, suddenly applies the brakes, causing all the rubber tires to skid. What force is exerted on the concrete pavement?

10. A metal box is to slide down an elm-wood plank. Find the angle of uniform slip. (*Ans.* 11.3°.)

11. A 50-lb box is tied with hemp rope. (a) Find the angle of uniform slip if the box is placed on an oak plank. (b) What force is required to pull this box up the plank when it is inclined 30° to the horizontal?

12. A truck weighing 4.2 tons starts from rest at the top of a 3% grade and coasts for a distance of 1 mi. If the coefficient of rolling friction is 0.025, find its final speed. (*Ans.* 41.1 ft/sec or 28.0 mi/hr.)

13. A car with a mass of 1200 Kg is traveling at a speed of 72 Km/hr. Suddenly the brakes are applied, causing all tires to skid. How far will the car travel before coming to a stop?

14. A 50-lb. wooden box falls from a truck going 60 mi/hr. If the coefficient of sliding friction between wood and concrete is 0.48, how far will the box slide along the pavement in coming to rest? (*Ans.* 252 ft.)

15. A sleigh with steel runners and weighing 350 lb is towed along a concrete road. What horizontal force is required?

16. A boy weighing 100 lb on a sled weighing 25 lb finds that he can slide with uniform speed on a hill road having a 8% grade. How big a force will be required when he goes to pull the sled back up the same hill? Assume the coefficient of friction to be the same in both cases. (*Ans.* 4.0 lb.)

17. A 1500-Kg car starts from rest at the top of a 5% grade and coasts for a distance of 400 m. What will be its speed at the bottom if the coefficient of rolling friction is 0.030?

18. A girl weighing 75 lb is on roller skates. Upon attaining a speed of 15 mi/hr, she starts coasting and comes to rest after covering a distance of 220 ft. Find the coefficient of rolling friction. (*Ans.* 0.0344.)

19. An airplane weighing 1600 lb is in a power climb. It maintains a constant speed when its angle of attack is 20° and its line of flight is 16°. Assuming a lift of twice the drag, calculate the forward thrust of the propeller.

20. A plane weighing 50,000 lb maintains constant speed in a power climb. If the angle of attack is 7°, the line of flight is 4°, and the thrust of the jet engine is 10,000 lb, find (a) the lift, and (b) the drag. (*Ans.* (a) 49360 lb, (b) 6500 lb.)

21. The motor of a plane weighing 3000 lb stalls while in flight, and the pilot sets the plane into a glide preparatory to making a forced landing. The speed of the gliding plane is constant, the angle of attack is 18° below the horizontal, and the line of flight is 24° below the horizontal. Find (a) the lift, and (b) the drag.

22. The motor of a plane stalls while in straight and level flight, and the pilot drops the nose of the ship into a glide preparatory to making a forced landing. The plane glides at a constant speed, the attitude becomes fixed at 16° below the horizontal, and the line of flight is at 20° below the horizontal. If the plane weighs 3600 lb, find (a) the lift, and (b) the drag. (*Ans.* (a) 3383 lb, (b) 1231 lb.)

23. Solve Prob. 6 for angles of 0°, 5°, 10°, 15°, 20°, and 25°. Plot a graph, and find the angle for which the applied force is a minimum.

24. Make a graph of the variation of sliding friction with speed using the values given on page 78. Show both origins at zero. What might be concluded about μ at higher speeds?

25. A 50-Kg wooden box falls from a truck traveling at a speed of 72 Km/hr along the highway. If the box slides for a total distance of 50 m before coming to rest, what is the coefficient of sliding friction?

26. An oak box with a mass of 40 Kg is to be pulled across a warehouse floor. If the coefficient of sliding friction is 0.25, find (a) the minimum horizontal force required to pull it. (b) What acceleration will be produced if the horizontal force is increased to 150 newtons? (*Ans.* (a) 98 newtons, (b) 1.30 m/sec².)

27. A box weighing 96 lb is pulled across a warehouse floor at constant speed with a horizontal force of 24 lb. Find (a) the coefficient of sliding friction. Find (b) the acceleration produced by increasing the force to 40 lb.

28. A 2-Kg block of wood slides down an inclined plane at constant speed when the plane makes an angle of 20° with the horizontal. Find (a) the coefficient of sliding friction, and (b) the acceleration of the block when the angle is increased to 30°. (*Ans.* (a) 0.364, (b) 1.81 m/sec² or 5.4 ft/sec².)

Chapter 12

Simultaneous and Relative Velocities

Since velocity has magnitude and direction, it is a vector quantity, and therefore subject to the principles of vector addition.

12.1. Velocity Is a Vector Quantity. When a body moves with two velocities simultaneously, the process of vector addi-

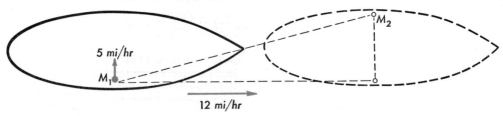

Fig. 12A *A body undergoing two simultaneous velocities.*

tion is applied to find its equivalent resultant velocity. To see what is meant by *simultaneous velocities* and a *resultant velocity,* consider the following problem.

While an ocean liner is sailing eastward with a velocity of 12 mi/hr, a man walks around the deck at the rate of 5 mi/hr. The problem is to find at all times the man's velocity with respect to the water. When he walks forward in the direction of the ship's motion, his velocity of 5 mi/hr is added to the ship's velocity of 12 mi/hr to give a resultant of 17 mi/hr eastward. As the man walks aft, however, his velocity of 5 mi/hr is subtracted from the ship's velocity of 12 mi/hr to give a resultant of 7 mi/ hr eastward.

In the first case, the vectors are parallel and in the same direction, and they add arithmetically, while in the second case they are oppositely directed and they subtract arithmetically.

When the man walks across the deck at right angles to the ship's motion, his resultant velocity is 13 mi/hr in a direction 22.6° north of east. To show how this answer is determined, a *space diagram* of the problem is given in Fig. 12A. The diagram at the left shows M_1 as the starting point of the man and boat, while the diagram at the right shows the position of the boat when the man reaches M_2 on the port side. The plane of the page represents the water.

The vector addition of the two velocities is shown at the top in Fig. 12B. The arrow *WB* is first drawn 12 units long and pointing in the direction of the boat's motion. *BM* is next drawn up from *B,* 5 units long, and pointing in the direction the man is walking on the boat. The triangle is then completed, the length of the side *WM* is measured from the graph, and the angle is measured with a protractor. The resultant *WM* = 13 mi/hr at 22.6° represents, both in magnitude and direction, the velocity of the man with respect to the water.

The Domino Method. A general procedure that can be applied to all problems involving simultaneous velocities is illustrated at the bottom in Fig. 12B. If we take

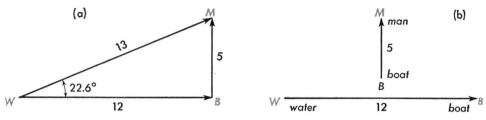

Fig. 12B *Vector addition of simultaneous velocities.*

the above problem as an example, each vector is first drawn separately with its proper magnitude and specified direction. Each is then labeled with the moving body at the head of the arrow and the object with reference to which it is moving at the tail. The vectors are then put together in a single diagram with like labels together, as in diagram (a).

12.2. Motion in a Moving Medium. The principles of vector addition are particularly useful when applied to the motion of a body in a medium which is itself moving. The drift of an airplane in a wind or the drift of a boat on a moving body of water are good examples.

The Airplane Problem. The pilot of a plane wishes to fly to a city directly to the north. If the plane has a cruising speed of 100 mi/hr, and a steady wind is blowing from the west with a velocity of 50 mi/hr, at what angle should the pilot head his plane into the wind? See Fig. 12C(a). Be-

cause this type of problem is often solved incorrectly, its correct solution should be noted with care. The procedure to be followed is that given in italics at the end of the preceding section.

Vectors are first drawn and labeled as shown in diagram (b). With both the direction and magnitude of the wind velocity known, the first vector is drawn toward the east, 50 units long. It is then labeled with the moving body, the wind W at the head, and the ground G to which the velocity is referred, at the tail. Since only the magnitude of the airplane velocity is known, a temporary arrow is drawn 100 units long, at an arbitrary angle, and then labeled with the moving body, the plane P, at the head, and the air or wind W, to which the velocity is referred, at the tail.

The next step is to combine the two vectors with their like labels, the wind W, as follows. After drawing the vector GW, a perpendicular line GX is drawn upward.

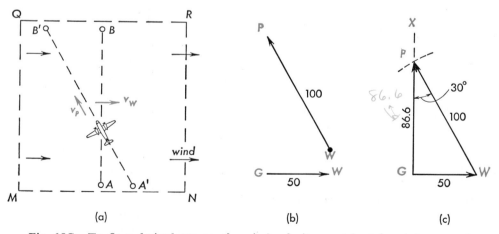

Fig. 12C *To fly a desired course, the wind velocity must be taken into account.*

With a compass of radius 100 units and the center at W, a short arc is drawn, intersecting the vertical line at P.

The vector WP is then completed, and the length of the side GP measured. The vector GP of 86.6 pointing north represents the velocity of the plane P with respect to the ground G, while the angle of 30°, measured from the triangle, gives the direction in which the plane must be headed.

Diagram (a) in Fig. 12C shows how the plane, heading in a direction 30° west of north, and flying through the air with a velocity of 100 mi/hr, follows the northward land course from A to B with a velocity of 86.6 mi/hr. In the air mass ($MNRQ$), the plane flies from A' to B'.

12.3. Relative Times for Two Planes. Because of its direct bearing upon Einstein's theory of relativity, the following problem should be of primary interest to every student. Suppose two pilots with identical planes are to fly to different cities equally far away. As shown in Fig. 12D, one

Starting out for city Y, the first pilot, cruising at velocity c, sets his course west of north so that his flight path, with respect to the ground, is due north, as shown by the left-hand vector diagram. To return to home base H, he sets his course west of south so that his flight path is due south, as shown by the upper velocity triangle. Since his ground speed GP is the same each way, by the Pythagorean theorem for a right triangle, we find that

$$GP = \sqrt{c^2 - v^2}$$

Starting out for city X, the second pilot, with the same air cruising velocity c, sets his course due east. Since his plane is flying *with* the wind, the ground speed GP is just the arithmetic sum of the two speeds:

$$GP = c + v$$

To return to home base H, the pilot sets his course due west. Flying against the

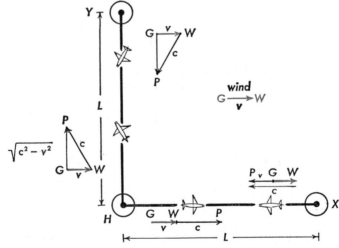

Fig. 12D *Comparisons of flight time for a plane flying downwind, upwind, and crosswind.*

pilot flies north to city Y, at right angles to the wind, and returns, while the other flies east to city X, parallel to the wind, and returns. We now wish to find whether the two total flight times are the same or whether they are different.

wind, the plane has a reduced ground speed equal to the arithmetic difference between the two speeds.

$$GP = c - v$$

To find the total flight time $t_\perp$ of the first

plane, we divide the total distance $2L$ by the velocity $\sqrt{c^2 - v^2}$.

$$t_\perp = \frac{2L}{\sqrt{c^2 - v^2}} \qquad (12a)$$

To find the total flight time $t_\parallel$ of the second plane, the two different velocities $c + v$ going, and $c - v$ returning must be used. Therefore, we have

$$t_\parallel = \frac{L}{c + v} + \frac{L}{c - v}$$

Placing these two terms over a common denominator, we obtain

$$t_\parallel = \frac{2Lc}{c^2 - v^2} \qquad (12b)$$

One way to compare these flight times is to divide the perpendicular flight time by the parallel flight time, and obtain

$$\frac{t_\perp}{t_\parallel} = \frac{2L}{\sqrt{c^2 - v^2}} \div \frac{2Lc}{c^2 - v^2}$$

Inverting the divisor and multiplying, we find

$$\frac{t_\perp}{t_\parallel} = \frac{2L}{\sqrt{c^2 - v^2}} \times \frac{c^2 - v^2}{2Lc} = \frac{\sqrt{c^2 - v^2}}{c}$$

from which we obtain the simplified result,

$$\boxed{\frac{t_\perp}{t_\parallel} = \sqrt{1 - v^2/c^2}} \qquad (12c)$$

This equation shows that flying with no wind blowing, $v = 0$, the ratio of the two flight times is unity, which means that they are equal, as one would expect. When the wind is blowing, however, the ratio is less than unity, and the plane flying parallel to the wind requires the greater time. If the wind velocity increases to nearly that of the cruising speed of the planes, the ratio tends toward zero. If the wind velocity exceeds the cruising speed of the planes, the ratio becomes imaginary: the first plane is blown off its course and the second plane cannot get back to home base.

It will be left as a problem for the student to show that the time of flight over both of these two courses is greater when the wind is blowing than when it is calm.

12.4. Different Frames of Reference. If two observers are moving with respect to one another, and both observers make measurements of any event, they could both be expected to come to the same conclusions as to what took place. In Fig. 12E we see

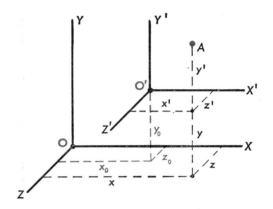

Fig. 12E *Diagram illustrating the coordinate distances of a point A measured in two different frames of reference.*

two sets of rectangular coordinates called *frames of reference.* In the space common to these two frames is a single point marked A, and it is to this point that measurements are to be made. The first observer O' in the upper right-hand frame measures the distance to A and finds the coordinates of this distance to be x', y', and z'. The second observer O in the lower left-hand frame measures the distance to A and finds coordinate distances x, y, and z.

Suppose that observer O' now wishes to make measurements from which he can determine x, y, and z as observed by O. To do this, he measures the distance from O' to O and finds the coordinates to be x_0, y_0, and z_0. He can now write down the following equalities,

$$x = x' + x_0 \qquad (12d)$$
$$y = y' + y_0 \qquad (12e)$$
$$z = z' + z_0 \qquad (12f)$$

Suppose observer O wishes to make his own determinations of x', y', and z' as observed by O'. To do this, he measures his distance from O to O' and finds the coordinates to be x_0, y_0, and z_0. He then writes down the equations

$$x' = x - x_0 \qquad (12g)$$
$$y' = y - y_0 \qquad (12h)$$
$$z' = z - z_0 \qquad (12i)$$

Note that both sets of these equations are the same and that they permit either observer to transform measurements made in his frame of reference to those made in the other. It is for this reason that such equations are called *transformation equations*.

12.5. Distance Measurements in Moving Frames of Reference. To transform measurements from one moving frame of reference to another, we will confine the motion to the line joining the two origins. It is along this straight line that x-axes are set up for two frames, as shown in Fig. 12F.

finds the distances to be x'_1 and x'_2. Each observer now decides to use the transformation equations to find the other observer's distance measurements. Observer O uses Eq.(12g) and writes

$$x'_1 = x_1 - vt \qquad \text{and} \qquad x'_2 = x_2 - vt \qquad (12j)$$

and observer O' uses Eq.(12d) and writes

$$x_1 = x'_1 + vt \qquad \text{and} \qquad x_2 = x'_2 + vt$$

In each case they arrive at the same equations. Each observer finds that upon taking the difference between his own measured distances,

$$x_2 - x_1 = x'_2 - x'_1$$

Each observer concludes, therefore, that the distance between A and B is the same whether viewed from one frame or the other. The transformation of measurements from one moving frame of reference to an-

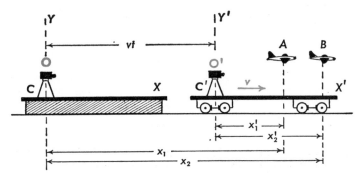

Fig. 12F   *Diagram showing distance measurements of two airplanes, A and B, from two frames of reference.*

Here one observer O is located on a stationary platform C and the other observer O' on a flat car C' capable of moving freely along a track. Observer O and reference frame C will be assumed at rest, while observer O' and car C' will be assumed moving along together with constant velocity v.

Both observers start their stop clocks at the instant O' is opposite O. At some later time, both observers simultaneously note the time and snap pictures of two airplanes, A and B, directly over the track. From their stereo-photographs, observer O finds the distances to be x_1 and x_2, while observer O'

other by means of the above equations is referred to as a *Galilean-Newtonian transformation*. Under such transformations, distances are said to be *invariant*, that is, they are the same.

We say, therefore, that in any Galilean-Newtonian system an object measured and found to have a length l in one reference frame will be found to have the same length l' when measured in any other reference frame.

$$\boxed{l' = l} \qquad (12k)$$

Note that this equality of results does not depend upon the value of v or of t, but does depend upon all observations being made at the same instant, that is, *simultaneously*. In other words, anything happening in one frame at an instant t' is observed from the other frame as occurring at the same instant t.

$$t' = t \qquad (121)$$

12.6. Velocity Measurements in Moving Frames of Reference. We have seen in the previous section that, under a Galilean-Newtonian transformation, the straight-line distance between two points is invariant. The question next arises as to whether the *velocity* of a moving body should be invariant, i.e., should the velocity be the same when observed from different frames which are themselves moving with different velocities? To find the answer to this question, we again make use of two observers, one stationary, and the other on a flat car as shown in Fig. 12G.

each of the two times. Applying the transformation equations, Eq.(12j), they can write

$$x'_1 = x_1 - vt_1 \qquad \text{and} \qquad x'_2 = x_2 - vt_2$$

To find the average velocity of the plane, observer O' takes his measured distance traveled, $x'_2 - x'_1$, and divides by his elapsed time $t'_2 - t'_1$. Taking the difference, he obtains

$$x'_2 - x'_1 = (x_2 - x_1) - (vt_2 - vt_1)$$

and dividing each term by either of the two equal time differences, he finds

$$\frac{x'_2 - x'_1}{t'_2 - t'_1} = \frac{x_2 - x_1}{t_2 - t_1} - \frac{v(t_2 - t_1)}{t_2 - t_1}$$

The term on the left represents the average velocity u' of the plane as observed by O', while the middle term represents the average velocity u observed by O.

$$u' = \frac{x'_2 - x'_1}{t'_2 - t'_1} \qquad \text{and} \qquad u = \frac{x_2 - x_1}{t_2 - t_1} \qquad (12\text{m})$$

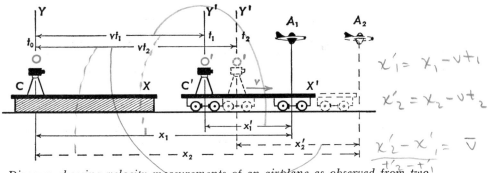

Fig. 12G *Diagram showing velocity measurements of an airplane as observed from two frames of reference.*

Both observers start their stopclocks at the instant the moving observer O' is opposite the stationary observer O. At some later time, both observers simultaneously note the time t_1 as they snap stereo-pictures of an airplane A_1 flying along and over the track. A short time later, both observers again note the time t_2 as they simultaneously snap pictures of the same plane at A_2. From their respective photographs each observer determines the plane's distance for

Observer O' can therefore write

$$u' = u - v \qquad (12\text{n})$$

Exactly the same equations can be written by observer O. Thus the two velocities measured by the two observers are not the same; they differ by the relative velocity of the two observers. We say that, *under a Galilean-Newtonian transformation, velocities are not invariant.*

12.7. Classical Relativity. Newtonian Mechanics. From the treatment of the kinematics of motion in the three preceding sections, we have seen how an observer in one reference frame can make measurements of something happening in another reference frame and, by applying simple transformation equations, find the measurements that apply to the second frame. We have seen that, if the relative velocity of the two frames is constant, the distance between two points, or the length of an object measured from either frame, is found to be the same. If the *acceleration* of an object is measured from both frames, the two results again come out the same, but if the *velocity* is measured, the two values are different. In other words,

Distances and accelerations are invariant and do not depend upon any relative velocity of an observer, while velocities are variant.

Even though velocities may be different for two observers, the transformation equations make the two velocities compatible. If measurements of the motion of a body in one frame of reference are transformed to find the measurements that would apply in another frame, we say that we are applying *classical or Newtonian mechanics.* These transformation equations are

$$\begin{aligned} x' &= x - vt \\ t' &= t \end{aligned} \qquad (12o)$$

A set of coordinates that is fixed relative to an observer is called the *observer's frame of reference.* Since Newton's laws of motion do not apply in an accelerated frame of reference, a frame that is not accelerated is called a *Galilean-Newtonian* or *inertial frame of reference.*

In setting up the Galilean-Newtonian transformation equations, it was assumed that all measurements were simultaneous, that is, that the light with which one sees an object travels with an infinite speed. If the relative velocities of moving frames are small compared with the speed of light (186,000 mi/sec), the speed of light can be assumed to be infinite, and the principles developed in this and the preceding chapters are valid. Newtonian mechanics applies, therefore, to velocities that are low compared with the speed of light, while a modified system called *relativistic mechanics* will apply to velocities comparable to the speed of light. (See Chap. 46.)

PROBLEMS

1. A man who can row a boat at 2 mi/hr wishes to cross a river 1 mi wide to a point 1 mi down the river. If the river flows with a velocity of $\frac{1}{2}$ mi/hr, (a) at what angle must he head the boat, and (b) how long will it take to get there?

2. A rowboat is headed straight across a river $\frac{1}{2}$ mi wide. If the water flows at the rate of 1.5 mi/hr, (a) what speed must the boat make in the water to land at a point $\frac{1}{4}$ mile down the river on the opposite bank, and (b) how long will it take to get there? (*Ans.* (a) 3 mi/hr, (b) 10 min.)

3. A motorboat capable of 10 mi/hr is headed straight across a river. If the water flows at the rate of 3 mi/hr, what will be the velocity of the boat with respect to the starting point on the bank?

4. At what angle must the boat in Prob. 3 be

headed upstream in order to land on the other bank 10° upstream? (*Ans.* 27.2° upstream.)

5. A submarine-chaser is headed due east at 30 knots while a 25-knot wind is blowing from the northeast. (a) What is the velocity of the wind with respect to the ship? (b) What angle will a smoke screen sent up by the ship make with the ship's course?

6. To an observer on a ship sailing east at 24 knots, it appears that a 16-knot wind is blowing from the northwest. Find the true wind velocity. (*Ans.* 37.1 knots at 17.7° south of east.)

7. A pilot with a plane having a cruising speed of 120 mi/hr leaves an airport and sets his course at 20° north of east. After flying for 1 hr, he discovers he is 104 mi directly east of his starting point. What is the average wind velocity that blew him off his course?

8. A ship sailing north at 18 knots, and a

12-knot wind is blowing from the west. What is the velocity of the wind with respect to the ship? What angle will the trail of smoke left by the funnels make witn the ship's course? (*Ans.* 21.6 knots at 33.7° east of south.)

9. A pilot with a plane having a cruising speed of 200 mi/hr wishes to fly from city *A* southwest to city *B*, 100 mi away. Before he leaves the airport, the weather report for that area gives the wind velocity as 30 mi/hr from the southwest. (a) In what direction should he set his course? (b) What velocity will he make with respect to the ground? (c) How long will it take to reach his destination?

10. A ship sailing south at 16 mi/hr leaves a smoke trail that makes an angle of 38° south of west. When the ship's course is changed to southwest, the smoke trail becomes due south. Find the velocity of the wind. (*Ans.* 27.3 mi/hr at 24.7° west of south.)

11. The trail of smoke left by a ship sailing east at 20 mi/hr makes an angle of 45° south of west. When the ship's course is changed to northeast, the line of smoke becomes due south. Find the velocity of the wind. *Solve graphically.*

12. Two pilots flying identical aircraft with a cruising speed of 200 mi/hr fly to equally distant cities 400 mi away, and return to their home base. City *X* lies to the east and city *Y* lies to the north as shown in Fig. 12D. Aloft, there is a 70-mi/hr wind blowing from the west. Find (a) the time of flight going to each city, (b) the time of flight returning, (c) the difference in total times of flight, and (d) the ratio of the two total flight times. (*Ans.* (a) 1.48 hr to *X*, 2.14 hr to *Y*; (b) 3.08 hr from *X*, 2.14 hr from *Y*; (c) 0.28 hr or 16.8 min; (d) 1.067.)

13. Two swimmers, starting simultaneously from the same anchored marker in a river, swim to distant markers and return. One marker *X* is directly downstream 500 ft, and the other, *Y*, is directly across-stream 500 ft. If both swimmers can make 3 mi/hr in the water, and the river flows at 2 ft/sec, (a) how long will it take each swimmer to reach his distant marker, (b) what is each swimmer's time to return, (c) what is the difference between their total times, and (d) what is the ratio of these times as determined from Eq.(12c)?

14. Two pilots flying identical aircraft with a cruising speed of 280 mi/hr fly to equally distant cities 300 mi away, and return to their home base. City *X* lies to the west, and city *Y* lies to the south of home base. Aloft there is an 80-mi/hr wind blowing from the west. Find (a) the time of flight going to each city, (b) each time of flight returning, (c) the difference in total time of flight times, and (d) the ratio of total flight times using Eq.(12c). (*Ans.* (a) 1.50 hr to *X*, 1.12 hr to *Y*; (b) 0.833 hr from *X*, 1.12 hr from *Y*; (c) 0.093 hr; (d) 1.04.)

15. A man rowing a boat upstream drops an empty bottle into the water as he passes a shore marker *A*. Continuing upstream for 15 min, he turns about and rows downstream, catching up with the bottle one mile downstream from *A*. Find the speed of the river.

16. A jet pilot, in a plane with a cruising speed of 480 mi/hr, sets his course due west. After flying for 30 min, a ground observer reports his position as 15 mi west and 20 mi north of where he should be. Calculate the average wind velocity that blew him off his course. (*Ans.* 50 mi/hr at 36.8° west of north.)

17. A river 1 Km wide flows with a speed of 4 Km/hr. A man, in a boat capable of making 10 Km/hr, wishes to cross the river to a point 0.5 Km upstream and then to return to the starting point. In what direction should he head his boat when going over and when coming back?

18. A pilot with a plane having a cruising speed of 200 mi/hr wishes to fly to another airport 100 mi to the north, and return. A steady wind of 30 mi/hr is blowing from the south. (a) What is his total flying time? (b) What would be his flying time if there were no wind? (c) Why are these times different? (*Ans.* (a) 1.023 hr, (b) 1 hr.)

19. A man in a boat capable of making 10 mi/hr heads upstream on a river. If the river flows with a speed of 4 mi/hr, and he travels upstream for 45 min, (a) how far will he be from his starting point, and (b) how many minutes will it take him to return?

20. A man in a boat capable of making 10 mi/hr, wishes to cross a river to a point directly across on the opposite shore. If the river flows at 5 mi/hr, and is 1 mi wide, (a) at what angle with the shore should he head his boat, (b) what will be his speed with respect to the shore, and (c) how long will it take him to cross the river? (*Ans.* (a) 60°, (b) 8.66 mi/hr. (c) 0.115 hr.)

Projectiles

13.1. Horizontal Projection. If one body falls freely from rest at the same time that another is projected horizontally from the same height, the two will strike the ground simultaneously. An experimental proof of this fundamental observation may be verified by an experiment of the type diagramed in Fig. 13A.

ground at the same time. Repetition of the experiment with higher or lower projection velocities and from different heights always ends with the same result: both marbles hit the ground together.

The first conclusion that may be drawn from this experiment is that the downward acceleration of a projectile is the same as

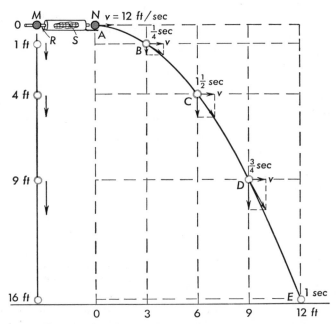

Fig. 13A *A body dropped from rest and another projected horizontally strike the ground at the same time.*

Two identical marbles, *M* and *N*, are supported by a rod and trough, respectively, in such a way that when the compressed spring *S* is released the rod *R* springs to the right, dropping *M* and projecting *N* horizontally. Marble *M*, falling with the acceleration of gravity *g*, and marble *N*, traversing the longer path *ABCDE*, strike the

a freely falling body and takes place independently of its horizontal motion. Furthermore, an experimental measurement of *times* and *distances* shows that the horizontal velocity of projection continues unchanged and takes place independently of the vertical motion.

In other words, a projectile carries out

two motions independently: (1) a constant horizontal velocity v; and (2) a vertically downward acceleration g.

With an initial horizontal velocity v, the horizontal distance x traveled is proportional to the time t and is given by the equation

$$x = vt \qquad (13a)$$

As the marble falls at the same time with an acceleration g, the vertical distance y is proportonal to the square of the time and is given by the equation

$$y = \tfrac{1}{2}gt^2 \qquad (13b)$$

An experimental verification of these two equations is illustrated by the numerical values given in the diagram. With an initial velocity of 12 ft/sec, marble N falls a distance of 1 ft in $\frac{1}{4}$ sec and at the same time travels a horizontal distance of 3 ft. In $\frac{1}{2}$ sec it falls 4 ft and travels horizontally 6 ft, etc. Since the motion obeys both formulas at the same time, the path traversed is a parabola.

As a proof, Eq.(13a) is first solved for t, then squared to obtain

$$t^2 = \frac{x^2}{v^2}$$

Substitute for t^2 in Eq.(13b).

$$y = \frac{1}{2}g\frac{x^2}{v^2}, \quad \text{or} \quad y = \frac{g}{2v^2}x^2 \quad (13c)$$

which is the equation of a parabola with the point of projection as the origin.

For the purposes of solving problems, the motions of projectiles are usually determined by calculating the horizontal and vertical motions separately and combining the results by vector addition.

Example 1. A stone is thrown horizontally with a velocity of 50 ft/sec from the top of a tower 100 ft high. How long will it take to reach the ground, and at what angle and with what velocity will it strike?

Solution. The time to reach the ground is the time of free fall given by Eq.(13b). By solving for t, we obtain

$$t = \sqrt{\frac{2y}{g}} = \sqrt{\frac{2 \times 100 \text{ ft}}{32 \text{ ft/sec}^2}} = \sqrt{6.25 \text{ sec}^2} = 2.5 \text{ sec}$$

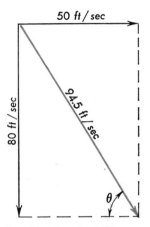

Fig. 13B *Combined velocities of a projectile.*

Upon striking the ground, the stone will have a horizontal velocity, $v_x = 50$ ft/sec, and a vertical velocity given by Eq.(5f),

$$v_y = gt \qquad (13d)$$

$$v_y = 32\,\frac{\text{ft}}{\text{sec}^2} \times 2.5 \text{ sec} = 80\,\frac{\text{ft}}{\text{sec}}$$

Combining these two velocities vectorially as shown in Fig. 13B, we find

$$v = \sqrt{v_x^2 + v_y^2} = \sqrt{(50)^2 + (80)^2} = 94.5\,\frac{\text{ft}}{\text{sec}}$$

The angle θ is seen from the right triangle to be given by

$$\tan \theta = \frac{80}{50} = 1.60, \text{ or } \theta = 58°$$

Another illustration of horizontal projection is to be found in the dropping of bombs or other loads by a low-flying plane in level flight. See Fig. 13C. Sweeping down in a dive from a greater height, a bomber may level off at a low elevation and, sighting on a target, release a bomb when the proper angle θ is reached. As the bomb falls with increasing speed, its horizontal velocity remains constant and equal to the velocity of the plane.

If air friction is neglected, the bomb should stay directly beneath the plane at all points along its path. To find the angle θ at which the bomb should be released, two factors must be taken into account: (1) the speed of the plane, and (2) the height

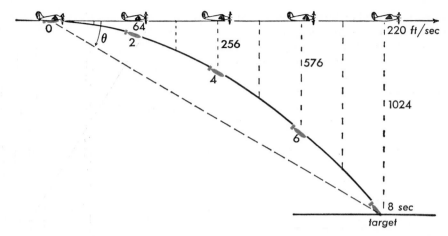

Fig. 13C *For the first few seconds after release, a falling bomb remains directly beneath
the plane. Later, wind resistance causes it to lag farther and farther behind.*

above the target. From the height y, the
time of fall can be calculated, and from
the time of fall the horizontal distance can
be computed.

If x represents the horizontal distance
traveled and y the vertical height, the right
triangle in Fig. 13B, gives

$$\tan \theta = y/x \qquad (13e)$$

where x and y are given by Eqs.(13a) and
(13b).

When bombs or other objects are
dropped from great heights, air friction
causes them to lag somewhat behind the
plane. Because the lag is negligibly small
in low-level bombing, and the plane is directly over the target when the bomb hits,
a delayed action mechanism in the bomb
has been used to avoid demolition of the
plane.

To give figures on the lag due to air friction, a bomb dropped from a plane making
about 200 mi/hr at 6000 ft will drop back
about 420 ft, having traveled horizontally
some 5580 ft to the plane's 6000 ft.

13.2. Projectiles. Many missiles when projected into the air follow a parabolic path.
Such is the case only for low speeds where
the retarding force of air friction is negligible. For high-speed projectiles the air continually slows the motion down and the
path departs from a parabola as indicated
in Fig. 13D. The higher the velocity, the

greater is the force of air friction and the
greater is the departure from a parabolic
path.

In general, it is convenient to neglect air
friction, calculate the theoretical path of a
projectile, and then if necessary make corrections for air friction. As a rule, the
known factors concerning a given projectile

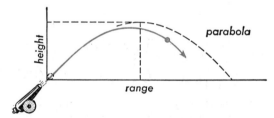

Fig. 13D *Projectiles tend to follow a parabolic
path. Because of air friction, they fall short.*

are v, the initial velocity of projection, and
θ the angle of departure. The latter is always measured from the horizontal, and in
the case of bullets and shells is the *elevation
angle* of the gun. The factors to be calculated are: (1) the *time of flight,* (2) the *maximum height* reached, and (3) the *range*
attained.

The time of flight of a projectile will
here be defined as the time required for it
to return to the same level from which it
was fired. The maximum height, called the
summit, is defined as the greatest vertical

distance reached, as measured from the horizontal projection plane, while the range is the horizontal distance from the point of projection to the point where the projectile returns again to the projection plane.

13.3. Calculation of Trajectories. To calculate the height and range of a projectile, the initial velocity of projection is resolved into two components, one vertical and the other horizontal. This is illustrated in Fig. 13E. Calling v the velocity of projection

time as another projected at an angle θ with a velocity v.

Since the time required to reach the highest point is equal to the time required to fall the same distance, the formula for free fall may be employed. The formula for an object falling from rest is

$$v_y = gt$$

By transposing, and substituting from Eq. (13f), we find

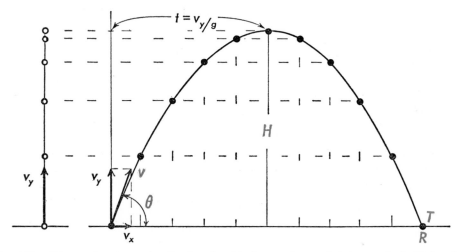

Fig. 13E   *The path of a projectile showing H the maximum height reached, T the time of flight, and R the range.*

and θ the elevation angle, the x- and y-components of velocity are given by the following trigonometric functions,

$$\sin \theta = \frac{v_y}{v} \quad \text{and} \quad \cos \theta = \frac{v_x}{v}$$

If v is transposed to the other side of each equation,

$$v_y = v \sin \theta \qquad (13f)$$
$$v_x = v \cos \theta \qquad (13g)$$

The traversal of the actual trajectory is a combination of two motions, one the motion of a particle projected vertically upward with an initial velocity v_y, the other a horizontal velocity v_x that remains constant. In other words, a particle projected vertically upward with a velocity of v_y will rise to the same height and in the same

$$t = \frac{v_y}{g} = \frac{v \sin \theta}{g} \qquad (13h)$$

Because t is the time to rise, or the time to fall, the total time of flight will be *2t*. Therefore,

$$T = 2 \frac{v_y}{g}$$

The time of flight is, therefore,

$$T = \frac{2v \sin \theta}{g} \qquad (13i)$$

To find the height H, the equation $v^2 = 2gs$ is used. See Eq.(5h). The letter s is replaced by H, and the letter v by v_y.

$$(v_y)^2 = 2gH$$

Transpose $2g$ to the other side of this equation, and obtain:

maximum height, $$H = \frac{(v_y)^2}{2g}$$

Using Eq.(13f) substitute $v \sin \theta$ for v_y, and we have,

$$H = \frac{(v \sin \theta)^2}{2g} \qquad (13j)$$

To find the range R, the equation $s = vt$ is used. Replacing the letter s by R, v by v_x, and t by the total time of flight $T = 2v_y/g$, we find

$$R = v_x T = v \cos \theta \times \frac{2v \sin \theta}{g}$$

or

$$R = \frac{2v^2 \sin \theta \cos \theta}{g}$$

To put this formula into another form, use is made of the trigonometric relation that $2 \sin\theta \cos\theta = \sin 2\theta$. Substitution gives

Range, $$R = \frac{v^2}{g} \sin 2\theta \qquad (13k)$$

In this form it is seen at once that, for a given velocity v, the range is a maximum when the $\sin 2\theta$ is a maximum. Since the sine has its maximum value of unity for an angle of 90°, the angle θ above will be 45°. Furthermore, the range for any angle any

number of degrees greater than 45° will be equal to the range for an equal number of degrees less than 45°. This is illustrated in Fig. 13F, for example, by the equal ranges of 100 ft for the 15° and 75° projections, and the equal ranges of 173 ft for the 30° and 60° projections.

Example 2. A baseball is thrown with a velocity of 50 ft/sec at an angle of 60° with the horizontal. Calculate (a) the time of flight, (b) the maximum height, and (c) the range.

Solution. To find the time of flight, direct substitution of the given quantities in Eq.(13i) gives

$$T = \frac{2v \sin \theta}{g} = \frac{2 \times 50 \times 0.866}{32} = \frac{86.6}{32} = 2.71 \text{ sec}$$

To find the maximum height, Eq.(13j) is used.

$$H = \frac{(v \sin \theta)^2}{2g} = \frac{(50 \times 0.866)^2}{2 \times 32} = 29.3 \text{ ft}$$

For the range, Eq.(13k) is used.

$$R = \frac{v^2}{g} \sin 2\theta = \frac{(50)^2 \times 0.866}{32} = 67.6 \text{ ft}$$

13.4. Monkey and Hunter Experiment. A hunter aims and shoots an arrow at a monkey in a tree. At the instant the arrow leaves the bow, the monkey drops from the branch upon which he has been sitting. The two should meet in mid-air regardless of the speed of the arrow. If gravity could be eliminated, the arrow, as shown in Fig.

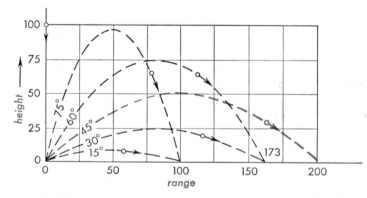

Fig. 13F *Diagram illustrating the shape of the trajectories of objects projected at different elevation angles. The vertical and horizontal scales are for the special case where the velocity of projection is 80 ft/sec.*

13G, would travel the straight line path *AM*, and the monkey would stay at *M* and be hit there. With gravity acting, however, the arrow travels the path *ABC* and the monkey drops from *M* to *C*. During each fraction of a second, indicated by $t = 1, 2,$

ing event will not be given here*, an analysis of some of the forces, velocities, and accelerations, to which the rocket and astronaut were subjected at several points of the flight, will be presented. The following cases are typical of space flight in general,

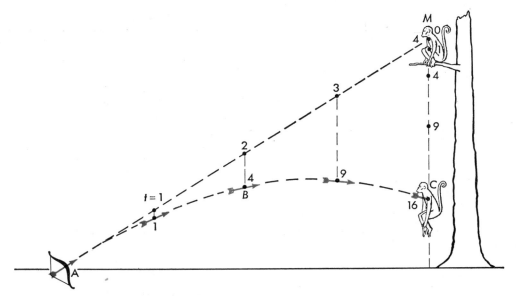

Fig. 13G   *Diagram illustrating the monkey and hunter experiment.*

3, and 4, both fall the same distance from their gravity-free positions and collide at *C*. The greater the speed of the missile, the shorter will be the distance *MC*.*

13.5. Rocket Flights into Space. The first American man to be launched into space by a rocket was carried aloft in a Mercury capsule boosted by a Redstone rocket from Cape Canaveral, Florida, on May 5, 1961. The astronaut, Alan Shepard, who piloted the pressurized space capsule in which he was jettisoned, followed a path similar to that shown in Fig. 13H.

Although the details of this history-mak-

* This experiment may be performed by blowing a small wooden marble through a tube (about a foot long). A toy monkey is released at *M* by a small electromagnet. Two fine copper wires completing the electric circuit are crossed just in front of the tube at *A*. When the projectile passes this point the circuit is broken, releasing *M*. The mass *M* should have a small piece of iron at the top for the magnetic attraction.

and the equations can be applied equally well to orbiting satellites and to future flights to the moon and planets. (See Chap. 18.)

Since the value of *g* in Shepard's flight diminished by less than 5% at an altitude of 115 mi, and its direction changed by less than 5 degrees over the 302-mi range, it will be assumed that *g* remains constant over the entire flight path.

Case A. Before Vertical Launch. When the entire rocket assembly is at rest on the launching pad, just prior to take-off, all velocities and accelerations are zero, and all forces are in equilibrium. (See Fig. 13I.) At this time there are two equal forces acting on the rocket, *W* the downward pull of the earth and *P* the upward push of the launching pad. The downward force is given by

* For details of Alan Shepard's space flight, see *Life Magazine,* May 12 and 19, 1961.

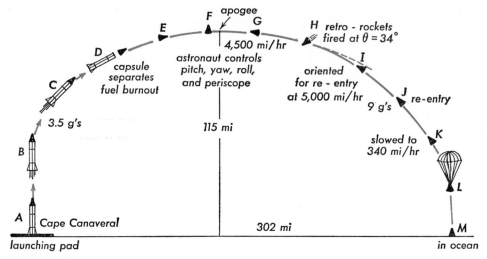

Fig. 13H *Diagram of the flight path taken by the first American astronaut to be launched into space, May 5, 1961.*

$$W = Mg \qquad (13l)$$

where M is the total mass of the rocket and its payload.

Assuming the upward direction as positive, g the acceleration due to gravity is

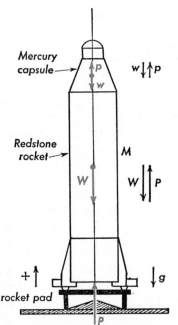

Fig. 13I *Diagram of a rocket and its manned space capsule at rest on its launching pad and ready for vertical take-off.*

negative, and so is W. Since the upward force P on the total mass M must be equal to W in magnitude,

$$P = -Mg \qquad (13m)$$

In a similar way the two equal but opposite forces acting on the astronaut are w, the downward pull of the earth, and p, the upward thrust of his supporting cradle. These forces are given by

$$w = mg \qquad (13n)$$
$$p = -mg \qquad (13o)$$

showing that for each kilogram mass of the rocket structure, or its contents, the force p is equal to 9.8 newtons, and for each slug of mass it is 32 lb. Under these conditions the force is said to be "1 g."

Case B. Vertical Climb. When the rocket is accelerating vertically upward after launching (see Fig. 13J), the two forces acting on the total mass M are P, the upward thrust of the rocket engines, and W, the downward pull of the earth. The force F giving rise to the upward acceleration a is the vector resultant of these two forces

$$\vec{P} + \vec{W} = \vec{F} \qquad (13p)$$

where

$$W = Mg \qquad (13q)$$

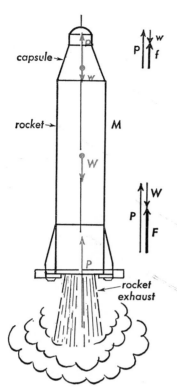

Fig. 13J *Force diagram for a rocket and its astronaut pilot during vertical flight under rocket thrust.*

To lift the rocket from the ground, P must be greater than W, and their vector resultant F will be the force that produces the upward acceleration.

$$F = Ma \qquad (13r)$$

Applying these same principles to the astronaut in the capsule shown at the top in Fig. 13J, we observe that

$$\vec{p} + \vec{w} = \vec{f} \qquad (13s)$$

where p is the thrust of the cradle on the astronaut's body and w is the downward pull of the earth on the same mass. The resultant f is the force that gives the astronaut the same upward acceleration as the rocket.

$$f = ma \qquad (13t)$$

Example 3. A 40-ton rocket with an astronaut of 160 lb aboard is climbing vertically upward with an acceleration of 96 ft/sec². Find the total force of the cradle on the man's body (a) in g's and (b) in lb.

Solution. Transposing Eq.(13s), we obtain for the thrust

$$\vec{p} = \vec{f} - \vec{w}$$

and substituting Eq.(13n) and Eq.(13t), we have

$$\vec{p} = \vec{ma} - \vec{mg} \qquad (13u)$$

Assuming $g = -32$ ft/sec², the astronaut's acceleration of 96 ft/sec², is just $-3 \times g$.

$$a = -3g$$

Direct substitution in Eq.(13u) gives for the thrust

$$p = -m(3g) - mg \qquad (13v)$$
or
$$p = -m(4g)$$

Ans. (a) The astronaut is said to be "taking 4 g's." This also means that all parts of his body are subjected to a force of four times their normal weight.

To find the thrust in pounds, direct substitution in Eq.(13v) gives

$$p = -\frac{160 \text{ lb}}{32 \text{ ft/sec}^2}\left(-4 \times 32 \frac{\text{ft}}{\text{sec}^2}\right)$$
$$p = 5 \text{ slugs} \times 128 \text{ ft/sec}^2$$
$$p = 640 \text{ lb}$$

Ans. (b) The astronaut's apparent weight is four times normal.

Case C. Inclined Rocket Thrust. When the rocket elevation angle θ is slowly altered from 90° to give the missile a predetermined direction at burnout, the rocket thrust is not directed along the flight path. In Fig. 13K the rocket is shown prior to burnout and at the instant its center of mass M passes a point (1) in its flight path.

Although the rocket axis determines the direction of total thrust P, the downward force W continually changes the direction of motion. The dashed red line, tangent to the flight path at (1), represents the instantaneous direction as the center of mass passes that point.

The two forces P and W acting on the rocket, and their resultant F, are shown in diagram (b). This resultant force gives rise to the acceleration a, in the direction of F, thus altering both in magnitude and direction the missile's velocity V.

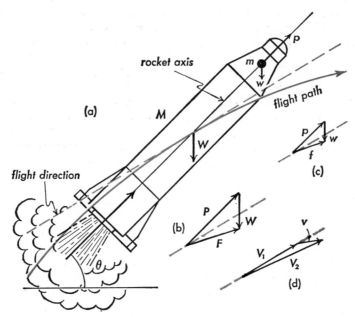

Fig. 13K *Force and velocity diagrams for a rocket and its astronaut pilot under rocket thrust at an angle.*

$$F = Ma \qquad (13w)$$

The two forces p and w acting on the astronaut, and their resultant f, are shown in diagram (c). This resultant force gives the astronaut the same acceleration as the rocket.

$$f = ma \qquad (13x)$$

A vector diagram of velocities is shown in diagram (d), where V_1 represents the instantaneous velocity of the missile as it passes point (1), v the additional velocity imparted by F during the time t it takes to go from point (1) to point (2), and V_2 the instantaneous velocity as it passes point (2). This added velocity v is given by

$$v = at \qquad (13y)$$

Note that p represents the force of the cradle on the astronaut's body mass m, and the magnitude of this force gives his apparent weight.

Case D. Free Jettisoned Space Capsule. After the space capsule carrying the astronaut has been jettisoned from the rocket, as shown at D in Fig. 13H, the vehicle becomes a free projectile. From point D

to point **H**, where the retro-rockets are fired, the downward pull of the earth W is the only force acting on the body. This force gives rise to a downward acceleration g and is responsible for the continually changing direction of the capsule as it travels along its flight path.

In the velocity diagram, Fig. 13L(b), V_1 represents the instantaneous velocity of the capsule as it passes point (1); v is the change

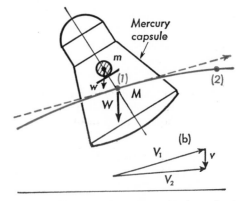

Fig. 13L *Diagram of a free jettisoned space capsule as it travels without rocket thrust along its flight path.*

in velocity imparted by W during the time it takes to reach point (2); and V_2 is the instantaneous velocity as it passes point (2).

$$v = gt \qquad (13z)$$

Since there is no thrust P from rocket motors for this part of the flight, the cradle exerts no force on the astronaut, and he exerts no force on the cradle. While the capsule, the astronaut, and the cradle fall with the same acceleration g, the concept

of weightlessness prevails throughout the moving system.

In Chap. 18, Sec. 18.4, we will see that, when the velocity of the capsule is great enough (about 17,500 mi/hr), it will orbit the earth as a satellite. In orbital flight the retro-rockets are necessary, to deflect and slow the capsule to begin its return to earth. In this particular flight of Shepard's, however, the retro-rockets were used only as a test of this manned capability.

PROBLEMS

1. A boy standing on a bridge 200 ft above the water throws a stone horizontally outward with a velocity of 50 ft/sec. (a) How long will it take to hit the water, and (b) how far away from the foot of the bridge will it strike?

2. A stream of water emerges in a horizontal direction from a hole in the side of a tank. If the hole is 20 m above the ground and the escape velocity is 14 m/sec, (a) how long is the water in the air, and (b) how far from the base of the tank does the water strike the ground? (*Ans.* (a) 2.02 sec, (b) 28.3 m.)

3. A mail plane flying at 180 mi/hr comes down to a 300-ft elevation where, in straight and level flight, it releases a mail bag to be caught in a net on the ground. What should be the horizontal distance between the plane and the net when the bag is released? Neglect air friction.

4. A supply plane making 180 mi/hr comes down to a 320-ft elevation where, in straight and level flight, it releases a large bundle of food to land on a ground marker. How far in advance of the marker, as measured along the ground, should the bundle be released? (*Ans.* 1180 ft.)

5. A smooth round stone is thrown from a sling with a speed of 49 m/sec. At what elevation angle should it be thrown to obtain a range of 245 m?

6. A baseball thrown by one player to another is in the air for 7 sec. How high did it rise? (*Ans.* 196 ft.)

7. A basketball thrown by one player to another is in the air for one second. How high did it rise?

8. Find the maximum theoretical range of a field artillery piece producing a muzzle velocity of 1600 ft/sec. What is the time of flight and the maximum height for this range? Neglect friction. (*Ans.* 15.1 mi, 70.7 sec, and 3.79 mi.)

9. An arrow shot with a speed of 200 ft/sec reaches a maximum height of 480 ft. Calculate (a) the time of flight, (b) the elevation angle, and (c) the range.

10. Calculate the time a rocket, launched at 4000 ft/sec 10 mi above the earth, spends above an altitude of 10 mi if its elevation angle at the 10-mi level is (a) 30°, and (b) 60°. Neglect friction and assume g to be constant. (*Ans.* (a) 125 sec, (b) 216.5 sec.)

11. A javelin is thrown with a speed of 80 ft/sec at an elevation angle of 42°. Find (a) the maximum height, and (b) the range. (c) How much farther would the throw have gone if the elevation angle had been 45°?

12. A smooth round stone is thrown from a sling with a speed of 300 ft/sec at an elevation angle of 20°. Calculate (a) its maximum height, (b) its range, and (c) its time of flight. (*Ans.* (a) 164 ft, (b) 1810 ft, (c) 6.41 sec.)

13. A shot-put is tossed for a distance of 52.0 ft. If the elevation angle of projection was 40°, how much more distance would have been obtained if it were thrown with the same speed at 45°?

14. A mortar hurls a 20-lb shell with a speed of 560 ft/sec. Neglecting friction, at what angle with the horizontal should it be aimed to hit a target on the ground 1600 yd away? (*Ans.* 14.7° or 75.3°.)

15. An anti-aircraft gun fires at an elevation angle of 55° at an enemy plane at 12,000 ft elevation and at 40° elevation angle. Calculate the muzzle speed.

16. A baseball is thrown with a speed of 35 m/sec at an elevation angle of 42°. Find (a) the position, and (b) the speed of the ball at the end of 2 sec. (*Ans.* (a) 27.2 m high and 52 m to the side, (b) 26.3 m/sec.)

17. A dart thrown with a speed of 160 ft/sec reaches a height of 320 ft. Calculate (a) the time of flight, (b) the angle of departure, and (c) the range.

18. A catapult hurls a stone at an elevation angle of 30° from the edge of a cliff 400 ft above the water. If the initial speed is 128 ft/sec, (a) to what height above the water does it rise, and (b) with what speed does it hit the water? (*Ans.* (a) 464 ft, (b) 205 ft/sec.)

19. An arrow is shot into the air with an initial velocity of 100 m/sec at an elevation angle of 40°. Find (a) the time of flight, (b) the maximum height, and (c) the range.

20. A mortar hurls a shell upward from the ground with a velocity of 500 ft/sec at an elevation angle of 30°. Find (a) the time of flight, (b) the maximum height reached, and (c) the range. (*Ans.* (a) 15.6 sec, (b) 977 ft, (c) 6770 ft.)

21. Calculate the total thrust of the rocket engines for Example 3 in Sec. 13.5, Case B, (a) in g's, (b) in pounds, and (c) in tons.

22. A 30-ton rocket with an astronaut of 120 lb aboard is climbing vertically upward with an acceleration of 144 ft/sec². Calculate the total force of the cradle on the man's body (a) in g's, and (b) in pounds. (*Ans.* (a) 5.5 g's, (b) 660 lb.)

23. A 25,000-Kg rocket with a 60-Kg astronaut aboard is climbing vertically upward. If the astronaut experiences an apparent weight of five times normal, find (a) the vertical acceleration, (b) the thrust of the rocket motors, and (c) the astronaut's apparent weight.

24. A 20,000-Kg rocket with a 70-Kg astronaut aboard is under full thrust of its rocket motors with its axis inclined at an angle of 30° with the horizontal. If the pilot finds his apparent weight to be given by 5 g's, find (a) the astronaut's real weight, (b) the thrust of the cradle against his body, and (c) the direction of the resultant force *f* on the astronaut's body. (*Ans.* (a) 686 newtons, (b) 3430 newtons, and (c) 17.5° from horizontal.)

25. If a large mass hangs by a wire as a pendulum in the space capsule of Figs. 13I, 13J, 13K, and 13L, in what direction would it hang for each case?

Chapter 14

Circular Motion

When a rigid body is set into rotation, its motion is generally described with reference to the axis about which it revolves. The *axis of rotation,* as it is generally called, is sometimes fixed within the body and sometimes beyond its outermost boundary. In the case of most wheels of machinery, for example, the axes of rotation are lines through the geometrical centers perpendicular to the planes of rotation. For a stone whirled on the end of a string, however, the axis is at the opposite end of the string, remote from the stone itself.

14.1. Angular Velocity. The speed with which a body rotates is called its *speed* or *frequency.* Either of these terms refers to the number of complete revolutions a body makes in unit time and is designated by the letter *n*.

n = number of revolutions per second

A flywheel, for example, might be said to have a speed of 10 revolutions per second (*abbr.* 10 rps). This is equivalent to a speed or frequency of 600 revolutions per minute (*abbr.* 600 rpm), and to a speed or fre-

quency of 36,000 revolutions per hour (*abbr.* 36,000 rph).

For formulating the laws of mechanics it will be found convenient to express all rotation in radians, not in degrees or revolutions. *The radian (abbr.* rad) *is a unit of angular measure* just as the centimeter is a unit of linear measure. It is defined as the angle subtended by the arc of a circle whose length is equal to the radius of the same circle. Referring to Fig. 14A the distance *s* measured along the arc is equal to the radius *r*, and the angle $\theta = 1$ radian.

Since the entire circumference of a circle is just 2π times the radius *r*, there are 2π radians in one complete circle.

$$2\pi \text{ radians} = 360°$$

Since $\pi = 3.1416$,

$$1 \text{ radian} = 57.3°$$

It follows from the above relations that the angle θ in radians between any two points on the circumference of a circle is given by *s*, the length of the arc between the two points, divided by the radius *r*. In other words,

$$\text{angle in radians} = \frac{\text{arc length}}{\text{radius}}$$

or, in algebraic symbols,

$$\theta = \frac{s}{r} \tag{14a}$$

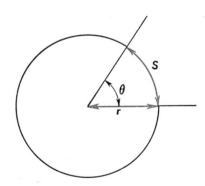

Fig. 14A *The radian is a unit of angular measure. When the arc s equals the radius r, the angle θ equals one radian.*

The reason for measuring angles in radians is that it simplifies all formulas for rotary motion. As an illustration, consider the speed of a stone being whirled on the end of a string as shown in Fig. 14B. The angular velocity of the motion is defined as

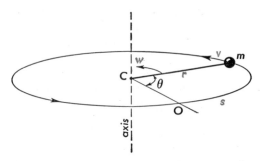

Fig. 14B *An illustration of circular motion.*

the angle turned through, divided by the elapsed time.

$$\text{angular velocity} = \frac{\text{angle turned through}}{\text{time}}$$

In algebraic symbols,

$$\omega = \theta/t \qquad (14b)$$

and is to be compared with the corresponding definition of linear velocity,

$$v = s/t \qquad (14c)$$

Angular velocity ω corresponds to linear velocity v, and angular displacement θ corresponds to linear displacement s. With θ measured in radians and t in seconds, the angular velocity ω has the units of radians per seconds, (*abbr.* rad/sec).

As a problem, suppose that a stone, when it is whirled on the end of a string 50 cm long, makes 8 complete revolutions in 2 sec, and we wish to find the angular velocity in radians per second. To employ Eq.(14b) the angle θ is first calculated as follows. Since 1 revolution = 2π radians, 8 revolutions are equivalent to

$$\theta = 2\pi \times 8 = 50.2 \text{ rad}$$

Substitution in Eq.(14b) gives

$$\omega = \frac{\theta}{t} = \frac{50.2 \text{ rad}}{2 \text{ sec}} = 25.1 \frac{\text{rad}}{\text{sec}}$$

To find the linear speed of the stone along its curved path, Eqs.(14a), (14b), and (14c) can be used by combining them as follows. By transposing Eq.(14a),

$$\boxed{s = r\theta} \qquad (14d)$$

Substitute $r\theta$ for s in Eq.(14c).

$$v = \frac{r\theta}{t} = r\frac{\theta}{t}$$

Replace θ/t by ω (from Eq. 14b).

$$\boxed{v = r\omega} \qquad (14e)$$

From the problem of the stone on a string in Fig. 14B, we can now calculate the speed of the stone from the known values of r and ω. Since the angular velocity $\omega = 25.1$ rad/sec, and the length of the string, r, is 50 cm, then, in 1 sec ($t = 1$ sec), the angle turned through will be 25.1 rad, and the velocity will be

$$v = 50 \text{ cm} \times 25.1 \frac{\text{rad}}{\text{sec}} = 1255 \frac{\text{cm}}{\text{sec}}$$

If it were required to find the distance traveled in 5 sec, Eq.(14c) could be transposed and used as follows:

$$s = vt = 1255 \frac{\text{cm}}{\text{sec}} \times 5 \text{ sec} = 6275 \text{ cm}$$

To find the total angle turned through in 5 sec, Eq.(14a) can be used.

$$\theta = \frac{s}{r} = \frac{6275 \text{ cm}}{50 \text{ cm}} = 125.5 \text{ rad}$$

Likewise, Eq.(14b) can be used by transposition and substitution.

$$\theta = \omega t = 25.1 \frac{\text{rad}}{\text{sec}} \times 5 \text{ sec} = 125.5 \text{ rad}$$

Note that all equations are consistent with each other and that the radian as a unit has no dimensions. The radian is the ratio between two lengths and therefore has the same value in all systems of units. It is for this reason that it can be canceled out where it is not needed, or added where necessary in the above answers.

14.2. Centripetal Force. When a stone is whirling on the end of a string, there is an inward force exerted by the string on the ball. This force is called the *centripetal force.* By Newton's third law of motion the ball exerts an equal but opposite force on the string. This is called the *centrifugal force.* Both forces are illustrated in Fig. 14C. Since the only force acting on the ball is inward, the ball is not in equilibrium but is being continually accelerated in the direction of the force, that is, toward the center.

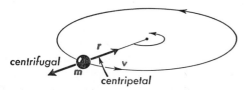

Fig. 14C *A mass m, moving in a circle, experiences an acceleration toward the center.*

This appears to be a physical paradox, for here is a body moving with constant speed in a circle and yet being accelerated toward the center of the circle without getting any closer to it. If the string were to break suddenly, the ball would fly off on a tangent to the circle and move with constant velocity according to Newton's first law.

To obtain a clearer picture of centripetal force and acceleration toward the center, motion in a circle, as illustrated in Fig. 14D(c), is to be compared with the motion of a projectile accelerated downward by the pull of gravity as shown in Fig. 13G. Due to

the earth's attraction of all bodies, a projectile is continually accelerated downward, away from the straight line of its original projection. In circular motion the mass is continually accelerated toward the center, always at right angles to its instantaneous velocity and away from any straight-line tangent along which it would travel if suddenly released.

The instantaneous velocity is shown at two points, *A* and *B*, in diagram (a) of Fig. 14D. The velocity, as indicated by the vectors *v*, is seen to be changing in direction but not in magnitude. Diagram (b) is a velocity diagram showing *v'* as the change in velocity that occurs in going from *A* to *B*. Since this velocity triangle is similar to triangle *ABC* in diagram (a), corresponding sides are proportional to each other, and the following can be written:

$$\frac{s}{r} = \frac{v'}{v}$$

Since the velocity *v'* is changing and is due to an acceleration, it can, by the equation $v = at$, be replaced by at. During the time *t*, the body moves from *A* to *B* a distance $s = vt$. For small angles θ the distance measured along the arc *AB* is approximately equal to the chord *s*, so that **to a** close approximation *s* can be replaced **by**

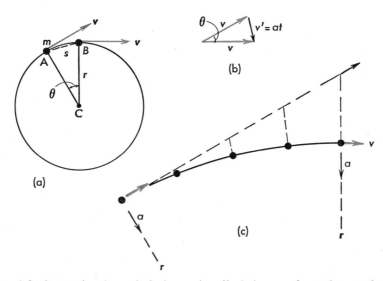

Fig. 14D *A body moving in a circle is continually being accelerated toward the center.*

vt. These two substitutions made in the equation above give

$$\frac{vt}{r} = \frac{at}{v}$$

By canceling *t* on both sides and transposing *v*, we obtain the relation

$$a = \frac{v^2}{r} \qquad (14f)$$

Thus, the *centripetal acceleration* is given by v^2/r.

As the angle θ in Fig. 14D is made smaller and smaller, the arc distance *s* becomes more and more nearly equal to the chord, while the change in velocity *v'*, which gives the direction of the acceleration *a*, becomes more nearly perpendicular to *v*. In the limit when θ becomes zero, Eq.(14f) holds true exactly and the acceleration is perpendicular to *v*.

If we substitute $r\omega$ for *v* (see Eq.(14f)), the centripetal acceleration can be expressed in terms of the angular velocity ω.

$$a = r\omega^2 \qquad (14g)$$

Centripetal force is defined as that constant force which, acting continuously at right angles to the motion of a particle, causes it to move in a circle with constant speed. Since by Newton's second law of motion, $F = ma$, the centripetal force is given by

$$F = m\frac{v^2}{r} \qquad (14h)$$

or in angular quantities by

$$F = mr\omega^2 \qquad (14i)$$

Example 1. A mass of 5 Kg is moving in a circle of 1-m radius with an angular velocity of 2 rad/sec. Find the centripetal force.

Solution. The known quantities substituted directly in Eq.(14i) give

$$F = 5 \text{ Kg} \times 1 \text{ m} \times 4\frac{\text{rad}^2}{\text{sec}^2} = 20\frac{\text{Kg m}}{\text{sec}^2}$$

$$= 20 \text{ newtons}$$

Note: Radians have no dimensions and are therefore dropped out in arriving at the force in any units.

14.3. Experiments Demonstrating Centripetal Force. Many interesting experiments can be performed to illustrate centripetal force. In Fig. 14E mercury and water

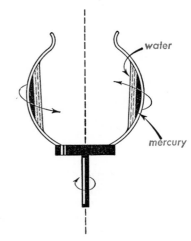

Fig. 14E *Mercury and water rotate in a dish; the water is inside the mercury. Centripetal force, like gravitational force, is greater for the more dense substance.*

have been placed in a dish and the dish set rotating rapidly about a vertical axis. Since mercury is 13.6 times as heavy as an equal volume of water, the centripetal force *F* on each gram of mercury is 13.6 times larger than on each gram of water. The mercury therefore takes the outermost position in the dish.

Although the earth is often said to be spherical, it is in reality an oblate spheroid, that is, a slightly flattened sphere. Accurate measurements show that the earth's diameter is 28 mi greater through the equator than it is through the poles. The cause for this flattening is illustrated in Fig. 14F by two circular metal strips. Diagram (a) shows the strips to be round when at rest, while (b) shows the flattening due to rapid rotation. The flattening of the earth is due to its own rotation of 2π radians every 24 hr. It is the enormous size of the earth and its lack of greater rigidity that makes it behave as though it were soft and semiplastic.

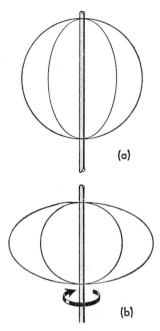

(a)

(b)

Fig. 14F *The flattening of the earth is due to its rotation about the polar axis.*

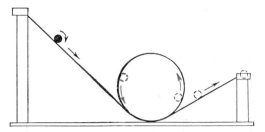

Fig. 14H *The ball will loop the loop if it starts rolling from a point high enough on the incline.*

the ball will fall. Such a behavior is similar to that of whirling a bucket of water in a circle up over the head and down, at arm's length, without spilling it. To find the critical velocity at the top of the circle, the centripetal force mv^2/r is equated to the body's weight mg. This is the same as equating the centripetal acceleration v^2/r to the acceleration of gravity g. For any given radius r, the critical speed becomes fixed by the equation,

$$g = \frac{v^2}{r} \qquad (14j)$$

When a stone on the end of a string is whirled in a vertical circle, gravity acts downward upon it at all times. At the bottom of its path, the weight must be added to the centrifugal force to obtain the tension in the string, while at the top of its path the weight must be subtracted. Whirled in a horizontal circle, the stone's weight is at all times perpendicular to centripetal force, and the string describes a cone. The tension in the string and its direction is given by the resultant of two forces, *centrifugal* and *weight*, composed at right angles.

The opening of the loop in a lariat as whirled and thrown by a cowboy is due to centripetal force. See Fig. 14I. Because of rotation, each small section of the rope, acting as an individual mass m, tends to fly off on a tangent and thus get as far from the center of rotation as possible. The average distance from the center of all sections of the rope is a maximum when the loop takes the form of a circle rotating

Mud or water clings to an automobile tire until the speed becomes too high and then it flies off on a tangent, as shown in Fig. 14G. To remain with the tire the required centripetal force cannot exceed the force of adhesion.

Fig. 14H shows a ball rolling down a looped track. The ball will stay with the track even at the top of the loop if the required centripetal force there is equal to or greater than the downward force of gravity. This means that the speed v must be greater than a certain critical speed or

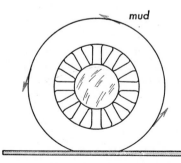

mud

Fig. 14G *Mud or water on a fast-turning wheel flies off on a tangent.*

Fig. 14I *A lariat takes a circular form because each small part tries to fly off on a tangent, thus getting as far from the center as possible. Centripetal force is responsible for keeping it in a circle.*

about an axis perpendicular to the plane of the loop.

When a small chain, as shown in Fig. 14J, is set rotating at high speed by an electric

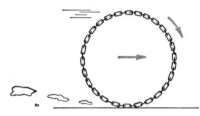

Fig. 14J *A chain turning at high speed will roll along the level as a rigid wheel.*

motor and then set free, it will roll along the floor as though it were a rigid metal hoop. Upon bumping into an obstacle, it will bounce into the air, and upon coming

down, will retain its circular form as it rolls on. The rigidity of the hoop is due to the enormous centripetal force attained at high angular velocities.

14.4. The Coriolis Force. When an object moves in a straight-line path above the surface of the earth, its path as seen from the earth appears to be curved. If a large gun, fixed in position on the earth's surface, fires a shell at a distant ground target, the projectile deflects to the right in the northern hemisphere and to the left in the southern. The explanation of this phenomenon, that it was due to the earth's rotation, was first given by the French scientist Coriolis about the middle of the last century.

Consider a demonstration in which a gun G, mounted on a turntable as shown in Fig. 14K, is aimed at targets T and P. The target P is off the table and in what is called a *stationary frame of reference,* while target T is on the table and in what is called a *rotating frame of reference.* If the table is not turning, the projectile leaving the gun with a velocity v', will pass through T and hit the target P.

If the table is rotating with an angular velocity ω, and the gun is fired at the instant the two targets are in line, the projectile will pass to the right of T and to the left of P.

Since the gun rotates with the table, the tip end of the gun barrel, at a distance r from the center of rotation C, will give the projectile an additional velocity v'' at right

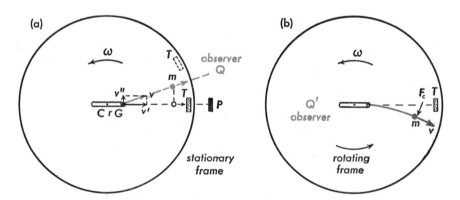

Fig. 14K *The projectile from the gun on the rotating table will miss both targets, because of the coriolis force.*

angles to v', and equal in magnitude to the product ωr.

$$v'' = \omega r \qquad (14k)$$

Since the projectile is given two simultaneous velocities v' and v'', with respect to the fixed frame of reference, a stationary observer will observe the mass m moving with a velocity v along the straight-line path GQ.

To the rotating observer shown in diagram (b), there appears to be a force F_c that deflects the projectile to the right of the

to the rotating observer, whose line of sight is now CH, to have traveled the path a, b, c, d, etc.

The stationary frame of reference may now be described as the frame of the fixed stars in the sky. In this space, sometimes called an "inertial frame," the projectile should follow a straight-line path and obey Newton's first law of motion. The rotating frame of reference may now be described as the earth as seen from the northern hemisphere. In this frame, a moving mass m has a force acting upon it which causes it

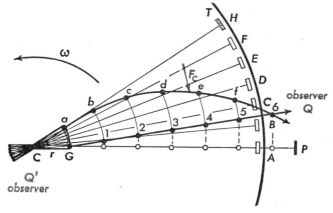

Fig. 14L *Diagram for the tracing out of the curved path of a body moving in a rotating frame.*

target T at which it is aimed. This apparent force is called the *coriolis force* and may be explained by the use of Fig. 14L.

Assume that the points 1, 2, 3, etc., mark the position of the projectile at the end of each second of time, as seen by the stationary observer Q. At the instant the projectile leaves the gun, the rotating observer Q' sees it at the point G. At the end of 1 sec, the projectile is seen at point 1, slightly to the right of the line of sight CB of the gun. This slight deflection to the right is transferred to position b, the same distance from the line of sight CH. At the end of 2 sec, the projectile is seen at point 2, a greater distance to the right of the line of sight CC of the gun. This deflection is transferred to position c, the same distance to the right of CH. When this process is carried out for 6 sec, the projectile is at point 6, appearing

to traverse a curved path. It can be shown that the coriolis force is given by the relation

$$\boxed{F_c = 2mv\omega} \qquad (14l)$$

coriolis force

A fine demonstration of the coriolis force and the curved path of a projectile in a rotating frame of reference is shown in Fig.

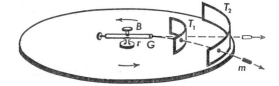

Fig. 14M *Apparatus for demonstrating the curved path of a projectile and the coriolis acceleration.*

14M. A rotating table made of plywood with a diameter of 4 ft contains a small spring gun and two metal frame targets, T_1 and T_2. The push button B for a trigger is located on the axis, and thin paper is glued over the target frames. When the table is set rotating at a relatively low angular speed, the trigger B is depressed, firing the small wood or aluminum pro-

jectile. When the table is stopped, the gun muzzle and the holes in the paper targets clearly indicate the curved path.

From measured distances and the angular velocity ω, the projectile velocity can be calculated from the coriolis acceleration.

$$a_c = 2v\omega \qquad (14m)$$
coriolis acceleration

PROBLEMS

1. A weight of 2 lb is whirled at 90 rpm in a horizontal circle at the end of a string 5 ft long. Taking gravity into account, find the tension in the string.

2. A 4000-lb car going 60 mi/hr rounds a curve of 800-ft radius. What is (a) the angular speed in rad/sec, (b) the centripetal acceleration, and (c) the centripetal force? (*Ans.* (a) 0.110 rad/sec, (b) 9.68 ft/sec², (c) 1210 lb.)

3. A locomotive weighing 45 tons is traveling at 60 mi/hr. Find the centrifugal force exerted by the wheels on the rails when it is rounding a curve of 900-ft radius. Assume that the road is not banked.

4. A 200-lb pilot is flying at 480 mi/hr when he pulls out of a dive. (a) What is the minimum radius allowed if his centripetal acceleration is not to exceed 6 times the acceleration of gravity, i.e., not to exceed 6g? (b) What is the total upward force on his body when he is at the lowest point in the dive? (*Ans.* (a) 2580 ft, (b) 1400 lb.)

5. A motorcycle and rider traveling 75 Km/hr round a curve of 100 m radius. At what angle will they lean from the vertical?

6. A man living at the equator accurately weighs himself and finds that he weighs 160.0 lb. What correction must be made for the earth's rotation? (*Ans.* +0.56 lb.)

7. A boy sits on the floor of a merry-go-round 20 ft from the center. If the coefficient of static friction is 0.5, at what angular speed will he start to slide?

8. What is the highest speed at which an automobile weighing 4200 lb can travel without skidding around a curve of 240-ft radius? Assume the roadway to be level and the coefficient of friction between tires and pavement to be 0.70. (*Ans.* 50.0 mi/hr.)

9. A 5-lb lead weight is whirled in a circle at the end of a wire 8 ft long. If the weight makes 90 rpm, find (a) the angular velocity, (b) the angle turned through in 5 sec, (c) the acceleration toward the center, and (d) the centripetal force in lb. Neglect gravity.

10. A mass of 5 Kg on the end of a wire 150 cm long is whirled in a circle at 240 rpm. Find (a) the acceleration toward the center, and (b) the centripetal force. Neglect gravity. (*Ans.* (a) 945 m/sec², (b) 4725 newtons.)

11. A merry-go-round 60 ft in diameter is rotating with an angular speed of 5 rpm. What will be (a) the speed, (b) the centripetal acceleration, and (c) the centripetal force of a person weighing 160 lb if he stands at the edge?

12. A 500-gm stone is whirled at 60 rpm in a circle at the end of a cord 60 cm long. If the plane of the circle is vertical, what is the tension in the string at (a) the top, and (b) the bottom of the circle? (*Ans.* (a) 6.9 newtons, (b) 16.7 newtons.)

13. How high above the level of the top of the circle of a loop-the-loop must a small car start in order to attain just enough speed to carry it around? Assume a radius of 20 ft.

14. A stone attached to a wire 1 m long travels in a horizontal circle, the wire describing the surface of a cone. Find the angular speed in rpm at which the wire will stand out at an angle of 60° with the vertical. (*Ans.* 42.3 rpm.)

15. Two 6-Kg masses are fastened to the ends of a steel wire 1 m long, and the system thrown whirling into the air at 120 rpm. Find the tension in the wire.

16. Two 8-lb weights are fastened to the ends of a steel wire 4 ft long, and the system thrown whirling into the air at 600 rpm. Find the tension in the wire. (*Ans.* 1972 lb.)

17. A car weighing 3000 lb and going 45 mi/hr rounds a curve of 500-ft radius. At what angle should the road be banked in order that there be no tendency to slip?

18. A curve in the road has a radius of 600 ft, and the road is banked at an angle of 15°. At what speed around this curve should a car travel without any tendency to skid? (*Ans.* 48.9 mi/hr.)

19. A pail held at arm's length is swung overhead in a circle of 1-m radius. What is the minimum angular velocity ω at the top to assure that no water spills out?

20. A chain of 125 links is 120 cm long and has a mass of 2 Kg. With the ends fastened together, it is set rotating at 3000 rpm. Find the centripetal force on each link. (*Ans.* 302 newtons.)

21. A merry-go-round is rotating with an angular velocity of 5 rpm. A 2-Kg ball starts rolling radially outward with a velocity of 4 m/sec. Calculate (a) the coriolis acceleration, (b) the coriolis force, and (c) the average radius of its path on the floor.

22. A small spring gun, as shown in Fig. 14K, fires a 100-gm projectile with a velocity of 15 m/sec. If the table turns at 3 rps, find (a) the coriolis acceleration, (b) the coriolis force, and (c) the average radius of the deflected path. (*Ans.* (a) 565 m/sec², (b) 56.5 newtons, (c) 0.398 m.)

23. A bicycle and rider must lean over at an angle of 20° to the vertical as they round a curve of 200-ft radius. What is their speed?

24. A pail is held at arm's length and is swung overhead in a circle of 3-ft radius. What is the minimum angular velocity it can have at the top of its swing to assure that no water spills out? (*Ans.* 3.26 rad/sec.)

25. A curve in the road has a radius of 500 ft, and the road is banked at an angle of 20°. At what speed (in ft/sec) around this curve should a car travel without any tendency to skid?

26. A stone attached to a wire 1 m long travels in a horizontal circle, the wire describing the surface of a cone. Find the angular speed in rps at which the wire will stand out at an angle of 70° with the vertical. (*Ans.* .893 rps.)

Chapter 15

Work, Energy, and Power

There is little doubt that the most important concept in all nature is energy. It is important because it represents a fundamental entity common to all forms of matter in all parts of the known physical world. Closely associated with energy is another concept, *work,* a term used in civil life to describe the expenditure of one's stored-up bodily energy. Because energy is most easily described in terms of work, this latter concept will first be treated in detail.

15.1. Work. In its simplest mechanical form, *work* is defined as *the force times the distance* through which the force acts.

work = force × distance

Algebraically, we write

$$\boxed{\text{work} = F \times s} \qquad (15a)$$

Consider the general problem of calculating the work done in lifting a mass m to a height s above the ground. See Fig. 15A. By Newton's second law of motion ($F = ma$) the force required to lift any mass m is equal to its own weight.

$$W = mg$$

If we substitute the weight mg for F in Eq.(15a),

$$\text{work done} = mg \times s \qquad (15b)$$

To give numerical values assume that a mass of 5 Kg is lifted vertically a distance of 2 m. By direct substitution in Eq.(15b),

$$\text{work} = 5\,\text{Kg} \times 9.8\,\frac{\text{m}}{\text{sec}^2} \times 2\,\text{m} = 98\,\frac{\text{Kg m}^2}{\text{sec}^2}$$

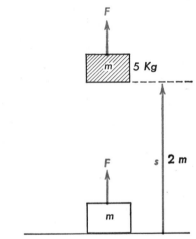

Fig. 15A *Work is defined as force × distance.*

Since *force,* in *newtons,* has the units Kg m/sec², the answer can also be written

$$\text{work} = 98\,\text{newton meters}$$

Work in the *mks* system is seen to have the absolute units Kg m²/sec², which are equal to the derived units, *newton meters.* In the *cgs* system, the corresponding absolute units are gm cm²/sec², which are equal to the derived units *dyne centimeters.* In the English, or engineering system, the units of work are *foot-pounds,* abbreviated ft-lb.

Example 1. Find the work done in lifting a weight of 5 lb to a height of 10 ft.

Solution. By direct substitution in Eq.(15a), we obtain

$$\text{work} = 5\,\text{lb} \times 10\,\text{ft} = 50\,\text{ft-lb}$$

15.2. Ergs and Joules. In the *cgs* system, the *dyne cm* as a unit of work is called the *erg*.

$$1 \text{ dyne cm} = 1 \text{ erg} \qquad (15c)$$

A force of 1 dyne acting through a distance of 1 cm in the same direction does 1 erg of work.

In the *mks* system of units, a force of 1 *newton* acting through a distance of 1 m in the same direction performs an amount of work equivalent to *1 joule*.

$$\boxed{1 \text{ newton meter} = 1 \text{ joule}} \qquad (15d)$$

Since the *newton* as a unit of force = 1 Kg × 1 m/sec² = 1000 gm × 100 cm/sec² = 10^5 dynes, the *newton meter* = 10^5 dynes × 100 cm = 10^7 dyne cm. In other words,

$$1 \text{ joule} = 10^7 \text{ ergs} \qquad (15e)$$

The *joule* as a unit of work is, therefore, much larger than the *erg* and in many practical problems is to be preferred, because of the smaller numbers involved in calculations.

Example 2. Calculate the work done in lifting a mass of 400 gm to a height of 250 cm.

Solution. The known quantities are $m = 400$ gm, $s = 250$ cm, and $g = 980$ cm/sec². Substitution in Eq.(15b) gives

$$\text{work} = 400 \text{ gm} \times 980 \frac{\text{cm}}{\text{sec}^2} \times 250 \text{ cm}$$

$$= 98{,}000{,}000 \frac{\text{gm cm}^2}{\text{sec}^2}$$

$$\text{work} = 98{,}000{,}000 \text{ ergs} \qquad (15f)$$

15.3. Work Done Against Friction. In sliding a mass of 5 Kg along a horizontal plane a distance of 2 m (see Fig. 15B) the work done *will not* in general be as great as that required to lift the same mass 2 m vertically.

Suppose, for example, that the coefficient of sliding friction for the block in the diagram is $\mu = 0.2$. By calculation then, the force of friction is (see Eq.(11f))

$$f = \mu N = 0.2 \times 5 \text{ Kg} \times 9.8 \text{ m/sec}^2$$
$$= 9.8 \text{ newtons}$$

Since a force of 9.8 newtons will slide the block, the work done, by Eq.(15b) will be

$$\text{work} = 9.8 \text{ newtons} \times 2 \text{ m}$$
$$= 19.6 \text{ newton meters}$$

This is only one-fifth as much work as that required to lift the same 5Kg mass an equal vertical distance of 2 m. (See Fig. 15A.) By reducing the friction between the block and the plane, the force F can be reduced still further. Such a reduction can be accomplished by smoothing and lubricating the sliding surfaces, or better by mounting the block on wheels. Could the friction be eliminated entirely, the work done in moving any object in a horizontal direction would be practically zero, for once started it would continue moving with constant velocity. A vertical lift, however, requires at least an amount of work equal to the weight mg times the height s.

When a force acting on an object is applied at an angle with the direction of motion, only the component of the force in the direction of motion is effective in doing work. This is illustrated in Fig. 15C where a force of 1000 dynes applied at an angle

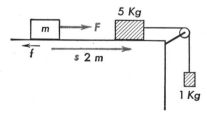

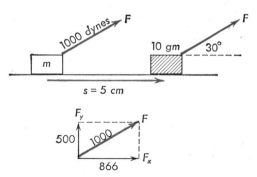

Fig. 15B *To slide a body horizontally, work must be done against friction.*

Fig. 15C *Force and distance are measured in the same direction in calculating work.*

of 30° moves a 10-gm mass a distance of 5 cm. In the right-hand diagram, F is resolved into two components, F_x horizontally and F_y vertically.

By calculation or by graphical construction,

$$F_x = F \cos 30° = 1000 \times 0.866 = 866 \text{ dynes}$$
$$F_y = F \sin 30° = 1000 \times 0.500 = 500 \text{ dynes}$$

The vertical force of 500 dynes, being perpendicular to the direction of motion, does no work since the distance moved upward is zero. Work is done only by the horizontal force F_x.

work = 866 dynes $\times$ 5 cm = 4330 ergs

While the vertical force does not enter directly into the calculation of work, it does help to lift the body and thereby reduce the friction between the sliding surfaces. As an illustration, consider the following problem.

Example 3. A trunk having a mass of 100 Kg is pulled 20 m across the floor by a rope making an angle of 35° with the horizontal. (See Fig. 15D.) If the coefficient of sliding friction is 0.25,

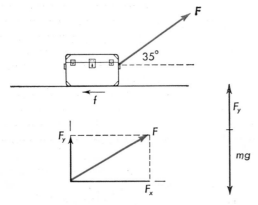

Fig. 15D *Work is done in sliding a trunk along the floor.*

find (a) the tension in the rope, and (b) the work done.

Solution. The force F is resolved into two components,

$$F_x = F \cos 35° = 0.819 \, F$$
$$F_y = F \sin 35° = 0.574 \, F$$

To find the horizontal force of friction ($f =$

μN), the normal force N is calculated as the resultant of two forces acting on the block; mg downward due to gravity and F_y upward due to the pull of the rope.

Therefore,

$$N = mg - F_y$$

and the force of friction is

$$f = \mu N = 0.25 \, (mg - F_y)$$

To overcome friction and slide the body, the component F_x must be at least equal to f. Set $f = F_x$,

$$F_x = 0.25 \, (mg - F_y)$$

Substitute for F_x and F_y from the above relations, and multiply out,

$$0.819 \, F = 0.25 \, mg - 0.25 \times 0.574 \, F$$

Collect factors containing F, on the left, and substitute for m and g,

$$0.962 \, F = 0.25 \times 100 \text{ Kg} \times 9.8 \, \frac{\text{m}}{\text{sec}^2}$$

Therefore

(a) $F = 255$ newtons

By Eq.(15a) the work done is $F_x \times s$,

work = 0.819×255 newtons $\times$ 20 m
(b)   work = 4177 joules

15.4. Work in the Engineering System of Units.
Because it is customary in engineering design and construction to measure loads and forces in pounds, it is proper to calculate work in *foot-pounds, i.e., force in pounds $\times$ distance in feet.* As an illustration consider the following problem.

Example 4. When loaded, the small car of a hoist weighs 240 lb. How much work is done in lifting this load 35 ft?
Solution. By Eq.(15a),

work = $F \times s$ = 240 lb $\times$ 35 ft = 8400 ft-lb

15.5. Potential Energy.
Mechanical energy is divided into two categories, *potential energy* and *kinetic energy. A body is said to have potential energy if by virtue of its position or state it is able to do work.* A car at the top of a hill or a wound clock spring is an example of an object with potential energy. The clock spring may keep a clock running for a certain length of time, and a car may, by coasting downhill, travel

a great distance. Potential energy is measured by the amount of work that is available. It is therefore measured in *ergs, joules,* or *foot-pounds.*

If a given mass m is raised to a specified height s, as illustrated in Fig. 15E, it then

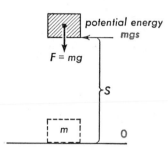

Fig. 15E *A body has potential energy by virtue of its position.*

has potential energy $F \times s$ by virtue of its position above the ground level from which it has been lifted. The *work done* in lifting it has been stored up as potential energy in the block. This energy can be regained by dropping the mass back to the ground, for in so doing it can be made to perform some kind of work. By definition,

$$\text{potential energy} = F \times s \qquad (15g)$$

or, in absolute units,

$$\boxed{\text{potential energy} = mg \times s}$$

Example 5. A mass of 5 Kg is raised to a height of 2.5 m above the ground. Calculate its potential energy.

Solution. If we substitute the known quantities in Eq.(15g),

$$\text{P.E.} = 5 \text{ Kg} \times 9.8 \frac{\text{m}}{\text{sec}^3} \times 2.5 \text{ m} = 122.5 \text{ joules}$$

If a body is lifted straight upward, carried up a staircase, or pulled up an inclined plane, the potential energy acquired is given by the *weight × vertical height* to which it is raised.

The meaning of positive, zero, or negative potential energy is illustrated in Fig. 15F. Located at any point above the *base plane* a body has positive potential energy, while at points below that line it has nega-

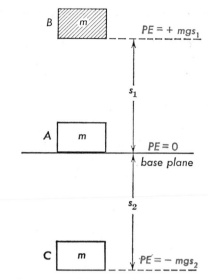

Fig. 15F *Potential energy with respect to a base plane may be plus or minus.*

tive potential energy. To lift the mass m from A to B, work is done, and the mass acquires a potential energy to the amount of mgs_1.

In returning from B to A, the mass loses potential energy, performing *work* $= mgs_1$ on some other body. Similarly, in going from A to C, the body loses energy and ends up at C with mgs_2 less energy than it had at A. To raise it again to A, an equivalent amount of work mgs_2 will have to be done on the body.

The choosing of a *base plane* as a zero energy level is a purely arbitrary selection. In most practical applications it is customary to select the lowest point to be reached by a body as the zero level, so that all displacements from there will be positive in sign. In the engineering system of units, *potential energy,* like *work,* can be expressed in foot-pounds, i.e., *pounds × vertical distance in feet.*

When a force is applied to a body to slide or roll it along the ground, the *work done* is not stored up as potential energy. Because of friction, the energy is transformed into heat, and as a practical matter is considered lost for further use. If the body ends up at the same level at which it started, all of the energy has gone into heat and the potential energy remains un-changed.

If a body is pulled up an inclined plane, on the other hand, part of the energy goes into heat and part into potential energy. The potential energy as illustrated in Fig. 15G is given by mgh, while the work done

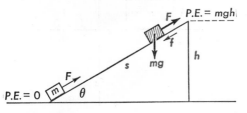

Fig. 15G *Part of the work done in sliding a mass up an incline goes into friction, and part into potential energy.*

is given by $F \times s$ and the frictional energy by $f \times s$.

$$F \times s = f \times s + mgh$$

work done = frictional energy
+ potential energy

15.6. Kinetic Energy. The kinetic energy of a moving body is defined as its ability to do work by virtue of its motion. A car moving along the highway has kinetic energy of translation, and a rotating wheel on a machine has kinetic energy of rotation. For a given mass m, moving in a straight line with constant velocity v, the kinetic energy is given by

$$\boxed{\text{kinetic energy} = \tfrac{1}{2}mv^2} \qquad (15\text{h})$$

Example 6. Calculate the kinetic energy of a 20-kg mass, moving with a velocity of 4 m/sec. *Solution.* By direct substitution in Eq.(15h),

$$\text{K.E.} = \frac{1}{2} \times 20 \text{ Kg} \times \left(4 \frac{\text{m}}{\text{sec}}\right)^2 = 160 \frac{\text{Kg m}^2}{\text{sec}^2}$$

This answer has exactly the dimensions of *work*, and *potential energy,* and can be written in the same derived units.

$$\text{K.E.} = 160 \text{ joules}$$

A moving body has energy, because in being brought to rest it must exert a force F on some other object, and this force act-

ing through a distance s does work. In other words, work can be done by a moving body. Conversely, by applying a constant horizontal force F on a body of mass m for a distance s, it will be given a kinetic energy $\tfrac{1}{2}mv^2$. See Fig. 15H.

$$F \times s = \tfrac{1}{2}mv^2 \qquad (15\text{i})$$

The above equation is known as the "work equation." In it, friction is entirely

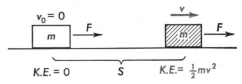

Fig. 15H *A body has kinetic energy by virtue of its motion.*

neglected and the body is presumed to start from rest. To derive Eq.(15i) from previous principles, Newton's second law of motion will serve as a starting point.

$$F = ma$$

Upon multiplying both sides of the equation by s,

$$F \times s = mas \qquad (15\text{j})$$

For the product as on the right, Eq.(4h) is used. The equation $v^2 - v_0^2 = 2as$ is transformed to give

$$as = \frac{v^2 - v_0^2}{2}$$

which, substituted in Eq.(15j), gives

$$F \times s = m\frac{v^2 - v_0^2}{2}$$

Then,

$$F \times s = \tfrac{1}{2}mv^2 - \tfrac{1}{2}mv_0^2 \qquad (15\text{k})$$

In the special case that a body starts from rest, $v_0 = 0$, the last term drops out and the equation becomes Eq.(15i).

Example 7. A constant horizontal force of 25 lb acts for a distance of 20 ft on a 500-lb box. If friction is neglected and the box starts from rest, what is its velocity? *Solution.* The known quantities are $v_0 = 0$, $m = 500$ lb/32 ft/sec², $s = 20$ ft, and $F = 25$ lb.

The special Eq.(15i) may, therefore, be applied. Transpose all but v^2 to one side of the equation.

$$v^2 = \frac{2(F \times s)}{m} = \frac{2(25 \text{ lb} \times 20 \text{ ft})}{500 \text{ lb}/32 \text{ ft/sec}^2}$$

$$v^2 = 64 \text{ ft}^2/\text{sec}^2 \quad \text{and} \quad v = 8 \frac{\text{ft}}{\text{sec}}$$

Note that in solving this problem the mass m must be in slugs, i.e., pounds weight divided by g in ft/sec^2.

15.7. Power. Power is defined as the rate of doing work or the rate at which work is being done.

$$\text{Power} = \frac{\text{work}}{\text{time}} \tag{15l}$$

$$\boxed{P = \frac{F \times s}{t}} \tag{15m}$$

The faster a given amount of work is done, the greater is the power. In other words, the smaller the time t in the above equation, the greater is the fraction $F \times s/t$ and the power P.

In the metric system, with work measured in *ergs* or *joules,* power is expressed either in *ergs per second* or in *joules per second.*

One joule per second is called the *watt,* a unit of power.

$$\boxed{1 \text{ joule/sec} = 1 \text{ watt}} \tag{15n}$$

The *kilowatt* is another unit of power and is equal to *1000 watts.*

In the engineering system, with work measured in foot-pounds, power is expressed in foot-pounds per second, and in horsepower (*abbr.* hp).

$$1 \text{ hp} = 550 \text{ ft-lb/sec} \tag{15o}$$

Example 8. Find the power of an engine capable of lifting 200 lb to a height of 55 ft in 10 sec.

Solution. By Eq.(15m),

$$P = \frac{200 \text{ lb} \times 55 \text{ ft}}{10 \text{ sec}} = 1100 \frac{\text{ft-lb}}{\text{sec}}$$

Divide this answer by 550 to get the horsepower,

$$\frac{1100}{550} = 2 \text{ hp}$$

If 550 ft-lb/sec is changed to the metric system (1 ft = 0.305 m, and 1 lb = 4.45 newtons),

$$1 \text{ hp} = 746 \frac{\text{joules}}{\text{sec}} = 746 \text{ watts} \tag{15p}$$

PROBLEMS

1. How much work is done in lifting a 25-Kg mass a vertical distance of 6.4 m?

2. How much work is required to lift a 255-lb engine to a height of 6 ft? (*Ans.* 1350 ft-lb.)

3. A small car of mass 500 Kg climbs to a height of 2000 m. Find the potential energy in joules.

4. A 10,000-Kg locomotive climbs a mountain grade, reaching a height of 500 m. Find the potential energy stored. (*Ans.* 4.9×10^7 joules.)

5. A 2000-Kg car moves along a straight and level road at 60 Km/hr. Find its kinetic energy.

6. A 3200-lb car travels along a straight road at 60 mi/hr. What is its kinetic energy? (*Ans.* 387,000 ft-lb.)

7. A 2000-Kg rocket takes off from its launching pad and acquires a vertical velocity of 70 m/sec at an altitude of 1800 m. Calculate (a)

its potential energy, (b) its kinetic energy, and (c) its total energy.

8. From what height must a 2000-lb boulder fall in order to have the same amount of kinetic energy as an 8-ton truck traveling with a speed of 60 mi/hr along a level road? (*Ans.* 968 ft.)

9. A fallen tree weighing 6 tons is pulled through the forest by a tractor for a distance of 500 ft. If the tow cable makes an angle of 20° with the horizontal, and the coefficient of sliding friction is 0.65, what is (a) the tension in the cable, and (b) the work done?

10. A metal box weighing 250 lb is pulled 16 ft up an oak plank inclined 20° with the horizontal. If the coefficient of friction is 0.25, find (a) the force applied parallel to the plank, (b) the work done, and (c) the potential energy at the top. (*Ans.* (a) 144.2 lb, (b) 2307 ft-lb, (c) 1370 ft-lb.)

11. An elevator car with 6 passengers weighs 1400 lb. (a) Calculate the power required to raise this car 4 ft/sec. (b) If the car's weight of 600 lb is counterbalanced by weights, what power is required?

12. An airplane weighing 50,000 lb climbs to a height of 1 mi in 5 min. Calculate the accomplished power in horsepower. (*Ans.* 1600 hp.)

13. The hopper of a concrete hoist weighs 750 lb when half loaded. If this hopper is raised 165 ft in 6 sec, find the power required in (a) ft-lb/sec, (b) horsepower, and (c) watts.

14. A mass of 200 Kg initially at rest is given a speed of 30 m/sec by a force of 500 newtons. Calculate (a) the distance over which the force acts, and (b) the kinetic energy in joules. (*Ans.* (a) 180 m, (b) 90,000 joules.)

15. A car weighing 3900 lb climbs to the top of a hill 500 ft high in 1 min. Neglecting friction, calculate (a) the potential energy stored up in ft-lb, and (b) the power of the car in horsepower.

16. A car weighing 4200 lb increases its speed from 30 to 60 mi/hr in 5 sec. (a) What is the change in kinetic energy, and (b) the power developed? (*Ans.* (a) 3.81×10^5 ft-lb, (b) 138 hp.)

17. An automobile weighing 3200 lb, and moving with a speed of 45 mi/hr, is brought to rest in 132 ft. Find (a) the time required to stop, (b) the acceleration, and (c) the power expended in the brakes.

18. How heavy a load can a 20-hp hoist lift at a steady speed of 168 ft/min without exceeding its rated output? (*Ans.* approx. 3928 lb.)

19. Find the power developed in a steam engine in which the steam exerts a force of 8000 lb on a piston and moves it forward and backward 120 times per min through a distance of 1 ft each way.

20. Water is pumped from a river into a reservoir, a total lift of 120 m, at a rate of 10 m³/hr. What is the minimum power required? One cubic meter of water weighs 1000 Kg. (*Ans.* 3.26 kw.)

21. A ski lift employs a 30-kw motor to keep the tow rope in motion. If the mass of the average person is 70 Kg, and the lift carries the skiers to an elevation 200 m above the base in 1 min, what is the maximum number of people that can be allowed on the lift at the same time?

22. An escalator carries persons from one floor to another 20 ft higher, and the steps move with a speed of 90 ft/min along the incline. The steps are 8 in. high and measure 18 in. from edge to edge along the incline. What size motor is needed to take care of an over-all load of 120 lb per step? (*Ans.* 4.36 hp.)

23. A funicular railway, in which the ascending car and descending car counterbalance each other, lifts 10 passengers whose average mass is 70 Kg a total height of 500 m in 10 min. What is the minimum power required if there are no passengers in the descending car?

24. A 10,000-Kg rocket takes off vertically from its launching pad and acquires a velocity of 100 m/sec at an altitude of 2000 m. Assuming the acceleration due to gravity to be constant at 9.8 m/sec², find (a) its potential energy, and (b) its kinetic energy. Assuming constant upward acceleration, find (c) the acceleration, (d) the total upward thrust of the motors, and (e) the power developed. (*Ans.* (a) 1.96×10^8 joules, (b) 5×10^7 joules, (c) 2.5 m/sec², (d) 123,000 newtons, (e) 6.15×10^3 kw.)

25. A 60,000-Kg jet plane is making 300 m/sec at an altitude of 10,000 m. Calculate its total energy.

26. A horizontal catapult 300 ft long launches a 32-ton reconnaissance plane from the deck of an aircraft carrier. If, starting from rest at one end, the plane acquires a take-off speed of 300 ft/sec at the other, find (a) the acceleration, (b) the average force, (c) the work done in ft-lb, and (d) the power developed, in ft-lb/sec. (*Ans.* (a) 150 ft/sec², (b) 3×10^5 lb, (c) 9×10^7 ft-lb, (d) 4.5×10^7 ft-lb/sec.)

27. A 30,000-Kg plane, starting from a standstill at the end of a runway, acquires a speed of 40 m/sec in a distance of 200 meters. Assuming uniform acceleration, find (a) the acceleration, (b) the force, (c) the final kinetic energy, and (d) the power developed. (*Ans.* (a) 4 m/sec², (b) 1.2×10^5 newtons, (c) 2.4×10^7 joules, (d) 2.4×10^6 watts.)

Chapter 16

Conservation of Energy and Momentum

16.1. Conservation of Energy. Most important of all the laws of nature is the law of the conservation of energy. Although the law has been stated in almost as many different ways as there are books written on the subject, they all have in reality the same meaning. The following three examples are typical statements:

(1) *In transforming energy from one form to another, energy is always conserved.*
(2) *Energy is never created or destroyed.*
(3) *The sum total of all energy in the universe remains constant.*

Everyone should be aware of the fact that there are many forms of energy. The most important forms are:

FORMS OF ENERGY

Mechanical	*Light*
Electrical	*Atomic*
Chemical	*Molecular*
Heat	*Nuclear*

In this chapter we are concerned with the law of conservation of energy only as it applies to the two forms of mechanical energy, *potential* and *kinetic*. The law will again be encountered in connection with the other forms in the chapters on heat, electricity, and atomic structure.

As an illustration of the transformation of one form of mechanical energy into another, consider the demonstration experiment shown in Fig. 16A.

Water in a tank escapes through an outlet pipe and falls on the blades of a paddle wheel. The water in the tank has potential energy *mgs*. As it falls with ever-increasing speed, that energy is converted into kinetic energy $\frac{1}{2}mv^2$. In turning the paddle wheel this energy of motion can be utilized to do mechanical work of one kind or another. On the other hand, it might well be made to turn an electric generator and convert mechanical energy into electrical energy. The electrical generator in turn can be connected to a toaster and convert electrical energy into heat, etc.

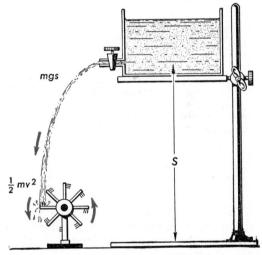

Fig. 16A *Demonstration of energy transformation.*

Consider the energy involved in a waterfall as shown in Fig. 16B. The water at the top of the fall has potential energy by virtue of its position above the base. As it falls over and then downward with ever-increasing speed, the kinetic energy $\frac{1}{2}mv^2$ increases, while the potential energy decreases. At the

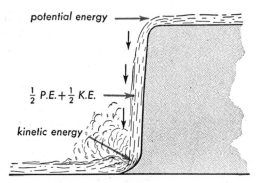

potential energy

$\frac{1}{2}$ P.E.$+\frac{1}{2}$ K.E.

kinetic energy

Fig. 16B *All the available energy at the top of a waterfall is potential. At the bottom it is kinetic.*

bottom of the fall, the potential energy approaches zero and the kinetic energy approaches its maximum value. At the top, the energy was practically all potential, while near the bottom it is mostly kinetic. Assuming the water to start from rest at the top and that no energy is lost in falling, the P.E. at the top of the falls equals the K.E. at the bottom.

$$(\text{P.E. at top}) = (\text{K.E. at bottom})$$

or
$$F \times s = \tfrac{1}{2}mv^2 \qquad (16a)$$

$$mgs = \tfrac{1}{2}mv^2 \qquad (16b)$$

Divide both sides of the equation by m and solve for v.

$$v^2 = 2gs$$

or
$$v = \sqrt{2gs} \qquad (16c)$$

This is the special Eq.(5h) derived for falling bodies in one of the preceding chapters from the laws of accelerated motion. Here the equation has been derived from the law of conservation of energy.

Example 1. A mass of 25 Kg is dropped from a height of 5 m. Find the kinetic energy and velocity just as it reaches the ground.

Solution. Since the P.E. at the top is equivalent to the K.E. at the bottom,

$$\text{P.E.} = 25 \,\text{Kg} \times 9.8 \,\frac{\text{m}}{\text{sec}^2} \times 5 \,\text{m}$$

$$= 1225 \,\text{joules} = \text{K.E.}$$

The velocity is found by Eq.(16c),

$$v = \sqrt{2 \times 9.8 \times 5} = 9.9 \,\text{m/sec}$$

When the falling body in the above problem is part way down, it has some P.E. and some K.E. Its total energy E is therefore of two kinds, *Total Energy*

$$E = \tfrac{1}{2}mv^2 + mgs \qquad (16d)$$

At the instant the body reaches the ground, it is suddenly stopped and all of the energy is quickly transformed into heat. The transformation of mechanical energy into heat is often demonstrated in the physics laboratory by an experiment in which a quantity of lead-shot is dropped from a height of several feet and its temperature measured before and after falling. By raising the shot and dropping it many times, the rise in temperature amounts to several degrees. (See page 239.)

16.2. The Inclined Plane. It can be shown that a body sliding without friction down an incline of height h should acquire at the bottom a velocity $v = \sqrt{2gh}$. This equation is readily derived from the law of conservation of energy.

Consider the demonstration experiment shown in Fig. 16C in which a small truck is

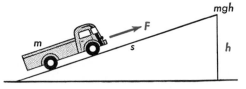

Fig. 16C *Conservation of energy.*

pulled up an incline. The work done to reach the top is given by the product of force F times the distance s. By conservation of energy, this must be equal to the stored-up potential energy mgh at the top. Therefore

$$F \times s = mgh \qquad (16e)$$

Now, if the truck is released, it will accelerate back down the incline, thereby converting the potential energy mgh into kinetic energy $\frac{1}{2}mv^2$. By conservation of energy we can write

total E at top = total E at bottom
P.E. + K.E. = P.E. + K.E.
$$mgh + 0 = 0 + \tfrac{1}{2}mv^2$$
$$mgh = \tfrac{1}{2}mv^2$$

Since the m on both sides refers to the same mass, we can divide by m and obtain

$$gh = \tfrac{1}{2}v^2, \qquad v = \sqrt{2gh} \qquad (16f)$$

When sliding friction is taken into account, the equation above must include an additional term. At the top of the incline the total energy E is all potential and $E = mgh$. In sliding down, part of this available energy, to the amount of $f \times s$, is used up in overcoming friction, and the rest goes into kinetic energy, $\frac{1}{2}mv^2$. By conservation of energy,

P.E. at top = frictional energy
+ K.E. at bottom
$$mgh = f \times s + \tfrac{1}{2}mv^2$$

In applying this formula to the solving of problems, the force of friction, $f = \mu N$, is found in the usual way by resolving the weight mg into components.

16.3. The Simple Pendulum. A similar energy treatment can be given for the swinging of a simple pendulum. At the extreme ends of each swing (see Fig. 16D) the bob comes momentarily to rest, and the energy E is all potential and equal to mgh. At the bottom of the swing the energy E is all kinetic and equal to $\frac{1}{2}mv^2$.

The motion of the pendulum bob is like that of a body sliding, without friction, down an inclined plane of changing angle. The kinetic energy acquired in going down one side is just sufficient to carry it up to an equal height on the other.

16.4. Conservation of Momentum. When two or more bodies collide, momentum is conserved. The law of conservation of momentum applies to all collision phenomena and states:

The total momentum before impact equals the total momentum after impact.

Consider as an example the "head-on" encounter of two balls as shown in Fig. 16E.

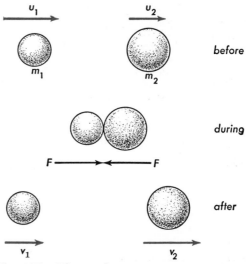

Fig. 16E *The total momentum of two bodies before impact is equal to the total momentum after impact.*

Before impact the mass m_1 is moving with a velocity u_1 and has a momentum $m_1 u_1$, while m_2 is moving with a velocity u_2 and has a momentum $m_2 u_2$. The total momentum before impact is therefore equal to the sum of the two momenta, $m_1 u_1 + m_2 u_2$.

By similar reasoning it is clear that after impact, m_1 and m_2, with their new veloci-

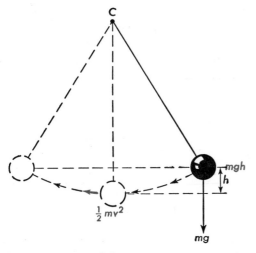

Fig. 16D *Potential energy of a pendulum changes to kinetic energy and back again.*

ties v_1 and v_2 have a total momentum $m_1v_1 + m_2v_2$. The law of conservation of momentum requires that

$$m_1u_1 + m_2u_2 = m_1v_1 + m_2v_2 \qquad (16g)$$

$$\frac{total\ momentum}{before\ impact} = \frac{total\ momentum}{after\ impact}$$

During impact, two equal but opposite forces are set up between the bodies, one the force exerted by m_1 on m_2, and the other the force exerted by m_2 on m_1. These two equal but opposite forces are an action and reaction pair explained by Newton's third law of motion. Each force acts for the same short interval of time, giving equal impulses Ft to both bodies. By Newton's second law, as expressed by the impulse equation $Ft = mv - mv_0$, equal impulses produce equal changes in momentum. One body gains as much momentum as the other loses. In other words, the total momentum remains constant.

Example 2. An ivory ball of mass 5 gm, moving with a velocity of 20 cm/sec, collides with another ivory ball of mass 10 gm moving in the same direction along the same line with a velocity of 10 cm/sec. After impact the first mass is still moving in the same direction but with a velocity of only 8 cm/sec. Calculate the velocity of the second mass after impact. Apply Eq.(16g).
Solution. By direct substitution in Eq.(16g),

$$(5 \times 20) + (10 \times 10) = (5 \times 8) + (10 \times v_2)$$
$$200 = 40 + 10v_2$$
$$10v_2 = 160 \qquad v_2 = 16\ cm/sec$$

After impact, the second mass has a velocity of 16 cm/sec.

If, in the above example, the total kinetic energy after impact is calculated and compared with the total kinetic energy before impact, the two will not be found equal. Employing the equation K.E. $= \frac{1}{2}mv^2$, we obtain

K.E. $= \frac{1}{2}(5 \times 20^2) + \frac{1}{2}(10 \times 10^2)$
$\qquad\qquad = 1500$ ergs, before impact
K.E. $= \frac{1}{2}(5 \times 8^2) + \frac{1}{2}(10 \times 16^2)$
$\qquad\qquad = 1440$ ergs, after impact

The difference in energy, to the amount of 60 ergs, has disappeared as mechanical energy and gone into heat. During impact,

both masses were slightly deformed in shape due to the mutually acting forces and a small amount of heat was generated internally. This heat raised the temperature of the two colliding bodies. It is only by including this heat energy of 60 ergs with the mechanical energy after impact that makes it possible to retain the law of conservation of energy.

This is just another way of stating that collisions in general are not perfectly elastic. If they were perfectly elastic, conservation of mechanical energy would hold, as well as conservation of momentum. Perfectly elastic collisions are known to occur between the *ultramicroscopic* atoms and molecules of a gas but not with the *macroscopic* bodies encountered in everyday life. The more inelastic the colliding bodies, the more energy is transformed into heat. A treatment of elasticity and its application to collision problems will be given in Chap. 23.

It is important to note from the discussion above that, *for all impact problems whether perfectly elastic or not, the law of conservation of momentum should be applied.*

16.5. The More General Problem of Impact. In general, the impact between two bodies is not a head-on collision but one in which a moving body collides with another body initially at rest, and the two bodies recoil in different directions from the impact. The diagram in Fig. 16F shows a mass m_1 moving with an initial velocity u_1 and colliding with a mass m_2 initially at rest.

After impact, mass m_1 recoils in a direc-

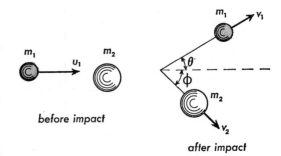

before impact

after impact

Fig. 16F   *Diagram of the impact between two bodies in which the collision is not head-on.*

tion θ with a veloicty v_1 while mass m_2 recoils in a different direction ϕ with a velocity v_2. Since momentum is a vector quantity, we can draw arrows to represent the momentum of bodies before impact, and after impact (shown in Fig. 16G).

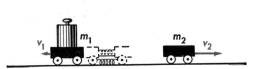

Fig. 16H *Conservation of momentum demonstration experiments.*

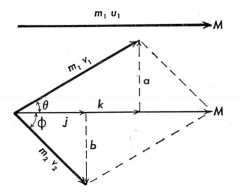

Fig. 16G *Momentum diagram for the impact of two bodies as shown in Fig. 16F.*

Before impact, the total momentum M is that of the moving mass m_1 and is just

$$M = m_1 u_1$$

After impact the total momentum M is the same as before and is composed of two parts as follows: The momentum $m_1 v_1$ is resolved into two components, component a perpendicular to M and component k parallel to M. Similarly, the momentum $m_2 v_2$ is resolved into two components, component b perpendicular to M and component j parallel to M.

By the conservation of momentum, the sum of the vectors j and k must be equal to the initial momentum M.

$$m_1 u_1 = m_1 v_1 \cos \theta + m_2 v_2 \cos \phi \quad (16h)$$

Since the initial momentum $m_1 u_1$ has no component perpendicular to its direction, the two components a and b must be equal in magnitude and opposite in direction.

$$m_1 v_1 \sin \theta = m_2 v_2 \sin \phi \quad (16i)$$

Hence, in any impact between two bodies, one initially at rest, these two equations must hold.

16.6. Experiments. An interesting experi-

ment that illustrates conservation of momentum is shown in Fig. 16H. Two small cars of equal mass, $m_1 = m_2$, are tied together with a compressed spring between them. Then, when the cord is burned with a match, releasing the spring, the two cars fly apart with equal velocities. Before the spring is released, the cars are at rest and the total momentum is zero. After the spring is released the total momentum is still zero because the two velocities are oppositely directed. Momentum being a vector quantity,

$$m_1 v_1 + m_2 v_2 = 0 \quad (16j)$$

With motions to the right taken as positive, v_2 is positive and v_1 negative, and the two momenta cancel.

If the experiment above is repeated with one of the cars heavily loaded as shown in diagram (b), the two fly apart as before but with unequal velocities. The lighter mass moves away with a high velocity while the heavier mass recoils with a low velocity. The product $m_1 \times v_1$, however, is equal in magnitude to the product $m_2 \times v_2$, and the sum of the two momenta is zero.

Example 3. A 60-Kg shell is shot with an initial velocity of 500 m/sec, from a gun having a mass of 2000 Kg. What is the initial velocity with which the gun recoils?

Solution. Applying Eq.(16j), and substituting directly the known quantities, we find

$$60 \text{ Kg} \times 500 \text{ m/sec} + 2000 \text{ Kg} \times v_2 = 0$$
$$30{,}000 \text{ Kg m/sec} + 2000 v_2 \text{ Kg} = 0$$
$$v_2 = \frac{30{,}000 \text{ Kg m/sec}}{-2000 \text{ Kg}} = -15 \text{ m/sec}$$

The gun recoils with a velocity of 15 m/sec. The law of conservation of momentum

Fig. 16I *Experiment with the duckpin balls, illustrating the law of conservation of momentum.*

can be derived from Newton's second law of motion as follows: An unbalanced force F acting on a body for a time t changes the momentum from its initial value mv_0 to a final value mv,

$$Ft = mv - mv_0 \qquad (16k)$$

If to a body, or system of bodies, no external unbalanced forces are applied, $F = 0$, and the impulse $Ft = 0$.

$$0 = mv - mv_0$$
$$\text{or} \qquad mv = mv_0$$

Forces between individual parts of a system of bodies are internal forces and always exist in pairs.

Another interesting experiment illustrating conservation of momentum may be performed with six or seven large balls or small marbles and a grooved board as shown in Fig. 16I. When one ball is rolled up to the others as shown in diagram (a), it will be stopped by collision with the others and the one on the extreme right-hand end will roll out with the same velocity. If two balls are rolled up as indicated in (b), two will roll out on the other end; and if three are rolled up as in (c), three will roll out. (Glass or steel marbles work best in this experiment, as they are highly elastic.)

When the two balls are rolled up, why doesn't just one roll off on the other side with twice the velocity, thus conserving momentum? The answer to this question involves conservation of energy, for if only one came off with twice the velocity, its kinetic energy would be twice the energy available from the original two.

The propelling force of a jet plane or rocket is derived from the principle of momentum. (See Fig 16J.)

As the gases are burned within the combustion chambers of the engine, they exert a large forward force $-F$ on the plane and an equal and opposite force $+F$ on the exhausting gases. As a result of the backward force the gases acquire a very high velocity v and a momentum mv. Flying at constant speed, the forward thrust $-F$ just balances the frictional resistance f of the air. To re-

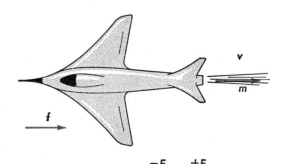

Fig. 16J *Conservation of momentum accounts for the forward thrust on a rocket plane or missile.*

late the thrust with the exhaust gas momentum, we write down the force equation:

$$F = ma$$

For uniformly accelerated motion we also have

$$v = at$$
$$\text{or} \qquad a = v/t$$

Direct substitution in the force equation gives

$$F = m\,\frac{v}{t}$$
$$\text{or} \qquad Ft = mv \qquad (16l)$$

To apply this equation, the *impulse equation,* to the jet or rocket engine, m represents the mass of gas exhausted in any chosen number of seconds t. The impulse $F \times t$ exerted on the gases is just equal and opposite to the impulse $-F \times t$ exerted on the plane.

PROBLEMS

1. Starting from rest, a 50-Kg stone falls 25 m before striking the ground. Find its maximum kinetic energy.

2. A 90-Kg paratrooper delays opening his parachute until he has fallen a distance of 200 m. Find his maximum kinetic energy. (*Ans.* 176,400 joules.)

3. If 15 m³ of water go over a waterfall 30 m high every second of time, find the power expended.

4. If 50 ft³ of water go over a waterfall 100 ft high every second of time, what horsepower is being expended? The weight-density of water is 62.4 lb/ft³. (*Ans.* 567 hp.)

5. A 5-lb stone is dropped from a height of 240 ft above the ground. Find the potential energy and the kinetic energy at a point 50 ft above the ground. Neglect friction.

6. A 5-Kg mass, moving with a constant velocity of 10 m/sec, overtakes and bumps a 2-Kg mass moving in the same direction with a constant velocity of 5 m/sec. If after impact the 2-Kg mass has a velocity of 12 m/sec, calculate (a) the velocity of the other mass, and (b) the energy lost in the form of heat. (*Ans.* (a) 7.2 m/sec (b) 1.4 joules.)

7. A 0.2-lb bullet, moving with a velocity of 2000 ft/sec, passes through a 1-lb ball of putty initially at rest. If the bullet leaves the putty at a velocity of 1400 ft/sec, what is the velocity of the ball of putty?

8. A 6-Kg block of wood hangs as a pendulum by a string 2 m long. When a 10 gm bullet is fired at close range into the block and becomes embedded there, the block swings to a height 20 cm above its rest position. Find (a) the recoil speed of the block, and (b) the muzzle speed of the bullet. (*Ans.* (a) 198 cm/sec, (b) 1190 m/sec.)

9. A 20-gm bullet, fired from a gun with a speed of 600 m/sec, embeds itself in a 980-gm block of wood suspended by a 15-m-long cord. (a) What is the recoil speed of the block, and (b) how high does the block rise?

10. An arrow having a mass of 200 gm is shot straight upward with a speed of 60 m/sec. (a) Calculate its initial kinetic energy. (b) From energy considerations, calculate how high it will rise. (*Ans.* (a) 360 joules, (b) 184 m.)

11. A stone having a mass of 2 Kg is projected straight upward with a speed of 80 m/sec. (a) Calculate its initial kinetic energy. (b) From energy considerations calculate the maximum height reached.

12. A man weighing 200 lb while sitting in a canoe weighing 80 lb fires a 2-oz bullet from a 5 lb gun. If the muzzle speed of the bullet is 2000 ft/sec, with what speed will the canoe recoil? (*Ans.* 0.871 ft/sec.)

13. A 10-lb box slides down an inclined plane 16 ft long and 8 ft high. With what speed will it reach the bottom (a) if the friction is neglected, and (b) if half of the energy is expended in friction?

14. A 600-gm block of wood lying on a fence is hit by a rifle bullet weighing 18 gm. If the bullet enters the block with a velocity of 550 m/sec and leaves the other side with a velocity of 250 m/sec, find (a) the recoil velocity of the block, and (b) the energy lost in the form of heat. (*Ans.* (a) 9 m/sec, (b) 2136 joules.)

15. A 30-gm bullet moving with a velocity of 600 m/sec enters and becomes embedded in a block of wood weighing 3.6 Kg. With what velocity will the block recoil if it was at rest before the impact?

16. A 250-gm ball is thrown upward with a speed of 25 m/sec. Upon returning to the thrower, it has a speed of 20 m/sec. (a) How much energy was lost in overcoming air resistance? (b) If 60% of this energy was lost on the way up, how high did the ball go? (*Ans.* (a) 28.1 joules, (b) 25 m.)

17. A 1200-lb gun is mounted on wheels. It fires a 20-lb shell at an elevation angle of 45°, with a muzzle speed of 1800 ft/sec. Calculate the horizontal recoil speed.

18. A box having a mass of 25 Kg starts from rest and slides down an inclined plane 8 m long and 5 m high. If its speed at the bottom is 7 m/sec, find (a) the energy loss due to friction,

(b) the force of friction, and (c) the coefficient of friction. (*Ans.* (a) 612.5 joules, (b) 76.6 newtons, and (c) 0.400.)

19. A 25-ton freight car moving at 10 ft/sec bumps into another of 30 tons moving 8 ft/sec in the same direction. If the cars lock together upon impact, find (a) their resultant speed, and (b) the energy lost during impact.

20. A 5-Kg mass, moving with a velocity of 8 m/sec, collides with a 10-Kg mass at rest. If they recoil at angles of 30° and 45°, respectively, with respect to the direction of the smaller mass before impact, find the velocities of the two masses after impact. (*Note:* Solve Eq.(16i) for v_2 and substitute in Eq.(16h); solve for v_1, simplify, and substitute numerical values. (*Ans.* 5.85 m/sec; 2.065 m/sec.)

21. A 2-Kg mass, moving with a velocity of 15 m/sec, collides with a 5-Kg mass at rest. If they both recoil at angles of 30° and 40°, respectively, with respect to the direction of the smaller mass before impact, find the velocities of the two masses after impact. (See note in Prob. 20.)

Center of Mass and Center of Gravity

In the kinematics and dynamics of motion, one often neglects the size and shape of a body and speaks of the object as if it were located at a point. Of course, this is done for convenience only and is justified as long as one's interests are not centered on structural details. Under certain conditions it is found necessary to take into account the structural details and still make use of the simplest forms of Newton's laws of motion. How this is accomplished is the subject of this chapter.

17.1. Center of Mass. *The center of mass of any given body, or system of bodies, is a point such that, if any plane is passed through it, the mass moments on one side of the plane are equal to the mass moments on the other.*

Consider, for example, two spheres of mass m_1 and m_2 as shown in Fig. 17A. The

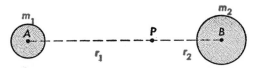

Fig. 17A *The center of mass of two bodies is located at some point on a line joining their centers of mass.*

center of mass (*abbr. c of m*) P lies on a line connecting the centers of the two bodies and in such a position that

$$m_1 \times r_1 = m_2 \times r_2 \qquad (17a)$$

For a vertical plane through P, perpendicular to the plane of the page, $m_1 \times r_1$ is the mass moment of m_1, and $m_2 \times r_2$ is the

mass moment of m_2. The mass moment of a body about any chosen plane is given by the mass of the body multiplied by its perpendicular distance to the plane.

Example 2. Find the *c of m* of two bodies $m_1 = 2$ gm, and $m_2 = 5$ gm, placed 14 cm apart.

Solution. Given is the distance $r_1 + r_2 = 14$ cm, from which

$$r_2 = 14 - r_1$$

Substitute all known quantities in Eq.(17a).

$$2r_1 = 5(14 - r_1) \qquad \text{or} \qquad 2r_1 = 70 - 5r_1$$

and

$$7r_1 = 70 \qquad \text{or} \qquad r_1 = 10$$

The substitution of this value of r_1 in Eq.(17a) gives

$$r_2 = 4 \text{ cm}$$

The *c of m* of a three-body system is found by an extension of the above principle. See Fig. 17B. To illustrate, two of the

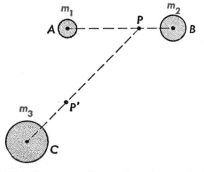

Fig. 17B *Diagram illustrating the method for finding the center of mass of a three-body system.*

masses like A and B are first selected and their c of m found by use of Eq.(17a). These two bodies are then treated as though they were one body located at P. With one mass $(m_1 + m_2)$ located at P and a second mass m_3 located at C, Eq.(17a) is applied to find P^1, the resultant c of m. If a system consists of more than three bodies, the above process is continued until all masses have been included.

The c of m of all regularly shaped bodies like those shown in Fig. 17C is at their ge-

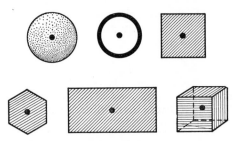

Fig. 17C   *Illustrating the center of mass of regularly shaped objects.*

ometrical center. A plane passed through the center of any of these figures will divide the body into two equal parts. Consider, for example, a thin ring of mass M as shown in Fig. 17D(a). By drawing straight lines

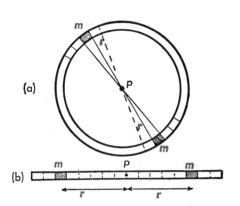

Fig. 17D   *Center of mass is at the geometrical center: (a) uniform ring, (b) uniform rod.*

through the geometrical center, the total mass can be divided up into pairs of small but equal masses. Since the masses m of each pair are equidistant from the center,

their c of m is at their midpoint P, and this is common to all pairs.

A similar process can be applied to a long thin rod or pole of equal cross section. Dividing the rod into an equal number of parts as shown in Fig. 17D(b) permits the pairing off of equal parts at equal distances from the center. Since the geometrical center is the c of m of each pair, it is also the c of m of the entire rod. It is now clear why the distances in Fig. 17A must be measured from the centers of the spheres; their centers give their c of m.

17.2. Rotation about the Center of Mass. In Fig. 17E two masses m_1 and m_2 are

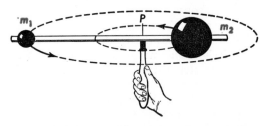

Fig. 17E   *Diagram illustrating the smooth rotation of two bodies around their center of mass.*

shown supported at the ends of a thin rod and rotating smoothly around a pin through the c of m. If the pin is located at any other point, for example halfway between the two masses, the experimenter will experience an unbalanced force on his hand, tending to make it "wobble."

Should the two-body system be thrown spinning into the air as shown in Fig. 17F,

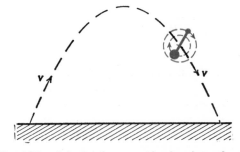

Fig. 17F   *A body thrown spinning into the air rotates smoothly about its center of mass, while the center of mass traces out the smooth trajectory of a projectile.*

it will be observed to rotate about its *c of m* while the *c of m* traces out the smooth trajectory of a projectile. Rotation is smooth around this point because the centripetal forces of the two bodies are counterbalanced there. The two centripetal forces are equal in magnitude but opposite in direc-

In a similar manner the earth and moon, considered as a single body, rotates with the sun as the second body about their *c of m*. Relatively, the bodies are similar to those in Fig. 17B, with m_1 and m_2 rotating about P, and the point P and mass m_3 rotating more slowly around P^1.

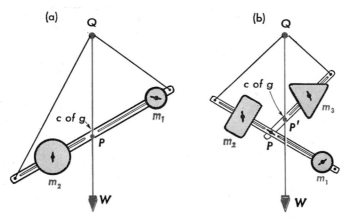

Fig. 17G   *Demonstration of an experiment for finding the center of gravity of a system of bodies.*

tion. Being in opposite directions, they exert no resultant force on the pivot.

To prove this result, consider the two-body system in Fig. 17A. If it is set into rotation about the *c of m*, the two centripetal forces are (see Eq.(14i)).

$$F_1 = m_1 r_1 \omega^2 \quad \text{and} \quad \vec{F_2} = m_2 r_2 \omega^2$$

ω being the angular velocity common to both masses. Setting these forces equal to each other as required $(F_1 = F_2)$, we get

$$m_1 r_1 \omega^2 = m_2 r_2 \omega^2$$

or

$$m_1 r_1 = m_2 r_2$$

the condition for the *c of m*.

The earth and the moon serve as a good illustration of two bodies rotating freely about their *c of m*. The mass of the earth is 81 times the mass of the moon, and the distance between them is approximately 240,-000 mi. A calculation, as in Example 2, gives $r_2 = 2927$ mi; nearly 3000 mi from the center of the earth and 1000 mi below the earth's surface.

17.3. Center of Gravity. The *c of m* of the two bodies in Fig. 17A is the one and only point about which the two bodies will, if pivoted, balance under the earth's gravitational pull. Furthermore, a single upward force applied at C, equal in magnitude to the weight of the two bodies, will maintain equilibrium; the system will not tend to move in any direction nor will it tend to rotate.

The *c of m* is therefore a point at which all of the weight can be considered as concentrated. For this reason, the *c of m* is often called the center of gravity (*abbr. c of g*).

The *c of g* of a system of bodies may be found by suspending it from a pivot point as shown in Fig. 17G. Both of these systems of masses may be turned to differently oriented positions by sliding the supporting string on the pin Q. No matter what orientation is assigned, the line of the plumb W will pass through the same point. The rigid system in diagram (b) is convenient for demonstrations since the rotation of m_1, m_2, or m_3 about their own centers of mass, or the turning of either bar at P to a new angle, will not shift the *c of g* from P'.

The *c of g* of any regular or irregular shaped body of uniform or nonuniform density can be found by suspending it from one pivot point and then another, as shown in Fig. 17H. With each suspension from a point P near the periphery, the body will hang with its *c of g* directly under that point. Lines drawn along the string supporting the plumb for each suspension will all cross at the common point, the *c of g*.

If pivoted at this point and set turning, or thrown spinning into the air, the rotation will be smooth about the *c of g*. (*Note:* Because the force of gravity decreases with altitude, the *c of g* of a body is not always at exactly the same point as the *c of m*. The lower part of a mass, for example, is closer to the earth's center than the upper part and therefore has a greater weight per unit mass. For all practical purposes, however, the two terms *c of g* and *c of m* are considered synonymous.)

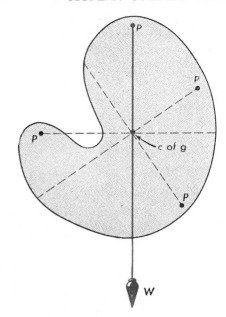

Fig. 17H   *The center of gravity of any freely suspended object lies at, or directly beneath, the point of suspension.*

PROBLEMS

1. Two bodies, 16 lb and 21 lb, respectively, are located 3 ft apart. Find their center of mass.

2. Two masses of 4 Kg and 9 Kg, respectively, are located 2 m apart. Find their center of mass. (*Ans.* 61.5 cm from 9 Kg.)

3. Two meteorites in free space have masses of 5 Kg and 9 Kg, respectively. Where is their center of mass if they are 8 m apart?

4. Two small solid spheres, with their centers 25 cm apart, have masses of 50 gm and 75 gm, respectively. Find the center of mass. (*Ans.* 15 cm from 50 gm.)

5. Two lead balls, located with their centers 24 m apart, have masses of 3 Kg and 9 Kg, respectively. Find their center of mass.

6. Three masses 4 Kg, 6 Kg, and 8 Kg are located at the corners of an equilateral triangle with sides 5 m long. Find the center of mass. (*Ans.* 2.42 m from 8-Kg mass and 3.37 m from 4-Kg mass.)

7. Three equal masses of 8 Kg each are located at the corners of a right triangle whose sides are 3 m, 4 m, and 5 m, respectively. Locate the center of mass.

8. Two weights, 3 lb and 5 lb respectively, are tied 2 ft apart at opposite ends of a rope and then thrown whirling into the air with an angular speed of 180 rpm. Calculate the tension in the rope. (*Ans.* 41.6 lb.)

9. Two stones with masses of 2 Kg and 4 Kg are tied 60 cm apart at opposite ends of a wire and then thrown whirling into the air with an angular speed of 20 rad/sec. Calculate the tension in the wire.

10. A uniform bar 8 m long has a mass of 4 Kg. Find the center of mass if a 10-Kg mass is fastened to one end. (*Ans.* 1.14 m from 10 Kg.)

11. A straight uniform pole 12 ft long has a weight of 30 lb. Find the center of gravity if a 20-lb mass is fastened at one end.

12. A uniform bar 6 ft long has a mass of 20 lb. Find the center of gravity if a 10-lb weight is fastened to one end and a 40-lb weight is fastened to the other. (*Ans.* 1.71 ft from 40 lb.)

13. A plywood board is 2 ft square and weighs 20 lb. A 5-lb weight is fastened to one corner. Find the center of gravity.

14. Two stones with masses of 5 Kg and 18 Kg are tied 90 cm apart at opposite ends of a wire and then thrown whirling into the air. About what point do these two rotate smoothly? (*Ans.* 19.6 cm from 18 Kg.)

15. A uniform bar *AB*, 8 m long, has a mass of 4 Kg and supports three masses: 5 Kg at *A*, 6 Kg 2m from *A*, and 3Kg at *B*. Find the center of the mass of the system.

16. A uniform bar 3 m long has a mass of 2 Kg. Find the center of mass if a 5-Kg mass is fastened to one end and a 1-Kg mass is fastened to the other. (*Ans.* 0.75 m from 5-Kg mass.)

17. A thin hoop with a mass of 3 Kg is 1 m in diameter. A mass of 2 Kg is fastened to the rim at one point and a mass of 4 Kg is fastened to a point diagonally opposite. Find the center of mass.

18. The center of gravity of an empty truck weighing 2600 lb is 7½ ft in front of the rear axle. The truck carries a load of 1.6 tons which is placed centrally with its center of gravity 2½ ft in front of the rear axle. Find the center of gravity. (*Ans.* 4 ft, 9 in. from rear axle.)

19. The center of mass of an empty wheel barrow 4 Kg is located 40 cm from the center of the wheel. A load of 20 Kg is centrally located in the barrow 60 cm from the center of the wheel. Find the center of mass.

20. A uniform ladder 6 m long has a mass of 20 Kg. Find the center of mass if a 70-Kg man is (a) 1 m from the bottom, and (b) 2 m from the top. (*Ans.* (a) 1.44 m from bottom, (b) 3.78 m from bottom.)

21. Five 2-Kg spheres are equally spaced around the periphery of a semicircle. If the diameter is 2 m and the two end spheres are diametrically opposite each other, find the center of mass.

Chapter 18

Satellites and Planetary Motion

According to astronomical history, it was the early Greek philosopher Pythagoras (530 B.C.) who said "the world is round and hangs in space." "The earth," he said, "does not stand still but revolves around a central fire, called Hestia. This fire is not the sun, for the sun is illuminated, as are the planets, by reflection from Hestia."

This idea lay dormant for two thousand years before Copernicus, at the beginning of the 16th century, said "the sun stands still and the earth and planets move in orbits around it." The observational and mathematical proof that all the planets move in elliptical orbits was first presented in 1609 when John Kepler* published a book containing two of his three laws which are now known as Kepler's laws of planetary motion.

18.1. Kepler's First Law.

The planets move in elliptical orbits with the sun at one of the foci.

An ellipse can be constructed by fastening the two ends of a piece of string to two pins, F_1 and F_2, as shown in Fig. 18A. By keeping the string tight with a pencil at P, the complete arc can be swung around, much the same as one draws a circle with a compass.

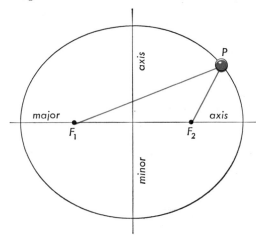

Fig. 18A *An ellipse can be drawn with two pins, a string, and a pencil.*

If the length of the string remains unchanged, and the foci F_1 and F_2 are brought closer and closer together, the major axis AB and the minor axis CD become more and more equal; in the limit when the foci coincide, the axes are equal and the ellipse becomes a circle. The real orbits of the planets are so nearly circular that, if they were drawn with a compass, the ellipse would differ from the circle by less than the thickness of the line.

The eccentricity e of an ellipse (see Fig. 18B) is defined as the ratio of the distance SQ and AQ.

---

* John Kepler (1571-1630), German astronomer and philosopher. Born in Weil of a poor but noble family, Kepler was educated at the University of Maulbroon. It was in his position as professor of astronomy at Gratz that he first became interested in the planets. When he heard that Tycho Brahe had recorded great quantities of data on the motions of hundreds of stellar objects, Kepler went to Prague. There he became a close and devoted friend of Tycho Brahe, and promised this grand old man that he would tabulate and publish the recorded observations. In 1609 Kepler published his *Commentaries on Mars,* in which his first two laws of planetary motion are to be found. The third law came a little later. Kepler was a religious, but sickly, man for most of his 59 years. He was twice married, but had no children of his own, and he died penniless.

$$e = \frac{SQ}{AQ}$$

where AQ is the semimajor axis a, and SQ is equal to ae. With the sun at one focus, the distance of closest approach AS is called *perigee*, and the greatest distance BS is

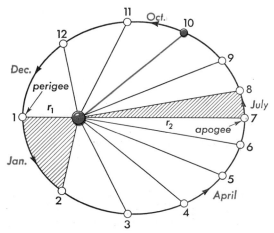

Fig. 18C *Elliptical orbit of a planet, or satellite, showing equal areas swept out by the radius vector in equal intervals of time.*

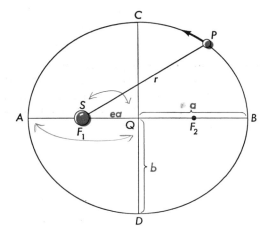

Fig. 18B *Elliptical orbit with an eccentricity $e = 0.5$.*

called *apogee*. A little study of Fig. 18B will enable the reader to find that

$$
\begin{aligned}
\text{apogee} &= a(1 + e) \\
\text{perigee} &= a(1 - e) \\
\text{semiminor axis} &= a\sqrt{1 - e^2}
\end{aligned}
$$

18.2. Kepler's Second Law.

The straight line joining the sun and any planet sweeps out equal areas in equal intervals of time.

As shown in Fig. 18C, the straight line referred to is called the *radius vector*; it varies in length from a minimum at perigee to a maximum at apogee. Although the orbit of the earth is nearly circular, the numbers 1, 2, 3, 4, etc., correspond to the position of the earth at the end of each of 12 equal months.

To cover these unequal orbital distances in equal intervals of time, the speed must be a maximum at perigee and a minimum six months later at apogee. During the periods 1 to 2 and 7 to 8, for example, the areas swept out are equal.

As the earth moves along its orbit in September, October, November, etc., the attractive force of the sun causes it to speed up. Upon reaching perigee at the end of December its speed is a maximum, and too fast to remain at this distance r_1 from the sun. During the months of March, April, May, etc., the earth is receding from the sun, and the attractive force of the sun slows the earth down. Upon reaching apogee at the end of June the speed of the revolving earth is a minimum, too slow to keep it at this greater distance r_2 from the sun. The average distance from the sun is 92,900,000 mi while the average orbital speed of the earth is 18.5 mi/sec.

18.3. Kepler's Third Law.

The squares of the orbital periods of the planets are proportional to the cubes of their mean distances from the sun.

The period T of a planet, or satellite, is defined as the time required to make one complete trip around its orbit; the mean distance r is defined as the average distance away from the sun. Important data on the eight major planets of the solar system are given in Table 18A. The constant ratios in column five verify Kepler's third law.

While Kepler's laws were originally de-

TABLE 18A. MEASURED CHARACTERISTICS OF THE PLANETS

Name	Period T (years)	Mean Distance		$\dfrac{T^2}{r^3}$	Mean Radius		Mass (Kg 10^{24})
		(mi $\times 10^6$)	(Km $\times 10^6$)		(mi)	(Km)	
Mercury	0.241	36.0	57.9	1.245	1504.3	2421.1	0.3244
Venus	0.615	67.1	108.1	1.252	3828.2	6161.0	4.861
Earth	1.000	92.9	149.5	1.247	3958.9	6371.0	5.975
Mars	1.881	141.5	227.8	1.249	2070.5	3332.1	0.6387
Jupiter	11.862	483.3	777.8	1.246	43429.0	69892.0	1902.1
Saturn	29.458	886.1	1426.0	1.247	35748.5	57532.0	569.4
Uranus	84.015	1783.0	2869.0	1.245	14727.0	23701.0	87.1
Neptune	164.790	2793.0	4496.0	1.246	13381.0	21535.0	103.1
Pluto	247.700	3665.0	5899.0	1.246	1781.4	2867.0	0.5?

rived from Tycho Brahe's careful observations, they are readily derived from the basic laws of classical laws of mechanics.

For simplicity we will assume that the orbit of the earth is circular, as shown in Fig. 18D. In this diagram, M is the mass of

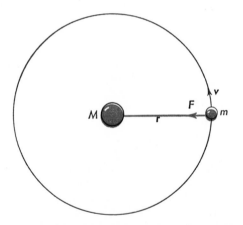

Fig. 18D *The gravitational force of attraction F is the centripetal force that keeps the earth in its nearly circular orbit around the sun.*

the sun, m is the mass of a planet like the earth, and r is the distance between their centers. The centripetal force F, as given by Eq.(9a), is just the force of gravitational attraction given by Eq.(14h). These are

$$F = m\frac{v^2}{r} \qquad\qquad F = G\frac{Mm}{r^2} \qquad (18a)$$

centripetal force

Newton's law of gravitation

where $\quad G = 6.66 \times 10^{-11}\dfrac{m^3}{\text{Kg sec}^2}$

Since these two equations are different expressions for the same force F, the right-hand sides may be placed equal to each other, which gives

$$G\frac{Mm}{r^2} = m\frac{v^2}{r}$$

Upon simplifying, this equation becomes

$$\frac{GM}{r} = v^2 \qquad\qquad (18b)$$

In mechanics the velocity of a body is given by $v = s/t$. If we choose the distance s to be once around the orbit, the time t then becomes the period T, and we obtain

$$v = \frac{2\pi r}{T} \qquad\qquad (18c)$$

By squaring both sides of this equation, and substituting the right-hand side for v^2 in Eq.(18b), we can write

$$\frac{GM}{r} = \frac{4\pi^2 r^2}{T^2}$$

or $\qquad T^2 = \left(\dfrac{4\pi^2}{GM}\right) r^3 \qquad (18d)$

Since all quantities in parentheses are constants, $T^2 \propto r^3$, and Kepler's third law is consistent with the laws of classical mechanics.

18.4. Satellites. When a space vehicle takes off from the ground to orbit the earth as a satellite, its initial take-off direction is vertically upward. See Fig. 13H. As the rocket gains height, control fins or jets are set to make it turn slowly toward a horizontal trajectory. To find the velocity that a space vehicle must acquire to circle the earth, consider the details of Fig. 18E.

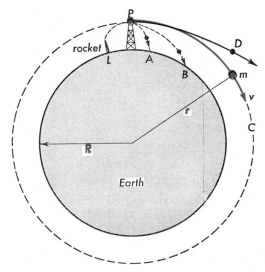

Fig. 18E *Horizontal projection from P with a high velocity v can cause a projectile m to circle the earth.*

Imagine a tower several hundred miles high, from the top of which projectiles are launched in a horizontal direction. With a low initial velocity the projectile will follow a nearly parabolic path as shown at *A*. At a somewhat higher velocity the trajectory will be that of path *B*. At a still higher velocity, the projectile in falling toward the earth will follow a circular path of radius *r*. This particular velocity is called the *orbiting velocity*. At still higher velocities, such as shown at *D*, the projectile will follow an elliptical path or escape from the earth completely.

By Newton's law of gravitation the force *F* exerted by the earth on a satellite of mass *m* is inversely proportional to r^2, and by his second law of motion the force is proportional to *a*. It follows, therefore, that the acceleration of a mass *m* toward the earth is

inversely proportional to the square of the distance.

Combining these two relations, we can write the following inverse square proportionality

$$\frac{a}{g} = \frac{R^2}{r^2} \qquad (18e)$$

where *a* is the inward acceleration of mass *m* at any distance *r*, and *g* is its inward acceleration at the distance *R*, i.e., at the surface of the earth. Transposing *g*, we obtain

$$a = g\frac{R^2}{r^2} \qquad (18f)$$

This inward acceleration for an orbiting satellite is just the centripetal acceleration required to keep it in orbit and to prevent it from flying off on a tangent. By Eq.(14f) we write

$$a = \frac{v^2}{r}$$

Equating these two relations, we obtain

$$\frac{v^2}{r} = g\frac{R^2}{r^2}$$

which, upon solving for *v*, becomes simply

$$v = \sqrt{g\frac{R^2}{r}} \qquad (18g)$$

orbiting velocity

If the orbit is very close to the earth's surface, we can write, to a first approximation, $r = R$, and Eq.(18g) becomes

$$v = \sqrt{gR} \qquad (18h)$$

(The acceleration due to gravity, $g = 9.80$ m/sec^2 is equivalent to 78,920 mi/hr^2.)

18.5. Gravitational Fields. A convenient and informative method of describing the gravitational attraction of one body for another at a distance is to define what is called the *gravitational field*. To see how this concept arises and how it is used, consider the following development.

In Fig. 18F a mass *M* is shown exerting a gravitational force *F* on a small mass *m*.

$$F = G\frac{M_1 M_2}{r^2} \qquad F = ma$$

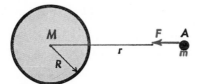

Fig. 18F   *Gravitational forces are always those of attraction.*

The magnitude of this force, as given by Newton's law of gravitation, is

$$F = G\frac{Mm}{r^2} \qquad (18i)$$

The field intensity I at any point A in the space surrounding any mass M is defined as the force per unit mass acting on any mass m placed there.

$$I = \frac{F}{m} \qquad (18j)$$

The small mass m is used in this description only as a means of detecting and measuring the gravitational field at the point A; whether m is large or small, the *force per unit mass* at the point will be the same. Double the mass m and F will be doubled, triple the mass m and F will be tripled, etc. To find an equation for the field intensity I, we need only obtain a value of F/m from Eq.(18i). Transposing m to the left side, we find that

$$\frac{F}{m} = G\frac{M}{r^2} \qquad \text{or} \qquad \boxed{I = G\frac{M}{r^2}} \quad (18k)$$

A diagram of the gravitational field around a spherical mass M is shown in Fig. 18G. The arrows show that the *direction* of the field is everywhere radially inward, and the spacing of the lines shows that the field is strongest at the surface. For every point at the same distance from the center, the field intensity I is the same, but as the distance increases the field decreases.

If m is transferred to the other side of Eq.(18j), we obtain the relation that

$$F = mI \qquad (18l)$$

Properly interpreted, this equation says

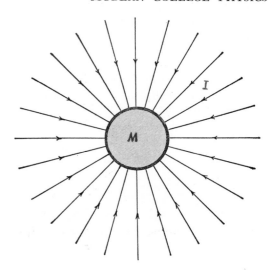

Fig. 18G   *The gravitational field around a spherical mass M is radially inward.*

that any mass m located in a gravitational field of intensity I experiences a force F acting upon it equal to the product of m and I.

At the surface of the earth the gravitational field is equal to g, the acceleration due to gravity.

This follows directly from Newton's second law of motion, which for freely falling bodies is written

$$F = mg$$

At the earth's surface, therefore, the gravitational field intensity

$$\boxed{I = g} \qquad (18m)$$

In mks units, $g = 9.80$ m/sec², and

$$1\frac{\text{newton}}{\text{kilogram}} = 1\frac{\text{meter}}{\text{second}^2}$$

Over a small volume of space, the gravitational field can be assumed to be constant in direction and magnitude. The path taken by a mass m, projected through a uniform gravitational field of intensity I, is the result of a constant force F. In free space the path is a parabola, as shown in Fig. 18H.

If the field is not uniform, as is the case

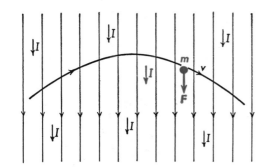

Fig. 18H *The path of a projectile in a uniform gravitational field is a parabola.*

over a large volume of space near the earth, the force is not constant and the path of a projectile is not that of a parabola.

18.6. Gravitational Potential. We have seen in Chap. 15 that the work done in raising a body of mass m to a height s is given by the product, force times distance.

$$W = F s \qquad (18n)$$

where the force F is given by Newton's second law, $F = mg$,

$$W = mgs$$

As a result of doing work on a body, we have stored within it, by virtue of its new position, an equivalent amount of potential energy.

$$P.E. = mgs$$

In setting up these defining equations in Chap. 15, it was assumed that the gravitational field intensity g is constant over the distance s through which the force acts. If the distance is large, however, the field intensity I is not constant, but varies inversely as the square of the distance from the center of the earth (see Eq.(18k)).

To calculate the work done by means of the defining equation, Eq.(18n), and with a continuously changing force, a mathematical procedure called *the calculus* is required. The calculus shows that the *work done* in carrying a mass m from a point at a distance r from the center of M, to a distance so great that the gravitational field is negligibly weak, is given by

$$W = F r \qquad (18o)$$

In this equation, F is just the force acting on m when it is at point A. (See Fig. 18I.) This simple result makes it easy to express the work done by the use of Eq.(18i). Upon the substitution of this value of F in Eq. (18o), we obtain

$$W = G \frac{Mm}{r} \qquad (18p)$$

The potential energy of a mass at that same point is, therefore,

$$\boxed{P.E. = -G \frac{Mm}{r}} \qquad (18q)$$

The minus sign indicates that the energy is negative with respect to the zero level, which is at infinity. As $r \to \infty$, the P.E. $\to 0$. Lifting a mass against the pull of a gravitational field requires the expenditure of energy.

We now define the gravitational potential P of any point in the space around a mass M as the potential energy per unit mass of any mass m located there.

$$P = \frac{P.E.}{m} \qquad (18r)$$

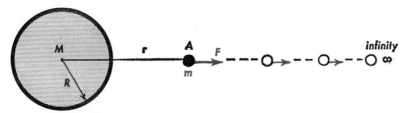

Fig. 18I *The force needed to remove a mass m from the earth decreases with increasing distance from the surface and becomes zero at infinity.*

Dividing both sides of Eq.(18q), by m and substituting from Eq.(18r), we obtain

$$P = -\frac{GM}{r} \qquad (18s)$$

Any mass m located at or near the surface of the earth M can be looked upon as being in a hole where the potential energy is negative, and to lift it out into free space (r infinite, and P.E. $= 0$) requires an amount of energy W.

$$W = -mP \qquad (18t)$$

We therefore arrive at the very simple result that the force on any mass is given by mI, and its potential energy is given by mP.

18.7. Escape Velocity. For a satellite to escape from the earth and never return, it must be launched with a velocity greater than that required to make it orbit. To find the *minimum escape velocity*, we make use of the gravitational potential as given in the preceding section.

To lift a mass m from any point at a distance r from the center of M requires the expenditure of energy in the amount given by Eq.(18t). (See Fig. 18J.) If we impart

$$v = \sqrt{2\frac{GM}{r}} \qquad (18u)$$

escape velocity

If we launch the mass m from the earth's surface, where $r = R$, we write

$$v = \sqrt{2\frac{GM}{R}} \qquad (18v)$$

If we wish to express this escape velocity in terms of g at the earth's surface, we can equate the force F given by Newton's law of gravitation with the force F given by his second law of motion:

$$G\frac{Mm}{R^2} = mg$$

from which we obtain

$$G = g\frac{R^2}{M} \qquad (18w)$$

Upon the substitution of this expression for G in Eq.(18v), we obtain

$$v = \sqrt{2gR} \qquad (18x)$$

escape velocity
from earth's surface

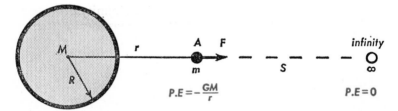

Fig. 18J   *The potential energy of a mass* m *near the earth is negative with respect to its potential energy at infinity.*

this energy by giving the mass a velocity, the total energy expended will be kinetic, $\frac{1}{2}mv^2$. By direct substitution in Eq.(18t) of $\frac{1}{2}mv^2$ for W, and $-GM/r$ for P (see Eq.(18s), we obtain

$$\frac{1}{2}mv^2 = m\frac{GM}{r}$$

Upon solving for v, we find that this equation gives

Note that this escape velocity is the square root of two greater than the orbiting velocity. (See Eq.(18h).)

$$v_{\text{escape}} = 1.41 \, v_{\text{orbit}} \qquad (18y)$$

This relation holds for any value of r.

18.8. Mechanical Well Model. The preceding sections of this chapter show that we on the surface of the earth are living at the bottom of a "gravitational well" thousands

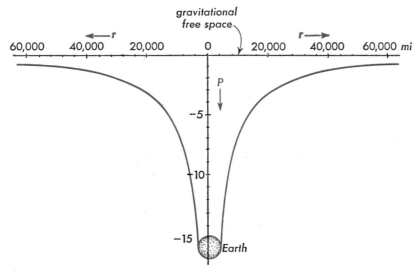

Fig. 18K *Potential energy graph illustrating the "well" analogy of the earth's gravitational field.*

of miles deep. To reach the moon, the planets, or other worlds, we must climb out of this well onto a horizontal plane we call *gravitationless free space.*

To see why we speak of a well, we plot a potential energy graph for the gravitational field around the earth like that shown in Fig. 18K. Such a graph is obtained by using Eq.(18s) and plotting the potential P vertically and the distance from the center of

the earth r *horizontally.* (For $r = 4000$ mi, assume $GM = -16$.)

For a distance r that is infinitely far away, $P = 0$. At smaller and smaller distances P increases, but is negative. The red curve in the diagram comes down to the earth's surface where r has the value of the earth's radius R.

A mechanical well model for demonstrating satellite orbits is obtained by rotating

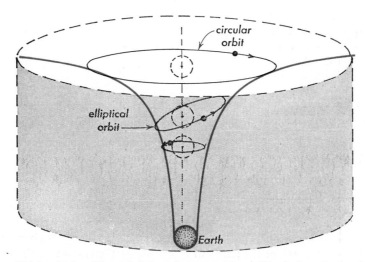

Fig. 18L *Mechanical well model for demonstrating elliptical and circular orbits.*

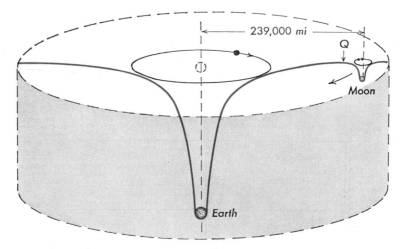

Fig. 18M *Mechanical well model for the earth and moon.*

this potential energy graph around the vertical axis. In so doing, the curve describes a cone-like surface as shown in Fig. 18L. If we make a solid body of some hard material with the shape of the shaded section, a small steel or glass marble can be rolled around in the cone to describe satellite orbits.

A great variety of orbits can be generated simply by varying the initial velocity of the marbles. When viewed from directly overhead, most orbits are elliptical or circular. Orbital distortion arising from rolling fric-

tion can be held to a minimum by using hard materials with smooth surfaces.

If orbits including the moon are desirable, a small potential crater, far out on the periphery of the earth model, can be made. (See Fig. 18M.) The rolling of a marble toward this crater, away from the earth, is analogous to the path of an earth-based satellite on its projected trip to or around the moon. At the saddle point Q the gravitational pull of the earth and moon are equal and opposite.

PROBLEMS

1. An ellipse is drawn with two pins placed 6 cm apart and a string 10 cm long. Find (a) the major axis, (b) the minor axis, (c) the eccentricity, (d) the apogee distance, and (e) the perigee distance.

2. An ellipse is to be drawn with a major axis of 8 m and a minor axis of 4 m. Find (a) the eccentricity, (b) the apogee distance, (c) the perigee distance, and (d) the distance between foci. (*Ans.* (a) 0.866, (b) 7.464 m, (c) 0.536, (d) 6.928 m.)

3. An ellipse is to be constructed with a major axis of 10 cm and a minor axis of 4 cm. Find (a) the eccentricity, (b) the apogee distance, (c) the perigee distance, (d) the distance between foci, and (e) the length of the string to be used.

4. A satellite is to orbit the earth at a height of 141 mi. Calculate (a) its speed, and (b) its period of revolution in min. (*Ans.* (a) 17460 mi/hr, (b) 89 min.)

5. A satellite is to orbit the earth 1000 mi above the surface. Calculate (a) its speed, and (b) its period of revolution in min.

6. A satellite orbits the earth 440 mi above the surface. Find (a) its speed, and (b) its period in min. (*Ans.* (a) 16,800 mi/hr, (b) 98.8 min.)

7. What must be the speed of a satellite if it is to orbit the earth 800 mi above the surface? (b) What will be its period?

8. Find the gravitational field intensity 2000 Km above the surface of the earth. (*Ans.* 5.68 newtons/Kg.)

9. Find the gravitational field intensity on the surface of the planet Mars.

10. Calculate the gravitational field intensity on the surface of the planet Saturn. (*Ans.* 11.5 newtons/Kg.)

11. Calculate the gravitational field intensity on the surface of the planet Jupiter.

12. Find the gravitational potential of any point on the earth's surface. (*Ans.* -6.25×10^7 joules/Kg.)

13. Find the gravitational potential of any point on the surface of the planet Mars.

14. Calculate the escape velocity in m/sec of a rocket if its fuel burns out at an elevation of 100 Km above the earth's surface. (*Ans.* 11,090 m/sec.)

15. What is the escape velocity in m/sec of a rocket if its fuel burns out 70 Km above the surface of Mars?

16. How much energy must be imparted to a 100-Kg rocket missile to carry it from the earth's surface out into free space? (*Ans.* 6.25×10^9 joules.)

17. A 1000-Kg rocket is to be put into orbit 1000 Km above the surface of the earth. Calculate (a) its potential energy, (b) its kinetic energy, and (c) the total energy required to put it into orbit.

18. Find the escape velocity for a missile leaving the surface of Mars. (*Ans.* 5050 m/sec.)

19. Find the escape velocity for a missile leaving the surface of Jupiter.

20. Find the escape velocity from the planet Saturn. (*Ans.* 36,300 m/sec.)

21. Find the escape velocity from the surface of the planet Venus.

22. Starting with Eqs.(18g) and (18p) in this chapter, derive the equation $E = mgR(1 - \dfrac{R}{2r})$, where E is the total energy that must be given a satellite to make it orbit the earth at an altitude r.

23. Calculate the speed of a satellite orbiting the planet Mars at a distance of 100 Km above the surface. Use Eq.(18b).

24. Calculate the speed of a satellite orbiting the planet Jupiter at a distance of 200 Km above the surface. Use Eq.(18b). (*Ans.* 42,500 m/sec, 153,000 Km/hr, or 95,200 mi/hr.)

25. Find the speed of a satellite orbiting the planet Venus at a distance of 100 mi above the surface. Use Eq.(18b).

26. Find the speed of a satellite orbiting the moon at a distance of 50 mi above the surface. See Fig. 9B, and use Eq.(18b). (*Ans.* 1700 m/sec 6,120 Km/hr, or 3,808 mi/hr.)

Chapter 19

Equilibrium of Rigid Bodies

In Chap. 10 it was shown how a body acted on by any number of forces is in equilibrium if the vector sum of all the forces is zero. If each of these forces is resolved into *x*- and *y-components* and the conditions of equilibrium applied, the summation of all the *x-components* of force must be zero, and the summation of all the *y-components* must be zero. Symbolically,

$$\Sigma F_x = 0, \qquad \Sigma F_y = 0 \qquad (19a)$$

If all of the forces acting on a body lie in one plane, the fulfillment of these two conditions is all that is necessary to assure *translational equilibrium.* If they are not all in one plane, however, a three-dimensional problem is involved, and each force should be resolved into three components, one along each of the three axes, *x, y,* and *z,* as shown in Fig. 19A. Equilibrium in three dimensions then requires that

$$\boxed{\Sigma F_x = 0 \quad \Sigma F_y = 0 \quad \Sigma F_z = 0} \qquad (19b)$$

These equations are commonly referred to as *the 1st condition of equilibrium.* Since all of the forces in most problems are confined to one plane, the third equation can be omitted by assuming the plane of the forces to be the *xy-plane.*

19.1. Couples. When a rigid body is acted upon by a number of forces, complete equilibrium is not assured with the satisfying of the 1st condition of equilibrium alone. In Fig. 19B, for example, a body is shown

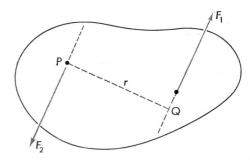

Fig. 19B *A "couple" acting on a rigid body tends to set it in rotation.*

acted upon by two equal but opposite forces. While Eq.(19a) is satisfied, the body is not in complete equilibrium; it is acted upon by a couple which tends to set it into rotation. To prevent this turning, the rigid body must be acted upon by another equal but opposite couple. In other words, to be in rotational equilibrium, couples must be balanced.

A couple is defined as two equal, but op-

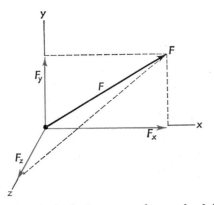

Fig. 19A *A single force may be resolved into three mutually perpendicular components, one along each of the three axes x, y, and z.*

positely directed, forces not acting along the same line. The magnitude of a couple is given by the product of one of the forces and the perpendicular distance between them. From the diagram,

$$\text{couple} = F_1 \times r \qquad (19c)$$

This product $F_1 \times r$ is called the moment of a couple and is to be compared with the moment of a force. A couple made up of large forces close together may have the same magnitude as a pair of small forces far apart.

A rigid body is defined as one whose various parts do not change their relative positions when forces are applied at different points. Actually, no known bodies strictly satisfy this condition, but for practical purposes most solid bodies may be regarded as rigid.

19.2. Torque. When a single force acting on a body tends to produce rotation, it is said to exert a *torque*. Torque is synonymous with *force-moment* and is defined as the product of force times lever arm, the lever arm being the perpendicular distance from the pivot point to the force. In Fig. 19C a body is shown acted upon by a

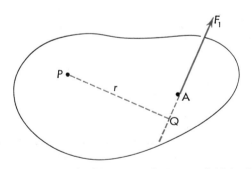

Fig. 19C *A single force acting on a rigid body pivoted at some point P exerts a torque L = $F_1 \times r$.*

torque. The force F is applied at the point A while the body is pivoted at the point P. The perpendicular distance r is equal to the line PQ, and the torque L is given by

$$\boxed{L = F_1 \times r} \qquad (19d)$$

If $F_1 = 5$ newtons, and $r = 3$ m,

$$L = 5 \text{ newtons} \times 3 \text{ m} = 15 \text{ newton m}$$

The dimensions *"newton m"* should not be confused with the units of *work* and *energy*. In the calculation of work, force and distance are measured in the same direction, while in torque the two are measured at right angles.

Because of its similarity to the general concept of moments, a torque is sometimes referred to as a force-moment. It is customary to ascribe a positive sign to all torques acting to turn a body counterclockwise and a minus sign to all torques tending to turn it clockwise.

19.3. Rotational Equilibrium. Consider the rigid body in Fig. 19D, pivoted by a pin at the point P and acted upon by four forces

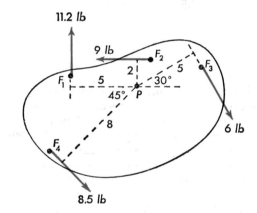

Fig. 19D *Diagram illustrating a rigid body in equilibrium under the action of four forces.*

$F_1, F_2, F_3,$ and F_4. With lever arms of 5, 2, 5, and 8, respectively, these forces constitute torques $L_1, L_2, L_3,$ and L_4. For this body to be in translational equilibrium the summation of all the forces, or the sums of their x- and y-components, must be zero. To be in rotational equilibrium, the summation of all the *torques* must be zero. This latter condition, the 2nd condition of equilibrium, can be expressed symbolically as

$$\boxed{\Sigma L = 0} \qquad (19e)$$

It will now be shown that the four forces

in Fig. 19D are in translational as well as rotational equilibrium. To apply the 1st condition of equilibrium, each of the forces is resolved into x- and y-*components* and each group added separately. From the angles given in the figure, and using Eq.(8b), we obtain

$$x\text{-}components$$

$F_1,$		0 lb
$F_2,$		-9 lb
$F_3,$	$6 \sin 30° =$	3 lb
$F_4,$	$8.5 \sin 45° =$	6 lb
	$\Sigma F_x = 0$	

$$y\text{-}components$$

$F_1,$		11.2 lb
$F_2,$		0 lb
$F_3,$	$6 \cos 30° =$	-5.2 lb
$F_4,$	$8.5 \cos 45° =$	-6 lb
	$\Sigma F_y = 0$	

Since $\Sigma F_x = 0$, and $\Sigma F_y = 0$, the conditions for translational equilibrium are satisfied.

Applying the 2nd condition of equilibrium,

L_1	$11.2 \times 5 = -56$
L_2	$9 \quad \times 2 = +18$
L_3	$6 \quad \times 5 = -30$
L_4	$8.5 \times 8 = +68$
	$\Sigma L = 0$

Because the sum of all the torques is zero, rotational equilibrium is assured. Since the body is in complete equilibrium, the pin P, acting as a pivot, cannot be exerting a force of any kind and it can therefore be removed. After removal it can be placed at any other point in the body and equilibrium is still assured. In other words, *if all of the forces acting on a rigid body maintain complete equilibrium about one pivot point, they also are in equilibrium about any other pivot point.*

Although the body in Fig. 19C is acted upon by a single torque and is set into rotation, the pin keeps it from being moved away. In other words, the body is in translational equilibrium; the pin is exerting a force on the body equal in magnitude to

F_1 and opposite in direction. Or, in other words, the force F, and the force exerted by the pin, constitute a couple.

19.4. Anatomical Mechanics. In the preceding chapters it has been seen that, to obtain a solution to many problems in mechanics, it is customary to neglect certain minor details like the weight of a bridge girder or the friction in a bearing, in order to simplify a problem and to arrive at some approximate yet practical numerical answer.

Although complicated, the general principles of muscle function in animals as well as in living human beings may also be simplified in much the same way by neglecting certain minor parts. As a result of such simplification, the bones of the body and the muscles that move them form the compression and tension members, respectively, of mechanical systems already classified as levers and machines. It is, therefore, the purpose of this chapter to show in what way some of the principles of mechanics may be found in, and applied to, the human anatomy.

One significant fact concerning muscles and their action is that their lever arms, that is, the perpendicular distance from some joint as a fulcrum to the line of action of the muscle, is relatively short. This means that, to overcome a relatively slight resistance at the extremity of some bone system, a muscle must be capable of exerting far greater forces than those offering the resistance to motion. It will be seen in what follows, therefore, that the large force of a muscle exerted through a short distance moves a lesser load through a greater distance. In other words, motion is magnified while the mechanical advantage is diminished.

When one part of the body is bent toward another, the action is called *flexion,* that is, bending; when the parts are straightened out, the motion is called *extension.* Even though a number of muscles are involved in the flexion of a joint, and another group in its extension, it is often true that some one particular muscle group may be considered to be the *prime mover* for flexion and another as the prime mover for extension.

Muscles that perform a minor role in any action are called *assistors*. The function of assistor muscles is to prevent undesired actions of the prime mover, such as inward and outward rotation.

19.5. Mechanics of the Foot. An elementary example of anatomical mechanics is found in an analysis of foot movement. (See Fig. 19E). In the flexion and extension of

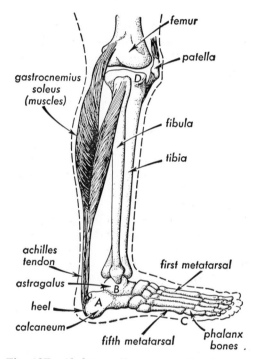

Fig. 19E *Skeleton diagram of the lower leg and foot showing the muscles and tendon used in rising on tiptoe.*

femur
patella
gastrocnemius
soleus
(muscles)
fibula
tibia
achilles
tendon
first metatarsal
astragalus
heel
calcaneum
fifth metatarsal
phalanx
bones .

the whole foot, the ankle acts as a hinge or pivot about which rotation in a vertical plane takes place. The top of the *astragalus* is like a ball fitting into and free to turn in the socket formed by the ends of the *fibula* and *tibia* bones of the leg. When a person attempts to rise on tiptoe, the strong muscles, the *gastrocnemius* and *soleus* forming the calf of the leg, act as prime movers. A sufficient tightening of these muscles causes the heel to rise, and the foot to bend

at *C* where the *phalanx* of the toes join the *metatarsals*.

A simple space diagram shown in Fig. 19F illustrates how rising on tiptoe involves

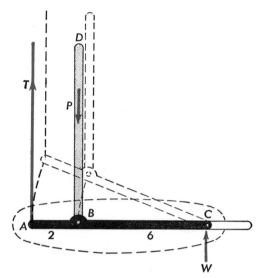

Fig. 19F *Schematic diagram showing the mechanical principle of the human foot when rising on tiptoe.*

the simplest type of torque action with a fixed pivot at *C*. The horizontal member *AC* represents the foot skeleton from *A* to *C* in Fig. 19E, and the vertical member (*BD*) the leg skeleton (*BD*) supporting the body. To calculate the tension required of the muscles and the load to be carried by the leg bones, the foot member *A* to *C* is drawn as a rigid body and all forces acting upon it are taken into account.

There are three forces acting on the horizontal member, an upward force at *A* due to tension in the muscles, a downward force at *B* due to the leg bones, and an upward force at *C* due to the floor. As a problem, let it be assumed that a person weighing 150 lb *stands on one foot* and then rises on tiptoe. Assign the dimensions of 2 in. for *AB* and 6 in. for *BC*, and calculate the tension force *T* and the compression force *P* as follows:

By taking moments about *A*, the counterclockwise torque is $W \times 8$ in. and the clockwise torque $P \times 2$ in.

Apply the 2nd condition of equilibrium.

$$W \times 8 \text{ in.} - P \times 2 \text{ in.} = 0$$

Substitute $W = 150$ lb and solve for P.

$$P = \frac{150 \text{ lb} \times 8 \text{ in.}}{2 \text{ in.}} = 600 \text{ lb}$$

Take moments about B, and apply the 2nd condition of equilibrium.

$$W \times 6 \text{ in.} - T \times 2 \text{ in.} = 0$$

Substitute and solve for T.

$$T = \frac{150 \text{ lb} \times 6 \text{ in.}}{2 \text{ in.}} = 450 \text{ lb}$$

If we now apply the 1st condition of equilibrium, it is observed that the total upward force $W + T$ of 600 lb equals the total downward force P of 600 lb.

It should be pointed out that tension is produced by a contraction of the large part or "belly" of a muscle, and not by the narrow section called the *tendon*.

19.6. Mechanics of the Lower Jaw. The *mandible*, or lower "jawbone," is a large, strong, horseshoe-shaped bone, forming the lower third of the facial skeleton. (See Fig. 19G.) A pair of *condyles* at the ends fit into

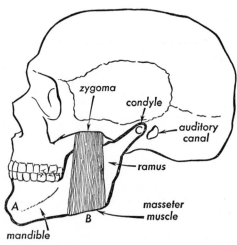

Fig. 19G *Diagram of the human skull.*

sockets, one on either side of the skull just in front of the auditory canal, and act as hinges about which the lower jaw pivots.

The *masseter* or "chewing muscle" is one of the strongest muscles in the body. As illustrated in the figure, it is located in the back part of the side of the face. Originating on the lower margin of the *zygoma,* the masseter passes downward to where it terminates on the lower edge of the *ramus* of the mandible.

The action of the two masseters, one on either side of the face, is such as to lift the lower jaw and at the same time draw it slightly forward. In principle, this is a torque action with a pivot at C, an upward force at B, and a load force at A introduced when chewing takes place between the teeth of the upper and lower jaws.

A schematic diagram of the torque action is shown at the right in Fig. 19H, with

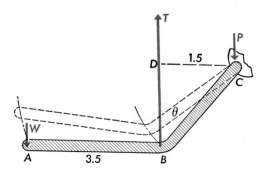

Fig. 19H *Schematic diagram showing the mechanics involved in chewing.*

selected values of the dimensions given in inches. When the mandible is selected as the rigid body, all of the acting forces, due to symmetry, are reduced to three, W, T, and P. To calculate the magnitudes of these forces, at least one of them must be known.

As a problem, let it be assumed that the lower jaw, in chewing with the front teeth, is able to exert a measured force of 20 lb. To calculate the tension T exerted by the two masseters, the point C is assumed as pivot, and the torques are equated as follows:

$$W \times 5 \text{ in.} = T \times 1.5 \text{ in.}$$

Inserting $W = 20$ lb, and solving for T,

$$T = \frac{20 \text{ lb} \times 5 \text{ in.}}{1.5 \text{ in.}} = 66.7 \text{ lb}$$

Equating downward forces to upward forces,

$$P + W = T$$

from which

$$P = T - W = 66.7 - 20 = 46.7 \text{ lb}$$

Each masseter therefore exerts $\frac{1}{2}$ of 66.7 lb or 33.35 lb, while the condyles each press against their sockets with a force of $\frac{1}{2}$ of 46.7 lb, or 23.35 lb.

19.7. The Biceps. The above procedure of solution will be applied to the muscle problem involved in the flexion of the lower arm. In Fig. 19I a skeleton of the

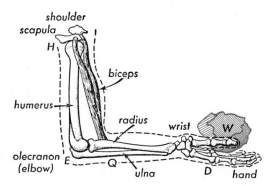

Fig. 19I *Skeleton diagram of the arm and hand showing the bicep used in lifting a load W.*

forearm is shown in a horizontal position supporting a stone in the palm of the hand. With a pivot point at the elbow joint, the forearm and hand form a compression member like the boom of a crane, while the *biceps* which assume the duty of prime mover in any flexor movement become the tension member.

The biceps originate on the *scapula* or shoulder, from where they pass downward and forward to terminate on the *radius* near the elbow.

A schematic diagram of this force problem is shown in Fig. 19J; the vertical member (*EH*) represents the *humerus;* the horizontal member (*ED*), 14 in. in length, the forearm and hand; and the tension member (*TQ*), the biceps. A weight of 10 lb is assumed held in the hand, while the weight of the forearm and hand is taken to be 2 lb

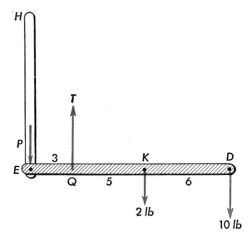

Fig. 19J *Mechanics of the forearm.*

and applied at the center of mass 8 in. from the elbow.

The problem to be solved resolves itself into one of calculating (a) the upward force exerted by the biceps and (b) the downward force exerted by the humerus on the elbow. With two unknown forces P and T, either one can be determined by eliminating one of them from torque calculations. Taking E as a pivot point and applying the 2nd condition of equilibrium, we write

$$10 \text{ lb} \times 14 \text{ in.} + 2 \text{ lb} \times 8 \text{ in.} - T \times 3 \text{ in.} = 0$$

Multiplying out and solving for the unknown T, we obtain

$$T = \frac{140 \text{ lb in.} + 16 \text{ lb in.}}{3 \text{ in.}} = 52 \text{ lb}$$

If Q is chosen as the pivot point, the 2nd condition of equilibrium gives

$$10 \text{ lb} \times 11 \text{ in.} + 2 \text{ lb} \times 5 \text{ in.} - P \times 3 \text{ in.} = 0$$

Multiplying out and solving for the unknown P, we find

$$P = \frac{110 \text{ lb in.} + 10 \text{ lb in.}}{3 \text{ in.}} = 40 \text{ lb}$$

The 1st condition of equilibrium is satisfied, since the only upward force is equal to the total of the downward forces, 40 lb + 2 lb + 10 lb.

19.8. The Quadriceps. The mechanics concerned with the extension of the lower limb involves a four-branched muscle called the *quadriceps.* One of the branches of this muscle originates above the hip on the anterior inferior spine of the ilium, and the other three on the front and two sides of the *femur,* respectively. See Fig. 19K. All

is similar to that of a pulley, as indicated in Fig. 19K. As a mechanical problem it is desired to find the tension required of the quadriceps to hold the lower part of the leg at any given angle with the horizontal, and the force exerted by the femur on the knee joint.

To make these calculations it is necessary

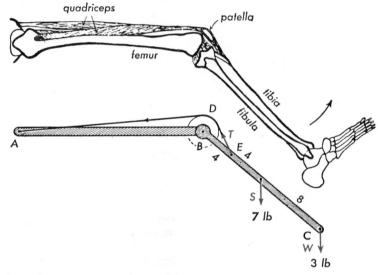

Fig. 19K *Skeleton diagram of the human leg (above) and its mechanical analogue (below).*

four unite around the small kneecap bone, the *patella,* and terminate as a strong tendon near the upper end of the *tibia.*

If, while the body is in a sitting position, the leg is extended as shown in the diagram, contraction in the quadriceps pulls the patella up over the knee joint. The action

to know the weights of the foot and lower leg, their centers of gravity, and the geometry involved at the knee joint. When these are known, the lower leg from *B* to *C* may be isolated and solved as a rigid body with a pivot at *B*. Such solutions will be left as problems on the following pages.

PROBLEMS

1. A uniform table weighing 50 lb is 8 ft long. A weight of 30 lb is located on the table directly over the legs at one end, and a boy weighing 100 lb stands on the table 2 ft from the other end. Find the upward force at each end of the table.

2. A uniform door weighing 40 lb is 7 ft high and 2.5 ft wide. The hinges are located 1 ft from each end. Assuming the weight of the door to be carried entirely by the lower hinge, find

the resultant force exerted on each door hinge. (*Ans.* 10 lb, and 41.2 lb at 14° for vertical.)

3. A truck having a 12-ft wheel base weighs 2½ tons when empty. Its center of gravity is 9 ft in front of the rear wheels. Where should a 3½-ton load be placed in order that all four wheels carry the same load?

4. The center of gravity of an empty truck weighing 5 tons is 10 ft in front of the rear

axle. The truck carries a load of 2 tons which is placed centrally with its center of gravity 4 ft in front of the rear axle. If the wheel base is 16 ft, find (a) the center of gravity, and (b) the load carried by each wheel. (*Ans.* (a) 8.3 ft in front of rear axle; (b) front wheels 3625 lb each, rear wheels 3375 lb each.)

5. If the greatest load a 150-lb man can lift, and still rise on his tiptoes with it, is 250 lb, what is the corresponding muscle tension he can exert through the Achilles' tendon? Referring to Fig. 19F, assume $AB = 1.75$ in. and $AC = 8.75$ in.

6. In applying the brake pedal of a truck, a man exerts a force of 15 lb with the ball of his right foot. If the dimensions of his foot are $AB = 1.6$ in. and $AC = 7.8$ in. (see Fig. 19F), find (a) the tension in the Achilles' tendon, and (b) the compressional force on the calcaneum. (*Ans.* (a) 58.1 lb, (b) 73.1 lb.)

7. A man weighing 175 lb and carrying a 100-lb bag rises on tiptoes. Calculate (a) the downward force on the astragalus of each foot, and (b) the tension in each Achilles' tendon if the dimensions of each foot (see Fig. 19F) are $AB = 1.45$ in. and $BC = 5.7$ in.

8. A boy pedaling a bicycle weighs 100 lb. When he puts all of his weight on the ball of one foot, what is the tension in the Achilles' tendon? The dimensions of his foot are $AB = 1.46$ in. and $AC = 7.20$ in. (See Fig. 19F.) (*Ans.* 393.2 lb.)

9. In biting down to crack a nut with his front teeth, a man exerts a force of 22 lb. Calculate the tension in the masseter muscles if the mandible has the following dimensions (see Fig. 19G): $AB = 9$ cm, $BC = 6.6$ cm, and $\theta = 48°$.

10. When chewing on a piece of dried venison, an Indian exerts a force of 14 lb with his front teeth. Find (a) the tension in each masseter, and (b) the force on each condyle. The mandible dimensions are (see Fig. 19G): $AB = 8.4$ cm, $BC = 6.5$ cm, and $\theta = 60°$. (*Ans.* (a) 25.1 lb, (b) 18.1 lb.)

11. A man holds a 7.5-Kg bowling ball in the palm of his hand. If his forearm is in the median position (see Fig. 19H), what is the tension exerted by the biceps? The dimensions of

his forearm are: $EQ = 10.0$ cm, $ED = 40.0$ cm, and $EH = 40.0$ cm. Assume the forearm and hand to weigh 2.50 Kg with the center of gravity 18.0 cm from the elbow.

12. An athlete holds a 12-lb shot-put in his hand with his forearm flexed to the median position. Calculate the force exerted by the biceps if the dimensions (see Fig. 19I) are $EQ = 2.2$ in. and $ED = 16$ in. Assume the forearm and hand to weigh 3.4 lb with the center of gravity 8 in. from E. *Note:* Take moments about the elbow. (*Ans.* 99.6 lb.)

13. Determine the tension T exerted by the quadriceps when the leg is held in the position shown in Fig. 19J. Assume the dimensions and weights given in the figure. Angle $DEB = 30°$ and $ABC = 135°$.

14. Assuming the weights and dimensions given for the lower leg in Fig. 19J, calculate (a) the tension exerted by the quadriceps, and (b) the magnitude of the force exerted by the femur on the knee joint. Take angle $ABC = 145°$ and angle $BED = 30°$. (*Ans.* (a) 42.6 lb, (b) 33.8 lb.)

15. A strong man weighing 210 lb lifts a 400-lb weight. If his foot dimensions as shown in Fig. 19F are as follows: $AB = 2.0$ in. and $AC = 9.0$ in., find (a) the tension in the Achilles' tendons, and (b) the compressional forces sustained by the bones of the lower leg.

16. The uniform boom of a crane is 20 ft long and has a mass of 50 lb. One end of the boom is pivoted at the base of the mast (or king post) and the other end is held up by a tie rope leading to the top of the mast. The boom makes an angle of 90° with the mast and the tie rope an angle of 30° with the mast. If a 500-lb load hangs from the far end of the boom, find the tension in the tie rope. (Make a diagram.) (*Ans.* 606 lb.)

17. A uniform ladder 20 ft long and weighing 50 lb makes an angle of 60° with the rough floor on which it stands. The upper end rests against a smooth, round horizontal bar so that the force exerted on the bar is normal to the ladder. A man weighing 200 lb stands on one step ¾ of the way up. Find the force exerted on the upper end of the ladder. (Make a force diagram.)

Chapter 20

Kinematics and Dynamics of Rotation

When a rigid body is acted upon by an unbalanced torque, it is set into rotation. Free to turn about an axis, such a body increases in angular velocity and acquires, when the torque ceases to act, some final speed. See Fig. 20A.

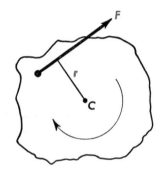

Fig. 20A   *A rigid body is acted upon by a torque, $F \times r$.*

20.1. Angular Acceleration. Just as the acceleration of a body in linear motion is defined as the rate of change of velocity, so the angular acceleration of a body in rotation is defined as the rate of change of angular velocity. By comparison these two definitions are expressed the same mathematically. See Eq.(4a).

$$a = \frac{v - v_0}{t} \qquad \boxed{\alpha = \frac{\omega - \omega_0}{t}} \qquad (20a)$$

linear motion   angular motion

In the equations above, α represents the angular acceleration and is analogous to the linear acceleration a; ω_0, the initial angular velocity, is analogous to v_0; and ω, the final angular velocity, is analogous to v. If the above equations are transposed, they become (see Eq. 4d)

$$v = v_0 + at \qquad \boxed{\omega = \omega_0 + \alpha t} \qquad (20b)$$

linear motion   angular motion

Angular velocity ω (see Eq.(14b)) is defined as θ, the angle turned through, divided by t the time.

$$v = \frac{s}{t} \qquad\qquad \omega = \frac{\theta}{t} \qquad (20c)$$

linear motion   angular motion

The following example will illustrate the meaning, as well as an application, of the above angular formulas.

Example 1. A flywheel starting from rest acquires, in 10 sec, a speed of 240 rpm. Find the acceleration.

Solution. Since the wheel starts from rest, $\omega_0 = 0$. The final velocity in radians per second is calculated by the use of Eq.(20c). Since there are 2π rad in 1 revolution,

$$\omega = \frac{2\pi \times 240}{60} = 25.1 \frac{\text{rad}}{\text{sec}}$$

Using (Eq.20a), we find that

$$\alpha = \frac{25.1 - 0}{10} = 2.51 \frac{\text{rad}}{\text{sec}^2}$$

It is clear from the above formulas that linear quantities s, v, and a in the linear equations have only to be replaced by the corresponding angular quantities, θ, ω, and α, to obtain the angular equations. This direct correspondence is the result of using the radian as a unit of angular measure and holds throughout all of the formulas in mechanics.

To derive a formula for the linear acceleration of a point around the periphery of an accelerated wheel, it is convenient to start with the definition of acceleration given by Eq.(20a) and substitute for the velocities v and v_0 the equality given by Eq.(14e), $v = r\omega$, and $v_0 = r\omega_0$. (See Fig. 20B.)

$$a = \frac{v - v_0}{t} = \frac{r\omega - r\omega_0}{t} = r\left(\frac{\omega - \omega_0}{t}\right) = r\alpha$$

The result, $a = r\alpha$, is to be compared with two previous formulas, Eqs.(14d) and

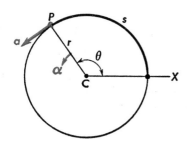

Fig. 20B   *A wheel free to rotate about its center is given an angular acceleration.*

(14e). The similarity is more conspicuous when written together.

$$s = r\theta$$
$$v = r\omega \qquad (20d)$$
$$a = r\alpha$$

These interrelation equations are well worth remembering, for they are found to be quite useful in the solving of many problems.

20.2. Average Angular Velocity. To calculate the total angle turned through by a rigid body undergoing constant angular acceleration, use is made of the *average angular velocity*. By analogy with linear motion (see Eq.(4e)), the *average angular velocity is defined as $\frac{1}{2}$ the sum of the initial and final angular velocities.*

Symbolically, we write

$$\bar{v} = \frac{v + v_0}{2} \qquad \bar{\omega} = \frac{\omega + \omega_0}{2} \qquad (20e)$$

linear motion   angular motion

Since $s = \bar{v}t$, and $\theta = \bar{\omega}t$, direct substitution gives

$$s = \frac{v + v_0}{2}t \qquad \boxed{\theta = \frac{\omega + \omega_0}{2}t} \qquad (20f)$$

linear motion   angular motion

Example 2. An airplane motor, while idling at 300 rpm, is suddenly accelerated. At the end of 3 sec it has acquired its maximum speed of 2400 rpm. Assuming constant acceleration, find (a) the average angular velocity, and (b) the total angle turned through.

Solution. We begin by changing the given speeds to radians per second.

$$\omega_0 = \frac{300}{60} \times 2\pi = 31.4 \frac{\text{rad}}{\text{sec}}$$

$$\omega = \frac{2400}{60} \times 2\pi = 251.3 \frac{\text{rad}}{\text{sec}}$$

To find (a), direct substitution in Eq.(20e) gives

$$\bar{\omega} = \frac{251.3 + 31.4}{2} = 141.4 \frac{\text{rad}}{\text{sec}}$$

To find (b), direct substitution in Eq.(20f) gives

$$\theta = 141.4 \times 3 = 424.2 \text{ rad}$$

20.3. Kinematics of Rotation. The term "kinematics of rotation" refers to a quantitative description of motion such as that given above. By combining two of the equations already studied, Eqs.(20b) and (20f), two other useful formulas may be derived.* Each of these is written here beside their analogous linear motions.

$$s = v_0 t + \tfrac{1}{2}at^2 \qquad \boxed{\theta = \omega_0 t + \tfrac{1}{2}\alpha t^2} \qquad (20g)$$
$$v^2 = v_0^2 + 2as \qquad \boxed{\omega^2 = \omega_0^2 + 2\alpha\theta} \qquad (20h)$$

linear motion   angular motion

Again note here that angular quantities θ, ω and α take the place of the corresponding linear quantities s, v, and a.

Example 3. An automobile engine running at 300 rpm is given an angular acceleration of 20 rad/sec² for 10 sec. Find (a) the angle turned through, and (b) the total number of revolutions.

---

* The derivations of Eq.(20g) and (20h) follow exactly the steps taken in obtaining the corresponding linear formulas, Eqs. (4i) and (4h).

Solution. First change 300 rpm to radians per second.

$$\omega_0 = \frac{300}{60} \times 2\pi = 31.4 \frac{\text{rad}}{\text{sec}}$$

Using Eq.(20g), we obtain

$$\theta = 31.4 \frac{\text{rad}}{\text{sec}} \times 10 \text{ sec} + \frac{1}{2} 20 \frac{\text{rad}}{\text{sec}^2} \times (10 \text{ sec})^2$$
$$= 1314 \text{ rad}$$

$$\theta = \frac{1314}{2\pi} = 209 \text{ rev}$$

20.4. Dynamics of Rotation.

In the treatment of angular acceleration given in the preceding sections of this chapter, neither the torques causing the acceleration, nor the mass of the rotating body, entered into the calculations. When these two factors are introduced into the equations the treatment is referred to as the *dynamics of rotation*.

When a specified torque is applied to a body free to rotate about some axis, the angular acceleration produced depends not only upon the size and shape of the body, but also upon the distribution of the mass with respect to the axis of rotation. To see how these factors are taken into account, consider the simplest kind of example, namely, that of a small mass m fastened to the end of a string and set into rotation as shown in Fig. 20C.

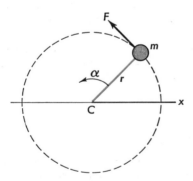

Fig. 20C *Angular acceleration depends upon torque and moment of inertia.*

By Newton's second law of motion, the acceleration a of the mass around the periphery of the circle should be given by

$$F = ma$$

Multiply both sides of this equation by the radius of the circle r.

$$F \times r = ma \times r$$

The product $F \times r$ on the left side represents the applied torque L. If we replace the acceleration a on the right by its equal, $r\alpha$, from Eq.(20d), the result is

$$L = mr^2\alpha \qquad (20i)$$

Since m and r for a given body are both constants, they may be replaced by a single constant I, and the equation written

$$L = I\alpha \qquad (20j)$$

where $I = mr^2$, and is called the *moment of inertia*. By the following comparison with the force equation,

$$F = ma \qquad \boxed{L = I\alpha}$$

linear motion   angular motion

the torque L is seen to be analogous to F, the angular acceleration α analogous to a, and the moment of inertia I analogous to m.

According to Eq.(20i), the angular acceleration α is inversely proportional to r^2. An experiment illustrating this fact is shown in Fig. 20D. Two masses m threaded on light horizontal arms, free to turn about a

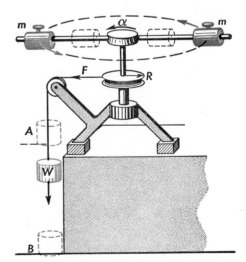

Fig. 20D *An experimental demonstration of moment of inertia.*

vertical axis, are acted upon by a constant torque $L = F \times R$.

When the masses are clamped at equal distances from, and halfway out on the arms, the angular acceleration is relatively large, and the weight W exerting the constant torque L quickly drops from A to B. When the masses m are moved to the outer ends of the arms where their distance r is doubled, the angular acceleration is reduced to $\frac{1}{4}$ and the weight W takes 2 times as long to go from A to B. By measuring the distance of each mass from the center, and the time of fall of the weight W for each part of the experiment, the product αr^2 is found to be constant.

20.5. Moment of Inertia. The moment of inertia of a body with respect to any axis is the sum of the products obtained by multiplying each elementary mass by the square of its distance from the axis. To illustrate, consider the uniform ring and the thin rod as shown in Fig. 20E.

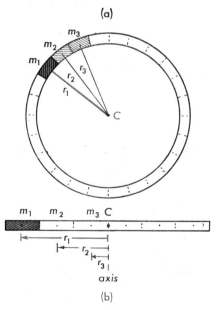

(a)

(b)

Fig. 20E *Diagram showing the division of (a) a ring, and (b) a rod, into small masses for calculating their moments of inertia.*

Both the ring and the rod are divided into small parts, as shown by the dotted lines and shaded areas, and the moment of inertia I is calculated from the formula

$$I = m_1r_1^2 + m_2r_2^2 + m_3r_3^2 + \ldots \quad (20k)$$

where m_1, m_2, m_3, ... represent the masses of each small part, and $r_1, r_2, r_3, \ldots$ their respective distances from the axis of rotation.

Since r has the same value for all masses around the ring, the subscripts on the r's can be dropped,

$$I = m_1r^2 + m_2r^2 + m_3r^2 + \ldots$$

and the common factor r^2 taken out as follows:

$$I = (m_1 + m_2 + m_3 + \ldots)r^2$$

Because the sum of all the masses $m_1 + m_2 + m_3 + \ldots$ equals M, the total mass of the ring,

$$\boxed{I_{\text{ring}} = Mr^2} \quad (20l)$$

This is the same as the formula for a mass on the end of a string.

When the same procedure is applied to the rod in Fig. 20E, the values of r vary from mass to mass, and the calculations, using Eq.(20k), give only an approximate value of its moment of inertia. It is not difficult to show that the larger the number of parts into which the rod is divided, the more nearly will Eq.(20k) give the true moment of inertia. A derivation of the formula by which the true moment of inertia is usually calculated requires the integral calculus and gives

$$I_{\text{rod}} = \frac{1}{12}Ml^2 \quad (20m)$$

where M is the total mass of the rod and l its total length. Because the calculus method is beyond the scope of this book, this formula should be assumed to be correct. To illustrate the approximate method and to compare it with this correct formula, consider the following example:

Example 4. A uniform rod 12 m long and having a mass of 30 Kg is pivoted to turn about an axis through its center, perpendicular to its

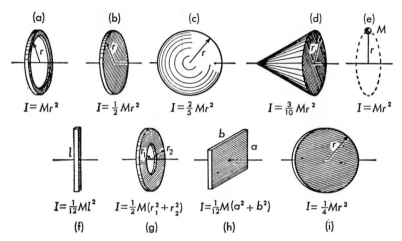

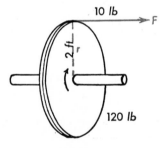

Fig. 20F *Formulas for the moment of inertia of certain regularly shaped bodies.*

length. Calculate its moment of inertia by (a) the true formula, and (b) the approximate formula.

Solution. (a) Direct substitution in Eq.(20m) gives

$$I = \frac{1}{12} \times 30 \text{ Kg} \times (12)^2 \text{ m}^2 = 360 \text{ Kg m}^2$$

as the true moment of inertia.

(b) By dividing the rod into six equal parts as shown in Fig. 20E, six masses are yielded of 5 Kg each with distances 5 m, 3 m, 1 m, 1 m, 3 m, and 5 m, respectively. Applying Eq.(20k), we obtain

$$I = 5 \times 5^2 + 5 \times 3^2 + 5 \times 1^2 + 5 \times 1^2$$
$$+ 5 \times 3^2 + 5 \times 5^2 = 350 \text{ Kg m}^2$$

a value nearly 3% lower than the true value.

Should the rod in part (b) have been divided into twelve equal parts, the same summation process would give 357.5 Kg m², a value less than 1% lower than (a). The student should confirm this last result as an exercise.

The true moments of inertia of a number of regular-shaped solid bodies are given in Fig. 20F. Diagram (a) represents a thin ring or hoop or radius r, (b) a disk of uniform density, (c) a solid sphere with an axis through the center, etc.

Two common moments of inertia not given in the figure are

Thin spherical shell—around any diameter,

$$I = \tfrac{2}{3} M r^2$$

Uniform ring—around any diameter,

$$I = \tfrac{1}{4} M (r_1^2 + r_2^2)$$

In the *cgs system,* the moment of inertia has the units of gm cm²; in the *mks system* as illustrated above, the units Kg m²; and in the *fps* system, the units slug ft² or lb ft-sec².

Example 5. A 120-lb flywheel, consisting of a uniform brass disk 4 ft in diameter, is mounted free to turn about an axis as shown in Fig.

Fig. 20G *A 4-ft flywheel weighing 120 lb is acted upon by a force of 10 lb applied tangent to the periphery.*

20G. A constant force of 10 lb is applied to its periphery by a cord wrapped around the wheel. Calculate the angular acceleration.

Solution. By definition, the applied torque is $L = F \times r,$

$$L = 10 \text{ lb} \times 2 \text{ ft} = 20 \text{ lb ft}$$

The moment of inertia of a disk equals

$$I = \frac{1}{2} \times \frac{120 \text{ lb}}{32 \text{ ft/sec}^2} \times 2^2 \text{ ft}^2 = 7.5 \text{ lb ft-sec}^2$$

Substitute known values in Eq.(20j).

$$20 \text{ lb ft} = 7.5 \text{ lb ft-sec}^2 \, \alpha$$

Solve for α, and cancel units.

$$\alpha = 2.67 \frac{\text{rad}}{\text{sec}^2}$$

20.6. Moment of Inertia About Any Axis.
It is to be noted in Fig. 20F that, with the
exception of (e), the moments of inertia are
referred to an axis through the geometrical
center. For bodies of uniform density, this
is also the center of mass. Analysis shows

that, if I_0 represents the moment of inertia
of a body about an axis through its center
of mass, the moment of inertia I about a
parallel axis, at a distance h away, is

$$I = I_0 + Mh^2 \qquad (20n)$$

Consider, for example, the narrow rod
in diagram (f). To find the moment of
inertia about the end of the rod, the axis
would have to be displaced from its present
position at the center to the end, a distance
equal to half its length, $l/2$. Therefore,

$$I = \tfrac{1}{12}Ml^2 + M\left(\frac{l}{2}\right)^2 = \tfrac{1}{3}Ml^2$$

The moment of inertia about the end is
$\tfrac{1}{3}Ml^2$.

PROBLEMS

1. An emery wheel 1 ft in diameter is making
3600 rpm. Find (a) tangential velocity of a
point on the rim, and (b) the distance traveled
in 5 sec by a point midway between the rim and
center.

2. An electric motor running at 1800 rpm
has 3 pulley wheels on its shaft. (a) Find the
linear speed of a belt when it is placed over
each wheel in turn. The pulley diameters are
3 in., 6 in., and 9 in., respectively. (b) If the
same belt passes over a similar pulley mounted
on another shaft, the 3 in. to the 9 in., the 6 in.
to the 6 in., and the 9 in. to the 3 in., what are
the 3 possible speeds of the adjacent shaft?
(*Ans.* (a) 23.56, 47.1, 70.7 ft/sec; (b) 600, 1800,
and 5400 rpm.)

3. A flywheel making 1200 rpm is slowed
down to 200 rpm in 10 sec by applying a brake.
Find (a) the acceleration, and (b) the angular
speed in rad/sec at the end of 3 sec, and (c) the
angle turned through in the first 3 sec.

4. Calculate the moment of inertia of an
emery wheel that weighs 12 lb and has a diameter of 9 in., (a) about its axis through the
center and perpendicular to the plane of one
face, and (b) about a parallel axis tangent to
the rim of the wheel. (*Ans.* (a) 0.0264 slug ft²,
(b) 0.0792 slug ft².)

5. Starting from rest, the large flywheel of a
steam engine acquires a speed of 450 rpm in 1
min. Find the angular acceleration in rad/sec².

6. An automobile engine is idling at 240 rpm.
Upon acceleration, it acquires a speed of 3600
rpm in 2 sec. Calculate (a) the angular acceleration, and (b) the angle turned through during
the acceleration. (*Ans.* (a) 175.9 rad/sec², (b)
402 rad.)

7. A uniform rod 50 cm long has a mass of
1 Kg and a rectangular cross section 4 cm by 6
cm. Calculate its moment of inertia about each
of three axes through its center of mass, perpendicular to (a) a 4-cm by 50-cm face, (b) a
6-cm by 50-cm face, and (c) a 4-cm by 6-cm face.

8. A uniform ring of 10-Kg mass has an internal diameter of 24 cm and an external
diameter of 30 cm. Find its moment of inertia
about an axis perpendicular to the plane of the
ring, and (a) through the center of mass, and
(b) through a point 50 cm from the center of
mass. (*Ans.* (a) 0.184 Kg m², (b) 2.68 Kg m².)

9. A uniform solid ball has a mass of 6 Kg
and a diameter of 30 cm. Calculate its moment
of inertia about an axis through the center of
mass, and (b) about an axis tangent to the ball.

10. A uniform door 7 ft by 30 in. weighs 40
lb. Calculate its moment of inertia about an
axis perpendicular to the plane of the door and
(a) through the center, and (b) through one
corner. (*Ans.* (a) 5.75 slug ft², (b) 17.3 slug ft².)

11. A baton consists of a uniform rod 60 cm
long, having a mass of 400 gm, with a 200-gm

hollow ball of 3-cm radius soldered to one end. Find its moment of inertia about the center of mass.

12. A 20-Kg flywheel of radius 0.20 m is free to turn about an axis as shown in Fig. 20F (b). A small, flat, circular disk with a mass of 4 Kg and radius 5 cm is welded off-center on one side of the flywheel so that the center-to-center distance is 12 cm. Find the moment of inertia about the center of mass. (*Ans.* 0.453 Kg m².)

13. A uniform disk has a mass of 500 gm and a diameter of 20 cm. With a string 90 cm long fastened to one edge of the disk, the system is suspended as a pendulum. Find the moment of inertia.

14. A uniform disk 10 cm in diameter has a mass of 1.5 Kg. One end of a 2-Kg rod 1.45 m long is welded to one edge of the disk to form a clock pendulum. Find the total moment of inertia about the top end of the rod. (*Ans.* 4.78 Kg m².)

15. A uniform flywheel weighing 40 lb has a diameter of 2 ft. What force applied tangent to this wheel will give it an acceleration of 0.5 rad/sec²?

16. A cylindrical grindstone 2 ft in diameter and weighing 40 lb is mounted on the same shaft with a pulley 1 ft in diameter and weighing 8 lb. A belt passes over the pulley and exerts a continuous force of 0.5 lb. Find (a) the

moment of inertia, (b) the angular acceleration, and (c) the angular speed at the end of 15 sec. Neglect the moment of inertia of the shaft and belt, and assume that the wheel starts from rest. (*Ans.* (a) 0.656 slug ft², (b) 0.381 rad/sec², (c) 5.71 rad/sec.)

17. A rectangular iron plate 0.5 m by 0.8 m has a mass of 120 Kg. It is free to rotate about an axis as shown in Fig. 20F(h). If a torque of 100 newton m is applied to set the plate rotating, find (a) the moment of inertia of the plate, (b) the angular acceleration, and (c) the angular speed at the end of 7 sec.

18. A rope is wrapped around the grinding surface of a large cylindrical grindstone 2 ft in radius, and a 10-lb weight hangs from the rope. If the wheel is free to rotate about a horizontal axis through its center, calculate (a) its angular acceleration, and (b) the tension in the rope. Assume a moment of inertia of 2 slug ft² for the grindstone. (*Ans.* (a) 6.15 rad/sec², (b) 6.15 lb.)

19. A dumbbell is composed of a uniform rod 42 cm long and 500-gm mass, and two solid spheres, one at either end, each with a diameter of 16 cm and a mass of 4000 gm. Find the moment of inertia about the center of mass.

20. The wheel of a water turbine having a moment of inertia of 250 Kg m², and rotating at a speed of 180 rpm, is brought to rest 26 min after the gate valve is closed. Find the torque applied. (*Ans.* 3.02 newton m.)

Chapter 21

Angular Momentum and Rotational Kinetic Energy

21.1. Angular Momentum. *Angular momentum* and *rotational kinetic energy* are to all rotating bodies what *linear momentum* and *kinetic energy* are to all bodies moving along a straight line. By definition, the angular momentum of a rotating body is equal to the product of its moment of inertia about the axis of rotation and its angular velocity.

$$\boxed{\text{angular momentum} = I\omega} \quad (21a)$$

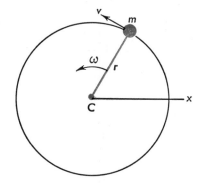

Fig. 21A *Angular momentum of a small mass m is given by mvr, or by mr²ω.*

In the special case of a small mass moving in a circle, as shown in Fig. 21A, the moment of inertia equals mr^2, and

$$\text{angular momentum} = mr^2\omega \quad (21b)$$

If ω is replaced by its equivalent, v/r,

$$\text{angular momentum} = mvr \quad (21c)$$

The first of the above equations applies to any rotating body regardless of size or shape, while the last two apply only to bodies considered small with respect to their distance from the center of rotation. To illustrate both cases, consider the following examples.

Example 1. A 20-Kg flywheel in the form of a uniform circular disk 1 m in diameter is making 120 rpm. Calculate its angular momentum.

Solution. To use Eq.(21a) the moment of inertia I and the angular velocity ω should first be calculated and expressed in the same system of units.

From the equation in Fig. 20F (b),

$$I = \tfrac{1}{2}Mr^2 = \tfrac{1}{2}20 \text{ Kg} \times (0.5\text{m})^2 = 2.5 \text{ Kg m}^2$$

By Eq.(20c),

$$\omega = 2\pi \times \frac{120}{60} = 4\pi \, \frac{\text{rad}}{\text{sec}}$$

By substituting in Eq.(21a), we obtain

$$\text{angular momentum} = 2.5 \text{ Kg m}^2 \times 4\pi \text{ rad/sec}$$
$$= 31.4 \text{ Kg m}^2/\text{sec}$$

Example 2. A boy weighing 100 lb rides at the outer edge of a merry-go-round, 40 ft in diameter. Calculate his angular momentum if the merry-go-round is making 3 rpm.

Solution. Since the boy is small compared with his distance from the center of rotation, Eq.(21b) can be used. First the angular velocity ω is found by Eq.(20c).

$$\omega = \frac{3 \times 2\pi}{60} = 0.314 \, \frac{\text{rad}}{\text{sec}}$$

Substitution of known values in Eq.(21b) gives

$$\text{angular momentum} = \frac{100 \text{ lb}}{32 \text{ ft/sec}^2} \times (20 \text{ ft})^2$$
$$\times 0.314 \, \frac{\text{rad}}{\text{sec}} = 392.5 \text{ lb ft-sec}$$

21.2. Theoretical Considerations. To understand why angular momentum is defined as $I\omega$, return to the fundamental equation for torque given in the preceding chapter, $L = I\alpha$. If in this equation the angular acceleration is replaced by its defining equation, $\alpha = (\omega - \omega_0)/t$,

$$L = I\frac{\omega - \omega_0}{t} \qquad (21d)$$

If t is transposed to the left side and multiplied out, an equation analogous to the impulse equation in translational motion is obtained.

$$Ft = mv - mv_0 \qquad Lt = I\omega - I\omega_0 \qquad (21e)$$
linear motion   angular motion

In linear motion, Ft is called the impulse and $mv - mv_0$, the change in momentum. By analogy, therefore, it is logical that Lt be called the *angular impulse* and $I\omega - I\omega_0$ the *change in angular momentum*. $I\omega_0$ is the initial angular momentum and $I\omega$ the final value.

Consider the flywheel shown in Fig. 21B. Starting from rest, and acted upon by a

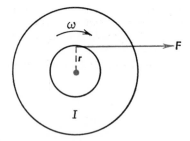

Fig. 21B *An acting torque sets a wheel rotating.*

torque $r \times F$ for a period of t seconds, the wheel acquires a final angular velocity of ω radians per second. In this special case of starting from rest, $\omega_0 = 0$, and Eq.(21e) reduces to

$$Lt = I\omega \qquad (21f)$$

Example 3. The wheel of a grindstone with a diameter of 30 cm and a mass of 5 Kg has applied at its axle, 4 cm in diameter, a constant tangential force of 98 newtons. Find (a) the angular momentum acquired at the end of 10 sec, and (b) the angular velocity.

Solution. (a) Since the wheel starts from rest ($\omega_0 = 0$), Eq.(21f) can be used. To determine $I\omega$ it is most convenient to calculate its equivalent, the angular impulse Lt.

Substitution of given quantities gives

$$Lt = 98\,\frac{\text{Kg m}}{\text{sec}^2} \times 0.02\text{ m} \times 10\text{ sec} = 19.6\,\frac{\text{Kg m}^2}{\text{sec}}$$

(b) Use Eq.(21f) and transpose.

$$\omega = \frac{Lt}{I} = \frac{19.6\text{ Kg m}^2/\text{sec}}{\frac{1}{2}5\text{ Kg} \times (0.15\text{ m})^2} = 348\,\frac{\text{rad}}{\text{sec}}$$

21.3. Conservation of Angular Momentum. If no external torque acts upon a body or system of bodies already in rotation, the angular momentum remains constant. Setting the torque L in Eq.(21e) equal to zero, $0 = I\omega - I\omega_0$, from which

$$\boxed{I\omega = I\omega_0} \qquad (21g)$$

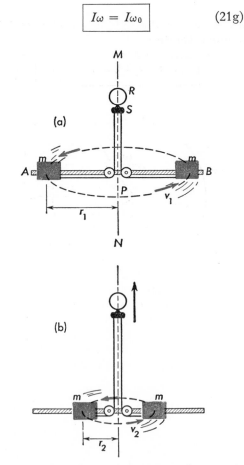

Fig. 21C *Experimental demonstration of the conservation of angular momentum.*

In words, the final angular momentum is always equal to the initial angular momentum.

An experiment illustrating a system of bodies in rotation is diagramed in Fig. 21C. Two equal masses m are mounted on a rod AB which is capable of rotation about a vertical axis MN. Cords fastened to each mass and leading over pulleys at P to the ring R enable the radial distance to be changed from r_1 in (a) to r_2 in (b) by simply pulling up on the ring R. The swivel S prevents the cords from twisting.

When the system is first set rotating as in (a) with an angular velocity ω_1, the angular momentum of each mass is $I\omega_1$. On pulling up on the ring R, the radius decreases to r_2 and the angular velocity ω_2 increases. Conservation of angular momentum requires that, for each mass m,

$$I_1\omega_1 = I_2\omega_2 \qquad (21h)$$

In terms of speed v,

$$mv_1r_1 = mv_2r_2 \qquad (21i)$$

Since the mass is not altered in value, the conservation of angular momentum requires that any decrease in r must be compensated for by an increase in speed. This is necessary to keep both sides of the above equation equal to each other.

Eq.(21i) shows for example that, if r is reduced to half value, the velocity v must double. With v doubled and the circle only half as large, the angular velocity increases fourfold.

Example 4. Suppose in Fig. 21C that $m = 10$ gm, $v_1 = 20$ cm/sec, and $r_1 = 16$ cm. What will be the new speed if the radius r_1 is decreased to half value, i.e., $r_2 = 8$ cm?

Solution. By direct substitution in Eq.(21i),

$$10 \text{ gm} \times 20\,\frac{\text{cm}}{\text{sec}} \times 16 \text{ cm} = 10 \text{ gm} \times v_2 \times 8 \text{ cm}$$

$$3200\,\frac{\text{cm}}{\text{sec}} = 80\,v_2$$

$$v_2 = 40\,\frac{\text{cm}}{\text{sec}}$$

An interesting experiment illustrating the same principle is diagramed in Fig.

Fig. 21D *Experiments illustrating conservation of angular momentum.*

21D. An observer stands on a turntable with weights in each hand. With arms fully extended horizontally, he is first set rotating slowly. Upon drawing the hands and weights in toward the chest, as shown, the angular velocity is considerably increased. This experiment is best appreciated by the turning observer who feels himself speeded up by what seems to be a mysterious force.

The force that increases the angular velocity when each mass is pulled in, or decreases it when each mass is allowed to move out, is the coriolis force described in Sec. 14.4. The force pulling each mass in, for example, is radially inward but the coriolis force is at right angles to r and accelerates each mass according to Eq.(14l).

This principle is used by expert figure skaters on the ice. They start into a whirl with their arms, and perhaps one leg extended, and then upon drawing the arms and leg in, obtain a greatly increased angular velocity.

21.4. Kinetic Energy of Rotation. In a previous chapter on linear motion, kinetic energy was seen to be given by $\frac{1}{2}mv^2$. By analogy the kinetic energy of a rigid body in rotation is given by $\frac{1}{2}I\omega^2$:

$$\text{KE}_{\text{trans}} = \tfrac{1}{2}mv^2 \qquad \boxed{\text{KE}_{\text{rot}} = \tfrac{1}{2}I\omega^2} \qquad (21j)$$

As a wheel rolls along a level road it has both kinetic energy of rotation and kinetic energy of translation. See Fig. 21E. In rotat-

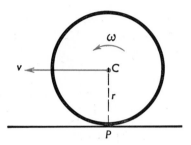

Fig. 21E *A rolling wheel has kinetic energy of rotation and kinetic energy of translation.*

ing about its geometrical center, it has a moment of inertia I_0 and kinetic energy $\frac{1}{2}I_0\omega^2$, while the center of gravity C, moving along a straight line with velocity v has kinetic energy $\frac{1}{2}mv^2$. The total kinetic energy is, therefore,

$$\text{K.E.}_{tot} = \tfrac{1}{2}I_0\omega^2 + \tfrac{1}{2}mv^2 \qquad (21k)$$

Total K.E. = rotational K.E.
                    + translational K.E.

21.5. Angular Momentum a Vector. Angular momentum, as illustrated by the rotating wheel in Fig. 21F, may be treated

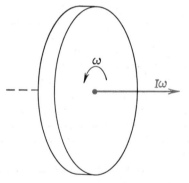

Fig. 21F *Angular momentum may be represented by a vector.*

as a vector quantity. To obtain an angular momentum vector, imagine grasping the axis of rotation with the right hand, the fingers pointing in the direction of rotation, the thumb then pointing in the direction of the vector. The length of the vector is given by the magnitude of $I\omega$.

Since angular momentum $I\omega$ is the result of an applied angular impulse Lt, the vec-

tor for $I\omega$ in Fig. 21F also represents Lt. In other words, Lt is a vector quantity and its direction and magnitude is that of $I\omega$. Torque is likewise a vector quantity. Its magnitude is given by $r \times F$, and its direction is given by the right-hand rule above.

The advantage of representing angular momentum and angular impulse by vectors becomes apparent when attempting to determine the resultant motion of a body that undergoes rotation about two or more axes simultaneously. The gyroscope in some of its varied forms serves as a good illustration of this.

21.6. The Spinning Top. A common top, set spinning like the one shown in Fig. 21G,

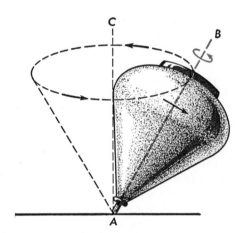

Fig. 21G *A spinning top precesses around a vertical axis.*

is but one of the many forms of a gyroscope. Spinning about its axis, the top precesses about its peg or pivot point, the line AB describing an inverted cone about the vertical line AC. If, when looking down from above, such a top is seen to be spinning in a clockwise direction, the precession is clockwise; spinning counterclockwise the precession is counterclockwise.

21.7. The Gyroscope. A fundamental study of gyroscopic precession may be readily made by the use of a top similar to those found in toy shops, and diagramed in Fig. 21H. The wheel W is designed to have a large moment of inertia, and is often ball-bearing mounted. Free rotation in any di-

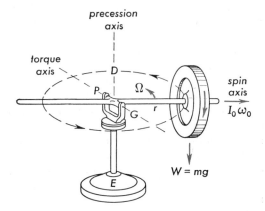

Fig. 21H *Experimental gyroscope for demonstrating precession.*

rection is permitted by the double pivot at the top of the stand E.

When the wheel is set spinning at high speed and released with its axis in a horizontal position, a smooth precession takes place around the vertical axis. This precessional motion is due to the external force exerted by the earth's gravitational pull downward on the wheel. Acting through the wheel's center of gravity, this downward force W, equal to mg, exerts a torque about a horizontal axis through PG. This torque L, given by $r \times W$, and acting for a time t, constitutes a torque impulse Lt and gives rise to a corresponding angular momentum $(I\omega)'$ about the same axis.

$$Lt = (I\omega)' \qquad (21l)$$

The top therefore has two angular momenta, one $I_0\omega_0$ due to spin and the other $(I\omega)'$ about a horizontal axis PG. Combining these vectorially, as shown in Fig. 21I, we obtain a resultant R equal in magnitude to the original $I_0\omega_0$ and now making an

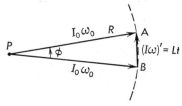

Fig. 21I *Vector diagram for precession of a gyroscope.*

angle ϕ with its direction. In other words, there has been a precession, a change in the direction of the spin axis. The angular momentum $I_0\omega_0$ is called the *spin vector*.

In the vector diagram the spin vector $I_0\omega_0$ is changing in direction by an amount $(I\omega)'$. Since $(I\omega)'$ is increasing with time and is due to a torque L, it can, by Eq.(21l) be replaced by Lt. For small angles ϕ, the distance measured along the arc AB is approximately equal to Lt and we can write

$$\phi = \frac{Lt}{I_0\omega_0} \qquad (21m)$$

Because the action gives rise to a uniform precession, angle ϕ is increasing at a uniform rate and may be written

$$\phi = \Omega t \qquad (21n)$$

where Ω is the precessional angular velocity.

Combining these two equations, we obtain

$$\Omega = \frac{L}{I_0\omega_0} \qquad (21o)$$

This, the precessional angular velocity in radians per second, is given by the torque L divided by the spin angular momentum.

By analogy, the treatment above is similar to that of circular motion given in Fig. 14D. There, a mass moves in a circle at constant speed because a constant inward force is exerted upon it. Although the acceleration is toward the center, the radius remains constant while only the direction of v changes.

In precessional motion, the magnitude of the angular momentum remains constant while its direction changes smoothly and continuously. And similar to the treatment of circular motion (see p. 107), as the angle ϕ is made smaller and smaller in Fig. 21I, the arc AB becomes more and more nearly equal to the chord AB, and the change is nearly perpendicular to the spin axis. In the limit when ϕ becomes zero, Eq.(21o) holds exactly and the spin vector and torque vector are mutually perpendicular.

21.8. The Product of Two Vectors. Since a vector may represent the magnitude and direction of any one of a number of physical quantities, it is impossible to say what the product of two vectors ought to be. By examining the various ways in which two vector quantities enter into physical concepts, however, two distinct kinds of vector products are found. One of these, called the *scalar product,* yields a scalar quantity; the other, the *vector product,* yields a vector quantity.

The Scalar or Dot Product. The scalar product of two vectors A and B, whose directions make an angle θ with each other, is equal to $AB \cos \theta$. The scalar product is written

$$\boxed{\mathbf{A} \cdot \mathbf{B} = AB \cos \theta} \qquad (21p)$$

Boldface capital letters represent vectors while italic capitals represent their magnitudes only. A graphical representation of these quantities is given in Fig. 21J. In

they are opposite in direction, $\cos \theta = -1$, and $\mathbf{A} \cdot \mathbf{B} = -AB$. The dot product of two vectors has magnitude but no direction, and is therefore a scalar quantity. It follows that the square of any vector is a scalar.

Example 5. A heavy box is pulled across the floor by a rope inclined at an angle of 30° with the horizontal. If the applied force F is 50 newtons, and the distance moved s is 12 m, the work done, and therefore the energy expended, is given by the dot product $\mathbf{F} \cdot \mathbf{s}$. (See Sec. 15.1.)

$$W = \mathbf{F} \cdot \mathbf{s} = Fs \cos \theta$$

Upon substitution, we obtain

$$W = 50 \text{ newtons} \times 12\text{m} \times 0.866$$
$$W = 520 \text{ newton meters}$$

The Vector or Cross Product. The vector product of two vectors $\mathbf{A}$ and $\mathbf{B}$, whose directions make an angle θ with each other,

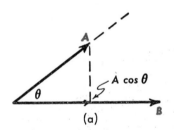 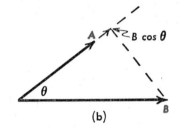

Fig. 21J   *Vector diagram illustrating the dot product.*

diagram (a), $A \cos \theta$ is the component of $\mathbf{A}$ in the direction of $\mathbf{B}$, positive or negative, depending on whether θ is less than or greater than 90°. In diagram (b), $B \cos \theta$ is the component of $\mathbf{B}$ in the direction of $\mathbf{A}$. Since the two right triangles in these diagrams are similar, corresponding sides are proportional and we can write $A:A \cos \theta = B:B \cos \theta$. Cross-multiplying, one obtains $AB \cos \theta = BA \cos \theta$. The order of the two vectors may, therefore, be reversed without changing the value of the product.

$$\mathbf{A} \cdot \mathbf{B} = \mathbf{B} \cdot \mathbf{A}$$

If the vectors are in the same direction, $\cos \theta = 1$, and $\mathbf{A} \cdot \mathbf{B} = AB$; and if they are at right angles, $\cos \theta = 0$, and $\mathbf{A} \cdot \mathbf{B} = 0$. If

is equal to a vector whose magnitude is $AB \sin \theta$, and whose direction is perpendicular to both $\mathbf{A}$ and $\mathbf{B}$, being positive relative to a rotation from $\mathbf{A}$ to $\mathbf{B}$.

The vector product is written

$$\boxed{\mathbf{A} \times \mathbf{B} = AB \sin \theta} \qquad (21q)$$

A graphical representation of these quantities is given in Fig. 21K. The resultant vector $\mathbf{A} \times \mathbf{B}$, has the same direction as the translation of a right-handed screw due to a rotation from $\mathbf{A}$ to $\mathbf{B}$. From this sign convention, it follows that the vector product $\mathbf{B} \times \mathbf{A}$ has the same magnitude as $\mathbf{A} \times \mathbf{B}$, but has opposite direction.

$$\mathbf{A} \times \mathbf{B} = -\mathbf{B} \times \mathbf{A}$$

A reversal of the order of the vectors reverses the sign of the product. For two parallel vectors, $\sin \theta = 0$, and the vector product $\mathbf{A} \times \mathbf{B} = 0$. If $\mathbf{A}$ and $\mathbf{B}$ are at right angles, $\sin \theta = 1$, $\mathbf{A} \times \mathbf{B} = AB$, and all three vectors $\mathbf{A}$, $\mathbf{B}$, and $\mathbf{A} \times \mathbf{B}$ are mutually perpendicular.

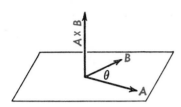

Fig. 21K *Vector diagram illustrating the cross product.*

Example 6. A heavy wheel, free to turn around its central axis, has a rope wrapped around its periphery. If a steady pull F of 24 newtons is applied to the rope, and the wheel radius r is 1.4 m, torque L acting upon it is given by the cross product $\mathbf{r} \times \mathbf{F}$.

$$L = \mathbf{r} \times \mathbf{F} = rF \sin \theta$$

Since the force vector F makes an angle of 90° with the radius vector r, $\sin 90° = 1$, and $L = rF$. The resultant torque L is perpendicular to both $\mathbf{r}$ and $\mathbf{F}$, and its magnitude is given by

$$L = 1.4 \text{ meters} \times 24 \text{ newtons}$$
$$L = 33.6 \text{ meter newtons}$$

Note that, although the units of this answer are the same as those for Example 5, torque is a vector quantity, whereas work, or energy, is a scalar quantity.

We have seen in Eq.(14e) that the instantaneous velocity v of a particle, moving in a circle of radius r, is given by $v = r\omega$. Since all three of these quantities are vectors, the equation is often written as a cross product

$$v = \omega \times r$$

Similarly, the coriolis acceleration of a body, moving in a rotating frame of reference, is seen in Eq.(14m) to be given by $a_c = 2v\omega$. It is customary to write this equation of the vector product:

$$a_c = -2\omega \times v$$

PROBLEMS

1. Two small spheres weighing 1 lb each are tied to opposite ends of a string so that their centers are 4 ft apart. A slip knot is tied in the center of the string, making the spheres 18 in. apart. In this condition they are thrown whirling into the air with an angular speed of 300 rpm. While in the air the slip knot comes untied. Calculate the new angular speed in rpm.

2. A bowling ball with a diameter of 10 in. and a weight of 12 lb rolls along the floor at 18 ft/sec. Calculate its total kinetic energy. (*Ans.* 85.0 ft-lb.)

3. A uniform hoop with an inside diameter of 0.2 m and an outside diameter of 0.24 m has a mass of 0.24 Kg. If this hoop is set rolling along a level floor at 5 m/sec, find (a) its moment of inertia about the geometrical center, (b) its angular speed, and (c) its total kinetic energy.

4. As a car is traveling along a road at 60 mi/hr, one of the tires comes off and rolls down the road. Calculate the kinetic energy of the tire if the inner diameter is 16 in., the outer diameter is 32 in., and it weighs 30 lb. Use the equation in Fig. 20F(g). (*Ans.* 8169 ft-lb.)

5. A uniform disk 3 ft in diameter weighs 40 lb. Calculate (a) the angular momentum, and (b) the rotational kinetic energy when it rotates as a wheel about its geometrical center at 1200 rpm.

6. A uniform solid sphere has a diameter of 50 cm and a mass of 100 Kg. It rotates at 720 rpm about an axis through its center of mass. Calculate (a) its angular momentum, and (b) its rotational kinetic energy. (*Ans.* (a) 188 Kg m²/sec, (b) 7106 joules.)

7. A uniform disk 1 ft in diameter and 8 lb in mass starts from rest and rolls down a 10% grade. If, at the bottom, it has a speed of 22 ft/sec, find (a) the total kinetic energy, and (b) the distance traveled.

8. A hollow ball with a diameter of 12 cm and a mass of 1 Kg rolls 20 m down a 20° in-

cline. Find (a) its moment of inertia, (b) its kinetic energy, and (c) its final speed. (*Ans.* (a) 0.0024 Kg m², (b) 66.9 joules, (c) 8.97 m/sec.)

9. A hoop 2 ft in diameter and weighing 5 lb starts from rest and rolls 20 ft down an incline making 30° with the horizontal. Find its speed at the bottom.

10. A uniform disk with a diameter of 20 cm and a mass of 50 gm rolls 10 m down a 20° incline. Find (a) its speed at the bottom, and (b) its kinetic energy. (*Ans.* (a) 6.68 m/sec, (b) 1.68 joules.)

11. A uniform solid ball rolls 10 m down a 10° incline. Find its speed at the bottom.

12. A solid uniform ball rolls along a level plane at 20 ft/sec. (a) If it comes to a 15° incline, how far up will it roll before coming to a stop? (b) How long does it remain on the incline? (*Ans.* (a) 33.8 ft, (b) 6.76 sec.)

13. A uniform rod, having a length of 120 cm and a mass of 10 Kg, can rotate about a transverse axis through its middle point. How many joules of work will be required to set it rotating at 300 rpm?

14. A flywheel, with a moment of inertia of 20 Kg m², has a rotational kinetic energy of 1000 joules. What is its speed of rotation in rpm? (*Ans.* 95.5 rpm.)

15. A hoop weighing 320 lb rotates about an axis through its center at 192 rpm. If its diameter is 4 ft, find its (a) moment of inertia, (b) angular velocity, (c) angular momentum, and (d) kinetic energy.

16. A boy's hoop has a mass of 1 Kg and a diameter of 1 m. It rolls along a level road at 2 m/sec. Calculate (a) the moment of inertia, (b) its angular speed, and (c) its total kinetic energy. (*Ans.* (a) 0.25 Kg m², (b) 4 rad/sec, (c) 4 joules.)

17. The rotating parts of an automobile motor have a moment of inertia equivalent to that of a uniform disk 1 ft in diameter and weighing 64 lb. (a) what is its moment of inertia? (b) Find its kinetic energy when rotating at 6000 rpm.

18. Each of the four propellers on the S.S. *Normandie* has a mass of 19 tons and a moment of inertia of 60,000 slug ft². The ship makes 29 knots when the propellers are turning over at 200 rpm. Calculate (a) the angular momentum, (b) the kinetic energy of each propeller, and (c) the advance of the ship with each turn. (*Ans.* (a) 1.25×10^6 slug ft²/sec, (b) 1.32×10^7 ft-lb, (c) 14.7 ft.)

19. A hollow ball starts from rest at the top of a sloping roof 6 m long. The roof makes an angle of 30° with the horizontal, and the edge of the roof is 5 m above the ground. Calculate (a) the velocity of the ball upon reaching the edge of the roof, (b) the time required to reach the edge of the roof, and (c) the point where the ball strikes the ground.

20. Let the two masses m in Fig. 21C weigh 5 lb each, their initial distance from the center of rotation be 2 ft, and the initial angular speed be 300 rpm. If the radius is decreased to 1 ft by pulling up the swivel S, calculate (a) the initial angular momentum, (b) the final angular momentum, (c) the initial kinetic energy, and (d) the final kinetic energy. (e) Where did the increased energy come from? (*Ans.* (a) 39.3 lb ft/sec. (b) 39.3 lb ft/sec, (c) 617 ft-lb, (d) 2467 ft-lb, (e) from work done in pulling the weights in.)

21. A 1-Kg solid sphere, with diameter 20 cm, starts from rest at the top of an inclined plane. Find its linear speed at the bottom if the inclined plane makes an angle of 30° with the horizontal and is 2 m long. For a sphere, $I = 2/5\ Mr^2$.

22. A metal disk with a mass of 1 Kg and diameter 20 cm starts from rest at the top of an inclined plane. Find its linear speed at the bottom if the inclined plane makes an angle of 30° with the horizontal and is 2 m long. For a disk, $I = \frac{1}{2}\ Mr^2$. (*Ans.* 362 cm/sec.)

23. A uniform flywheel (a disk) has a mass of 10 Kg and a diameter of 60 cm. If it is turning with an angular speed of 900 rpm, find (a) the tangential speed of a point on the periphery, (b) the angular velocity, (c) the angular momentum, and (d) the kinetic energy. (The moment of inertia of a uniform disk is given by $I = \frac{1}{2}\ Mr^2$.)

24. An emery wheel (a uniform disk) is 20 cm in diameter, has a mass of 2 Kg, and rotates at 2600 rpm. Find (a) the angular velocity in rad/sec, (b) the tangential speed of a point on the rim, (c) the angular momentum, and (d) the kinetic energy. (The moment of inertia of a uniform disk is given by $I = \frac{1}{2}\ Mr^2$.) (*Ans.* (a) 272 rad/sec, (b) 27.2 m/sec. (c) 2.72 Kg m²/sec. (d) 370 Kg m²/sec².)

Chapter 22

The Atomic Structure of Matter

In dealing with the physical properties of matter it is convenient to divide substances into three forms or states: (1) *the solid state,* (2) *the liquid state,* and (3) *the gaseous state.* Most substances may be made to take on any one of these three forms simply by altering the temperature.

The atomic theory of matter assumes that all matter in the universe is made up of ultra-microscopic bodies called atoms and that these are at all times in a rapid state of motion. The nature of this motion and its activity depends upon the temperature and the state of the matter in question, as well as upon the kinds of atoms of which it is composed.

22.1. Kinds of Atoms. Although there are thousands of different substances known to the scientific world, they are all, when broken down into their smallest component parts, found to be composed of one or more kinds of atoms. A substance that contains atoms of one kind only is called an *element,* while those containing more than one kind are called *compounds* or *mixtures.* Iron, copper, aluminum, platinum, mercury, hydrogen, and helium are examples of elements; whereas water, salt, brass, wood, and air are examples of compounds and mixtures.

The technical names and chemical abbreviations of a few of the more commonly known elements are given in Table 22A. A complete table of the nearly 100 known elements is given in the Appendix.

With each element it is customary to associate two numbers; one is called the *atomic number,* the other the *atomic weight.* The

TABLE 22A. SOME OF THE CHEMICAL ELEMENTS

Atomic No.	Element	Symbol	Atomic Weight
1	hydrogen	H	1.0078
2	helium	He	4.004
3	lithium	Li	6.940
4	beryllium	Be	9.02
6	carbon	C	12.01
7	nitrogen	N	14.01
8	oxygen	O	16.000
10	neon	Ne	20.183
13	aluminum	Al	26.97
26	iron	Fe	55.84
29	copper	Cu	63.57
47	silver	Ag	107.88
50	tin	Sn	118.70
78	platinum	Pt	195.23
79	gold	Au	197.2
80	mercury	Hg	200.61
82	lead	Pb	207.18
88	radium	Ra	225.95
92	uranium	U	238.17
94	plutonium	Pu	239.18

atomic number, given at the left in the tables, specifies the position that element always occupies with respect to all the others, while the atomic weight on the right gives the average weight of one atom of that element relative to the average weight of an oxygen atom, which is 16. On this basis, the lightest known element, hydrogen, has an average weight of approximately unity.

To illustrate the minuteness of individual atoms, the actual masses in kilograms and approximate diameters in meters of the lightest element, hydrogen, and the very heavy element, plutonium, are as follows:

1. hydrogen $\begin{cases} \text{mass} = 1.66 \times 10^{-27} \text{ Kg} \\ \text{diameter} = 1 \times 10^{-10} \text{ m} \end{cases}$

94. plutonium $\begin{cases} \text{mass} = 3.9 \times 10^{-25} \text{ Kg} \\ \text{diameter} = 6 \times 10^{-10} \text{ m} \end{cases}$

The actual mass of any atom in kilograms can be obtained by multiplying the atomic weight of that element by the unit atomic mass 1.66×10^{-27} Kg.

Although the intricate structure of each atom plays an important part in its physical and chemical behavior, we will neglect this detailed structure for the time being and think only of each atom as being a tiny sphere-like particle with a very small mass. Later, in other chapters where it is pertinent to do so, the structure of individual atoms will be considered in detail.

22.2. Molecules. One of the most important properties of atoms is their ability to act upon one another at a distance. Some

will move about and behave as a unit particle under various physical conditions.

Molecules in general may contain almost any number of atoms. Those having but one atom are called *monatomic molecules,* those with two are called *diatomic molecules,* and those with three *triatomic molecules.* In the free state of a gas, some atoms, like helium, neon, and krypton, prefer to exist alone, whereas others like hydrogen, nitrogen, and oxygen prefer to combine and move about in pairs.

Examples of monatomic molecules are helium (He), neon (Ne), and krypton (Kr); of diatomic molecules are hydrogen (H_2), nitrogen (N_2), oxygen (O_2), and carbon monoxide (CO); and of triatomic molecules are ozone (O_3), carbon dioxide (CO_2), water (H_2O), and hydro-cyanic acid (HCN). (See Fig. 22A.) Besides these simplest atomic

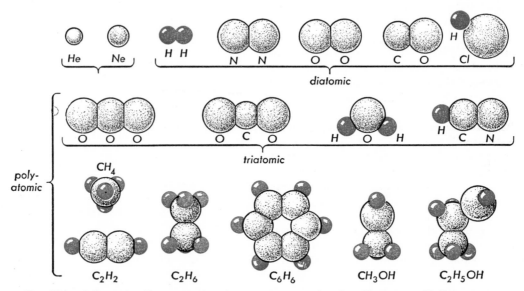

Fig. 22A *Schematic diagrams of a few common molecules. First row: Helium, neon, hydrogen, nitrogen, oxygen, carbon monoxide, hydrochloric acid. Second row: Ozone, carbon dioxide, water, hydrocyanic acid. Third row: Methane, acetylene, benzene, methyl alcohol, ethyl alcohol.*

atoms, when they come close together attract each other, while others exhibit a force of repulsion. When, at the close approach of two or more atoms, attraction occurs, the atoms may combine to form a molecule. Once a molecule has formed, it

aggregates, there are molecules known to contain many atoms. Along with triatomic molecules they are called polyatomic molecules.

It is clear from the diagrams in Fig. 22A that the atoms of a molecule may be of the same kind or may be different. The question as to why some atoms cling together in pairs and others do not is a subject involving the structure of the atoms themselves. If the individual atoms of a molecule are brought much closer together than their normal separation, they repel each other and are pushed apart. If they are pulled farther apart, the forces become attractive, pulling them together. In other words, they act as though they were connected by springs as shown in Fig. 22B. Pushed closer

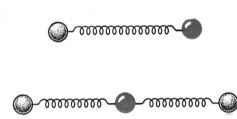

Fig. 22B   *The forces between atoms in a molecule behave like springs.*

together or pulled farther apart, they tend to move back to some equilibrium distance. In terms of energy they occupy a position of *minimum potential energy.* To push them closer together or to separate them requires work.

At large distances, all atomic forces become very weak so that if by some means or other the atoms of a molecule are pulled far enough apart they become completely separated as free atoms.

A graph of the forces between atoms is shown in Fig. 22C. The horizontal scale giving the distance *r* between atoms will be slightly different for different atoms, but the

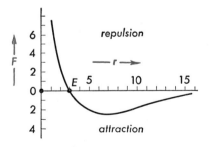

Fig. 22C   *Typical graph of the force between two atoms of a diatomic molecule.*

equilibrium position E is approximately 3×10^{-10} m.

22.3. Molecular Weight. The molecular weight of a substance is defined as the sum of the atomic weights of the atoms which make up one molecule of that substance. A carbon dioxide molecule, for example, has two oxygen atoms of weight 16 and one carbon atom of weight 12. The molecular weight of carbon dioxide is therefore $16 + 16 + 12 = 44$. Similarly the molecular weight of nitrogen is 28, oxygen 32, and helium 4. To find the mass of a molecule in grams, its molecular weight should be multiplied by unit atomic mass 1.66×10^{-24} gm.

22.4. Three States of Matter. As already stated, matter may exist in three states: (1) the solid state, (2) the liquid state, and (3) the gaseous state. If a solid is heated sufficiently it can be made to melt or liquefy, and by continued heating it can be boiled or vaporized. As a vapor, it is in the gaseous state. If, on the other hand, a gas is cooled sufficiently, it will condense and become a liquid. The continued cooling of a liquid will cause it to solidify or freeze. In the case of water, nature performs all these changes of state: ice is melted to become water, and water is vaporized to become steam; water vapor or clouds condense to become rain, and rain freezes to become ice or hail. Although it may sometimes require extreme heat or extreme cold, all substances can be transformed from any one state to another.

22.5. The Gaseous State. When a substance is in the gaseous state, it is in an extremely rarefied condition. Most of the atoms are grouped together into molecules which, on the average, are very far apart. These molecules are not at rest but are moving about with extremely high velocities, bumping into each other and into the walls of the container. It is the bumping of many millions of molecules against the walls of the containing vessel that gives rise to what is called gas pressure.

A good example of gas pressure is to be found where air has been pumped into an automobile tire or into a toy balloon. Since there are so many more air molecules bombarding the rubber walls inside than outside, the walls are held out by greater bombardment. In addition to moving linearly, a gas molecule, made up of two or more atoms, also vibrates and rotates about its center of mass. As the temperature of the gas is raised, all of these motions increase in speed, causing an increase in pressure. As the temperature is decreased, the atomic motions slow down, decreasing the pressure.

Molecular motion can be illustrated by means of a mechanical model as shown in Fig. 22D. Small steel marbles are placed be-

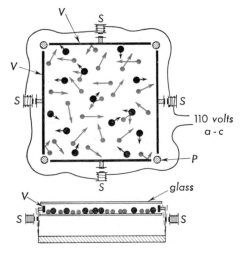

Fig. 22D *Mechanical model illustrating the random motion of molecules in a gas.*

tween two parallel glass plates and set into motion by means of vibrating metal strips around the sides. Each strip *V* is mounted at the end of a short strip of spring steel and is set into vibration by means of small electromagnets *S*. As the steel balls bump into these strips, they are bounced off with high speed. On the average, the small steel marbles move considerably faster than the larger ones. This is characteristic of the different-sized molecules in a mixture of two different gases like helium and neon. By increasing the vibrations of the strips the steel marbles move faster. This is analogous to the heating of a gas to a higher temperature.

22.6. The Liquid State. When a gas is continually cooled, the molecular motion slows down until at a certain temperature the gas condenses into a much smaller volume and changes into a liquid. Although the molecules continue to move, they no longer move as rapidly as they did in the gaseous state. Being much closer together, however, they now attract each other with sufficiently strong forces to cause them to move in closely packed swarms.

The swarming of honeybees as they fly through the air is comparable to the molecules of a gas, while their subsequent collection on the branch of a tree corresponds to condensation into the liquid state.

22.7. Brownian Motion. Although no one has ever observed directly the random motions of molecules, it is possible to observe in a microscope the resultant recoils of larger particles under their continual bombardment. The effect was first discovered in 1827 by Robert Brown, a British botanist, who observed the irregular but lifelike motions of small particles suspended in a liquid. These microscopic particles appear to be continually agitated and make a succession of quick jumps first one way and then another. The path of a single particle is illustrated in Fig. 22E. Such motions are called Brownian movements, after their discoverer. These curious Brownian move-

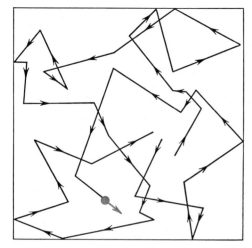

Fig. 22E *Diagram of the random path of a single molecule.*

ments were first explained by Sir William Ramsey in 1879 and may be observed in either liquids or gases. The invisibly small molecules of air or water, as the case may be, move at relatively high velocities and, bombarding the larger visible particles vigorously from all sides, make them dart here and there. The larger the particles, the slower their Brownian movement.

One method of observing Brownian motion in a gas is illustrated in Fig. 22F.

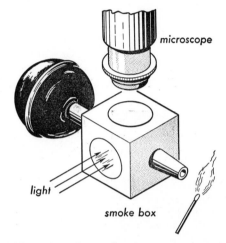

Fig. 22F *Experimental arrangement for observing the Brownian motion of smoke particles.*

Smoke from the tip of a match, just extinguished, is drawn into a small box by squeezing and releasing the rubber bulb. A strong beam of light from a carbon arc, entering the box through a glass lens in the side, illuminates the smoke particles, enabling them to be seen from above with a high power microscope. The tiny smoke particles appear as bright starlike points darting first one way and then another.

To observe Brownian movement in a liquid, a small amount of powdered gamboge (an orange-yellow gum resin) is first put into some distilled water, and one drop of this solution put on a microscope slide. By illuminating the slide with a strong light, the microscopic gamboge particles will be seen to dance about as they are continually being hit by water molecules. If one remembers that the gamboge particles are thou-

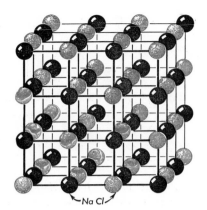

Fig. 22G *Atomic model for sodium chloride (NaCl is common table salt).*

sands of times heavier than the water molecules, it will be realized that the latter must be moving with very high speeds to cause such visible recoils.

22.8. The Solid State. As the temperature of a liquid is lowered, the molecular activity decreases. This permits the molecules to pack a little more closely together and accounts for the slight contraction of a liquid on cooling, and conversely for its expansion on heating. As the molecules come closer and closer together, the tendency of each molecule to wander through the liquid decreases. If the temperature is lowered still further a point is ultimately reached where the liquid freezes and becomes a solid.

In the solid state, each molecule is confined to a definite small space between neighboring molecules. This is illustrated in Figs. 22G, 22H, and 22I by atomic mod-

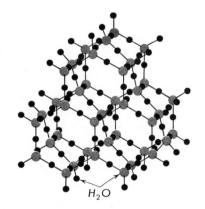

Fig. 22H *Atomic model for ice (H_2O).*

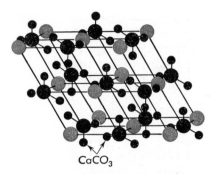

CaCO₃

Fig. 22I *Atomic model for iceland spar, or calcite, CaCO₃.*

els of ultramicroscopic crystals. The model in Fig. 2G illustrates a cubic lattice, a simple type of structure in which the atoms take positions at the corners of cubes. Com-

oxygen atoms of *quartz*, chemically SiO_2, take on a somewhat similar structure, and in the natural state also exhibit its hexagonal structure. (See Figs. 22K and 80Q.)

The third model, Fig. 22I, shows the atomic structure for a crystal of calcite. Calcite, which chemically is calcium carbonate ($CaCO_3$), is a clear transparent crystal found in nature. Because of its particular structure it has interesting optical properties, which will be discussed in a later chapter on polarized light. Note how the calcium and carbon atoms form the corners of parallelograms, with each carbon atom surrounded by three oxygen atoms.

Although some elements or compounds always seem to form the same crystal pattern on solidifying, others are known to take

Fig. 22J *Photographs of snow crystals exhibiting hexagonal structure.*

mon table salt with its two kinds of atoms, sodium and chlorine, always forms such a cubic lattice, the individual atoms alternating in kind in each of the three directions, Na, Cl, Na, Cl, Na, etc.

The crystal model in Fig. 22H is of the hexagonal lattice form in which the principal structure presents parallel hexagonal "holes" through the crystal. Water, in freezing to form ice, or snowflakes, takes on this form. (See Fig. 22J.) Note that within the atomic lattice each oxygen atom is bound by connecting links between four hydrogen atoms, while each hydrogen atom is linked between two oxygen atoms. The silicon and

on any one of a number of different forms. Some forms are found in nature, while others have been produced in the laboratory. Diamond, one of the several known crystal

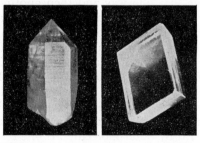

Fig. 22K *Natural crystals of quartz and calcite.*

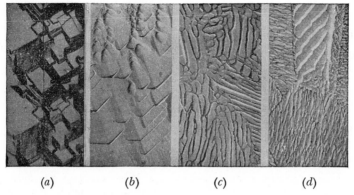

(a)   (b)   (c)   (d)

Fig. 22L *Electron microscope photographs showing the crystalline-like structure of metals: (a) pure aluminum 5600x, (b) magnesium-aluminum alloy 13,000x, (c) polished steel 14,000x, and (d) polished copper 14,000x.* (Courtesy, R. D. Heidenreich, Dow Chemical Co.)

forms of carbon atoms alone, is a closely packed crystal that has, until recently, defied laboratory reproduction. While some crystal types present a more open structure than others, the actual size of each atom in the models shown above has been reduced in order to reveal the positions of others behind.

Metals in general, when they cool down from the molten state, solidify into ultra-microscopic crystals that pack closely together to form a three-dimensional mosaic. This is well illustrated by the electron-microscope photographs reproduced in Fig. 22L. Note the clear-cut cubic structure of pure aluminum.

Actually, the atoms in most liquids begin to form localized crystal arrays before solidi-fication takes place but, due to the rapid state of atomic vibration, each localized crystal region can move with respect to another. A liquid may therefore be looked upon as a transition state between the gas where individual molecules exist and the solid where individual atoms become part of a crystal structure and can no longer be associated with any particular molecule. The average distance between atoms in all solids, crystal or amorphous, is of the order of 3×10^{-10}m.

While each atom or molecule in a solid is confined to a definite space within the body lattice, it is in a state of motion within that space. As the temperature decreases, this motion becomes slower and slower until at absolute zero, $-273°C$, all molecular

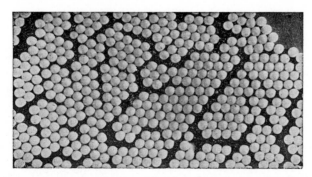

Fig. 22M *Electron microscope photograph of polystyrene molecules, showing natural hexagonal packing. Diameter 5×10^{-3} cm.* (Courtesy, Robley Williams.)

motion ceases. By molecular motion is meant the motion of the molecule as a whole. At absolute zero, however, the atoms of certain solids are still vibrating. This residual energy of vibration is known to be an inherent property of some solids, which cannot be utilized or taken away.*

* For an introductory book on crystal structure, see Alan Holden, and Phylis Singer, *Crystals and Crystal Growing*, Doubleday, New York.

QUESTIONS

1. What are the three states of matter? How do these states differ from each other? Which, in general, is the most compact?

2. How many known elements are there? What constitutes an element?

3. What is meant by (a) atomic number and (b) atomic weight?

4. Give an example of (a) a monatomic molecule, (b) a diatomic molecule, (c) a triatomic molecule, and (d) a polyatomic molecule.

5. What general treatment of most solids will change their state to the liquid or gas?

6. What is Brownian motion? How is it observed?

7. What can you say about the arrangement of atoms in a solid, like iron? In a solid like common table salt?

8. How could you set up an experiment to demonstrate the forces between the atoms of a linear triatomic molecule? If you were to push the outer atoms of a molecule toward each other and suddenly release them, what kind of motion do you think would ensue?

Chapter 23

Properties of
Solids—Elasticity

In the following treatment of elasticity, the *gram* and *kilogram* are frequently treated as units of force. Such usage is justified since the actual applied forces are directly proportional to the masses that produce them: $W \propto m$. We therefore introduce the *gram weight* and *kilogram weight (abbr.* gm-wt and Kg-wt) as units of force. *One kilogram weight, for example, is defined as a force equivalent in magnitude to the downward pull of the earth on a one kilogram mass:* $W = mg$.

23.1. Stretching of a Spring. If a vertically mounted rod, wire, or spring is supported rigidly at its upper end, and weights are added to its lower end, the amount by which it is stretched is found to be proportional to the weight applied. This is known as Hooke's law. The stretching of a spring is illustrated in Fig. 23A. Due to an added

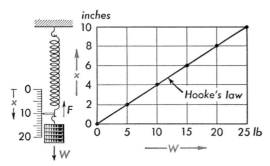

Fig. 23A *Experiment illustrating Hooke's law.*

weight W, the spring is stretched a distance x. If a second equal weight is added, the total distance stretched will be twice that for the first one. If a third weight is added, the total distance stretched will be three

times that for the first one, etc. This is illustrated by the graph shown at the right in Fig. 23A. Each value of x is plotted vertically and the corresponding loads W are plotted horizontally.

More specifically, when the first 10-gm weight is added, the stretch or elongation is 2 cm. With two 10-gm weights the total elongation is 4 cm, and with three weights $x = 6$ cm, etc. A continuation of this shows, as does the graph at the right in Fig. 23A, that each 10-gm weight produces an added elongation of 2 cm. To make an equation of this, we write

$$W = kx \qquad (23a)$$

where k is a constant and equal in this experiment to 5. Each value of x multiplied by 5 gives the corresponding weight W. When the spring in Fig. 23A is stretched a distance x, the spring itself exerts an upward force F equal but opposite in direction to W. For the spring, then,

$$\boxed{F = -kx} \qquad (23b)$$

The minus sign indicates that x and F are in opposite directions. This equation is often referred to as Hooke's law.*

23.2. The Stretching of a Wire. Because

* Robert Hooke (1635-1703), English experimental physicist known principally for his contributions to the wave theory of light, universal gravitation, and atmospheric pressure. He originated many physical ideas but perfected few of them. Hooke's scientific achievements would undoubtedly have received greater acclaim had his efforts been confined to fewer subjects. He had an irritable temper, and made many virulent attacks on Newton and other men of science, claiming that work published by them was due to him.

a wire or rod will not stretch very far before reaching the breaking point, one must, in order to check Hooke's law, resort to some method of measuring extremely small changes in length. This is frequently done by means of a device known as the optical lever. As shown by the experiment diagramed in Fig. 23B, a beam of light is re-

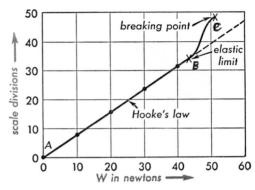

Fig. 23C   *A graph of the stretching of a wire showing Hooke's law, the elastic limit, and the breaking point.*

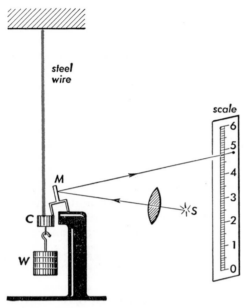

Fig.   23B   *The stretching of a wire under increasing tension can be measured by an optical lever.*

flected from a small mirror M mounted on a small three-legged stool, two legs of which rest on a stationary platform, as shown, and the third on a small clamp C at the lower end of the wire. As the wire stretches under an added weight W, the mirror tips back and the light beam is reflected up a measurable amount on the distant scale.

Like the stretching of a spring described in the preceding section, the stretching of a wire obeys Hooke's law. The amount stretched is directly proportional to the force applied and is illustrated by the straight part of the graph AB in Fig. 23C. If the weights are removed, the wire will return to its original length. If weights are continually added, the forces applied will eventually become too great, and Hooke's

law will no longer hold as the elongation will increase too rapidly. This is the region BC on the graph. Carried too far in this direction, the wire will break. The point B at which Hooke's law ceases to hold is called the *elastic limit*. If the wire is stretched beyond this point, it will be permanently stretched and will not return to its original length when the weights are removed.

23.3. Stress and Strain. When a force of any magnitude is applied to a solid body, the body becomes distorted. Whether the distortion is large or small, some portion of the body is moved with respect to some neighboring portion. As a result of this displacement, atomic forces of attraction set up restoring forces which resist the alteration and tend to restore the body to its original shape. The greater the applied force, the greater will be the deformation, which in turn sets up greater atomic restoring forces that bring about equilibrium. (See Fig. 22C.)

It is a common engineering practice to describe the restoring forces in a distorted body as a stress and to give to this term the quantitative definition of *force per unit area.* The actual deformation of the body produced by an applied force involves a change in geometrical form called *strain.* Strain is defined as a quantitative measure of deformation.

23.4. Hooke's Law. Hooke's law, as described above for the stretching of a spring or wire, applies equally well to other types of deformation. In general, Hooke's law states that *stress is proportional to strain.* The stress set up within an elastic body is proportional to the strain caused by the applied load.

$$\text{stress} \propto \text{strain} \qquad (23c)$$

To make an equation of this, a proportionality constant K is introduced:

$$\text{stress} = K \text{ strain}$$

Upon transposing,

$$K = \frac{\text{stress}}{\text{strain}} \qquad (23d)$$

The constant K has a value characteristic of the material of the elastic body and is called the *modulus of elasticity.*

23.5. Young's Modulus. Consider the experiment, diagramed in Fig. 23B, where a wire or rod is clamped at one end and a load is applied at the other. Let l represent the wire's original length, A its cross-sectional area, and e the elongation produced by the applied load F. (See Fig. 23D.)

By definition, stress is the force per unit area, and strain is the elongation per unit length.

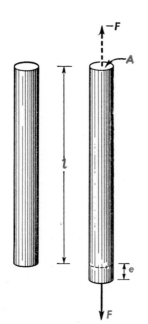

Fig. 23D *Young's modulus for the stretching of a wire or rod is given by Fl/Ae.*

$$\text{stress} = F/A \quad (23e) \qquad \text{strain} = e/l \quad (23f)$$

When these defining equations are substituted in Eq.(23d) the modulus of elasticity K is called *Young's modulus,** written as Y, and is given by

$$Y = \frac{F/A}{e/l} \quad \text{or} \quad \boxed{Y = \frac{Fl}{Ae}} \quad (23g)$$

Young's modulus Y is a very practical constant, for, if its value is known for any given material, the amount of stretch produced in any size of wire or rod of that material can be calculated. Careful laboratory experiments have established such values for many common substances. (See columns 2 and 3 in Table 23A.)

Example 1. A copper wire 3 m long and 2 mm² in cross-sectional area hangs from the ceiling. What will be its elongation if a 2-Kg mass is suspended from the lower end?

Solution. Transpose Eq.(23g) to solve for e, and substitute known dimensions and Young's modulus for copper from Table 23A.

$$e = \frac{Fl}{AY} = \frac{2000 \text{ gm} \times 980 \text{ cm/sec}^2 \times 300 \text{ cm}}{0.02 \text{ cm}^2 \times 12.5 \times 10^{11} \text{ dynes/cm}^2}$$
$$= 0.0235 \text{ cm}$$

Care must be taken in solving such problems as this to express the force F in the same units as the force in the modulus.

Table 23A also includes values of the elastic limit E and of the breaking point P. These constants are of practical value where it is essential to know the stress required to reach the elastic limit of a material or the minimum load that would cause it to break. (See Fig. 23C.) The necessity for giving ranges of values for metals is due to the various work treatments applied to them in

* Thomas Young (1773-1829), English scientist. Born of a Quaker family, young Thomas had read the Bible twice through at the age of four and at fourteen could speak seven languages. He studied medicine in London, Edinburgh, Göttingen, and Cambridge, and at twenty-eight he was appointed professor of physics at the Royal Institution. Young is best known for his experiments proving the wave theory of light, but he also made valuable contributions to mechanics, medicine, and to the mechanism of sight and vision. He was one of the first to decipher successfully Egyptian hieroglyphic inscriptions.

TABLE 23A. YOUNG'S MODULUS. ELASTIC LIMIT. BREAKING POINT

Material	Young's Modulus Y		Elastic Limit E Stress		Breaking Point P	
	dynes/cm²	lb/in.²	dynes/cm²	lb/in.²	dynes/cm²	lb/in.²
Aluminum	7×10^{11}	10.2×10^6	13×10^8	19×10^3	15×10^8	22×10^3
Brass	9.02 "	13.09 "	7-15 "	10-22 "	35-60 "	51-56 "
Copper	12.5 "	18.0 "	1-10 "	1.5-15 "	23-47 "	32-67 "
Iron	21.0 "	30.0 "	15-18 "	21-26 "	30-37 "	42-52 "
Steel (mild)	19.2 "	27.9 "	17-21 "	25-30 "	34-41 "	50-60 "
Tendon (human)	1.6 "	2.3 "	..	..	6.2-6.4 "	9.0-9.2 "
Muscle (human)	0.009 "	0.013 "	..	..	0.35-0.4 "	0.5-0.6 "
Bone (tension)	22 "	32 "	..	..	9-12 "	13-17 "
Bone (compression)	22 "	32 "	..	..	3-10 "	4-23 "
Nerve	0.1850 "	0.2680 "	..	..	1.38 "	2.00 "
Vein	0.0085 "	0.0123 "	..	..	0.18 "	0.26 "
Artery	0.0005 "	0.0007 "	..	..	0.14 "	0.20 "

their fabrication. Some are cast, others are drawn or rolled, and some are annealed.

Example 2. Calculate for the copper wire in Example 1 the load that must be applied to reach (a) the elastic limit and (b) the breaking point. (Use minimum values listed.)

Solution. Since the values in Table 23A represent the stress that must not be exceeded, Eq. (23e) is used. Substitute the *elastic limit E* for the *stress,* and transpose.

$$F = E \times A = 1 \times 10^8 \frac{dynes}{cm^3} \times 0.02 \text{ cm}^2$$
$$= 2 \times 10^6 \text{ dynes}$$

Substitute *P* for the stress, and transpose.

$$F = P \times A = 23 \times 10^8 \frac{dynes}{cm^2} \times 0.02 \text{ cm}^2$$
$$= 46 \times 10^6 \text{ dynes}$$
$$F = 460 \text{ newtons}$$

23.6. Compression. When a load *F* is applied to the ends of a rod to compress it as shown in Fig. 23E, the decrease in length is the same in amount as the elongation it would acquire when the same load is applied as a tension. In other words, Hooke's law applies to compression, the values of Young's modulus for stretching are valid, and Eq.(23g) can be used for all calculations within the elastic limit.

The simple proportionality between the force applied to a body and the amount stretched or compressed is consistent with the intermolecular force diagram of Fig.

22C. The straightness of the graph for a short distance on each side of the equilibrium position is an indication of why Hooke's law holds for limited amounts of stretch or compression.

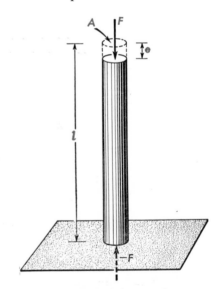

Fig. 23E *Young's modulus for the compression of a rod is given by Fl/Ae.*

23.7. Impact of Elastic Bodies. When two bodies collide, as shown in Fig. 23F, the law of conservation of momentum states that the total momentum before impact is equal to the total momentum after impact. This law is not sufficient, however, to determine

Fig. 23F   *The total momentum of two bodies before impact is equal to the total momentum after impact.*

what the individual velocities of each of the two bodies will be. Different kinds of material behave differently at impact and will move apart with different velocities.

Experimental observations show that hard bodies in collision are highly resilient and rebound from each other quite rapidly, while soft bodies are less resilient and rebound much more slowly. *Resilience is de-*

Referring to the two bodies in Fig. 23F,

$$r = \frac{v_2 - v_1}{u_1 - u_2} \qquad (23i)$$

One method of determining r for two bodies in collision is to employ spheres of the material and mount them as pendu-

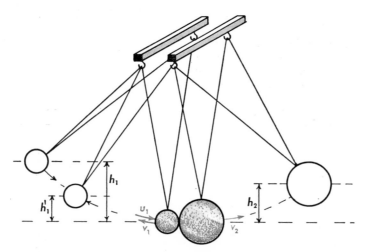

Fig. 23G   *Experiment for determining the coefficient of restitution.*

fined as the ability of a body to undergo a compression, or rapid deformation, without the development of permanent deformation. The vigor with which a body restores itself to its original shape after a deformation is called *restitution.*

The coefficient of restitution r *is defined as a number expressing the ratio of the velocity with which the two bodies separate after collision to the velocity of their approach before collision.*

$$r = \frac{\text{velocity of separation}}{\text{velocity of approach}} \qquad (23h)$$

lums, as shown in Fig. 23G. With m_2 hanging freely at rest, m_1 is raised to a height h_1 and released. From the rebound heights h_2 and h_1' the velocities before and after collision can be determined from the equation $v = \sqrt{2gh}$. (See Eq.(16f).) By substitution of the calculated velocities in Eq.(23i), the value of r is found.

We have seen in Chap. 16 that, for all bodies in collision, the law of conservation of momentum must apply. (See Eq.(16g).)

$$m_1u_1 + m_2u_2 = m_1v_1 + m_2v_2 \qquad (23j)$$
$$\text{before impact} \qquad \text{after impact}$$

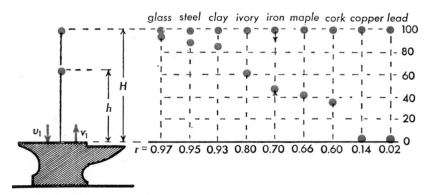

glass steel clay ivory iron maple cork copper lead

$r = 0.97 \quad 0.95 \quad 0.93 \quad 0.80 \quad 0.70 \quad 0.66 \quad 0.60 \quad 0.14 \quad 0.02$

Fig. 23H   *The bouncing marble experiment, illustrating the resilience of different substances.*

This relation, along with Eq.(23i), may be applied to many practical problems, for, with two equations relating initial and final velocities, two unknowns may always be calculated. Suppose for example that the masses of two bodies, their initial velocities, and the coefficient of restitution are known. The two final velocities can then be calculated. By solving Eqs.(23i) and (23j) simultaneously for the final velocity v_1, we obtain

$$v_1 = u_1 - \frac{m_2}{m_1 + m_2}(u_1 - u_2)(1 + r) \quad (23k)$$

and for the final velocity v_2, we get

$$v_2 = u_2 - \frac{m_1}{m_1 + m_2}(u_2 - u_1)(1 + r) \quad (23l)$$

These equations are particularly impor-

tant in atomic and molecular collisions where perfectly elastic impacts are the common occurrence. For such collisions $r = 1$, and the above equations simplify.

The simplest method of finding the coefficient of restitution for two bodies at impact is shown in Fig. 23H. Spheres of different substances are dropped successively, all from the same height, onto the smooth top surface of a large anvil and allowed to bounce to their various heights. Contrary to one's preconceived ideas of elasticity, a glass or steel marble will bounce to a greater height than will a ball made of the best Pará or India rubber. A lead ball or marble, on the other hand, hardly bounces at all.

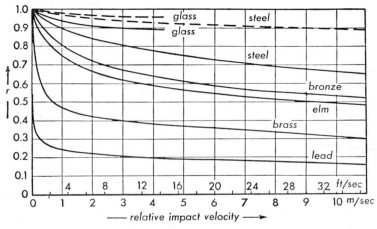

Fig. 23I   *Coefficients of restitution measured for the impact of two spheres of similar material. Dotted curves at top are for small spheres dropped on thick flat plates of similar material.*

If we apply Eq.(23i) to these bouncing marbles, we note that the very great mass of the anvil reduces its recoil velocity v_2 to practically zero. Under these conditions we can write $u_2 = 0$ and $v_2 = 0$, and u_1 and v_1 are given by the law of freely falling bodies,

$$u_1 = \sqrt{2gH} \qquad v_1 = \sqrt{2gh}$$

Upon substitution in Eq.(23i), we obtain

$$r = \frac{\sqrt{2gh}}{\sqrt{2gH}} \qquad \boxed{r = \sqrt{\frac{h}{H}}} \qquad (23m)$$

As illustrated in Fig. 23H, H is the height from which a marble falls and h is the height to which it rebounds. For a very elastic substance, like glass or steel, colliding with steel, r has a value of 0.95 or better, whereas for a very inelastic substance, like lead, colliding with steel, r is extremely small. It is seen from Eq.(23i) that the smallest value that r can have is zero, while the largest value is unity.

Curves showing how the coefficient of restitution varies with impact velocity are given in Fig. 23I.

PROBLEMS

1. A 2-Kg mass suspended from the lower end of a spring, stretches it a distance of 6.5 cm. Find the value of Hooke's law constant in newtons per meter.

2. If the Hooke's law constant for the stretching of a spring is 320 newtons per meter, what mass in Kg, suspended from the lower end, will stretch this spring 2.5 cm? (*Ans.* 0.816 Kg.)

3. An iron wire 3 ft long and cross-sectional area 0.03 in.² is subjected to a tension of 5.1 lb. Calculate (a) its elongation, and (b) the tension required to reach the elastic limit.

4. A steel wire 9 ft long and cross-sectional area of 0.024 in.² is subjected to a tension of 100 lb. Calculate (a) its elongation, and (b) the tension required to reach the elastic limit. Assume $E = 28 \times 10^3$ lb/in.² (*Ans.* (a) 1.61 in., (b) 672 lb.)

,0/6/5

5. A brass wire 2.5 m long and 2.0 mm in diameter hangs from the ceiling. If a mass of 2.2 Kg is suspended from the lower end, what will be (a) the elongation? Calculate the load required to reach (b) the elastic limit, and (c) the breaking point.

6. A copper wire 20 m long and diameter 0.4 cm hangs from the ceiling. If a mass of 10 Kg hangs from the lower end, find (a) the elongation. Calculate the load required to reach (b) the elastic limit, and (c) the breaking point. Assume $E = 2 \times 10^8$ dynes/cm², and $P = 25 \times 10^8$ dynes/cm². (*Ans.* (a) 1.25 mm, (b) 2.51×10^7 dynes, and (c) 3.14×10^8 dynes.)

7. Find the elongation of a tendon 5 cm long and 0.4 cm in diameter if it is put under a tension of 1470 newtons. Assume Young's modulus to be 1.6×10^{11} dynes/cm².

8. What tension in lb would be required to break a tendon whose diameter is 0.16 in? Assume $P = 9.1 \times 10^3$ lb/in². (*Ans.* 183 lb.)

9. An artery has a length of 10 cm and a cross-sectional area of 0.30 cm². Find (a) the elongation under a tension of 40 newtons, and (b) the force required to break it.

10. A blood vein has a length of 2 cm and a cross-sectional area of 0.25 cm². Find (a) the elongation under a tension of 20 newtons, and (b) the force required to rupture it. (*Ans.* (a) 0.188 mm, (b) 45 newtons.)

11. A golf ball, when dropped from a height of 4 ft and allowed to hit a concrete pavement, bounces to a height of 2.5 ft. Calculate the coefficient of restitution.

12. A glass marble is dropped from a height of 28 in. onto a smooth heavy steel plate. Calculate the height to which it will bounce. (*Ans.* 26.3 in.)

13. An ivory ball weighing 8 oz and moving with a speed of 10 ft/sec collides head-on with another ball of the same mass at rest. After collision the two balls have speeds of 1.5 ft/sec and 8.5 ft/sec. Find the coefficient of restitution.

14. An ivory ball with a mass of 200 gm, moving with a speed of 300 cm/sec, collides head-on with another ivory ball of the same mass and size, at rest. If the coefficient of restitution is 0.65, find the velocity of each ball after collision. (*Ans.* 52.5 cm/sec, and 247.5 cm/sec.)

15. A croquet mallet of 300 gm, moving with a speed of 500 cm/sec, hits a 200-gm croquet ball at rest. If the coefficient of restitution is 0.60, find the velocity of the croquet ball after impact.

16. A steel ball with a mass of 0.5 Kg and a velocity of 3.5 m/sec, collides with a 2.4-Kg iron ball at rest. If the coefficient of restitution is 0.40, find the velocity of both masses after impact. (*Ans.* 0.845 m/sec, and −0.55 m/sec.)

17. A mass of 48 gm, moving with a velocity of 20 m/sec, makes a head-on collision with a mass of 6 gm initially at rest. If the coefficient of restitution is 0.80, what will the final velocities of the two masses be?

18. Two ivory balls, each with a mass of 500 gm, are suspended by cords each 1 m long, so that they rest in contact. If one ball is moved away until its cord makes an angle of 30° with the horizontal and is then released, find (a) its speed just before impact, and (b) the speed of each ball after impact. The coefficient of resti-

tution of ivory on ivory is 0.65. (*Ans.* (a) 3.13 m/sec, (b) 0.55 m/sec, and 2.58 m/sec.)

19. An atom of mass 5×10^{-25} Kg, moving with a velocity of 2×10^7 m/sec, makes a head-on collision with another atom of mass 15×10^{-25} Kg, at rest. Assuming a perfectly elastic collision, what are the two velocities after impact?

20. A molecule of mass 7.5×10^{-25} Kg, moving with a speed of 6.8×10^6 m/sec, makes a head-on collision with another molecule of mass 15×10^{-25} Kg, at rest. Assuming a perfectly elastic collision, what will their two velocities be after impact? (*Ans.* −2.27 m/sec, +4.53 m/sec.)

21. Starting with Eqs.(23i) and (23j), derive Eq.(23k). (*Note:* Solve each equation for v_2 and set the right-hand sides equal to each other.)

22. Reduce Eqs.(23k) and (23l) to their simplest form for the special case of perfectly elastic spheres.

Chapter 24

Properties of Liquids

The properties of solids like bending, twisting, and stretching do not exist in liquids. Liquids, however, can be put under compression and, if placed in a thoroughly cleaned vessel or container, can be subjected to very high tensions. Although these properties are of considerable interest, they have not proved to be of much practical importance. There are physical properties of liquids, on the other hand, that are considered to be of general importance. These are pressure, buoyancy, surface tension, and viscosity.

24.1. Pressure. It is frequently necessary to determine the pressure at various depths within a liquid, as well as the pressure on the bottom and sides of any containing vessel. The rule regarding pressure states that the magnitude of the pressure at any depth is equal to the weight of a column of liquid of unit cross section reaching from that point to the top of the liquid.

At a depth of l_1, as illustrated in Fig. 24A (a), the pressure p_1 is given by the weight of a column of liquid 1 sq cm in cross section and l_1 centimeters in height. At a greater depth of l_2, the pressure p_2 is given by the weight of a column of liquid 1 sq cm in cross section and l_2 cm in height.

This can be demonstrated with a glass cylinder and a thin lightweight disk as shown at the right. With water surrounding the empty cylinder, the force, f, pushing up, holds the disk tightly against the end. If the cylinder is gradually filled with water, an increasing downward force is exerted on the disk. Just as the water inside reaches the level of the water outside, the disk drops from the end of the cylinder, showing that the downward force and upward force at that point and at that instant become equal.

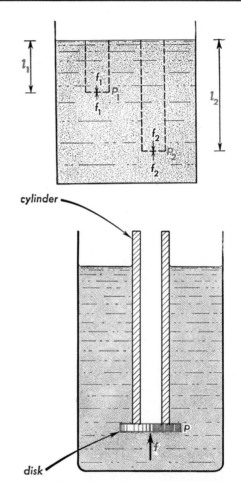

Fig. 24A   *The pressure at any given depth in a liquid is equal to the weight per unit cross section of the liquid directly above.*

We can conclude from this experiment that not only is the pressure at any given point in a liquid given by the weight of the liquid per unit area above it, but that the pressure at one point is equal to the pressure at any other point at the same level.

Pressure in a liquid is defined as the normal force exerted by the liquid per unit area and is usually measured in *pounds per square inch, dynes per square centimeter,* or *newtons per square meter.* Because of its dimensions, pressure is not a vector.

24.2. Pressure Acts in All Directions. In a liquid at rest, the force exerted by the liquid upon any surface is perpendicular to the surface. At any given point, the force exerted on an element of surface is independent of the orientation of that surface. This can be illustrated in many ways. For example, in Fig. 24B a hollow steel ball

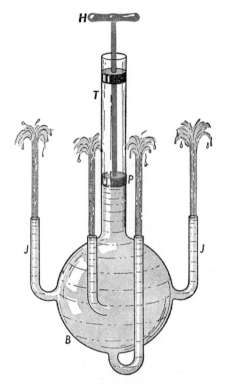

Fig. 24B *Experimental demonstration of equal pressures in all directions.*

B, with a uniform steel tube *T*, is filled with water. By pushing down on the handle *H*, the plunger *P* forces water out of the several metal tubes, *J*, leading from the sides and the bottom of the ball. Equal force in all directions is indicated by the water jets all coming to the same height as drawn.

24.3. Pressure on a Surface. Because of pressure, the force *f* exerted by a liquid at rest is perpendicular to the wall with which the liquid is in contact. As a proof, suppose the force were not perpendicular but at some angle to the surface. Such a force could be resolved into two components, one normal and the other tangent to the surface. But, the tangent component cannot exist, for, if it did, the wall would exert an equal and opposite force on the liquid and the liquid would move. Since the liquid is assumed to be at rest the force *f* must be normal to the surface.

The vessels shown in Fig. 24C are known as Pascal's vases.* Three glass vessels, of

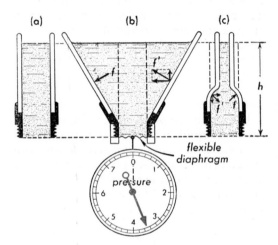

Fig. 24C *Demonstration with Pascal's vases.*

different shape but of the same height, have screw-in metal bases that fit into the same pressure meter shown at the lower center. The three vases are inserted one after the other and filled with water to the same height *h*. Even though the amount of water is greatly different in each vase, the pressure, as measured by the meter, is the same.

The experimental fact that the small

* Blaise Pascal (1623-1662), French religious philosopher, physicist, and mathematician. He is noted principally for his discoveries in pure mathematics and for his experiments with the barometer. His experiments and his treatise on the equilibrium of fluids entitle him to rank with Galileo and Stevinus as one of the founders of the science of hydrostatics and hydrodynamics.

amount of water in vessel (c) can exert the same downward force as the large amount in vessel (b) may be considered as a verification of equal pressure. Let f represent the force of the water on the unit area of the wall, and f' the equal and opposite force of the wall on the water. The latter is shown resolved into vertical and horizontal components. The vertical component in (b) is upward and supplies the additional force needed to support the extra amount of water, while in (c) the vertical component is downward and supplies the additional force equivalent to the missing column of water above.

24.4. Density and Specific Gravity. The density of matter, whether in the solid, liquid, or gaseous state, is defined in metric units as the mass per unit of volume. Algebraically, this may be expressed as

$$\text{density} = \frac{\text{mass}}{\text{volume}} \qquad \boxed{\rho = \frac{M}{V}} \quad (24a)$$

The Greek letter ρ is commonly used to represent density. In the *cgs* system, density is given in *grams per cubic centimeter*. Since the gram is defined as the mass of 1 cm³ of water, the density of water is 1 gm/cm³. In the *mks* system, density is given in *kilograms per cubic meter*.

Example 1. If 25 cm³ of mercury have a mass of 340 gm, what is the density?
Solution. Direct substitution in Eq.(24a) gives

$$\rho = \frac{340 \text{ gm}}{25 \text{ cm}^3} = 13.6 \frac{\text{gm}}{\text{cm}^3}$$

If the volume and density of a body are known, the mass is given by Eq.(24a) as

$$M = V \times \rho \qquad (24b)$$

Specific gravity is another term frequently used to express the relative weights of matter. Specific gravity is defined as the ratio between the weight of a given volume of substance and the weight of an equal volume of water.

Specific gravity

$$= \frac{\text{weight of a given substance}}{\text{weight of equal volume of water}} \quad (24c)$$

TABLE 24A. DENSITIES AND WEIGHT-DENSITIES OF A FEW COMMON SUBSTANCES

Material		gm/cm³	lb/ft³
Liquids			
alcohol	(20°C)	0.79	49.3
benzine	(0°C)	0.90	56.2
blood	(37°C)	1.04	65.0
gasoline	(0°C)	0.69	41.2
mercury	(20°C)	13.6	849
olive oil	(15°C)	0.918	57.3
water	(0°C)	1.000	62.4
Metals			
aluminum		2.7	168.7
brass		8.5	530
copper		8.9	556
gold		19.3	1205
iron		7.9	493
lead		11.4	712
platinum		21.5	1342
silver		10.5	655
tin		7.3	456
zinc		7.1	446
Wood			
balsa		0.11-0.13	7-8
cedar		0.49-0.57	30-35
cork		0.22-0.26	14-16
maple		0.62-0.75	39-47
oak		0.60-0.90	37-56
Miscellaneous			
glass		2.4-2.8	150-175
ice		0.91	57.2
quartz		2.65	165

According to this definition, the specific gravity of a substance is given by the same numerical value as the density in the *cgs* system. Since it is the ratio between like quantities, specific gravity has no dimensions and is therefore the same in all systems of units. For example, the specific gravity of aluminum is 2.7, which means that any solid piece of aluminum weighs 2.7 times as much as an equal volume of water.

24.5. Calculation of Pressure and Total Force. For convenience only, engineers, as well as others, in this country usually employ the quantity *weight per unit volume* for the term *density*. For example the density of water is commonly said to be 62.4 lb per cubic foot. Since the pound is a unit of force, it is proper to distinguish such a quantity from density as defined by Eq.(24a) by calling it weight-density.

$$\text{weight-density} = \rho g$$

where ρ is the density in *slugs/ft³*, and g is the acceleration due to gravity, 32 ft/sec².

Since *pressure* is defined as *force per unit area* and its magnitude is given by the weight of a column of fluid above it, calculations of fluid pressure usually involve the use of the fluid density ρ. For example, to find the weight of a column of fluid, we multiply the mass of the fluid by g (the weight per unit mass). Since the mass M of a fluid is given by Eq.(24b) as $V\rho$, the weight w of any volume of fluid is given by

$$w = V\rho g \qquad (24d)$$

For a fluid column of unit cross section and height h, the weight w is numerically equal to the pressure p, and the volume V is numerically equal to the height h. Therefore

$$p = h\rho g \qquad (24e)$$

This latter equation gives the pressure at any depth in a liquid of uniform density and may be used to calculate the total force acting on any wall.

Consider for example the cross-section diagram of the square-bottomed tank in Fig. 24D. Over each square inch of the bottom surface of area A, the pressure p is

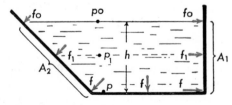

Fig. 24D *Liquid pressure is normal to the surface, and varies with the depth.*

the same, and f is normal to the surface. The total downward force F on the bottom, therefore, is

$$F = pA \qquad (24f)$$

On the side walls, however, the pressure is not constant but varies with the depth. The pressure p at the bottom is twice as great as the pressure p_1 at the middle, while the pressure p_0 at the top is zero.

To calculate the total force on either side of the tank, the average pressure, that is, the pressure p_1 at the center, is multiplied by the area of the surface. On the slanted wall, for example, the pressure of the depth of $\frac{1}{2}h$ is, by Eq.(24e), equal to $\frac{1}{2}p$, and the total force is, therefore,

$$F = \frac{1}{2}pA_2$$

If p is in newtons/m² the force F is in newtons. If p is in dynes/cm² the force F is in dynes, and if p is in lb/in.² the force F is in lbs.

24.6. The Ocean Depths. Only recently has man descended to very great depths in the ocean to observe one of the most interesting regions of the earth's crust. The *bathysphere,* a hollow but thick-walled steel sphere about $4\frac{1}{2}$ ft in diameter, descended with its two American observers, Beebe and Barton, in 1931, to a depth of 1400 ft, and in 1934 to a depth of 3000 ft.

Auguste Piccard, the Swiss professor who once set a balloon record into the stratosphere (see Fig. 25B of the next chapter), set another record in 1953 by diving into the Mediterranean, just off the coast of Italy. Accompanied by his son Jacques, they descended in their *bathyscaph* to a depth of 10,300 ft. (See Fig. 24E.) In January of 1960, Jacques Piccard and Lt. Donald Walsh, U.S.N., descended into the Pacific, just off the coast of the island of Guam, to a depth of 37,800 ft. The pressure at this great depth of over seven miles amounts to 16,400 lb/in.² These bathyscaphs had steel walls 3 to 5 in. thick and small portholes through which observations and photographs could be made.

At these great depths fish were observed.

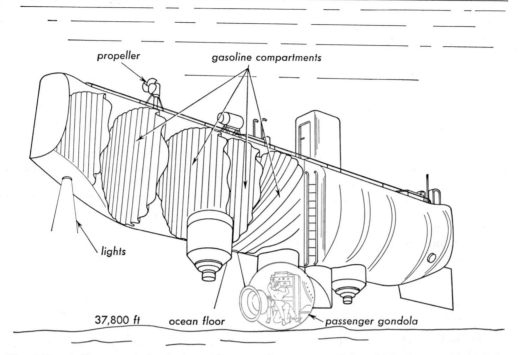

Fig. 24E *A diagram of the bathyscaph, an underwater vessel in which Jacques Piccard and Lt. Donald Walsh, U.S.N., descended to an ocean depth of 7 mi, in January 1960. The bathyscaph operates much the same as a balloon. The main part of the vessel is a thin-walled, multiple-celled tank, supporting a small, thick-walled, passenger gondola at the bottom. While the buoyancy of a balloon is due to the lightweight gas it contains, the bathyscaph obtains its buoyancy by being filled with lighter-than-water gasoline. To descend, the divers release gasoline; to rise, they release ballast. Propellers on top permit the vessel to maneuver for short periods of time.*

How do these fish live and withstand such pressures? The answer is to be found in the fact that water circulates freely within and permeates the fish to such an extent that the pressure inside the fish is the same as the pressure outside. The entire organism is therefore in equilibrium, for the inside forces pushing out are everywhere equal to the outside forces pushing in. If such fish are brought to the surface too suddenly, the inside pressure will not be sufficiently relieved and the fish will explode. A gradual ascent enables some of the water within to escape slowly, thus reducing the pressure inside as well as outside, and the fish can be brought to the surface alive. These fish do not live long, however, for their natural existence requires great pressures.

Example 2. Calculate the water pressure exerted on the bathyscaph at a depth of 10,330 ft.

Solution. Table 24A gives the weight-density of water as 62.4 lb/ft³. Then, the weight of a column of water 1 ft high and 1 in.² in cross section is 62.4/144 = 0.433 lb. We now multiply this weight by the depth in ft to obtain

$$0.433 \times 10{,}330 = 4473 \text{ lb/in.}^2$$

The salt content of ocean water increases this result by a relatively small amount.

24.7. Adhesion and Cohesion. All matter is composed of atoms and molecules of one kind or another. As already stated, these ultramicroscopic particles attract each other with forces which depend upon the kinds of atoms or molecules involved and upon the distance between them. The closer two

read but ≠ problems

atoms or molecules are together, the greater is the attractive force between them. The attractive force between different kinds of molecules is called *adhesion*, and the attractive force between two like kinds of molecules is called *cohesion*.

Although the force of attraction between two molecules is extremely small, the combined attraction of billions of molecules contained within a very small bit of matter is astonishingly great. A steel cable 1 in. in diameter, for example, will support a maximum load of 25 or more tons without breaking. This is a direct measure of the cohesive forces between hundreds of billions of atoms.

The difference between adhesion and cohesion can be demonstrated by an experiment diagramed in Fig. 24F. A glass plate

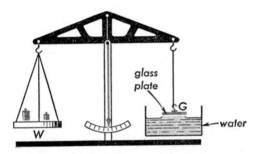

Fig. 24F   *Experiment illustrating the forces of adhesion between glass and water.*

G is supported by one arm of a beam balance. The plate, after being balanced by weights on the left-hand scale pan, is brought into contact with the surface of water, as shown. Additional weights are next added at W until the plate breaks free from the water surface. Upon examining the glass, water is found clinging to the under-surface, showing that the break came between water molecules only. The adhesive forces between glass and water molecules therefore exceed the cohesive forces between water molecules. The weight added in the experiment is therefore a measure of the cohesive forces between water molecules.

If mercury is substituted for the water in the above experiment and the glass plate

pulled away from the mercury surface, the added weights will measure adhesion, the force of attraction between the glass and mercury molecules. This is shown by the fact that no mercury clings to the bottom of the glass plate. Thus the cohesion between the mercury molecules is greater than the adhesion between mercury and glass.

24.8. Surface Tension. The cohesion of molecules gives rise in liquids to a phenomenon called surface tension. According to this aspect of molecular attraction, the surface of a liquid acts at all times as though it has a thin membrane stretched over it, and this membrane is under tension and trying to contract. It is for this reason that fogdrops, raindrops, soap bubbles, etc., assume a spherical shape as they fall through the air. (For any specified volume of matter, a sphere has a smaller surface area than any other geometrical figure.)

An experiment designed to illustrate the spheroidal state of a liquid drop is shown at the left in Fig. 24G. Alcohol and water are poured carefully into a glass vessel where they form a separation boundary, the water with its greater density going to the bottom. Olive oil, which is not soluble in either water or alcohol, is then dropped into the liquid. The drops quickly take on a spherical form and, due to their intermediate density, settle slowly to the boundary level where they remain suspended.

A second illustration of surface tension is the floating needle experiment. A common sewing needle lowered horizontally to the surface of water in an open dish will be found to float as shown in Fig. 24G(b). (If the needle is first drawn through the fingers, a thin film of grease is deposited on the surface, making it easier to float. The adhesion between water and grease is very weak.) For the needle to break through the surface, water molecules must be pulled apart. Rather than do this, the surface becomes depressed until the upward buoyant force $-W$ is equal in magnitude to W, the weight of the needle. Surface tension T keeps the film intact.

An interesting experiment is performed by fastening a bit of soap to the back of a

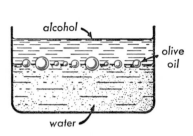

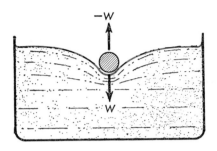

Fig. 24G   (a) *Demonstration of the spheroidal state.* (b) *A steel needle can float by itself on water.*

small wooden boat and then placing the boat on the surface of a pond of water. As the soap goes into solution, the surface tension of the water is greatly weakened behind the boat and surface tension in front pulls the boat forward. As soon as a soap film covers the whole of the water surface, the boat will stop.

A similar experiment is to scrape small bits of camphor into a dish of water. Like the boat, each tiny camphor flake is propelled rapidly around on the surface of the water. The camphor, going into solution most rapidly at the pointed end of each flake, reduces surface tension more at that point than at any other.

Surface tension in the laboratory is usu-ally measured by an arrangement illustrated in Fig. 24H. A small wire frame of length l is dipped into water and then pulled slowly out. As a result of both cohesion and ad-hesion, a thin film of water is formed in the frame. This film pulls down by a force which can be measured by suspending the frame from the arm of a beam balance. Weights are slowly added to the other scale pan (not shown), until the film breaks. The maximum weight added without breaking the film is a direct measure of surface ten-sion, which arises from the cohesive forces of the water molecules.

Surface tension is defined as the force of contraction across a line of unit length, the line and the force being perpendicular to each other, both lying in the plane of the liquid film. If F is the maximum force applied in the above experiment and l is the length of the wire frame, the surface tension T is given by

$$T = \frac{F}{2l} \qquad (24g)$$

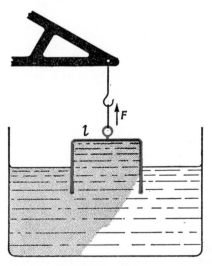

Fig. 24H   *A simple laboratory experiment for measuring surface tension.*

TABLE 24B. SURFACE TENSION OF A FEW LIQUIDS

Liquid	T in dynes/cm		
	0°C	20°C	50°C
acetone	26.3	23.7	19.9
alcohol	24.0	22.3	19.8
benzine	31.5	28.9	25.0
mercury	508	480	445
water	75.6	72.7	67.9

The factor 2 enters because there are two surfaces to a thin film, thus making the effective length of the surface equal to $2l$.

It was Laplace who first proved by a mathematical analysis that the pressure p on the concave side of a single curved surface of radius r is greater than the pressure p' on the convex side by the factor $2T/r$.

$$p - p' = \frac{2T}{r} \qquad (24h)$$

The pressure inside a fog particle or raindrop is, therefore, greater than the pressure outside. Furthermore, the smaller the drop, the smaller is the radius, and the greater is the internal pressure. Due to this large pressure, tiny fogdrops have rigidity properties like those of solids. A good illustration is to be found in the ease with which ice skates slide over the surface of smooth ice. Under the enormous pressures exerted on the ice by the sharp metal edges of the skate, ice melts, and the runners run along on the tiny drops as if they were on ball bearings.

24.9. The Theory of Surface Tension. The following theory of surface tension and capillarity is based upon atomic and molecular forces. Let the horizontal line in Fig. 24I represent the free surface of a liquid, and the three dots at the center of the circles represent three individual atoms or molecules of the liquid. Around each molecule we imagine a sphere to be drawn of such a size that molecules inside the sphere are close enough to be attracted by the one at the center, while those outside are too far away to be taken into account. While such spheres of influence have no definite

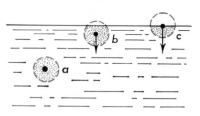

Fig. 24I *Each molecule in a liquid exerts an attractive force on all other molecules within a certain radius.*

boundary, it is known that the attractive forces from much beyond three molecules away may be neglected.

Consider molecule (a) which is well below the surface; surrounded by equal numbers of molecules in all directions, there is no resultant force acting upon it. Molecule (b) near the surface, with more molecules in the lower half of its sphere of influence than in the upper half, experiences a small downward force. Molecule (c), in the liquid surface, experiences the greatest possible downward force since all molecules inside its sphere of influence lie below it.

It is clear from these considerations that, to move a molecule from the interior of the liquid to the surface and thus increase the surface area, would require work to be done. An outward force would have to be exerted on the molecule for a finite distance. Therefore a minimum surface area for a given volume of water represents a minimum of potential energy. The tendency to reduce the surface to a minimum exhibits itself as a surface tension, and agrees with a well-known principle in mechanics that the condition of minimum potential energy of a system is the most stable.

PROBLEMS

1. A hemispherical bowl 40 cm in diameter is filled with oil of density 0.8 gm/cm³. Find the maximum pressure exerted on the wall.

2. What pressure must a diver withstand when he is lowered 60 ft below the surface of the ocean? Assume the specific gravity of sea water to be 1.03. (*Ans.* 26.8 lb/in.²)

3. A water tank is 6 ft in diameter and 10 ft tall. Find (a) the pressure on the bottom, and (b) the total weight of water it contains when full.

4. A V-shaped trough 5 ft long with sides 3 ft wide making an angle of 90 degrees with each other is filled with water. Find the total force

exerted by the water on each side. (*Ans.* 991 lb.)

5. A U-shaped wire having a length of 4.5 cm is lowered into benzine at 20°C. What force is required to break the film that forms as the wire is slowly raised? (See Fig. 24H.)

6. Find the difference in air pressure between the inside and outside of a soap bubble 4 cm in diameter if the surface tension for the soap film is 16 dynes/cm. *Note:* A soap bubble has two surfaces. (*Ans.* 32 dynes/cm^2.)

7. A fogdrop, as seen under a microscope with a micrometer eyepiece, is found to have a diameter of 0.00286 mm. Calculate the pressure inside this drop, in atmospheres, if the temperature is 20°C. Assume the air pressure outside the drop is 1 atm and equal to 1,013,000 dynes/cm^2.

8. An air bubble just below the surface of water is 0.05 mm in diameter. If the temperature is 20°C, find the pressure inside the bubble. Assume the air pressure on the surface of the water to be 1 atm and equivalent to 1.013 × 10^6 dynes/cm^2. (*Ans.* 1.071 × 10^6 dynes/cm^2.)

9. A spherical drop of mercury has a diameter of 1 mm. Find the difference in pressure between the inside and outside if the temperature is 20°C.

10. What is the diameter of a spherical drop of water at 50°C in which the pressure inside exceeds that on the outside by 2 atm. The pressure outside is equal to 1 atm or 1,013,000 dynes/cm^2. (*Ans.* 0.00067 mm.)

11. Auguste Piccard and his son Jacques descended to a depth of 10,300 ft in the ocean, in 1953. Calculate the pressure at this depth. Assume the average specific gravity of the water to be 1.03.

12. The water level in a farmhouse well is 60 ft below the ground. A pump lifts this water to a tank where the outlet of the pipe is 30 ft above the ground. Find the minimum pressure required to pump this water into the tank. (*Ans.* 39.0 lb/in.^{2})

13. Find the difference in air pressure between the inside and outside of a soap bubble 0.40 cm in diameter. Assume the surface tension to be 15 dynes/cm.

14. If raindrops have an average diameter of 2.5 mm, what is the average pressure increase inside the drops? Assume a temperature of 20°C, and an outside air pressure of 1 × 10^6 dynes/cm^2. (*Ans.* 1163 dynes/cm^2.)

15. A square loop of wire 10 cm on a side is suspended from a thread, by fastening the thread at the middle of one side, and then lowered into water at 50°C. When it is slowly raised, a rectangular film of water is formed between the upper edge and the water. What upward force is required to break the film? Assume the surface tension to be 68 dynes/cm.

16. A square loop of wire 6 cm on a side is suspended from a thread by fastening the thread at the middle of one side. The loop is then lowered into water at 20°C. When it is slowly raised, a rectangular film of water is formed between the upper edge and the water. What upward force is required to break the film? Assume the surface tension to be 73 dynes/cm. (*Ans.* 876 dynes.)

Chapter 25

Properties of Gases

25.1. The Earth's Atmosphere. We on the earth's surface, although little conscious of the fact, are submerged in a great sea of air called the atmosphere. This air, which to the earth is the most common of all gases, is really a mixture of well-known gases: about 77% nitrogen, 21% oxygen, and 1% argon. The remaining 1% includes small quantities of such gases as carbon dioxide, hydrogen, neon, krypton, helium, ozone, and xenon.

Being most dense at sea level (see Fig. 25A), the atmosphere extends upward to a

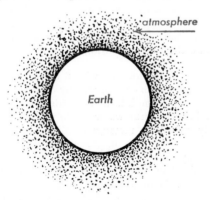

Fig. 25A *Illustration of the air surrounding the earth. The height is exaggerated to bring out the decrease in density with altitude. (If drawn to scale, the earth's atmosphere would form a layer much thinner than the line shown here representing the earth's surface.)*

height of many miles. The air gets thinner and thinner the higher one goes and finally thins out into interstellar space. Observations show that even interstellar space, which is often referred to as the most perfect vacuum, contains a small but definite amount of matter: several particles per cubic centimeter.

Fig. 25B is a schematic cross section of the atmosphere up to a height of 25 miles. It will be noted on the right-hand side of the diagram that 50% of the earth's atmosphere lies below $3\frac{1}{2}$ mi, and that 99% lies below 20 mi. While this accounts for most of the atmosphere, experiments with radio waves show that the small amount of air existing at a height of several hundred miles is sufficient to reflect radio waves back to the earth.

Living as most of us do near sea level, we are constantly subjected to an enormous pressure due to the weight of the air above us. Unbelievable as it may seem, the air exerts a pressure of close to 15 lb for every square inch of surface. This, the atmospheric pressure, is given by the weight of a column of air 1 in.² in cross section and reaching from sea level to the top of the atmosphere.

A pressure of one atmosphere is defined as the average atmospheric pressure at sea level. This is taken to be 14.7 lb/in.², or 1,013,000 dynes/cm².

25.2. The Density of Air. That air has weight may be shown by one of the simplest of experiments. A hollow brass ball with a volume of 1 liter (1 liter = 1000 cm³) is first weighed when it is filled with air, and again when it is evacuated. See Fig. 25C. With the air removed, the vessel is found to be lighter than before by 1.29 gm. If the scales are first balanced with the sphere evacuated, and then the air is allowed to enter, a mass of 1.29 gm must be added to the opposite scale pan to restore balance. Since this is the mass of 1000 cc of air, the mass of 1 cc will be 0.00129 gm. This is the density of air.

If the above experiment is repeated at

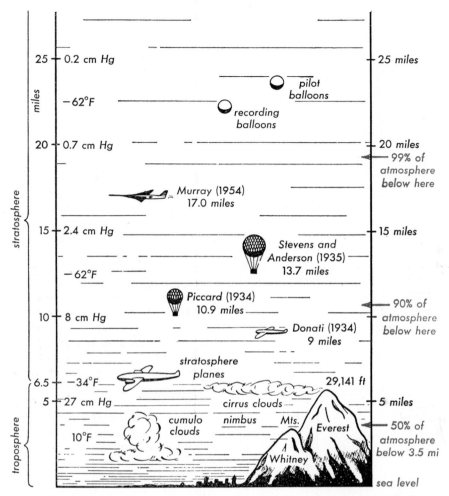

Fig. 25B *Illustration of important facts concerning the troposphere and the strato-sphere and the relative heights reached by man in balloons and airplanes.*

an elevation of 5 mi, the air in the brass vessel will weigh only one third as much as at sea level. The reason for this is that the lower pressure at a height of 5 mi admits only one-third as much air to an evacuated vessel.

If, on the other hand, air is pumped into the hollow sphere, the weight can be made to increase considerably, thus giving a greater than normal density. The density of a gas is therefore standardized and defined as the mass of 1 cc of the gas measured at standard pressure and temperature. Standard pressure is defined as a pressure of one atmosphere and standard tempera-

ture as zero degrees centigrade. The densities of a few common gases are given in Table 25A. The reason for specifying temperature is that gases expand with a rise in

TABLE 25A. DENSITIES OF SIX COMMON GASES

Gas	gm/cm³	lb/ft²
Air	0.00129	0.080
CO_2	0.00198	0.124
Helium	0.000178	0.011
Hydrogen	0.00009	0.005
Nitrogen	0.00125	0.078
Oxygen	0.00143	0.089

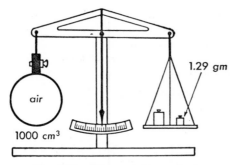

Fig. 25C   *The weighing of air.*

temperature. This subject will be treated in Chap. 28. on expansion.

25.3. The Mercury Barometer. A barometer is a device for measuring the atmospheric pressure. There are in common use today two kinds of barometers—the mercury barometer and the aneroid barometer. The mercury barometer was invented by the Italian physicist, Evangelista Torricelli, some 300 years ago. Torricelli's experiment is illustrated in Fig. 25D. A long glass tube

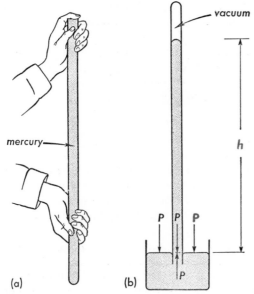

Fig. 25D   *Torricelli's experiment. The making of a mercury barometer.*

is filled with mercury and the finger placed over one end as shown in diagram (a). This tube is then inverted and with the open end

in a dish of mercury the finger is removed as in diagram (b). At the instant the finger is removed, the mercury level drops in the tube to a height *h* as shown. The mercury drops until the pressure due to its own weight inside the tube (at the level *P*) is equal to the atmospheric pressure outside.

At sea level the height at which the mercury column stands is about 76 cm or 30 in. This height will be the same regardless of the diameter of the tube or the length of the vacuum space at the top. Torricelli's experiment shows that a column of air 1 cm² in cross section and reaching to the top of the atmosphere is equal in weight to a column of mercury of the same cross section and 76 cm high.

It was the French philosopher and mathematician, Blaise Pascal, who first showed that when a mercury barometer is taken to a high elevation like the top of a mountain, the height of the mercury column drops considerably. It drops because there is less air above that point and hence a lesser downward pressure on the free mercury surface.

Fig. 25E is a diagram of an experiment demonstrating that it is the atmosphere outside of a barometer pushing down on the exposed mercury surface which supports the mercury column inside, and not the vacuum in the space above drawing it up. An entire barometer is placed in a tall cylinder and the air removed by means of a vacuum pump. As the air slowly leaves, the mercury column drops steadily. When the cylinder is well evacuated, the level of the mercury inside the tube is the same as the level in the small reservoir outside. A return of the air forces the mercury back into the tube and up to its original height, *h*.

The height of the mercury in a barometer measures directly the atmospheric pressure. Instead of specifying the pressure in lb/in.² or in dynes/cm², it is customary to give the height of the mercury column in inches or centimeters. The pressure so expressed in centimeters of Hg (the chemical symbol for mercury is Hg) is given at each 5-mi interval at the left in Fig. 25B.

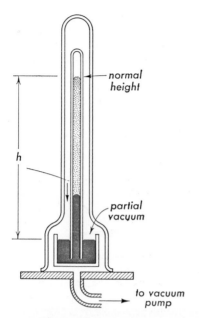

normal height

h

partial vacuum

to vacuum pump

Fig. 25E *Experimental arrangement demonstrating that atmospheric pressure supports the column of mercury in a barometer tube. When the air is removed, the mercury column drops from its normal height.*

If a barometer were made to employ water in place of mercury, the barometer tube would have to be at least 13.6 times as high, or 1034 cm. This is equivalent to about 34 ft. Such an instrument would be too cumbersome to be of much practical value.

25.4. The Aneroid Barometer. The desirability of a small portable pressure measuring instrument has led to the development of the aneroid barometer. This device is frequently used as an altimeter and barometer combined. A cross-sectional diagram of such an instrument is shown in Fig. 25F and photographs are reproduced in Fig. 25G. A small flat metal box, evacuated and with a flexible top, is attached at A to a multiplying system of levers. The end of the lever system is connected to a small cable C which is wrapped around a spindle N, carrying a pointer, I. If the atmospheric pressure P increases, the flexible boxtop is pushed down at A. This lowers the end of the lever system at B, and with

a pivot at D raises the point C. The cable winds up on the spindle N, turning the pointer, I, to the right to a scale reading of higher pressure. The scale of the aneroid is calibrated by a standard mercury barometer, so the pressure is always given in centimeters or inches of mercury.

Since the atmospheric pressure decreases as one goes to higher altitudes, a barometer is often used to determine elevation. As a matter of fact, aneroid barometers are frequently made with an altitude scale attached. Such instruments, called *altimeters*, are to be found on the instrument panel of every airplane and dirigible. Some of these instruments are small enough to be carried in the pocket like a watch, and others are so sensitive that they will indicate a change in elevation of 1 ft. The altitude scale usually has its zero mark near the sea-level pressure as shown in Fig. 25F.

Atmospheric pressure not only varies with altitude but also with time. Although these time variations are small and do not follow any regular law, they can be and are used by the weather bureau as an aid to predicting weather conditions. If at any place the exact height of a barometer is measured carefully throughout the day and the season, slight changes will be observed. When the barometric pressure begins to fall, it is a sign of changing weather. If the pressure continues to fall, rain usually follows. As the storm passes, the barometer rises again. So, by keeping close watch of changing barometric pressure in the vicinity of an observer, the weather for that locality can be forecast.

25.5. Standard Atmospheric Pressure. Standard atmospheric pressure is defined as the pressure equivalent to a column of mercury 76 cm high when the temperature is 0°C. This is equivalent to 29.92 in. of mercury at 32°F. Standard atmospheric pressure is equivalent to 14.7 lb/in.² The approximate value of 15 lb/in.² is frequently quoted and used.

To calculate the equivalent pressure in dynes per square centimeter, multiply by the density of mercury and the acceleration of gravity.

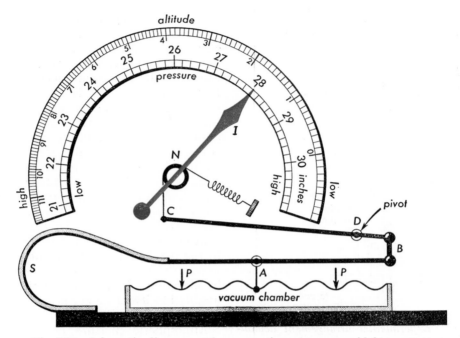

Fig. 25F   *Schematic diagram and cross section of an aneroid barometer.*

$$76 \times 13.6 \times 980 = 1.013 \times 10^6$$

$$\boxed{1 \text{ atmosphere} = 1.013 \times 10^6 \text{ dynes/cm}^2}$$

$$(25a)$$

It is common practice in meteorology to measure atmospheric pressure in bars and millibars.

$$1 \text{ bar} = 1,000,000 \text{ dynes/cm}^2$$
$$1 \text{ millibar} = 1000 \text{ dynes/cm}^2$$

On this basis,

$$1 \text{ atm} = 1.013 \text{ bars} = 1013 \text{ millibars} \quad (25b)$$

The United States Weather Bureau obtains daily records of the barometric pressure from hundreds of places over the country. These records are obtained automatically at each station by means of a specially designed aneroid like the one shown in Fig. 25G(b). A pen or stylus from the barometer itself moves up and down on a slowly rotating drum, thus recording the pressure at every instant. These records are then compiled by the United States Weather Bureau, and maps are published daily of the equal pressure areas over the

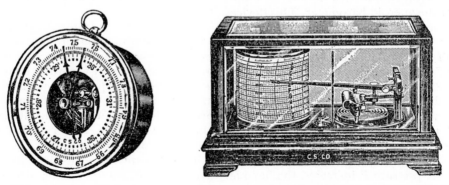

Fig. 25G   (*a*) *Aneroid barometer used for measuring atmospheric pressure.* (*b*) *Self-recording aneroid barometer, or barograph.* (Courtesy, Central Scientific Co.)

country. One such map is shown in Fig. 25H, the irregular lines representing points of equal pressure. It is standard practice now to give the pressure in millibars (see Eq.(25b)).

LOW areas, indicating stormy weather, move slowly and continuously across the country, sometimes growing in intensity and at other times breaking up and disappearing. Particularly noticeable in the diagram is the *HIGH* pressure region on the Atlantic sea coast and the pronounced *LOW* pressure region just northwest of the

25.6. Experiments Illustrating Atmospheric Pressure. Normal atmospheric pressure of 15 lb/in.^{2} does not ordinarily impress a person as being very great. Taken over a considerable area, however, such a pressure gives rise to a tremendous force. Consider the evacuated bulb of an incandescent lamp 3 in. in diameter. A sphere of this diameter has an area of about 28 in.^{2}, and hence a total of 28×15 or 420 lb is exerted inward upon its walls. The thin glass walls can withstand this because the force is distributed uniformly over the

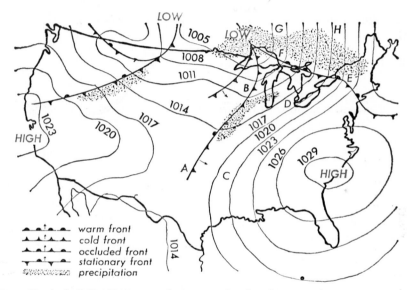

Fig. 25H   *Typical daily U. S. weather map showing barometric pressures, warm and cold air fronts, and precipitation.*

Great Lakes. Like the arms of a great windmill, the cold and warm air masses around every pronounced *LOW* rotate in a counterclockwise direction. As cold air fronts like *AB* sweep down from the polar regions and advance upon warm air masses like *CD*, they push the warm air ahead of them, up over a slowly moving or stationary cool front like *EF*. There, at *EFGH*, the warm air above the cold is cooled below its saturation temperature, and the precipitation of snow or rain takes place. The slipping of some warm air up over the advancing cold front, *AB*, causes some precipitation there as shown.

whole surface. If it were all applied at one small point, the bulb would surely break. A spherical or cylindrical vessel can have thin walls and yet stand enormous pressures whereas a vessel with flat sides may not. It is for this reason that all large vessels used for storing liquids or gases have curved walls instead of flat ones.

An experiment illustrating atmospheric pressure is diagramed in Fig. 25I. In diagram (a) a thin sheet of rubber is first tied over the top end of a jar. When this is done, the air pressure inside is the same as that outside. If now the inside force, upward on the rubber, is removed by means of a

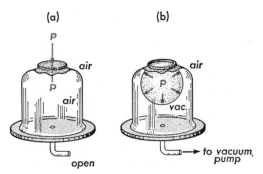

Fig. 25I *Experiments illustrating the magnitude of atmospheric pressure.*

vacuum pump, the outside force pushes the rubber down inside as shown in diagram (b).

The principles of breathing in the human body are demonstrated in Fig. 25J. Muscular contraction in pulling down on the *diaphragm* creates a low pressure around the lungs and atmospheric pressure pushes air into the lungs. Retraction of

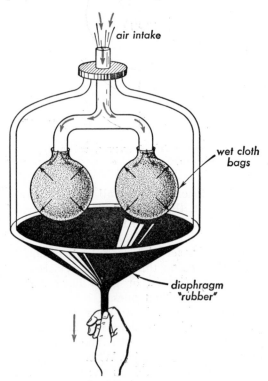

Fig. 25J *Experimental demonstration of the principles of breathing by the human body.*

the diaphragm raises the pressure and compresses the lungs, forcing air and carbon dioxide out.

25.7. The Magdeburg Hemispheres. In the year 1654, Otto von Guericke* performed before the Emperor Ferdinand III, at Regensburg, the celebrated experiment of the "Magdeburg hemispheres." Two copper hemispheres, about 22 in. in diameter, were placed together to form a sphere as shown in Fig. 25K. A ring of

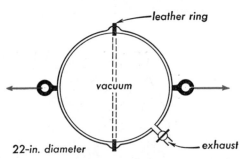

Fig. 25K *The Magdeburg hemisphere designed by Otto von Guericke.*

leather soaked in oil and wax was set between them to make an airtight joint. When the sphere was evacuated, two teams, consisting of eight horses each, were unable to pull the hemispheres apart. This is not to be wondered at, for the force required to pull them apart is easily calculated; it amounts to nearly three tons.

25.8. Measurement of Gas Pressure. There are many kinds of gauges used for measuring gas pressure. One of the simplest instruments used in fixed installations is the manometer. As shown in Fig. 25L, these devices are U-shaped glass tubes containing mercury, alcohol, water, or other liquids.

In the open-tube manometer at the left, atmospheric pressure, p_0, acts downward on the exposed liquid surface at B. The pressure at the level A in the right-hand column is therefore p_0 plus the pressure due to the

* Otto von Guericke (1602-1686), German philosopher, lawyer, physicist, and magistrate. Incited by the discoveries of Galileo, Pascal, and Torricelli, he produced the first vacuum and made the first air pump. From researches in astronomy he predicted the periodic return of comets.

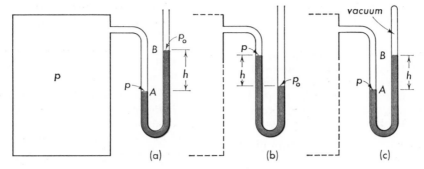

Fig. 25L *Diagrams of open and closed manometer tubes as used in measuring gas pressure.*

liquid column of height, h. Since this must be equal to the pressure at the same level, A, in the left-hand column,

$$p = p_0 + h\rho g \qquad (25c)$$

This is the pressure, p, exerted by the enclosed gas on the liquid surface and the container walls. If p and p_0 are in dynes/cm², then h is in centimeters, ρ, is the density of the liquid in the manometer in gm/cm³, and g is the acceleration due to gravity in cm/sec².

If the liquid in the manometer is mercury, it is customary to specify p, p_0, and h in centimeters of mercury.

$$p = p_0 + h \qquad (25d)$$

A similar reasoning applied to the open manometer tube of diagram (b) shows that the absolute pressure p inside the vessel (indicated by dotted lines) is less than atmospheric pressure by an amount equal to the mercury column h,

$$p = p_0 - h \qquad (25e)$$

The closed-tube manometer, shown at the right, is frequently used where pressures of only a fraction of 1 atm are to be measured.

The right-hand side of the U-tube is closed at the top and evacuated. With the atmospheric pressure thus eliminated, the gas pressure to be measured is given by the mercury column, h.

$$p = h \qquad (25f)$$

25.9. Absolute Pressure. When an automobile tire goes flat from a puncture, the small amount of air remaining in the tire is at atmospheric pressure, the same as the air outside. This is roughly 15 lb/in.² If the tire is repaired and pumped up to a pressure of 30 lb/in.², as read on a standard air pressure gauge, the absolute pressure of the enclosed gas is $30 + 15$ or 45 lb/in.² In other words, a pressure gauge gives the difference between atmospheric pressure outside and the air pressure inside.

In the manometer tubes of Fig. 25L, the mercury column, h, is the gauge pressure, and to this is added the atmospheric pressure, p_0, to get the absolute pressure. In the closed-tube diagram (c) h measures directly the absolute pressure. Bourbon gauges are usually adjusted to a zero reading when disconnected, so that atmospheric pressure must be added to their reading to obtain the absolute pressure.

PROBLEMS

1. A hollow glass sphere 20 cm in diameter is evacuated. Calculate the total inward force on the outside surface under standard atmospheric pressure.

2. A circular screen of a television tube is 19 in. in diameter. With the tube thoroughly evacuated and with standard atmospheric pressure outside, what is the total inward force on

the screen? Assume the screen to be flat and standard atmospheric pressure to be 15 lb/in.² (*Ans.* 4250 lb.)

3. Magdeburg hemispheres with an internal diameter of 10 cm are put together and thoroughly evacuated. What minimum force will pull them apart at (a) sea level, and (b) 3.5-mi elevation where the atmospheric pressure is 50% that at sea level?

4. Magdeburg hemispheres 0.2 m in diameter are thoroughly evacuated. Calculate the minimum force required to pull them apart (a) at sea level, and (b) at an altitude of 3.5 mi. (*Ans.* (a) 3180 newtons, (b) 1690 newtons.)

5. If a barometer contains water in place of mercury, how high will the water column be (a) at sea level, and (b) at an altitude of 3.5 mi?

6. A brass cylinder 2 cm in diameter and 5 cm high is being weighed on an accurate beam balance. What is the mass equivalent of the buoyant force of the air on the cylinder? (*Ans.* 19.9 dynes.)

7. A cylindrical pipe 12 in. in diameter has flat brass plates clamped on the ends. If the pipe is thoroughly evacuated, find the total inward force exerted by the outside air on each plate.

8. If a cylindrical tin can 10 cm in diameter and 12 cm tall were thoroughly evacuated, what would be the force on each end? (*Ans.* 796 newtons.)

9. One Magdeburg hemisphere 2 ft in diameter has a thick glass plate placed over the opening and then evacuated. Calculate the total inward force on the glass plate.

10. A jet airplane maintains standard atmospheric pressure inside the cabin when flying at an altitude of 3.5 mi. If the open end of a mercury manometer, Fig. 25L(a), were exposed to the air pressure outside, what would be the mercury column height, h? (*Ans.* 36 cm.)

11. If a jet airplane maintains standard atmospheric pressure inside the cabin when flying at an altitude of 10 mi, Fig. 25B, what would be the total outward force on a window having an area of 1 ft²? Assume standard atmospheric pressure to be 15 lb/in.²

12. An open-tube mercury manometer used to measure the pressure inside a cylindrical tank shows a reading of $h = -16$ cm Hg. (See Fig. 25L(b).) What total force would be exerted on a small circular glass window mounted over a circular opening 10 cm in diameter in the end of the tank? Assume an outside pressure of 1.013 dynes/cm². (*Ans.* 168 newtons.)

13. The original Magdeburg hemispheres had an internal diameter of 22 in. Find the force in lb required to pull them apart if they were highly evacuated. Assume the atmospheric pressure to be 14.7 lb/in.²

14. The inside diameter of a pair of Magdeburg hemispheres is 4 in. What force is required to pull them apart if they evacuated? Assume atmospheric pressure to be 15 lb/in.² (*Ans.* 189 lb.)

15. A pair of Magdeburg hemispheres have an external diameter of 6 in. If, instead of evacuating them, they are submerged to a depth of 100 ft in water, what force is required to pull them apart? (Assume the weight of a column of water 1 ft high and 1 in.² in cross section is 0.43 lb.

Chapter 26

Fluids in Motion

The term fluid applies to any substance capable of flowing and includes gases as well as liquids. Since all fluids have mass, Newton's second law of motion implies that unbalanced forces are required to set them in motion. As a matter of practical interest, we shall consider the various means by which such forces are obtained, how they are applied to fluids, and what factors control the resultant motion. In these discussions the student would do well to keep in mind the fact that liquids are practically incompressible.

26.1. Velocity Through an Orifice. Many city water supply systems store water in reservoirs on some hilltop or in a nearby water tower and from these sources run the water through pipes into houses, stores, and factories in and around the city. Such an arrangement is called a "gravity system."

When a hole is opened in the side of a vessel containing a liquid, the velocity of flow through the orifice increases with depth. Here the unbalanced force setting the liquid in motion is gravity acting through the liquid as pressure. We have already seen how the pressure at any given depth is given by $p = h\rho g$ and is the same in all directions. At a depth h_1 (see Fig. 26A), the liquid exerts a pressure p_1 against the walls, and the walls exert an equal and opposite pressure against the liquid.

The instant an opening is made in the side of the vessel, the wall pressure is destroyed at that point and the liquid pressure inside pushes the liquid directly in front of the hole, giving it an acceleration outward and normal to the plane of the opening. To find the velocity of escape, consider the potential energy of the liquid

body in the vessel when the hole is first opened and then a short time later when a small amount of liquid has escaped, dropping the surface level a distance t.

As far as energy is concerned, the change is the same as though the top layer of water had fallen a distance h_1 and its potential

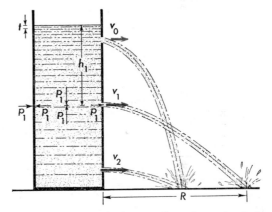

Fig. 26A *The velocity of efflux through a hole in the side of a vessel of water increases with depth.*

energy mgh_1 converted into kinetic energy $\frac{1}{2}mv_1{}^2$ as it becomes the emerging stream. By conservation of energy,

$$mgh_1 = \tfrac{1}{2}mv_1{}^2 \qquad (26a)$$

Since m is the same on both sides, one may divide by m, giving

$$v_1 = \sqrt{2gh_1} \qquad (26b)$$

the same as the law of falling bodies. In other words, the velocity of efflux at any depth, h, is equivalent to the velocity acquired by free fall from the same height.

201

This relation, first discovered by Torricelli* is known as Torricelli's theorem.

It is interesting to note that the parabolic path followed by an emerging stream of liquid is such that the greatest horizontal range R (see diagram) is obtained from an orifice midway between any base level and the top surface of the liquid and that holes equidistant above and below this point have lesser but equal ranges. The proof of this will be left as a problem for the student.

26.2. Measuring the Velocity of a Stream.

One method of measuring the velocity of water in a trough or river bed is to use an L-shaped tube called a "pitot tube." (See Fig. 26B.) If the water were at rest, it would rise in the vertical arm to the height of the surface outside.

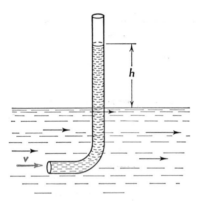

Fig. 26B   *A pitot tube is often used to measure the velocity of water in a stream.*

The pressure exerted by the moving stream, however, raises it to a height h above the surface. This, it may be recognized, is Torricelli's theorem in reverse, the height h measuring the velocity of the moving stream through Eq.(26a). We obtain

$$h = \frac{v^2}{2g} \qquad (26c)$$

The right-hand term $v^2/2g$ is called the *velocity head* of the moving stream.

*Evangelista Torricelli (1608-1647). An Italian physicist and mathematician and disciple of Galileo. He is most noted for his scientific articles on fluid motion, on the theory of projectiles, and on geometrical optics.

The simplest method of measuring the velocity of a jet of water is to turn it straight upward and, from the height of rise, calculate the velocity from the law of falling bodies, Eq.(26b).

26.3. Flow Through a Pipe.

One of the factors determining the flow of water, oil, or gas through a pipe, or the flow of blood through the arteries and veins of the body is the resistance to flow offered by the confining walls. Consider the experiment shown in Fig. 26C in which water from a vertical tank at the left is made to flow through a horizontal glass tube at the bottom. The pressure at five equally spaced points along the tube is measured by vertical standpipes, and the velocity of flow is controlled by the valve at the right. By means of a "water supply" and "over-flow" pipe, the water level in the tank is maintained at a constant level, thus assuring a constant pressure and hence a steady flow.

With the valve closed, the water "seeking its own level" soon brings all standpipes to the same level, *sr*. Their heights thereby indicate equal pressures at all points along the pipe to *E*. When the valve is partially opened and a steady flow is attained, the water in each pipe drops to different levels similar to those shown. The more the valve is opened, the more rapid is the flow and the steeper is the straight line *abcde*.

Since at all times the heights of columns *aA, bB, cC, dD,* and *eE* measure the pressures at the points *A, B, C, D,* and *E,* respectively, the straight line *ae* indicates a smooth and uniform drop in pressure all along the pipe from *A* to *E*. Such a drop in pressure, designated h_f in the figure, is due to *fluid friction* in the pipe and is called the *friction head*. By measuring the friction head for different rates of flow, a comparison of the results will show that h_f is proportional to the square of the velocity. This may be expressed as an equation:

$$h_f = Kv^2 \qquad (26d)$$

where K is the proportionality constant.

The pronounced drop in level from *s* in the tank to *a* in the first standpipe meas-

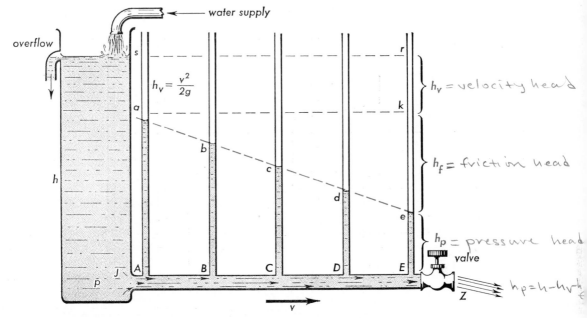

Fig. 26C   *Flow of water through a pipe showing the velocity head h_v, the friction head h_f, and the presure head h_p.*

ures the drop in pressure at A where the water is practically at rest in the tank and is then speeded up to a velocity, v, upon entering the pipe. Just as in Torricelli's theorem, the drop in potential energy from s to a is converted into kinetic energy in the stream, and by Eqs.(26b) or (26c),

$$h_v = v^2/2g \qquad (26e)$$

Here h_v equals sa and is the *velocity head*. The final pressure at the point E, where the water is being drawn from the pipe is directly measured by the height of the liquid column Ee, and is called the *pressure head*, h_p. Thus, with a total pressure, h, available at the tank, there is first a velocity-head drop of h_v, and then a friction-head drop h_f, giving as the final pressure $h_p = h - h_v - h_f$. For all points along a uniform pipe, the velocity head is constant while friction head increases proportionally with the distance from the source.

The above equations also apply to the flow of gas through a pipe provided that the pressure is relatively small. If the pressure is large, the formulas must be modified to allow for the compressibility of the gas.

26.4. Bernoulli's Principle. When a river runs through broad open country, the water runs slowly, but when it comes to a narrow rocky gorge its velocity increases many fold. Similarly when a gas or liquid flowing through a pipe comes to a narrow constricted section, the velocity increases as it enters the constriction and decreases again as it leaves the other end. This is illustrated by an experiment diagramed in Fig. 26D.

The arrangement is the same as in Fig. 26C except that the horizontal flow pipe contains a short section, DE, having only half the cross-sectional areas as elsewhere. When the valve is opened and a condition of steady flow exists, the water in the standpipes will have dropped from sr to new levels like a, b, d, etc., as shown. It is to be noted that, as the water enters the constriction at C, the velocity of flow increases and the pressure drops from c to l. Farther along where it leaves the narrow tube at F, the velocity decreases and the pressure rises from f to k.

This illustrates Bernoulli's principle which may be stated as follows: "where the

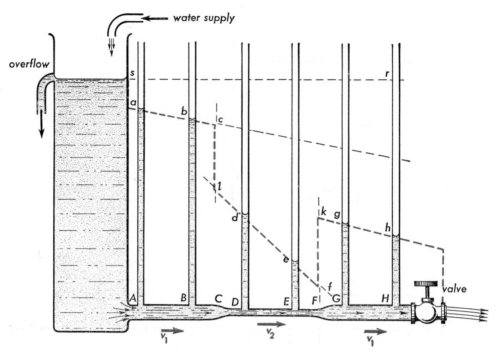

Fig. 26D *Where the velocity of a fluid increases, the pressure drops; and where the velocity of a fluid decreases, the pressure rises.*

velocity of a fluid is high the pressure is low, and where the velocity of a fluid is low the pressure is high." The drops in pressure from a to b, d to e, and g to h represent friction heads for the pipe sections AB, DE, and GH, respectively. The drop from s to a gives directly the velocity head $v_1^2/2g$ for the pipe sections, AB and GH, and to this must be added the drop from c to l to obtain the velocity head $v_2^2/2g$ for the narrow pipe section, DE. The simplest of laboratory measurements confirm the result that narrowing the tube to half the cross section doubles the velocity and quadruples the velocity head.

26.5. Experiments Illustrating Bernoulli's Principle. Bernoulli's principle is often referred to as a physical paradox and is the basis of many interesting phenomena. Seven experiments involving this principle are diagramed in Fig. 26E. In the first illustration (a) a blast of air from a nozzle is blown between two sheets of cardboard suspended about 3 in. apart by cords. Instead of being blown apart, as one might expect, they

come together. The reason for this action is that between the two sheets where the velocity of the air is high the pressure p_2 is low. On the two outside surfaces where the air is not moving, the pressure p_1 (atmospheric pressure) is high and pushes the two sheets together.

In the second diagram (b) air is blown through a hole in the center of a disk AB as shown. When a piece of paper CD is placed close to the opening, it is not blown away but is drawn toward the disk. Where the velocity of air between the disk and paper is high, the pressure is low, and the higher pressure p_1 on the underside of the paper pushes it up against the disk.

One often hears it said that, during a certain wind storm, tornado, or hurricane, the roofs of one or more houses were blown off without otherwise damaging the house. This is not as freakish an accident as one might think, for there is a simple explanation. A high wind blowing over the roof, as shown in Fig. 26E(c), creates a low pressure p_2 on top, and the atmospheric pressure p_1

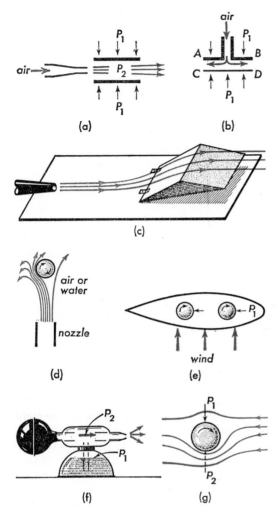

Fig. 26E *Demonstrations of Bernoulli's principle.*

The same principle has been applied to the historical *Flettner rotor ship* which, instead of using sails, employed two tall rotating cylinders, motor-driven. As shown by the top view diagram (e), a wind from broadside the ship produces a forward force. Such a ship, carrying a cargo, crossed the Atlantic twice not many years ago. Although the trips were successful, the uncertainty of a strong wind makes shipping with such boats unreliable.

The sixth diagram (f) represents a common form of perfume atomizer. Squeezing the bulb sends a stream of air through the central tube, which creates a low pressure p_2 inside. The atmospheric pressure, p_1, on the liquid surface pushes the liquid up the stem to be blown out the right-hand tube with the air stream.

Most of the baseballs thrown by a pitcher are curves, some up or down, and others in or out, i.e., to right or left. This is an art, accomplished by throwing the ball so that it spins rapidly about some particular axis. To produce a downward curve, i.e., a *drop ball*, the ball is given a top spin as shown in diagram (g). Here, instead of having the ball moving to the right, we can imagine the ball standing still, but spinning, and the air to be moving from right to left. At the top surface where the wind and ball are moving in opposite directions, the air is slowed down by friction, giving rise to a high pressure region. On the underside the surface moving with the wind keeps the velocity high, thus creating a low pressure region. The resultant downward force thus causes the ball to drop faster than usual.

26.6. The Lift of an Airplane Wing.

The major part of the lift of an airplane wing is due to the top surface. This discovery has been made in laboratory wind tunnels by setting up sections of air foils in fast moving currents of air and measuring the pressure at various regions of the surface with pressure gauges. Fig. 26F shows how this can be done with mercury manometers connected by long tubes to small openings on the top and bottom surfaces.

When the air is still, all manometer tubes show equal heights in their two arms and

inside, where the wind is not blowing, lifts the roof off.

If a small "ping-pong" ball is placed in a vertical stream of air or water, it will rise to a given height above the nozzle and stay at that level, spinning and bobbing around without falling. If the ball goes to one side as illustrated in diagram (d), the fluid going by on the left side causes the ball to spin as shown. The velocity's being high on the left means a low pressure. The higher pressure on the right where the velocity is low pushes the ball back into the stream.

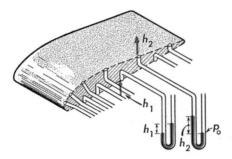

Fig. 26F *Experimental arrangement of mercury manometers, showing how the air pressure can be measured at various points over the surface of an airfoil.*

normal atmospheric pressure, p_0, exists at all points inside the hollow wing, as well as outside. When the air stream is set in motion, manometers connected to the top surface show a drop from atmospheric pressure while those connected below show a rise. Since atmospheric pressure on the outside surfaces was previously counterbalanced at all points by the atmospheric pressure inside the hollow wing, the manometer readings h_1 and h_2 give directly the resultant pressures on the two wing coverings.

A graphical representation of the manometer pressures is shown below in Fig. 26G. Note the very large effect of the up-

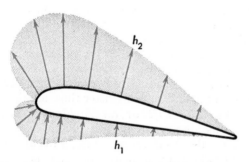

Fig. 26G *Diagram of an airfoil showing pressure differences over the surfaces.*

per surface as compared with the lower surface, particularly near the leading edge.

26.7. Blood Circulation in the Human Body. It has been estimated that the circulation of blood through the human body involves a vessel system containing several thousand arteries and veins and well over one billion capillaries. Any attempt to analyze the mechanical principles involved in circulation, therefore, must of necessity simplify the problem in one way or another. While this has been done successfully by numerous research studies, only the most elementary considerations can be presented here.

A schematic diagram of the circulation is given in Fig. 26H, and shows a combination of series and parallel paths between the *left ventricle* where the blood leaves the heart and the right *atrium* where it enters again. The pulsating heart is a force pump that contains two chambers, the right and left ventricles, joined into a single unit and pumping in synchronism. During the compression stroke of the heart, called *systole,* the blood in the *right ventricle* is forced out through the valve above into the lungs, while the blood in the left ventricle is forced into the *aorta.* During the filling stroke, called *diastole,* blood from the veins and right atrium enters the right ventricle while blood from the lungs enters the left atrium and left ventricle.

The entrance and exit valves of the right and left ventricles consist of two or three flaps or leaves attached to the edge of each opening and meeting at the center. These cusps are free to move apart when the flow is in one direction, but are forced together and thus close the opening when the flow attempts to reverse.

Upon leaving the largest artery, the aorta, the blood enters the main arteries leading to all parts of the body. After branching into smaller *arterioles,* and then into the numerous small capillaries, the blood emerges into the many small venous branches, the *venules,* and finally into the large veins where it is returned to the heart.

While passing through the capillaries of the lungs the red corpuscles in the blood stream take in oxygen by diffusion, while upon passing through the capillaries in other parts of the body, they give it up and acquire carbon dioxide by diffusion through the cell walls. The tubular capillaries in man are about 8 microns in diam-

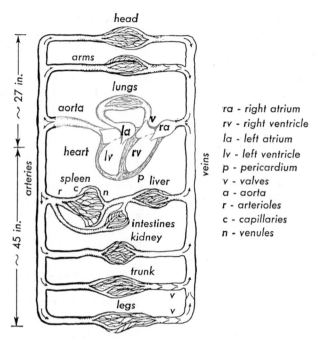

Fig. 26H   *Schematic diagram of blood circulation, showing the series and parallel circuits between the large systemic arteries and the large veins.*

eter and the red blood cells average 7.5 microns (1 micron = 10^{-4} cm).

During systole the maximum pressure reached in the aorta (called *systolic pressure*) is about 120 mm, while during diastole the pressure (called *diastolic pressure*) drops to about 80 mm. Both of these extreme pressures vary considerably with the health and age of the individual.

In considering variations in blood pressure throughout the entire circulation system, it should be kept in mind that all vessels are semi-elastic tubes instead of rigid pipes. The two principal functions of this elasticity are (1) to smooth out the pulsating outflow from the heart into a more steady flow through the arteries and capillaries, and (2) to allow contraction by muscles, thus diverting blood through some channels in preference to others when conditions require it.

As the blood is forced out of the heart, the aortic wall expands under the pressure, and part of the energy of the ejected blood is stored momentarily as potential energy in the distended wall. This distension trav-

els along the aortic wall and arteries as a kind of transverse wave. As the wave passes by, the stored potential energy is returned to the blood, thereby smoothing out the flow.

A patient's blood pressure is generally measured at the same horizontal level as the heart by means of a thin-walled rubber tube wrapped around the upper arm. As air is pumped in, the expansion of the tube squeezes the arm until the *brachial artery* is collapsed. The pressure of the air in the tube is then measured with an attached U-tube mercury manometer or a Bourdon gauge (see Fig. 25L). When the air pressure in the tube is slowly reduced by means of an escape valve, a point will be reached (about 110 to 120 mm) where small pressure pulses due to the heart action may be observed on the gauge. The gauge reading is then taken to be the systolic blood pressure.

The effect of gravity on venous pressure in different parts of the body differs markedly between *prone, sitting,* and *standing positions*. Pressure in the arteries varies too, but not to so great a degree, for muscular action partially compensates for hydrostatic pressure differences. Laboratory experiments on blood pressure measured with the body in the prone position have resulted in the pressure curve shown in Fig. 26I. The very small pressure drop through

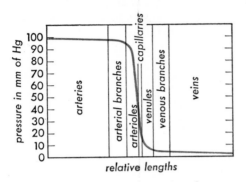

Fig. 26I *Blood pressure curve for the average human body in a prone position. (Lengths of capillaries greatly exaggerated.)*

the arteries and veins as compared with the long drop through the capillaries is readily understood from the relative diameters, as may be seen from the following tabulated data.

the top of the head, overcoming gravity as well as friction. Gravity alone is sufficient to return the blood through the veins. The vessels leading to the lower extremities and back again are like an inverted siphon.

The pressure gained in the arteries leading to the feet is transmitted through the capillaries to the veins where it is used to raise the blood again to the heart level.

Example. What minimum pressure is required to force blood from the heart to the top of the head if the vertical distance is 27 in.? Assume the density of blood to be 1.04 gm/cm³, and neglect friction.

Solution. The pressure will be equivalent to the weight of a column of liquid 27 in. in height. Changing inches to centimeters gives

$$27 \times 2.54 \times 1.04 = 71.3 \text{ gm/cm}^2$$

Divide by the density of mercury to convert this to an equivalent mercury column.

$$\frac{71.3}{13.6} = 5.24 \text{ cm} = 52.4 \text{ mm}$$

The following observation will demonstrate the wide variation in blood pressure with elevation above or below the heart.

	Number	Diameter, mm	Length, cm
Aorta and large arteries...........	40	3-10	40-20
Arterial branches.................	2400	0.6-1.0	1-10
Arterioles......................	40,000,000	0.02	0.2
Capillaries.....................	1,200,000,000	0.008	0.1
Venules.......................	80,000,000	0.03	0.2
Venous branches.................	24,000	1.5-2.4	1-10
Vena cava and large veins........	40	6-12	40-20

Note the enormous cross section of a large vein or artery as compared with a capillary. Maximum flow velocity in the aorta may reach as high as 40 cm/sec.

When the body is upright, the variations in blood pressure with height above or below the heart level are quite appreciable. First of all, the pressure developed by the heart must be sufficient to pump blood to

With the hand held palm down at waist level, observe the bulging of the veins on the back of the hand. Now slowly raise the hand higher and higher and notice carefully the height at which the bulges disappear. At this height the pressure in the veins has become zero at the hand level and, due to gravity, the blood flows downward through the arm to the heart.

PROBLEMS

1. At what speed will benzine emerge from a hole in the side of a tank if the hole is 10 m below the liquid surface?

2. At what speed will the velocity head of a stream of water be equal to 25 cm of mercury? (*Ans.* 8.16 m/sec.)

3. A pipe enters a water tank at a point 20 ft below the surface of the contained water. What is the water pressure in this pipe?

4. A cylindrical tank 30 ft high and full of water develops a hole in its side 6 ft below the top. How far from the base of the tank will the emerging water strike the ground? (*Ans.* 24.1 ft.)

5. The following measurements were made for the experiment shown in Fig. 26C. Distance $ab = 10$ cm, $aK = 40$ cm, and $CD = 5$ cm. The internal diameter of the tube is 0.8 cm. Find (a) the velocity of flow through the tube, (b) the friction head between K and D, and (c) the quantity of water delivered in 1 min.

6. Assuming the blood in a large artery to have a velocity of 34 cm/sec, what pressure drop is attributed to the velocity head? (*Ans.* 0.433 mm of Hg.)

7. Assuming the aorta to be a rigid pipe 0.9 cm in diameter, how much blood would be pumped through the heart with each pulse? Assume a pulse rate of 65 per min and a velocity of flow through the aorta of 35 cm/sec.

8. Water flowing with a velocity of 2 m/sec in a 2-cm-diameter pipe enters a short section having a diameter of only 1 cm and then a section having a diameter of 4 cm. Calculate (a) the velocity in hte last two pipes, and (b) the velocity head in all three. (*Ans.* (a) 8 m/sec, and 50 cm/sec; (b) 20.4 cm, 327 cm, 1.27 cm.)

9. Water flowing in a 4-in. pipe at the rate of 1.4 ft/sec comes to a small ½-in. pipe, and then a 2-in. pipe. Find (a) the velocity in the last two pipes, and (b) the velocity head in all three pipes.

10. A water tank is located on a platform 20 ft above the ground. If the water is 8 ft deep at the time that a hole develops in the side of the tank very close to the bottom, how far away from the platform and tank will the escaping stream of water strike the ground? (*Ans.* 25.3 ft.)

11. In a laboratory experiment performed with apparatus like that shown in Fig. 26D, the following measurements were made: $sA = 150$ cm, and $sa = 5$ cm. The diameter of the middle section DE of the horizontal tube equals 1 cm, and the diameter of the end sections AB and GH equal 2 cm. Find the speed of the water in (a) AB, and (b) DE. (c) What is the pressure drop cl in cm of water?

12. A pressure gauge on a pipe leading from the bottom of a water tank indicates a pressure of 40 lb/in.² When a valve in the pipe is opened to let water flow out, the gauge pressure drops to 36 lb/in.² Find the speed of the water in the pipe. (*Ans.* 24.3 ft/sec.)

13. A gauge on a water pipe shows a pressure of 25 lb/in.² When a faucet is opened to let water flow out, the gauge reading drops to 17 lb/in.² What is the speed of the water in the pipe?

14. A gauge on a water pipe shows a pressure of 60 lb/in.² When a valve is opened, the gauge reading drops to 45 lb/in.² (a) What is the water velocity? (b) How long will it take for 2 ft³ of water to flow out if the internal pipe diameter at the gauge is 1 in? (*Ans.* (a) 47.0 ft/sec. (b) 7.80 sec.)

15. If the internal diameter of a water pipe is 1 in., and 5 ft³ of water flow through in 1 min, what is (a) the velocity, and (b) the velocity head?

Chapter 27

Temperature, Specific Heat, and Change of State

27.1. Thermometers. The first authentic record of a thermometer dates back to the time of Galileo. Galileo's thermometer, as illustrated in Fig. 27A, consists of a narrow glass tube with an opening at one end and a bulb at the other. The open end of the tube is filled with colored water and inverted in a dish of water. When the temperature of the surrounding air rises, the air within the bulb expands, forcing the water down the tube. If the bulb is cooled, the air inside contracts, drawing the water up. (To be exact, atmospheric pressure outside pushes the water up.) A scale attached to the narrow tube can be calibrated to any temperature scale, low temperatures at the top and high temperatures at the bottom.

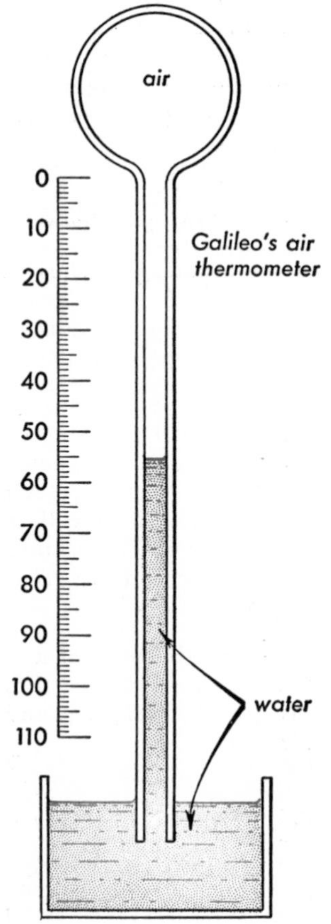

Of the many forms of temperature measuring devices, the mercury thermometer is the most common. A mercury thermometer, as shown in Fig. 27B, consists of a narrow glass tube (called a capillary), the bottom end sealed to a small bulb and the top end closed. The bulb and part of the capillary are filled with mercury, and the remaining section is evacuated. When the temperature rises, the mercury and the glass bulb both expand. The mercury, however, expands more than the glass, forcing a small part of the mercury up the narrow capillary. A scale is engraved on the glass to read temperature.

27.2. Temperature Scales. There are in general use today four different temperature scales. These are the Fahrenheit, Rankine, Centigrade, and Kelvin or Absolute. Each scale is shown by a diagram in Fig. 27C. The thermometers are all identically made but each has a different scale. In the United States, the Fahrenheit scale is commonly used in civil life, and the Rankine scale is used by engineers. The Centigrade and Kelvin scales are used in all countries for scientific measurements.

Fig. 27A *Air on heating expands and pushes the water down in the tube. On cooling, the air contracts and the water rises.*

210

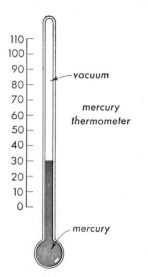

Fig. 27B *On heating a thermometer, the mercury expands more than the glass tube and the mercury level rises.*

Most of the manufactured thermometers are calibrated to one of these four scales. To calibrate a thermometer, the bulb is first placed in a mixture of ice and water, and the height of the mercury column marked on the side of the stem. It is next placed in steam just above boiling water and again marked. These two marks then determine the end points for whatever scale is to be used.

Between the temperatures of melting ice and boiling water there are 180° on the Fahrenheit and Rankine scales, as compared with 100° on the Centigrade and Kelvin scales. The ratio of these numbers is 9 : 5. This comparison shows that a temperature rise of 9°F, or 9°R, is equivalent to a rise of only 5°C, or 5°K.

The lowest temperature ever reached is approximately −273.16°C, or −459.69°F. For theoretical reasons, which will be given later, this is the lowest temperature that can ever be attained. The Kelvin and Rankine scales start with the lowest possible temperature as *absolute zero*. On the basis of the Centigrade and Farhenheit scale divisions, this locates the freezing point of water, to the nearest whole number, at 273°K or 492°R, and the boiling point at 373°K or 672°R.

It is frequently necessary to change temperature readings from one temperature scale to another. Rather than develop formulas for such changes, it is more conven-

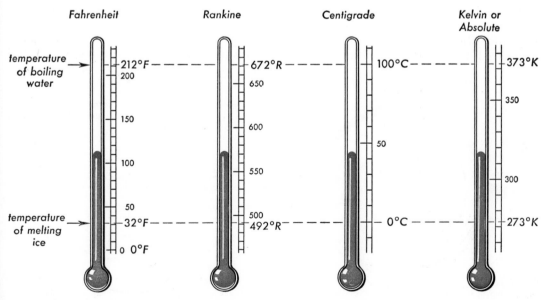

Fig. 27C *Mercury thermometers illustrating the four common temperature scales.*

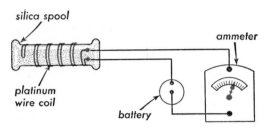

Fig. 27D *Electrical-resistance thermometer showing connections between the platinum wire coil, the battery, and the ammeter.*

ient to work out the simple mathematical steps by the inspection of a diagram like Fig. 27C.

27.3. Electrical Thermometers. If very low or very high temperatures are to be measured, other than mercury thermometers must be employed. At temperatures below −39°C, mercury freezes and becomes a solid; at high temperatures, glass melts and becomes a liquid. For both of these temperature extremes, electrical thermometers are commonly used. These instruments operate upon the principle that the resistance a wire offers to a flow of electric current through it changes with temperature. The higher the temperature, the greater is the resistance.

A diagram of an electrical thermometer is shown in Fig. 27D. A fine piece of platinum wire is wound around a small spool made of silica. The ends of this wire are connected to a battery and an ammeter.

The purpose of the battery is to supply the electric current, and the ammeter is used to determine its exact value. When the temperature of a hot body like a furnace is to be measured, the spool of platinum wire is placed inside the furnace and the battery and ammeter outside. A rise in temperature causes the resistance of the platinum wire to increase, and the current, therefore, to decrease. When the platinum wire reaches the temperature of the furnace, its resistance reaches a constant value and the ammeter pointer indicates a steady current. In many cases the ammeter scale is calibrated to give the temperature directly in degrees.

Another form of electrical thermometer, called a *thermocouple*, is illustrated in Fig. 27E(a). This temperature recording device is based upon a principle, discovered in 1821 by Seebeck, known as the *thermoelectric effect*. Two pieces of wire, one copper and one iron, are joined together at the ends to form a complete loop. When one junction is heated and the other kept cool, an electric current flows around the loop in the direction indicated by the arrows. The greater the difference in temperature between the two junctions, the greater is the electric current.

Diagram (b) in Fig. 27E represents a thermocouple connected by wires to an ammeter. If the junction of the thermocouple is first placed in melting ice and then in boiling water, the two scale readings of the am-

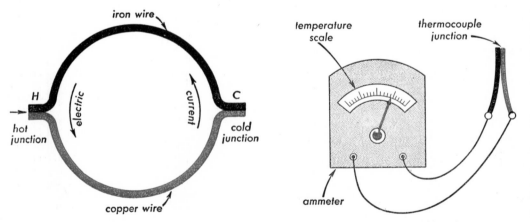

Fig. 27E (a) *A thermocouple.* (b) *A thermocouple thermometer circuit diagram.*

meter can be marked 0°C and 100°C at the appropriate points. These determine the scale of the instrument, making of it a direct reading thermometer.

Thermocouples are not always made of copper and iron as shown in Fig. 27E. Any two different metals when brought into contact will exhibit a thermoelectric effect. Some combinations of two metals, however, produce larger currents than others. For very high temperature measurements, platinum and platinum-iridium alloys are used, owing to their very high melting point temperatures. (See Table 27C.)

A set of thermocouples, when connected

cools, the atomic motions decrease and the body shrinks. That heat is a form of energy and is due to the kinetic energy of molecular motion was first proposed by Count Rumford in the latter part of the 18th century.*

It is not always clear to the beginning student that the temperature and the quantity of heat are different entities. The difference between the two can be illustrated by the heating of two pans of water. More gas must be burned to heat a large pan of water than a small pan. Although both are started at the same temperature and both are raised to the same boiling point, 100°C,

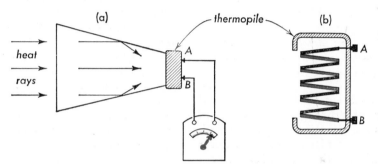

Fig. 27F *Cross section of a thermopile for measuring heat radiation from hot bodies.*

as shown in Fig. 27F, form what is commonly called a *thermopile*. Small rods of two different metals are joined alternately as shown in diagram (b). One set of junctions is usually protected by placing them at the back of a small box container, and the other set is exposed to heat rays through the opposite side which is left open. A funnel or horn-shaped reflector mounted over the open side will collect more heat rays from a distant hot object and thereby increases the electric current. Thermocouples containing several hundred elements can be made so sensitive that they will detect the heat of a candle flame several hundred feet away.

27.4. Specific Heat. According to the kinetic theory of matter, the individual atoms of which all substances are made are in a state of rapid motion. As a body is heated to a higher temperature this atomic motion increases and the body expands. As a body

the larger pan has required more thermal energy, called heat.

The difference between the temperature and quantity of heat is well illustrated by the following experiment. See Fig. 27G. Five marbles, all of the same size but made of different materials, are heated in boiling water to a temperature of 100°C. At a given instant they are all placed on a sheet of

* Benjamin Thompson was born in Woburn, Massachusetts, in 1753. He spent most of his adult life abroad, notably in Bavaria, which was then a part of the Holy Roman Empire. Among other ventures, he managed a Bavarian artillery factory. From his observations about the heat developed in boring cannon, he was able to show that heat is not a pervading fluid, but a form of internal energy of the atoms or molecules forming the substance. His own expression was that heat was a mode of motion of these particles. For these and other services, Thompson was appointed a count of the Holy Roman Empire; he chose the name of his wife's former home in New Hampshire, Rumford, as his title.

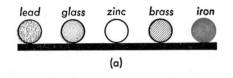

(a)

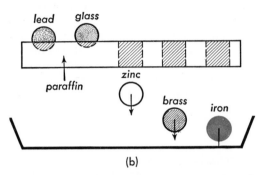

(b)

Fig. 27G *Experiment demonstrating the different heat capacities of different substances of the same size.*

paraffin about 0.5 cm thick and permitted to melt their way through. The iron and brass marbles are observed to drop through first, but the lead and glass marbles never do. This illustrates the fact that the heat content of the iron and brass, even though raised to the same temperature as the others, is considerably greater than the heat content of the glass and lead.

In order to determine the exact heat capacity of a substance, we must first define the *calorie* and the *British thermal unit*.

The amount of heat required to raise the temperature of 1 gm of water 1C° is called the calorie (abbr. cal).

The quantity of heat required to raise the temperature 1 lb of water 1F° is called the British thermal unit (abbr. Btu.)

The ratio between these two units is readily computed and found to be

$$1 \text{ Btu} = 252 \text{ cal} \qquad (27a)$$

Once the calorie or the Btu is defined, the amount of heat required to raise any amount of water from one temperature to another may be calculated by simply multiplying the mass of water by the temperature rise. For example, to raise 25 gm of water from 10°C to 50°C requires $25 \times 40 = 1000$

cal, or to raise 6 lb of water from 32°F to 60°F requires $6 \times 28 = 168$ Btu.

While 1 cal of heat will raise 1 gm of water 1C°, a different number of calories will be required to raise the temperature of 1 gm of some other substance 1C°. For example, to raise 1 gm of iron 1C° requires only $\frac{1}{10}$ of a calorie, while to raise 1 gm of lead 1C° requires only $\frac{1}{30}$ of a calorie. In other words, the thermal capacities of equal masses of different materials have different values.

The thermal capacity of a substance is defined as the number of calories required to raise 1 gm of that substance through 1C°, or the amount of heat to raise 1 lb 1F°.

The ratio between the thermal capacity of a substance and the thermal capacity of water is called specific heat.

Numerically, specific heat has the same value as thermal capacity; being a ratio, however, it is like *specific gravity* and has no units.

The specific heats or thermal capacities of a few common substances are given in the following table.

TABLE 27A. SPECIFIC HEATS
(Thermal Capacities)

	c
Aluminum	0.220
Brass	0.092
Copper	0.093
Glass	0.160
Gold	0.031
Glycerine	0.60
Ice	0.50
Iron	0.105
Lead	0.031
Mercury	0.033
Silver	0.056
Zinc	0.092
Steam	0.50
Water	1.000

To illustrate the use of this table, consider the calculation of the heat content of the marbles used in the above experiment. The measured mass of each marble is given in the second row of the following tabulation and the corresponding thermal capacity in the next row. The product of these two quantities gives the values shown in the third row; they represent the amount of heat required to raise that marble 1°C. Since all marbles were raised from room temperature 20°C to the boiling point of water, 100°C, the values in the third row have been multiplied by the rise in temperature 80°C to obtain the total heat values in the last row.

til it has all turned to water does the temperature begin to rise. As the water becomes hotter and hotter, it eventually reaches a temperature of 100°C where vigorous boiling sets in. Here again the temperature stops rising and, as heat is added, more and more water is boiled away to become steam. Finally, when all has become steam at 100°C the temperature begins to rise once more.

TABLE 27B. TABULATED RESULTS OF THE MARBLE EXPERIMENT

	Lead	Glass	Zinc	Brass	Iron
Mass in grams..................	45	10	24	30	28
Thermal capacity, cal/gm deg...	0.031	0.160	0.092	0.092	0.105
Heat to raise 1°C, cal...........	1.39	1.60	2.20	2.76	2.94
Heat to raise 80°C, cal..........	111	128	176	221	235

These numbers clearly indicate that, in the experiment above, iron and brass should melt through the paraffin first: they have available within them the largest amounts of stored thermal energy, 235 and 221 cal, respectively.

The definition of thermal capacity and the calculation of total heat content may be summarized by a generally useful formula of the following form:

$$H = m \times c \times (t_2 - t_1) \qquad (27b)$$

H represents the total amount of heat in calories or Btu, m the mass of the body to which it is added, c the thermal capacity, and $t_2 - t_1$ the rise in temperature.

27.5. Change of State. The continuous addition of heat to a solid or liquid mass will eventually bring about a change of state. The general behavior of many substances can be illustrated by a detailed description of the changes that occur with the most common of all liquids, water. If a block of ice at a temperature of −50°C is placed in a pan and put on a stove to heat, its temperature will rise slowly until it reaches 0°C.

At 0°C the temperature stops rising and the ice begins to melt. More and more ice is melted as heat is continually added; not un-

All of these changes of temperature and changes of state are shown by a graph in Fig. 27H. The horizontal sections represent changes of state without change in tempera-

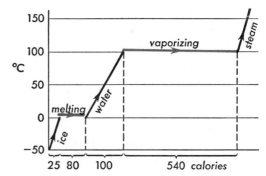

Fig. 27H *Heat-temperature graph for one gram of ice starting at −50°C. Illustrating the latent heat of fusion and vaporization.*

ture, while the slanted sections on either side represent changes in temperature without abrupt changes in state.

27.6. Melting Point. The melting point is defined as the temperature at which a substance under normal atmospheric pressure changes from the solid to the liquid state, or vice versa. Every substance has its own melting point, which for water is at 0°C. As shown by a few common substances listed in Table 27C, some substances melt at very low temperatures while others require extremely high temperatures.

Recent studies of the atomic structure of certain liquids show that, at temperatures approaching the freezing point, the lattice formation assumed by the individual atoms is essentially that of the solid state, whereas others show no such resemblance or similarity right up to the freezing temperature.

quires 80 cal, and to melt 1 lb requires 143 Btu. Similar heat determinations for other solids show that they too require a definite amount of heat to melt them without a rise in temperature. To melt 1 gm of gold requires 16 cal, 1 gm of silver 21 cal, etc. These values, the so-called *latent heat of fusion,* are tabulated for a number of elements in Table 27C.

TABLE 27C. MELTING POINT, LATENT HEAT OF FUSION, BOILING POINT, AND HEAT OF VAPORIZATION OF SOME COMMON SUBSTANCES

Substance	Melting Point °C	Heat of Fusion cal/gm	Boiling Point °C	Heat of Vaporization cal/gm
Air	−212	5.5	−191	51
Aluminum	658	77	1800	..
Copper	1080	42	2310	..
Gold	1063	16	2500	..
Helium	−271	..	−268	6
Hydrogen	−259	14	−252	108
Iron	1530	6	2450	..
Lead	327	5.9	1525	..
Mercury	−39	2.8	357	65
Nitrogen	−210	6.1	−195	48
Oxygen	−219	3.3	−184	51
Platinum	1760	27	3910	..
Silicon	1420	..	3500	..
Silver	962	21	1955	..
Sulfur Dioxide	73	24	−10	95
Tin	232	14	2270	..
Tungsten	3400	..	5830	..
Water	0	80	100	540

27.7. Boiling Point. The boiling point is defined as the temperature at which a substance, under normal atmospheric pressure, changes from the liquid to the vapor state, or vice versa. These temperatures, too, are listed in Table 27C. A knowledge of melting and boiling points is of considerable practical importance. Solid carbon dioxide, liquid air, liquid hydrogen, and liquid helium are used as refrigerants for cooling, whereas metals like tungsten and platinum are used in furnaces designed for the heating of bodies to very high temperatures.

27.8. Latent Heat of Fusion. We have seen above that, when ice is melting, heat is continually added, with no resultant rise in temperature. To melt 1 gm of ice re-

The latent heat of fusion is defined as the quantity of heat necessary to change 1 gm of solid to 1 gm of liquid with no change in temperature.

The reverse of fusion is *solidification,* a process in which heat is liberated by the substance. The amount of heat liberated by matter on solidification is equal to the amount of heat taken in on fusion; pure water on freezing gives up 80 cal/gm, gold 16 cal/gm, silver 21 cal/gm, etc. Letting L represent the latent heat of fusion and m the mass of a given substance to be fused or solidified, the quantity of heat required or liberated, as the case may be, is given by

$$H = mL_f \qquad (27c)$$

If m is the mass in grams, then L_f should be in cal/gm and H will be in calories. If m is in pounds, then L_f should be in Btu/lb, and H will be in Btu.

27.9. Heat of Vaporization. When water is being boiled, heat is continually being added without a rise in temperature. This added heat is not retained by the liquid, but is carried off by the vapor through the boiling process. To vaporize 1 gm of boiling water requires 540 cal, and to vaporize 1 lb requires 970 Btu. These values, the so-called *heat of vaporization,* are tabulated along with others for a number of substances in Table 27C. (For metals with very high melting points, the heat of vaporization has never been measured.)

The same Eq.(27c) used for calculating heat quantities during fusion may be used to determine heat quantities during vaporization. If we let L_v be the heat of vaporization and m the mass of substance to be vaporized, the quantity of heat H required is given by

$$\boxed{H = mL_v} \qquad (27d)$$

This is also the amount of heat liberated by the same amount of vapor when it condenses to the liquid state.

Since heat is a form of energy and its addition to a body raises the average kinetic energy of the molecules, the absolute temperature increases proportionately. During fusion and vaporization, however, heat is added without a temperature change. During change of state, the heat energy goes into the potential energy of the molecules, exerting forces through collision which push the molecules farther apart against their attractive forces.

Example. Calculate the amount of heat required to change 50 gm of ice at $-20°C$ to steam at $140°C$.

Solution. To heat the ice from $-20°C$ to the melting point at $0°C$, use Eq.(27b) and the thermal capacity of ice from Table 27A.

$$H_1 = mc(t_2 - t_1) = 50 \times 0.50 \times 20 = 500 \text{ cal}$$

To melt the ice to water at $0°C$, use Eq.(27c) and the heat of fusion from Table 27C.

$$H_2 = mL_f = 50 \times 80 = 4000 \text{ cal}$$

To heat the water from $0°C$ to the boiling point at $100°C$, use Eq.(27b) and the thermal capacity of water.

$$H_3 = mc(t_2 - t_1) = 50 \times 1 \times 100 = 5000 \text{ cal}$$

To vaporize the water to steam at $100°C$, use Eq.(27d) and the heat of vaporization of water.

$$H_4 = 50 \times 540 = 27,000 \text{ cal}$$

To heat the steam from $100°C$ to steam at the desired temperature $140°C$, use Eq.(27b) and the thermal capacity of steam.

$$H_5 = mc(t_2 - t_1) = 50 \times 0.5 \times 40 = 1000 \text{ cal}$$

By adding all of these equations we obtain the total required heat.

$$H = 500 + 4000 + 5000 + 27,000 + 1000$$
$$= 37,500 \text{ cal}$$

PROBLEMS

1. Name and diagram the four temperature scales.

2. Diagram and explain the principle of the thermocouple.

3. If a Centigrade thermometer indicates a temperature of $35°C$, what would a Fahrenheit thermometer read in the same room?

4. What temperature on the Centigrade scale and the Rankin scale is equivalent to the following: (a) $50°F$, (b) $77°F$, (c) $95°F$, (d) $85°F$, and (e) $-40°F$. (*Ans.* (a) $10°C$, $510°R$, (b) $25°C$, $537°R$, (c) $35°C$, $555°R$, (d) $29.4°C$, $545°R$, and (e) $-40°C$, $420°R$.)

5. Find the number of calories of heat required to raise the temperature of 2 Kg of lead from $20°C$ to $100°C$.

6. Calculate the amount of heat required to raise 2 Kg of gold from $68°F$ to $302°F$. (*Ans.* 8060 cal.)

7. Calculate the heat required to change 50 gm of ice at $-5°C$ to water at $30°C$.

8. Find the heat necessary to change 4.2 Kg of water at $20°C$ to steam at $100°C$. (*Ans.* 2.60×10^6 cal.)

9. How much heat is required to melt 5 lb of lead at $327°C$?

10. How much heat will vaporize 1.6 Kg of mercury at 357°C? (*Ans.* 1.04 × 10⁵ cal.)

11. A small crucible containing 300 gm of gold is heated to the temperature of a small furnace and then the gold dropped into 1 Kg of water at 10°C. If the final temperature comes to 20°C, find the temperature of the furnace. Neglect the heat losses to any container.

12. An aluminum pan with a mass of 250 gm holds 200 cm³ of water. How much heat is required to raise the temperature of the pan and the water from 20°C to 100°C? (*Ans.* 20,400 cal.)

13. An iron kettle having a mass of 10 Kg contains 50 Kg of ice at 0°C. How much heat is required to melt the ice and bring the water to the boiling point?

14. A 3-Kg block of lead at 20°C is to be melted. What is the minimum amount of heat required? (*Ans.* 46,250 cal.)

15. What is the minimum amount of heat required to melt 2 Kg of iron if the initial temperature is 30°C?

16. A mass of 5 Kg of lead is placed in a 2-Kg iron pot at 27°C. What is the minimum amount of heat required to melt the lead? (*Ans.* 139,000 cal.)

Chapter 28

Heat Transfer and the Atmosphere

There are numerous methods by which heat may be transmitted from one place to another. Some of these methods are slow and roundabout, while others are very fast and straight to the point. A careful study of all known methods has led to the realization that there are but three general types of heat transfer: *conduction, convection,* and *radiation.* Conduction is a slow process by which heat is transmitted through a substance by molecular activity. Convection is a more rapid process involving the motion of heated matter itself from one place to another. Radiation of heat from one place to another takes place in the same manner and with the same speed as light, 186,000 mi/sec.

28.1. Conduction. Not all bodies are good conductors of heat. Metals like copper and silver are much better for this purpose than are other substances like wood, glass, paper, and water. The ability of a given substance to conduct heat is called its *thermal conductivity.*

The relative conductivities of different substances can be illustrated by an experiment performed as follows: Similar rods of six different metals, copper, aluminum, brass, tin, german silver, and lead, are coated with a special yellow paint and arranged as shown in Fig. 28A. The ends of the rods, mounted in rubber corks, project through holes in a metal tube where their lower ends are heated to 100°C by steam passing through the tube. As the heat travels slowly up each rod, the yellow paint turns to red. After 5 or 10 min running, the height to which the paint has turned color is approx-

imately as shown by the stippled areas in the figure. Of these six metals, copper is observed to be the best conductor and lead the poorest.

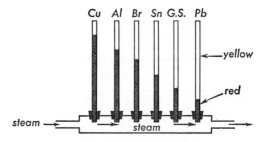

Fig. 28A *Experiment illustrating the relative heat conductivities of six different metals: copper, aluminum, brass, tin, German silver, and lead.*

In order to heat an object, it is customary to bring it into contact with some other body at a higher temperature. A pan of water, for example, is generally heated by placing it over an open flame. The combustion of natural gas first sets the gas molecules into a rapid state of motion. These molecules, striking the bottom of the pan, set the molecules of the metal into rapid vibration. They in turn strike other metal molecules, thus transferring the motion through to the other side. This is called heat conduction. The metal molecules set the first layer of water molecules moving, and they in turn set others moving. Thus molecular motion, called heat, has been given to the body of water.

Laboratory experiments show that the amount of heat flowing through a rod is proportional to the time, the cross-sectional area, and the difference in temperature between the ends, and is inversely proportional to the length.

Using appropriate symbols for each of these factors and inserting a proportionality constant, we can set up the following equation:

$$H = k \frac{A(t_2 - t_1)}{L} T \qquad (28a)$$

H is the amount of heat flowing through the body of length L and cross section A, k is the thermal conductivity, T is the time interval of flow, t_2 is the temperature of the hot end, and t_1 is the temperature of the cold end. It is quite clear to almost everyone that if the temperature difference $t_2 - t_1$, or the area A is increased (see Fig. 28B),

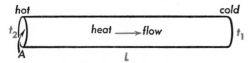

Fig. 28B *Diagram illustrating the various measurable factors involved in the flow of heat through a body by conduction.*

the amount of heat passing through is increased. It is not as obvious, however, that an increase in the length L causes a decrease in the heat flow, or that a decrease in length produces an increase. The latter will be illustrated by two experiments.

Although paper is a poor conductor, the flow of heat through it can be made very great by increasing A, the cross-sectional area, and decreasing L, the distance it has to flow. Diagram (a) in Fig. 28C illustrates

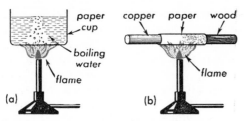

Fig. 28C *Illustration of the conduction of heat through paper.*

thermal conductivity by the boiling of water in a paper cup. Although the gas flame plays directly against the surface of the paper, the cup will not burn. The reason for this is that the heat from the lower surface of the paper is conducted through to the water fast enough to keep the temperature of the paper from rising too high. If the paper is thick, the lower surface will burn. Strange as it may seem, the thinner the paper, the less is the chance of burning.

In diagram (b) of Fig. 28C, a thin piece of paper is wrapped once around a rod made half of wood and half of copper. When the flame is brought up, as shown, the paper burns only where it is in contact with the wood, and not at all where it is in contact with the copper. Copper, being a good conductor, carries the heat into the interior of the metal and away from the metal surface. Since wood is a poor conductor it cannot conduct the heat away from the surface fast enough, and the paper heats up and soon burns.

The thermal conductivities of a few common substances are given in Table 28A.

TABLE 28A. THERMAL CONDUCTIVITIES, k, in cal cm/sec cm² C°

Substance	k
Silver	0.97
Copper	0.92
Aluminum	0.50
Brass	0.26
Iron	0.16
Lead	0.08
German Silver	0.10
Mercury	0.02
Tile	0.002
Glass	0.0025
Water	0.0014
Wood	0.0005
Paper	0.0003
Felt	0.00004

The number k is the quantity of heat in calories that in 1 sec will pass through a 1-cm cube when two opposite faces are maintained at 1C° difference in temperature. Knowing the value of k for a given substance, it is possible to calculate, by means of Eq.(28a), the amount of heat flowing through any sized object made of that same substance.

Example. One end of an aluminum rod 40 cm long and 5 cm² in cross section is maintained at a temperature of 100°C, and the other end at 20°C. Find the amount of heat that will flow through the rod in 2 min.

Solution. Substitution in Eq.(28a) gives

$$H = 0.50 \frac{5(100 - 20)}{40} 120 = 600 \text{ cal} \quad (28b)$$

28.2. Convection. Why is it that a poor conductor of heat like water can be heated so quickly when it is placed in a pan over a hot fire? It is due to the second method of heat transfer known as *convection.* Water on the bottom of a pan is heated first. Because of a rise in temperature it expands. Being lighter than the cold water above, it then rises to the top, permitting cold water to come to the bottom from the sides. This action sets up a flow of water called a *convection current.* (See Fig. 28D.) Convection

Fig. 28D *Convection currents in a pan of water being heated over a stove burner.*

currents thus keep the water stirred up as it heats.

Convection currents set up by the heating of a vessel of water are illustrated in Fig. 28E(a). A glass tube in the shape of a letter O is filled with water and then heated at one of the lower corners as indicated. A drop of ink admitted at the top opening will mix with the water and quickly flow around the tube in a counterclockwise direction. This circulation is the basis of the hot water heating systems used in some houses. As illustrated in diagram (b), hot water from a supply tank in a lower room or basement rises and flows through several

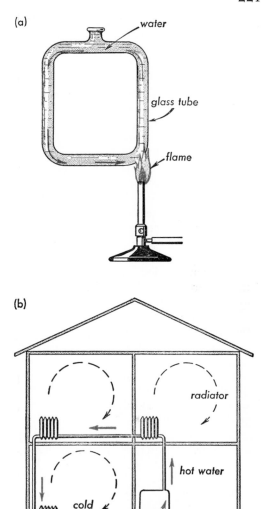

Fig. 28E *Illustrations of heat convection by the circulation of water in a pipe and air in a room.*

radiators, only to return, somewhat cooled, to the tank where it is reheated.

Convection currents in the atmosphere are quite noticeable and account for the wind. Along the sea coast, cool air from over the ocean comes as a sea breeze due to convection. The sun's rays are absorbed more readily by the land than they are by water, and the warmed air over the land rises while cooler air from the ocean comes in to take its place. At night the land cools quickly by radiation back toward the cold sky and soon the air over the water is the warmer, and rising it causes a reversal in air movement. The wind blows from the land to the sea. These air currents are easily observed by smoke from a fire built on the seashore. During the day the smoke blows inland, and at night it blows seaward.

Pilots are well aware of rising air currents over certain local areas of ground. Solar radiation being absorbed more completely by a newly plowed field, for example, will warm the air sufficiently to cause convection. Flying into such an upward draft of air, the plane receives a sudden lift. During certain seasons these updrafts of warm air are cooled by the air layers above and water vapor is condensed to form clouds.

28.3. Radiation. When the sun comes over the horizon in the early morning, the heat can be felt as soon as the sun becomes visible. This heat, called radiant heat or radiation, travels with the speed of light, 186,000 mi/sec.

Radiant heat is but one of the many forms of energy and is readily detected by means of a radiometer, thermocouple, thermister, thermometer, etc. A Crooke's

Fig. 28F   *A Crooke's radiometer.*

radiometer, shown in Fig. 28F, will often be found in a jewelry store window. In daylight or under a bright light the little pinwheel, made of very thin mica, will be found spinning around as if by perpetual motion.

Each vane of such a radiometer is shiny on one face, and blackened on the other. The black faces absorb more radiant energy than the polished surfaces, so that the adjacent air is heated. The faster recoiling air molecules therefore exert a larger force on the blackened sides, driving it around.

Should a radiometer be so highly evacuated that little air remains inside, light waves in bouncing off the polished surfaces will exert twice the force they do in being

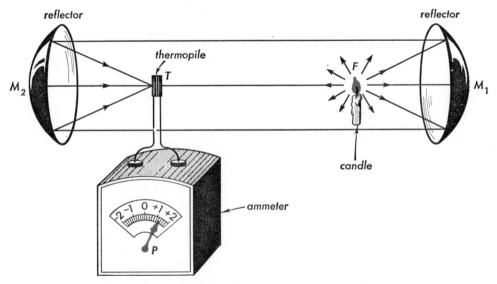

Fig. 28G   *Reflection of heat rays by concave mirrors.*

absorbed on the blackened side, and the pinwheel will spin the other way.

Radiant heat rays, like visible light, are electromagnetic waves and have all the general properties known to visible light. The essential difference between the two is that heat waves, sometimes called *infrared rays,* are not visible to the human eye.

A demonstration of the reflection of infrared rays is diagramed in Fig. 28G. A candle flame acting as a source at F emits light and heat rays in all directions. Of these rays, only the ones traveling toward the concave mirror M_1 are reflected into a parallel beam. Arriving at the second concave mirror M_2, these rays are again reflected, being brought together to a focus on the exposed junctions of a thermopile T. As the junctions of the thermopile warm up, an electric current is produced, which causes the ammeter pointer P to move to the right. When the candle is removed, the pointer returns to zero.

A practical example of heat radiation is to be found in every home where a fireplace is used as a means of heating. Contrary to most beliefs, the heat entering a room from a fireplace is practically all in the form of infrared rays originating in the flames, the coals, and the hot stone or brick walls. The air that is heated within the fireplace does not enter the room but is carried up the chimney as a convection current. See Fig. 28H. This rising current of air draws fresh air into the room and into the fire, thus supplying fresh oxygen to the burning wood or coal.

A Dewar-flask or "Thermos bottle" is an example of a practical device in which the conduction, convection, and radiation of heat are reduced as much as possible. As shown by the cross-sectional diagram in Fig. 28I, a Thermos bottle consists of a dou-

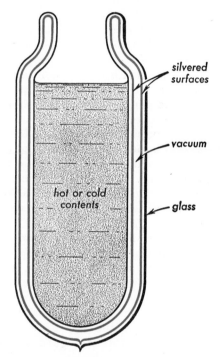

Fig. 28I *The Dewar-flask, or "Thermos" bottle, minimize conduction by using glass, convection by evacuating, and radiation by silvering.*

ble-walled glass vessel silvered on the inside. The purpose of the silvering is to reflect all radiant heat attempting to enter or leave the vessel. The space between the walls is highly evacuated to prevent convection, and the glass, being a poor conductor, minimizes conduction through the walls of the neck. With the exception of the vacuum space between walls, a calorimeter of the type commonly used in laboratories is similar to a Dewar-flask.

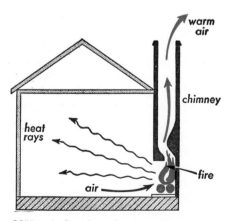

Fig. 28H *A fireplace heats a room by radiation from the flame, the coals, and the stove walls. Convection currents set up a draft and carry warm air and smoke out the chimney.*

Another type of heating system for public buildings and private dwellings has recently been developed. Known to engineers as *panel heating,* this system heats the walls of the rooms by hot air or water pipes that run through them. Even though the windows are open on the coldest days, radiant heat keeps the occupants warm.

28.4. Emission and Absorption. The rate at which a body radiates or absorbs heat depends not only upon the absolute temperature, but upon the nature of the exposed surfaces as well. Objects that are good emitters of heat are also good absorbers of the same kind of radiation. This is known as *Kirchoff's law of radiation.* A body whose surface is blackened is an excellent emitter as well as an excellent absorber. If the same body is chromium-plated it becomes a poor emitter and a poor absorber.

If the outside surface of a hot coffee cup were painted a dull black, the rate of cooling would be more rapid than if it were chromium-plated. A highly polished surface, as in the Dewar-flask, would help by reflection to keep radiant heat from crossing the boundary.

Black clothes should not be worn on a hot day since black is a good absorber of the sun's radiant heat. While black is also a good emitter, the external temperature is higher than the body temperature and the exchange rate is therefore such as to heat the body. White clothes are worn in hot climates because white is a good reflector and therefore a poor absorber.

28.5. Black Body Radiation. The relation between the radiant heat E emitted by a body and its temperature was first made through the extensive laboratory experiments of Josef Stefan. The same law was later derived from theoretical considerations by Ludwig Boltzmann, and is now known as the *Stefan-Boltzmann law.**

* Ludwig Boltzmann (1844-1906), Austrian theoretical physicist, was educated at Linz and Vienna. At 23 he was appointed assistant at the physical institute in Vienna. Later he became professor at Graz, then at Munich, and finally back at Vienna. His first publication was on the second law of thermodynamics, and was followed by numerous papers on molecular motion, on viscosity and diffusion of

$$E = kT^4 \qquad (28c)$$

Here E represents the energy radiated per second by a body at an absolute temperature T, and k is a proportionality constant. The law applies only to so-called "black bodies."

A black body is defined as one that absorbs all of the radiant heat that falls upon it.

Such a perfect absorber would also be a perfect emitter.

If E represents the heat in calories radiated per second per square centimeter of a black body, then $k = 1.36 \times 10^{-12}$. If E is measured in ergs/cm^2 sec, then $k = 5.7 \times 10^{-5}$.

The best laboratory approach to a black body is a hole in a blackened box. Practically all heat entering such a hole would be absorbed inside. Black velvet cloth or a surface painted dull with lampblack will absorb about 97% of the radiant heat falling on it, and may for many purposes be considered a black body. Polished metal surfaces, however, are far from black bodies; they absorb only about 6% of the incident energy and reflect the remainder. Most other substances have absorption ratios between these two extremes.

28.6. Prevost's Law of Heat Exchange. Laboratory experiments, as well as the Stefan-Boltzmann law, show that all bodies, whether they are hot or cold, radiate heat. The words "hot" and "cold" are only relative terms, since even ice radiates heat. The greater the absolute temperature of a body, the greater is the rate at which it radiates, and ice at 0°C is 273° above absolute zero.

If a cold block of metal is brought into a warm room, it radiates heat to the walls of the room and the walls of the room radiate heat to the rock. Because the walls are at a higher temperature, they give more heat per second to the block than the block gives up in return. See Fig 28J. Due to this unequal exchange of heat, the temperature

gases, on Maxwell's electromagnetic theory, on Hertz's electrical experiments, and on Stefan's law for black body radiation.

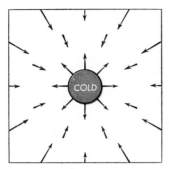

Fig. 28J   *A cold body warms up to room temperature.*

of the cold block rises until it comes to the same temperature as the room, at which time it radiates and absorbs at exactly the same rate.

Prevost's law of heat exchange states that a body at the temperature of its surroundings is radiating and receiving heat at equal rates.

When a person stands near a fireplace, he feels warm because his body receives more heat from the fire than it emits. If he stands next to a cold window, he feels chilly because he radiates more heat than he absorbs. The side of his body facing the window gets noticeably colder than the other.

28.7. Radiant Heat from the Sun. Instruments designed to measure solar radiation are called pyroheliometers. See Fig. 28K. A

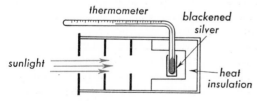

Fig. 28K   *Abbot's pyroheliometer for measuring the heat radiated by the sun.*

beam of sunlight of known cross-sectional area is allowed to fall upon the blackened surface of a silver disk where it is absorbed. A drill hole in the metal disk admits the narrow bulb of a sensitive mercury thermometer, the latter being bent and threaded through a hole in the heat-insulated box as shown in the diagram. Knowing the heat capacity of the metal and its

rise in temperature, the total number of calories per minute can be calculated.

Measurements of this kind by various observers are in remarkable agreement with each other and give a value of 1,938 cal/cm²/min. This number, called *the solar constant,* is defined as the average amount of energy falling in 1 min on 1 cm² of surface placed at right angles to the sun's rays. Multiplying the solar constant by the area of a sphere 93 million mi in radius, we obtain the figure 9×10^{25} cal/sec as the total heat radiated by the sun.

An appreciation of these figures can be had by the following comparison. If all of the energy radiated by the sun could be used to heat the oceans of the earth, the temperature would rise from the freezing point to the boiling point in less than 2 sec. Where all this heat comes from within the sun has long been a puzzle to astronomer and physicist alike. A satisfactory answer to the problem has recently been found and will be given in Sec. 78.7.

28.8. The Seasons. The reason for the earth's polar ice caps and warm equator, as well as the difference in temperature between winter and summer, is to be attributed to the different angles at which the sun's rays arrive at the earth's surface. When it is summer in the northern hemisphere the sun's rays strike the earth's surface from the direction shown in Fig. 28L.

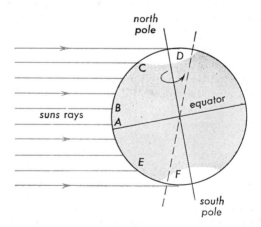

Fig. 28L   *Solar radiation is spread over a bigger area at the earth's poles than it is at the equator.*

It will be noted that a given bundle of rays near the poles is spread over a much larger area C to D and E to F, than an equal bundle of rays near the equator A to B.

With the arrival of less heat per unit area, the resulting temperature will be lowest near the poles and highest near the equator. As the earth moves slowly in its orbit around the sun, the South Pole is in darkness for many months and it is winter in the southern hemisphere; the North Pole is in the light and it is summer. Six months later, when the orientation of the sun's rays with respect to the earth is like that shown by the dotted axis in the diagram, the conditions and the seasons are reversed.

Not all of the solar radiation coming toward the earth gets through the atmosphere to be absorbed by the surface. While a small per cent is absorbed by the atmosphere on the clearest of days, fog and clouds in regions away from the equator and toward the polar caps often absorb 30% to 40% and reflect a similar amount back into space. Under such conditions only a small amount of heat may get to the ground.

On clear cold nights the temperature at the earth's surface drops rapidly, because of direct heat radiation into space. An intervening cloud blanket, however, will prevent this and the resultant surface temperature will remain considerably higher.

28.9. Convection Currents of Air Around the Earth. The earth's atmosphere is not a stationary body of air but one that is continually moving. A "wind pattern" showing the average air currents around the earth is given in Fig. 28M. Warm air masses at the equator rise because of convection and colder air from both sides rushes in to take its place. The rising currents divide high up in the atmosphere and return to the earth at other regions north and south.

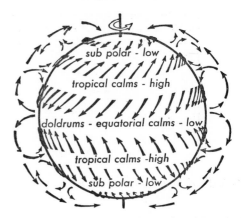

Fig. 28M *Air current pattern for the earth, due to convection and the earth's rotation.*

This circulation of air is altered by the earth's rotation from east to west about its polar axis. The air masses that move north and south from the regions of tropical calms move to a region of lower or higher ground speeds with the result that the air gets ahead of the earth's rotation or behind, respectively. This gives rise to the diagonal movements of the trade winds which are good illustrations of the coriolis forces described in Sec. 14.4. Where the air currents rise at the equator, the average barometric pressure is less than in the regions of tropical calms where the currents are down.

The absorption of the sun's rays by the earth and its lower atmosphere causes the temperature at sea level to be greater than the temperature at higher altitudes. Normally the temperature decreases steadily with height until an altitude is reached beyond which the temperature remains constant at −67°F. This altitude, which is about 5 mi at the poles and 10 mi at the equator, is the upper limit of the so-called *troposphere.* This layer contains about 80% of the atmospheric mass.

PROBLEMS

1. A large leaded window contains 25 panes of glass, each one of which is 20 cm by 30 cm and 0.5 cm thick. If the snow outside maintains the outer surface at 0°C, and the heat of the room maintains the inner surface at 12°C, how much heat will be conducted through the glass in 1 hr?

2. The bottom of an aluminum boiler is 1.2 mm thick and has a cross-sectional area of

2500 cm². If the upper surface is maintained at 50°C and gas flames keep the under surface at 60°C, how much heat will flow through in 2 min? (*Ans.* 1.25 × 10⁷ cal.)

3. A brass rod is 6 cm long and 1 cm in diameter. How much heat will flow through this rod in 5 min if one end is maintained at −40°C and the other end at +40°C?

4. One end of a copper rod 20 cm long and with cross-sectional area 6 cm² is maintained at 30°C and the other end at 250°C. How much heat will flow through the rod in 2 hr? (*Ans.* 437,000 cal.)

5. The rear wall of a brick fireplace has an effective open area of 1 m². Find the number of calories radiated per minute if this area is maintained at 127°C. Assume the surface to be a black body.

6. The wooden handle on a frying pan is 3.0 cm in diameter and 14 cm long. If the pan temperature is 180°C and the free end of the handle is kept at 30°C, how much heat will flow through in 5 min? (*Ans.* 11.4 cal.)

7. A small copper ball 4 cm in diameter is coated with lampblack and heated to a temperature of 827°C. How much heat is radiated from this sphere in 1 min?

8. In cold climates where the temperature falls below freezing, the touching of an iron railing with the bare hand tends to make the fingers stick to the metal. This does not happen so readily with a wooden railing. Explain.

9. A silver bar is 20 cm long and 1 cm² in cross section. One end is maintained at 200°C and the other end at 50°C. How much heat will flow through in 5 min?

10. A silver ball 6 cm in diameter is coated with lampblack and its temperature maintained at 227°C. (a) How much heat will this body radiate each second of time? (b) If the walls of the room are maintained at 27°C, how much heat will this ball absorb each second of time? Assume black body surfaces. (*Ans.* (a) 9.61 cal/sec, (b) 1.25 cal/sec.)

11. The coil heater of an electric hot plate has a surface area of 200 cm², and when heated maintains a temperature of 527°C. (a) How much heat will this unit give off each second of time? (b) If the walls of the room are maintained at 27°C, how much heat will this unit absorb each second of time? Assume all surfaces to be black bodies.

12. Calculate the amount of heat radiated by the sun per second of time. Assume the earth to be 93 million miles from the sun, and the solar constant to be 2 cal/cm² min. (*Ans.* 9.34 × 10²⁵ cal/sec.)

$$E = KT^4$$

$$K = 1.36 \times 10^{-12} \text{ cal/cm}^2 \text{ sec}$$

$$K = 5.7 \times 10^{-5} \text{ ergs/cm}^2 \text{ sec}$$

Chapter 29

Change of State
and Refrigeration

29.1. Expansion and Contraction on Fusion. When molten metal of one kind or another is poured into a mold for casting, the metal may contract or expand on solidifying and then, on cooling down to room temperature, contract or expand according to its coefficient of thermal expansion. Cast iron, for example, is a substance which, on solidifying, expands slightly but then, on cooling down to room temperature, contracts about 1% of its length. It is therefore well suited to casting since slight expansion on solidifying aids in the reproduction of every detail in the mold. To allow for shrinkage in cooling, however, an increase of $\frac{1}{8}$ in. per ft must be introduced in the wood pattern that is used in making the mold.

plug is screwed in tightly the bomb is packed in a freezing mixture of cracked ice and salt. After some minutes the freezing water explodes the bomb with a dull thud.

29.2. Effect of Pressure on Freezing. The freezing point of liquid is affected only slightly by the pressure to which it is usually subjected. *For liquids that contract on freezing, an increase of pressure raises the freezing point. For liquids that expand upon freezing, an increase of pressure lowers the freezing point.* These statements are consistent with molecular structure and activity, since increased pressure should tend to prevent expansion and consequently hold off solidification until a lower temperature is reached.

A curve showing the behavior of water is

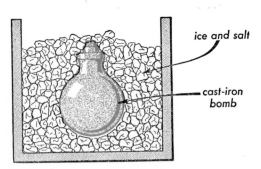

Fig. 29A *When the water inside the bomb freezes, the expansion bursts the cast-iron walls.*

An experiment illustrating the enormous expansion forces of freezing water is diagramed in Fig. 29A. A small cast iron bomb, about 2 in. in diameter and $\frac{1}{8}$ in. thick, is completely filled with water at a temperature close to 0°C. After the threaded iron

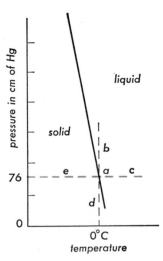

Fig. 29B *Pressure-temperature curve for water at the freezing point.*

given in Fig. 29B. The slope of the curve is greatly exaggerated; it should be more nearly vertical. Since the curve extends upward and slightly to the left, an enormous pressure of 110 atmospheres is required to lower the melting point but 1°C. To better understand the meaning of the graph, consider the conditions represented by the point *a* near the bottom. Here at 0°C and 76 cm of Hg, water and ice can exist together without change. To raise the temperature at this same pressure (point *c*), heat would have to be added, first to melt the ice, and second to raise the temperature of the water.

To lower the temperature at this same pressure (point *e*), heat would first have to be given up by the water to freeze it, and then additional heat given up to lower the temperature of the ice. To raise the pressure without a change in temperature (point *b*), heat would have to be added to melt the ice, whereas to lower the pressure without a change in temperature (point *d*), heat would have to be given up to freeze the water.

In the diagram, therefore, the region to the right of the line represents all possible temperatures and pressures for the existence of the *liquid state,* while the region to the left represents all possible conditions for the existence of the *solid state.* The line itself gives the pressure and temperature conditions under which the liquid and solid can exist together in equilibrium.

29.3. Regelation. If two small blocks of ice are held in opposite hands and two of their relatively flat surfaces pressed tightly together, upon release they will be stuck together. The explanation is that, where contact is made between the blocks, high pressure at localized spots lowers the melting point sufficiently to melt the ice. In order to melt, the ice must acquire heat (80 cal/gm); it gets this by conduction from the nearby ice. The water then flows to one side and, returning the heat it had taken away from the nearby ice, freezes, thus sealing the blocks together. This is a process called *regelation.* The same process explains why snow, when squeezed in the

hands, sticks together to form well-packed snowballs.

Glaciers are well known to seemingly "flow" around hard jutting rocks as they move slowly down a rocky ravine. The ice melts under the pressure it receives from a rock on one side, and the water that flows down and around to the open gap on the other side freezes again to go on as if the rock had never been there.

A simple laboratory experiment demonstrating this principle is shown in Fig. 29C.

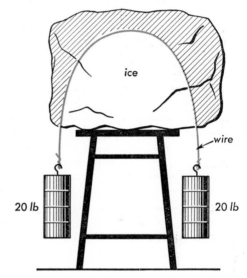

Fig. 29C *Ice melts under pressure, allowing the wire to work its way through.*

A small wire with heavy weights attached is hung over a block of ice and allowed to remain for some time. Slowly, the wire is observed to melt its way through the ice. On completion of the cut, the block of ice is still in one piece, the gap made by the wire having frozen shut. The high pressure under the wire melts the ice, and the water flows around to the other side where it freezes again.

29.4. Cooling by Evaporation. When water is left in an open dish it slowly evaporates, i.e., it goes spontaneously into the gaseous state. Evaporation therefore is a free expansion, and expansion is always accompanied by cooling. This phenomenon of cooling by evaporation, which is so important from the standpoint of its many commercial applications, is explained by the kinetic theory of matter.

Due to the random motions of the molecules of a liquid, some molecules obtain, momentarily, a very high velocity. If a molecule at the surface is given a high velocity in an upward direction, it may escape into the air above. Some of these escaped molecules soon find their way back into the liquid by chance collisions with air molecules from above the surface, but many of them do not. (See Fig. 29D.) The

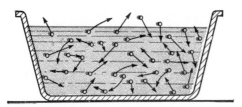

Fig. 29D *Evaporation of water from an open dish is due to the rapid motion of the water molecules and their occasional escape into the air space above.*

sporadic escape of molecules may be speeded up by blowing air across the surface. The air carries the newly escaped molecules away before they have a chance to return to the liquid.

By virtue of the high speed of the molecules escaping from a liquid surface, considerably more than the average kinetic energy is carried away with them. A lowering of the average kinetic energy of the remaining liquid molecules means a lowering of the temperature. The more rapid the evaporation, therefore, the faster will be the cooling. This is strikingly demonstrated by pouring a small amount of ether or alcohol on the finger. Either of these liquids, and particularly ether, evaporates very rapidly, cooling the surface of the finger quickly. Ether is often used in this way by surgeons, in place of an anesthetic, to freeze local spots of the body before beginning a minor operation.

Cooling by evaporation can be demonstrated to a large group by pouring a small quantity of ether over the bulb of an air

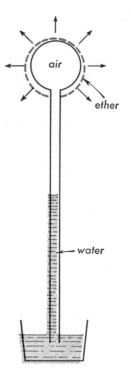

Fig. 29E *Experiment demonstrating the cooling effect produced by the evaporation of ether.*

thermometer as shown in Fig. 29E. Due to the cooling of the glass bulb, the air inside contracts, drawing more water up into the stem of the thermometer.

29.5. Humidity. When water molecules escape by evaporation from the free surface of a liquid, they mix with the air molecules

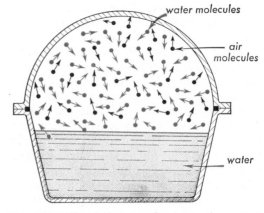

Fig. 29F *Illustration of the saturation of air with water vapor.*

above. If the space above the liquid surface is enclosed, as shown in Fig. 29F, this mixture cannot escape. Under these circumstances the water will continue to evaporate until the air above becomes saturated with water vapor, that is, until it can hold no more. When this condition is reached, as many free water molecules will be returning to the liquid every second as there are water molecules escaping.

The maximum amount of water the air can hold in the vapor state depends upon the temperature, and very little upon the air pressure. This is illustrated by the values given in Table 29A. The temperature of the air is given in one column and the maximum amount of water that can exist in the vapor state in a cubic meter of air is given in the other.

TABLE 29A. MASS OF WATER VAPOR IN ONE CUBIC METER OF SATURATED AIR

Temperature	Water Vapor
0°C or 32°F	4.8 gm
5°C or 41°F	6.8 gm
10°C or 50°F	9.3 gm
15°C or 59°F	12.7 gm
20°C or 68°F	17.1 gm
25°C or 77°F	22.8 gm
30°C or 86°F	30.0 gm
35°C or 95°F	39.2 gm

It is clearly seen from the table that the hotter the air, the greater is the amount of water it can hold in the vapor state.

The atmosphere, which we might term free air, is not always saturated with water vapor. If it contains very little or no water vapor, we say the air is dry; if it contains a great deal we say it is damp.

The quantity of water vapor present in 1 cu m of air is called the absolute humidity. It is, therefore, a measure of the dampness of the air. It may be measured by the number of grams of water vapor present in 1 m³ of air. For example, the absolute humidity might be said to be 14 gm/m³.

It is customary, in speaking of the dampness of air, not to specify the absolute humidity but the relative humidity.

Relative humidity is defined as the ratio of the quantity of water vapor actually present in any volume of air to the quantity required to saturate the same volume of air at the same temperature.

To illustrate this, suppose the air at the present time contains 5.7 gm/m³ of water vapor and the temperature is 25°C. If the air were saturated at this temperature (see Table 29A) it would contain 22.8 gm/m³. Therefore the

$$\text{relative humidity} = \frac{5.7}{22.8} = 0.25 \quad (29a)$$

It is customary to express such answers in per cent, to say that the relative humidity in this case is 25%.

If air that is saturated with water vapor is cooled to a lower temperature, some of the water vapor may condense to the liquid state. These are the conditions under which rain and fogdrops are formed. The reason for this condensation is that, at the lower temperature and equilibrium conditions, less water can exist in the vapor state and still saturate the air. If the air cools without the formation of rain or fog, the air takes on an unstable state in which it is supersaturated.

29.6. The Dew Point. When the temperature of a glass of water is slowly cooled, a temperature is reached at which water condenses on the outside. The temperature at which this occurs is called the *dew point,* and signifies that the air has become saturated with water vapor. Any measurement of the dew-point temperature therefore offers a means of determining the relative humidity.

Suppose, for example, the following experiment is performed in a room whose temperature is 35°C. A polished metal cup containing water and a thermometer is slowly cooled by adding cracked ice. The first appearance of moisture on the outside is noted to occur at 20°C. According to Table 29A, the saturated density for 20°C is 17.1 gm/m³, and for 35°C is 39.2 gm/m³. The first of these densities gives the actual amount of water vapor present in the room, and the latter gives the amount the air in the room could hold when saturated. The absolute humidity is therefore 17.1 gm/m³, and the

$$\text{relative humidity} = \frac{17.1}{39.2} \times 100 = 43.6\%$$

Meteorologists often determine relative humidity from the dew point by means of a *sling-psychrometer*. Such a device consists, as shown in Fig. 29G, of two identical mer-

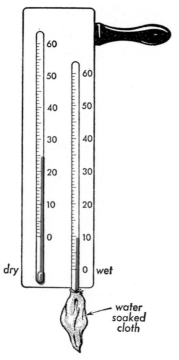

Fig. 29G *Sling psychrometer with wet- and dry-bulb thermometers for determining the dew point and relative humidity.*

cury thermometers mounted on a base with a convenient handle for whirling. One bulb is exposed to the air and is called the *dry bulb* while the other, with a water-soaked cloth tied to it, is called the *wet bulb*. When the psychrometer is whirled in the air for several minutes, being stopped occasionally to observe the temperature readings, the wet bulb will be observed to drop to some value and remain there during any subsequent whirling.

The lowest obtainable wet-bulb tempera-

ture is not the dew point, even though whirling causes evaporation and evaporation produces cooling. By applying a correction from well-known tables, the dew point can be determined from the wet- and dry-bulb readings. Equation (29a) is then applied to the densities read from Table 29A.

29.7. Vapor Pressure. The presence of water vapor in the air increases the atmospheric pressure. To explain why it does so, consider again Fig. 29F. As more and more water evaporates into the space above, the pressure due to the bombardment of the walls by the water molecules becomes greater and greater, reaching a maximum at saturation. The water molecules exert pressure and the air molecules exert pressure, each independent of the other.

Vapor pressure is usually expressed in centimeters of mercury and at saturation is referred to as the saturated vapor pressure. Values of saturated vapor pressure are given in Table 29B for every five degrees between 0°C and 100°C, and at ten-degree intervals to 160°C.

As an illustration of the meaning of Table 29B, assume that we have dry air at normal atmospheric pressure of 76 cm of Hg and room temperature of 25°C, and we then proceed to saturate it with water vapor. From the table the saturated vapor pressure at 25°C is found to be 2.37 cm of Hg. Adding these two quantities, the total gas pressure becomes 76 + 2.37 or 78.37 cm of Hg. The 76 cm represents the *partial pressure* of the air, and 2.37 represents the *partial pressure* of the water vapor.

This relation between partial pressures and total pressure was first discovered by the English chemist and physicist, John Dalton, and is known as *Dalton's law. The total pressure exerted by a mixture of two or more gases that do not chemically combine is equal to the sum of the pressure which the several gases would exert separately if each were permitted to occupy the entire space alone at the same temperature.* In other words, each gas in a mixture exerts its own pressure, independent of the pressure exerted by the other gases.

TABLE 29B. SATURATED VAPOR PRESSURE
OF WATER

Temp., °C	Pressure cm Hg
0	0.458
5	0.654
10	0.921
15	1.28
20	1.75
25	2.37
30	3.18
35	4.22
40	5.53
45	7.19
50	9.25
55	11.80
60	14.94
65	18.75
70	23.37
75	28.91
80	35.51
85	43.36
90	52.58
95	63.39
100	76.00
110	107.4
120	148.9
130	202.6
140	271.1
150	357.0
160	463.6

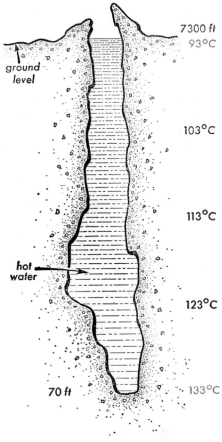

Fig. 29H *Diagram illustrating the principles of a geyser like "Old Faithful" in Yellowstone National Park.*

29.8. Boiling. The boiling of a liquid is but a state of rapid evaporation. As the temperature of water is raised, the rate of evaporation increases until at the boiling temperature it reaches a maximum. Beyond this temperature, water can exist only in the vapor state.

When water boils at normal atmospheric pressure, evaporation takes place throughout the liquid as well as at the surface. Evidence of this is seen in the bubbles of saturated vapor that form near the bottom of a vessel and increase in size as they rise to the surface. The bubbles are able to form because the saturated vapor pressure at 100°C (see Table 29B) is 76 cm of Hg and equal to the external pressure of the atmosphere. Boiling cannot occur unless the saturated vapor pressure is equal to the pressure exerted on the liquid.

29.9. Geysers. One of the great wonders of the western world is the spontaneous eruption almost hourly of the mammoth geyser "Old Faithful" in Yellowstone National Park. The following explanation of geyser activity was first given by Bunsen in 1847, and is based upon the above explanation of boiling.

Water from nearby streams seeps into the vertical shaft or hole where, due to volcanic heat below, it is gradually heated to the boiling point. (See Fig. 29H.) Because the water is heated from below, and convection currents are shut off by the narrowness of the shaft, a temperature considerably higher than 100°C must be reached before the water at the bottom can boil. Since atmospheric pressure exists at the surface, the water there will boil at 100°C. Far down the shaft, however, the added pressure of nearly 70 ft of water requires a temperature of 130°C to produce boiling. Because the water is heated from below, this high temperature is reached near the bottom and boiling begins there before it does at the top. When a sufficiently high temperature is reached, the vapor pressure deep down exceeds the pressure due to the air and water column above and the rise of numerous bubbles, by pushing out the column of hot water above, starts an eruption. As the superheated water nears the surface, its vapor pressure is so high that the remaining water is pushed out with great force.

An excellent demonstration of these principles can be performed by an experimental geyser of the form shown in Fig. 29I. Such

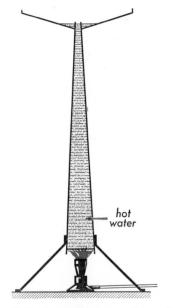

Fig. 29I   *Experimental geyser that will erupt periodically.*

models can be made almost any size from one foot in height to 10 ft or more. The period of their eruption depends upon size as well as the quantity of applied heat.

29.10. Boiling at Low Temperatures. Just as water can be made to boil at temperatures higher than 100°C by increasing

the pressure, so can it be made to boil at temperatures below 100°C by reducing atmospheric pressure. Because of the practical importance of this basic fact, a detailed explanation should be given. Fig. 29J is a

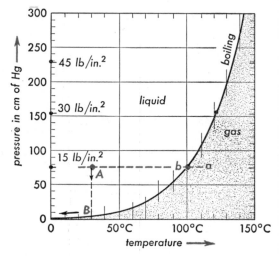

Fig. 29J   *Boiling-point curve for water as it changes with temperature.*

graph of the saturated vapor pressures of water given in Table 29B. This curve represents conditions under which water and saturated water vapor can exist together in equilibrium.

Since boiling at the surface of water takes place when the saturated vapor pressure becomes equal to the atmospheric pressure, it follows that by lowering the atmospheric pressure a lower vapor pressure can bring about the conditions for boiling. The curved line in the graph is therefore a boiling point curve; all pressures and temperatures to the right represent the vapor state, all points to the left the liquid state.

Consider, for example, water at the normal boiling point of 100°C and 76 cm of Hg. To raise its temperature without raising the pressure, point *a*, heat must be added to vaporize the water and additional heat added to raise the temperature of the resultant steam. To lower its temperature (point *b*), heat must be given up to liquefy the steam and additional heat removed to lower the temperature of all the water.

To go one step farther, suppose water at room temperature, 25°C, is placed in a vacuum jar as shown in Fig. 29K and the pressure is slowly reduced by means of a

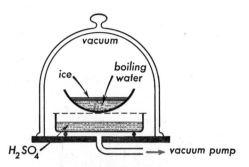

Fig. 29K *The boiling point of a liquid like water is lowered by lowering the atmospheric pressure. Water in a vacuum will boil and freeze at the same time.*

vacuum pump. Starting at the point A on the graph, the pressure decreases until it reaches B, about 2.37 cm of Hg, where bubbles form and the water begins to boil.

To vaporize water requires heat, which is taken from the remaining water, thus cooling it to a lower temperature. Continued reduction in pressure causes continued boiling and lowering of temperature, until finally the freezing point at approximately 0°C is reached. Continued evaporation cools the surface of the water until ice forms over the surface of the boiling water. Here then is a condition in which water boils and freezes at the same time and at 0°C. (The small dish of sulfuric acid, H_2SO_4, placed in the vacuum chamber, absorbs water vapor, thus aiding the pumps in keeping the pressure sufficiently low.)

Although water under normal atmospheric pressure at sea level boils at 100°C, water at higher altitudes boils at lower temperatures. Evidence of this fact is well known to those who like to camp in the higher mountains. There, at reduced atmospheric pressure, it takes longer than usual to cook all kinds of foods. The boiling points given in Table 29C show specific values for different elevations.

At high altitudes the water in water-

TABLE 29C. PRESSURE AND BOILING POINT OF WATER AT VARIOUS DISTANCES ABOVE AND BELOW SEA LEVEL

Altitude in Air	Boiling Point	Atmospheric Pressure	
ft	°C	cm of Hg	lb/in.²
100,000	9.8	0.82	0.16
50,000	48.9	8.75	1.7
40,000	58.8	14.1	2.7
30,000	69.2	22.5	4.4
20,000	79.6	35.0	6.7
15,000	84.4	42.4	8.2
10,000	89.8	52.2	10.1
8,000	92.1	56.8	11.0
6,000	94.0	61.0	11.8
4,000	96.0	65.6	12.7
2,000	98.0	70.2	13.7
Sea Level	100.0	76.0	14.7
−20	113.7	121.0	23.4
−40	123.3	165.0	32.0
−60	131.2	210.0	40.7
−80	138.0	255.0	49.4
−100	144.0	300.0	58.0
−120	149.0	345.0	66.7
ft	°C	cm of Hg	lb/in.²
Depth in Water	Boiling Point	Total Pressure Atmosphere + Water	

cooled airplane engines boils at lower temperatures. At a height of 6 mi, gasoline boils at the normal temperature of −65°C. At 12-mi elevation, blood boils at the body temperature of 98.6°F (37°C).

29.11. Sublimation. Under certain conditions many substances will go from the solid to the vapor state without passing through the liquid phase. A good illustration of this is the heating of iodine crystals or the evaporation of so-called "dry ice." Iodine crystals, when placed in a test tube at room temperature and pressure, and slowly heated, pass directly into iodine vapor. This is called sublimation.

Dry ice, which chemically is carbon dioxide, CO_2, is normally at a temperature of −78.5°C and, when standing in the open air, evaporates directly without liquefying.

The visible fumes rising from it are water vapor from the surrounding air condensed by the cold CO_2 gases that leave.

Ice over the ponds and lakes in cold climates sublimes slowly at the surface. By enclosing the space above ice at below 0°C, the saturated vapor pressure can be measured just as it is for water, as shown in Fig. 29F.

The result of such measurements is represented by the sublimation curve PS in the "triple point" graph in Fig. 29L. The

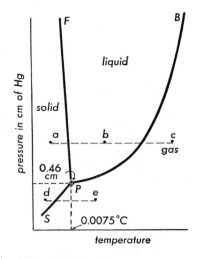

Fig. 29L *Triple point graph for water.*

curve PF is the freezing point curve of Fig. 29B and PB is the boiling point curve of Fig. 29J. Every point along PF represents the conditions of equilibrium for ice and water, and every point along PB represents the conditions of equilibrium for water and water vapor. The experimental fact that these curves intersect at one common point, the so-called *triple point,* means that at that pressure and temperature all three states, *solid, liquid,* and *gas,* can exist in equilibrium. These were the conditions attained in the experiment in Fig. 29K.

29.12. Refrigeration. A refrigerator in the home or corner grocery store is now a commonplace. It is not the purpose here to describe any particular commercial refrigerator but to present the physical principles underlying the operation of a typical ma-

chine. It is probably safe to say that nearly all refrigerators are based upon the principle that the rapid evaporation of a liquid or the expansion of a gas produces cooling. The most common fluids used in the machines today are liquid ammonia (NH_3), sulfur dioxide (SO_2), and methyl chloride (CH_3Cl). & Freon 4 & 12

A schematic diagram of an electrically operated refrigerator is shown in Fig. 29M.

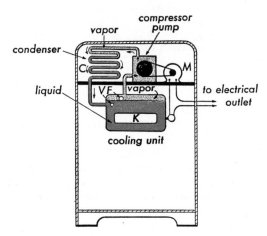

Fig. 29M *Schematic diagram of the working parts of a common electrically operated refrigerator.*

The three principal parts of this machine are (1) the cooling unit, (2) the compressor, and (3) the condenser. The cooling unit K and the condenser coils are partly filled with one of the above-mentioned liquids, and the remaining parts with vapor. By means of an electric motor and pump, the vapor is removed from the top of the cooling unit and pumped into the hollow coiled pipes of the condenser. The low pressure in the cooling unit causes the liquid to boil, resulting in the cooling of the entire unit by evaporation. In pumping more and more vapor into the condenser, the compression heats the vapor considerably above room temperature. Before and after the motor stops running, the heated vapor cools and condenses into a liquid by transferring heat into the room.

When the liquid in the cooling unit falls to a certain low level, the float F opens a valve V, letting in liquid from the condenser. Being cold, the cooling unit absorbs heat from the refrigerator and warms up. When the temperature rises to a certain value, the thermostat makes electrical contact and starts the motor. The pump then lowers the pressure, which in turn causes evaporation and cooling. At the moment the temperature of the cooling unit and thermostat drops to the desired value, the thermostat opens the electric circuit, stopping the motor and the pump.

PROBLEMS

1. At what altitude will water boil at 95°C?

2. If air at a temperature of 35°C has a relative humidity of 80%, how much water vapor will be condensed per m³ of air if the temperature is lowered to 20°C? (*Ans.* 14.26 gm.)

3. If the relative humidity is 38% and the temperature is 75°F, what is the absolute humidity?

4. If the absolute humidity is 12 gm/m³ and the temperature is 95°F, what is the relative humidity? (*Ans.* 30.6%.)

5. Plot a temperature vs. water-vapor graph for saturated air. Use the Fahrenheit scale for temperatures as given in Table 29A, and extrapolate the curve to 104°F.

6. Plot a graph of the boiling point of water vs. altitude in meters. Cover the range 0 to 30,000 m.

7. If the air contains 14.5 gm of water vapor per m³ of air when the temperature is 86°F, what is the relative humidity?

8. If the air contains 15 gm of water vapor per m³ of air when the temperature is 32°C, what is the relative humidity? (*Ans.* 45%.)

9. Plot a temperature vs. water-vapor graph for standard air. Use the Centigrade values given in Table 29A, and extrapolate the curve to 40°C.

10. The dew point is found to be 48°F when the room temperature is 70°F. What is the relative humidity? (*Ans.* 48%.)

11. A sling-psychrometer is whirled until the dew point is found from the wet-bulb and conversion tables to be 8°C. Calculate the relative humidity if the dry-bulb temperature is 30°C.

12. At what temperature will water boil at an altitude of 9000 ft? (*Ans.* 91.0°C.)

13. If the relative humidity is 42% when the temperature is 41°F, what will it be if the temperature rises to 68°F?

14. At what temperature will water boil at the bottom of a geyser 130 ft deep? Assume standard atmospheric pressure of 14.7 lb/in.² above ground. (*Ans.* 151°C.)

15. At what temperature will water boil 20 m below the surface of the water in a geyser?

16. At what depth in a geyser will water begin to boil at 125°C? (*Ans.* 13.6 m or 45 ft.)

17. An air conditioning system in a building delivers 2000 m³/hr of air. When the air is 25°C and the relative humidity is 90%, the system removes 7.6 Kg of water per hr without changing the temperature. Find the final (a) relative humidity, and (b) absolute humidity.

18. If, at a temperature of 68°F, the relative humidity is 50%, how much water per m³ will be condensed if the temperature goes down to freezing, that is, 32°F? (*Ans.* 3.75 gm.)

Chapter 30

Heat Energy
and Low Temperatures

30.1. Thermodynamics. Thermodynamics is that branch of physics dealing with the conversion of mechanical energy into thermal energy, and the reverse process, heat into work. There are numerous ways of carrying out either of these transformations. By rubbing the palms of the hands together, for example, heat is produced; by rubbing two sticks of wood together a fire may be started. If a weight falls freely from some height, heat is developed when the weight strikes the ground. The bearings of a car motor or the wheels of a freight car, if not lubricated, will get hot and either "burn out" or lock together, as in a "hot box." These are all examples of mechanical energy being transformed into heat.

The reverse process of transforming heat into mechanical energy is illustrated by present-day steam, diesel, gasoline, and jet propulsion engines. In all of these engines, fuel is burned to produce heat and by expanding gases the heat is turned into mechanical energy. Jet propulsion is not a new idea. A simple device based upon the principle of jet propulsion is to be found in the writings of some of the ancient philosophers of Archimedes' time.

An interesting demonstration is shown in Fig. 30A. A small hollow brass tube, mounted on the shaft of an electric motor, has a few drops of water in the base and a cork driven into the open end. A wooden clamp, like the one shown at the lower right, is squeezed tightly around the tube as it spins. Because of friction the tube gets hot, boils the water, and steam pressure suddenly blows the cork out as if from a gun.

30.2. The First Law of Thermodynamics. The first law of thermodynamics is frequently referred to as *the mechanical equivalent of heat*. It is to the painstaking work of Joule (1843)* that we attribute this fundamental verification of the universal law of conservation of energy. With his apparatus he was able to show that, when a moving body is brought to rest, the energy that disappears is directly proportional to the amount of heat produced. In his most famous experiment, he set water into motion in a bucket by means of rotating paddles and then brought the water to rest by stationary paddles. He was able to show that, if all of the work used in churning the water goes into producing heat, then the same amount of work will always produce

* James Prescott Joule (1818-89), English physicist, was born on December 24, 1818, near Manchester. Although he owned a large brewery, he devoted his life to scientific research. At the age of 22, he discovered the law giving the relation between electrical energy and heat, and a short time later the law known as the first law of thermodynamics.

Fig. 30A *Cork gun. Friction heat boils water, and steam blows cork out.*

the same amount of heat regardless of the method used to carry out the transformation. In other words, the calorie, which is a unit of heat energy, is equivalent to a definite number of ergs of mechanical energy.

The number of energy units, which upon conversion gives one heat unit, is called the mechanical equivalent of heat. By experiment

$$1 \text{ cal} = 41,800,000 \text{ ergs}$$

and

$$1 \text{ Btu} = 778 \text{ ft-lb} \qquad (30a)$$

As an equation,

$$\frac{\text{work}}{\text{heat}} = \text{mech. equiv. of heat} \qquad \boxed{\frac{W}{H} = J}$$

$$(30b)$$

Because of the fundamental importance of this relation, many experimenters have devoted considerable time and effort to obtain a more accurate value of the constant J. In 1879, the famous American physicist Rowland, using an improved form of Joule's apparatus, obtained the value $J = 4.179 \times 10^7$ ergs/cal. Since that time, simpler experiments have been devised that make use of a method first employed by Joule, namely, that of heating by electric currents. Such an experiment will be described in a later chapter.

In honor of Joule and his most important discovery, it is customary to express the mechanical equivalent of heat as

$$\boxed{1 \text{ cal} = 4.18 \text{ joules}}$$

where 1 joule $= 10^7$ ergs.

30.3. Experiments on Mechanical Equivalent of Heat. There are numerous ways of transforming mechanical energy into heat. By rubbing the palms of the hands together, for example, heat is produced by friction. Again, if a weight is dropped from any height, heat is developed when it strikes the ground. A 1-lb weight dropped $3\frac{1}{2}$ ft will, on stopping, produce 1 cal.

One simple laboratory method of measuring the mechanical equivalent of heat is to place a measured amount of lead shot (about 100 gm) in a tube about 5 cm in diameter and about 100 cm long. After reading the temperature of the shot with a thermometer, the tube is turned end for end about 50 to 200 times, stopping each time in a vertical position to allow the shot to fall the full distance and strike the bottom. (See Fig. 30B.) The temperature of the shot

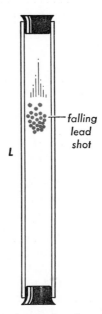

L

falling lead shot

Fig. 30B *Experiment for determining the mechanical equivalent of heat.*

is then measured again. From the known mass of shot, m, its specific heat c, and the rise in temperature, $t_2 - t_1$, the total *heat gained* can be calculated, $H = mc(t_2 - t_1)$. From the mass of the shot m, the acceleration due to gravity g, the number of tube inversions n, and the length of the tube l, the input energy is calculated. Since *work done* equals *force times distance*, $W = mg \times nl$. Substituting in Eq.(30b),

$$J = \frac{W}{H} = \frac{mg\,nl}{mc(t_2 - t_1)} = \frac{g\,n\,l}{c(t_2 - t_1)} \qquad (30c)$$

The canceling of m is to be expected since, for example, the dropping of twice the amount of shot will produce twice as much heat, but this will be divided between twice the amount of lead.

Consider as a problem the calculation of the mechanical equivalent of heat from the following data taken in such a laboratory experiment.

Initial temperature of lead shot . . . .   23.4°C
Final temperature of lead shot . . . . .   30.9°C
Length of tube . . . .   104 cm
Number of falls   100

By substituting these values in Eq.(30c), and the specific heat of lead from Table 27A, we obtain

$$J = \frac{980 \times 100 \times 104}{0.031(30.9 - 23.4)} = 4.38 \frac{\text{joules}}{\text{cal}}$$

The difference between any experimental result and its accepted value, divided by the accepted value, and multiplied by 100 gives the percentage error.

$$\text{Per cent error} = \frac{4.38 - 4.18}{4.18} \times 100 = 4.8\%$$

While the type of experiment just described is not capable of high accuracy, it does illustrate the relation between mechanical energy and heat. The inaccuracies are due chiefly to the method of temperature measurement and to the absorption of heat by the tube and tube ends. The latter may be reduced by using materials having a low thermal conductivity.

The transformation of potential energy into heat usually occurs by first changing it into kinetic energy. In the above experiment, for example, the lead shot acquired a velocity in falling and its kinetic energy $\frac{1}{2}mv^2$ was changed into heat at the bottom. Due to the impact the molecules of the colliding bodies were given additional kinetic energy.

Example 1. A 1-Kg hammer, moving with a velocity of 50 m/sec, strikes a 200-gm iron rod lying on the ground. If half of the energy goes into heating the iron rod, what will be its rise in temperature?
Solution.

KE of hammer $= \frac{1}{2}mv^2 = \frac{1}{2} \times 1000$ gm
$\qquad \times (5000 \text{ cm/sec})^2 = 12.5 \times 10^9$ ergs

From Eq.(30c), the heat produced will be

$$H = \frac{W}{J} = \frac{12.5 \times 10^9}{4.18 \times 10^7} = 299 \text{ cal}$$

Since one-half goes to heat 200 gm of iron of specific heat 0.105

$$149.5 \text{ cal} = 200 \times 0.105(t_2 - t_1)$$

Solving for the rise in temperature $(t_2 - t_1)$ gives

$$t_2 - t_1 = \frac{149.5}{200 \times 0.105} = 7.1°C$$

30.4. Kinetic Theory of Gases. According to the kinetic theory of matter, the pressure exerted by a gas upon the walls of the containing vessel is due to the continual bombardment of the walls by the rapidly moving gas molecules. If the temperature of the gas is raised, the molecules move faster and the pressure rises, whereas if it is lowered they move slower and the pressure decreases. The absolute temperature of a gas is proportional to the average kinetic energy of translation of the molecules.

The more gas that is pumped into a vessel of constant volume, the more molecules there are to bombard the walls per second and the greater is the resultant pressure. At any given instant of time some molecules are moving in one direction and some in another; some are traveling fast, some slow, and a few are momentarily at rest.

In any reasonably large volume of gas, there are many molecules (about 10^{24} molecules/ft³ at normal atmospheric pressure and room temperature) and, according to the mathematical laws of probability, some average speed can be determined which, if possessed by all the molecules, would correspond to the same temperature and would give rise to the same wall pressure. Denoting this average speed by $\bar{v}$, we shall now derive a formula for the pressure.

Consider a cubical vessel whose volume, as shown in Fig. 30C, is l^3. Because the total number of molecules present, N, is very large, the calculations are simplified by assuming that one-third are moving in the x direction, one-third in the y direction and one-third in the z direction.

Select now the one-third that are moving in the x direction. Each molecule as it ap-

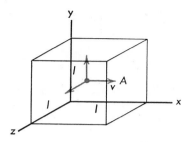

Fig. 30C *Gas molecules in a closed compart-ment create pressure by virtue of their impact against the walls.*

proaches the right-hand wall of the vessel is moving with a velocity $\bar{v}$ and after collision it rebounds with a velocity $-\bar{v}$. There has been a change in velocity of $2\bar{v}$. Since the impulse Ft exerted on the wall is given by the change in momentum, we may write

$$Ft = 2m\bar{v} \qquad (30d)$$

Bouncing back and forth between opposite walls of the vessel, each molecule will make many impacts on the same wall in unit time. Now, t is the average time required for the molecule to make the round trip, $2l$, from the right-hand wall to the left-hand wall and back. Therefore

$$t = 2l/\bar{v}$$

Since the impulse, Ft, is given by the change of momentum, we may write

$$F \times 2l/\bar{v} = 2m\bar{v} \qquad \text{or} \qquad F = m\bar{v}^2/l$$

For $\frac{1}{3}N$ molecules, then, the force will be $N/3$ times that for one molecule, or

$$F = \frac{Nm\bar{v}^2}{3l}$$

Since pressure is the force per unit area, and the area of the wall is l^2

$$p = \frac{F}{l^2} = \frac{Nm\bar{v}^2}{3l^3} \qquad (30e)$$

Since the number of molecules N multiplied by the mass of a single molecule gives the total mass of the gas, and l^3 gives its volume, the density ρ is given by

$$\rho = \frac{Nm}{l^3}$$

By substituting ρ for Nm/l^3 in Eq.(30e), we obtain for the pressure

$$p = \tfrac{1}{3}\rho\bar{v}^2 \qquad (30f)$$

The average velocity of molecules in a gas of density ρ, under an absolute pressure p, is given by rearranging the terms.

$$\boxed{\bar{v} = \sqrt{3p/\rho}} \qquad (30g)$$

Example 2. Calculate the average velocity of hydrogen molecules in a gas of normal atmospheric pressure and room temperatures.

Solution. From the gas densities in Table 25A and the value for standard atmospheric pressure,

$$\bar{v} = \sqrt{\frac{3 \times 1,013,000 \text{ dynes/cm}^2}{0.000090 \text{ gm/cm}^3}} = 184,000 \frac{\text{cm}}{\text{sec}}$$

This is considerably faster than a rifle bullet or the shells from the largest guns.

The formula above shows that the greater the density of a gas, the lower is the average speed of its molecules. For a gas like oxygen, with sixteen times the density of hydrogen, the molecules will be moving with only one-quarter the average speed of the hydrogen molecules. This is well illustrated by the mechanical model shown in Fig. 22D, representing the case of a mixture of two gases of different density.

30.5. Liquefaction of Air. The present method of liquefying air and other gases is based upon the principle of cooling by expansion. It was by this method that Dewar liquefied oxygen for the first time in 1891, and Linde liquefied air in 1895. Oxygen gas becomes a liquid at the extremely low temperature of $-184°C$ and air at $-191°C$. On the Fahrenheit scale these correspond to $-300°F$ and $-312°F$, respectively.

A schematic diagram of the two absolute temperature scales in common use is given in Fig. 30D. The zero point of both these scales is called *absolute zero* and represents the temperature at which all molecular motion ceases. While all molecular motion is said to cease at absolute zero, the atoms of which some substances are composed would still have inherent motions that cannot be eliminated.

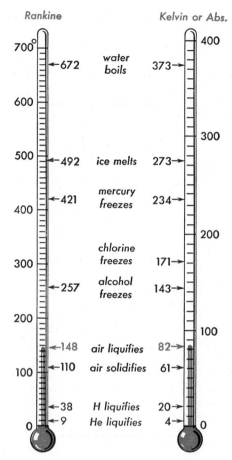

Fig. 30D *Rankine and Kelvin, or Absolute, temperature scales.*

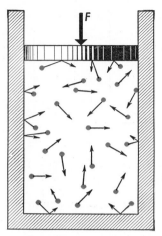

Fig. 30E *Illustration of the random motions of atoms and molecules in a gas.*

On the Kelvin scale, water boils at 373°K and freezes at 273°K. Air becomes a liquid at 82°K and a solid at 61°K. Hydrogen gas becomes a liquid at 20°K and freezes at 14°K. Helium liquefies at 4°K and becomes a solid only at 2°K.

The compression of a gas causes heating, and the expansion of a gas causes cooling. To obtain a clear understanding of how this comes about, consider the action of a piston as it moves down, compressing the gas in a cylinder as shown in Fig. 30E. Gas molecules striking the side walls and bottom of the cylinder will bounce away with the average velocity of those throughout most of the volume.

Molecules colliding with the downward moving piston, however, will on the aver-

age bounce away with a higher velocity. The piston action on the molecules is analogous to a bat as it swings and hits a ball.

As the piston rises in the cylinder, the molecules colliding with it rebound with a lower average velocity, much the same as a ball rebounds with little or no velocity when a batter draws his bat backward in a "bunt."

In the liquid air machine (see Fig. 30F) air is compressed by a pump to a pressure of about 3000 lb/in.[2] Because of compression this air is heated to a fairly high temperature. It must therefore be cooled by running it through a cooling tank. This cold compressed air passes through the inner tube of a double-walled coil *B* and escapes through the very narrow opening of a needle valve, *V*. The escaping air expands so much that its temperature is lowered considerably below room temperature.

The continual pumping of the compressor draws this cold air up through the outer tube of the coil, thus cooling the compressed air on its way down to the needle valve. This air is compressed again and cooled to go around the circuit again. The cycle continues until the temperature in the region of *V* is so low that drops of liquid air form in the jet from the needle valve. These drops fall into the Dewar flask and accumulate, to be drawn off later as needed.

30.6. Liquid Air Experiments. The physical properties of matter are quite different at extremely low temperatures than they are at room temperatures. This may be illustrated by a number of experiments with a small quantity of liquid air.

evaporated air, just as the water drops ride around on a steam layer.

Mercury and gasoline will freeze when cooled in liquid air. An interesting demonstration is to make a small cardboard box

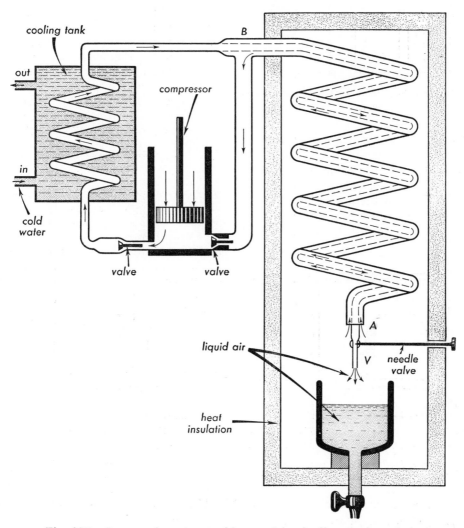

Fig. 30F *Cross section of a machine used in the liquefaction of air.*

First of all, liquid air has the same general appearance and density as water. When a little is poured out onto the table top or into an open dish, it runs around over the surface in little spherical drops and behaves just like water drops on the flat surface of a hot stove. The drops of liquid air move quickly over the surface, riding on a film of

about 1 in. × 1 in. × 2 in., fill it with mercury, and clamp a small wooden stick into it as shown in Fig. 30G. Liquid air poured over the box will soon freeze the mercury. When it is well frozen, the carboard can be peeled off, and the resulting small mercury hammer used to drive nails in a block of wood.

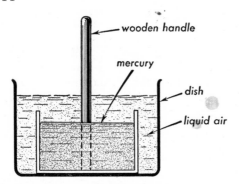

Fig. 30G   *How to make a small mercury hammer.*

Take a good rubber ball, hollow and about 2 in. in diameter, and put it into a vessel containing liquid air for several minutes. When the liquid quiets down, indicating that the rubber's temperature is closely that of liquid air, remove the ball and drop it to the floor. Instead of bouncing, it will

Fig. 30H   *Cooled to the temperature of liquid air, a lead bell will ring.*

break into many small pieces as if it were made of glass. A small bunch of grapes, or a flower, cooled in liquid air will behave the same way and break like fine glass.

An interesting demonstration can be performed by hammering or molding a small bell out of lead metal. Such a bell at room temperature will give only a dull thud, but after being cooled in liquid air, it will ring quite well. See Fig. 30H.

A piece of wire solder can be wound into a coil spring and suspended from a clamp stand as shown in Fig. 30I. At room tem-

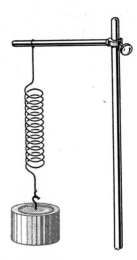

Fig. 30I   *At liquid-air temperature, a coil of lead solder becomes a spring.*

perature it will neither show elastic properties nor support a mass of several hundred grams. Cooled to liquid-air temperature, however, it will exhibit springlike action.

PROBLEMS

1. A 50-gm steel bullet having a velocity of 800 m/sec is shot into the ground. Find its rise in temperature if half of the energy goes into the bullet.

2. A train weighing 5000 tons and traveling 45 mi/hr is brought to a stop by applying the brakes. Find the heat developed. (*Ans.* 8.75 × 10⁵ Btu.)

3. A boy weighing 100 lb, riding a bicycle weighing 40 lb, is going 15 mi/hr. When the

brakes are applied to come to a stop, how much heat is developed?

4. A 10-Kg mortar shell fails to explode when it hits the ground traveling with a speed of 150 m/sec. How much heat is developed? (*Ans.* 26,900 cal.)

5. A heavy box having a mass of 200 Kg is pulled along the floor for 15 m. If the coefficient of sliding friction is 0.40, how much heat is developed?

6. A horizontal force of 60 lb is required to pull a heavy trunk along the floor. How much heat is developed for each 50 ft it slides? (*Ans.* 3.86 Btu.)

7. The water drops 80 m in a large waterfall. Assuming the available energy all goes into heat, find the temperature difference between the water at the bottom and the water at the top.

8. A 12-lb lead shotput is dropped from a tower 250 ft high. Assuming half the energy goes into heating the lead, find the rise in temperature. (*Ans.* 5.2°F.)

9. Compute the average velocity of the nitrogen molecules in the air at normal temperature and pressure.

10. Find the average velocity of the oxygen molecules in the air at normal temperature and pressure. (*Ans.* 461 m/sec.)

11. Calculate the average velocity of helium atoms in a gas at normal atmospheric pressure and 0°C.

12. Find the average velocity of carbon dioxide molecules in a gas at normal temperature and pressure. See Table 25A. (*Ans.* 392 m/sec.)

13. A racing car and driver have a combined weight of 3840 lb. When moving at a speed of 150 mi/hr, the brakes are applied bringing the car to rest. If we assume that 75% of the total energy goes into heat, how much heat is produced?

14. A 100-Kg box slides down a metal chute a distance of 25 m. If the chute makes an angle of 35° with the horizontal, and all of the energy goes into heat, how many calories are produced? (*Ans.* 3360 cal.)

Chapter 31

Vibration and Waves

31.1. Simple Harmonic Motion. Any motion, simple or complex, which repeats itself in equal intervals of time, is called *periodic motion*. There are many examples in everyday life which give rise to a special kind of periodic motion called *simple periodic motion*. The swinging of the clock pendulum, the turning of the balance wheel of a watch, or the vibration of a tuning fork, are good examples of such motions. The term "simple periodic motion" applies to these because each can be described in terms of one of the simplest known types of periodic motion—namely, *uniform circular motion*.

Simple harmonic motion is defined as the projection on any diameter of a point moving in a circle with uniform speed.

This motion is illustrated in Fig. 31A.

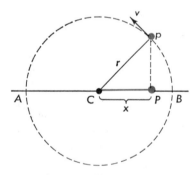

Fig. 31A *Diagram illustrating simple harmonic motion along a straight line.*

The point p moves around the circle of radius r with uniform speed v. If at every instant a perpendicular is drawn from p to the diameter AB, the intercept P will move with simple harmonic motion. Moving back and forth along the straight line from A to B, the velocity v_x is continually changing.

At the center point C it has its greatest velocity, while at A and B it is momentarily at rest. Starting from either end of its path, the velocity increases until it reaches C; from there it slows down again, coming to rest at the opposite end of its path.

The *displacement* of a simple harmonic motion is defined as the distance from the center C to the point P. As shown in Fig. 31A, the displacement x varies in magnitude from zero at C up to r, the radius of the *circle of reference,* at A or B.

The *amplitude* r is defined as the maximum value of the *displacement* x, and the *period* is defined as the time required to make one complete vibration.

If a vibration starts at A, it is not completed until the point moves across to B and back again to A. If it starts from C and moves to B and back to C, only half a vibration has been completed. The amplitude r is usually measured in centimeters and the period T in seconds.

The frequency of a harmonic motion is defined as the number of complete vibrations per second. For example, if a particular vibrating object completes one vibration in one-half second (the period $T = \frac{1}{2}$ sec), then it will make two complete vibrations in 1 sec (the frequency $n = 2$ vib/sec). If again a body completes one vibration in one-tenth of a second, $T = \frac{1}{10}$ sec, it will make ten vibrations in 1 sec, $n = 10$ vib/sec. In other words, n and T are reciprocals of each other.

$$\text{Period} = \frac{1}{\text{frequency}}$$

or
$$\text{frequency} = \frac{1}{\text{period}} \tag{31a}$$

In algebraic symbolism,

$$T = \frac{1}{n} \qquad n = \frac{1}{T} \qquad \text{(31b)}$$

31.2. Theory of Simple Harmonic Motion.

It is intended here to derive a general formula for the period of vibrating bodies executing simple harmonic motion. Referring to Sec. 31.1, the period T is defined as the time required to make one complete vibration. Referring to Fig. 31B, the point

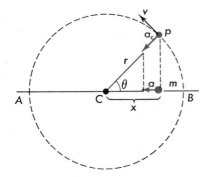

Fig. 31B *In any simple harmonic motion, the acceleration is always toward the central equilibrium position.*

p, moving with a speed v, will travel once around the circle of reference, a distance $2\pi r$, in a time T. Applying the relation that *time equals distance divided by velocity*, we get

$$T = \frac{2\pi r}{v} \qquad \text{(31c)}$$

We have seen in Sec. 14.2 that an object moving in a circle with uniform speed v has a constant acceleration toward the center given by Eq.(14f) as

$$a_c = \frac{v^2}{r}$$

As this acceleration a_c changes in direction, its component a along the x axis changes in magnitude and is given by $a_c \cos \theta$.

$$a = \frac{v^2}{r} \cos \theta$$

Since $\cos \theta = x/r$

$$a = \frac{v^2}{r} \cdot \frac{x}{r} \qquad a = \frac{v^2}{r^2} x$$

By transposing and taking the square root, we obtain

$$\frac{r^2}{v^2} = \frac{x}{a} \qquad \text{and} \qquad \frac{r}{v} = \sqrt{\frac{x}{a}}$$

Substitution in Eq.(31c) gives

$$T = 2\pi \sqrt{\frac{x}{a}}$$

When the displacement is $+$, the acceleration a is toward the center and therefore $-$. Conversely when x is $-$, a is $+$. For this reason the period should be written,

$$T = 2\pi \sqrt{-\frac{x}{a}} \qquad \text{(31d)}$$

This is a useful equation because it gives the period of vibration in terms of the displacement x and the corresponding acceleration.

31.3. Vibrating Spring.

Any elastic body may be set into a state of vibration by first distorting it in some way and then releasing it. This is demonstrated by a weight on the end of a spring as shown in Fig. 31C. In

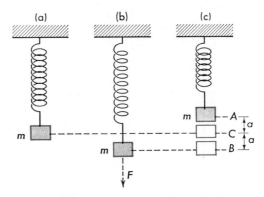

Fig. 31C *A mass on the end of a spring executes simple harmonic motion.*

diagram (a), the spring S and mass m hang in a state of equilibrium. At (b) a force F has been applied to stretch the spring, displacing the mass a distance a. After being released, the mass m moves up and down with simple harmonic motion. In diagram

(c) the spring is shown compressed with m at its highest point. The amplitude a of the vibration is determined by the original distance to which the spring is stretched, and the period T is given by the algebraic equation:

$$\boxed{T = 2\pi\sqrt{m/k}} \qquad (31e)$$

where m is the mass of the vibrating body and k a number expressing the stiffness of the spring. (See Sec. 23.1.) The constant k is the force in dynes required to stretch the spring 1 cm. This formula shows that, if m is made larger, the period is increased and that, when a stiffer spring is used (k being in the denominator), the period is decreased.

In accordance with Hooke's law (see Sec. 23.1), the stretch of a spring is given by the relation

$$F = -kx$$

where F is the applied force, x the displacement, and k the same as above. Since a force of magnitude F acts to accelerate the mass m, $F = ma$, gives

$$ma = -kx \qquad \text{or} \qquad -x/a = m/k$$

The substitution of m/k for $-x/a$ in Eq.-(31d) gives Eq.(31e).

31.4. Vibrating Strips. If a strip of wood or metal is clamped tightly at one end, as shown in Fig. 31D, it may be set into a natural state of vibration. Pulled to one side and then released, the free end of the strip will move back and forth with simple harmonic motion. If the mass m clamped to the free end is increased, the frequency of vibration will decrease; whereas, if the strip is made stiffer either by increasing its thickness or decreasing its length, the frequency will increase.

Shown in diagram (b) is a tuning fork used by musicians to determine pitch. Striking one prong of a fork against some object sets both prongs vibrating simultaneously in opposite directions. The thinner the prongs of the fork, the lower is the frequency of vibration; the shorter the prongs of the fork, the higher is the frequency of vibration.

Besides being used as standards of pitch by musicians, tuning forks are used for scientific purposes. As scientific instruments they perform one very useful function of marking off short but equal intervals of time. A common fork used for this purpose has a frequency of 1000, $n = 1000$ vib/sec, and is frequently kept vibrating by means of an electrical circuit similar to that of a doorbell.

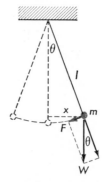

Fig. 31E   *A pendulum bob executes simple harmonic motion along a curved path.*

31.5. The Simple Pendulum. If a simple pendulum, as shown in Fig. 31E, is set swinging in an arc which is not too big, its period T is given by the following formula,

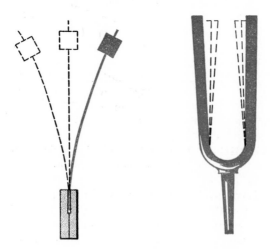

Fig. 31D   *A weighted leaf spring, or reed, and a tuning fork.*

$$T = 2\pi\sqrt{\frac{l}{g}} \qquad (31f)$$

T is the time of one complete vibration, l is the length of the pendulum, and g is the acceleration due to gravity. If the angle of swing is much greater than $5°$, the period will be slightly increased.

The statement can now be made that the bob of a simple pendulum moves along its arc with *simple periodic motion*. At the ends of its swing the velocity is momentarily zero and at the center is a maximum. The driving force which starts the bob at one end of its path and accelerates it until it reaches the center and then decelerates it, bringing it to rest at the other end, is the component F of the force of gravity W. The component F_2 is the tension in the cord supporting the mass m.

The fact that the mass of a pendulum bob does not appear in Eq.(31f) signifies that pendulums of equal length but different mass should have the same period T. Started together, and with small amplitudes (see Fig. 31F), simple pendulums of different mass will swing in synchronism.

The effect of the acceleration of gravity g on the period is illustrated in Fig. 31G. If the pull of gravity could be increased, the

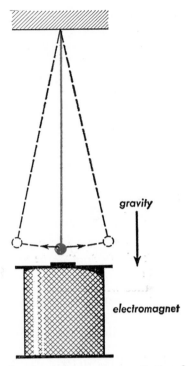

gravity

electromagnet

Fig. 31G *An increase in gravitational attraction, like the downward pull of the magnet, will shorten the period of a simple pendulum.*

period of all pendulums would decrease, that is, they would swing faster. If gravity could be decreased, the periods would be greater, that is, they would swing more slowly. In the diagram the pull of gravity is imitated by means of an electromagnet. When the magnet is turned on, it pulls down on the iron bob and makes it swing more quickly.

The effect of the length l on the period is shown in Fig. 31H. Two pendulums of lengths l and $4l$ are shown at the same instant a short time after having started simultaneously at their respective origins S. While the pendulum l has made one complete swing, the pendulum of length $4l$ has made but half a swing. This shows that to double the time of swing the length must be made four times as large. This is in agreement with Eq.(31f) in which the length occurs under the square root sign.

A derivation of Eq.(31f) can be obtained from Fig. 31E as follows. The downward

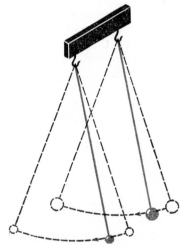

Fig. 31F *Two simple pendulums of the same length but different mass have the same period of vibration.*

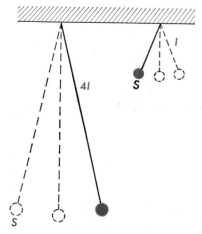

Fig. 31H *To double the period of a simple pendulum, the length must be increased four-fold.*

pull of gravity on the bob of mass m is W, and this has been resolved into two components, one parallel to the support l and the other F perpendicular to it. Because of equal angles θ in the two right triangles and the theorem that corresponding sides of similar triangles are proportional, we may write

$$\frac{F}{W} = \frac{x}{l}$$

Since the force F accelerates the mass m in the direction opposite to x, and the weight W is equal to mg, substitution in the above proportionality gives

$$\frac{ma}{mg} = \frac{-x}{l} \quad \text{or} \quad -\frac{x}{a} = \frac{l}{g}$$

Substituting l/g for $-x/a$ in Eq.(31d), we obtain

$$T = 2\pi\sqrt{l/g}$$

31.6. Sources of Waves. The motion of any material object may be considered as a source of waves. A board striking the water, the snap of a finger, or a bowed violin string are examples of this.

Suppose that the far end of a rope is fastened to a post, as shown in Fig. 31I, and that the other end (a), which is held in the hand, is given a sudden flip up and down. The disturbance sent out along the rope

travels down the rope to the post, as shown, and is then reflected back again toward the hand. This kind of wave is called a *single-wave pulse*. If instead of a sudden pulse the hand is moved up and down with simple harmonic motion, a *train of waves*, like that shown in diagram (b), travels down the rope.

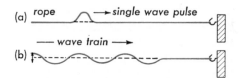

Fig. 31I *Examples of transverse waves sent out along a rope.*

When the prongs of a tuning fork are made to vibrate, they set the surrounding air into periodic motions. Each prong periodically strikes the air molecules next to it and these molecules in turn strike others, thus transmitting the disturbance outward. Traveling outward in all directions, such periodic disturbances constitute sound waves.

31.7. Transverse Waves. Transverse waves are those in which each particle vibrates along a line perpendicular to the direction of propagation. Along any one line of travel all particles are vibrating in one plane only. Such waves are illustrated in Fig. 31J by means of a wave machine designed for this purpose. As the handle H is turned one way or the other, the small round balls at the top move up and down with simple harmonic motion. As they move up and down, each along its own line, the wave form *ABCDEF* will move to the right or to the left. Light is an example of transverse wave motion.

31.8. Longitudinal Waves. Longitudinal waves are those in which the vibrations of the particles are along straight lines parallel to the direction of propagation. This type of wave is illustrated in Fig. 31K by another wave machine. As the handle is turned, each small ball moves horizontally and in the plane of the page with simple harmonic motion. In so doing, the regions of rarefaction B and D and the regions of

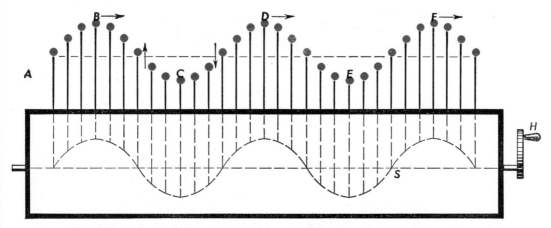

Fig. 31J *Diagram of a wave machine for demonstrating transverse waves.*

condensation A, C, and E move to the right, always keeping their same relative distances.

Sound waves in air are examples of longitudinal waves. Each air molecule vibrates back and forth about some equilibrium position as the wave train passes by.

31.9. Standing Waves. Nearly all sounds emanating from musical instruments are the result of standing waves. Standing waves may be produced in any substance, whether it is a solid, liquid, or gas, by two wave trains of the same frequency traveling in the same medium in opposite directions. One of the ways in which this is done is illustrated in Fig. 31L. One end of a rope is fastened to a post, and the other end, held taut, is moved up and down with simple harmonic motion. As the waves reach the

fixed end of the rope, they are reflected back to meet succeeding waves just coming up. If the waves have just the right frequency, the rope will sustain both wave trains by dividing into sections as shown. The points L_1 to L_5, where the rope has a maximum up and down motion, are called *anti-nodes*, and the points of no motion halfway between are called *nodes*. The heavy line represents the rope at one instant and the other lines represent it at other instants. The entire wave section between two consecutive nodes is called a *loop*.

Standing waves with longitudinal vibrations may be demonstrated with a long flexible spring as shown in Fig. 31M(a). The right-hand end of the spring is fixed and

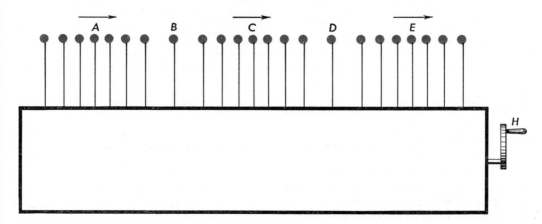

Fig. 31K *Diagram of a wave machine for demonstrating longitudinal waves.*

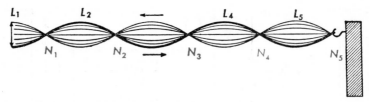

Fig. 31L   *Standing waves produced by reflecting a train of transverse waves from the fixed end of a rope.*

the left-hand end is moved back and forth with simple harmonic motion. If the impressed vibration has the proper frequency, the waves traveling to the right in meeting the reflected waves traveling to the left set up *nodes* and *anti-nodes*. The nodes N correspond to points where there is no motion, and the anti-nodes L to points where the motion is a maximum. The dots in diagram (b) show the relative positions and motions of each individual coil of the spring at nine different times during one complete vibration. The dots at the nodes remain fixed at all times while those at the anti-nodes move back and forth as shown by the arrows in diagram (c). At one instant (3), compressions are formed at the odd-numbered nodes N_1, N_3, and N_5 and rarefactions at the even-numbered nodes N_2, N_4, and N_6.

Half a vibration later (7), they change; the nodes of compression become nodes of rarefaction, and vice versa.

A direct comparison of standing transverse and standing longitudinal waves is given by diagrams (b), (c), (d), and (e) in Fig. 31M. The numbers (1), (2), (3), etc., indicate the corresponding states in the vibrations of each. Diagram (c) indicates the amplitudes of the longitudinal motions at the anti-nodes of the spring, and diagram (e) the transverse motions at the anti-nodes of the rope.

It should be explained that the dots in diagram (b) also represent the motions of air molecules when sound waves are reflected from a flat wall, back on themselves, to produce standing waves. As we shall see in the next chapter, these are like the sus-

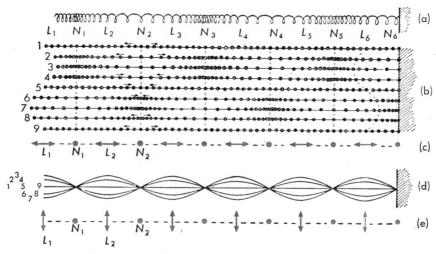

Fig. 31M   *Illustration of standing waves as they are produced with (a) the longitudinal waves of a spring, (b) the longitudinal waves of sound in the air, and (d) the transverse waves of a rope. (c) and (e) indicate the direction of vibration at the antinodes.*

tained vibrations of the air in an organ pipe, a flute, or some other musical wind instrument.

While sound waves in air are longitudinal vibrations, it is customary, for convenience only, to draw them as transverse waves. It is for this reason that the comparisons in Fig. 31M are made here. In the following two chapters, therefore, sound waves will usually be drawn as though they were transverse.

31.10. Wavelength. When a vibrating object sends out waves through a homogeneous medium, the waves travel with constant velocity. If the source vibrates with simple harmonic motion and the waves are transverse, they have the general appearance of the waves shown in Fig. 31N. The *wave-*

This is equal to the frequency of the source and is usually designated by n. It is customary to express frequency in *vibrations per second* or in *cycles per second*.

From the definitions of velocity, frequency, and wavelength, the following very simple relation exists between them:

$$V = n\lambda \qquad (31g)$$

The length of one wave, λ, times the number of waves per second, n, equals the total distance traveled in 1 sec, V.

Since the period is defined as the time required for one wave to pass by a given point, the relation between frequency and period given for vibrating sources in Eq. (31b) also applies to waves.

$T = \frac{1}{N}$

$N = \frac{1}{T}$

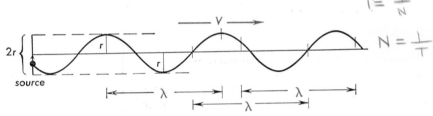

2r

source

λ λ λ

Fig. 31N *Illustration of the wavelength λ as the distance between corresponding points on two consecutive waves, and the amplitude r as the maximum displacement.*

length is defined as the distance between two similar points of any two consecutive waves, and is represented by the Greek letter lambda, λ. The distance between two consecutive wave crests, for example, is equal to one wavelength.

The amplitude of a wave is defined as the maximum value of the displacement. This is illustrated by r in Fig. 31N, the amplitude of the waves being proportional to the amplitude of the source. The frequency of a train of waves is defined as the number of waves passing any given point per second.

Example. If a train of waves moving along a rope has a velocity of 100 ft/sec and a wavelength of 20 ft, what is the frequency and period of the source?

Solution. By inserting these values in the proper places of Eq.(31g), we obtain

$100 \text{ ft/sec} = n \times 20 \text{ ft}$ or $n = {}^{100}\!/_{20} = 5 \text{ vib/sec}$

By Eq.(31b),

$$T = \tfrac{1}{5} = 0.2 \text{ sec}$$

The frequency is 5 vib/sec, and the period is 0.2 sec.

PROBLEMS

1. The amplitude of a particle executing simple harmonic motion is 20 cm; the period is 0.5 sec. Calculate (a) the maximum acceleration of the particle, and (b) its maximum velocity.

2. The maximum velocity of a particle moving with simple harmonic motion is 36 cm/sec. If its period of vibration is 2 sec, what is (a) the amplitude, and (b) the maximum acceleration? (*Ans.* (a) 11.5 cm, (b) 113 cm/sec².)

3. A small mass moves with simple harmonic motion. If it has an amplitude of 1 cm and a period of 0.01 sec, find (a) its maximum speed, and (b) its maximum acceleration.

4. A mass of 125 gm, fastened to the end of a lightweight spring and set vibrating up and down, is found to have a frequency of 2.6 vib/sec. Calculate the frequency when the mass is reduced to 50 gm. (*Ans.* 4.12 vib/sec.)

5. When a 5-lb weight is fastened to the lower end of a spring as shown in Fig. 31C, it stretches the spring a distance of 3 in. If the suspended weight is then set vibrating, what will be its frequency?

6. A mass of 400 gm is suspended from a spring as shown in Fig. 31C. If the mass is set vibrating and the frequency is found to be 12 vib/sec, what is the value of the spring constant k? (*Ans.* 2.27×10^6 dynes/cm.)

7. When a mass of 100 gm is suspended from a spring as shown in Fig. 31C, it stretches the spring a distance of 5 cm. If the 100-gm mass is now replaced by one of 30 gm, and then set vibrating up and down, what will be the frequency?

8. When a 20-lb weight is suspended from a spring as shown in Fig. 31C, the spring stretches 4 in. After the 20-lb weight is removed, a man jumps up and hangs on to the lower end. If in doing so he is set vibrating with a period of 2.0 sec, how much does he weigh? (*Ans.* 195 lb.)

9. A pendulum has a length of 50 cm. Find its period and frequency.

10. A simple pendulum is to have a period of $\frac{1}{10}$ sec. How long should it be if $g = 32.00$ ft/sec²? (*Ans.* 0.0973 in.)

11. A clock pendulum swings with a period of 1 sec where g = 32.26 ft/sec². How many sec will it lose in 24 hr if it is taken to a high mountain where g = 32.10 ft/sec²?

12. A clock pendulum made of aluminum has a length of 100 cm when the temperature is 20°C. How many sec will this clock lose in 24 hr if the temperature is maintained at 30°C? (See Eq.(29a).) (*Ans.* 11 sec.)

13. A simple pendulum, generally called a Foucault pendulum, is 30 m long and hangs from the dome of a cathedral. From such an arrangement, the effect of the earth's rotation can be observed. Find the period of the pendulum.

14. A tiny pendulum 4 mm long is made of a quartz fiber and a quartz bead. Calculate (a) its period, and (b) its frequency. (*Ans.* (a) 0.128 sec, (b) 7.8 vib/sec.)

15. A train of waves moves along a cable with a speed of 30 ft/sec. Find the frequency and period of the source if their wavelength is 3 in.

16. A vibrating source with a frequency of 36 vib/sec sends waves along a rope with a velocity of 5 m/sec. Find (a) the period of the source, and (b) the wavelength of the waves. (*Ans.* (a) 0.0278 sec, (b) 13.9 cm.)

17. The velocity of radio waves is 3×10^8 m/sec. What is the wavelength from a station broadcasting on a frequency of 550 kilocycles/sec?

18. A radio station broadcasts on a wavelength of 20 meters. What is the frequency in megacycles/sec if the velocity of radio waves is 3×10^{10} cm/sec? (*Ans.* 15 Mc/sec.)

Chapter 32

Sound, Its Transmission and Detection

32.1. Sound Transmission. The transmission of sound from one place to the other, from source to receiver, requires a material medium through which to travel. This is to be contrasted with light which travels best through a vacuum.

That sound is transmitted by air, or any other gas, may be demonstrated by placing a small bell in an evacuated jar. This is illustrated in Fig. 32A. As the air is slowly

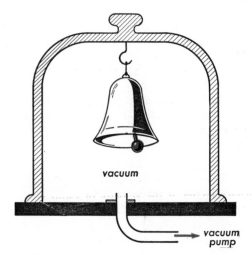

Fig. 32A *A bell ringing in a vacuum cannot be heard.*

the adjacent air molecules and they in turn strike others. Upon reaching the side of the jar, the glass walls are periodically bombarded by the molecules and set vibrating. The walls in turn set the outside air vibrating. Arriving at the observer's ear, the disturbance strikes the eardrum, setting it into motion. Without air to transmit the vibrations from the bell to the inside surface of the glass jar, no sound could ever leave the jar.

The transmission of sound by liquids may be illustrated by an experiment shown in Fig. 32B. A tuning fork with a disk at-

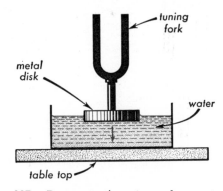

Fig. 32B *Demonstration of sound waves traveling through water.*

removed from the jar, the ringing of the bell grows fainter and fainter until, when a good vacuum is obtained, no sound can be heard. As soon as the air is admitted, however, the ringing becomes clearly audible again. The vibrating bell strikes air molecules, knocking them away from the metal surface. These fast moving molecules strike

tached to its base is set vibrating and then touched to the surface of a dish of water. The vibrations of the fork and disk travel through the water to the bottom of the dish and to the table top. The table top itself is set into vibration with the same frequency as the fork, thus acting like a *sounding board* to make the sound louder.

The transmission of sound by solids is

illustrated in Fig. 32C. A vibrating tuning fork is brought into contact with the end of a long wooden rod. The longitudinal vibrations travel down the length of the rod, which causes the hollow wooden box at the other end to vibrate. Sound is clearly heard coming from the box.

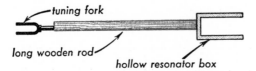

Fig. 32C *Demonstration of sound waves traveling through wood.*

Sound waves, whether they travel through solids, liquids, or gases, are longitudinal in character. In Fig. 32D the prongs of a tuning fork are shown vibrating back and forth with simple harmonic motion. By collisions with air molecules, each one sends out longitudinal waves through the atmosphere.

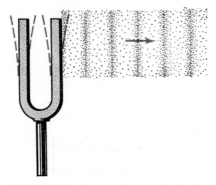

Fig. 32D *Sound waves are longitudinal waves.*

32.2. Velocity of Sound. Although light and sound both travel with a finite velocity, the velocity of light is so great in comparison that an instantaneous flash may be regarded as taking no time to travel many miles. When we see the light of a distant lightning flash and hear the thunder later, we know that the difference in time is due to the relatively low velocity of sound. Knowing that sound requires 5 sec to travel 1 mi, the distance of a passing thunderstorm can be noted by the second hand of a watch.

Similarly, when a distant train starts up and we watch for the first puff of smoke as it starts out, the arrival of the accompanying sound is not heard until an appreciable time afterward.

The earliest successful attempts to measure the velocity of sound in air were made in 1640 by Marin Mersenne, a French physicist, and in 1656 by Giovanni Borelli and Vincenzo Viviani, Italian physicists. Since that time many experimenters have improved upon these earliest measurements by using various different methods and devices. The most recent and probably the most accurate measurements are those made in 1934 by Miller.* With coast defense guns as a source of sound and a set of receivers located at certain distances apart, very accurate velocity determinations were made. The results gave a velocity of 331 m/sec at a temperature of 0°C. This is equivalent to 1087 ft/sec.

As a general rule, sound travels faster in solids and liquids than it does in gases. This is illustrated by the measured velocities for a few common substances given in Table 32A.

It is well known that the temperature has a small but measurable effect upon the velocity of sound. For each degree centigrade rise in temperature, the velocity in air increases by 61 cm/sec, or its equivalent of 2 ft/sec. Written as an equation,

$$V = V_0 + 0.61t \qquad (32a)$$

where V_0 is the velocity in m/sec at 0°C, and t is the temperature in °C. For each degree on the Fahrenheit scale, the velocity increases by 1.1 ft/sec. This is an approximate relation.

* Dayton C. Miller (1866-1940), American physicist, noted for his experiments on the quality of musical sounds and on the ether drift. He collected and had in his possession the largest collection of flutes in the world. These instruments he turned over to the Smithsonian Institute in Washington, D.C., where they are now on exhibit. A member of the National Academy of Sciences, and one-time president of the American Physical Society, he has been awarded the Elliott Cresson Medal and the Cleveland Distinguished Service Medal.

TABLE 32A. VELOCITY OF SOUND
IN DIFFERENT SUBSTANCES

Substance	Velocity (m/sec)	Velocity (ft/sec)
Air (at 0°C)...	331	1,087
Hydrogen.....	1,269	4,165
Water........	1,435	4,708
Alcohol.......	1,213	3,890
Iron.........	5,130	16,820
Glass........	5,000	16,410

A velocity of 1087 ft/sec is equivalent to 740 mi/hr. High in the stratosphere where the daytime temperature reaches 200°F, the velocity of sound increases 185 ft/sec. There the velocity of 1272 ft/sec is equivalent to 867 mi/hr.

32.3. Pitch. The pitch of a musical note refers to its position on a musical scale, and is determined by the frequency of the sound impulses sent out by the vibrating source. The dependence of pitch upon frequency can be demonstrated in many ways. Diagram (a) of **Fig. 32E** represents a toothed

ergy as well as the sound is derived from compressed air which is blown through small holes in the hollow container C. The air issuing from these jets passes through similar holes in a rotating disk W. With the holes drilled at an angle as shown in detail in (d), the air blasts from the stationary holes below exert a force on one side of the holes in W, causing the disk to turn. As the disk turns, each blast of air is momentarily cut off until another hole arrives just above it. The intermittent pulses of air issuing from the disk give rise to a musical note.

Diagram (c) in Fig. 32E represents a siren in which a single blast of air is interrupted by a rotating disk containing several rings of holes. Detailed experiments with many musically trained and untrained observers alike show that pitch and frequency are not identical.

Pitch is a *subjective* measurement and is therefore a sensory magnitude depending upon the individual, while frequency is a *physical* measurement of the number of vibrations per second. As the intensity of a

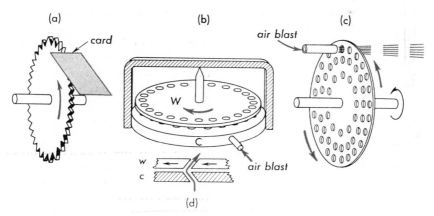

Fig. 32E *Sound demonstrations illustrating the relation between pitch and frequency.*

wheel (called Savart's wheel) rotating at high speed. A small card held against the teeth is set into vibration, giving out a musical note. As the wheel slows down, the vibration frequency of the card decreases and the note lowers in pitch.

Diagram (b) is a siren similar to those commonly used as factory whistles. The en-

pure tone of 300 vib/sec is increased, for example, it appears to most observers to change in quality and at the same time to decrease slightly in pitch. Conversely, at a high frequency, an increase in the intensity seems to increase the pitch.

32.4. Detection of Sound. By far the most important instrument by which sound is detected is the ear. This hearing mechanism, which is sensitive to very faint as well as loud sounds and to very high as well as low frequencies, is treated in detail in Sec. 32.7.

Various electrical devices, commonly called microphones, have been invented for detecting sound waves and transforming them into varying electric currents. These currents may then be amplified, transmitted long or short distances, and then reconverted into sound. Sometimes they are fed into an oscilloscope for a study of wave mo-

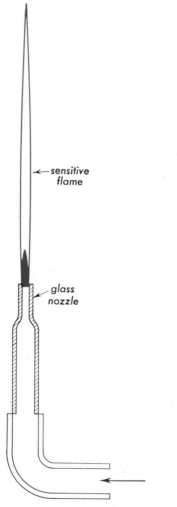

Fig. 32F *Diagram of a gas flame, sensitive to high-pitched sound waves. As the waves pass the tip of the nozzle, the flame dips down.*

tion, a "cutting head" for recording, a light source for sound recording on film, or an electromagnet for recording on wire or tape. Some of these devices are considered in detail in later chapters.

Sound may also be detected by a rather interesting but impractical device known as the sensitive flame. This detector, as illustrated in Fig. 32F, consists of a tall, thin gas flame produced by gas issuing from a small nozzle. As sound waves pass by the tip of the nozzle, the gas stream is disturbed and the flame becomes unstable and drops in height. This action is particularly noticeable with high-pitched sounds like those from a blowing whistle, or those from a jingling bunch of keys.

32.5. Reflection of Sound. The reflection of sound waves may be demonstrated in various ways. One arrangement is shown in Fig. 32G in which a Galton whistle sounding a high-pitched note acts as a source of sound and a sensitive flame as the receiver. A solid screen between the two casts a "sound shadow," thus permitting only the reflected waves from the wall of the room to reach it.

When the whistle, blown by compressed air, is sounded continuously, the flame will remain unstable. If, under these conditions, the experimenter walks beside the wall through the sound path, the flame will be quite unstable when he reaches *A*, *C*, or *E*, but will burn smoothly when he intercepts the beam at *B* or *D*.

Sound shadows of the kind shown in this experiment are characteristic of high-pitched notes only and demonstrate that short waves tend to travel in straight lines. The longer waves of low-pitched sounds, however, tend to bend around corners. This latter effect, known as *diffraction*, is quite noticeable where a carillon of large bells is being played. On walking around the corner of a nearby building, one notices that the sharp cutoff in the intensity of the high-pitched bells is quite marked, while the low-pitched bells continue in good strength. It should be pointed out that high-pitched notes also show diffraction, but to a lesser degree. This phenomenon is due to

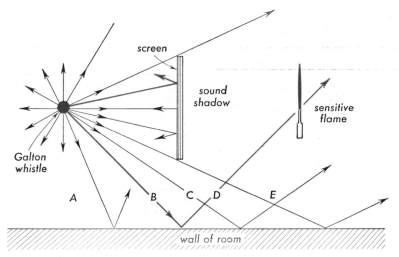

Fig. 32G *Experiment demonstrating the reflection of sound waves from the wall of a room.*

the wave nature of sound, and will be explained in principle in the case of light waves in another chapter.

32.6. Refraction of Sound Waves. The bending of sound waves in layers of air at different temperatures is called *refraction*. The phenomenon, which can be observed in various ways, is due to the greater velocity of sound in warm air than the velocity in cold (see Sec. 32.2).

A good illustration is found in the frequent observation while boating on a lake or river of being able to hear the music from a quite distant radio or phonograph at night but not in the daytime. The reason for this is shown in Fig. 32H. At night, the air near the water is colder than it is higher up, so that the higher velocity in the warmer air bends the waves back down. During the day, the air close to the water is warmer and the waves bend up away from the water as shown.

Recent experiments of this kind have been performed with the very loud sounds from big guns. Sound waves refracted back from high up in the stratosphere indicate with some degree of certainty the existence of very warm layers of air at altitudes of 25 to 40 mi. Refraction in such cases as this is similar to reflection from a mirror surface, since the waves travel in more or less

straight lines, going up and back, but bend over when they enter, more or less abruptly, a warmer layer.

32.7. Intensity of Sound. There are three fundamental characteristics of all sounds:

Objective	*Subjective*
intensity	loudness
frequency	pitch
wave form	tone quality

The intensity of sound is characterized by its loudness and is measured scientifically by the amount of energy in a given volume of the space through which the sound is traveling. In other words, sound waves constitute a flow of energy through matter. This may be demonstrated by an experiment, arranged as shown in Fig. 32I. A vibrating tuning fork is placed near one opening of a Helmholtz* resonator, and a very lightly constructed pinwheel is placed near the other. Air pulses from the vibrating prongs of the fork traveling through

* Hermann Helmholtz (1821-1894), noted German physicist, who during his lifetime made outstanding contributions to the subjects of light, sound, and electricity. Probably his greatest contribution was his explanation of tone quality in musical notes. He demonstrated that quality depends upon the number and intensity of the overtones or harmonies present in the musical tone.

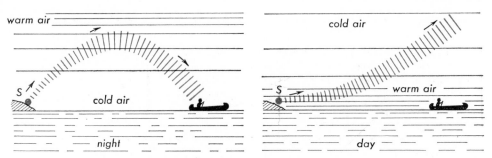

Fig. 32H   *The higher velocity of sound waves in warm air causes sound waves to be refracted down at night and up in the daytime.*

the resonator come out reinforced at the other opening and strike the vanes of the pinwheel. When the fork is removed the pinwheel stops rotating. *Loudness is a subjective measurement of sound power and is therefore a sensory magnitude. Intensity, on the other hand, is an objective measurement of the sound power being delivered.*

One method of specifying the intensity of a sound is to state the amount of energy flowing through unit area per sec. Since the rate of flow of energy in most common sounds is extremely small, the ordinary unit of power, the *watt*, is too large to be practical. Consequently, a unit one million times smaller, the *microwatt*, is used. One microwatt equals 10^{-6} watt. *Sound intensity is defined as the power flowing through unit area taken normal to the direction of the waves* (see Fig. 32J). One microwatt is equivalent to 10^{-6} joules/sec, or 10 ergs/sec.

A common method of specifying intensity is to compare the power in a given sound with the power in another. *When the power in one sound is ten times that in another, the ratio of intensity is said to be 1 bel.* The bel is so called in honor of Alexander Gra-

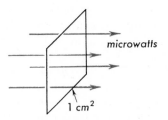

Fig. 32J   *Sound intensity is measured in microwatts flowing through 1 cm² of area.*

ham Bell, the inventor of the electric telephone. According to this definition, an intensity scale in bels is a logarithmic scale of power.

$$B_{bels} = \log_{10} \frac{E}{E_0} \qquad (32b)$$

where E is the intensity, or power, of one sound and E_0 that of another. The following tabulation will illustrate this equation.

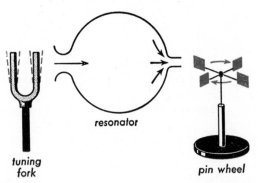

Fig. 32I   *A pin wheel may be set rotating by sound waves from a tuning fork, demonstrating that sound waves have energy.*

TABLE 32B. SOUND INTENSITY
SCALE IN BELS

Relative Power E/E_0	Relative Intensity B_{bels}
1	0
10	1
100	2
1000	3
10000	4

The numbers at the right are just the logarithms of those at the left. According to these figures, a sound with 1000 times the power of another is 3 bels louder.

Because the *bel* represents large differences in intensity, a smaller unit, the *decibel* (abbr. db), has been introduced and used by telephone and radio engineers, as well as by physicians (ear specialists). According to this smaller unit, the bel is divided into ten equal ratios by the following equation.

$$b_{\text{db}} = 10 \log_{10} \frac{E}{E_0} \qquad (32c)$$

The following tabulation will illustrate specific values from this equation.

TABLE 32C. SOUND INTENSITY
SCALE IN DECIBELS

Relative Power E/E_0	Relative Intensity b_{db}
1.00	0
1.26	1
1.58	2
2.00	3
2.51	4
3.16	5
3.98	6
5.01	7
6.31	8
7.94	9
10.00	10

Each power ratio in the left column is 26% greater than the preceding value. Because such a change is just detectable by the human ear, the decibel is considered a practical unit. The sounds from several common sources are compared in different units, in Table 32D.

An audiogram for the normal human ear is given in Fig. 32K. The lower curve gives the faintest sounds that can be heard, and the upper curve the loudest that can be heard without pain. It will be noted that the ear is most sensitive to frequencies between 2000 and 4000 cycles and that the sensitivity diminishes rapidly at higher and lower frequencies.

As a practical matter, sound experts have adopted as a zero level of sound intensity, $E_0 = 10^{-10}$ microwatts/cm² at a frequency of 1000 cycles. This is the limit of audibility of the average human being for a thousand-cycle note.

To see how intensity affects the frequency limits of audibility, consider the horizontal line at 20 db. At this intensity level, with a flow of energy 100 times that necessary to hear the faintest thousand-cycle note, frequencies below about 200 and above 15,000 cannot be heard. At 40 db with a flow of energy 10,000 times the threshold of audibility at 1000 cycles, the lowest frequency to be heard is about 100 cycles/sec, whereas the upper limit may be as high as 20,000 cycles/sec.

The amplitude of the sound waves at the threshold of audibility at 1000 cycles has been determined and found to be about 1×10^{-8} cm. This is about the diameter of a hydrogen atom and gives some idea of the enormous sensitivity of the human ear. When a sound becomes so loud that it is painful to the ear, the amplitude is of the order of one or two millimeters.

TABLE 32D. COMMON SOUND LEVELS

	Intensity in microwatts/cm²	Sound Level in bels	Sound Level in decibels
Threshold of hearing.........	10^{-10}	0	0
Rustling leaves..............	10^{-8}	2	20
Talking (at 3 ft)............	10^{-6}	4	40
Noisy office or store.........	10^{-4}	6	60
Subway car.................	1	10	100
Threshold of feeling.........	100	12	120

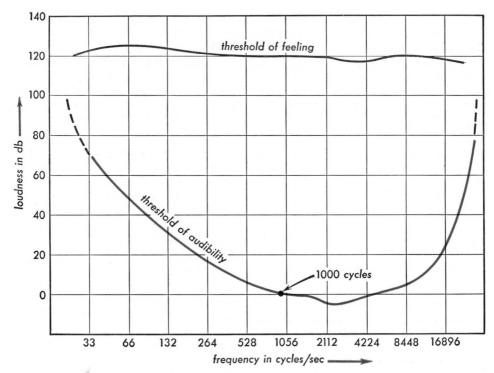

Fig. 32K   *Audiogram of the average human being, showing the threshold of hearing for different frequencies of sound.*

32.8. Inverse Square Law. Theory indicates, and experiments prove, that the intensity of sound is inversely proportional to the square of the distance from the source. As an equation,

$$E = \frac{E_0}{d^2} \qquad (32d)$$

where E_0 is the intensity at unit distance (1 cm, 1 m, or 1 ft) and E is the intensity at any distance d in the same units. This is called the *inverse square law*.

If S in Fig. 32L represents a source of sound, the waves travel outward in straight lines. Whatever sound energy flows through area A at 1 m, the same energy will flow

through area B at 2 m, and area C at 3 m. Since these areas have the ratios 1:4:9, the energy flow per sec, through unit area at each distance, will be E_0, $E_0/4$, and $E_0/9$, respectively.

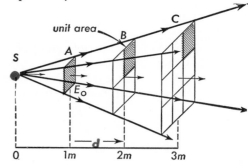

Fig. 32L   *Illustration of the inverse square law.*

PROBLEMS

1. Find the velocity of sound in mi/hr for air at 77°F.

2. Determine the velocity of sound in m/sec at 50°C. (*Ans.* 361.5 m/sec.)

3. Calculate the velocity of sound in air when the temperature is 30°C.

4. Determine the velocity of sound in air at an altitude of 6.5 mi where the temperature is −34°F. (See Fig. 25.2.) (*Ans.* 1014 ft/sec.)

5. The noise from a racing car motor is 60 db at a distance of 10 ft. What is the noise level at 200 ft?

6. At a distance of 5 m from a jet plane, the noise level on open throttle is 85 db. What is the noise level when the plane flies overhead at an altitude of 3000 m? (*Ans.* 29.5 db.)

7. At 1 mi the sound level of a fire siren is 20 db. What is the intensity at a distance of only 10 ft?

8. If one sound is 35 db louder than the other, what are their relative energies? (*Ans.* 3160:1.)

9. If one sound is 15 db louder than another, what are the relative energies?

10. Two ft in front of a radio loud-speaker the sound level is 35 db. Calculate the intensity at a distance of 18 ft. (*Ans.* 15.9 db.)

11. To one standing in front of a flight of steps, a sharp clap of the hands will produce a sound wave that is reflected back to the observer from each step. If the step treads are 14 in. deep, what frequency is heard by the observer? Assume a temperature of 68°F.

12. If one sound is 50 db more intense than the other, what are their relative powers? (*Ans.* 100,000:1.)

13. If the intensity of sound 1 ft from a source is 5 microwatts/cm^2, what is the intensity at a distance of 40 ft?

14. If the intensity of a sound 2.5 m from a source is 1 microwatt/cm^2, what is the intensity at a distance of 1000 meters? (*Ans.* 6.25 × 10^{-6} microwatts/cm^2.)

15. The noise from a racing car motor is 60 db at a distance of 1 m. How loud is it at a distance of 10 m?

16. If one sound is 8 db louder than another, what are their relative powers? (*Ans.* 6.31.)

Chapter 33

Resonance, Beats,
Doppler Effect, and Interference

33.1. Resonance. An experimental demonstration of resonance is easily set up, as shown in Fig. 33A. Two simple pendulums are suspended from a flexible support. One, *A*, has a heavy bob made of metal, and the other, *B*, a bob made of wood.

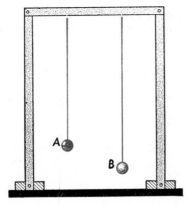

Fig. 33A *A demonstration of resonance can be performed with two pendulums.*

The heavy bob *A* is pulled to one side and released to swing freely. The horizontal support responds to the motion and, in swaying back and forth in step with *A*, acts to set the other pendulum swinging. The response of pendulum *B* to this forced vibration depends upon the relative lengths of the two pendulums. If there is considerable difference in their lengths, the response is ever so slight, and the closer they are to the same length the greater is the response.

When *A* and *B* have the same length, their natural periods become equal, and *B* responds to the swaying support and swings with a large amplitude. It responds in sympathy, or resonance, to the driving pendulum *A*.

If two violin strings are tuned to the same frequency and one is set vibrating, the other stationed some distance away will soon pick up the vibrations and give out the same note. This too is a case of resonance, a phenomenon which occurs only if two objects have the same natural frequency of vibration.

Another experimental demonstration of resonance is illustrated in Fig. 33B. Two

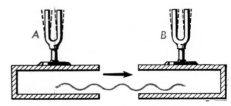

Fig. 33B *Tuning forks mounted on resonator boxes for demonstrating resonance.*

tuning forks with exactly the same pitch are mounted on separate hollow boxes as shown. Fork *A* is first set vibrating for a moment and then stopped by touching the prongs with the fingers. Fork *B* will then be found vibrating. If we take into account the hollow boxes, whose purpose it is to act as sounding boards and thus intensify the sound, we find that the explanation is quite simple. Each sound pulse that emerges from the box with each vibration of fork *A* passes into the other box, pushing out the sides at just the right time to make the prongs of fork *B* move in the proper direction.

33.2. Beat Notes. When two notes of slightly different pitch are sounded at the same time, beats are heard. This phenomenon is used in organ pipes to produce the familiar vibrato effect. Two pipes tuned to slightly different frequencies are used for every note.

The phenomenon of beats may be demonstrated by two tuning forks mounted as shown in Fig. 33C. One fork is made slightly

about 1 and 6 vib/sec, the ear perceives an intertone halfway between the two sounded, but periodically waxing and waning in intensity. As the beat frequency increases, the smooth rise and fall gives way to a succession of pulses, then to a sensation of roughness, and finally to two clearly perceived tones.

33.3. The Doppler Effect. Nearly everyone has at some time, perhaps without re-

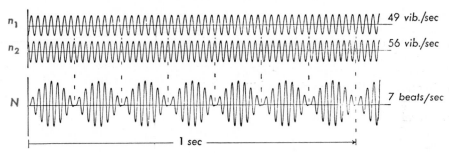

Fig. 33C   *Wave graphs illustrating how beat notes are produced by two different frequencies.*

out of tune with the other by looping rubber bands *tightly* around the prongs. If the two forks are sounded simultaneously, the intensity of the sound rises and falls periodically. This is illustrated by means of vibration graphs as shown in Fig. 33C. The upper curve represents the sound vibrations arriving at the ear from one fork, and the second curve the vibrations from the other. Both waves arriving at the ear are first in phase, i.e., in step with each other, then out of phase, then in phase, then out of phase, etc.

The resultant action of these two waves on the eardrum is represented by the third line. When the waves are in phase, the resultant has a large amplitude equal to the sum of the amplitudes of the two. When they are out of phase the amplitude becomes zero. The number of beats per sec, N, is determined by the difference between n_2 and n_1, the respective frequencies of the two sources producing the sound.

$$\boxed{\text{beat frequency } N = n_2 - n_1} \quad (33a)$$

When the beat frequency lies between

alizing it, observed the *Doppler effect*. The sounding horn of a car passing at high speed on the highway exhibits the phenomenon. The pitch of the horn, as the car goes by, drops as much as two whole notes on the musical scale. A similar observation can be made by listening to the roar of the motor of a racing car as it approaches and recedes from an observer at the race track. The motor seems to slow down as it passes by. Again, the pitch of the whistle on a fast moving train sounds higher as the train approaches the observer than it does after the train has passed by.

This change in pitch is due to the relative motions of the source of sound and the observer. To see how this produces the effect, consider the following example. When the whistle on a train at rest is blown, it sends out waves traveling with the same velocity in all directions. To all stationary observers, no matter in what direction they are located, the true pitch of the whistle is heard, since just as many waves arrive at the ear per second as there are waves leaving the whistle. If, on the other hand, the train is moving as shown in Fig. 33D, the whistle is moving away from the waves traveling to the rear and toward the waves traveling forward. The result is that the waves behind are considerably drawn out while those in front are crowded together. With each new wave sent out by the source, the train is farther from the preceding wave sent out to the rear and nearer to the one sent out ahead. Since the velocity of sound is the same in all directions, an observer at O_1 therefore hears more waves per second and an observer at O_2 hears fewer.

To an observer O_3 or O_4, at right angles and at some little distance from the moving source, the pitch remains unchanged. For these side positions the source is neither approaching nor receding from the observer, so that approximately the same number of waves are received per second as there are waves leaving the source.

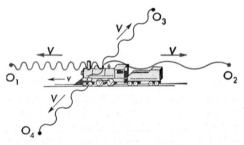

Fig. 33D *The Doppler effect. The pitch of a whistle on a fast-moving train sounds higher to an observer in front of the train, lower to an observer in back, and normal to observers off at the sides.*

The general relations for the Doppler effect are given by the following single equation:

$$\frac{n_o}{V - v_0} = \frac{n_s}{V - v_s} \qquad (33b)$$

where n_s is the frequency of the source, n_o is the frequency heard by the observer, V is the velocity of sound, v_s the velocity of the source, and v_o the velocity of the observer. *The direction of the velocity of sound V at the observer is positive, and its direction is taken as the positive direction for all velocities.* Either v_o or v_s is positive if it is directed

along the positive direction, and negative if it is oppositely directed.

Case 1. If the source and observer are approaching each other, v_s is +, and v_o is −.

Case 2. If the source and observer are moving in the same direction, v_s and v_o are both +.

Case 3. The observer is at rest and the source is approaching at a velocity $v_s = 2V$. Here $v_o = 0$ and v_s is +. This is an interesting case since n_o is the negative of n_s. The observer hears the sound backward, as if played backward on a tape recorder, and it is heard after the source has passed him.

Example. A racing car passes the grandstand traveling at a speed of 150 mi/hr. If the noise from the exhaust has a frequency of 540 vib/sec, what frequency is heard by the audience as the car approaches the grandstand? Assume the speed of sound to be 1120 ft/sec.

Solution. Employing the Doppler formula, Eq.(33b), we solve for the unknown n_o, and write

$$n_o = \frac{n_s(V - v_o)}{V - v_s}$$

Since the source of the sound is moving in the same direction as the sound waves arriving at the grandstand, V_s is +150 mi/hr, or +220 ft/sec. Substituting the known quantities, we obtain

$$n_o = \frac{540(1120 - 0)}{1120 - 220}$$

and

$$n_o = \frac{540 \times 1120}{900} = 672 \frac{\text{vib}}{\text{sec}}$$

33.4. Interference. Everyone has at one time or another dropped a stone in a still pond of water and watched the waves spread outward in ever-widening circles. Such waves are represented by concentric circles as shown in Fig. 33E. The solid-line circles represent crests of waves and are therefore one wavelength apart, while the dotted-line circles represent the troughs of the waves, which are also one wavelength apart.

If two stones are dropped simultaneously into the water, two sets of waves will spread outward as shown in Fig. 33F. As these waves cross each other, they act one upon the other, producing what is called an

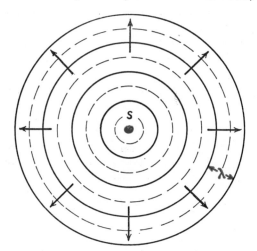

Fig. 33E *Concentric waves traveling outward from a single source* S.

interference pattern. Where the crests of two waves come together at the dotted intersections, they are *in step,* or in phase, and the amplitude of the water surface is increased. Where the crest of one wave and the trough of another come together, they are out of step, or out of phase, and the amplitude of the water surface is reduced. The *in-phase* regions of the waves move outward along the dotted lines, such as *x, y,* and *z,* and we have what is called *constructive interference.* The *out-of-phase* regions

move outward along the solid lines, such as *a* and *b,* and we have what is called *destructive interference.*

An instantaneous photograph of such a wave pattern is shown in Fig. 33G. Note how clearly the interference regions of the waves stand out. Photographs of this kind, as well as direct observations of such wave patterns, are readily made as follows. A glass tray for maintaining a shallow water layer can be made from a piece of window glass and a wooden frame. A thin metal strip, clamped at one end and set vibrating up and down over the water, is used as a source. A piece of wire, fastened to the vibrating end of this strip, should have one wire end dipping into the water for a single-wave source, and both ends dipping into the water for a double source. Intermittent viewing of the waves through a slotted disk, or illumination by means of a stroboscopic light source, enables one to make the wave pattern appear to stand still, or to progress in *slow motion.*

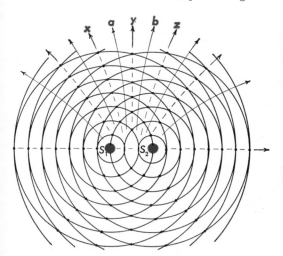

Fig. 33F *Concentric waves traveling outward from a double source, producing what is called an interference pattern.*

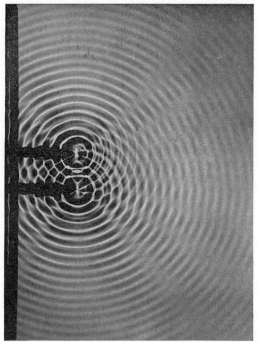

Fig. 33G *Ripple tank photograph of the interference of water waves from two sources.* (Courtesy, Physical Sciences Study Committee Project.)

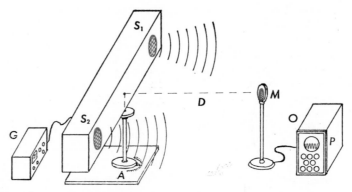

Fig. 33H *Experiment for demonstrating the interference of sound waves from two sources.*

An experiment for demonstrating the interference of sound waves is shown in Fig. 33H. Two small radio loudspeakers S_1 and S_2 are mounted, about 150 cm apart, in a hollow box. The box is free to pivot about a vertical axis midway between the speaker centers. When both speakers are connected to an electronic sound generator, G, the speakers vibrate in phase and send out identical waves into the surrounding air. A microphone, M, about 2 m away, is an excellent detector, and an oscilloscope connected to it will indicate the relative amplitudes of the resultant sound waves arriving at M. As the box is turned slowly in one direction, the amplitude of the oscilloscope signal P rises and falls periodically, indicating constructive and destructive inter-

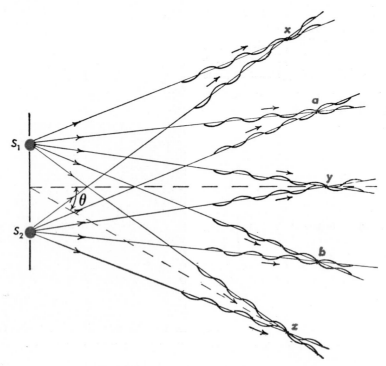

Fig. 33I *Diagram showing the in-phase and out-of-phase of waves at certain points.*

ference. As it is turned slowly back again, maxima and minima are again observed at the same angle positions.

An instructive diagram showing the arrival of pairs of waves at the microphone, for maximum and minimum response positions, is shown in Fig. 33I. Points x, y, and z correspond to points x, y, and z in Fig. 33F, where the waves arrive in phase, while points a and b correspond to those where they arrive out of phase.

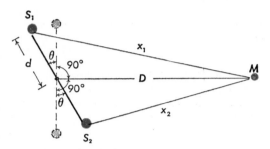

Fig. 33J *Geometrical relations for finding the wavelength of sound waves from a double source.*

By measuring the angles, θ, at which maximum response occurs for the experiment shown in Fig. 33H, as well as the distance, d, between S_1 and S_2, and the distance D, the wavelength of the sound waves can be calculated. The geometry for this calculation is shown in Fig. 33J.

When the line between the two speakers makes an angle of 90° with the perpendicular bisector D, the sources are equidistant from M, the waves arrive in phase, and we have point y of Figs. 33F and 33I. When the sources are turned to position z, the line between the speakers has been turned through an angle θ, the waves arrive in phase again, but the path x_1 is exactly one wavelength longer than the path x_2. At some greater angle θ, the path x_1 can be made exactly two wavelengths longer than x_2, and at some still greater angle it can be made three wavelengths longer, etc. For all these particular angles where the waves are in phase, we can write the single equation

$$x_1 - x_2 = n\lambda \qquad (33c)$$

where $\qquad n = 0, 1, 2, 3, ----$ (33d)

We can now apply the law of cosines to the two large triangles in Fig. 33J, and calculate the distances x_1 and x_2.

For the upper triangle, we write

$$x_1^2 = d^2 + D^2 - 2dD \cos(90° + \theta) \quad (33e)$$

and for the lower triangle, we write

$$x_2^2 = d^2 + D^2 - 2dD \cos(90° - \theta) \quad (33f)$$

By substituting the measured values of D, d, and θ in these two equations, the values of x_1 and x_2 can be calculated. Substituting these values in Eq.(33c), along with the appropriate value of n, makes it possible to calculate the wavelength λ.

PROBLEMS

1. Two tuning forks have frequencies of 297 and 396 vib/sec, respectively. What is the beat frequency?

2. Three tuning forks with frequencies of 264, 352, and 495 vib-sec, respectively, are sounded at the same time. What are the frequencies of the beat notes arising from these sources? (*Ans.* 88, 143, and 231 vib/sec.)

3. A violinist playing in harmonics sounds the A and E strings simultaneously. If the frequencies of these two sounds are 440 and 660 vib/sec, what is the frequency of the beat note?

4. The following musical triad is sounded on the strings of a harp: 264, 352, and 440 vib/sec. Find the frequencies of all the beat notes produced. (*Ans.* 88, 88, and 176 vib/sec.)

5. The horn of a car is blown as the car approaches an intersection at 60 mi/hr. If the frequency heard by an observer standing at the intersection is 200 vib/sec, what is the frequency of the horn? Assume a temperature of 77°F.

6. The siren of a ranger station along the highway is sounded with a frequency of 600 vib/sec. What frequency is heard by motorists traveling 60 mi/hr along the highway if they are (a) approaching, and (b) receding from the

station? Assume a temperature of 30°C. (*Ans.* (a) 646 vib/sec, (b) 554 vib/sec.)

7. To one standing in front of a flight of steps, a sharp clap of the hands will produce a sound wave that is reflected back to the observer from each step. If the step treads are 12 in. deep, what frequency is heard by the observer? Assume a temperature of 92°F.

8. A train making 90 mi/hr sounds its whistle, pitched to a frequency of 600 vib/sec. What frequency would be heard by an observer on the ground (a) ahead of the train, and (b) behind the train? Assume the speed of sound to be 1100 ft/sec. (*Ans.* (a) 682 vib/sec, (b) 536 vib/sec.)

9. A car traveling 60 mi/hr on the highway, sounds its horn as it overtakes and passes another car traveling 30 mi/hr in the same direction. If the horn frequency is 400 vib/sec, what is the frequency heard by the driver in the slower car (a) before passing, and (b) after passing? Assume the speed of sound to be 1150 ft/sec.

10. Two radio speakers sounding the same frequency are placed 2 m apart in a box as shown in Fig. 33H. A microphone is located 3 m away on the perpendicular bisector. As the box is slowly turned, the first maximum response is observed when the angle θ is 30°. (See Fig. 33J.) Find the wavelength of the sound waves. (*Ans.* $\lambda = 0.96$ m.)

11. In performing the experiment shown in Fig. 33H, the distance between speaker centers is measured to be 1.5 m and the distance between the box and the microphone to be 2.5 m. As the sound box is turned from its 90° position (see Fig. 33J), the second maximum response of the microphone is observed when $\theta = 36°$. Find the wavelength of the sound waves.

Chapter 34

Sources of Musical Sounds

34.1. Stringed Instruments. There are two principal reasons why stringed instruments of different kinds do not sound alike as regards *tone quality*—first, the design of the instrument, and second, the method by which the strings are set into vibration. The violin and cello are bowed with long strands

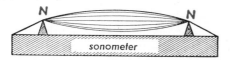

Fig. 34A *Single string vibrating with its fundamental frequency.*

of tightly stretched horsehair, the harp and guitar are plucked with the fingers or picks, and the piano is hammered with light felt mallets.

Under very special conditions a string may be made to vibrate with nodes at either end as shown in Fig. 34A. In this state of motion the string gives rise to its lowest

possible note, and it is said to be vibrating with its *fundamental frequency*.

Every musician knows that a thick heavy string has a lower natural pitch than a thin one, that a short strong string has a higher pitch than a long one, and that the tighter a string is stretched the higher is its pitch. The *G* string of a violin, for example, is thicker and heavier than the high-pitched *E* string, and the *bass* strings of the piano are longer and heavier than the strings of the *treble*.

34.2. Harmonics and Overtones. When a professional violinist plays "in harmonics" he touches the strings lightly at various points and sets each one vibrating in two or more segments, as shown in Fig. 34B. If a string is touched at the center, a node is formed at that point and the vibration frequency, as shown by Eq.(34c), becomes double that of the fundamental. If the string is touched lightly at a point one-third the distance from the end, it will vibrate

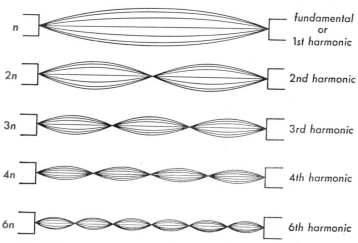

Fig. 34B *Vibration modes for strings of musical instruments.*

271

in three sections and have a frequency three times that of the fundamental.

In the elementary theory of string instruments, it is assumed that each string is thin, uniform, and highly flexible, and that it vibrates with small amplitude between unyielding supports. For such an ideal string, the above vibration modes have frequencies exactly equal to whole number multiples of the fundamental frequency n, and are called *harmonics*. To show how closely a real string meets these ideal conditions, the measured frequencies of a piano string whose fundamental frequency is 32.70 vib/sec are given in the following table.*

TABLE 34A. HARMONIC FREQUENCIES
OF A PIANO STRING

Mode Number	Meas. Freq.	Harmonic Freq.	Ratio
1	32.70	32.70	1.000
2	65.52	65.40	2.003
3	98.39	98.10	3.008
4	131.4	130.8	4.018
5	164.7	163.5	5.038
6	198.4	196.2	6.066
7	232.4	228.9	7.106
8	266.8	261.6	8.159

It is not difficult to set a string vibrating with its fundamental and several of its higher modes at the same time. This is accomplished by plucking or bowing the string vigorously. As an illustration a diagram of an ideal string vibrating with two normal modes at the same time is shown in Fig. 34C. As the string vibrates in two loops

Fig. 34C *String vibrating with its first and second harmonics simultaneously.*

with a frequency $2n$, it also moves up and down as a single loop with the fundamental frequency n.

* See R. W. Young, *American Journal of Physics,* Vol. 20, p. 177 (1952).

The sound wave sent out by such a vibrating string (see Fig. 35E(c)) is composed of two frequencies, the fundamental or first harmonic of frequency n, diagram (a); and the second harmonic or first partial with the frequency $2n$, diagram (b).

An interesting experiment with a vibrating string is diagramed in Fig. 34D. Light from an arc lamp is focused on the central section of a stretched steel string, which, except for a small vertical slot, is masked by a screen. An image of the slot and the string section seen through it is focused on a screen by a second lens, after reflection from a rotating mirror. As the string vibrates up and down, only a blurred image of the short section of string is seen, but when the mirror is rotated the wire section draws out a clearly visible curve W.

If the string is plucked gently near the center, a smooth wave form (a) is drawn out on the screen, but, if it is plucked hard near the end to produce a harsh sounding note, the wave form is more complex as shown in (b). In the first case, the string is vibrating only with its fundamental mode, while in the second case various overtones, or partials, are also present.

As a string vibrates with *transverse waves,* it strikes air molecules all around it, sending periodic impulses through the air as *longitudinal waves.*

34.3. The Theory of Vibrating Strings. A string set into vibration with nodes and loops is but an example of standing waves (see Fig. 31L). A disturbance produced at one end, as in the plucking or bowing of a string, sends a wave or train of waves along the string to be reflected back and forth from end to end. When traveling in one direction the wave is on top and, upon reflection, it flips to the under side. Because the wave is always on top when moving to the right, and on the bottom when moving to the left, a flipping up and down of the string results.

Since the fundamental frequency of vibration is equal to the number of times per sec that the wave arrives at the same end, the pitch will depend upon the velocity of

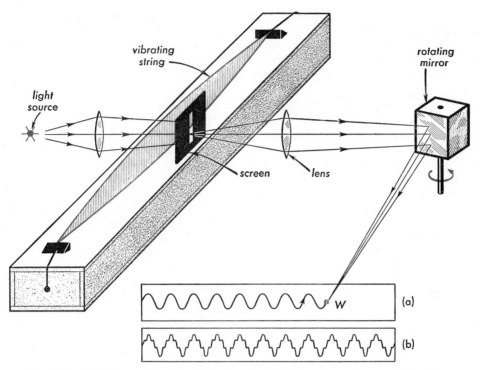

light
source

vibrating
string

rotating
mirror

screen   lens

W   (a)

(b)

Fig. 34D *Experiment for observing the detailed vibrations of a stretched string.*

the waves and the distance they have to travel.

The velocity of transverse waves along a rope or string under tension is given by

$$V = \sqrt{F/m} \qquad (34a)$$

where F is the tension and m is the mass per unit length of string. When standing waves are produced, the distance L between any two consecutive nodes is just equal to half a wavelength, $\frac{1}{2}\lambda$. Accordingly,

$$\lambda = 2L \qquad (34b)$$

To obtain an equation for the fundamental frequency of a vibrating string, the general wave equation $V = n\lambda$ (see Eq. (31g)) is used. If we transpose and then substitute the above values for V and λ, we obtain

$$n = \frac{1}{2L} \sqrt{F/m} \qquad (34c)$$

Accurate measurements with vibrating strings and musical instruments confirm this equation.

Example. A piano string that sounds three octaves below middle C is 110 cm long. Calculate the tension on the string when, in proper tune, its frequency is 33 vib/sec. Assume the mass of the string to be 160 gm.

Solution. The *mass per unit length* of string is $m = 160$ gm/110 cm $= 1.45$ gm/cm. Transpose $2L$ to the left side of Eq.(34), square both sides, and transpose m, so that the frequency equation becomes $F = 4n^2L^2m$. By direct substitution,

$$F = 4 \times (33)^2 \times (110)^2 \times 1.45$$
$$= 76,400,000 \text{ dynes}$$

Dividing by 980 changes dynes to gm-wt; and then dividing by 454 changes gm-wt to lb. The result is

$$F = 172 \text{ lb}$$

The vibration of a string brought about by bowing is associated with friction. Because starting friction is greater than sliding friction, the resinous bow periodically engages the string, pushing or pulling it to one side. During one-half the vibration the string clings to the bow and is carried along by it. When the tension becomes too great and exceeds starting friction, the string slips back to the opposite side of its vibration. There it stops and upon reversal in direction is grabbed again by the bow.

34.4. Wind Instruments. Musical instruments, often classified as "wind instruments," are usually divided into two subclasses, "wood winds" and "brasses." Under the heading of wood winds, we find such instruments as the *flute, piccolo, clarinet, bass clarinet, saxophone, bassoon,* and *contra bassoon;* and under the brasses such instruments as the *French horn, cornet,*

trumpet, tenor trombone, bass trombone, and *tuba* (or *bombardon*).

The fundamental principles involved in the vibration of an air column are demonstrated by means of an experiment shown in Fig. 34E. A vibrating tuning fork which acts as a source of sound waves is held over the open end of a long hollow tube containing water. Traveling down the tube with the velocity of sound in air, each train of sound waves is reflected from the water surface back toward the top. If the water is raised or lowered to the proper level, standing waves will be set up and the air column will resonate to the frequency of the tuning fork.

The first resonance occurs at N_1 when the water level is but a short distance from the top. The second resonance occurs at N_2, three times the distance of N_1 below the top, and the third N_3 at five times the distance, etc. The reason for these odd fractions is that only a *node* can form at the closed end of the pipe, i.e., at the water surface, and an *antinode* at the open end.

Standing waves in air are longitudinal in character, and they are difficult to represent in any drawing (see Fig. 31M). For convenience only, it is quite customary to indicate the positions of nodes and loops as if they were transverse standing waves (dotted lines in the diagram). If the frequency of the tuning fork used in the above experiment is known, the velocity of sound in air can be calculated. The distance between consecutive nodes is equal to $\lambda/2$, so that λ is equal to the length of two segments $N_3 - N_1$, $N_4 - N_2$, or $N_5 - N_3$, as shown in the diagram. In an actual experiment when the temperature is 27°C, and a tuning fork is sounding 512 vib/sec, the nodes are 13.37 in. apart. Substitution of these values in the general wave equation, Eq.(31g) gives

$$V = n\lambda = 512 \times 26.74 = 13690 \text{ in./sec}$$

Dividing by 12, we get $V = 1141$ ft/sec.

34.5. Vibrating Air Columns. The various modes in which air columns may vibrate in open or closed pipes are shown in Fig. 34F. Starting at the left, a pipe open at both ends may vibrate with (1) a single node

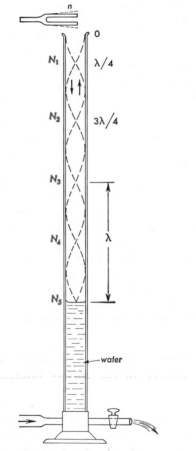

Fig. 34E   *Sound waves from tuning fork set up standing waves in an air column adjusted to proper length.*

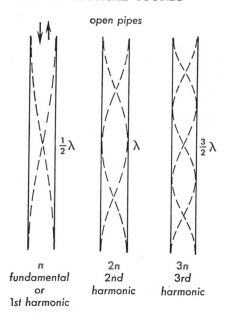

open pipes

$\frac{1}{2}\lambda$ λ $\frac{3}{2}\lambda$

n	2n	3n
fundamental	2nd	3rd
or	harmonic	harmonic
1st harmonic		

closed pipes

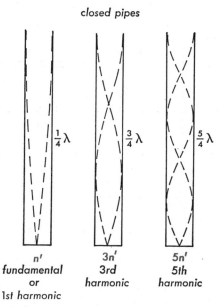

$\frac{1}{4}\lambda$ $\frac{3}{4}\lambda$ $\frac{5}{4}\lambda$

n'	3n'	5n'
fundamental	3rd	5th
or	harmonic	harmonic
1st harmonic		

Fig. 34F *Air columns in open and closed pipes have definite frequencies of vibration.*

at the middle and an antinode at both ends, (2) two nodes and three antinodes, or (3) with three nodes and four antinodes, etc. On the other hand, a pipe closed at one end and open at the other may vibrate with (1) one node and one antinode, (2) two nodes

and two antinodes, or (3) three nodes and three antinodes, etc. *In all vibrating air columns, an antinode always forms at an open end and a node at a closed end.*

The various possible frequencies to which a pipe may resonate are definite and fixed in value, and depend only upon the length of the pipe and the velocity of sound in air. If, for example, the pipes in Fig. 34F are all 2 ft long and the velocity of sound in air is 1120 ft/sec, $V = n\lambda$ shows that they will vibrate with the following respective frequencies:

n	2n	3n	n'	3n'	5n'
280	560	840	140	420	700

With an open pipe, the lowest possible vibration frequency is called the *fundamental;* the others, with whole numbered multiples of the fundamental frequency, $2n$, $3n$, $4n$, etc., are called *harmonics.* With closed pipes, the lowest frequency is again the fundamental and the others with odd integral multiples, $3n'$, $5n'$, $7n'$, etc., are harmonics. All these vibration modes are referred to as natural modes and their corresponding frequencies as natural frequencies. *The fundamental is also called the first harmonic.* It should be noted that with one end of a pipe closed, all even numbered harmonics cannot be sounded.

The existence of standing waves in a resonating air column may be demonstrated by a long hollow tube filled with illuminating gas as shown in Fig. 34G. Entering through an adjustable plunger at the left, the gas escapes through tiny holes spaced at regular intervals in a row along the top. Sound waves from an organ pipe enter the gas column by setting into vibration a thin paper sheet, stretched over the right-hand end. When resonance is attained by sliding the plunger to the correct position, the small gas flames will appear as shown. Where the nodes occur in the vibrating gas column, the air molecules are not moving (see Fig. 31M(b)); at these points the pressure is high and the flames are tallest. Halfway between are the antinodes—regions where the molecules vibrate back and forth with large amplitudes, and the flames

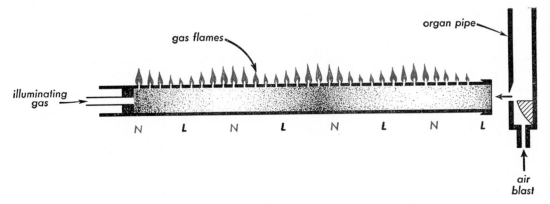

Fig. 34G   *Standing waves in a long tube containing illuminating gas.*

are low. Bernoulli's principle is chiefly responsible for the pressure differences (see Sec. 26.4), for, where the velocity of the molecules is high the pressure is low, and where the velocity is low the pressure is high.

In many of the wind instruments of the orchestra, the vibrating air columns are not entirely uniform and the far open end is considerably flared. Because of this non-uniformity, the nodes are not equally spaced nor are the possible frequencies exactly harmonics of the fundamental. As an example of how nearly the various normal modes come to being harmonics of a fundamental, the following measured frequencies of the *open notes* of a B♭ cornet are given in the table below: ($n = 116.7$ vib/sec).

Open notes are those for which all valves

are open and the entire air column is vibrating.

34.6. Theory of Vibrating Air Columns. The various notes produced by most wind instruments are brought about by varying the length of the vibrating air column. This is illustrated by the organ pipes in Fig. 34H.

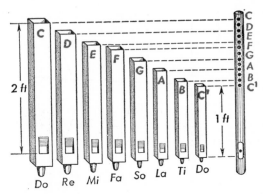

Fig. 34H   *Organ pipes arranged in a musical scale. The longer the pipe, the lower is its fundamental frequency and pitch. The vibrating air column of the flute is terminated at various points by openings along the tube.*

The longer the pipe, the lower the fundamental frequency or pitch of the note. In a regular concert organ, the pipes vary in length from about 6 in. for the highest note to almost 16 ft for the lowest. For the middle octave of the musical scale, the open-ended pipes vary from 2 ft for middle C to 1 ft for C^1, one octave higher. In the

TABLE 34B. HARMONIC FREQUENCIES
OF A B♭ CORNET

Mode Number	Meas. Freq.	Harmonic Freq.	Ratio
1	116.7	116.7	1.000
2	233.4	233.4	2.000
3	349.8	350.1	2.998
4	467.5	466.8	4.007
5	587.7	583.5	5.037
6	706.2	700.2	6.058
8	948.6	933.6	8.130

The seventh harmonic was not sounded.

wood winds, like the flute, the length of the column is varied by openings in the side of the instrument; and in many of the brasses, like the trumpet, by means of valves. A valve is a piston which, on being pressed down, throws in an additional length of tube.

Since a vibrating air column is a condition of standing waves, the frequency of vibration will depend upon two factors, the length of the pipe and the velocity of waves through it. The velocity of longitudinal waves in a gas is given by Newton's formula as modified by Laplace,

$$V = \sqrt{K \frac{p}{\rho}} \qquad (34d)$$

where K is a number representing the compressibility of a gas, p is the gas pressure in dynes/cm², and ρ its density in gm/cm³. For monatomic gases, $K = 1.67$; for diatomic gases, $K = 1.40$; and for triatomic gases, $K = 1.33$.

For all standing waves, the distance L between any two consecutive nodes, that is, the length of one segment, is just equal to half a wavelength, $\lambda/2$. Accordingly,

$$\lambda = 2L$$

By substituting this relation and the velocity above in the general wave equation, Eq.(31g), we get the general formula.

$$n = \frac{1}{2L} \sqrt{K \frac{p}{\rho}} \qquad (34e)$$

Measurements with resonating pipes confirm this relation.

The effect of the density of a gas on the pitch of a note may be demonstrated by a very interesting experiment with the human voice. Voice sounds originate in the vibrations of the vocal cords in the larynx (see Fig. 34I). This source of vibration, which determines the fundamental pitch of the speaking or singing voice, is controlled by muscular tension on the cords. The quality of the voice is determined by the size

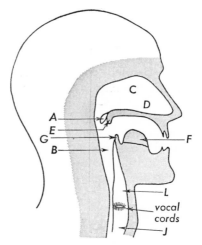

Fig. 34I *Cross-section diagram showing the vocal chords in the larynx. (A) Soft palate, (B) pharynx, (C) nasal cavity, (D) hard palate, (F) tongue, (G) epiglottis, and (J) windpipe.*

and shape of the throat, the mouth, and the nasal cavities.

If a gas lighter than air is breathed into the lungs, the above equation shows that the voice quality should change. The demonstration can be best and safely performed by exhaling completely, and then filling the lungs with helium gas (hydrogen is unsafe). Upon speaking, the experimenter will be observed to have a very peculiar high-pitched voice, which must be heard to be appreciated. The peculiarities arise from the fact that the fundamental pitch, due to the vocal-cord frequency, remains practically normal, while the harmonics from the resonating mouth, throat, and nasal cavities are raised by about $2\frac{1}{2}$ octaves.

34.7. Edge Tones. Although the pitch of the note sounded by any wind instrument is determined by the vibration of an air column according to principles of resonance, the method by which the air is set into vibration varies widely among instruments. In instruments like the saxophone, clarinet, oboe and bassoon, air is blown against a thin strip of wood called a reed, setting it into vibration. In most of the brasses the musician's lips are made to vibrate with certain required frequencies, while in certain wood winds, like the flute and piccolo and in organs and whistles, air is blown across the sharp edge of an opening near one end of the instrument, setting the air into vibration. A brief discussion of these source vibrations is therefore important here.

When wind or a blast of air encounters a small obstacle, little whirlwinds are formed in the air stream behind the obstacle. This is illustrated by the cross section of a flue organ pipe shown in Fig. 34J.

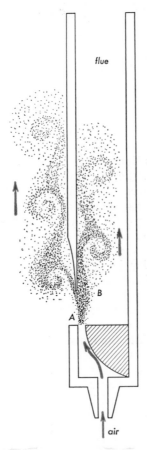

Fig. 34J   *A steady stream of air blown across the lip of an organ pipe sets up whirlwinds along both sides of the partition.*

Whether the obstacle is long, or a small round object, the whirlwinds are formed alternately on the two sides as shown (see Fig. 11H). The air stream at B waves back

and forth, sending a pulse of air first up one side and then the other. Although the wind blows through the opening A as a continuous stream, the separate whirlwinds going up each side of the obstacle become periodic shocks to the surrounding air. Coming at perfectly regular intervals, these pulses give rise to musical notes often described as "edge tones."

The number of whirlwinds formed per second, and therefore the pitch of the edge tone, increases with the wind velocity. When the wind howls through the trees, the pitch of the note rises and falls, its frequency at any time denoting the velocity of the wind. For a given wind velocity smaller objects give rise to higher-pitched notes than large objects. A fine stretched wire or rubber band, when placed in an open window or in the wind, will be set into vibration and will give out a musical note. Each whirlwind shock to the air reacts on the obstacle (the wire or rubber band), pushing it first to one side and then the other. These are the pushes that cause the rope of a flagpole to flap periodically in the breeze, while the waving of the flag at the top of a pole shows the whirlwinds that follow each other along each side.

The air column in an organ pipe, flute, or piccolo, has its own natural frequency of vibration which may or may not coincide with the frequency of an edge tone. If it does coincide, resonance will occur, the air column will vibrate with a large amplitude, and returning pulses of air down the tube with each vibration will force the air stream out at just the right moment, thus aiding in building up the natural frequency of the pipe. If the edge tone has a frequency different from the fundamental of the string, or air column, vibrations will be set up but not as intensely as before. If the frequency of the edge tone of an organ pipe, for example, comes close to double that of the fundamental, and this can be obtained by a stronger blast of air, the pipe will resonate to double its fundamental frequency and give out a strong note one octave higher.

By blowing more sharply against the opening in a piccolo or flute, the entire scale of notes can be raised one octave above normal playing range of the instrument. In all instruments like those mentioned above where air is blown across the sharp edge of an opening to make it sing, as in the organ pipe of Fig. 34J, an antinode is formed at that end. Whether an antinode or node forms at the other end depends upon whether it is open or closed, respectively.

the lower is its frequency of vibration and pitch.

The xylophone is a musical instrument based upon the *transverse vibrations* of wooden rods of different lengths. Mounted as shown for the marimba in Fig. 34K(b), the longer rods produce the low notes and the shorter ones the higher notes. The marimba is essentially a xylophone with a

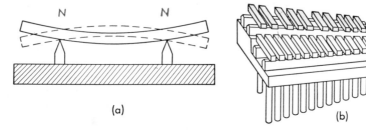

Fig. 34K   *The bars of the marimba or xylophone vibrate transversely with nodes near each end.*

34.8. Percussion Instruments. Vibrating Rods.

If a number of small sticks are dropped upon the floor, the sound that is heard is described as a noise. If one stick alone is dropped, one would also describe the sound as a noise, unless, of course, a set of sticks of varying lengths were arranged in order of length and each one dropped in its order. If this is done, one notices that each stick gives rise to a rather definite musical note and that the set of sticks could be cut to the proper length to form a musical scale. The use of vibrating rods in a musical instrument is found in the *xylophone,* the *marimba,* and the *triangle.* Standing waves in a rod, like those in a stretched string, may be any one of three different kinds—transverse, longitudinal, and torsional. Only the first two of these modes of vibration will be treated here.

Transverse waves in a rod are usually set up by supporting the rod at points near each end and striking it a blow at or near the center. As illustrated in Fig. 34K (a), the center and ends of the rod move up and down, forming nodes at the two supports. Like a stretched string of a musical instrument, the shorter the rod the higher is its pitch; and the longer and heavier the rod,

long straight hollow tube suspended vertically under each rod. Each tube is cut to such a length that the enclosed air column will resonate to the sound waves sent out by the rod directly above. Each resonator tube, being open at both ends, forms a node at its center.

The tuning fork depends for its pitch upon the transverse vibrations of a bar. Sounding its fundamental as shown in Fig. 34L, an antinode forms at both ends. Due

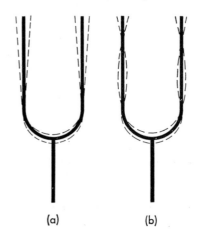

Fig. 34L   *Vibration nodes of a tuning fork show (a) fundamental and (b) first overtone.*

to the bend in the center, the two nodes are closer together than in a straight bar, and the antinode at the center transmits forceful vibrations of small amplitude through the shaft to any surface on which it is rested.

34.9. Vibrating Plates. Although the drum or the cymbals should hardly be called musical instruments, they are classified as such and are used in nearly all large orchestras and bands. The sound given out by a vibrating drumhead or cymbal plate is in general due to the high intensity of certain characteristic overtones. These overtones in turn are due to the very complicated modes of vibration of the source.

Cymbals consist of two thin metal disks with handles at the centers. Upon being struck together, their edges are set into vibration with a clang. A drumhead, on the other hand, is a stretched membrane of leather held tight at the periphery, and is set into vibration by being struck a blow at or near the center.

To illustrate the complexity of the vibrations of a circular plate, two typical sand patterns are shown in Fig. 34M. The sand

bow is drawn down over the edge at a point L. Nodes are formed at the stationary points N_1 and N_2, and antinodes in the regions of L_1 and L_2. The grains of sand bounce away from the loops and into the nodes, the regions of no motion. At one instant the regions marked with a ($+$) sign all move up, while the regions marked with a ($-$) sign all move down. Half a vibration later, the $+$ regions are moving down and the $-$ regions up. Such diagrams are called *Chladni's sand figures.*

With cymbal plates held tightly at the center by means of handles, a node is always formed there, and antinodes are always formed at the periphery. With a drumhead, on the other hand, the periphery is always a node and the center is sometimes, but not always, an antinode.

34.10. Bells. In some respects a bell is like a cymbal plate, for when it is struck a blow by the clapper, the rim in particular is set vibrating with nodes and loops distributed in a symmetrical pattern over the whole surface. The vibration of the rim is illustrated by a diagram in Fig. 34N (a) and

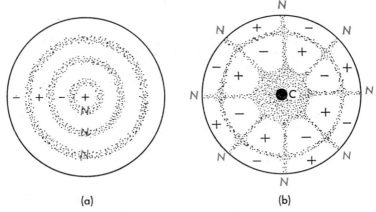

(a)   (b)

Fig. 34M *Chladni's sand figures showing the nodes and loops of (a) a vibrating drumhead (clamped at the edge), and (b) a vibrating cymbal plate (clamped at the center).*

pattern method of studying the motions of plates was invented in the eighteenth century by Chladni, a German physicist. A thin circular metal plate is clamped at the center C and sand is sprinkled over the top surface. Then, while touching the rim of the plate at two points N_1 and N_2, a cello

by an experiment in diagram (b). Small cork balls are suspended by threads around, and just touching, the outside rim of a large glass bowl. A violin bow drawn across the edge of the bowl will set the rim into vibration with nodes at some points and loops at others. The nodes are always even in

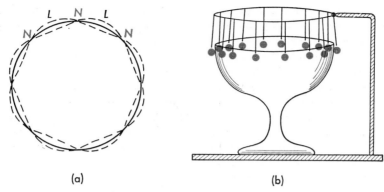

(a)   (b)

Fig. 34N   *Experiment illustrating how the rim of a bell or glass vibrates with nodes and loops.*

number just as they are in cymbal plates and drumheads, and alternate loops move in while the others move out.

Strictly speaking, a bell is not a very musical instrument. This is due to the very complex vibrations of the bell surface which give rise to so many loud overtones. Some of these overtones harmonize with the fundamental, while others do not.

PROBLEMS

1. Find the mass per unit length of a violin string 35 cm long if, under a tension of 500 newtons, it has a vibration frequency of 440 vib/sec.

2. Find the frequency of (a) the fundamental, and (b) the 7th harmonic of a 16-ft organ pipe, closed at one end and open at the other. Assume a temperature of 68°F. (*Ans.* (a) 17.6 vib/sec, (b) 123 vib/sec.)

3. A violin string 35 cm long has a mass of 0.05 gm/cm length. Find the tension in newtons if the frequency of vibration is 660 vib/sec.

4. A piano string 30 cm long has a frequency of 528 vib/sec, and a mass of 0.06 gm/cm length. Find the tension in newtons. (*Ans.* 602.)

5. An organ pipe 50 cm long, with both ends open, is used to produce the sound waves in the experiment shown in Fig. 34G. If the velocity of sound in air is 1100 ft/sec, and in the illuminating gas used is 1400 ft/sec, what is the distance between consecutive points where the flames are a maximum?

6. Calculate the velocity of sound in CO_2 if at 0°C and 76-cm Hg pressure the density is 1.98×10^{-3} gm/cm³. (*Ans.* 261 m/sec.)

7. A steel wire 1 m long has a total mass of 20 gm. If this wire is fastened at both ends and then put under a tension of 200 newtons, what is the theoretical frequency of its third harmonic?

8. A string 2 m long has a mass of 120 gm. Find the speed with which waves will travel along this string if it is put under a tension of 5 newtons. (*Ans.* 9.13 m/sec.)

9. An organ pipe filled with air at 0°C has a fundamental frequency of 220 vib/sec. What would be its fundamental frequency if the air were replaced by CO_2? The speed of sound in CO_2 is 261 m/sec.

10. A whistle has a fundamental frequency of 6000 vib/sec at a temperature of 0°C. If anti-nodes are formed at both ends, find the length of the air column. (*Ans.* 2.76 cm.)

11. What is the shortest length of pipe, open at both ends, that will resonate to a tuning fork of frequency 440 vib/sec? Assume a temperature of 68°F.

12. An organ pipe with one end closed has a fundamental frequency of 594 vib/sec when the temperature is 80°F. Find its frequency when the temperature drops to 40°F. (*Ans.* 571 vib/sec.)

13. Calculate the velocity of sound in nitrogen at normal atmospheric pressure and 0°C. Assume the density of N under these standard conditions is 1.25×10^{-3} gm/cm^3.

14. A tuning fork of frequency 256 vib/sec is used in the experiment shown in Fig. 34E. Find the distance between consecutive nodes if the temperature is 68°F. (*Ans.* 2.20 ft.)

15. Find the mass per unit length of a violin string 35 cm long if, under a tension of 500 newtons, it has a vibration frequency of 440 vib/sec.

16. A violin string 35 cm long has a mass of 0.066 gm/cm length. Find the tension in newtons if the frequency is 440 vib/sec. (*Ans.* 6.25 $\times$ 10^7 dynes.)

17. The lowest pitched note from a bugle has a frequency of 66 vib/sec. What are the frequencies of the lowest six notes it can produce?

18. Waves travel along a stretched steel wire at 50 m/sec. What is the tension in the wire if its mass is 0.08 gm/cm length? (*Ans.* 2×10^6 dynes.)

19. The E string of a violin has a fundamental frequency of 660 vib/sec. Find the wavelengths of the 5th and 10th harmonics if the speed of sound is 1120 ft/sec.

20. The longest organ pipe in a cathedral organ is 32 ft long. Find the frequency of the 5th and 10th harmonics if the speed of sound is 1140 ft/sec. (*Ans.* 89 vib/sec, 178/sec.)

21. A piece of water pipe 3 ft long is open at both ends. What is the frequency of the 20th harmonic of the enclosed air column if the speed of sound is 1160 ft/sec?

22. A harp string with a length of 30 in. is tuned to a frequency of 396 vib/sec. What is the wavelength of the 5th harmonic (a) on the string, and (b) in the air? Assume the speed of sound to be 1155 ft/sec. (*Ans.* (a) 12 in., (b) 7.0 in.)

Chapter 35

The Science of the Musical Scale

From the scientific point of view, the musical scale is based upon the relative frequencies of different sound waves. The frequencies of the various notes are so chosen that they produce the greatest amount of *harmony*. Two or more notes are said to be *harmonious* or *concordant* if they are pleasing to the ear. If they are not pleasant to hear, they are *discordant*.

The general form of the musical scale is illustrated by the *notes, letters, intervals,* and *scale ratios* given in Fig. 35A. The

dle *C* on the piano. In the history of modern music the standard of pitch has varied so widely and changed so frequently that no set pitch can universally be called standard.*

Most symphony orchestras today tune their instruments to a musical scale based upon a frequency of 440 vib/sec for the *A* string of a violin. Usually the first violinist tunes his *A* string to a standard pitch pipe or tuning fork of this frequency, and the other musicians tune their instruments to this violin.

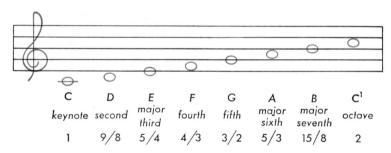

C	D	E	F	G	A	B	C¹
keynote	second	major third	fourth	fifth	major sixth	major seventh	octave
1	9/8	5/4	4/3	3/2	5/3	15/8	2

Fig. 35A *Diagram giving the names, and fractional ratios of the frequencies, of the different tone intervals on the diatonic musical scale.*

numbers indicate frequency ratios. Whatever frequency is selected for the keynote C, the frequency of the octave C¹ will be twice as great, the frequency of the fifth, G, will be three-halves as great, the fourth F will be four-thirds as great, etc. These fractions are important because they have the same values in all octaves of the musical scale.

The musical pitch of an orchestral scale is usually determined by specifying the frequency of the *A* string of the first violin, although sometimes it is given by the mid-

In some of our older science laboratories, a number of tuning forks may still be found with frequencies based upon middle *C* of the musical scale having a frequency of 256 vib/sec.

35.1. The Diatonic Scale. The diatonic musical scale, first introduced by Zarlino in

* For a brief historical discussion of normal standards of pitch, the student is referred to the book, *The Science of Musical Sounds,* by D. C. Miller. For other treatments of the science of music see *Sound,* by Capstick, *Science and Music,* by James Jeans, *Sound and Music,* by J. A. Zahn, and *Hearing,* by Stevens and Davis.

	major tone	minor tone	semitone	major tone	minor tone	major tone	semitone	major tone
scale notes	C	D	E	F	G	A	B	C¹
vocal notes	Do	Re	Mi	Fa	So	La	Ti	Do
ratio numbers	24	27	30	32	36	40	45	48
frequencies	264	297	330	352	396	440	495	528
scale ratios	1	9/8	5/4	4/3	3/2	5/3	15/8	2
tone ratios		8:9	9:10	15:16	8:9	9:10	8:9	15:16	8:9

Fig. 35B *The diatonic musical scale illustrated by the middle octave with C as the tonic and A = 440 as the standard pitch.*

1558, is based entirely on harmonious tone intervals. The middle octave of the scale is given in Fig. 35B assuming as a standard of pitch $A = 440$ vib/sec. The *frequencies* of all the notes are given in the fourth row. These numbers represent the actual frequencies of the vibrating source producing the note, as well as the frequencies of the waves that travel through the air and reach the ear.

Of equal importance are the *ratio numbers* in the third row. These are the smallest whole numbers that are proportional to both the *scale ratios* and to the actual *frequencies*. They are readily used to calculate the frequencies for all octaves of the scale. If the ratio numbers in row three are multiplied by 11 they give the actual frequencies in the fourth row. If these same ratio numbers are multiplied by 22, they will give the frequencies of the first octave above, while multiplied by 5.5 they will give the first octave below the middle.

The various octaves above the middle are labeled with numerical superscripts as shown here, while the octaves below the middle are designated by subscripts.

Each of the *tone ratios* given at the bottom of the table in Fig. 35B represents the ratio between the frequencies of two consecutive notes. The fraction representing the frequency ratio designates what is called an *interval*. Throughout the scale, it will be noted that between successive notes there are but three different intervals

—*major tones* with a frequency ratio 9/8, *minor tones* with a ratio 10/9, and *diatonic semitones* with a ratio of 16/15. The semitone, it will be noted, is a little larger than half of either a major or minor tone.

C_2	D_2	E_2	F_2	G_2	A_2	B_2
66	74.2	82.5	88	99	110	123.8
C_1	D_1	E_1	F_1	G_1	A_1	B_1
132	148.5	165	176	198	220	247.5
C	**D**	**E**	**F**	**G**	**A**	**B**
264	**297**	**330**	**352**	**396**	**440**	**495**
C^1	D^1	E^1	F^1	G^1	A^1	B^1
528	594	660	704	792	880	990
C^2	D^2	E^2	F^2	G^2	A^2	B^2
1056	1188	1320	1408	1584	1760	1980
C^3	D^3	E^3	F^3	G^3	A^3	B^3
2112	2376	2640	2816	3168	3520	3960

A better understanding and appreciation of the diatonic scale is to be had by a study of other intervals and their frequency ratios. Of interest to every composer of music are the following intervals:

Perfect Consonances	octave	1:2	C C¹
	fifth	2:3	C G
	fourth	3:4	C F

Imperfect Consonances	major third	4:5	C E
	minor third	5:6	E G
	major sixth	3:5	C A
	minor sixth	5:8	E C¹

Dissonant Intervals
$\begin{cases} \text{second} & 8:9 & C\ D \\ \text{major seventh} & 8:15 & C\ B \\ \text{minor seventh} & 9:16 & D\ C^1 \end{cases}$

A study of these tone intervals clearly indicates that harmony* is associated with the simplicity of the ratios between frequencies. The smaller the whole numbers expressing the ratio of any two notes, the more *harmonious* or *consonant* is the musical effect. The larger the whole numbers, the more *discordant*, or *dissonant*, is the effect.

According to this notion the *octave,* with a frequency ratio 2:1, is the most harmonious of all intervals. This becomes evident when it is recalled how natural it is for male and female voices to sing one octave apart. A bass or baritone voice, in accompanying a melody sung by a soprano voice, will naturally sing one octave lower.

The next perfect consonant, the *fifth,* has a frequency ratio of 3:2. Musicians call the fifth note above the keynote the *dominant,* and the fifth note below, the *sub-dominant.* When C is the keynote, G is the dominant and F_1 is the sub-dominant. Next in the order of consonance comes the perfect *fourth* as a musical interval with its frequency ratio of 4:3.

In the *diatonic scale* of Fig. 35B it will be seen that a fifth (like CG) added to a fourth like GC^1) is one octave. To add two tone intervals, their frequency ratios are multiplied. For example, a fifth plus a fourth is written $3/2 \times 4/3 = 2$, or 2:1, an exact octave. Similarly, a fourth (like CF) subtracted from a fifth (like CG) always gives a major tone. To subtract one interval from another, the frequency ratios are divided. For example, a fifth minus a fourth is written $3/2 \div 4/3 = 9/8$, an exact major tone.

---

* The essential difference between *melody* and *harmony* is quite generally recognized by everyone. Melody consists of a succession of notes and conveys the idea of motion that should go on and on, while harmony consists of the simultaneous and often sustained sounding of several notes like a chord, followed by other similar combinations of notes. The latter seems to stand still, each chord of notes being more or less complete in itself.

35.2. Chords. The simultaneous sounding of two or more notes, each of which forms a *concordant* interval with the others, constitutes a chord. An added restriction is that the highest and lowest notes be not more than one octave apart. Two notes sounded together constitute a *dyad,* three notes a *triad,* and four notes a *tetrad.* The *octave, fifth,* and *fourth,* considered in detail in the previous section, are examples of *harmonious dyads.*

Musicians generally agree that there are six harmonious triads, which are listed as follows:

Harmonic Triads or Chords

1. Major third followed by minor third
2. Fourth   followed by major third
3. Minor third followed by major third
4. Minor third followed by fourth
5. Major third followed by fourth
6. Fourth   followed by minor third

Frequency Ratio Example

1. 4:5:6 $C\ E\ G$
2. 3:4:5 $C\ F\ A$
3. 5:6, 4:5 $E\ G\ B$
4. 5:6, 3:4 $E\ G\ C^1$
5. 4:5, 3:4 $C\ E\ A$
6. 3:4, 5:6 $E\ A\ C^1$

The first chord in the tabulation above is generally called a perfect major chord, and the second a perfect minor chord. It is quite common practice to add the octave to each of these triads to form the tetrads $CEGC^1$ and $CFAC^1$.

35.3. The Chromatic Scale. Contrary to the belief of many, the sharp of one note and the flat of the next higher major or minor tone are not of the same pitch. The reason for this false impression is that on the piano the black keys represent a compromise. The piano is not tuned to the diatonic scale but to an *equal tempered scale*. Experiments with eminent musicians, and particularly violinists, have shown that they play in what is called *pure intonation,* that is, to a *chromatic scale* and not according to *equal temperament,* as will be described in the next section.

On the chromatic scale of the musician, the ratio between the frequency of one note and the frequency of its sharp or flat is 25:24. This interval, the smallest usually

scale. Each octave is divided into 12 equal ratio intervals as illustrated in Fig. 35C. The *whole tone* and *half tone* intervals shown represent the white keys of the

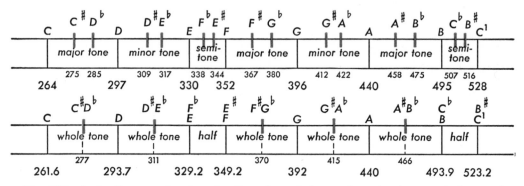

Fig. 35C *Scale diagrams showing the diatonic and chromatic scale above and the equal tempered scale below.*

used in music, is just the difference between a diatonic semi-tone and a minor tone, i.e., $15/16 \div 9/10 = 25/24$. The actual frequencies of the various sharps and flats for the middle octave of the chromatic scale, based upon $A = 440$, are shown in Fig. 35C. C♯, for example, has a frequency of 275, whereas D♭ is 285. This is a difference of 10 vib/sec, an interval easily recognized at this pitch by almost everyone.

35.4. The Equal Tempered Scale. The white keys of the piano are not tuned to the exact frequency ratios of the diatonic scale; they are tuned to an *equal tempered*

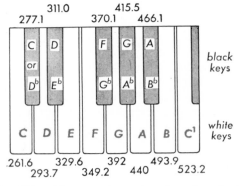

Fig. 35D *The equal tempered scale of the piano illustrating the frequencies of the middle octave based upon A = 440 as the standard pitch.*

piano, as indicated in Fig. 35D, and the sharps and flats represent the black keys. Including the black keys, all 12 tone intervals in every octave are exactly the same. The frequency of any note in the equal tempered scale turns out to be 6% higher than the one preceding it. More accurately, the frequency of any one note multiplied by 1.05946 gives the frequency of the note $\frac{1}{2}$ tone higher. For example, $A = 440$ multiplied by 1.05946 gives A♯ or B♭ as 466.1 vib/sec. Similarly, 466.1×1.05946 gives 493.9.

The reason for tuning the piano to an equal tempered scale is to enable the pianist to play in any key and yet stay within a given pitch range. In so doing, any given composition can be played within the range of a given person's voice. In other words, any single note can be taken as the tonic or keynote of the musical scale.

Although the notes of the piano are not quite as harmonious as if they were tuned to a diatonic scale, they are not far out of tune. This can be seen by a comparison of the actual frequencies of the notes of the two scales in Fig. 35C.

35.5. Quality of Musical Notes. Although two musical notes have the same pitch and intensity, they may differ widely in tone quality. Tone quality is determined by the number and intensity of the harmonics present. This is illustrated by a detailed examination of either the vibrating source or of the sound waves emerging from the source. There are numerous experimental methods by which this is accomplished.

A relatively convenient and simple demonstration is given in Fig. 34D where the vibrating source of sound is a stretched piano string. If the string is made to vibrate with its fundamental alone, its own motion or that of the emitted sound waves have the form shown in diagram (a) of Fig.

G^1, C^2, E^2, G^2, X, and C^3. All of these except X, the seventh harmonic, belong to some harmonic triad. This very overtone is discordant and should be suppressed. In a piano this is accomplished by striking the string $\frac{1}{7}$ of its length from one end, thus preventing a node at that point.

The different wave forms in Fig. 35F represent the sound vibrations coming from different musical instruments all playing the note $A = 400$ vib/sec. Observe that each wave form is repeated three times in the same time interval but that the overtones,

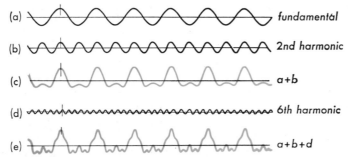

Fig. 35E *Sound wave vibrations from a string vibrating with its fundamental and the second and sixth harmonics.*

35E. If it vibrates in two segments or six segments (see Fig. 34B), the wave forms will be like those in diagram (b) and (d) respectively of Fig. 35E. Should the string be set vibrating with its fundamental and second harmonic simultaneously, Fig. 34C, the wave form will appear something like diagram (c) in Fig. 35E. If, in addition to the fundamental, a string vibrates with the second and sixth harmonics, the wave will look like diagram (e). This is like diagram (c) with the sixth harmonic added to it.

It is difficult to make a string vibrate with its fundamental alone. As a rule there are many harmonics present. Some of these harmonics harmonize with the fundamental and some do not. Those that harmonize are called *concordant overtones,* and those that do not are called *discordant overtones.* If middle $C = 264$ is sounded with its next seven harmonics, they will have 2, 3, 4, 5, 6, 7, and 8 times 264 vib/sec. These on the diatonic scale will correspond to notes C^1,

the small "wiggles" in the curves are different in every case.

When complicated sound vibrations enter the ear, they are analyzed into their component frequencies. One set of nerve endings responds to the fundamental frequency while other sets respond to the various overtones. The fundamental frequency generally has most of the energy and therefore the greatest amplitude, while the overtones with their higher frequencies have relatively small amplitudes.

An excellent experiment for demonstrating the wave forms of musical sounds is diagramed in Fig. 35G. A small mirror M is connected to the voice coil V of a radio loud-speaker by three small aluminum wires L. As the voice coil vibrates, moving the paper cone C back and forth to produce sound, the tiny mirror M tips back and forth around the pivot P. As the voice coil and cone move out to the right the mirror tips forward, and when the voice coil and

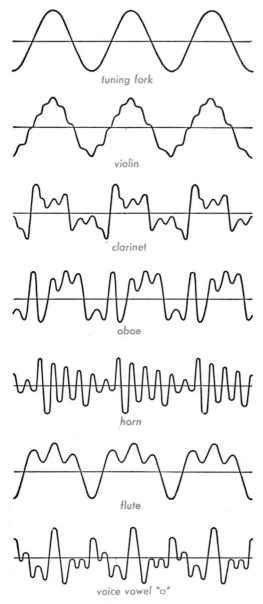

tuning fork

violin

clarinet

oboe

horn

flute

voice vowel "a"

Fig. 35F   *Wave forms of sounds from different musical instruments playing the same note.*

tracing out the vibrations as shown. Each of the four mirrors on R sweeps out a wave across the screen. If the sound is a sustained note, the successive wave forms are alike and may be made to overlap, whereas if the notes are continually changing, each wave form is different. Persistence of vision enables the observer to see a long wave instead of a moving point. (With distances of several feet between mirrors and screen, wave amplitudes of at least 1 ft are readily obtained on a large screen or on the walls of a room.)

35.6. The Ranges of Musical Instruments. A chart showing the ranges of various musical instruments and singing voices is given in Fig. 35H. The male speaking voice has an average fundamental frequency of about 150 vib/sec with a singing range of about six notes up and six down, whereas the average female voice has a frequency of about 230 vib/sec with approximately the same singing range. The *quality*, or *timbre*, depends almost entirely on two sets of overtones. Good-quality singing voices emphasize two sets of overtones or partials, one around 500 cycles and the other around 2400 to 3200 cycles. The lower frequency seems to be the natural frequency of the *pharynx* (see Fig. 34I) and the higher frequencies to other throat, mouth, and nasal cavities.

35.7. Aural Harmonics. Research experiments show that, when a pure note of one frequency is sounded with medium intensity, one and only one region of nerve endings in the basilar membrane is stimulated to audibility. As the intensity is continuously raised, however, successive *harmonics* appear at successively higher levels, thereby stimulating other nerve endings at regular intervals along the basilar membrane. (See Fig. 35I.)

The origin of these harmonics, with their frequencies of 2, 3, 4, etc., times the frequency of the source, is attributed largely to what is called the *nonlinear* response of the middle and inner ear to large amplitudes.* Although each harmonic is from

cone move to the left, the mirror tips back.

Light from an arc lamp and lens is reflected as a narrow beam from the vibrating mirror M to a rotating mirror R and then to a screen as shown. The beam from M to R moves up and down with the exact motion of mirror M, and the rotation of R sweeps the beam across the screen, thus

* See Stevens, S. S., and Davis, H., *Hearing: Its Psychology and Physiology,* Chap. 7, Wiley, New York, 1938.

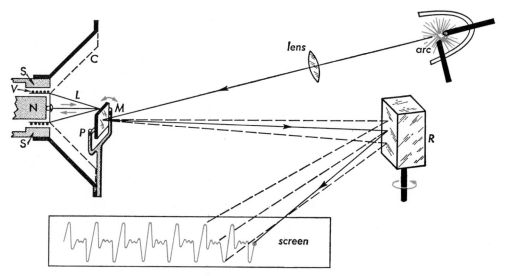

Fig. 35G *Radio loud-speaker attachment and apparatus for observing the wave forms of musical sounds.*

10 to 30 db lower in intensity than its predecessor, its apparent loudness may be relatively high, particularly if it comes in a frequency range of high aural sensitivity. (See Fig. 32K.)

35.8. Aural Combination Tones. When two pure tones are sounded simultaneously, the basilar membrane may respond not only to the two frequencies and their respective harmonics but to their *sum-* and *difference tones* as well. For example, if U and L represent the frequencies of the upper and lower notes, respectively, *summation tones* with frequencies given by $pU + qL$ and *difference tones* given by $pU - qL$ can be heard. Here p and q are whole numbers and pU and qL correspond to the harmonics of U and L.

$$N = pU \pm qL \qquad (35a)$$

On the average, the relative loudness of combination tones as well as harmonics is given by the order number, $N = p + q - 1$. The smaller the value of N, the louder the tone.

35.9. A Physical Basis for Harmony. It would appear from present knowledge that harmony, as sung by vocalists and played by musicians, may be traced directly to the regularity of the stimulus pattern set up on the basilar membrane. In general it can be said that *the more nearly the ratios of the primary frequencies sounded are to small whole numbers the more consonant is the interval, the more harmonious is the combination, and the more regular is the stimulated pattern on the basilar membrane.*

As an illustration, consider the sounding of two pure tones $C = 264$ vib/sec and $G = 396$ vib/sec. Together, this harmonious dyad, with a frequency ratio 2:3, constitutes a *perfect fifth.* Sounded separately or together, the wave forms reaching the ear are similar to those shown in Fig. 35J. As heard by the ear, however, there will in general be the two fundamentals as well as their harmonics and combination tones, given by

Harmonics, $U, 2U, 3U, 4U, \ldots, L,$
$\qquad\qquad 2L, 3L, 4L, \ldots$
Summation tones, $U + L, 2U + L, 3U + L,$
$\qquad U + 2L, U + 3L, 2U + 2L, \ldots,$
Difference tones, $U - L, 2U - L, 3U - L,$
$\qquad U - 2L, U - 3L, 2U - 2L, \ldots,$

The stimulated nerve endings in the ear present a regularly spaced pattern like that shown in diagrams (a), (b), and (c) in Fig. 35K. When a discordant dyad like $C = 264$ and $D = 297$ is sounded, no such regular pattern as this is established,

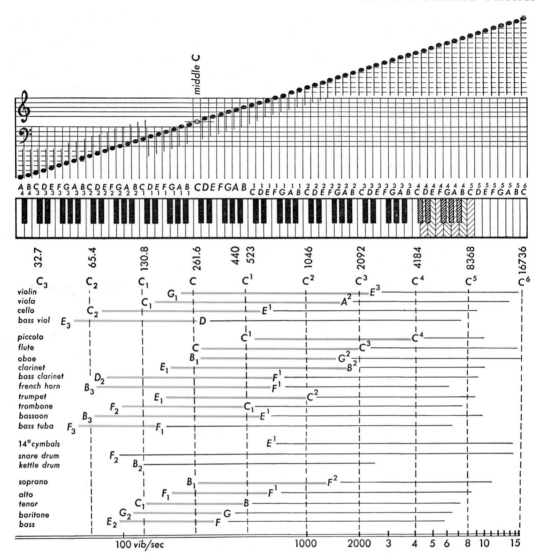

Fig. 35H   *Chart showing the frequency range of various musical instruments.*

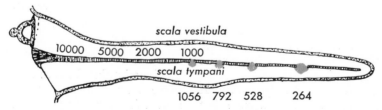

Fig. 35I   *Cross section of the cochlea of the ear, showing the nerve centers stimulated by the sounding of a loud pure tone C = 264 vib/sec.*

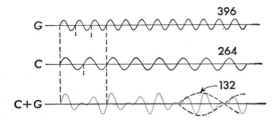

Fig. 35J *Sound wave vibrations for the musi-cal notes of a perfect fifth. Two notes are sounded, but quite a number may be heard.*

What has just been said of an harmonic dyad like the perfect fifth can also be said of a chord. If, for example, $E = 330$ vib/sec is added to the C and G discussed above to form a perfect major chord CEG, some of

the many combination-tones produced strengthen those already set up by C and G (diagram c), while the rest stimulate new regions halfway between them. Thus a regular stimulation pattern is produced as shown in diagram (d) with a spacing of 66 vib/sec. Similarly, when a *perfect fourth* like C and F are sounded, and then A is added to make the *perfect minor chord* CFA, the regular two-note pattern with an 88 vib/sec spacing retains the same spacing when A is added, but the combination tones already there are strengthened and add richness to the sound. Adding the octave $C = 528$ vib/sec to either of these chords to form tetrads goes to further strengthen many combination tones already present.

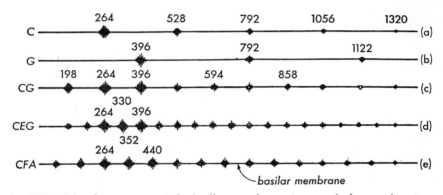

Fig. 35K *Stimulus patterns of the basilar membrane for certain harmonious tones.*

PROBLEMS

1. Calculate the frequencies of the second, third, and fourth octaves above the middle octave of the diatonic musical scale based on $A = 480$ vib/sec.

2. Calculate the frequencies of the middle octave of the diatonic musical scale based upon $A = 420$ vib/sec. (*Ans.* 252, 283.5, 315, 336, 378, 420, 472.5, 504.)

3. Calculate the frequencies of $D_1\sharp$ and $D_1\flat$ based upon the diatonic musical scale with $A = 440$ vib/sec.

4. Calculate the frequencies of $A\flat$ and $G\sharp$ based upon the diatonic musical scale with $A = 450$ vib/sec. (*Ans.* 432, 422 vib/sec.)

5. Make a list of the first eight harmonics of the fundamental 396 vib/sec. Where possible,

denote the scale note to which each harmonic corresponds in the diatonic scale based on $A = 440$.

6. Solve Prob. 5 for fundamental frequency of 330 vib/sec. (*Ans. E, E[1], B[1], E[2], X, B[2], X, E[3].*)

7. Two pure tones are sounded separately and then together, $E = 330$, and $B = 495$. Make separate lists of the following: (a) the first three aural harmonics of E, (b) the first three aural harmonics of B, (c) the summation tones for (a) and (b) together, and (d) the difference tones for (a) and (b) together.

8. Find answers to parts (a), (b), (c), and (d) of Prob. 7, if the two notes sounded are $A = 440$ vib/sec, and $E = 330$ vib/sec. (*Ans.* (a) 440, 880, 1320. (b) 330, 660, 990. (c) 770, 1100, 1210,

1430, 1540, 1650, 1870, 1980, 2310. (d) 110, 220, 330, 550, 660, 990.)

9. Calculate the frequencies of the notes forming the middle octave of an equal tempered scale based upon $A = 460$ vib/sec.

10. What three notes on the diatonic scale form an harmonic triad with G as the lower frequency, if the two intervals consist of a major third followed by a minor third? (*Ans. G B D¹.*)

11. What three notes on the diatonic scale form an harmonic triad with G as the lower frequency if the two intervals consist of a fourth followed by a major third?

12. (a) Find the frequencies and the beat frequencies for the tetrad C E G $C¹$. (b) What are the smallest ratio numbers for all these frequencies? (*Ans.* 66, 132, 198, 264, 330, 396, 528. Ratios 1:2:3:4:5:6:8.)

13. The three notes of a chord are C, F, and A. (a) Taking these notes in pairs, what beat frequencies are produced? (b) Since the ear can hear both the notes and their beat notes, make a list of all frequencies heard when this triad is sounded. (c) What are the smallest whole numbers that give the ratios of all these frequencies?

14. Calculate the frequencies of the middle octave of a diatonic scale based upon middle C with a frequency of 276 vib/sec. (*Ans.* 276, 310.5, 345, 386, 414, 517.5, 552.)

15. What are the frequencies of the triad C, E, G, based upon $A = 480$ vib/sec?

16. Find the frequencies of the triad E, G, B, based upon the keynote $C = 312$ vib/sec. (*Ans.* 390, 468, 585 vib/sec.)

Chapter 36

Properties of Light

Light and its various phenomena present some of the most interesting studies in the whole realm of physics. They are interesting because the results of many experiments are revealed through the sense of vision as color phenomena. Equally important and every bit as interesting is the historical development and discovery of the various principles, concepts, and properties of light which give rise to these phenomena.

All of the various known properties of light are conveniently described in terms of the experiments by which they were discovered and the many and varied experiments by which they are now continually demonstrated. Numerous as they are, these experiments may be grouped together and classified under one of the three following heads: (1) *geometrical optics,* (2) *physical optics,* and (3) *quantum optics.* Each of these may be subdivided as follows:

> *Geometrical Optics*
> rectilinear propagation=st. lines
> finite velocity
> reflection
> refraction
>
> *Physical Optics*
> diffraction
> interference
> polarization
> double refraction
>
> *Quantum Optics*
> photoelectric effect
> Compton effect
> atomic excitation
> pair production

The first group, geometrical optics, treated in this chapter and the following chapter, deals with those optical phenomena that are most easily described with straight lines and plane geometry. The second group, physical optics, dealing with the wave nature of light, is treated in Chaps. 43, 44, and 45, whereas the third group, dealing with the quantum aspects of light, is treated in Chaps. 68, 69, 70, and 71.

36.1 The Rectilinear Propagation of Light. The rectilinear propagation of light is another way of saying that "light travels in straight lines." The fact that objects may be made to cast fairly sharp shadows is an experimental demonstration of this principle. Another illustration is the image formation of an object produced by light passing through a small opening, as diagramed in Fig. 36A. In this figure, the object is an ordinary incandescent light bulb. In order to see how an image is formed, consider the rays of light emanating from a single point *a* near the top of the bulb. Of the many rays of light radiating in all directions, the ray that travels in the direction of the hole passes through to the point *a'* near the bottom of the image screen. Similarly, a ray leaving *b* near the bottom of the bulb and passing through the hole will arrive at *b'* near the top of the image screen. Thus it may be seen that an inverted image is formed.

If the image screen is moved closer to the pinhole screen, the image will be proportionately smaller, whereas if it is moved farther away the image will be proportionately larger. The same thing happens when either the object or the pinhole is moved. Excellent photographs can be made with this arrangement by making a pinhole in one end of a small box and placing a photographic film or plate at the other. Such an

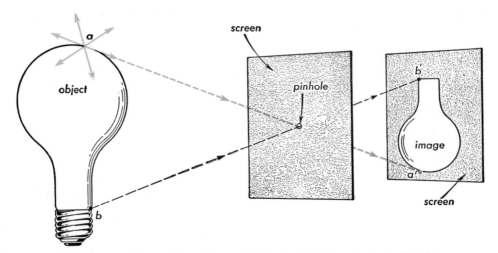

Fig. 36A   *An illustration of the principle that light travels in straight lines.*

arrangement is called a pinhole camera. For good, sharp photographs the hole must be very small, because its size determines the amount of blurring produced. The photograph shown in Fig. 36B was taken with such a camera. Note the undistorted perspective lines of the building.

Fig. 36B   *Photograph taken with a pinhole camera.*

36.2. Candlepower. Candlepower (*abbr.* cp) refers to the *luminous intensity* of any light source; it is a term commonly employed to specify the total light output of a lamp. The *standard candle,* or *international candle,* as it is frequently called, is the luminous intensity of the flame of a certain make of candle, the constituents of which were at one time specified by international agreement. Many years ago, this form of standard was found to be unsatisfactory and it has since been replaced by the light emitted by an incandescent platinum metal surface. Platinum metal, at its freezing temperature of 2033°K, has a luminance of 60 candles/cm² of projected area.

Ordinary tungsten filament light bulbs used in general house lighting give a little more than one candlepower per watt of electrical power used. A 60-watt lamp, for example, has a luminous intensity I of about 66 cp and a 100-watt lamp a luminous intensity of about 127 cp, etc. (see Table 36A). Luminescent tubes, on the other hand, have considerably higher efficiency and yield about 4 cp/watt. The construction and electrical operation of all kinds of light sources are treated in detail in Chap. 59.

36.3. The Inverse Square Law. One direct consequence of the rectilinear propagation of light is the inverse square law. This law applies to the illumination of a surface due to the luminous intensity of a point source of light. While no source of light is actually confined to a point, many are so small in comparison with the distances to illuminated areas that they may be regarded as point sources.

The illumination of a surface, called *il-*

TABLE 36A. EFFICIENCY OF GAS-FILLED
TUNGSTEN FILAMENT LIGHT BULBS

Input (watts)	Output (c. p.)	Output (lumens)	Efficiency (lumens/watt)
25	20.7	260	10.4
50	55.0	695	13.9
100	125	1580	15.8
200	290	3640	18.2
500	800	10,050	20.1
1000	1640	20,700	20.7

luminance, is defined as the amount of light falling on a unit area. If a screen is placed one foot from a point source of one candle-power, the illuminance will be one foot-candle (*abbr.* ft-c). One foot from a 50-candle-power source, the illuminance will be 50 ft-candles, etc.

When the top surface of a table is illuminated by a single light directly above it and then the light raised to twice the height, the illuminance on the surface will only be $\frac{1}{4}$ as great. If it is raised to three times the first height the illuminance will only be $\frac{1}{9}$ as great, etc. In other words, *illuminance is proportional to the luminous intensity of the light source and is inversely proportional to the square of the distance.* This, the inverse square law, is illustrated in Fig. 36C by the three shaded patches of equal

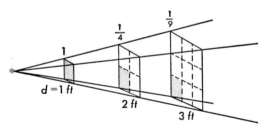

Fig. 36C   *Illustration of the inverse square law.*

area. If the letter I represents the luminous intensity of a light source in candles and d the distance to the illuminated surface in feet, the illuminance E in foot-candles will be given by

$$E = \frac{I}{d^2} \qquad (36a)$$

To illustrate this equation, consider the following example.

Example 1. The illuminance on the road directly under a street light suspended 25 ft above the ground is 1.2 ft-c. Calculate the candle power of the lamp.

Solution. Transposing Eq.(36a) and substituting the known values, $E = 1.2$ ft-c, and $d = 25$ ft, we find that

$$I = Ed^2 = 1.2 \times (25)^2 = 750 \text{ cp}$$

36.4. Foot-Candle Meter. Many different kinds of direct reading instruments for measuring the illuminance on a surface have been devised and manufactured. Most of these employ a *photoelectric cell* of one kind or another, and are classified as *illuminometers.* One such instrument using a special kind of photoelectric cell that requires no batteries is shown in Fig. 36D.

Fig. 36D   *Weston type of foot-candle meter. (Courtesy, Weston Instruments Co.)*

Light falling on the photocell in the upper half of the instrument gives rise to an electric current, which in turn activates a highly sensitive ammeter and pointer shown in the lower half. If the scale under the pointer is calibrated in foot-candles as in the photograph, the instrument is called a *foot-candle meter,* but if it is calibrated with an arbitrary number scale it may be labeled an *exposure meter* of the kind used by photographers. The useful range of such instruments can be greatly extended by placing a screen with holes of a known size over the sensitive photocell area.

When using a foot-candle meter to measure the illuminance on a desk top, the face of the photocell should be placed parallel to the surface. If it is turned at an angle, the amount of light intercepted by the sensitive area may be quite different. The change in illuminance produced by a change in the direction of the incident light is shown diagrammatically in Fig. 36E. A

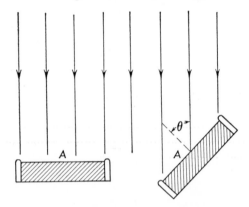

Fig. 36E *Illumination is usually measured normal to the incident light rays.*

maximum amount of light is intercepted by a given plane area A when it is perpendicular to the incident light rays, as shown at the left. When it is turned at an angle θ, the effective area is smaller and given by $A \cos \theta$. If, therefore, the inverse square law, as given in Eq.(36a), is to be applied to general problems, the factor $\cos \theta$ should be included.

$$E = \frac{I}{d'^2} \cos \theta \qquad (36b)$$

Example 2. The top of a drafting table, inclined at an angle of 30° with the horizontal, is illuminated by a single 250-cp lamp suspended 4 ft directly above the center. Calculate the illuminance on the table top directly beneath the lamp.

Solution. The given quantities in this problem are $I = 250$ cp. $d = 4$ ft, and $\theta = 30°$. By direct substitution in Eq.(36b), we obtain

$$E = \frac{250}{16} 0.866 = 13.5 \text{ ft-c}$$

36.5. The Law of Reflection. Experiment shows that, whenever a ray of light is reflected from a plane surface, the nature of the reflected light can be described in terms of a number of simple and well-defined laws. The simplest of these is the one known as the law of reflection. According to this law, the angle at which a ray of light strikes the reflecting surface is exactly equal to the angle the reflected ray makes with the same surface. Instead of measuring the angle of incidence and the angle of reflection from the mirror surface, however, it is customary to measure both from a line perpendicular to the plane of the mirror. This line as shown in Fig. 36F is called the *normal*.

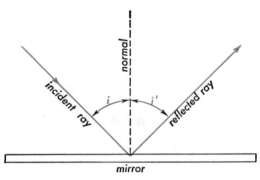

Fig. 36F *Diagram illustrating the law of reflection from a plane surface.*

As the angle i increases, the angle i' increases by exactly the same amount so that, for all angles of incidence,

$$\text{angle } i = \text{angle } i' \qquad (36c)$$

A second part of this law stipulates that the reflected ray lies in the plane of incidence, the plane of incidence being defined as the plane containing the incident ray and the normal. In other words, *the incident ray, the normal, and the reflected ray all lie in the same plane.*

In speaking of a mirror surface, one does not necessarily mean a silvered plate of glass; a mirror is any surface smooth enough to produce regular reflection as it has just been described.

36.6. Image in a Plane Mirror. The image of one's self seen in a mirror is formed by rays of light traveling in straight lines which are reflected according to the law of reflection. All objects seen in a plane mirror are images formed by reflection. This can be demonstrated by the experiment shown in Fig. 36G. A lighted candle O is placed on the table near a plate of glass MN. With the candle itself hidden in the box H, the observer at E sees only the reflected image at I. If a glass of water is placed at B, this image appears as a real candle burning under water.

As shown in the top view, all rays of light leaving the source O are reflected according to the law of reflection. To an observer anywhere between L and R on the right side of the mirror, all light appears to come from the same point I. This image point is just as far behind the mirror as the object O is in front of it, and the two lie on the same perpendicular to the mirror.

The image one sees in a plane mirror is not a real image but a virtual image. A virtual image is one from which rays seem to radiate but actually do not. In the figure

the rays do not come from I', they come from O and by reflection reach the observer.

This experiment illustrates a trick commonly used to make ghostlike figures appear to move about a room or stage. Light from real persons or objects, located below or above the stage, is reflected from a large sheet of plate glass at the front of the stage. With proper drapes and a darkened room, the illusion is very effective.

If one looks at his own face in a plane mirror, the image observed is technically described as *perverted*. The image is the same as though the face were reproduced as a rubber mask and the mask turned inside out and viewed from the new front. The right ear of the subject becomes the left ear of the image, and vice versa.

To see one's face as others see it, two front silvered mirrors should be placed 90° apart and touching each other along one edge as shown in Fig. 36H. The observer's right ear will then be seen, because of two reflections, as the right ear of his image, etc. This experiment must be performed to be

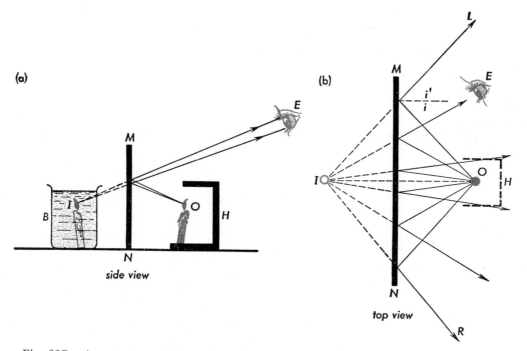

Fig. 36G *An experiment illustrating reflection from a mirror or plate of glass. Light from the candle flame at O appears to come from I.*

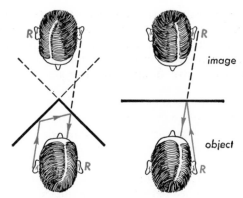

Fig. 36H *One's own image seen in 90° mirrors is normal; that seen in a plane mirror is perverted.*

appreciated, since many people's faces are, unknowingly, slightly unsymmetrical. Seen in 90° mirrors, all such irregularities are reversed; they therefore appear double in magnitude and are very noticeable.

36.7. Galileo's Experiment on the Velocity of Light. History tells us that Galileo once tried to measure the velocity of light, but without success. Galileo stationed himself on one hilltop with one lamp and an

greater distances between observers, Galileo came to the conclusion that they could not uncover their lamps fast enough and that light probably travels with an infinite speed. Knowing as we do now that light travels with the amazing speed of 186,000 mi/sec, it is easy to see why Galileo's experiment failed.

36.8. Fizeau's Experiment. The first terrestrial method of measuring the velocity of light was devised by Fizeau in 1849.* His experimental arrangement is shown in Fig. 36I. Light from an intense source S was reflected from a semitransparent mirror G and then brought to a focus at the point O by means of a lens L_1. After being made into a parallel beam by a second lens L_2, the light traveled a distance of 5.39 mi to a hilltop, where a mirror M and lens L_3 reflected the light back again. Returning by the same path, some of the light passed through the mirror G and entered the eye of the observer at E.

The purpose of the rotating toothed wheel was to chop the light beam into short flashes and to measure the time it takes each of these signals to travel over to the far mir-

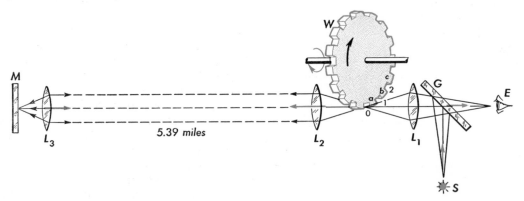

Fig. 36I *Experimental arrangement used by Fizeau in determining the velocity of light.*

assistant on another hilltop with a similar lamp. Galileo would first uncover his lamp for an instant, sending a short flash of light to the assistant. As soon as the assistant saw this light he uncovered his own lamp, sending a flash back to Galileo, who noted the total time elapsed. After numerous repetitions of this experiment at greater and

ror and back. With the wheel at rest and in such a position that the light passes through an opening between two teeth at O, the ob-

* H. L. Fizeau (1819-1896). Born of a wealthy French family, he was financially independent and free to pursue his hobby—the velocity of light. His experiments were carried out in Paris, the light traveling between Montmartre and Suresnes.

server at *E* will see an image of the light source *S*. If the wheel is now set rotating with slowly increasing speed, a condition will soon be reached in which the light passing through 0 will return just in time

and improvements stand out above the rest. Replacing the toothed wheel by a small eight-sided mirror and increasing the light path to about 44 mi, Michelson in 1926 obtained a value of 299,796 Km/sec.

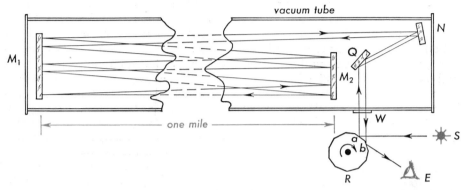

Fig. 36J *Diagrams of the two ends of the 1-mile-long vacuum tube used by Michelson, Pease, and Pearson in measuring the velocity of light in a vacuum.*

to be stopped by *a*, that passing through opening 1 will return just in time to be stopped by *b*, etc. Under these conditions the image will be completely eclipsed from the observer. By further increasing the speed, the light will reappear, increasing in intensity until a maximum is reached. This will occur when the flashes sent out through the openings 0, 1, 2, 3, etc., return just in time to get through the openings 1, 2, 3, 4, etc., respectively. With a wheel containing 720 teeth, Fizeau observed this maximum at a speed of 25 rps. The time required for the light to travel over and back can therefore be calculated as 1/25 times 1/720, or 1/18,000th of a second. This, from the measured distance over and back of 10.78 mi, gave a velocity of 194,000 mi/sec, or 313,000 Km/sec.

36.9. Michelson's Measurements of the Velocity of Light. In the years that followed these earliest experiments, several investigators improved upon Fizeau's apparatus and methods of observation, and obtained more accurate values for the velocity of light. Of these, Michelson's* contributions

* Albert A. Michelson (1852-1931). Distinguished American physicist, celebrated for the invention and development of the interferometer, an optical

Believing that a still more accurate value could be obtained by measuring the velocity of light in a vacuum, Michelson, with the help of Pease and Pearson, constructed a vacuum tube 1 mi long. The form of the apparatus used is shown diagrammatically in Fig. 36J. Light from a carbon arc is reflected from *a*, one of the 32 faces of a rotating mirror *R*, into the vacuum pipe through a window *W*. After reflection from the mirrors *Q* and *N*, the light travels back and forth from one end of the tube to the other by reflection from the large flat mirrors *M₁* and *M₂*. Returning after the tenth traversal to *N* and *Q*, the light leaves through the same window *W* to strike *b*, an adjacent face of *R*, from where it is reflected to the observer at *E*.

Driven as an air turbine by a steady blast of air, the mirror *R* is rotated faster and

instrument, now named the Michelson stellar interferometer in his honor. This instrument is used to establish the length of the standard meter in terms of the wavelength of light, to make ether drift experiments (see Chap. 46 on Relativity), to determine the rigidity of the earth, to measure the distances and the diameters of giant stars, and to measure the velocity of light. He was the first American scientist to be awarded the Nobel Prize (1907).

faster until a condition is reached where the light reflected from each face at the position *a* will return just in time to be reflected to the observer by the same mirror face when it reaches the position *b*. The exact speed required to do this was found by a stroboscopic* comparison of the rotating mirror with a standard electrically driven tuning fork to be 582 rps.

Michelson died in 1931, and the experiments were completed three years later by Pease and Pearson. From 2885 individual measurements, these observers obtained the following average value for the velocity of light, $c = 299,774$ Km/sec. This is lower than any of the values previously obtained, but is undoubtedly the most nearly correct.

An extensive and critical study of the values of the velocity of light measured by all observers has been made by Birge.† He concludes that the most probable value at the present time is as follows:

$$c = 299,790 \text{ Km/sec} \qquad (36d)$$
or $$c = 186,280 \text{ mi/sec}$$

For practical purposes where calculations are to be made, the velocity of light in air or in a vacuum may be assumed to be 300,000 Km/sec, or 3×10^{10} cm/sec. One is justified in using this round-number value since it differs from the more accurate value in Eq.(36d) by less than $\frac{1}{10}$th of 1%.

36.10. The Velocity of Light in Stationary Matter. In 1850, Foucault completed and published the results of an experiment in which he had measured the velocity of light in water. This was a crucial experiment, for it settled a long existing controversy concerning the nature of light. According to Newton and his followers, light was believed to be made up of small parti-

† Raymond T. Birge (1887-   ), American physicist. Noted for his valuable contributions to the analysis of band spectra as a method of determining the structure of diatomic molecules; for his discovery, with A. S. King, of the carbon isotope 13; and for computations of the best probable values of the general physical constants. He served as chairman of the Department of Physics at the University of California from 1933 to 1957 and was elected to the National Academy of Sciences in 1932.

cles or corpuscles emanating from a source. Huygens, on the other hand, regarded light as being composed of waves, similar in nature perhaps to water waves or sound waves. Now, Newton's corpuscular theory required light to travel faster in a dense medium like water than it did in a less dense medium like air, whereas Huygens' wave theory required it to travel slower. By sending light back and forth through a long tube of water, Foucault found its velocity to be less than that in air. This was a strong confirmation of Huygens' wave theory.

Years later, Michelson also measured the velocity of light in water and found a value of 225,000 Km/sec. This is just $\frac{3}{4}$ the velocity in a vacuum. In common glass, the velocity is still lower, being about $\frac{2}{3}$ the velocity in vacuo, or 200,000 Km/sec. In air, the velocity is very little less than the velocity in a vacuum, differing only by about 70 Km/sec at sea level and less at higher altitudes where the air is less dense. For most practical cases this difference can be neglected, and the velocity in air can be said to be the same as in a vacuum.

36.11. The Refractive Index. The ratio between the velocity of light in a vacuum and the velocity in a medium is called the *refractive index,* or the *index of refraction* of the medium.

$$\frac{\text{Velocity of light in vacuo}}{\text{Velocity of light in a medium}} = \text{refractive index}$$

Symbolically, we write

$$\boxed{\frac{c}{v} = \mu} \qquad (36e)$$

The Greek letter μ (mu) is frequently used to represent this ratio. Substituting the velocities given in the preceding section, we may calculate the following refractive indices:

$$\text{for water, } \mu = 1.33 \qquad (36f)$$
$$\text{for glass, } \quad \mu = 1.5 \qquad (36g)$$
$$\text{for air, } \quad \mu = 1.00 \qquad (36h)$$

Very exact measurements of the refractive index of air give a value 1.00029.

PROBLEMS

1. A 50-watt tungsten filament lamp has an efficiency of 1.10 c/watt. How far above a table top should this lamp be placed to produce an illuminance of 5 ft-c?

2. A 150-cp source is located 3 ft above a table top. What additional lamp at the same point will bring the illuminance up to 30 ft-c? (*Ans.* 120-cp.)

3. How many 1000-watt tungsten filament lamps located 5 ft above an operating table are required to produce an illuminance of 500 ft-c? Assume an efficiency of 1.25 c/watt.

4. Five 100-watt tungsten filament lamps are located 5 ft above a table top. How many additional lamps of the same size, located 5 ft above the same table, will bring the total illuminance to 50 ft-c? Assume an efficiency of 1.25 c/watt. (*Ans.* 5 lamps.)

5. A chandelier at the center of the ceiling in a theatre is located 25 ft above the floor. How many 60-watt tungsten filament lamps must it contain to produce an illuminance of 5 ft-c on the floor? Assume an efficiency of 1.1 c/watt.

6. A table is illuminated by two 100-watt lamps spaced 4 ft apart and 3 ft above the top. Calculate the illuminance in ft-c on the top (a) at a point directly under one lamp, and (b) at a point halfway between them. Assume an efficiency of 1.25 c/watt. (*Ans.* (a) 17.9 ft-c, (b) 19.2 ft-c.)

7. A book lying on a table is illuminated by three 60-watt lamps placed in a line, spaced 4 ft apart, and 3 ft above the top. Calculate the illuminance in ft-c on the book if it lies directly under one of the end lamps. Assume efficiency of 1.1 c/watt.

8. Solve Prob. 7 if the book lies directly under the center lamp. (*Ans.* 10.5 ft-c.)

9. Find the velocity of light in gasoline if the refractive index is 1.425. Assume the velocity of light in a vacuum to be 186,300 mi/sec.

10. Find the velocity of light in carbon bisulfide if the refractive index is 1.670. Assume the velocity of light in a vacuum to be 186,300 mi/sec. (*Ans.* 11.16×10^4 mi/sec.)

11. At the earth's closest approach to the sun, it is 91×10^6 mi away. Find the time it takes the sunlight to reach the earth.

12. Sirius, the "dog star," is about 4 light years away, that is, it takes 4 years for the light to reach the earth. Calculate its distance in miles. (*Ans.* 2.35×10^{13} mi.)

13. If the distance to one of the nearest stars is 2.46×10^{13} mi, how many years does it take its light to reach the earth?

14. If Fizeau's velocity of light experiment (see Fig. 36I) were performed with a distant mirror 7 mi away, and a wheel having 180 teeth, how fast would the wheel have to turn for each pulse of light returning through the first succeeding opening to be seen? Assume the velocity of light to be 186,300 mi/sec. (*Ans.* 73.9 rps.)

15. What must be the length of a mirror in order for a man to see a full view of himself in it?

Chapter 37

Refraction

When light falls upon the smooth surface of a transparent substance like water or glass, part of it is reflected according to the law of reflection and the rest is refracted into the medium (see Fig. 37A). This bend-

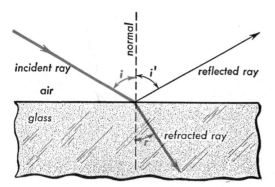

Fig. 37A *Reflection and refraction of light at the boundary of a glass surface.*

ing is due to the change in the velocity of the light upon entering the second medium. The direction of the refracted ray, like the incident and reflected rays, is always measured by the angle it makes with the normal.

The angle of refraction, r, is found by experiment to depend upon two factors: (1) *the angle of incidence i* and (2) *the index of refraction μ.* As defined in Sec. 36.11, *the index of refraction is the ratio of the speed of light in vacuo to the speed of light in the medium.*

To determine the angle of refraction from these two factors, we perform the following graphical construction (see Fig. 37B). A parallel beam of light of width PQ is incident at an angle i on the surface of water. From the point A where the beam first strikes the surface, a line is drawn per-

pendicular to the beam intersecting QC at B.

Assuming a refractive index of $\mu = 1.33$ for water, the line BC is divided into four equal parts. With a radius of three of these units and a center at A, the arc of a circle is scribed as shown. From the point C a tangent is drawn intersecting the arc at D. The refracted ray ADR is then drawn in and the other edge of the ray C drawn parallel to it.

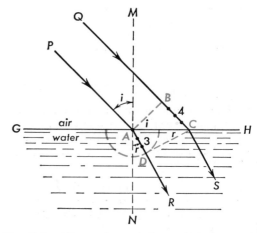

Fig. 37B *Illustration of the graphical method of determining the angle of refraction.*

The law of refraction may now be stated in terms of the lines BC and AD as follows:

$$\frac{BC}{AD} = \mu \qquad (37a)$$

It was the Dutch astronomer and mathematician, Willebrord Snell, who first discovered from experiment that the ratio of these two lines for a given substance is the same for all angles of incidence. In other

302

words, μ is a constant. The relation as given by Eq.(37a) is therefore called Snell's law.* The reason for the constancy of this ratio is that, while the light travels from B to C in air, it travels the corresponding lesser distance AD in water. The ratio $4/3 = 1.33$ $= \mu$. For common glass with a refractive index, $\mu = 1.5$, the same two lines should be divided into 3 and 2 parts, respectively.

37.1. Snell's Law of Refraction. It is customary, in treating the refraction of light, to express Snell's law in trigonometric terms. Referring to Fig. 37B, triangles ABC and ACD are right triangles. Since line PA is $\perp$ to AB and line MA is $\perp$ to AC, angle $i =$ angle BAC. By similar relations, angle $r =$ angle ACD. From triangles ABC and ACD,

$$BC = AC \sin i, \quad \text{and} \quad AD = AC \sin r$$

Substitution for BC and AD in Eq.(37a) gives

$$\frac{BC}{AD} = \frac{AC \sin i}{AC \sin r} = \frac{\sin i}{\sin r} = \mu$$

or

$$\boxed{\mu = \frac{\sin i}{\sin r}} \tag{37b}$$

This latter form is the most useful form of Snell's law. For any given transparent substance, the ratio of the sine of the angle of incidence to the sine of the angle of refraction is the same for all angles of incidence and is equal to the refraction index, μ. Since μ is the ratio of the velocities of light in the two media (see Sec. 36.11), Snell's law may also be written

$$\frac{\sin i}{\sin r} = \frac{v_1}{v_2} = \mu \tag{37c}$$

where v_1 represents the velocity in the first

---

* Willebrord Snell (1591-1626), Dutch astronomer and mathematician, was born at Leyden in 1591. At the age of twenty-two he succeeded his father as professor of mathematics at the University of Leyden. In 1617, he determined the size of the earth from measurements of its curvature between Alkmaar and Bergen-op-Zoom. In 1621, he discovered the law of refraction which now carries his name.

medium and v_2 the velocity in the second medium.

Example 1. Light, in air, is incident at an angle of 45° on the surface of a glass plate for which the refractive index is 1.52. Through what angle is the light deviated upon refraction at the top surface?

Solution. First find the angle of refraction r by use of Eq.(37b). By transposing and substituting the given quantities, we obtain

$$\sin r = \frac{\sin i}{\mu} = \frac{\sin 45°}{1.52} = \frac{0.707}{1.52} = 0.465$$

If we look up 0.465 in a table of natural sines, we find that angle $r = 27.7°$. Since the deviation of the light is the difference between angle i and angle r (45° − 27.7°),

$$\text{deviation} = 17.3°$$

37.2. Displacement in a Parallel Plate. One very useful principle concerning the behavior of light is *the reversibility of light rays*. If, in any of the experiments or illustrations already described, the light rays could be reversed in direction, they would be found to retrace their paths exactly.

If a beam of light, on being refracted into a denser medium like glass, is bent toward the normal, the light passing through and out of this denser medium into the air should be bent away from the normal. This can be demonstrated by sending light through a plane-parallel plate of glass as illustrated in Fig. 37C. In (c) the light is incident on the first surface at an angle i and is refracted at an angle r. This internal ray is now incident on the second surface at the same angle r and is refracted into the air at the same angle i. The light thus emerges in a direction parallel to the original beam, but displaced from it laterally.

This lateral displacement is zero for normal incidence as in diagram (a) and increases with the angle i as shown in diagrams (b), (c), and (d), respectively. If the parallel plate is very thin, as in the case of an ordinary windowpane, the displacement is quite small and for most practical purposes can be neglected.

37.3. Refraction by a Prism. When light passes through a prism, it is refracted at two surfaces, once on the way in and once

(a)   (b)   (c)   (d)

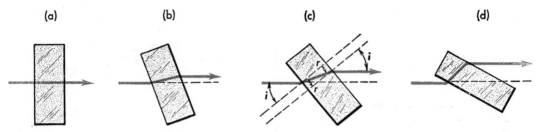

Fig. 37C   *Illustration of the lateral displacement of a beam of light as it passes through a parallel plate of glass.*

on the way out. If the two sides involved are parallel, as they are in Fig. 37D, diagram (a), the emergent ray is always parallel to the incident ray. If the sides are not parallel, as in diagrams (b), (c), and (d), the emergent ray has a different direction. The larger the angle A between the two refracting surfaces, the larger is the angle of deviation D. Upon entering the prism at the first surface (see diagram (d)), the light is bent toward the normal. Emerging into the air from the second surface, the light is bent away from the normal. Note in Fig. 37D that neither the apex nor the base of the prism has any effect on the deviation of the light.

In verifying these results by experiment, light of only one color should be used, because white light will spread out into a spectrum of colors. Light of one color only is readily obtained by inserting a piece of red or green colored glass into a beam of white light.

A relatively simple graphical method of tracing a given ray of light through a prism is shown in Fig. 37E. Here we have a ray of light VP incident at an angle i on the first face of a prism of angle A and refractive index μ. In this diagram $A = 60°$, $\mu = 1.5$, and $i = 60°$.

Starting at one side, a line EF is first drawn parallel to the incident ray VP. With a center at any point O, and with radii, in this particular case, of 1.0 unit and 1.5 units, arcs CS and BR are drawn of indefinite length. From the intersection C a line is now drawn parallel to the normal M, intersecting the second arc at R. The line OR is drawn next, and from the point P of the prism a parallel line is drawn intersecting the second face at Q. Starting at R, a line is next drawn parallel to the normal N, intersecting the first arc at S. Finally the line OS is drawn in, and from the point Q on the second prism face a parallel line QW is drawn as the emergent ray.

In triangle OCR the length of side OC is 1.00, the length of side OR is 1.5 or μ, and the angle opposite side OR is $180° - i$. If we now apply the laws of sines to this triangle, we can write

$$\frac{\sin (180° - i)}{\mu} = \frac{\sin r}{1}$$

The sine of any angle i is always equal to the sine of $180°$ minus that same angle.

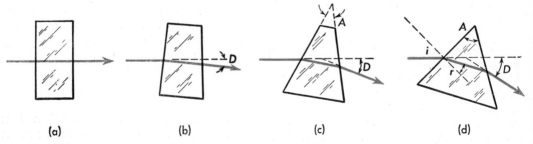

(a)   (b)   (c)   (d)

Fig. 37D   *Illustration of the bending of a beam of light by prisms made of the same glass.*

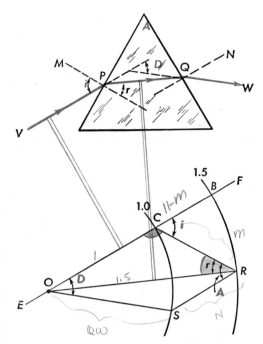

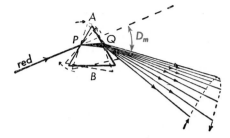

Fig. 37F *Light refracted by a prism has a min-*
imum angle of deviation D_m.

Fig. 37E *Graphical construction for refraction*
by a prism.

the *angle of minimum deviation,* and occurs at that particular angle of incidence
where the refracted ray inside the prism
makes equal angles with the prism faces P
and Q.

Therefore,

$$\frac{\sin i}{\mu} = \frac{\sin r}{1}$$

from which we obtain

$$\frac{\sin i}{\sin r} = \mu$$

To derive a formula from which the angle of minimum deviation D_m can be calculated, reference is made to **Fig. 37G.** To

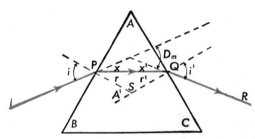

Fig. 37G *Geometrical relations for minimum*
deviation in a prism.

The same derivation can be applied to
the triangle ORS.

Since the above construction obeys Snell's
law, the accuracy of the graphical results depends upon the sharpness of the pencil used
and the care with which the diagram is
made. Furthermore the lower diagram as
well as the prism diagram includes all of
the angles involved in the prism, including
the angle of deviation D.

37.4. Minimum Deviation. If, during the
time a beam of light is refracted by a prism,
the prism is rotated continuously in one direction about an axis parallel to the refracting edge A, the angle of deviation will be
observed to decrease, reach a minimum,
and then increase again as shown in Fig.
37F. The smallest deviation angle is called

start with, $i = i'$, and $r = r'$. To prove these
angles equal, assume i does not equal i'
when minimum deviation occurs. Reversal
of the direction of the light rays will give
the same angle of minimum deviation, yet
the incident angle is now different from
what it was before. This would mean that
there are two different angles of incidence
capable of giving minimum deviation. Since
by experiment there is only one, the two
angles, i and i', must be equal.

By geometrical construction,

$$\angle i = \angle i' \qquad \angle r = \angle r' \qquad \text{and} \qquad \angle x = \angle x'$$

Since two of the angles in the four-sided
figure $APSQ$ are right angles, the sum of
the other two angles, $A + S = 180°$. Fur-

thermore, for a straight angle, $A' + S = 180°$. Therefore,

$$\angle A = \angle A'$$

In the isosceles triangle PQS, the exterior angle A' equals the sum of the interior angles, $r + r'$. Similarly, the exterior angle D_m equals the sum of the interior angles $x + x'$.

Consequently,

$$A = 2r \qquad D_m = 2x \qquad \text{and} \qquad i = r + x$$

If we solve these three equations for angle i and angle r,

$$r = \tfrac{1}{2}A \qquad i = \tfrac{1}{2}A + \tfrac{1}{2}D_m$$
or $\qquad i = \tfrac{1}{2}(A + D_m)$

Since, by Snell's law, $\mu = \sin i / \sin r$,

$$\boxed{\mu = \frac{\sin \tfrac{1}{2}(A + D_m)}{\sin \tfrac{1}{2}A}} \qquad (37d)$$

This is the formula we set out to derive.

When, in the manufacture of optical glass, the refractive index of a given melt must be determined, a small prism is made from a sample of the glass and angles A and D are determined experimentally. The measured values are then substituted in Eq.(37d), and μ is calculated. Almost without exception, the light used for such measurements is the yellow light from a sodium lamp.

Example 2. Glass of known refractive index $\mu = 1.52$ is ground and polished into a prism having a refracting angle $A = 60°$. Calculate the angle of minimum deviation.

Solution. Since D_m is the unknown quantity, Eq.(37d) is transposed and the known values A and μ are substituted as follows:

$$\sin \tfrac{1}{2}(A + D) = \mu \sin \tfrac{1}{2}A = 1.52 \sin \tfrac{1}{2}60°$$
$$= 1.52 \times 0.50$$
$$\sin \tfrac{1}{2}(A + D) = 0.760$$

Looking up the angle whose sine is 0.760, we find

$$\tfrac{1}{2}(A + D) = 49.5°$$
and $\qquad A + D = 99°$

which, on substituting $A = 60°$, gives

$$D = 99 - 60 = 39°$$

37.5. Critical Angle of Refraction. When light passes from a medium, such as air, into a more dense medium, like glass or water, the angle of refraction is always less than the angle of incidence. As a result of this decrease in angle, there exists a range of angles for which no refracted light is possible. To see what this range of angles is, consider the diagram in Fig. 37H, where

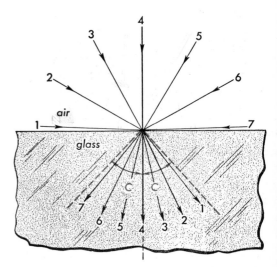

Fig. 37H *Diagram illustrating the critical angle.*

for several angles of incidence the corresponding angles of refraction are shown. It is to be noted that, in the limiting case where the incident rays approach the angle of 90°, i.e., where they graze along the surface, the refracted rays approach a certain angle c, beyond which no refracted light is possible. In any medium this limiting angle, called *the critical angle,* depends for its value upon the index of refraction.

To calculate the critical angle of refraction, one takes the angle of incidence $i = 90°$ and angle $r = $ angle c. Since $\sin 90° = 1$, Snell's law becomes

$$\mu = \frac{1}{\sin c} \qquad \text{or} \qquad \sin c = \frac{1}{\mu} \qquad (37e)$$

For the most common of crown glass $\mu = 1.515$, substitution in this formula gives $c = 41.3°$. For water of index $\mu = 1.33$, it gives

$c = 49°$. It should be noted in particular that the critical angle is measured from the normal, and not from the refracting surface.

37.6. Total Reflection. Another experiment illustrating the reversibility of light rays is shown in the diagram of Fig. 37I. A

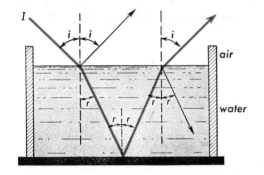

Fig. 37I *Illustration of reflection and refraction.*

beam of light is refracted at an angle r into a tank of water. From there it is reflected from a silvered mirror at the bottom of the tank, illustrating the law of reflection in a medium other than air. The reflected ray arriving at the upper surface at the same angle r is refracted into the air at the incident angle i. At each refraction at the air-water boundary, a small amount of the incident light is reflected, as indicated by the fine-lined arrows.

When a beam of light within a medium like water or glass approaches the surface at an angle greater than the critical angle, all of the light is reflected back into the medium. In other words, a water-to-air or glass-to-air surface acts under these conditions like a perfect reflector. This phenomenon is called *total internal reflection.* Since no light can be refracted into the water at such an angle (see Fig. 37H), none inside the water at large angles of incidence can be refracted out. The experiment is illustrated with a tank of water as shown in Fig. 37J. If light is sent into the water through a glass plate in one end, the light approaches the upper surface at an angle greater than c, there to be totally reflected back into the water as shown.

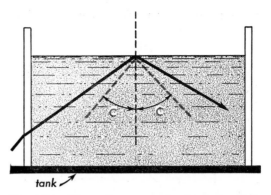

Fig. 37J *Illustration of total reflection and the critical angle c.*

An interesting demonstration can be performed with a clear glass or plastic rod bent into almost any form as shown in Fig. 37K. Light, on entering one end, reflects from wall to wall by total reflection, causing it to follow the rod to the end and emerge as a divergent beam. Various instruments used by physicians and surgeons employ this principle for internal body observations.

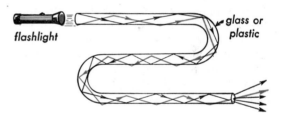

Fig. 37K *Light follows a bent rod by total reflection.*

Another demonstration consists of placing a lighted tungsten lamp in the bottom of a pitcher of water and pouring the water slowly into a larger vessel. The light follows the stream of water and produces an interesting display of light where it splashes into the other vessel. (Care should be taken to avoid electrical shock from this experiment.)

Total reflection is also employed in optical instruments such as telescopes, microscopes, prism binoculars, spectroscopes, etc. The optical parts employing this principle are known as *total reflection prisms.* Such prisms are usually made of common glass with one angle a right angle and the other two 45° angles. As illustrated in Fig. 37L there are three ways in which these prisms may be used. Incident normally upon the first surface, as in (a), the light enters the

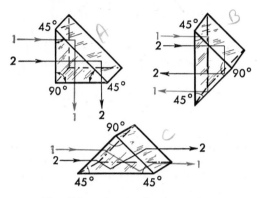

Fig. 37L   *Total reflection prisms.*

prism without deviation. Arriving at the second surface at an angle of 45°, just 3° greater than the critcial angle, the light is totally reflected according to the law of reflection. Having thus been deviated through 90°, the light passes normally through the third surface without further deviation. The prism has therefore acted like a plane mirror with its reflecting surface at 45°.

In diagram (b), the light enters normally near one end of the long diagonal face of the prism. When it arrives at the second surface at 45°, total reflection takes place exactly as in diagram (a). A second reflection occurs at the third surface, sending the light out near the bottom of, and normal to, the first surface. The light has thus been reversed in direction. Used in this way, the

prism performs the function of two prisms, each used as in diagram (a).

In diagram (c) the light enters the first prism face at an angle. After refraction, the light is totally reflected from the second face and then refracted out of the third surface to be parallel to the original beam. Used in this way the prism is called an *erecting prism*. The incident ray, *l*, which is on top, reverses its position and emerges from the prism at the bottom.

Three special prisms of considerable interest are shown in Fig. 37M. The first, called a *pentaprism,* is commonly used in range finders, whereas the second is a *roof-prism* and is used in various optical instruments for erecting images that would otherwise be inverted. The third, called a *triple prism,* is like the corner of a cube with three mutually perpendicular faces; it has the unusual property of returning every beam of light that enters it back in the exact direction from which it came. Although the same results can be obtained with mirrors in all cases, prisms have the principal advantage that they are rigid and the reflecting faces cannot be put out of alignment with each other by jarring. The back faces of the pentaprism must be silvered.

37.7. Reflecting Power. Thus far in the treatment of reflection and refraction, little has been said concerning the relative intensities of the refracted rays for different angles of incidence. At and near normal incidence on glass (see Fig. 37N), the reflected light contains only 4% of the incident light and the refracted light contains the remainder or 96%. As the angle of incidence increases, the intensity of the reflected beam increases, slowly at first and then more rap-

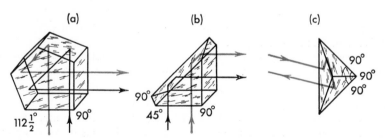

Fig. 37M   *Special prisms: (a) pentaprism, (b) roof-prism, and (c) triple prism.*

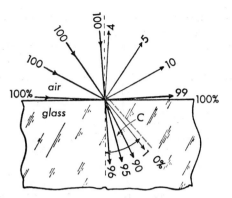

Fig. 37N *Diagram showing the relative intensities of the reflected and refracted rays for different angles of incidence.*

idly, approaching 100% at 90°. At the same time the refracted ray decreases in intensity and vanishes as the angle of refraction reaches the critical angle.

Although formulas for the reflecting power of all kinds of substances have been derived, they are generally quite complicated. For nonmetallic substances at normal incidence, however, the relations are considerably simplified.

$$\text{reflecting power} = \frac{(\mu - 1)^2}{(\mu + 1)^2} \quad (37f)$$

This formula also holds for internal reflection where the incident light is in the medium of index μ and comes to an air or vacuum boundary. To express reflecting power in per cent, multiply Eq.(37f) by 100. Polished metal surfaces in general have a high reflecting power at all angles of incidence. Silver and aluminum, for example, have a reflecting power of 90% or better at normal incidence, and for this reason are commonly used on glass mirrors.

PROBLEMS

1. Light is incident at 50° on the surface of a clear crystal whose refractive index is 1.25. Construct a refraction diagram similar to Fig. 37B, and determine the angle of refraction. Check your result by calculation.

2. Light is incident at 60° on the surface of water whose refractive index is 1.33. (a) Use the graphical method of Fig. 37E to find the angle of refraction. (b) Use Snell's law to calculate this same angle. (*Ans.* (a) 41°, (b) 40.6°.)

3. A plastic cube is 4 cm on each side and has a refractive index of 1.40. A ray of light incident on one side at 50° passes through the cube and out the opposite side. Use the graphical method of Fig. 37E to find the lateral displacement.

4. A glass cube 2 in. on a side has a refractive index of 1.620. A ray of light incident on one side at 45° passes through the cube and out the opposite side. What is the lateral displacement? (*Ans.* 0.728 in.)

5. A rectangular aquarium with glass sides and filled with water is 1 ft thick. Find the lateral displacement of a beam of light incident on one of the sides at 30°. Neglect the thickness of the glass.

6. A 60° glass prism has a refractive index of 1.60. Using the graphical method of Fig. 37E, find the angle of deviation for a ray incident on one surface at an angle of 50°. (*Ans.* 46.5°.)

7. A 50° glass prism has a refractive index of 1.75. Using the graphical method of Fig. 37E, find the angle of deviation for a ray incident on the first surface at 60°.

8. A 60° plastic prism has a refractive index of 1.414. Calculate (a) the angle of minimum deviation, and (b) the angle of incidence that gives minimum deviation (*Ans.* (a) 30°, (b) 45°.)

9. A dense flint glass prism of index 1.67 has a refraction angle of 50°. Calculate the angle of minimum deviation.

10. A 50° prism exhibits an angle of minimum deviation of 41°. Calculate the refractive index. (*Ans.* 1.69.)

11. A 50° prism exhibits an angle of minimum deviation of 34°. Calculate the refractive index.

12. A 60° glass prism has a refractive index of 1.60. Using the graphical method of Fig. 37E, find the angle of minimum deviation. *Note:* Start with the internal ray as making

equal angles with the two prism faces. (*Ans.* 46.2°.)

13. Calculate the critical angle of refraction for plastic of index 1.48.

14. Find the critical angle of refraction for a dense flint glass of index 1.75. (*Ans.* 34.9°.)

15. The critical angle of a crystalline substance is measured to be 35.5°. What is its refractive index?

16. If the critical angle of a certain glass is 36, what is its refractive index? (*Ans.* 1.70.)

17. Green light is incident at 50° on one face of a 60° glass prism. Find the total deviation of the light if the refractive index is 1.50.

18. Calculate the reflecting power for diamond at normal incidence if its refractive index is 2.42. (*Ans.* 17.2%.)

19. Yellow light is incident at an angle of 55° on one face of a 60° prism. Find the total deviation of the light if the refractive index is 1.50.

Chapter 38

Dispersion

38.1. Dispersion. It was known to the ancients that sunlight, on passing through transparent crystals and jewels of various kinds, would produce brilliant colors of light. The early philosophers, attempting to explain the phenomenon, attributed the origin of the colors to the crystal itself. It was Newton who first demonstrated with prisms that the colors were already present in the white sunlight and that the function of the prism was to separate the colors by refracting them in different directions.

We have already seen how light of one color is refracted at the boundary of a medium like glass or water, and how it is deviated by a prism. It may be seen in Fig. 38A how, *with white light, each color is*

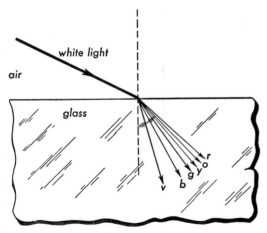

Fig. 38A *Refraction of white sunlight into its spectrum colors.*

refracted by a different amount to produce its own angle of deviation. *Red light is refracted least and violet light is refracted most.* The angular spread of all the colors produced by sending white light through a

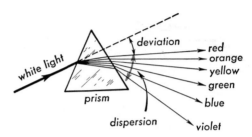

Fig. 38B *Refraction at both surfaces of a prism produces higher dispersion.*

prism is called the *dispersion* and the band of color so produced is called *a spectrum.* (See Fig. 38B.)

If white light is sent through a group of similar prisms made of different substances, each prism will be found to have a different dispersion. This can be demonstrated for solids by *flint* and *crown glass prisms,* and for liquids by *kerosene (carbon bisulfide)* and *water.* It will be noted that the two glass prisms in Fig. 38C, one of flint glass and the other of crown glass, produce quite different dispersions. The liquid prisms, produced by filling thin-walled glass troughs with liquid, also disperse light by different amounts.

Since different colors are refracted by different amounts, the index of refraction is different for each color. In a vacuum all colors travel with the same speed, 186,300 mi/sec, but in a transparent medium, like glass or water, they travel considerably slower and at different speeds. Among the spectrum colors, red travels the fastest and violet the slowest, with the speeds of all other colors somewhere in between. In air there is very little dispersion and in a vacuum there is absolutely none. This latter statement is proved by the fact that, when the dark star of an eclipsing binary passes

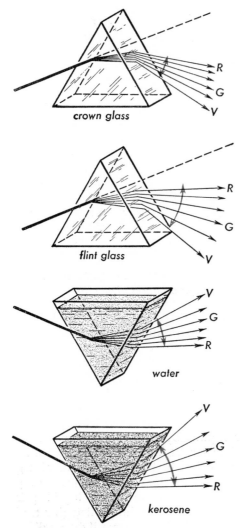

Fig. 38C *Illustration of the relative dispersions of solid as well as liquid prisms.*

in front of its brighter companion, all colors disappear and reappear simultaneously. If one color were to travel slightly faster than another, the dip in stellar intensity for that color would have plenty of time in its many years of travel to the earth to get ahead.

The refractive indices for a number of transparent solids are given in Table 38A. It will be noted that, although the values for any one substance do not vary greatly between colors, the values for blue and violet are the largest and those for orange and red are the smallest. Note the relatively high values for diamond and strontium titanate and the relatively low values for ice.

In the physics laboratory the index of refraction is determined with a prism, usually one having an angle of 60°. The prism is placed on a spectrometer where the spectrum of white light is observed in a small telescope, and the angle of minimum deviation is measured for each color separately. As the prism is slowly turned, the spectrum widens or narrows continuously and each color goes through its own angle of minimum deviation just as the rays of that same color make equal angles with the two prism faces.

38.2. Prism Combinations. While substances that produce large deviations also produce large dispersions, the two properties are by no means proportional to each other. If a flint glass prism, for example, produces twice the dispersion of a crown glass prism, it is not true that the deviation of each color by the flint prism is twice that of the crown glass prism. Useful devices

TABLE 38A. REFRACTIVE INDEX FOR SEVERAL TRANSPARENT SOLIDS

Substance	Color wavelength $\lambda \times 10^{-8}$ cm					
	Violet 4100	Blue 4700	Green 5300	Yellow 5900	Orange 6100	Red 6700
Crown glass.........	1.5380	1.5310	1.5260	1.5225	1.5216	1.5200
Light flint..........	1.6040	1.5960	1.5910	1.5875	1.5867	1.5850
Dense flint.........	1.6980	1.6836	1.6738	1.6670	1.6650	1.6620
Quartz.............	1.5570	1.5510	1.5468	1.5438	1.5432	1.5420
Diamond...........	2.4580	2.4439	2.4260	2.4172	2.4150	2.4100
Ice................	1.3170	1.3136	1.3110	1.3087	1.3080	1.3060
Strontium titanate ...	2.6320	2.5130	2.4460	2.4060	2.3980	2.3730

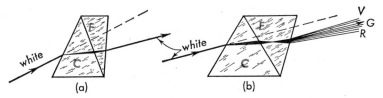

Fig. 38D *Prism combinations: (a) achromatic prism giving deviation without dispersion,
(b) direct vision prism giving dispersion without deviation.*

illustrating this fact can be demonstrated by combining two prisms in opposition as shown in Fig. 38D.

For the achromatic combination in (a), the angles of both prisms are so selected that each prism alone will produce the same total dispersion. Since flint glass has the higher dispersive power, the flint prism will have a smaller angle as shown. Placed in opposition, the crown glass spreads the colors out and the flint prism bends them back parallel to each other again. Since the deviation produced by the two prisms is not the same, light will emerge as white light but in a different direction from that in which it first entered.

For the direct vision combination in (b), the angles of the prisms are so selected that each prism alone will produce the same deviation for green light. For two such matched prisms the flint prism will produce the greatest dispersion. Combined in opposition, the green light comes out on the far side, parallel to the incident white light on the left and the other spectrum colors on either side as shown.

38.3. The Rainbow. The rainbow is nature's most spectacular display of the spectrum of white light. The required conditions for the appearance of the phenomenon are that the sun be shining in one part of the sky and the rain be falling in the opposite part of the sky. Turning one's back to the sun, the bright primary bow and sometimes the fainter secondary bow, with colors reversed, are seen as the arcs of circles. From a high vantage point or an airplane, these bows may form complete circles whose common center lies in the direction of the observer's shadow.

The elementary theory of the rainbow was first given by Antonius de Demini in the year 1611 and later developed more exactly by Descartes. The general characteristics of the *primary* and *secondary bows* are satisfactorily accounted for by considering only the reflection and refraction of light by spherical raindrops. To understand how the phenomenon arises, we first confine our attention to an individual raindrop as shown in Fig. 38E. A ray of sunlight is shown

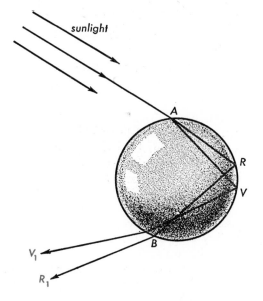

Fig. 38E *Dispersion of sunlight by a single raindrop. (Primary rainbow.)*

entering a single raindrop at a point *A* near the top. At this point some of the light is reflected (not shown), and the remainder is refracted into the liquid sphere. At this first refraction the light is dispersed into its spectrum colors, violet being deviated the most and red the least.

Arriving at the opposite side of the drop, each color is partly refracted out into the air (not shown) and partly reflected back into the liquid. Reaching the surface at the lower boundary, each color is again reflected (not shown) and refracted. This second refraction is quite similar to that of a prism (see Fig. 38B), where refraction at the second surface increases the dispersion already produced at the first. This is the path of the light in thousands of drops giving rise to the bright primary rainbow.

In Fig. 38F, a ray of sunlight, coming

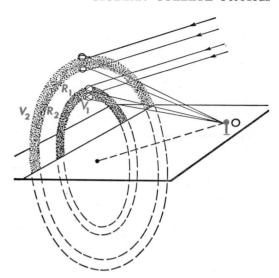

Fig. 38G   *The primary and secondary rainbows as seen by an observer at O.*

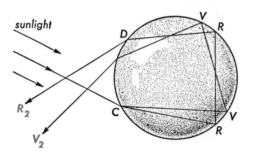

Fig. 38F   *Dispersion of sunlight by a single raindrop. (Secondary rainbow.)*

from the same direction as in Fig. 38E, is shown entering a single raindrop at a point C near the bottom. After one refraction and two internal reflections the light is again refracted and dispersed, this time in a direction not greatly different from that in Fig. 38E. This is the path of the light in thousands of drops giving rise to the fainter secondary rainbow with its colors reversed.

Of all the sun's rays falling on one face of each individual drop, only a small part of them are responsible for the main features of both rainbows. The reasons for excluding the others will be explained in later paragraphs. Assuming for the present that the two rays shown are the only rays to be considered, let us see why the bows appear as they do in the sky.

As shown in Fig. 38G, the primary bow appears inside the secondary bow and arises from sunlight entering the tops of drops properly located. Those in a region R_1 refract red light toward the observer's eye at

O, and the violet and other colors over his head. Drops in the region of V_1 refract violet light to the observer's eye at O, and the red and other colors toward his feet. In other words, the light seen from any one drop is but one color, all drops giving this color lying on the arc of a circle. The reason they lie on the arc of a circle is that the angle between the incident sunlight and the refracted light of any one color is of necessity the same for each drop. In the primary bow, this angle is 42° for the red light and 40° for the violet.

The secondary bow is formed by similar reasoning and appears at higher angles of elevation, and with the colors reversed. The angles subtended by the secondary bow are 50° for the red and 54° for the violet.

38.4. The Theory of the Rainbow. The complete theory of the rainbow was first proposed by Thomas Young, and later worked out in detail by Potter and Airy. To understand why the particular rays shown in Fig. 38E are responsible for the rainbow, and that other rays which certainly enter the drop can be neglected, see Fig. 38H. Here, in the parallel beam of sunlight entering a single drop, our attention is confined to the rays of only one color. By this simplification, the phenomenon of

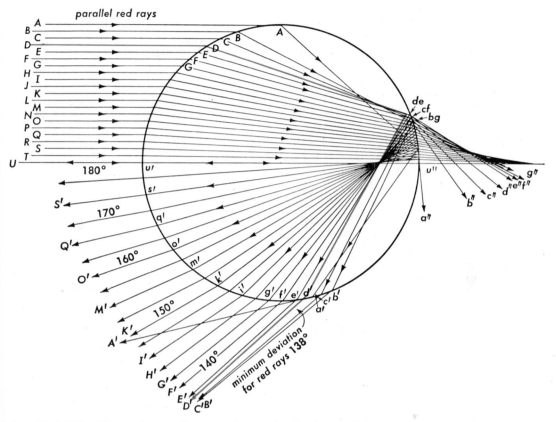

Fig. 38H   *Illustration of the refraction and reflection of light by a single raindrop and the minimum deviation of certain rays that produce the primary rainbow.*

dispersion is dispensed with and we consider only the reflection and refraction of red light. As each of the parallel red rays *A, B, C,* etc., from the sun enter the drop, they are deviated according to the law of refraction. At the opposite side of the drop, in the region *d* to *u″*, these rays are partly reflected to the lower left boundary at *a′, b′, c′,* etc., where, by refraction, they pass out into the air in the directions of *A′, B′, C′,* etc., respectively, and are partly refracted in the direction of *a″, b″, c″,* etc., respectively.

From the diagram it will be noted that a ray like *A*, entering at the very edge of the drop, is deviated through an angle close to 180°, that is, it emerges in almost the opposite direction to that in which it entered. The same is true of a ray like *Q* nearer the center of the drop. Ray *U* is

exactly reversed in direction and therefore deviated exactly 180°. Ray *D*, on the other hand, is seen to be deviated least of all and is therefore referred to as the ray at minimum deviation. In going from *A* to *U* with the incident light, the emergent light is deviated less and less until it reaches a minimum for *D′* and then increases again, reaching 180° with the axial ray *UU′*. The net result of this behavior is seen to be a slight crowding together of a considerable number of nearly parallel rays at minimum deviation where the light emerges as an intense and nearly parallel beam *B′* to *G′*.

It should be noted that raindrops are spheres and not circles, as represented in the figures, and that the refracted rays emerge as cones of light. If Fig. 38H is rotated about the axial ray *UU′*, the emerging rays *A′, B′, C′,* etc., are confined to a cone bounded at the edges by the rays that have suffered the least deviation. In the direction of D', the edge of the cone, the radiation is very intense, and inside the cone the rays are divergent and the radiation feeble. Outside the cone there is no light. Thus the selected ray A of the incident light in Fig. 38E is the ray D in Fig. 38H.

Similar diagrams for other colors lead to angles of minimum deviation and cones of light whose angles decrease in the order of the spectral colors red, orange, yellow, green, blue, and violet. An experimental demonstration of this can be made by sending a beam of parallel light from a carbon arc through a round glass bulb filled with water. The refracted cones of light falling on a screen in back of the arc source forms a complete primary rainbow. Outside this primary bow, and with colors reversed, is the fainter secondary bow.

To understand the secondary rainbow, additional rays must be added to Fig. 38H. Internally reflected rays from the points a', b', c', etc., are drawn up to where they again strike the surface of the drop and are there refracted out into the air. Out of these rays, a given set of rays, like those for the primary bow, will have a preferred direction in which the light is most intense. When the figure is rotated about the axial line UU', the rays form a secondary cone of light, the inner edge of which is sharply defined.

It is interesting to point out that no light emerges in the region between the primary and secondary cones of light. This agrees with the observations that the region between the two rainbows is quite dark, whereas outside the secondary bow and inside the primary bow a considerable amount of light is visible.

Theoretically three, four, and five reflections within raindrops should give rise to other rainbows. The third and fourth bows are located between the observer and the sun and, because the direct sunlight is so bright compared with the faint bows, the phenomenon has probably never been observed. The fifth bow, however, occurs in the same part of the sky as the primary and secondary bows, and would be seen except for the faintness of the light.

On occasions when the primary and secondary rainbows are particularly bright, a third bow just inside the primary, and a fourth bow just outside the secondary bow, may be seen. These are called supernumerary bows, and are due to peculiar interference effects of light. This interference occurs between pairs of rays that are parallel to each other on emergence, but which have traveled different paths within the drop. Such pairs of rays, for example, are D' and E', C' and F', B' and G', and A' and Q'. The two rays in each of these pairs are just those that cross each other at the reflecting surface d to u''; they are therefore symmetrical with the corresponding incident pairs of rays.

38.5. Coronas and Lunar Bows. Lunar bows may be seen under favorable conditions. When the full moon appears in one part of the sky and rain is falling in another part of the sky, an observer with his back to the moon may observe a barely visible rainbow. As a rule only the brighter colors, red and yellow, are visible.

At times when the sun or moon shines through a thin veil of fog, we observe a circular colored bow with the sun or moon at the geometrical center. Such a corona, as it is technically called, is due to the diffraction of light around the tiny fog particles. Popularly called a ring around the sun or a ring around the moon, a corona appears close to the luminary with red on the outside. It should not be confused with the larger rings or halos with red on the inside.

38.6. Halos. Halos are commonly observed as faint rainbow-like rings around the sun or moon, and are due to tiny ice crystals floating in the upper atmosphere. Such crystals are hexagonal in shape and, acting like prisms, refract and disperse white light into a spectrum. Two halos are frequently observed, the brighter one making an angle of 22° with the luminary and the fainter one an angle of 46°. Both exhibit confused spectrum colors with a decided red tint on the inside.

Crystals, like prisms, have an angle of minimum deviation for each color of light and, because they are oriented at random in space, millions of them appear to each observer to concentrate the light in a circle with the luminary at the center. As shown in Fig. 38I, the angle of minimum deviation

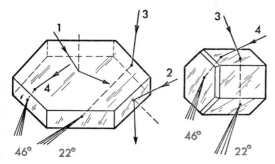

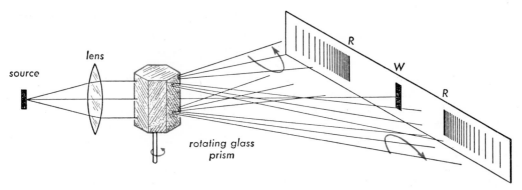

Fig. 38I *Typical forms of ice crystals showing reflected and refracted rays of sunlight that give rise to halos and "mock suns."*

for light entering and leaving different faces of either plate-like or rod-like crystals is 22° and 46°. The 22° angle arises from rays like (3) where the two refracting surfaces are alternate faces that make an angle of 60° with each other. The 46° angle arises from rays like (4) where the two refracting surfaces make an angle of 90°. (The refractive index of ice for red light is 1.3030.)

of white light. Dispersed light refracted by alternate faces sweeps in from either side of the screen, slows down and stops at minimum deviation, and then retreats again. The blurred patches of light on the screen are brightest at the minimum deviation angles R.

38.7. "Mock Suns" or "Sundogs." Another natural phenomenon of great interest, and one which is quite spectacular, is the formation of "mock suns" or "sundogs." Although the phenomenon is most commonly seen in the polar regions, it is occasionally observed at low latitudes and at a time of day when the sun is not far from the horizon (see Fig. 38K).

This display too is caused by myriads of tiny ice crystals in the upper atmosphere, reflecting and refracting the light according to the well-established laws of optics. As shown in Fig. 38K, there are, in addition to the two rainbow-like halos at 22° and 46°, four radial streaks of white light, two vertical and two horizontal. Where these streaks of white light cross the halos, the colors appear intensified and form what are called *mock suns* or *sundogs*.

The explanation of the halos is the same as explained above, while the white streaks are due to reflection from all crystal faces. The plate-like crystals, falling freely under

Fig. 38J *Experiment demonstrating colors produced at minimum deviation by a single rotating prism.*

A demonstration of such color effects can be produced as shown in Fig. 38J by means of an hexagonal or octagonal glass prism rotated rapidly about its axis in a strong beam

gravity, flutter slowly downward like leaves from a tree. Wobbling slightly about a horizontal plane, they present vertical and horizontal faces from which light is reflected.

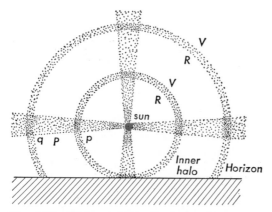

Fig. 38K *Halos and "mock suns" or "sundogs" as seen frequently in polar regions, and occasionally at lower latitudes. P, parhelic circle; p, mock suns or parhelia; q, paranthelia.*

38.8. Mirages and Flying Saucers. When walking across the desert sands or driving along a straight and level highway on a hot day, one notices that the sand or the dark asphalt in the distance seems to be covered with water. The water, of course, is just a reflected image of the sky, and a distant object above the horizon will appear upside down below the horizon. The air in contact with the ground has been heated to a high temperature and, because its refractive index is lowered due to expansion, light rays are reflected as if from a plane mirror.

Oftentimes at night, when the air at the ground is cooler than the air above, the bending of light rays will occur in the opposite direction, and distant objects, like a row of bright city street lights, can be seen against the sky. This and similar phenomena, explain the "flying saucer" observations,* first observed centuries ago and reported so frequently in the last decade.

* See *Flying Saucers*, by D. H. Menzel, Harvard University Press.

At positions close in line between the sun and observer, the light reflected toward the observer is incident at a grazing angle, an angle where the reflecting power for all transparent solids is high. (See Fig. 37N.)

PROBLEMS

1. White light is incident at 85° on one face of a diamond. Calculate the dispersion produced by one surface, that is, the angle between the red and violet rays.†

2. White light is incident at 75° on the surface of quartz. Calculate the dispersion produced by one surface, that is, the angle between the red and violet rays.† (*Ans.* 26.5′ or 0.41°.)

3. White light is incident at 20° on one face of a quartz prism having a refractive angle of 45°. Find the dispersion produced between the red and violet rays.†

4. White light is incident at 40° on one face of a dense flint glass prism having a refractive angle of 50°. Find the dispersion produced between emergent red and violet rays. For refractive indices, see Table 38A. (*Ans.* 2°43′ or 2.72°.)

† All answers given here are calculated using five-place trigonometry tables.

5. A six-sided prism is rotated in a beam of white light like that shown in Fig. 38J. If the prism is made of crown glass of index 1.62, what will be the angle between the two minimum deviation positions *RR*?

6. An eight-sided prism is rotated in a beam of white light like that shown in Fig. 38J. If the prism is made of quartz with a yellow index of 1.5438, what will be the total angle between the two minimum deviation positions *RR*? (*Ans.* 54.8°.)

7. Solve Prob. 6 if the prism is twelve-sided.

8. A parallel beam of green light is incident on a spherical raindrop as shown in Fig. 38F. Calculate the angle of deviation for a ray like *F*, at a distance ¾ of the way up from the center line toward the edge. Assume the refractive index to be 1.3333. (*Ans.* 140°16′ or 140.27°.)

9. Solve Prob. 8 for the ray *K*, at a distance halfway up from the center line toward the edge.

Chapter 39

Lenses

39.1. Lenses. The primary function of a lens is to form images of real objects. Although most lenses are made of common glass, a few special lenses are made of other

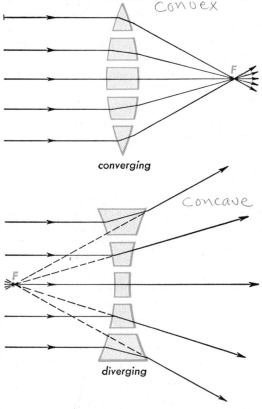

Fig. 39A *Matched sets of prisms illustrating lenslike action.*

transparent materials like *quartz* and *fluorite*. To understand the principles upon which a lens functions, imagine a set of several matched prisms and blocks of glass arranged in the order shown in Fig. 39A. In the first arrangement, the prisms are made

so as to refract the incoming parallel light rays and to converge them to a focus at *F*. In the second arrangement, the parallel rays are made to diverge as if they had come from a common point *F*. In each system the greatest deviation occurs at the outermost prisms, for they have the greatest angle between the two refracting surfaces. No deviation occurs for the central rays, for at that point the glass faces are parallel to each other.

A real lens is not made of prisms, as indicated in Fig. 39A, but of a solid piece of glass with surfaces ground to the form of a sphere. Cross sections of several standard forms are shown in Fig. 39B. The first three

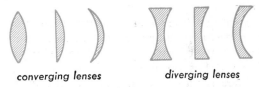

converging lenses · · · · diverging lenses

Fig. 39B *Cross sections of standard forms of common lenses.*

lenses, which are thicker in the center, are called *converging* or *positive lenses,* while the last three, which are thinner in the center, are called *diverging* or *negative lenses.* Special names attached to each of the six lens types shown are: (1) *double convex,* (2) *plano-convex,* (3) *convex miniscus,* (4) *double concave,* (5) *plano-concave,* and (6) *concave miniscus.*

There are two good reasons why lenses have spherical surfaces: first, with this shape they form reasonably good images; and second, a spherical form is by far the most practical shape to which smooth polished surfaces can be ground.

Diagrams showing the refraction of light

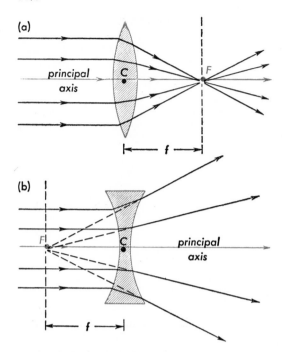

Fig. 39C *Converging and diverging lenses.*

from which parallel light rays appear to originate. *By symmetry every lens has two principal foci, one on each side of the lens and at the same distance from the center of the lens.* The distance from the focal point to the center of the lens is called the focal length.

$$CF = \text{focal length} = f$$

A plane perpendicular to the principal axis which passes through either principal focus is called the *focal plane.* Parallel light rays entering the lens from any other direction than shown in the diagrams will come to a focus at some point on the focal plane. This point is readily located by remembering that a ray through the center of the lens does not change in direction.

The greater the curvature of the two surfaces of a lens, the shorter is its focal length. The reason for this, as can be seen from the diagrams, is that the greater the curvature the greater is the deviation of the light rays passing through, near the edges of the lens.

One important principle concerning lenses is the reversibility of light rays. If a point source of light is placed at F in Fig. 39C(a), the rays of light that strike the lens will be refracted into a parallel beam of light moving to the left. Similarly, in Fig. 39C(b), if light rays are converging toward the focal point F they will be refracted by the lens into a parallel beam.

39.2 Image Formation. When an object

by converging and diverging lenses are given in Fig. 39C. The principal axis in each case is a straight line passing through the center of a lens perpendicular to the two faces at the points of intersection. The principal focus F lies on the principal axis; it is defined for a converging lens as the point where parallel light rays are brought together, and for a negative lens as a point

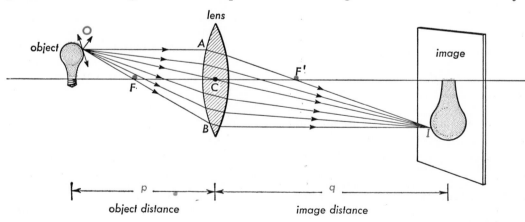

Fig. 39D *Ray diagram illustrating the formation of a real image by means of a single converging lens.*

is placed on one side of a converging lens beyond the principal focus, a real image will be formed on the opposite side of the lens. This is illustrated in Fig. 39D. If the object is moved closer to the focal point, the image will be formed farther away from the lens and will be bigger, that is, magnified. As the object is moved farther away from the lens, the image is formed closer to the focal point and is smaller in size.

In general there are two ways of accurately determining the position of an image: one is by graphical construction and the other is by use of the lens formula.

$$\frac{1}{p} + \frac{1}{q} = \frac{1}{f} \qquad (39a)$$

where *p is the object distance, q the image distance*, and *f the focal length.*

The graphical method is illustrated in Fig. 39E. Consider the light emitted by some one particular point like O in the object. Of the rays going out from this point in all

point, by the principle of the reversibility of light rays, will be refracted parallel to the principal axis, crossing the other ray at I, as shown.

The use of the lens formula can be illustrated by the following example. Let an object be placed 60 cm in front of a lens of focal length 20 cm. If we solve Eq. (39a) for q, we obtain the expression:

$$q = \frac{pf}{p - f} \qquad (39b)$$

Then substituting the known quantities, we obtain

$$q = \frac{60 \times 20}{60 - 20} = 30 \text{ cm}$$

The image is formed 30 cm from the lens or 10 cm from F.

The size of the image can be calculated from the following simple relation:

$$\frac{\text{size of image}}{\text{size of object}} = \frac{\text{image distance}}{\text{object distance}}$$

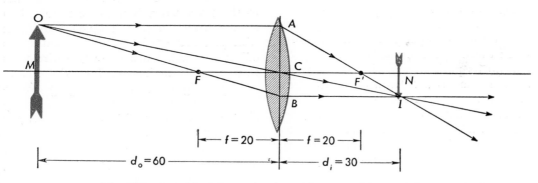

Fig. 39E   *Graphical determination of image position and size.*

directions, the ray OA traveling parallel to the principal axis will be refracted to pass through the focal point F (see Fig. 39C(a)). The ray OC arriving at the center of the lens where the faces are parallel will pass straight through, meeting the other ray at some point I. These two rays locate the tip of the image at I. All other rays from the point O which strike the lens will be brought to a focus at this same point. To check this, note that the ray OF, which passes from O through the left-hand focal

This is the image formula,

$$\frac{I}{O} = -\frac{q}{p} \qquad (39c)$$

in which the ratio I/O is called the *magnification*. If we substitute known values of O, p, and q from the above problem, as an example, we obtain

$$m = \frac{I}{O} = -\frac{30}{60} \qquad I = -\tfrac{1}{2}O$$

The answer shows that the image is half the size of the object and that the magnification is $\frac{1}{2}$. The minus sign means that the image is inverted.

If a centimeter rule is used to construct this problem graphically, the resultant diagram will be similar to Fig. 39E. Each line

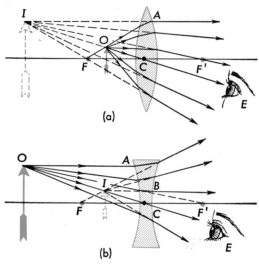

(a)

(b)

Fig. 39F   *The formation of virtual images.*

is drawn in its proper position and size, and when the image is located by rays (1), (2), and (3) its position and size are measured by the same scale. Drawn carefully, the graphical results will agree in every detail with those calculated by the above formulas.

39.3. Virtual Images. The images formed by the lenses in Figs. 39D and 39E are *real*. *Real images* are defined as those that can be formed on a screen and are characterized by the fact that rays of light are actually brought together to a focus there. *Virtual images* are not real, they cannot be formed on a screen, and the rays from different points on the object do not pass through corresponding points in the image. Virtual images may be observed with a converging lens by placing an object close to the lens and inside the focal point, or by a diverging lens with the object at any point. These two examples are illustrated in Fig. 39F.

In the first case the lens is used as a magnifier, or reading glass. Rays of light radiating from the point of the object at O

are refracted in the proper direction, but are not sufficiently deviated to come to a focus. To the observer's eye at E, these rays appear to be coming from a point I back of the lens. This is a *virtual image, right side up and magnified*. To find this image graphically, we observe that the ray FOA must be refracted parallel to the principal axis. The ray OC through the center of the lens goes on undeviated. These two refracted rays extended backward intersect at I. If the lens formula, Eq.(39b), is used to find the image in such a case, the image distance q will come out as a negative quantity, showing it to be a virtual image on the same side of the lens as the object.

In the case of a negative lens the image is always virtual, closer to the lens, and smaller in size than the object. As shown in Fig. 39F(b), light rays diverging from the object point O are made more divergent by the lens. To the observer's eye at E, these rays appear to be coming from the point I back of, but close to, the lens. To find this image we observe that the ray OA parallel to the principal axis must be refracted in such a direction that it appears to come from F. The ray OC through the center goes on undeviated. Since these two directions intersect at I, the image is formed there.

In applying the lens formula to a diverging lens, the focal length f is always *negative* in sign. To illustrate this, consider the following example.

Example 1. An object is placed 30 cm in front of a diverging lens of focal length of 15 cm. Locate the image position.

Solution. Direct substitution in Eq.(39b) gives

$$q = \frac{30 \times (-15)}{30 - (-15)} \quad \text{or} \quad q = \frac{-450}{45}$$

From which

$$q = -10 \text{ cm}$$

The image is found at 10 cm from the lens, the negative sign indicating that it is virtual and, therefore, on the same side of the lens as the object.

A convenient sign convention for all lens problems solved with Eq.(39b) is the following:

(1) Numerical values of real object distances are always positive.

(2) Numerical values of real image distances are positive; numerical values of virtual image distances are negative.

(3) Numerical values of focal lengths of convergent lenses are positive, of divergent lenses are negative.

39.4. Conjugate Foci. Since the lens equation, Eq.(39a), is symmetrical in p and q, it follows that a real image and the object from which it was formed may be interchanged. For example, in Figs. 39D and 39E, if the object is located at I, the image would be located at O. The distances p and q are called *conjugate distances, O and I conjugate points,* and the intersections of the optic axis with the object and image planes *conjugate foci.*

In demonstrating conjugate distances with a lens and screen, the object and the image can be interchanged in position, or the lens can be moved. If, for example, an object distance $p = 30$ cm and an image distance $q = 50$ cm, the lens may be moved to a new position $p = 50$ cm. The image will be formed at $q = 30$ cm. In other words, for a fixed distance between object and image screen, there are two lens positions of good image formation (see Fig. 39G). Because of the image-object relation, Eq.(39c), the two images will differ in size, the one being smaller than the object by the ratio 3:5 as shown by the solid arrow, and the other larger by the ratio 5:3 as shown by the dotted arrow.

39.5. The Lens Maker's Formula. To grind and polish a lens to some predetermined focal length, the refractive index of the glass should be known. Usually the refractive index is specified for the particular wavelength of yellow light emitted by a sodium lamp. With the index known, the radii of curvature of the two spherical surfaces can be calculated from the equation:

$$\frac{1}{f} = (\mu - 1)\left(\frac{1}{r_1} - \frac{1}{r_2}\right) \qquad (39d)$$

The sign convention for r_1 and r_2 is based upon the following rules:

(1) Light rays entering and passing through a lens are always drawn from left to right.

(2) When such a ray encounters a convex surface, the radius r is positive.

(3) When a light ray encounters a concave surface, the radius r is negative.

To illustrate the use of the lens maker's formula, consider the following example.

Example 2. A plano-convex lens having a focal length of 50 cm is to be made of glass of refractive index 1.52. Calculate the radius of curvature of the grinding and polishing tools that must be used to make this lens.

Solution. Since a plano-convex lens has one flat surface, the radius of curvature for that surface is infinite, and r_1 in Eq.(39d) is replaced by ∞. r_2 is the unknown. Direct substitution of all known quantities in the formula gives

$$\frac{1}{50} = (1.52 - 1)\left(\frac{1}{\infty} - \frac{1}{r_2}\right) \qquad (39e)$$

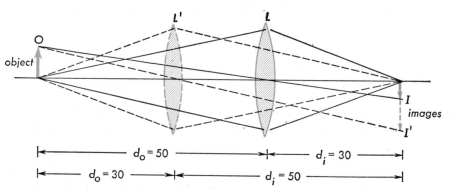

Fig. 39G *Conjugate foci for a single converging lens.*

Transpose and solve for r_2.

$$\frac{1}{50} = (0.52)\left(0 - \frac{1}{r_2}\right), \qquad \frac{1}{50} = -\frac{0.52}{r_2}$$

which gives

$$r_2 = -50 \times 0.52 = -26.0 \text{ cm}$$

39.6. Defects of the Image. Although a simple converging lens may be made to form a relatively clear image of almost any object, there is present in every image a number of common defects tending to blur it. These defects are known as *spherical aberration, chromatic aberration, curvature of field, astigmatism, distortion,* and *coma.* Although some of these *aberrations,* as they are called, can be partly or almost entirely corrected by one means or another, they cannot all be eliminated entirely. These corrections are refinements that are usually considered in the design of lenses and are of some importance in the understanding of the principal action of a lens. We will be content to consider briefly the first three defects mentioned above—namely, spherical aberration, chromatic aberration, and curvature of field.

39.7. Spherical Aberration. Spherical aberration is an undesirable defect in the focusing properties of single glass lenses and is attributed to the fact that spherical surfaces are not exactly the correct surfaces to which a lens should be ground and polished. The reason they are not correct is shown for a double convex lens in Fig. 39H. Rays

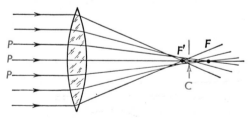

Fig. 39H *Spherical aberration of a lens. P, paraxial rays; C, circle of least confusion.*

of light parallel to the principal axis which pass through the outer parts of the lens are not brought to exactly the same focus as those rays passing through the central por-tion. The result is that nowhere can a sharply defined image of a distant object be formed on a screen.

When a screen is placed between F and F' and a blurred image is obtained, it is not difficult to find a position where the least blurring occurs. This point, C in the diagram, is called the *circle of least confusion.*

There are various ways in which spheri-cal aberration in a lens may be reduced. Some of these are easily carried out, while others require expert lens design.

(1) The easiest way to reduce spherical aberration is to place a circular diaphragm in front of the lens and allow only the central bundle of rays to pass through. Such a procedure reduces the size of the circle of least confusion and thereby produces sharper images. This is one of the functions of the *iris diaphragm* in the lens cell of a camera. The smaller the effective diameter of a lens, the more sharply defined are its image-focusing properties. Reduced aper-ture, however, reduces the light-gathering power and for some purposes is not desir-able.

Rays passing through or near the center of a lens, and at the same time making rela-tively small angles with the principal axis, are called *paraxial rays.* It is for such rays only that reasonably sharp focus is obtained and the equations used in the preceding sec-tions can be applied.

(2) Because peripheral rays are deviated through too great an angle (see Fig. 39H), any method that will bring about lesser de-viation from the outer edges of a lens will result in better focusing. The principle of minimum deviation offers one such method, because by carefully selecting the radii of curvature for the two lens faces, the periph-eral rays can be brought to much more nearly the same focal point as the paraxial rays (see Fig. 39I). In diagram (a), parallel rays entering normal to the flat surface of a plano-convex lens are refracted at the sec-ond surface only, the outer rays being de-viated through too great an angle. In (b), the outer rays, because they enter one face and leave the other at nearly the same

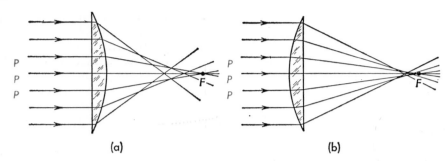

Fig. 39I *Spherical aberration for parallel rays is different on the two sides of a plane-convex lens. P, paraxial rays.*

angle, are near minimum deviation and cross the axis farther out. If, for any given object distance and image distance, the radii of curvature r_1 and r_2 are so chosen that *the peripheral rays pass through the lens at minimum deviation*, the lens will have a minimum of spherical aberration.

(3) To correct for spherical aberration, the two lens surfaces are sometimes ground and polished to other than a spherical form. Such a process, called *aspherizing*, is not only tedious and difficult, but any lens so made is good for only one pair of object and image distances.

(4) A fourth method of correcting spherical aberration is to combine a positive crown glass lens with a negative flint glass lens. Although both lenses have spherical surfaces, the curvatures of the two can be so chosen that the errors of one practically cancel those of the other.

39.8. Chromatic Aberration. When white light passes through a lens close to the edge,

it is dispersed in much the same way that it is when passing through a large angle prism (see Fig. 39J). The violet light, being deviated the most, comes to a focus nearer the lens than the red. The ray passing through the center of the lens and along the principal axis is not dispersed. For white light a single lens, therefore, cannot possibly form a sharply defined image.

To correct a lens for chromatic aberration, use is made of the principle of the achromatic prism (see Fig. 38C(a)). Two prisms, one of crown glass, the other of flint glass, are so chosen that when placed in opposition they produce deviation without dispersion.

A similar combination can be constructed of flint and crown glass lenses, as illustrated in Fig. 39K, whereby the dispersion in one lens is compensated for by the opposite dispersion in the other, and yet the light is deviated to bring all colors to a common focus. Such a combination is called an

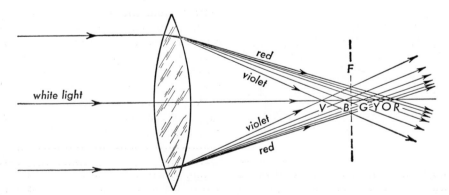

Fig. 39J *Ray diagram illustrating chromatic aberration with a single converging lens.*

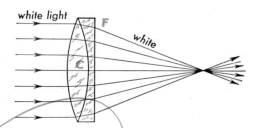

Fig. 39K *Achromatic lens combination.*

achromatic lens. All first-class optical instruments use achromatic lenses. By the proper selection of surface curvatures, spherical aberration as well as chromatic aberration can be minimized with two lenses. The two exposed surfaces are chosen to give minimum deviation, and the two inner surfaces adjusted to correct chromatic aberration.*

* For a more complete account of geometrical optics, see *Optics,* by Jenkins and White, McGraw-Hill.

When two *thin* lenses are placed in contact, the combination behaves as a single lens with a focal length of its own. If f_1 and f_2 represent the focal lengths of the two lenses, respectively, the equivalent focal length f of the combination is given by

$$\frac{1}{f} = \frac{1}{f_1} + \frac{1}{f_2} \qquad (39f)$$

Example 3. An achromatic lens is composed of two lenses: a converging crown glass lens with a focal length of 8 in. and a diverging flint glass lens with a focal length of 12 in. Find the equivalent focal length.

Solution. The two focal lengths given are $f_1 = +8$ in., and $f_2 = -12$ in. Substitution in Eq.(39f) gives

$$\frac{1}{f} = \frac{1}{8} - \frac{1}{12} \qquad \frac{1}{f} = \frac{3}{24} - \frac{2}{24} \qquad \frac{1}{f} = \frac{1}{24}$$

from which $f = 24$ in.

PROBLEMS

1. A converging lens has a focal length of +12 in. Find the position and size of the image if an object 3 in. high is located in front of the lens at a distance of (a) 60 in., (b) 30 in., (c) 18 in., (d) 12 in., (e) 8 in., and (f) 4 in.

2. A converging lens has a focal length of +16 cm. Find the position and size of the image if an object 4 cm high is located in front of the lens at a distance of (a) 80 cm, (b) 32 cm, (c) 20 cm, (d) 16 cm, and (e) 8 cm. (*Ans.* (a) 20 cm, −1 cm; (b) 32 cm, −4 cm; (c) 80 cm, −16 cm; (d) ∞, ∞; (e) −16 cm, +8 cm.)

3. Solve Prob. 2 if the lens is diverging.

4. Solve Prob. 1 if the lens is diverging. (*Ans.* (a) −10, +0.5; (b) −8.57, +0.857; (c) −7.2, +1.2; (d) −6.0, +1.5; (e) −4.8, +1.8; (f) −3.0, +2.25 in.)

5. An object 5 cm high is located 12 cm in front of a converging lens of focal length +8 cm. Find (a) the position, and (b) the size of the image by the lens formula and by the graphical method.

6. An object 2 in. high is located 30 in. in front of a converging lens of focal length +18 in. Find (a) the position, and (b) the size of the

image by the lens formula and by the graphical method. (*Ans.* (a) 45 in., (b) −3.0 in.)

7. An object 2 ft high is located 10 ft in front of a diverging lens whose focal length is −6 ft. Find the position and size of the image.

8. An object 5 cm high is located 20 cm in front of a diverging lens of focal length −8 cm. Find the size and position of the image. (*Ans.* +1.43 cm, −5.72 cm.)

9. A double convex lens of index 1.50 has the following radii: $r_1 = +20$ cm, and $r_2 = -12$ cm. Find its focal length.

10. A double convex lens of index 1.75 has the following radii: $r_1 = +7$ cm, and $r_2 = -21$ cm. Calculate its focal length. (*Ans.* +7.0 cm.)

11. A concave miniscus lens with radii $r_1 = -24$ cm and $r_2 = -6$ cm. Find its focal length if the refractive index is 1.58.

12. A miniscus lens with radii $r_1 = -40$ in. and $r_2 = -8$ in., has an index 1.55. Find its focal length. (*Ans.* +18.1 in.)

13. A growing flower is planted 9 ft from a wall. Where should a lens be placed to form a real image on the wall if its focal length is +2 ft?

14. A lens with a focal length of +20 cm is used to form a real image on a screen 120 cm from an object. How far from the object should the lens be placed? (*Ans.* 25.3 cm or 94.7 cm.)

15. An object 5 cm high is located 60 cm in front of a converging lens of focal length +15 cm. A diverging lens of focal length −60 cm is located 5 cm beyond the first lens. (a) Where is the final image located, and (b) what is its size and nature?

16. An object 3 cm high is located on the axis 60 cm in front of a lens of focal length +20 cm. A second lens of focal length +40 cm is located 5 cm beyond the first lens. (a) Where is the final image located, and (b) what is its size and nature? (*Ans.* Real, inverted, .92 cm high, and at 15.4 cm from second lens.)

17. Sunlight falls on a divergent lens with a focal length of 20 cm. If a converging lens with a focal length of 20 cm is located 5 cm beyond this lens, where should a screen be placed to receive the sun's image?

18. Three lenses with focal lengths of +20 cm, −20 cm, and +20 cm, respectively, are spaced in line with their centers 2 cm apart. If the sunlight enters the first lens along its axis, where will the final image of the sun be located? (*Ans.* 18 cm from the third lens.)

19. Where should an object be placed in front of a lens of +20 cm focal length if the image to be formed is twice the size of the object and (a) real, and (b) virtual?

20. Where should an object be placed in front of a lens of focal length +12 in. if the image to be formed is three times the size of the object and is real and inverted? (*Ans.* 16 in.)

21. The radii of the two surfaces of a double convex lens are measured as 10 cm and 30 cm, respectively. If its focal length is measured to be +28 cm, what is the refractive index of the glass?

22. The radii of a concave miniscus lens are measured as −20 cm and −5 cm. If its focal length is measured to be +9.0 cm, what is the refractive index of the glass? (*Ans.* 1.741.)

23. A plano-concave flint glass lens with an index 1.65, and an equi-convex crown glass lens with an index 1.53 are placed in contact to make an achromatic lens. If all curved surfaces have radii of 50 cm, find the equivalent focal length.

24. An equi-convex crown glass lens with an index 1.63 and a plano-concave flint glass lens with an index 1.52 are placed in contact to make an achromatic telescope objective lens. If all curved surfaces have radii of 40 cm, find the equivalent focal length. (*Ans.* 54.0 cm.)

Chapter 40

Spherical Mirrors

40.1. Concave Mirrors. The concave mirror is an optical device which, like a glass lens, may by pure reflection form images on a screen. Such mirrors are often used in optical instruments in place of a lens. There are several very good reasons for this, one of them being that the concave mirror does not exhibit chromatic aberration, and another that there is but one curved surface to prepare and polish instead of two or more.

A spherical mirror has the form of a circular section of a hollow sphere as shown in cross section in Fig. 40.A. The center

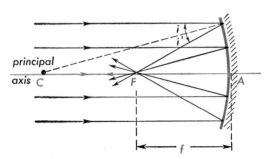

Fig. 40A   *The focal point F and focal length f of a concave mirror.*

point *A* of the section is called the *vertex,* and a line from the center of curvature of the sphere through the vertex is called the *principal axis.* The radius of the sphere *r* is called the *radius of the mirror.*

Because spherical mirrors are symmetrical about their axes, cross-section diagrams are sufficient to show their optical properties. If the mirror is silvered on the inner surface, it is called a *concave mirror,* while if silvered on the outer surface, it is a *convex mirror.*

The cross-section diagram of Fig. 40A

shows how a beam of parallel light is reflected by a concave mirror. Each ray striking the mirror obeys the law of reflection, namely, that the angle of incidence *i* equals the angle of reflection *i'*.

The point *F* where the rays cross the principal axis is called the *principal* focus, and the distance *A* to *F* is called the *focal length f.*

If the mirror is silvered on the outer surface as in Fig. 40B, it becomes a **convex**

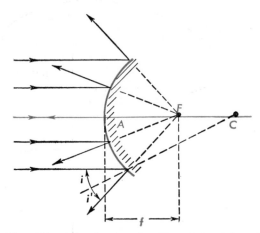

Fig. 40B   *The focal point F and focal length f of a convex mirror.*

mirror, and parallel incident light rays are reflected as if they came from a point *F* on the axis. The different rays, each obeying the law of reflection, diverge after reflection and never come to a focus.

Nevertheless, the distance *A* to *F* is called the *focal length* of the convex mirror and it is assigned a minus sign in all optical formulas.

40.2. Image Formation. If an illuminated object *O* is located in front of a concave

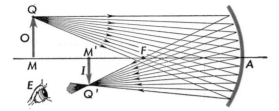

Fig. 40C   *A concave mirror forms a real image.*

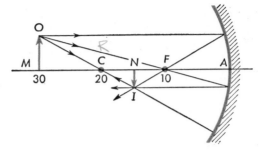

Fig. 40D   *Graphical construction for locating the image formed by a concave mirror.*

mirror as shown in Fig. 40C, a real image *I* can be formed nearby. All rays emitted by the object point *Q* and reflected by the mirror come to a focus at *Q'*. All rays emitted by the object point *M* (not shown) would upon reflection come to a focus at *M'*. For every object point in *QM* emitting rays, there will be a corresponding image point in *Q'M'* where focus is produced.

If the eye is located at *E*, the illuminated object will appear at *Q'M'*, but inverted. If a screen is located at *Q'M'*, a sharply defined image will be observed there. Because the image can be formed on a screen, it is called a *real image*.

The geometry of the reflection from a concave or convex mirror is such that the focal length *AF* is always equal to ½ the radius of curvature *r*, where *r* = *AC*, and *C* is the center of curvature. As an equation,

$$AF = \tfrac{1}{2}AC \quad \text{or} \quad f = -\frac{r}{2} \quad (40a)$$

Furthermore the lens formula, Eq.(39a), holds for mirrors as well as for lenses, *p*, *q*, and *f* having the same meaning as before.

$$\boxed{\frac{1}{p} + \frac{1}{q} = \frac{1}{f}} \quad (40b)$$

As an illustration of the image-forming properties of a concave spherical mirror, consider the graphical construction in Fig. 40D. An object *O* is located 30 cm from a concave mirror of radius *r* = −20 cm, center at *C*. By Eq.(40a) *F* must be halfway between *A* and *C*, giving *f* = +10 cm.

A light ray from *O* parallel to the principal axis is reflected, by definition of the focal point, through *F*. By the reversibility of light rays, another ray from *O* passing

through *F* is reflected parallel to the principal axis. Where these two rays cross at *I*, the image is formed. A third ray from *O* through the center of curvature *C* strikes the mirror normally and is reflected back on itself where it passes through *I*. Any two of these three rays are sufficient to locate the image. The third ray is then a check upon the other two.

To solve this mirror arrangement as a problem, Eq.(40b) can be applied directly. Given are the quantities, *p* = 30 cm, *f* = +10 cm. By substitution

$$\frac{1}{30} + \frac{1}{q} = \frac{1}{10} \qquad \frac{1}{q} = \frac{1}{10} - \frac{1}{30} \qquad \frac{1}{q} = \frac{3}{30} - \frac{1}{30}$$

from which

$$\frac{1}{q} = \frac{2}{30} \quad \text{and} \quad q = \frac{30}{2} = 15 \text{ cm}$$

An interesting experiment can be performed with a large concave mirror under the conditions illustrated in Fig. 40E. A flower hanging upside down in a box and placed just below the center of curvature

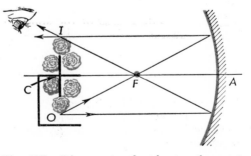

Fig. 40E   *Diagram for the phantom bouquet.*

$$f = -\left(\frac{-20}{2}\right) = 10$$

will form a real and erect image at O directly above. An observer to the left cannot see the flower directly but can see the real image. So real is this image that it cannot be distinguished from a real object; the rays of light as shown in the diagram diverge from I, the same as they would if the object were located there.

In Fig. 40F an object is placed inside the focal point; the rays after reflection

virtual and cannot be formed on a screen. When in using Eq.(40b) the focal length of a convex mirror is known, its value is substituted with a minus sign.

Although spherical mirrors do not produce chromatic aberration, they do exhibit other aberrations common to lenses. In Fig. 40G the focusing property of a large aper-

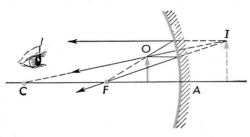

Fig. 40F   *Diagram showing the formation of a virtual image.*

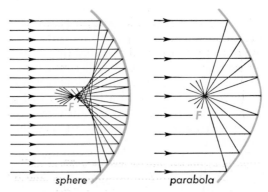

Fig. 40G   *Diagrams showing the caustic curve obtained with a spherical mirror and the point focus with a paraboloidal mirror.*

diverge as if they had come from the point I. To the eye of an observer at E, a virtual image is seen magnified and right side up at I. As a problem, let the object distance $p = 10$ cm, the focal length $f = +20$ cm. Substitution of these in Eq.(40b) gives

$$\frac{1}{10} + \frac{1}{q} = \frac{1}{20} \quad \frac{1}{q} = \frac{1}{20} - \frac{1}{10} \quad \frac{1}{q} = \frac{1}{20} - \frac{2}{20}$$

from which

$$\frac{1}{q} = -\frac{1}{20} \quad \text{or} \quad q = -20 \text{ cm}$$

The image is located 20 cm from the mirror, the minus sign indicating that it is virtual and on the opposite side of the mirror from the object.

No matter where a real object is located in front of a convex mirror, the image is

ture mirror is compared with that of a parabolic mirror. Like a spherical lens, a spherical mirror deviates the outer rays to a shorter focus than those near the center. This focusing defect is called *spherical aberration*. The parabola, on the other hand, brings all rays to focus at one point. A small source of light located at the focal point of a parabolic reflector becomes a parallel beam after reflection, a principle used in spotlights, searchlights, and automobile headlights.

Spherical aberration for a spherical mirror is reduced by reducing the aperture or, what is the same thing, by keeping the focal length large compared with the reflector diameter.

PROBLEMS

1. An object 3 cm high is located 15 cm in front of a concave mirror $r = -12$ cm. Find graphically and by formula the (a) position, and (b) size of the image.

2. An object 9 in. high is located on the axis and 20 in. from a concave mirror of radius $r = -16$ in. Find graphically and by formula (a) the position, and (b) the size of the image. (*Ans.* (a) 13.3 cm in., (b) −6 in.)

3. Solve Prob. 2 if the mirror is convex with $r = +20$ in.

4. Solve Prob. 1 if the mirror is convex with $r = +10$ cm. (*Ans.* (a) −3.75 cm, (b) +0.75 cm.)

5. An object 2 cm high is located 20 cm in front of a concave mirror of 16-cm radius. Find the image distance (a) graphically, and (b) by formula. (c) What is the image height?

6. An object 1 cm high is located 10 cm in front of a concave mirror of 12-cm radius. Find the image position (a) graphically, and (b) by formula. (c) What is the image height? (*Ans.* (a) +15 cm, (b) +15 cm, (c) −1.5 cm.)

7. An object 1.5 cm high is located 4 cm in front of a concave mirror having a 20-cm radius. Find the image position (a) graphically, and (b) by formula. (c) Find the image height.

8. An object 2 cm high is located 5 cm in front of a concave mirror having a 30-cm radius. Find the image position (a) graphically, and (b) by formula. (c) Find the image height. (*Ans.* (a) −7.5 cm, (b) −7.5 cm, (c) +3.0 cm.)

9. An object 2 in. high is located 12 in. in front of a convex mirror of 16-in. radius. Find (a) the image position, and (b) the image size. (c) Find the image graphically.

10. An object 3 cm high is located 5 cm in front of a convex mirror of 10-cm focal length. (a) Where is the image formed? (b) Is the image real or virtual? (c) Find the image graphically. (*Ans.* (a) −3.3 cm, (b) virtual, (c) −3.3 cm.)

11. An object 1.5 cm high is located 6 cm in front of a convex mirror of 24-cm radius. (a) Find the image distance. Graphically find (b) the image distance, and (c) the image height.

12. An object 2 cm high is located 6 cm in front of a convex mirror of 6-cm focal length. (a) Find the image distance. (b) Graphically find the image distance. (*Ans.* (a) −3.0 cm, (b) −3.0 cm.)

13. A concave mirror has a focal length of 10 in. Where should an object be placed if the image distance is to be three times the object distance?

14. A concave mirror has a focal length of 12 cm. Where should an object be placed to form a virtual image twice as far from the mirror? (*Ans.* +6.0 cm.)

Chapter 41

Optical Instruments

41.1. The Camera. Since the photographic camera employs but a single lens unit, it may be considered as one of the simplest of all optical instruments. As illustrated by the roll-film camera in Fig. 41A, a converging lens forms a *real* and

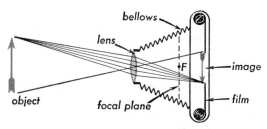

Fig. 41A *Diagram of the image formation by a camera.*

inverted image on the film. If the object is far away, the light rays approaching the lens are nearly parallel and the image is formed at the focal plane. If the object is close up, the image will be formed beyond the focal plane as shown in the diagram. To permit distant landscapes or "close ups" to be taken with the same camera, a bellows is used, allowing the lens distance to be varied at will. Motion of the lens to the proper image distance is called *focusing.*

Only a simple converging lens is used in the cheapest of cameras, which means that all of the common defects of images are present to give rise to a slightly blurred or diffuse image. In more expensive cameras, however, the most objectionable defects are fairly well corrected by a compound lens made of several individual lenses. As a rule, a good camera lens will contain from three to five lens elements and will partially correct for *chromatic aberration, spherical aberration, astigmatism,* and *curvature of field.*

The purpose of an iris diaphragm is to decrease the effective aperture of a lens and hence increase its *f*-number. Such practice is desirable in photographing still objects because the smaller the lens opening, the sharper will be the focus of near and far as well as central and peripheral objects.

The f-number of a lens is equal to its focal length divided by its diameter.

41.2. The Eye. Some aspects of this most remarkable optical instrument, the human eye, have been presented in Chap. 1. There it was pointed out that a single eye is in principle an exceptionally fine camera, with an elaborate lens system on one side and a sensitive screen or photographic film called the *retina* on the other.

When light from a distant object passes through the lens system of the eye, it is refracted and brought to a focus on the retina. There a real but inverted image of the object is formed. It is a most amazing fact that, while all retinal images are inverted, as shown in Fig. 41B, they are interpreted as being erect.

Accommodation is the ability to focus the eyes on near and far objects. In a camera the focusing of a picture on the photographic film or plate is accomplished by moving the lens toward or away from the film. In the human eye, however, *focusing is brought about by changing the shape of the crystalline lens.* This is accomplished by a rather complicated system of ligaments and muscles. Due to a tension which exists in the lens capsule (see Fig. 1B), the crystalline lens, if completely free, would tend to become spherical in shape. The edge of the

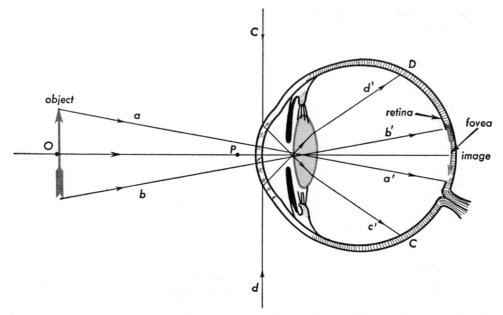

Fig. 41B   *The human eye is similar to a camera. All retinal images are inverted.*

lens is surrounded by the *ciliary muscle* which, by contracting, causes the lens to bulge out. This reduces the focal length of the lens, bringing nearby objects to focus on the retina. When the ciliary muscle relaxes, the suspensory ligaments, being under tension, pull at the edges of the lens, thus tending to flatten it. Under these conditions the focal length increases, bringing distant objects to focus on the retina. This is the accommodation process.

The normal eye is most relaxed when it is focused for parallel light, i.e., for objects far away. To study the detail of an object,

however, the object should be brought close to the eye. The reason for this is that the closer the object is to the eye, the larger is the image formed on the retina. A distance of about 10 in. is found to be the distance of most distinct vision. Prolonged observation at distances of 10 in. or less will result in a considerable amount of fatigue and eyestrain.

41.3. Eye Correction with Spectacle Lenses. As the average person grows older the crystalline lens of the eye tends to harden and the muscles that control it to grow weaker, thus making accommodation

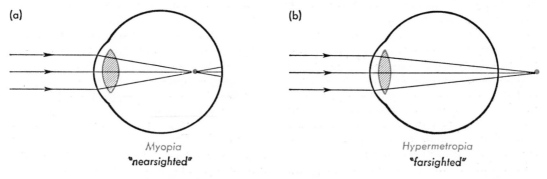

Fig. 41C   *Typical eye conditions of certain humans.*

more and more difficult. The existence of these conditions is referred to as *presbyopia*. The speed of the hardening varies among individuals. If the length of the eyeball is such that parallel incident rays converge to a point in front of the retina (see Fig. 41C(a)), the person is nearsighted and is said by the eye specialist to have *myopia*. If parallel incident rays converge to a point behind the retina, as in diagram (b), the person is farsighted and is said to have *hypermetropia*.

To correct these defects a diverging spectacle lens of the proper focal length is placed in front of the myopic eye and a converging lens of the proper focal length in front of the hypermetropic eye. The function of such lenses is shown in Fig. 41D.

mology to express the focal length of any lens in *diopters* and to speak of the power of a lens in such terms.

The power of a lens in diopters is given by the reciprocal of the focal length in meters.

$$\frac{1 \text{ meter}}{\text{focal length in meters}} = \text{diopters}$$

$$\boxed{\frac{1}{f} = P} \qquad (41a)$$

A lens with a focal length of $+50$ cm, for example, has a power of $+2$ diopters (D), $P = +2$ D, whereas one of $+20$ cm focal length has a power of $+5$ D, $P = +5$ D, etc. Converging lenses have a plus power while

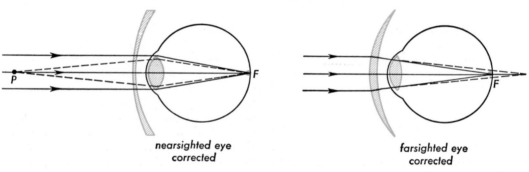

nearsighted eye
corrected

farsighted eye
corrected

Fig. 41D *Nearsighted and farsighted eyes can be corrected by the proper selection of spectacle lenses.*

For the nearsighted eye, rays from a nearby object at some point P will, in the absence of spectacles, come to focus on the fovea F. Insertion of the proper diverging lens will now diverge parallel rays as if they came from P and thus bring a distant object to focus at F. For the farsighted eye, a converging lens adds some convergence to the incoming rays before they meet the eye lens and thus enables distant objects to be seen in good focus. To see close at hand, this same eye requires the use of a converging lens of still greater power. In other words this person should wear bi-focals, lenses whose upper and lower halves have different focal lengths.

It is customary in optometry and ophthal-

diverging lenses have a minus power. Spectacle lenses are made to the nearest quarter of a diopter, thereby reducing the number of grinding and polishing tools required in the optical shops. Furthermore, the sides next to the eyes are always concave to permit free movement of the eyelashes and yet keep the lens as close to the eye as possible as they turn one way and then another.

When, with age, practically all accommodation has been lost, even the normal eye will require a lens of about $+3$ D to obtain good vision of objects at a normal reading distance. As illustrated by the dotted lines in Fig. 41E(a), parallel rays entering the unaided eye are brought to a good focus on the retina R. For an object

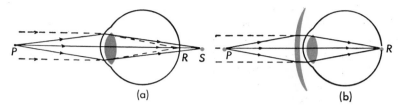

Fig. 41E *The normal eye, having lost accommodation because of age, sees distant objects in good focus. To see nearby objects in focus requires spectacle lenses.*

close by, however, the power of the eye lens is not great enough and the rays converge toward a point S beyond the retina. With an object P located $33\frac{1}{3}$ cm away and a $+3$ D lens in front of the eye, diagram (b), parallel rays enter the eye from the lens and are brought to a good focus on the retina R.

The principal advantage of the diopter system of measuring lens action is that, when two or more thin lenses are placed in contact, their combined power is just the sum of their separate powers. From Eq.(39f), and the use of Eq.(41a) for power,

$$\frac{1}{f} = \frac{1}{f_1} + \frac{1}{f_2}$$

or

$$P = P_1 + P_2 \tag{41b}$$

The power P of a combination of two thin lenses is equal to the sum of the powers of the two separately. As an illustration, two lenses of $+2\frac{1}{4}$ D and $+3\frac{1}{2}$ D respectively give, in combination, a power of $+5\frac{3}{4}$ D; and two lenses of $+3\frac{1}{2}$ D and $-2\frac{1}{4}$ D, respectively, give a power of $+1\frac{1}{4}$ D.

Example. A person with hypermetropia (see Fig. 41C) requires a $+1\frac{1}{4}$ D spectacle lens to see objects clearly at a great distance (see Fig. 41E(b)). What power spectacles will this person require to see objects at 20 in. (or 50 cm)?

Solution. Since lens powers are additive, a lens can be added to the one already present, and of such a power that it will take the rays from any point on an object 50 cm away and make them parallel. A lens of focal length 50 cm will do just this, and by Eq.(41a) corresponds to a power of $+2$ D. Combining a $+2$ D lens with the $+1\frac{1}{4}$ D already required gives an equivalent power of $3\frac{1}{4}$ D. Therefore, spectacle lenses with a power of $+3\frac{1}{4}$ D should be worn.

It frequently happens that the cornea acquires a greater curvature in one plane than in another. Such irregularities are called *astigmatism.* Whether accommodation by the crystalline lens has been lost or not, such eyes require astigmatic spectacle lenses, that is, lenses that have more curvature in one direction than at right angles. The surfaces of such lenses are not spherical and are a little more difficult to grind and polish.

41.4. The Telescope. History informs us that the first telescope was probably constructed in Holland in 1608 by an obscure spectacle lens grinder, Hans Lippershey. A few months later Galileo, upon hearing that objects at a distance may be made to appear close at hand by means of two lenses, designed and made with his own hands the first authentic telescope. The elements of this telescope are still in existence and may be seen on exhibit in Florence, Italy.

Astronomical telescopes today are practically the same in principle as they were in the earliest days of their development. A diagram of a small telescope is shown in Fig. 41F. Light rays from a single point of a far distant object are shown entering the objective lens as a parallel beam. These rays are brought to a focus and form a point image at I. In a similar manner, parallel sets of rays from other points of the same object (not shown) will form point images in the focal plane of the objective. Assuming that the distant object is an arrow pointing upward, the image, as shown in the diagram by a black arrow, is *real* and *inverted.*

The function of the second lens in a telescope is to magnify the image formed

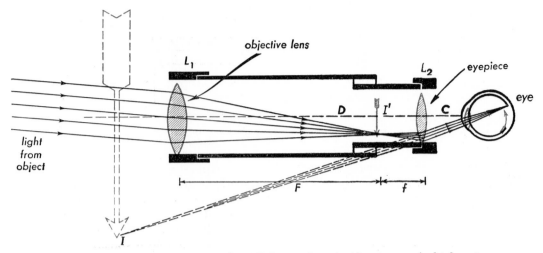

Fig. 41F   *Illustration of the paths of light rays in a simple astronomical telescope.*

by the objective. For this purpose a converging lens of short focus, called the *eyepiece,* is usually used. If the eyepiece is moved to a position where the image *I* is just inside its focal plane, a magnified image *I'* will be seen by the eye. For normal observation, the image *I* and the focal planes of both lenses are in conjunction, and the light emerging from the eyepiece is parallel. The image *I'* under these conditions appears to be far off to the left of L_1, "at infinity," and is of approximately the same angular size as shown in the diagram. Actually, of course, the final image is the one formed on the retina by rays that appear to have come from *I'*.

The magnifying power of a telescope is defined as the ratio between the angle subtended at the eye by the final image *I'* and the angle subtended at the eye by the object itself. In other words, it is the number of times larger an object appears to be when viewed with the telescope. When plane geometry is applied to a simple light-ray diagram of a telescope, it is found that the magnifying power is equal to the ratio of the focal lengths of the two lenses.

$$\text{magnifying power} = -\frac{F}{f} \quad (41c)$$

where *F* is the focal length of the objective,

and *f* is the focal length of the eyepiece.

As an illustration, suppose the objective lens of a small telescope has a focal length of one yard and that it is used with an eyepiece having a focal length of 1 in.; the magnifying power would be 36/1 or 36. Distant objects viewed through this telescope would appear to be 36 times as tall and 36 times as wide as when viewed with the unaided eye. If an eyepiece with a focal length of only half an inch is used with the same objective, the magnification will be twice as great, or 72.

This would seem to indicate that the magnification of a telescope can be increased indefinitely, but this is not the case. There are a number of factors that set a practical upper limit, the chief one of which for small telescopes is the diameter of the objective lens.

If a telescope is to be used for astronomical purposes only, an inverted image is of no consequence to the observer, but if it is to be used to observe objects on the earth the magnified images should be right side up. Instruments that give erect images are called *terrestrial telescopes.* To right the inverted image in a telescope, any one of several methods may be employed: one is to use a third lens, and another is to insert an erecting prism of the type shown in Fig. 37L(c) just in front of the eyepiece in place of the converging lens. A third method is the arrangement devised by Galileo in his first telescopes, and now commonly used in *field* and *opera glasses* (see Fig. 41G).

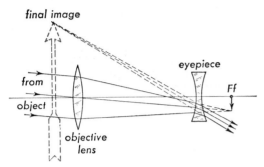

Fig. 41G *Lens and ray diagram of an opera glass, or Galilean telescope.*

41.5. Prism Binoculars. Prism binoculars are in reality a pair of twin telescopes mounted side by side, one for each of the two eyes. The objective lenses in front and the eyepieces at the rear are converging lenses as in the astronomical telescope, but each pair of total reflecting prisms (see Fig. 41H) inverts the rays to give erect images.

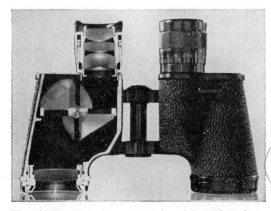

Fig. 41H *Cutaway of a prism binocular showing the lenses and reflecting prisms.* (Courtesy, Bausch & Lomb Optical Company)

The doubling-back of the light rays has the advantage of enabling long-focus objective lenses to be used in short tubes, thus giving higher magnification. In addition to good achromatic lenses and accurately ground prisms, there are three features that go to

make up good binoculars: these are (1) *magnification*, (2) *field of view*, and (3) *light-gathering power*.

For hand-held use, binoculars with a 6-, 7-, or 8-power magnification are most generally useful. Glasses with powers above 8 are desirable but require a tripod mount to hold them steady. For powers less than 4, lens aberrations usually offset the magnification and the average person can usually see better with the unaided eyes.

The field of view is determined principally by the eyepiece aperture and should be as large as is practical. For 7-power binoculars, a 6° field taken in by the objective is considered large since, in the eyepiece, the same field is spread over an angle of 7 × 6 or 42°.

The diameter of each objective lens determines the light-gathering power, and is important at night only when there is so little light available.

Binoculars with the specification of 6 × 30 have a magnification of 6 and objective lenses with an effective diameter of 30 mm. The specification 7 × 50 means a magnification of 7 and objective lenses 50 mm in diameter. Although glasses with the latter specifications are excellent day or night, they are considerably larger and more cumbersome than daytime glasses specified as 6 × 30's or 8 × 30's. For general civilian use, the latter two types are by far the most useful.

41.6. The Reflection Telescope. Nearly all of the very large astronomical telescopes in the world today employ concave mirrors instead of lenses. There are several advantages to this: first, a concave mirror does not exhibit chromatic aberration, thereby requiring but one piece of glass and one surface to be ground; and second, greater stability of the telescope is attained by having the large and heaviest optical part at the bottom of the instrument.

A diagram of the great 100-in. reflecting telescope of the Mt. Wilson Observatory is shown in Fig. 41I. Parallel light rays entering the telescope tube are brought to a focus at *F*. Instead of viewing or photographing images at this point, a small mir-

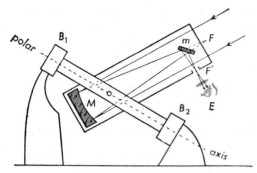

Fig. 41I *Diagram of the 100-in. reflecting telescope of the Mt. Wilson Observatory.*

ror *m* reflects the convergent rays to a focus at *F'*. Here, out of the path of the incoming light, the star images can be observed and photographed. While the small mirror *m* casts a shadow on the objective mirror *M*, the shadow area is relatively small so that only a small per cent of the light is lost.

The new 200-in. telescope now in operation on Palomar Mountain in Southern California is of the same optical design. The objective mirror is a little over 16 ft in diameter and has a hole 40 in. in diameter through its center. This hole cuts out only 4% of the mirror's total area. For various kinds of observations, photographic instruments and cameras of one kind or another are located in an observing booth 40 in. in diameter and located at the focal plane, *F*, in Fig. 41I. On other occasions a 40-in. con-

vex mirror is placed at *m*, and the light is reflected back down the telescope tube through the hole in the big objective where it is brought to a focus below the telescope.

41.7. The Microscope. The simplest of microscopes is just a single converging lens of short focus used as a magnifier as shown in Fig. 39F(a). Since the shortest focal length lenses produce the greatest magnification, it is not surprising that small glass beads in the form of perfect spheres were the first really successful microscopes. Lenses of this description were used by the famous Dutch microscopist, Van Leeuwenhoek, when in 1674 he discovered and gave an accurate account of the red corpuscles in blood.

The compound microscope, which now exceeds by far the magnifying power of a simple microscope, was invented by Galileo in 1610. Like a telescope, these instruments consist of an optical train of two lenses, one called the objective and the other the eyepiece. The objective of the microscope differs from the telescope, however, in that, instead of having a long focus, it has a short focus and it is placed close to the object as shown in Fig. 41J. This lens forms a real and magnified image at a point *I* just in front of the eyepiece. Since the eyepiece is another short focus lens, it is used as a simple microscope or magnifying glass to produce a magnified virtual image at *I'*.

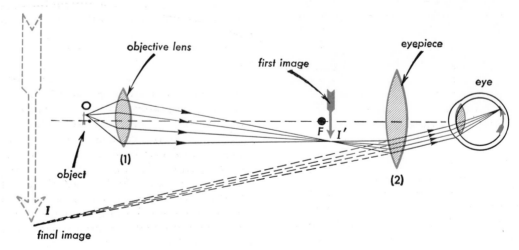

Fig. 41J *Lens and ray diagram of a compound microscope.*

Early forms of the compound microscope displayed so much chromatic aberration that only low magnifying powers were attained. High-powered microscopes of today overcome this and other defects by using an objective containing as many as eight or ten lenses and an eyepiece containing two or more. Under suitable illumination, magnifying powers of a little more than 2000 diameters are commonly attained. Although this is not an upper limit to the magnification for optical microscopes of the future, we know from the wave nature of light that the ultimate limit is not many times that which has already been attained. This is not a pessimistic attitude but a scientific truth based upon our present knowledge of the atomic structure of matter itself.

The electron microscope, capable of magnifications 50 to 100 times that of the best optical microscope, is described in Sec. 65.8.

41.8. The Kellner-Schmidt Optical System. The Kellner*-Schmidt optical system combines a concave spherical mirror with an aspheric lens as shown in Fig. 41K. The

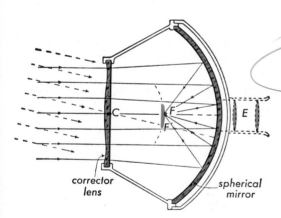

corrector lens   spherical mirror

Fig. 41K   *Kellner-Schmidt optical system (speed f/0.5).*

purpose of the lens is to refract incoming parallel rays in such a direction that, after reflection from the spherical mirror, they all come to focus at the same axial point F. Since the lens is located at the mirror's center of curvature, parallel rays entering

* American Patent No. 969785; published 1910.

the system at large angles with the principal axis are brought to a relatively good focus at F'. The focal surface of such a system is a spherical surface with its center at C.

Such an optical system has several remarkable and useful properties. First as a camera, with a small film at the center or a large film curved to fit the focal surface, it has a very high speed and covers a wide angle of 45° or more. In photographer's terminology, the system has an *f-number* of 0.5. Because of their large light-gathering power, Kellner-Schmidt systems are used by astronomers to obtain photographs of faint stars. They are used for similar reasons in television receivers to project the images from an oscilloscope tube onto a relatively large screen. In this case the convex oscilloscope screen is placed in the focal plane FF' so that light from the bright image screen is reflected by the mirror, through the corrector lens to the observing screen.

If a convex silvered mirror is located at FF', rays from any distant source will, on entering the system, form a point image on FF' and after reflection emerge again as a parallel bundle in the exact direction of the source. Used in this fashion the device is referred to as an *auto-collimator,* and is similar in its action to a *triple prism* as shown in Fig. 37M(c). If this small convex mirror is coated with fluorescent paint, ultraviolet light from a distant invisible ultraviolet light source will form a bright spot at some point on FF', and visible light emitted from this spot will emerge only in the direction of the source. Should an opening be made in the center of the large concave mirror, and an eyepiece be inserted to view the fluorescent screen in the focal plane, ultraviolet light sources can be seen as visible sources. As such, the device becomes a wide-angled ultraviolet telescope.

41.9. Endoscopes. Endoscopes are long narrow telescopes used by physicians and surgeons, and are designed to be inserted through a body opening into a cavity for the purpose of visually examining the cavity walls. A majority of such instruments are manufactured for specific purposes and

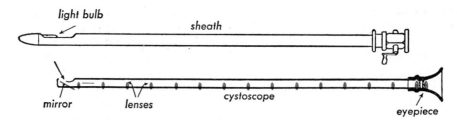

Fig. 41L   *Diagram of a cystoscope and sheath showing the principal optical parts.*

listed under the titles, *bronchoscopes, cystoscopes, gastroscopes,* and *laryngoscopes.* All of these instruments are based on the same principles but differ from each other chiefly in their length and diameter, or in their arrangement and number of mirrors, prisms, lenses, and miniature light bulbs.

The far-end section of many endoscopes is usually removable and has interchangeable optical and surgical attachments that can be manipulated from the outside. Oftentimes a sheath is first introduced into the body opening and then the telescope is inserted. A cross-section diagram is shown in Fig. 41L as a typical example of a cystoscope.

Since the outside diameter of a cystoscope must be kept small, the telescope tube (usually about 6 mm in diameter) contains a long train of some 30 small, accurately spaced, lenses. The image formed by the objective end is passed on from one set of lenses to the next without magnification until it reaches the eyepiece. There a two- or three-fold magnified image may be seen. In some cases the eyepiece is replaced by a special camera, thereby permitting photographs of the cavity walls to be made.

PROBLEMS

1. A camera lens has a focal length of +8 in. Calculate image distances for the following object distances: (a) infinity, (b) 20 ft, (c) 10 ft, (d) 5 ft, (e) 3 ft, and (f) 2 ft. Make a scale 4 in. long, showing $\frac{1}{4}$- and $\frac{1}{2}$-in. divisions, and put marks on it at the calculated image distances but labeled with the corresponding object distances.

2. A portrait camera lens has an aperture of 1.8 in. and an *f*-number of 2.8. What is its focal length? (*Ans.* +5.04 in.)

3. The lens of a camera has an aperture of 4.0 cm and a focal length of +11.2 cm. What is its *f*-number?

4. A telephoto lens has a 30-cm focal length. Calculate image distances for the following object distances: (a) infinity, (b) 10 m, (c) 5 m, (d) 3 m, (e) 2 m, and (f) 1 m. Make a millimeter scale 5 cm long, mark it with lines at the proper image distances, and label them with the corresponding object distances. (*Ans.* 30.0, 30.9, 31.9, 33.3, 35.3, 42.9 cm.)

5. A woman with *hypermetropia* requires +1.25 D spectacle lenses to see clearly at a distance. What power spectacle lenses will she require to read a book at 18 in.?

6. A student with *presbyopia* sees distant objects clearly. Calculate to the nearest quarter diopter the power of the spectacle lenses that will enable him to see objects (a) 5 ft away, and (b) to read a book at 18 in. (*Ans.* (a) +0.66 D, (b) +2.19 D.)

7. A nearsighted person sees objects clearly at a distance of 20 cm. Having lost his accommodation, what power spectacle lenses will enable him to see distant objects clearly?

8. An astronomical telescope objective has a focal length of +100 cm. What focal length eyepiece will give it a magnification of 75? (*Ans.* +1.33 cm.)

9. To an observer on the earth, the moon subtends an angle of approximately 0.5°. If a telescope objective lens with a focal length of +20 ft is used to photograph the moon, what will be the diameter of the image formed at the focal plane of the lens?

10. The objective lens of an astronomical telescope has a focal length of +5 ft, while the eyepiece has a focal length of +1.5 in. What is its magnifying power? (*Ans.* 40.)

11. The eyepiece of a 12-power astronomical telescope has a focal length of +0.75 in. What is the focal length of the objective?

12. The objective and eyepiece of a telescope have focal lengths of 52 cm and 3 cm, respectively. The objective lens has a diameter of 4.0 cm. Calculate (a) the magnifying power, and (b) the size and position of the image of the objective lens formed by the eyepiece. (*Ans.* (a) 17.3, (b) 0.231 cm in diameter, 3.17 cm beyond the eyepiece.)

13. A Kellner-Schmidt optical system is used as an astronomical telescope. The mirror has a 2-m radius of curvature, the corrector lens a diameter of 50 cm, and the circular focal surface a diameter of 20 cm. Find (a) the *f*-number of the system, and (b) the angular field it can photograph in one picture.

14. A small lens with a focal length of 1.5 cm is to be used as the eyepiece of an inexpensive reflecting telescope. To what radius of curvature should the objective mirror be ground if the instrument is to have a magnifying power of 90? (*Ans.* 270 cm concave.)

15. A pair of Navy-type binoculars has the designation 11 × 60. If the eyepieces have a focal length of 2.5 cm, (a) what are the diameters, and (b) the focal lengths of the objective lenses?

16. The objective lenses of a pair of 7 × 50 binoculars have a focal length of 25 cm. The eyepieces have an effective diameter of 2.7 cm. Find (a) the focal length of the eyepieces. (*Ans.* (a) 3.57 cm.)

17. A person with *presbyopia* finds that he must hold the telephone book at a distance of 60 cm from his eyes in order to see the print clearly. What power lenses should he have in order to see clearly when the book is 25 cm from his eyes?

18. A pair of binoculars has the designation 8 × 40. If the eyepieces have a focal length of 2.5 cm, (a) what are the diameters, and (b) the focal lengths of the objectives? (*Ans.* (a) 40 mm, (b) 20 cm.)

19. A telescope objective lens, with a focal length of 50 cm and an aperture of 8.5 cm, is used as a telephoto lens on a camera. What is the *f*-number?

20. The objective lens of a telescope has a focal length of 60 cm and a diameter of 7.5 cm. (a) What focal length eyepiece should be used to obtain a magnification of 75? (b) What is the size of the image of the objective lens formed by the eyepiece? (*Ans.* (a) 0.80 cm, (b) 0.10 cm.)

21. A pair of binoculars has objective lenses with a focal length of 25 cm, and a designation 8 × 40. Find (a) the focal length of the two eyepieces. (b) What is the diameter of each objective lens? (c) What is the size of the image of the objective lens as formed by the eyepiece?

Chapter 42

The Science of Color

Color vision is perhaps the most valued gift of nature. While color is for the most part a physiological phenomenon, its origin is considered by some to belong to the realm of physics. There is, on the one hand, the theory of *color mixing* and, on the other, the theory of *color vision*. The first of these theories deals with the action of matter on light before it reaches the eye, and the second with the visual functions of the eye. The science of color mixing has been made possible through the discovery that all colors can be completely analyzed by spreading them out into a prismatic spectrum. The science of color vision, on the other hand, involving the optics of the eye as well as the physiological functions of the entire vision mechanism, is not completely understood. Both of these subjects will be treated in this chapter on the science of color.

42.1. Effect of Illumination on Color. To see a body in its true color, that body must be illuminated by light of the same color. If a red rose, as an illustration, is placed in the different colors of a prismatic spectrum it will appear a brilliant red in red light and grey or black in all the others.

Another experiment is illustrated in Fig. 42A where yellow light from a sodium arc lamp is shown illuminating a row of colored skeins of yarn. When the lamp is turned on, only the yellow yarn appears with its true color; the white yarn is yellow and the others are black or grey. If the same set of colored yarns is illuminated with red light, only the red yarn will appear in its true color; the white yarn will now be red, and the others will be grey or black. In other words, unless the source emits the proper colors, the body cannot be seen in its true color. Sunlight will show each yarn in its true color, for sunlight contains all colors of the spectrum.

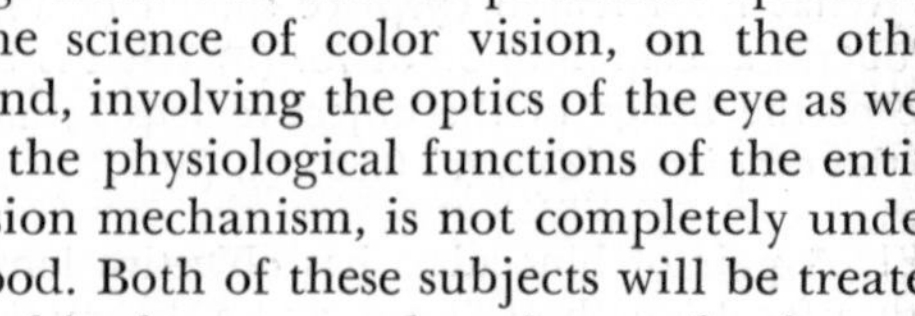

42.2. Surface Color. The above experiments demonstrate what is called *surface color.* When sunlight falls on a red rose, red yarn, red paint, or red glass, all of the colors

white red yellow green blue violet brown

colored yarns

sodium lamp
or flame

Fig. 42A *Experiment with colored skeins of yarn showing that, to see an object in its true surface color, it must be illuminated by the proper light.*

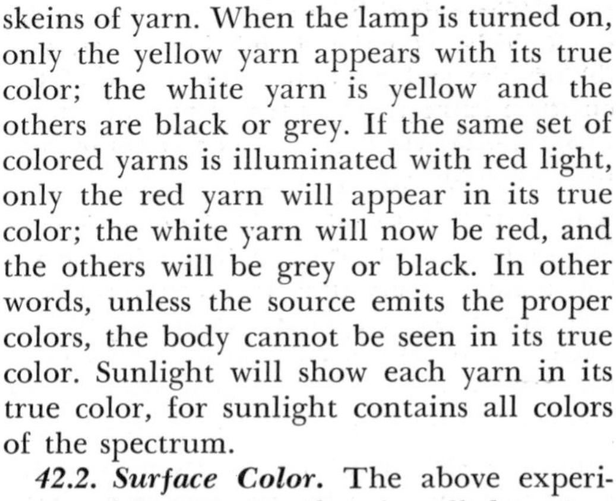

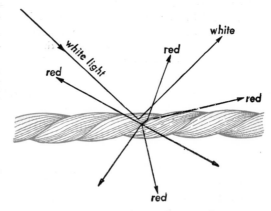

Fig. 42B *Illustration of color.*

except red are absorbed and do not get through or out again. The red, as it passes through, is reflected and refracted by the fine grains of pigment and comes out in all directions as shown in Fig. 42B(a).

Not all of the other colors are completely absorbed, for a small amount of each color is reflected from the first surface the white light strikes. This may be illustrated by a polished sheet of red glass. Although the glass appears red from both sides, a small amount of white light is reflected from the top surface, obeying the law of reflection. The red, on the other hand, is reflected and refracted in the usual way at each surface.

The three aspects of surface color are *hue, brightness,* and *saturation.* Hue refers to the *name* of a color, brightness to the relative *magnitude* of the sensory response, and saturation to the color *strength.* Hue is qualitative and is the most distinctive aspect of color, for without hue there is no color. Hue cannot be defined but only exemplified: red, yellow, green, blue, violet, purple, and various intermediaries between these are hues. *Brightness is a subjective intensity and may exist alone, as in white light.* White is devoid of hue and hence is devoid of color. Hue cannot exist alone, for if we have hue it has a certain brightness and saturation. Illustrations of these three concepts are shown in Fig. 42H.

Colors that do not contain any trace of white light are said to be *saturated.* The more white they contain, the less saturated they become. Pink is not a saturated color since it is a mixture of red and white. This may be demonstrated by mixing a small amount of red pigment with white paint, or, what is still more striking, by pulverizing a piece of red glass. As the glass is ground finer and finer the amount of white light reflected is increased by the increasing surface area, until the powder becomes almost white. Although the red light is still present, the white light by comparison is much stronger. A similar effect is produced by transparent substances like crystals and window glass; when powdered they become white. *The smaller the amount of white light mixed in with a color, the greater is the saturation.*

42.3. Metallic Color. Some substances appear to be one color by reflected light and a different color by transmitted light. This is particularly true of metals and of certain aniline dyes. Gold, for example, is always yellow-orange by reflected light but, if thin

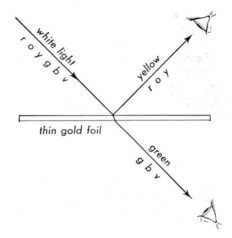

Fig. 42C *A thin gold foil appears yellow-orange by reflected light and blue-green by transmitted light.*

enough, is blue-green by transmitted light (see Fig. 42C).

White light, composed of the spectrum colors, red, orange, yellow, green, blue, and violet, is incident on the thin film of gold. Although all of these colors are partially reflected and partially transmitted, the predominant colors in the transmitted light are green, blue, and violet, while those in the reflected light are red, orange, and yellow. To the eye the mixture of reflected colors appears yellow, and the mixture of transmitted colors appears green.

Graphs of the reflecting power of copper, silver, and gold are reproduced in Fig. 42D. Copper, it will be noted, reflects about 80%

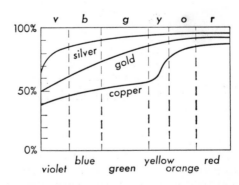

Fig. 42D *Graphs showing the reflecting power of metals for different colors of the spectrum.*

of all red light incident upon it and only 40% of the violet. Curiously enough, all metals are good absorbers of colors they best reflect, so that white light incident on a thin copper foil is partly robbed of red, orange, and yellow by having some of each of these colors reflected and some absorbed. Since smaller amounts of the green, blue, and violet are reflected and absorbed, these colors will predominate in the transmitted light, giving it, like gold, a blue-green or cyan appearance. If the metal is too thick, it becomes opaque to all colors. In a rough way the curves in Fig. 42D represent the absorption of light by metals as well as the reflecting power. Silver, like so many other metals, is a good reflector of all colors and therefore is nearly white.

42.4. Mixing Spectrum Colors. Over a period of many years, different color charts and color theories have been proposed, some of them good and some of them bad. Because the most successful theories have, of necessity, been detailed and complicated, some simplification of their concepts and an explanation of their common principles will be given here.

As a starting point, consider the experiment shown in Fig. 42E in which a narrow

tion are brought to a focus on a translucent glass rod where, combined again, they produce white. A large white card is next held in front of the mirror to act as a screen to control the colors that are permitted to mix at the rod. By screening off violet, blue and green, for example, the remaining colors, red, orange, and yellow, come together and the rod appears orange.

We now proceed to divide the spectrum up into three equal parts, as shown at the lower left in Fig. 42F, and to call these parts the *additive primaries*. When red and orange are allowed to mix, the rod appears a bright red; when yellow and green are mixed the rod appears bright green, and when blue and violet are mixed it appears blue-violet. As colors these additive primaries, red, green, and blue, appear like the three large circular areas at the upper left in Fig. 42F.

The next step is to mix the *primary colors* two at a time and to observe their resultant color mixture. When primary red and primary green mix at the glass rod, they produce yellow; red and blue produce magenta; and green and blue produce cyan, a light blue-green. These, the so-called *subtractive primaries* are shown by the three

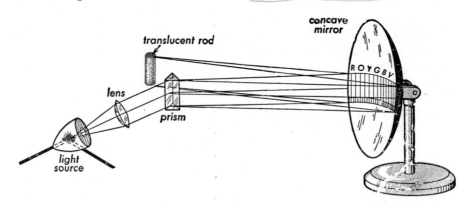

Fig. 42E *Experimental arrangement for mixing pure spectrum colors to form all primary colors.*

beam of white light from a carbon arc and lens falls on a glass prism and is spread out into a complete spectrum. With the prism located near the center of curvature of a large concave mirror, all colors after reflec-

large circles at the upper right in Fig. 42F, and the overlapping areas at the upper left. The pure spectrum colors that go to make up each subtractive primary are shown at the lower right.

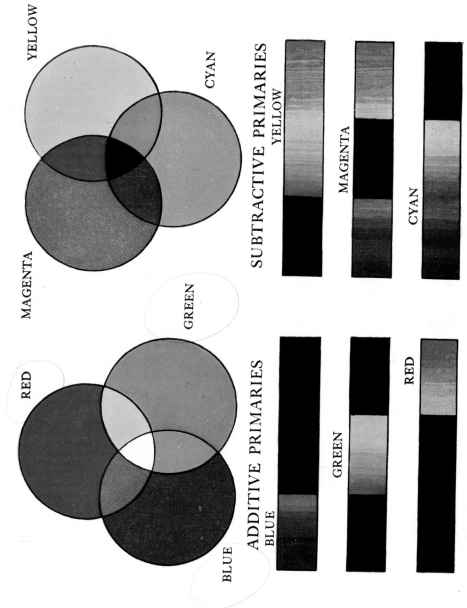

Fig. 42F *Primary colors showing their combinations and component spectral colors.*

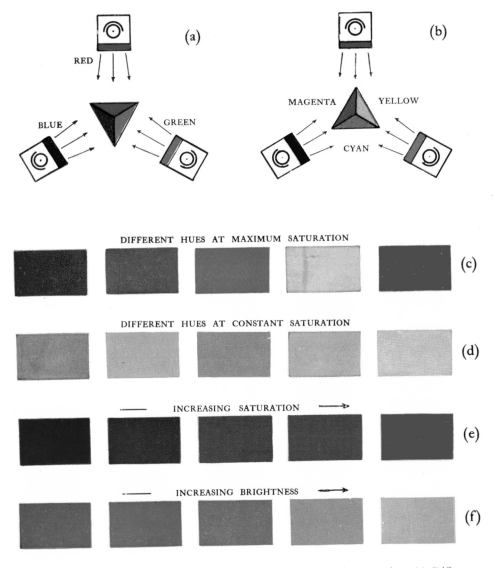

Fig. 42H (a) *Additive primaries.* (b) *equal mixing of primary pairs.* (c) *Different hues at their maximum saturation values.* (d) *Different hues at constant saturation and equal brightness.* (e) *The same hue at constant brightness but increasing saturation.* (f) *The same hue at constant saturation but increasing brightness.*

42.5. The Color Triangle. The color triangle, as illustrated in Fig. 42G, is a triangular arrangement of the additive and subtractive primaries with white at the center. Red, green, and blue are located at the corners, while magenta, yellow, and cyan are located at the sides. The order of the colors is such that the sum of any two additive primaries at the corners gives the subtractive primary between them on the sides, and the sum of all three primaries gives white at the center.

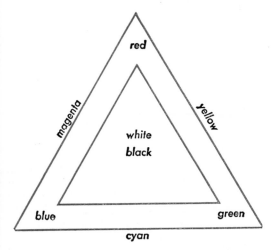

Fig. 42G   *Diagram of the color triangle, with the additive primaries at the corners and the subtractive primaries at the sides.*

Colors opposite each other on the color triangle are *complementary.*

Two colors are said to be complementary if when added together they produce white. Magenta and green are complementary, for when added together, as can be seen from their spectral distributions in Fig. 42F, they contain all of the spectrum colors of white light. Similarly red and cyan, as well as yellow and blue, are complementary.

42.6. Additive Method of Color Mixing. The mixing of colored lights described in the two preceding sections is called the additive method of color mixing and differs greatly from the subtractive method to be described in the following section. An interesting experiment for demonstrating the additive method is shown in Fig. 42H.

Three boxes containing white lights are arranged to illuminate separately the three sides of a white pyramid. A matched set of glass filters, one for each of the additive primary hues, red, green, and blue, respectively, are placed in front of each box opening, thereby illuminating the pyramid faces as shown in the left-hand diagram.

Upon rotating the pyramid slowly a point is reached, as shown in the right-hand diagram, where pairs of lights mix in equal amounts on each of the three faces. These mixtures are the subtractive primaries, magenta, yellow, and cyan. As the pyramid turns from position (a) to position (b), all variations of two colors are seen on the pyramid faces. Television in full color is produced by the additive method of color mixing.

42.7. Subtractive Method of Color Mixing. This is the method most familiar to everyone, the method used in the mixing of pigments to produce various colored paints. For this purpose the subtractive primaries, *magenta, yellow,* and *cyan,* often referred to by artists as *red, yellow,* and *blue,* are the most useful. The mixing in equal amounts of any two subtractive primaries will produce the additive primary lying between them on the color triangle. When cyan and yellow paints are mixed, the result is green.

At first it seems strange that yellow and cyan, neither one of which has the appearance of an additive primary, should produce green when mixed together. A spectrum analysis of these two colors, as shown at the lower right in Fig. 42F, shows that green and yellow are spectrum colors common to both.

Mixing by the subtractive method is demonstrated with prisms and filters in Fig. 42I. To see what happens to each spectral hue in each filter, the white light is first spread out into its complete spectrum. To illustrate, the yellow filter alone in diagram (h) absorbs blue and violet, and the cyan filter alone in (f) absorbs red and orange. When both are inserted as in diagram (d), only green and yellow are transmitted. To the eye this mixture appears bright green. The other two pairs of filters in diagrams

(e) and (i) give the other two primaries, red and blue.

To carry these experimental demonstrations to the mixing of paint, each little grain of pigment is like a piece of colored glass (see Fig. 42J). Assuming the oil in

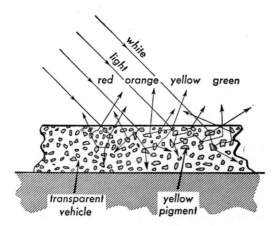

Fig. 42J *Illustration of the absorption of blue and violet light by yellow paint and the emission of red, orange, yellow, and green.*

which the yellow pigment is imbedded to be transparent, white light entering the paint is reflected and refracted as shown. Wherever blue or violet rays pass through pigment grains, they are absorbed. After many reflections and refractions the red, orange, yellow, and green can still escape. Together these four colors (see Fig. 42F) appear as yellow.

When yellow and cyan pigments are mixed together as illustrated by the detailed diagram in Fig. 42K, only green and yellow light is transmitted by both pigments.

The essential difference between the additive method and subtractive method of color mixing is just that suggested by the name; in the additive method the resultant color is just the *sum* of the two constituents used to produce it, and in the subtractive method it is just the *difference* between the two. Addition always produces a brighter color, and subtraction produces a darker color. Just as the additive mixing of red, green, and blue produces white, so the subtractive mixing of magenta, yellow, and

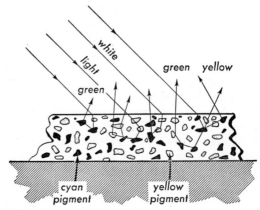

Fig. 42K *When blue and yellow paints are mixed together, green and yellow are the only pure spectral colors transmitted by both pigments.*

cyan produces black. Similarly, two complementary colors, when mixed additively, produce white, and when mixed subtractively produce black.

42.8. Color Vision. When radiant energy at different wavelengths of the spectrum falls upon the retina of the normal human being, the visual sensations vary as shown at the top in Fig. 42L. The maximum, which occurs in the green at $\lambda = 5550$A, is assigned the arbitrary value of 1000. On either side of this maximum the response falls off smoothly toward the violet at one end and the red at the other.

The *standard luminosity curve* is experimentally determined by matching the brightness of one color against that of another for each part of the spectrum and then measuring the relative amounts of energy in each of the two color fields. In comparing green and red, for example, much less intensity is required to give green light a brightness apparently equal to that of a red light. The solid curve is therefore a plot of *photometric energy magnitudes* and not relative brightness.

Brightness is a *sensory magnitude* in light just as loudness is a sensory magnitude in sound. Both vary over a wide range of values as the logarithm of the energy. To double the brightness of a surface, its emission must increase many fold. A

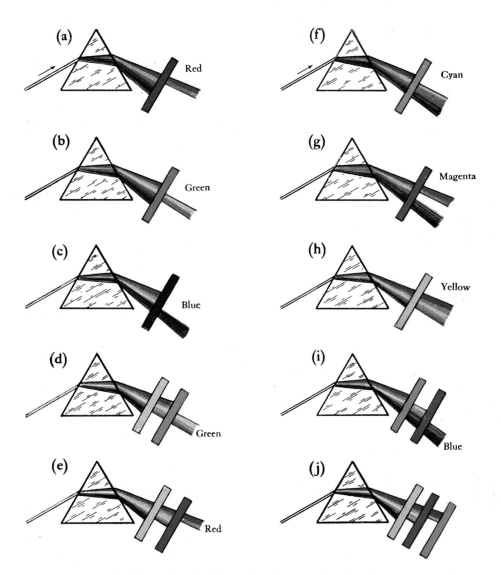

Fig. 421 *Diagram illustrating the absorption of spectral colors by colored filters and the subtractive method of color mixing.*

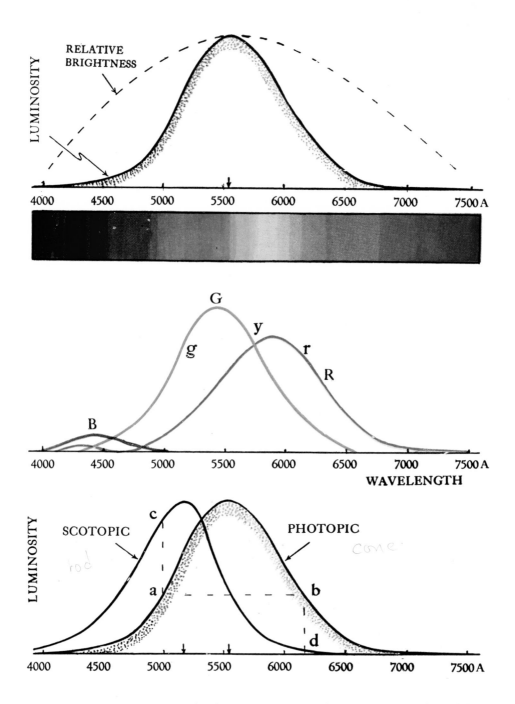

Fig. 42L (a) *Standard luminosity and relative brightness curves for the visible spectrum,* (b) *Tri-stimulus curves for the red, green, and blue sensitive cones of the retina,* (c) *Photopic and scotopic curves comparing cone vision by day with rod vision by night.*

plot of the logarithms of the luminosity gives the *relative brightness* curve for an equal energy spectrum. In other words, the dotted curve represents the relative brightness of the colors of a constant energy spectrum and clearly indicates the rather abrupt cutoff at either end.

During the past century, many attempts to formulate a scientific theory of color vision have been made. While some of these theories have met with considerable success, none of them has been able to explain every known phenomenon. The most successful theory was first advanced by the English scientist, Thomas Young, and later improved by the German scientist, Von Helmholtz. According to the Young-Helmholtz theory, the tiny cones in the retina of the eye (see Fig. 1B) are of three kinds. One set of cones produces the visual sensation of red, the second set gives the sensation of green, and the third set the sensation of blue. A set of sensation graphs for each of these color-sensitive cones is given by the center curves in Fig. 42L. The R-curve shows that, to stimulate the red-response cones, any wavelength from spectral violet to red is satisfactory, but wavelength 6000A will produce the maximum response. Similarly the B- and G-cones are seen to be stimulated by a whole range of different wavelengths.

When pure spectrum yellow enters the eye, as represented by y in the diagram, both the R- and G-cones respond equally and the sensation is yellow. If pure spectral red and pure spectral green are permitted to enter the eye (like r and g in the diagram), both the R- and G-cones again respond equally and the sensation produced is yellow. Because of the stimulus equality, the brain is unable to tell the difference from the y-stimulus, and the mixture has neither *redness* nor *greenness*. It is therefore possible to obtain a yellow hue with no spectral yellow present. A similar behavior occurs near wavelength 5000A where the B- and G-cones are stimulated equally to produce a *cyan hue*.

If the eye is subjected to faint light of wavelength 4500A, the visual sensation is *blue,* but when the intensity is raised the hue turns to violet or purple, indicating a noticeable stimulation of the R-cones. This is the evidence for the small "bump" in the R-curve in Fig. 42L. White is produced by the presence of all wavelengths in equal amounts, but it can also be produced by as few as three wavelengths only.

By the additive process of three primary responses, red, green, and blue, all of the thousands of recognized hues can be produced. The power of the eye and the brain to synthesize colors is to be compared with the reverse process by which the ear and brain are able to analyze musical tones into components.

42.9. Color Deficiency and Color Blindness. About 8% of males and 1% of females are color deficient or color blind, that is, do not have normal color vision. Although there are many forms and degrees of this defect, the two most common types are called *protanopia* and *deuteranopia.** Numerous tests and experiments indicate that protanopia is due to the absence of R-cones in the retina (see Fig. 42L(b)), whereas deuteranopia arises wherever the G-cones have the same spectral response as the normal R-cones.

The true *protanope* is characterized by his observation that the long wavelength end of the spectrum is green and stops at about 6800A, instead of the normal 7600A. Although he is able to match colors reasonably well, the number of hues seen by this individual is only a small fraction of those seen by the normal person. With only two primary colors, blue and green, at his disposal, he sees only those hues produced by their mixture in all possible proportions.

To the *deuteranope,* the spectrum is not shortened at the ends, but, since the G- and R-cones are equally stimulated with all the longer wavelengths, he sees only yellow

* Both of these forms of *dichromacy* are hereditary, recessive, and sex-linked. Theoretically, one woman in seven is a genetic carrier who does not herself exhibit color deficiency but transmits it *through* half of her daughters and *to* half of her sons. If one of these dichromatic males marries a normal woman, all of their children will be normal but the daughters will all be carriers.

from about 5700A on. With only red and blue primaries, only hues described by the normal as yellow, blue, or white are produced. Although various methods have been devised for detecting color deficiencies, the most sensitive and accurate determinations are made with an optical instrument known as the *anomaloscope.*

Color vision with but two primaries, as in protanopia and deuteranopia, is called *dichromacy,* whereas vision with only a partial deficiency of one of the three cone types is called *anomalous trichromacy.* In the *anomalous trichromat,* there is a reduction in the brightness of either red, green, or less commonly blue, but the number of possible hues is greater than with the *dichromat* and, in many cases, approaches the *normal* individual who is a *trichromat.*

42.10. Photopic and Scotopic Vision. In a well-lighted room or in bright sunlight, the peak sensitivity of the eye is in the yellow-green part of the visible spectrum. When the light is extremely faint, however, the maximum shifts to the blue green region and practically all color discrimination disappears. Two brightness sensitivity curves, one for high-level illumination and the other for very low illumination are shown in Fig. 42L. Although the peaks are drawn to the same height, the vertical scales for the two are different. The P curve is actually thousands of times higher than the S curve.

Under daytime illumination, normal vision is acquired by what is called *photopic vision,* a condition whereby the color sensitive cones in the retina of the eye are responsible for visual sensations. On dark nights, however, when the illumination is very low, the highly sensitive rods account for what little vision is attained, and we have what is called *scotopic vision. Photopic vision is cone vision; scotopic vision is rod vision.* The normal eye contains about 7 million cones and 130 million rods.

An interesting demonstration may be performed with an ordinary projection lantern, a slide that is half red and half blue, and an iris diaphragm located in front of the projection lens. The red and blue glass of the slide should be matched for equal brightness under normal projection on a white screen. As the iris diaphragm is narrowed down, the red field will appear to fade more rapidly than the blue, and finally to disappear altogether. The persistence of the blue is more strikingly observed by directing the eyes to one side of the two colored fields. If the original matching of red and blue corresponds to equal brightness points like (a) and (b) in Fig. 42L, the reduced illumination corresponds to the unequal brightness points (c) and (d). This observed phenomenon is called the *Purkinje effect.*

42.11. Color Photography. Out of the scientific research laboratories of the world, there has come in recent years a number of processes by which photographs in full color can be faithfully reproduced. For example, there are the "Lumière" process developed in France, the "Agfa" process developed in Germany, and the "Kodachrome" and "Technicolor" processes developed in the United States.

Many of the full color pictures printed in the magazines of today are reproduced from photographs that were originally taken with a somewhat complicated three-color process. The rapid growth of this industry of color photography justifies a brief description here of the most recent and successful processes.

For "still pictures," a special box camera having one lens and three separate film holders is often used (see Fig. 42M). Instead of taking but one picture at a time, as in the ordinary camera, three pictures are taken simultaneously. This is accomplished by the use of two lightly silvered mirrors. The first mirror M_1 reflects $\frac{3}{4}$ of the light to one photographic film at P_1, the second mirror M_2 reflects $\frac{1}{2}$ of the remaining light to a film at P_2, and the remainder travels straight through to a film at P_3. Before reaching each photographic film, the light is made to pass through glass plates, colored to transmit only the *primary colors, red, green, and blue* (see Fig. 42F). Light from a red object, for example, will pass through the red filter, but not through the green and blue filters.

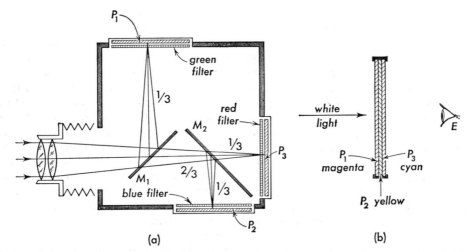

Fig. 42M (a) *Camera arrangement for taking three-color photographs.* (b) *Superposition of three colored films to produce the final photograph.*

After a picture is taken, the films are developed as "black and white" negatives as shown by the contrast illustrations in Fig. 42N. Instead of printing these films on white paper as in the ordinary photographic processing, they are either put through a reversing process whereby white is made black and black is made white, or

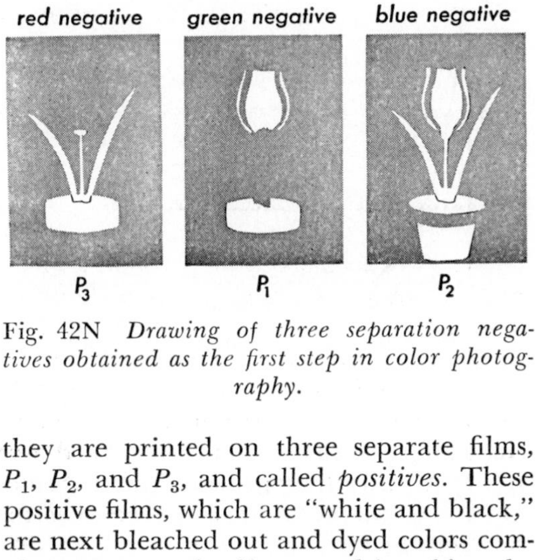

red negative   **green negative**   **blue negative**

P_3 P_1 P_2

Fig. 42N *Drawing of three separation negatives obtained as the first step in color photography.*

they are printed on three separate films, P_1, P_2, and P_3, and called *positives*. These positive films, which are "white and black," are next bleached out and dyed colors complementary to the filters used in taking the corresponding negatives. As shown at the top of Fig. 42O, film P_1 is dyed magenta, P_2 is dyed yellow, and P_3 is dyed cyan.

Where a color was bright in the original scene the positive is now transparent, and where there was no light it is now colored with the dye.

The three colored films are next superimposed as shown at the right in Fig. 42M, and when they are viewed with white light the result will appear as at the left center in Fig. 42O. Where the red tulip petals are located in the original scene, the positive P_1 is magenta, P_2 is yellow, and P_3 is transparent. Of all the colors in white light, only red and orange will be transmitted at this point, for only red and orange get through the magenta-yellow combination. Where the original background was white, light was transmitted by all three filters in the camera and each of the colored positives is transparent. Where the scene contained black, no light reached any of the negatives and the positives are all colored. When superimposed, no light can get through all three. Thus, by the subtractive method of color mixing, a colored photograph exhibiting all the natural colors is obtained. Even pastel shades of pink, blue, and green are quite faithfully rendered.

42.12. Color Printing. If the average color picture in a book or magazine is examined with a microscope it will be found, as shown in the lower part of Fig. 42O, to be made up of thousands of tiny colored dots. In the illustration the background of the three squares is the resultant color effect of three sets of dots shown magnified 20-fold in the corresponding circles. Viewed from a distance of 20 to 30 ft, the circles of large dots blend with their own background.

A careful examination of the dot patterns will show that three separate screens, one for each of the primary colors, is used. With their rows 60° apart with respect to each other, these screens print rectangular patterns of dots one on top of the other. The amount of each color is regulated by the size of the dots and, because each color is printed separately, the overlapping of dots is quite random. As illustrated in the upper right-hand square, yellow is produced by large yellow dots covering almost the entire field, the small red and cyan dots contributing only a slight darkening effect.

Green, as shown in the lower right-hand circle, is produced by large yellow and cyan dots with negligibly small magenta dots. Where the yellow and cyan overlap, green is produced by subtractive color mixing. White light to be reflected from the white paper underneath must go through both yellow and cyan, so that only spectrum green and yellow emerge as explained in Sec. 42.7. Where the dots do not overlap, additive color mixing takes place. The yellow dots reflect spectrum red, orange, yellow, and green; while cyan dots reflect yellow, green, blue, and violet. Because both reflect spectrum yellow and green, and all remaining spectrum colors are present, the net effect is white light with a preponderance of green and yellow. Hence green is produced by both the additive and subtractive processes. The darkening that results from overlapping areas can be brightened by white areas so that any desired effect is produced by increasing or decreasing the dot size. In some processes black dots are added to darken some color fields and left out where brighter hues are desired.

42.13. The ICI Chromaticity Diagram.
Well-planned steps toward a quantitative

measurement of color were taken by the International Commission on Illumination in 1931. At that time three additive primaries, red, green, and blue, were adopted, in which the visible spectrum was divided into three overlapping spectral response curves somewhat similar to those in Fig. 42L. Although a treatment of this standard ICI system[*] must be left for more advanced studies, it should be mentioned here that any given color sample can be measured with a spectroscope in terms of the three adopted primaries, and the results of the measurements can be expressed by two numbers. These two numbers can then be plotted on a graph.

When the pure spectrum colors *ROYGBV* are matched against a mixture of the standard primaries, a smooth curve as shown in Fig. 42P is obtained. With white at the

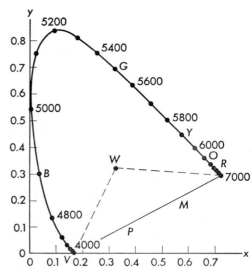

Fig. 42P   *ICI Chromaticity diagram.*

center, the complete gamut of all possible color mixtures lies within the enclosed area *RGBVW*, with the purples *P* and magentas *M* confined to the region *RWV* between the two ends of the spectrum.

---

[*] For a treatment of the ICI color system, see Sears, F. W., *Principles of Physics,* Chap. 13, Addison-Wesley Press.

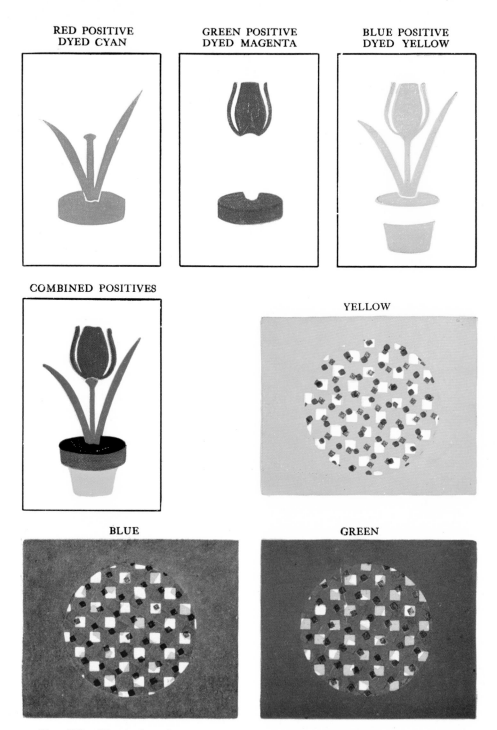

RED POSITIVE
DYED CYAN

GREEN POSITIVE
DYED MAGENTA

BLUE POSITIVE
DYED YELLOW

COMBINED POSITIVES

YELLOW

BLUE

GREEN

Fig. 420 *Illustrating the processes of color photography and color printing.*

PROBLEMS

1. The following pairs of colors are mixed additively. What is their resultant color? (a) red and green, (b) red and blue, (c) blue and green, (d) blue and yellow, and (e) red and cyan.

2. The following pairs of colors are mixed subtractively. What is their resultant color? (a) yellow and cyan, (b) magenta and cyan, (c) magenta and yellow, (d) magenta and green, and (e) red and cyan. (*Ans.* (a) green, (b) blue, (c) red, (d) black, (e) black.)

3. Make charts showing the various parts of the pure spectrum colors belonging to each of the additive and subtractive primaries.

4. Diagram the color triangle from memory.

5. Draw scotopic and photopic curves for day and night vision, and briefly explain the Purkinje effect.

6. Yellow and magenta are mixed (a) additively, and (b) subtractively. What are the resultant colors in each case? (*Ans.* (a) pink, (b) red.)

7. (a) What color added to red will give white? (b) What color subtracted from red will give black?

8. What colors are complementary to each of the following: (a) red, (b) yellow, (c) green, (d) cyan, (e) blue, (f) magenta, (g) white, and (h) black? (*Ans.* (a) cyan, (b) blue, (c) magenta, (d) red, (e) yellow, (f) green, (g) black, (h) white.)

9. How can it be shown that the actual colors of the spectrum combine to form the colors shown on the color triangle? Describe the experiment.

10. What are complementary colors? When two complementary colors are added together, what spectrum colors would be present? If they are mixed subtractively, what spectrum colors would be present?

11. Which of the two methods of color mixing produces brighter colors as the result of mixing?

12. What color added to red will give (a) white, (b) magenta, and (c) yellow? (*Ans.* (a) cyan, (b) blue, (c) green.)

13. What color mixed subtractively with yellow will produce (a) green, (b) red, and (c) black?

14. Make a diagram and briefly explain how yellow and cyan pigments when (a) mixed as paints can produce green. (b) Do the pigment particles themselves become green?

Chapter 43

Physical Optics

43.1. Shadows. When light passes close to the edge of any object, it is bent in its path and travels on in a new direction. This bending of light around corners is called *diffraction.* In the preceding chapters, light

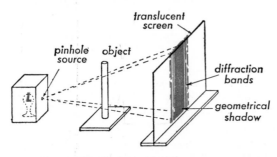

Fig. 43A *The shadow cast by the light from a small source is not sharp at the edges, but exhibits a banded structure.*

has been assumed to travel in straight lines and to obey the laws of reflection and refraction. Furthermore, according to the rectilinear propagation of light, it is customary to assume that an object will cast a sharp and well-defined shadow. A close ex-amination of every shadow, however, shows that the edges are not sharp, but blurred and diffused.

If one is careful to choose a small source of light, such as the light emanating from a pinhole in a screen, the shadow of an object cast on a distant screen is bounded at the edges by narrow bands or fringes of light. To observe these effects, the following simple experiment may be performed in a darkened room. A box containing a light bulb and a pinhole is placed on one side of the room and a ground-glass observing screen or photographic film is placed on the other. The objects whose shadows are to be observed are then placed about halfway between the source and the screen as shown in Fig. 43A. This is the arrangement used in obtaining the original photographs reproduced in Figs. 43B and 43C. The latter is an enlarged photograph of the light diffracted by a small circular opening.

43.2. Huygens' Principle. The phenomenon of diffraction was explained in the time of Newton by assuming that light is composed of small particles or corpuscles obey-

Fig. 43B *Photographs of the shadows cast by small objects. The narrow bands are due to the diffraction of light.*

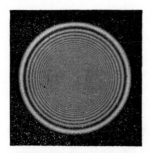

Fig. 43C *Diffraction of light by a small circular opening. (Original photograph by Hufford.)*

ing the ordinary laws of mechanical motion. And so it was that Newton and his followers held for many years to the idea that a source of light is a source of high-speed particles radiated in all directions.

Although such a viewpoint was believed for many years, it was later abandoned in favor of a wave theory of light, according to which a beam of light is made up of many waves of extremely short wavelengths. By adopting the wave hypothesis, a complete and adequate account of *reflection, refraction, diffraction, interference,* and *polarization* phenomena on a mathematical basis was finally formulated by Augustin Fresnel, a French physicist, at the beginning of the 19th century. The wave theory of light was first proposed by the English physicist, Robert Hooke, in 1665, and improved twenty years later by the Dutch scientist and mathematician, Christian Huygens.*

Everyone has at some time or another dropped a stone in a still pond of water and watched the waves spread slowly out-

* Christian Huygens (1629-1695), famous Dutch physicist and contemporary of Isaac Newton. Born at The Hague in 1629, young Christian got his first ideas about waves and their propagation by watching the ripples on the canals about his home. Although his chief title-deed to immortality is his development of the wave theory of light, he made many and valuable contributions to mathematics and astronomy. He improved upon the method of grinding telescope lenses and discovered the Orion nebula, part of which is now known by his name. He was elected to the Royal Society of London in 1663, and delivered before that august body the first clear statement of the laws governing the collision of elastic bodies. He died a confirmed bachelor at The Hague in 1695.

ward in ever-widening concentric circles. In the analogous case of a point source of light, the spreading waves form concentric spheres moving outward with the extremely high velocity of 186,300 mi/sec. This is represented diagrammatically in Fig. 43D.

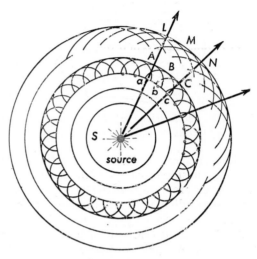

Fig. 43D *Diagram of waves spreading out from a point source. The secondary wavelets and new wave fronts illustrate Huygens' principle.*

Each circle represents the crest of a wave so that the distance between consecutive circles is one wavelength.

According to Huygens' principle, every point on any wave front may be regarded as a new point source of waves. Regarding each of any number of points like *a, b, c,* etc., as point sources like *S,* secondary wavelets spread out simultaneously as shown. The envelope of these an instant later is the new wave front *A, B, C,* etc., and still later the wave front *L, M, N,* etc. Although Huygens' principle at first hand might seem to be a useless play with circles it has quite general application to many optical phenomena.

43.3. Reflection and Refraction of Waves.

A diagram illustrating the application of Huygens' secondary wavelets to reflection is shown in Fig. 43E. A parallel beam of light of width *KM* is incident at an arbitrary angle on the polished surface of

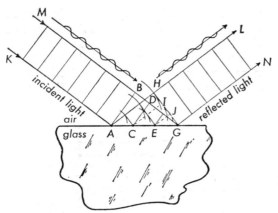

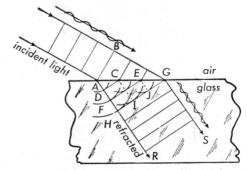

Fig. 43F   *The application of Huygens' principle of secondary wavelets of refraction.*

Fig. 43E   *Applications of Huygens' principle
of secondary wavelets of reflection.*

a piece of glass. As indicated by the wavy
lines at the side of each beam, the crests of
the waves are represented by equidistant
lines perpendicular to the direction of motion.

At the instant one end of a crest strikes
the surface at *A*, the opposite end is at *B*.
While this upper edge travels from *B* to *G*,
the lower side is reflected and travels an
equal distant *AH*. Each of the points *A*, *C*,
E, and *G* at the instant a wave arrives there
act as new point sources, and send out a
secondary wavelet, to form the new wave
front *HG*. If, from other points between *A*
and *G* on the mirror, secondary wavelets
are drawn, they will all fall tangent to the
reflected wave fronts, traveling off in the
direction shown. The geometry of the diagram shows that the angle of incidence
equals the angle of reflection.

A similar diagram illustrating refraction
is given in Fig. 43F. The same points *A*,
C, *E*, and *G*, acting as point sources of light
for the reflected light, also send out second-

ary wavelets into the medium. Since the
velocity of light is less in the medium than
in air, the waves are shorter, i.e., the wavelets are crowded together. If we assume a
refractive index of 1.5, the wavelets and the
new wave fronts in the glass will be only
$\frac{2}{3}$ as far apart as they are in the air. Their
new directions are found by setting a compass at the points *A*, *C*, *E*, and *G* and drawing arcs of circles $\frac{2}{3}$ as far apart as the waves
in air. Wavefronts *AC*, *DE* and *FG* are next
drawn tangent to the wavelets, followed by
lines *AR*, *CI* and *EJ*, drawn through the
points of tangency, perpendicular to the
new wave fronts.

When the beam is refracted from the
lower face of the glass plate in Fig. 43F, the
secondary wavelets emerge from the lower
boundary into the air again. In this instance the distance between the wave fronts
returns to that for the incident light. The
direction of the refracted beam, which is
left as an exercise for the student, will be
found to be parallel to the incident beam.

The action of a converging lens on light
waves is illustrated in Fig. 43G. If a point
source of light is placed at the focal point,

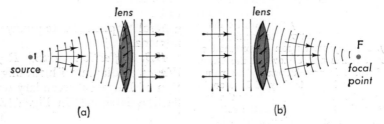

(a)   (b)

Fig. 43G   *The behavior of light waves as they pass through a converging lens.*

as in diagram (a), the expanding waves pass through the lens and come out as plane waves, i.e., as parallel light. In diagram (b), incident plane waves are shown emerging from the lens as contracting waves which come to a focus at F. The change brought about by the lens can be explained by the fact that light travels faster in air than it does in glass.

43.4. Diffraction at a Single Small Opening. A direct experimental demonstration of Huygens' principle is illustrated in Fig. 43H. Plane waves approaching a barrier

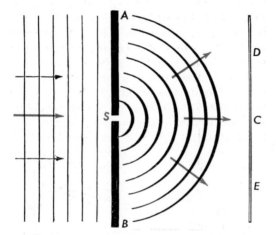

Fig. 43H *Diagram of the diffraction of waves at a small opening. Huygens' principle.*

AB from the left are reflected or absorbed at every point except at S, where they are allowed to pass on through. When the experiment is carried out with water waves, one can see the waves spreading out in all directions as if S were a point source.

If AB is an opaque screen and S is a pinhole small in comparison to the wavelength of light, the light waves will spread out in hemispheres with S at their center. If S is a long narrow slit (perpendicular to the page), the waves spread out with cylindrical wave fronts. Cross sections of all of these cases are represented by the semicircles, the light traveling in the direction of the arrows.

43.5. Young's Double-Slit Experiment. The crucial test between Newton's corpus-

cular theory of light and Huygens' wave theory came in 1801 when Thomas Young performed his now famous interference experiment. This is represented schematically in Fig. 43I. Sunlight from a pinhole S was

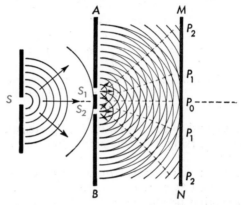

Fig. 43I *Diagram of Young's double-slit experiment illustrating the interference of light waves.*

allowed to fall on a distant screen containing two pinholes, S_1 and S_2. The two sets of spherical waves emerging from the two holes interfered with each other in such a way as to form a symmetrical pattern of bands on another screen MN. This experiment is now regarded as the first definite proof that light is a wave motion. Cf. Fig. 33G.

For convenience it is now customary to repeat Young's experiment with narrow slits in place of pinholes. If S, S_1, and S_2 in Fig. 43I represent the cross sections of three narrow slits, the light falling on the farther screen MN has the appearance of equidistant bands or fringes, as shown by the photograph in Fig. 43J. The bright fringes

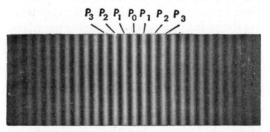

Fig. 43J *Interference fringes produced by a double-slit as in Young's experiment.*

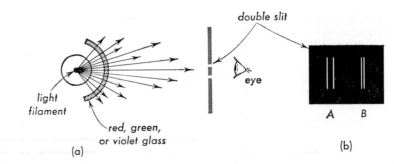

(a)   (b)

Fig. 43K   (a) *Experimental arrangement for observing interference fringes by Young's double-slit experiment.* (b) *Detail of double-slit showing two pairs of slits.*

correspond to the points P_o, P_1, P_2, etc., and the dark fringes to the points halfway between.

As the waves travel outward from each slit S_1 and S_2, they cross each other only at points that lie along the dotted lines shown in the diagram. These lines represent the areas where the crests of two waves come together and produce a maximum brightness. About halfway between these dotted lines lie other areas where the crest of one wave and the trough of another cancel each other and produce darkness. This is the same phenomenon illustrated by water waves in Fig. 33G and is called *interference.* Where the bright fringes are formed with light waves there is *constructive interference,* and where the dark fringes appear there is *destructive interference.*

One of the simplest methods of demonstrating interference fringes with light is illustrated in Fig. 43K(a). The best source for this purpose is a light bulb of clear glass with a vertical, single-wire filament. Small pieces of photographic plate about 1 in. square can be made for each observer. Two sets of slits, as shown in diagram (b), are made in the photographic emulsion by drawing the point of a pen-knife across the plate. If one holds either pair of slits close to one eye as shown in diagram (a) and looks at the source, a number of closely spaced colored fringes will be seen. The smaller the double slit spacing the wider the fringe spacing.

43.6. Measuring the Wavelength of Light. A formula for the wavelength of light can be derived from the geometry of

Young's double-slit experiment as shown in Fig. 43L. Let P be the position of any bright fringe on the screen, and x its distance from the central fringe at P_o. P_o is located on the perpendicular bisector of the double slit, S_1 and S_2. A straight line from each slit to the point P is drawn in, and with a compass of radius S_1P the arc of a circle S_yM is scribed. By this construction, line MP is made equal to S_1P, and the short line S_2M

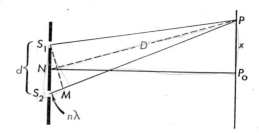

Fig. 43L   *Geometrical relations for the double-slit experiment.*

becomes the extra distance that light must travel from the lower slit. To produce a bright fringe at P, the interval S_2M must be equal to one whole wavelength, two whole wavelengths, three whole wavelengths, etc., for only then will the waves from S_1 and S_2 arrive at P in phase. Therefore, S_2M must be equal to $n\lambda$, where n is a whole number, $n = 0, 1, 2, 3, 4$, etc., and λ is the wavelength of the light.

Since the distance d between slit centers is extremely small compared with the distance D to the screen, line S_1M may be considered straight and at right angles to all three lines S_1P, NP, and S_2P. With corresponding sides mutually perpendicular to each other, the triangles S_1S_2M and NPP_0 are similar to each other. From the well-known theorem that corresponding sides of similar triangles are proportional,

$$\frac{n\lambda}{d} = \frac{x}{D} \quad \text{or} \quad \lambda = \frac{xd}{nD} \quad (43a)$$

If we let x_1 be the distance from the central fringe to the first one on either side, then $n = 1$, and the equation becomes

$$\boxed{\lambda = x_1 \frac{d}{D}} \quad (43b)$$

Because the fringes are evenly spaced, x_1 represents the spacing all along the pattern. By measuring the three distances d, x, and D, the wavelength of light can be calculated. Repeated experiments, carefully performed, give the following results.

Red, $\lambda = 0.000066$ cm
Orange, $\lambda = 0.000061$ cm
Yellow, $\lambda = 0.000058$ cm
Green, $\lambda = 0.000054$ cm
Blue, $\lambda = 0.000046$ cm
Violet, $\lambda = 0.000042$ cm

As illustrated by the waves in Fig. 43M, red light has the longest waves.

A scale of wavelengths showing the range over which each of the visible colors ex-

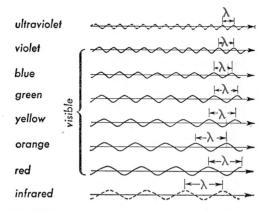

Fig. 43M   *Diagram showing the relative wavelengths of light.*

tends is shown in Fig. 42L. The above wavelengths, measured by the double-slit experiment, are therefore average values since each color corresponds to a range of different wavelengths.

43.7. The Diffraction Grating. The diffraction grating is an optical device widely used in place of a prism for studying the spectrum and measuring the wavelengths of light. Gratings are made by ruling fine grooves with a diamond point, either on a glass plate to produce a transmission grating or on a polished metal mirror to produce a reflecting grating. As illustrated in Fig. 43N the rulings are all parallel, and

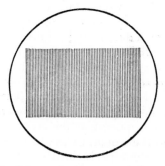

Fig. 43N   *Schematic diagram of the grooves or rulings on a diffraction grating.*

equally spaced. The best gratings are several inches in width and contain from 5000 to 30,000 lines/in.

The transmission grating and its effect on light is idealized by the cross-section diagrams in Fig. 43O. The heavy black lines represent the lines that permit no light to get through, and the open intervals between them represent the undisturbed parts of the glass which transmit the light and act like parallel slits as in Young's double-slit experiment. In diagram (a), parallel light is shown arriving at the grating surface as a succession of plane waves. The light then passing through the openings spreads out as Huygens' wavelets, and forms new wave fronts parallel to the grating face. These wave fronts, parallel to the original waves, constitute a beam of light W traveling on in the same direction as the original beam.

These are not the only wave fronts, however, for other beams of parallel light are to

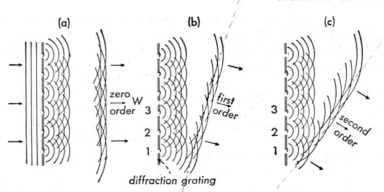

Fig. 43O *Diagrams showing the formation of wave fronts forming the various orders of interference observed with a diffraction grating.*

be found traveling away from the grating in other directions. Two other such wave fronts are illustrated in diagrams (b) and (c). In (b), a dotted line is drawn tangent to the seventh wave from opening 1, the eighth wave from opening 2, the ninth wave from opening 3, etc., to form what is called a wave front of the first order of interference. In (c), a line is drawn tangent to the fourth wave from opening 1, the sixth wave from opening 2, the eighth wave from opening 3, etc., to form what is called a wave front of the second order of interference. Similarly, by taking every third wave or every fourth wave from consecutive slits, other parallel wave fronts corresponding to the third or fourth orders are found moving off at greater angles. By symmetry all of the orders found on one side of the zeroth order are also found at the same angle on the other side.

Experimentally there are two methods of observing the various orders of interference from a small diffraction grating: one is to place the grating directly in front of the eye as illustrated by the double slit in Fig. 43K, and the other is to place it in the parallel beam of light between two lenses as shown in Fig. 43P. In the latter case, the second lens is shown converging the various wave fronts of the different orders to a focus on a distant screen. If the source is a slit as shown at the left, and a colored glass filter is used to let through any one color of light, like violet, the light falling on the screen will appear as shown in the top photograph in Fig. 43Q. Each vertical line is an image of the slit source and is violet in color.

If the three diagrams in Fig. 43O are redrawn for light of a longer wavelength, i.e., a greater distance between waves, the central beam of light *W* would travel on in

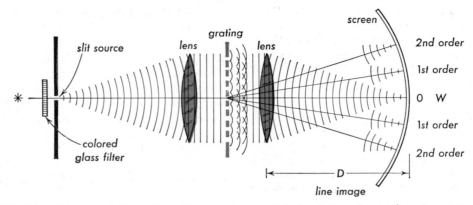

Fig. 43P *Diagram showing how the wave fronts of the various orders of interference are brought to a focus by the same lens.*

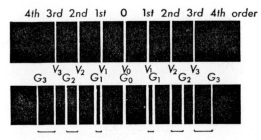

4th 3rd 2nd 1st 0 1st 2nd 3rd 4th order

V_3 V_2 V_1 V_0 V_1 V_2 V_3
G_3 G_2 G_1 G_0 G_1 G_2 G_3

Fig. 43Q *Photographs of the different orders of interference of violet and green light obtained with a diffraction grating as shown in Fig. 43P.*

the same direction as before, but the various *orders of interference* would be diffracted out at greater angles. Should green light of one wavelength be used in Fig. 43P, the slit images formed on the screen would be

order for all colors comes to the same point, the central image is white. Because the width of each spectrum is proportional to the order, the higher orders overlap one another more and more. The violet of the third order, V_3 for example, falls on the red of second order, R_2. It is for this reason that only the first and second orders of the spectrum from any grating are the ones generally used in practice.

The general appearance of a spectrum, produced by a diffraction-grating spectrograph, can be seen in the photographs reproduced in Chap. 59.

43.8. Mathematical Theory of the Diffraction Grating. The theory of the diffraction grating is similar to that of the double slit and is shown in its simplest form in Fig. 43S. These diagrams derive their con-

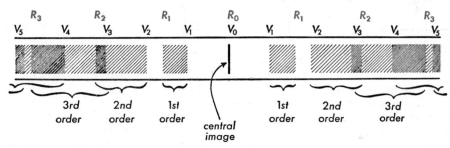

R_3 $\quad$ R_2 $\quad$ R_1 $\quad$ R_0 $\quad$ R_1 $\quad$ R_2 $\quad$ R_3
V_5 $\quad$ V_4 $\quad$ V_3 $\quad$ V_2 $\quad$ V_1 $\quad$ V_0 $\quad$ V_1 $\quad$ V_2 $\quad$ V_3 $\quad$ V_4 $\quad$ V_5

3rd order   2nd order   1st order   central image   1st order   2nd order   3rd order

Fig. 43R *Diagram of the first several orders of the continuous spectrum as displayed by a diffraction grating.*

farther apart than for violet light, as illustrated by the images marked *G* in Fig. 43Q(b). This lower photograph was taken with both violet and green light from a mercury arc passing through the grating. These line images are called *spectrum lines*.

It will be noted that the separation of the spectrum lines *V* and *G* in the *third order* is three times as great as in the *first order*. In other words, any two spectrum lines are separated by an amount that is proportional to the order of interference.

If white light is sent through a grating, all of the different wavelengths, corresponding to the different colors, form their own characteristic wave fronts and produce a complete and continuous spectrum in each order of interference. This is illustrated by a diagram in Fig. 43R. Since the zeroth

struction from Fig. 43O. The wave fronts for the first order emerge at such an angle θ that the difference in path between the rays from any two consecutive rulings, like *A* and *B*, is just one wavelength. Since any tangent drawn to any circle is always per-

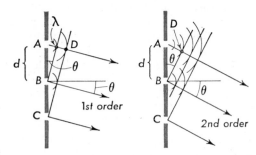

Fig. 43S *Geometry for the wave theory of the diffraction grating.*

pendicular to the radius drawn through the point of contact, triangle ABD is a right triangle, and $\sin \theta = \lambda/d$. Transposing, we obtain

$$\lambda = d \sin \theta \qquad (43c)$$

where λ is the wavelength of the light, d is the grating spacing, and θ is the angle that the emergent light of the first order makes with the grating normal.

By similar reasoning, and by the use of diagrams like the one shown for the second order, it will be seen that the second, third, fourth, etc., order spectra are formed at such angles θ that the difference in path between consecutive slits is 2λ, 3λ, 4λ, etc. In general, the side AD of the right triangle ABD must be equal to $n\lambda$, where $n = 1, 2, 3, 4,$ etc., and $\sin \theta = n\lambda/d$. If we transpose as

before, we obtain the general formula

$$\boxed{n\lambda = d \sin \theta} \qquad (43d)$$

In this general grating formula, n is the spectrum order.

Example. Red light of one particular wavelength falls normally on a grating having 4000 lines per cm. If the second order spectrum makes an angle of 36° with the grating normal, what is the wavelength of the light?

Solution. Since the grating has 4000 lines per cm, the spacing between the lines is 1/4000, or $d = 0.00025$ cm. The other given quantities are $\theta = 36°$ and $n = 2$. Substituting in Eq.(43d), and solving for λ, we get

$$\lambda = \frac{0.00025 \times \sin 36°}{2} = \frac{0.00025 \times 0.588}{2}$$
$$= 0.0000735 \text{ cm}$$

PROBLEMS

1. Red light of wavelength 6×10^{-5} cm is used in observing the interference fringes produced by a double slit. If the centers of the two slit openings are 0.5 mm apart, and the distance to the observing screen is 2 m, what is the fringe spacing?

2. Yellow light of wavelength 5.7×10^{-5} cm falls on a double slit; 2 m away, on a white screen, interference fringes are formed 4 mm apart. Calculate the double-slit separation. (*Ans.* 0.285 mm.)

3. Monochromatic light falls upon a double slit. The distance between the slit centers is 1.1 mm, and the distance between consecutive fringes on a screen 5 m away is 0.3 cm. What is the wavelength and the color of the light?

4. A beam of parallel light, $\lambda = 6 \times 10^{-5}$ cm, falls normally on a grating, and the third order is diffracted at an angle of 40° with the grating normal. How many lines per cm are on the grating? (*Ans.* 3570.)

5. Parallel blue light of wavelength 4.6×10^{-5} cm falls normally on one side of a diffraction grating having 5000 lines per cm. Calculate the angle between the first order spectrum on opposite sides of the grating normal.

6. A diffraction grating with 10,000 lines per cm is used with two lenses, each of 2-m focal length, as shown in Fig. 43P. Find the width of the first order spectrum of white light as it is

formed on the screen. Assume $\lambda = 4 \times 10^{-5}$ cm and $\lambda = 7 \times 10^{-5}$ cm for the shortest and longest wavelengths and a curved screen of radius 200 cm. (*Ans.* 72.5 cm.)

7. A grating having 2000 lines per cm is set up with 1-m, focal-length lenses as shown in Fig. 43P. What fourth order wavelength will be diffracted at the same angle as the third order of $\lambda = 60 \times 10^{-5}$ cm?

8. Red light of wavelength 6500×10^{-8} cm from a narrow slit falls on a double slit of separation 0.025 cm. If the interference pattern is formed on a screen 100 cm away, what will be the linear separation between fringes on the screen? (*Ans.* 0.26 cm.)

9. Green light of wavelength 5200×10^{-8} cm is incident on a double slit of separation 0.35 mm. If the interference pattern is formed on a screen 50 cm away, what will be the linear separation between fringes?

10. Yellow light of wavelength 5800×10^{-8} cm is incident on a double slit. If the over-all separation of 10 fringes on a screen 160 cm away is 1.2 cm, find the double-slit separation. (*Ans.* 0.077 cm.)

11. Violet light of wavelength 4×10^{-5} cm falls as a parallel beam on a diffraction grating containing 10,000 lines per cm. At what angle will the second order spectrum be located?

Chapter 44

Diffraction and Interference

If a beam of light is allowed to pass through a narrow slit, it is found to spread out into the region of the geometrical shadow. This effect has already been de-

symmetrically located on either side. For these photographs the distance $S'L$ was 25 cm, and L_2P was 100 cm. The width of slit S' was 0.10 mm and S was 0.090 mm. When

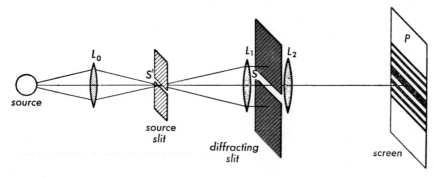

Fig. 44A *Experimental arrangement for obtaining the diffraction pattern of a single slit. Fraunhofer diffraction.*

scribed in Sec. 43.1 as a failure of light to travel in straight lines; it is called *diffraction*. The phenomenon is most easily explained by assuming a wave character for light.

44.1. Diffraction by a Single Slit. A *single slit* is a rectangular aperture, long in comparison to its width. An adjustable slit S is set up as shown in Fig. 44A, with its long dimension horizontal, and illuminated by parallel light of one wavelength. This beam of *monochromatic* light is obtained by the use of a source of light with a filter, a very narrow slit S' and two lenses L_0 and L_1.

Two actual photographs of the light falling on the screen at the right are reproduced in Fig. 44B. The upper photograph, made with a shorter time exposure, shows a band of light fading out at the edges. The longer exposure below shows this central band somewhat widened, and narrow bands

S' was widened to more than 0.3 mm, the details of the pattern began to disappear. On the original photograph the total width of the central band was 9.68 mm. The light source was a small mercury arc and a violet glass filter transmitting only the mercury violet light, $\lambda = 4358 \times 10^{-8}$ cm.

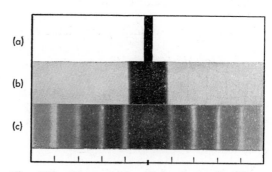

Fig. 44B *Photographs of the single-slit diffraction pattern.* (a) *The slit itself,* (b) *short exposure,* (c) *long exposure.*

This diffraction pattern can easily be observed by ruling a groove on an unused photographic plate with a penknife, and holding it in front of the eye as shown in Fig. 43K.

The explanation of the single-slit pattern lies in the interference of the Huygens secondary wavelets described in Fig. 43D. These wavelets can be thought of as sent out from every point on a wave crest at the instant that it crosses the plane of the slit.

The cross-section diagram of Fig. 44C

now choose a point P_1 on the distant screen where the light intensity is observed to be zero, corresponding to the point P_1 in Fig. 44E. This is a point where the length of the light path BP_1 is one whole wavelength λ greater than the light path AP_1.

To see why this is just the right condition for no light on the screen, consider the wave diagram in Fig. 44D. The points marked a, b, c, etc., correspond to the relative phases of the wavelets arriving at P_1 at the same instant from all 12 of the slit elements.

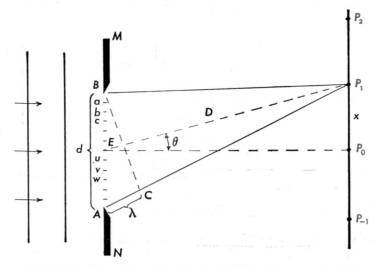

Fig. 44C   *Geometry of the single-slit diffraction experiment.*

shows a slit *MN*, of width d, with parallel wave crests approaching from the left. The wave crest at the slit is shown divided into 12 imaginary segments of equal width. Each of these segments may be thought of as a new source for a secondary wavelet. Let us

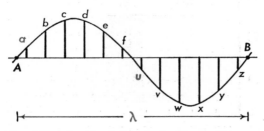

Fig. 44D   *Graph of the single-slit wavelet contributions from the first dark band, point P_1 of Fig. 44C.*

The heights of the vertical lines give the relative magnitudes of the wavelet contributions at P_1 due to the different elements. Note that the wavelet from a has a small upward displacement, while the wavelet from u has an equal downward displacement. One cancels the other to produce darkness. At this same instant the wavelet from b has a larger upward displacement while the wavelet from v has an equal downward displacement, thereby canceling each other. Similarly the elements c and w may be paired off with opposite displacements, and the process continued across the slit. Each pair of displacements is seen to cancel out and to produce destructive interference, or darkness, at P_1.

Suppose we now consider a point higher

up on the screen corresponding to the center of the next dark band, P_2, of Fig. 44D. For this point in Fig. 44C, the light path BP_2 will be two whole wavelengths longer than the path AP_2. If the slit is again divided into an equal number of small segments, the phases of the light wavelets arriving at P_2 will again be found to cancel in pairs.

When this treatment is applied to the point P_0 at the center of the screen, all the paths are the same, all wavelets arrive in phase, and we obtain the bright band center.

$$\frac{n\lambda}{d} = \sin\theta$$

from which we can write,

$$n\lambda = d\sin\theta \qquad (44b)$$

dark bands

This formula shows that by widening the slit the diffraction bands become narrower, and vice versa. By increasing the wavelength the bands become wider.

In making this derivation, certain approximations are made in assuming the triangles ABC and P_1EP_0 similar. As the dis-

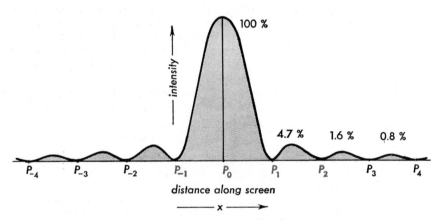

Fig. 44E *Single-aperture diffraction pattern.*

44.2. The Single-Aperture Diffraction Pattern.
If the above treatment of pairing-off light contributions from small elements of a single aperture are carried out over all angles of θ, complete cancellation will be found to occur only when the path difference AC is exactly a whole-number multiple of one wavelength, i.e., $AC = 1\lambda$, 2λ, 3λ, 4λ, etc. For the dark bands, then, we can write $AC = n\lambda$, where $n = 0, 1, 2, 3,$ etc. Since line BC is $\perp$ to EP_1 and line AB is $\perp$ to EP_0, the two triangles can be assumed similar, and the following proportions between corresponding sides can be written

$$\frac{AC}{AB} = \frac{P_0P_1}{EP_1} \quad \text{or} \quad \frac{n\lambda}{d} = \frac{x}{D} \quad (44a)$$

But $x/D = \sin\theta$, and we may write

tance to the screen D is made larger and larger in comparison to the slit with d, this similarity becomes more and more nearly exact. For most practical cases D is very large compared with d, and Eq.(44a) agrees with experiment to a high degree of accuracy.

If the path difference AC in Fig. 44C is not equal to a whole number of wavelengths λ, the wavelet contributions to those points on the screen will not cancel out, and this accounts for the bright bands.

A more detailed theory than that given above shows that the light intensity on the screen should have a distribution like that graphed in Fig. 44E. If we call the central intensity 100%, the maximum intensity of the side bands reaches the relatively low values of 4.7%, 1.6%, 0.83%, etc. Note carefully that the dark points P_0, P_1, P_2, etc., are equally spaced, but that the maxima do not come exactly halfway between. Furthermore, if the observing screen is not far away compared with the slit opening, the dark bands will be modified somewhat, and the minima will not be zero.

Example. A parallel beam of monochromatic light falls on a single slit 1 mm wide. When the diffraction pattern is observed on a screen 2 m away, the central band is found to have a width of 2.5 mm. Find the wavelength of the light.

Solution. The given quantities in this problem are $D = 200$ cm, $d = 0.10$ cm, $n = 1$, and $2x = 0.25$ cm. Upon substitution in Eq. (44a), we obtain

$$\frac{1\lambda}{0.10} = \frac{0.125}{200}$$

from which

$$\lambda = \frac{0.10 \times 0.125}{200} = 6.25 \times 10^{-5} \text{ cm}$$

The light, $\lambda = 6.25 \times 10^{-5}$ cm, is red in color.

44.3. Diffraction by a Circular Aperture.

The diffraction pattern formed by light passing through a circular aperture is of considerable importance, as it applies to the resolving power of telescopes and other optical instruments. The resolving power refers to the ability of an instrument to reveal fine detail in the object being viewed.

Due to the diffraction of light waves as explained in the preceding section, light through a circular aperture produces a diffraction pattern having the same general intensity variations as given by Fig. 44E. Being circular, however, the parallel bands of light from a slit aperture are replaced by concentric circles with a bright disk at the center. It is as if the graph of Fig. 44E were rotated around the center line.

A lens acts as a circular aperture for light passing through it, and the image it forms for every bright spot in any object is a tiny diffraction pattern. The photograph in Fig. 44F shows that, with pinholes in a screen as objects, the images formed by a single lens are composed of tiny disks surrounded by faint concentric rings of light. The

larger the lens aperture, the smaller the diffraction patterns. The distant stars act as point objects, and their images formed by a telescope objective are diffraction patterns of this kind.

Fig. 44F *Photographs of diffraction images of one point source taken with a circular aperture, two points close together, and two point sources farther apart.* Top: *Short exposure.* Bottom: *Longer exposure.*

We can see from this why the magnification by a telescope or microscope is limited, and cannot exceed certain values. If the eyepiece of an instrument has too high a magnifying power, each point in the object is observed as a disk, and the image appears blurred.

The radius x of the central disk of the diffraction pattern formed by a circular aperture of diameter d is given by Eq.(44a) but with n replaced by 1.22.

$$x = 1.22 \frac{\lambda D}{d} \qquad (44c)$$

Sound waves from the circular aperture of a radio loud-speaker will form diffraction patterns of the same kind. Such behavior gives rise to marked changes in sound quality at different points around a room. The microwaves from a radar reflector radiate outward as a single-aperture diffraction pattern, with a central maximum radiated straight forward.

44.4. Michelson Interferometer.

The Michelson interferometer is an optical device that employs the principle of the interference of two beams of light. Its treatment here is important because of its general application to many practical problems, and because historically it led to Einstein's theory of relativity.

The form of the Michelson interferometer generally found in the science laboratory is that shown in Fig. 44G. The opti-

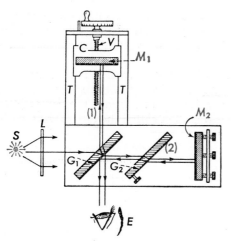

Fig. 44G   *Diagram of the Michelson interferometer.*

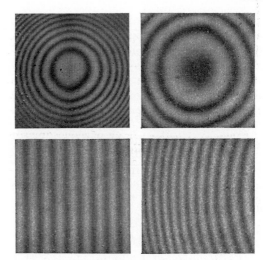

Fig. 44H   *Interference fringe patterns as photographed with a Michelson interferometer.*

cal parts consist of two mirrors, M_1 and M_2, and two parallel plates of glass, G_1 and G_2. Oftentimes the rear side of plate G_1 is lightly silvered (shown heavy in the figure) so that light coming from the source S is divided into (1) a reflected and (2) a transmitted beam of equal intensity. The light returning from M_1 passes through G_1 a third time before reaching the eye. The light returning from M_2 is reflected from G_1 and into the eye. The purpose of plate G_2 is to render the total path in glass equal for the two rays.

The mirror M_1 is mounted on a well-machined guide and can be moved along slowly by means of a screw V. When mirror M_2 is made exactly perpendicular to M_1 by screws on its back face, interference fringes similar to those found with a double slit may be seen, or photographed, at E. Photographs of typical fringes when mirror M_1 is at different distances are shown in Fig. 44H.

When monochromatic light is used as a source and the mirrors are in exact adjustment, circular fringes are observed as shown

in photographs (a) and (b). If the mirrors are not exactly at right angles to each other, fringes like those in photographs (c) and (d) are obtained. If circular fringes are observed, and mirror M_1 is slowly moved along by the turn of the screw V, the circular fringe pattern will expand or contract; if it expands, new fringes will appear as a dot at the center, widen, and expand into a circle; and if it contracts, fringes grow smaller, become a dot, and vanish at the center. If straight or curved fringes are observed, the motion of M_1 causes the fringes to drift across the field at right angles to the fringe lines.

The expansion, contraction, or drift in the pattern for a distance of one fringe corresponds to M_1 moving a distance of exactly $\frac{1}{2}$ wavelength of light. When M_1 moves back a distance of $\frac{1}{2}\lambda$, the total light path (1) increases a whole wavelength. If M_1 moves 1λ, the pattern will move two fringes because the total light path (1) has changed by 2λ. Any bright fringe that one observes is caused by both beams coming together in phase. When the one path is changed by $\frac{1}{2}\lambda$, 1λ, $\frac{3}{2}\lambda$, etc., the two beams arriving at the same field points will again be in phase.

By counting the number of fringes required to move the mirror M_1 a given dis-

tance, the wavelength of light can be calculated. This would appear to be the most direct and accurate method for the wavelength measurements of different light sources. Knowing the accurate wavelength of any light source, one can then use the interferometer to accurately measure distances.

It is by means of the Michelson interferometer that the standard meter was determined in terms of the wavelength of orange light, $\lambda = 6057.80$ A of krypton, element 36.*

$$1 \text{ meter} = 1,650,763.73 \text{ wavelengths}$$
(for orange light of krypton)

44.5. Velocity of Light in Moving Matter. In 1859, the French physicist Armand Fizeau measured the velocity of light in a moving stream of water and found that the light was carried along by the stream. A schematic diagram of his apparatus is shown in Fig. 44I.

Light from a monochromatic source S is separated into two beams by means of a lens L_1. These two beams pass through tubes

and the fringes formed at S', where the beams came together, will shift. Using tubes 1.5 m long and a water speed of 7.0 m/sec, Fizeau found a shift of 0.46 of a fringe upon a reversal of the water stream. This shift corresponds to a decrease in the speed of light in one direction, and an increase in the other, of about half the speed of the water. In other words, the moving water has a dragging effect upon the light waves.

In 1818, the French physicist Augustin Fresnel * derived a formula for this dragging effect, based upon the existence of what was then called the *ether*. His formula gives v' the increase in the velocity of light in any medium, due to motion.

$$v' = v \left(1 - \frac{1}{\mu^2}\right) \qquad (44\text{d})$$

where v is the velocity of the medium, and μ is the index of refraction. For water, with an index of 1.33, $v' = 0.43v$ in reasonably good agreement with Fresnel's observations.

44.6. The Michelson-Morley Experiment. This, the most famous experiment in optics, was first performed by Michelson and

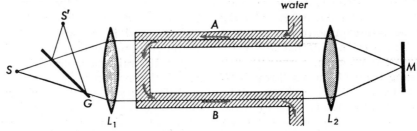

Fig. 44I *Fizeau's experiment for measuring the velocity of light in a moving medium.*

A and B which contain water flowing rapidly in opposite directions. After reflection from M the beams traverse opposite tubes, so that upon arrival at L_1 one has traversed streams A and B in the direction of flow, while the other has traversed both tubes but always against the flow.

If the light travels faster by one path than the other, the time will be different

* Adopted as the international legal standard of length on October 14, 1960, by the General Conference on Weights and Measures in Paris, France.

Morley in 1881, in an effort to detect the motion of the earth through space. If the

* Augustin Fresnel (1788-1827), French physicist. Although starting his career as a civil engineer, Fresnel became interested in optics at the age of 26. His mathematical development of the wave theory of light and its complete validation of experiment have marked this man as an outstanding genius of the nineteenth century. His true scientific attitude is illustrated by a statement from one of his memoirs, "All the compliments that I have received from Arago, Laplace, and Biot never gave me so much pleasure as the discovery of a theoretic truth, or the confirmation of a calculation by experiment."

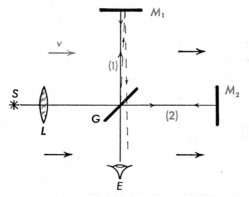

Fig. 44J *The Michelson interferometer ar-rangement for detecting an ether drift.*

transmission of light through space requires an ether, that is, a medium for it to move in, then light should be dragged along by this ether as the earth moves along through space. In order to detect such a drift, the Michelson interferometer appeared to be the most sensitive instrument to use.

In principle the ether drift test consists simply of observing whether there is any shift of the interference fringes of light in the Michelson interferometer when the en-tire instrument is turned through an angle of 90°. Let us assume that the interferom-eter and the earth are at rest and that the ether is moving by with a velocity v as shown in Fig. 44J. If no ether drag is effec-tive, light paths (1) and (2) will be out and back, as shown by the solid lines and ar-rows, and a set of interference bands like those shown in 44H(d) will be observed.

If we now suppose the light to be dragged along by an ether, the time it takes for light to traverse path (1) at right angles to the ether stream, and the time it takes to tra-verse path (2), first with and then against the stream, will both be increased. This is identical in principle with the problem of the two airplanes treated in detail in Chap. 12 (see Fig. 12D).

The times to traverse paths (1) and (2) are given by Eqs.(12a) and (12b) as

$$t_\perp = \frac{2L}{\sqrt{c^2 - v^2}} \qquad t_\parallel = \frac{2Lc}{c^2 - v^2} \quad (44e)$$

where c is the velocity of light *in vacuo*, and v is the very much slower drift velocity.

A little study of these equations will show that, while both times have been increased a slight amount, the increase is twice as large in the direction of motion. Further-more, the ratio of the two times is given by Eq.(12c), as

$$\frac{t_\perp}{t_\parallel} = \sqrt{1 - \frac{v^2}{c^2}} \quad (44f)$$

An ether drift should, therefore, cause a shift in the fringes observed in the inter-ferometer. Since neither the earth's motion, nor the ether, can be stopped, in an effort to observe this shift, a rotation of the inter-ferometer through 90° should have a simi-lar effect. By interchanging paths (1) and (2), the time difference $t_\parallel - t_\perp$ is reversed, and any fringe shift should be doubled.

Michelson and Morley made the light paths as much as 11 m long by reflecting the light back and forth between 16 mirrors, as shown in Fig. 44K. To prevent distortion by the turning of the instrument, the entire apparatus was mounted on a concrete block floating in mercury, and observations of the fringes were made as it rotated slowly and continuously about a vertical axis.

If we assume the ether velocity v to be 18.6 mi/sec (the speed of the earth in its orbit around the sun), and the speed of light c to be 186,000 mi/sec, a shift of $\frac{1}{2}$ a fringe should have been observed. No shift as great as $\frac{1}{10}$ of this was observed. Such a negative result was so surprising and so dis-appointing that others have repeated the experiment. The most exacting work was done by D. C. Miller who used Michelson and Morley's arrangement, but with optical paths of 64 m in place of 11 m. While Miller thought he found evidence for a shift of $\frac{1}{30}$ of a fringe, the latest analysis of Miller's data makes it probable that no shift exists.

This negative result of an ether drift forms the basis of the special theory of rela-tivity proposed by Einstein in 1905, and treated in Chap. 46.

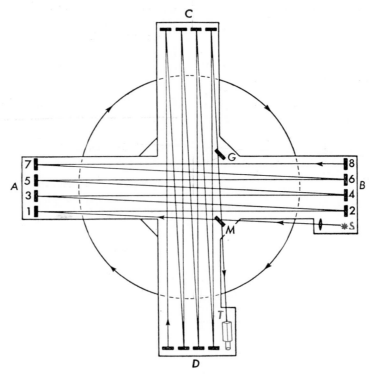

Fig. 44K   *Miller's elaborate arrangement of the Michelson-Morley experiment to detect ether drift.*

PROBLEMS

1. A parallel beam of green light, of wavelength 5.5×10^{-5} cm, falls on a single slit 0.8 mm wide. Find the total width of the central band of the diffraction pattern formed on a screen 2.4 m away.

2. Violet light of wavelength 4.2×10^{-5} cm falls on a single slit and forms a diffraction pattern on a screen 5 m away. If the central bright band has a total width of 4 mm, what is the slit width? (*Ans.* 1.05 mm.)

3. A parallel beam of monochromatic light falls on a single slit 1.2 mm wide. A diffraction pattern is formed on a screen 1.6 m away. If the equally spaced dark bands on either side of the central maximum are found to be 0.75 mm apart, what is the wavelength of the light?

4. Monochromatic light falling on a slit 1 mm wide forms a diffraction pattern on a screen 1.4 m away. If the equally spaced dark bands on either side of the central maximum are 0.6 mm apart, what is the wavelength of the light? (*Ans.* 4.29×10^{-5} cm.)

5. Light of wavelength 5×10^{-5} cm, passing through a circular hole 5 mm in diameter, falls on a screen 2 m away. Find the diameter of the central disk of the diffraction pattern.

6. Light of wavelength 5.5×10^{-5} cm passes through a circular aperture 2 mm in diameter, and falls on a screen 1.6 m away. Find the diameter of the central disk of the diffraction pattern. (*Ans.* 1.07 mm.)

7. A telescope objective lens has a diameter of 10 cm and a focal length of 1.0 m. Find the diameter of the central disk of the diffraction patterns formed in the focal plane of the lens when the distant stars are the objects being observed. Assume a wavelength of 5.5×10^{-5} cm.

8. A telescope objective lens has a diameter of 50 cm and a focal length of 8 m. Find the diameter of the central disk of the diffraction patterns formed in the focal plane of the lens when the distant stars are the objects being

observed. Assume a wavelength of 5.5×10^{-5} cm. (*Ans.* 0.0215 mm.)

9. Sound waves with a frequency of 5000 vib/sec are given out by a radio loud-speaker with a diameter of 12 in. If the speed of sound in air is 1100 ft/sec, find the angle θ away from the forward direction at which the intensity first drops to 0.

10. A sodium lamp is used with a Michelson interferometer for measuring the wavelength of the yellow light. Upon turning the traveling screw and counting 600 fringes, the experi-

menter moves the mirror, as observed on the micrometer scale, a distance of 0.177 mm. Calculate the wavelength of the light. (*Ans.* 5.900×10^{-5} cm.)

11. If a krypton lamp is used with a Michelson interferometer, how many fringes of orange light must be counted, crossing the interference pattern, to move the mirror exactly 1 mm?

12. If the stream of water in Fizeau's experiment (see Fig. 44I) had a speed of 20 m/sec, what would be the increased speed of light traveling through it? (*Ans.* 8.69 m/sec.)

The Polarization of Light

The experiments described in the two preceding chapters illustrating the *diffraction* and *interference* of light are generally regarded as proof that *light is a wave motion*. Although such experiments enable the experimentalist to measure accurately the wavelengths of light, they give no information of the kinds of waves involved. The reason for this is that all types of waves, under the proper conditions, will exhibit diffraction and interference. The desired information in the case of light waves is found in another group of phenomena known as *polarized light*. Some of the phenomena, which will be described in this chapter, are considered to be a proof that *light is a transverse wave motion* in contrast with the longitudinal wave motion in sound.

In the case of longitudinal waves the vibrations are always parallel to the direction of propagation, so that in a plane at right angles to the direction of travel there is no motion and hence there is perfect symmetry. If light is a transverse wave motion, the vibrations of a beam of light are all at right angles to the direction of propagation and there may or may not be perfect symmetry around the direction of travel. If perfect symmetry does not exist for a beam of light the beam is said to be *polarized*.

The experimental methods by which light may be polarized are classified under one of the following heads: (1) *reflection,* (2) *double refraction,* (3) *selective absorption,* and (4) *scattering*.

45.1. Plane-Polarized Light. A better understanding of the experiments to be described in this chapter can best be attained by first presenting the graphical methods of representing transverse waves. We assume at the outset that each light wave is a trans-verse wave whose vibrations are along straight lines at right angles to the direction of propagation (see Fig. 31J). Furthermore, we assume that a beam of ordinary light consists of millions of such waves, each with its own plane of vibration, and that there are waves vibrating in all planes with equal probability. Looking at such a beam end-on as in Fig. 45A, there should be just

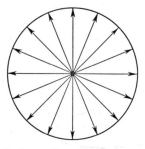

Fig. 45A *End-on view of a beam of unpolarized light illustrating schematically the equal probability of all planes of vibration.*

as many waves vibrating in one plane as there are vibrating in any other. This then can be referred to as perfect symmetry.

If, by some means or other, all the waves in a beam of light are made to vibrate in planes parallel to each other, the light is said to be plane-polarized. Diagrams illustrating such light are shown in Fig. 45B. The top diagram (a) represents plane-polarized light waves traveling to the right and vibrating in a vertical plane, while the second diagram (b) represents a ray of plane-polarized light vibrating in a horizontal plane. The dotted line indicating waves in diagram (a) is usually omitted.

It can be shown that a beam of ordinary unpolarized light, vibrating in all planes, may be regarded as being made up of two

370

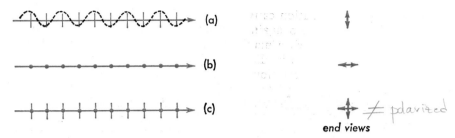

end views

Fig. 45B *Diagrams illustrating plane-polarized rays of light.*

kinds of vibrations only, half of the waves vibrating in a vertical plane as in diagram (a) and the other half vibrating perpendicular to it as in diagram (b). The reason for this is that waves not vibrating in either of these two planes can be resolved into two components, one component vibrating in a vertical plane and the other vibrating in a horizontal plane. Although these two components may not be equal to each other, the similarly resolved components from all waves will average out to be equal. Diagram (c) is regarded therefore as being equivalent to ordinary unpolarized light.

45.2. Polarization by Reflection. When ordinary unpolarized light is incident at an angle of about 57° on the polished surface of a plate of glass, the reflected light is plane-polarized. This fact was first discovered by Etienne Malus, a French physicist, in 1808. The experiment usually performed to demonstrate his discovery is illustrated in Fig. 45C.

A beam of unpolarized light *AB* is incident at an angle of 57° on the first glass surface at *B*. This light is again reflected at the same angle by a second glass plate *C* placed parallel to the first, as in diagram (a). If now the lower plate is rotated about the line *BC* by slowly turning the pedestal on which it is mounted, the intensity of the reflected beam *CD* is found to decrease slowly and vanish completely at an angle of 90°. With further rotation the reflected beam *CD* appears again, reaching a maximum at an angle of 180° as shown in dia-

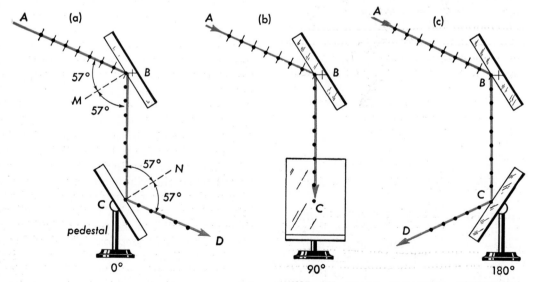

Fig. 45C *Common experiment performed to demonstrate the polarization of light by reflection from a smooth glass surface.*

gram (c). Continued rotation causes the intensity to decrease to zero again at 270°, and to reappear and reach a maximum at 360°, the starting point as in diagram (a). During this one complete rotation the angle of incidence on the lower plate, as well as the upper, has remained at 57°.

If the angle of incidence on either the upper or lower plate is not 57°, the beam CD will go through maxima and minima every 90° as before, but the minima will not go to zero. In other words, there will always be a reflected beam CD.

A complete mathematical theory of the polarization of light by reflection was first given by Fresnel in 1820. The remarkable confirmation of this theory, in every detail, by experimental observations on the behavior of light and measurements, establishes Fresnel as the greatest contributor to the whole field of optics.

The explanation of the above experiment is made clearer by a detailed study of what happens to ordinary light when it is reflected at the polarizing angle of 57° from glass. As illustrated in Fig. 45D, 8% of the

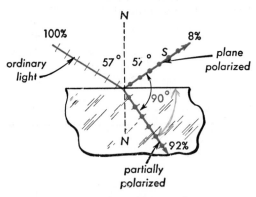

Fig. 45D *Light reflected from glass at an angle of 57° is plane-polarized, while the refracted light is only partially plane-polarized.*

light is reflected as plane-polarized light vibrating in the plane at right angles to the plane of incidence, and the other 92% is refracted as partially plane-polarized light, 42% vibrating perpendicular to the plane of incidence and 50% vibrating parallel to the plane of incidence. The plane of inci-

dence is defined as the plane passing through the incident ray and the ray normal NN. In nearly all diagrams the plane of the page is the plane of incidence.

If in Fig. 45D the angle of incidence is changed to some other value than 57°, the reflected beam will not be plane-polarized but will contain a certain amount of light vibrating parallel to the plane of incidence. In general, the light reflected from a transparent medium like glass or water is only partially plane-polarized; only at a certain angle, called the *polarizing angle*, is it plane-polarized. It was Sir David Brewster, a Scottish physicist, who first discovered that *at the polarizing angle the reflected and refracted rays are 90° apart.* This is now known as *Brewster's law*. The polarizing angle for water is 53°, for at this angle the reflected and refracted rays make an angle of 90° with each other.

Because these two rays make 90° with each other, the angle of incidence i and the angle of refraction r are complements of each other and sin r in *Snell's law* (sin i/sin $r = \mu$) can be replaced by cos i, giving

$$\frac{\sin i}{\cos i} = \mu \qquad \text{or} \qquad \boxed{\tan i = \mu} \qquad (45a)$$

This formula is useful in calculating the angle of polarization. For example, with water, $\mu = 1.33$, angle $i = 53°$; whereas for glass with $\mu = 1.52$, angle $i = 57°$.

Returning to the experiment demonstrated in Fig. 45C, we observe that the reflected light from the first mirror is plane-polarized as shown, and that the refracted light goes into the glass plate where it is absorbed by the black paint on the back face. The second mirror acts as a testing device or analyzer for polarized light. A certain fraction of the incident waves is reflected when the vibrations are perpendicular to the plane of incidence, and all are refracted (to be absorbed) when the vibrations are parallel to the plane of incidence.

45.3. Double Refraction. The double refraction of light by Iceland spar (calcite) was first observed by a Swedish physician, Erasmus Bartholinus, in 1669, and later studied in detail by Huygens and Newton.

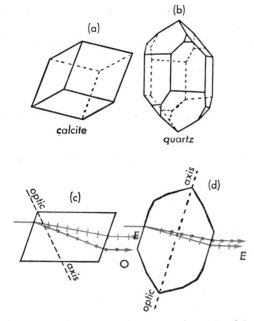

Fig. 45E *Diagrams and cross sections of calcite and quartz crystals showing double refraction and polarization.*

Nearly all crystalline substances are now known to exhibit the phenomenon. The following are but a few samples of crystals that show this effect: *calcite, quartz, mica, sugar, topaz, selenite, aragonite,* and *ice.* Calcite and quartz are of particular importance because they are used extensively in the manufacture of special optical instruments.

Calcite, as found in nature, always has the characteristic shape shown in Fig.

45E(a), whereas quartz has many different forms, the most complicated of which is illustrated in diagram (b). (For photographs of crystals, see Fig. 22K.) Each face of every calcite crystal is a parallelogram whose angles are 78° and 102°. Chemically, calcite is a hydrated calcium carbonate, $CaCO_3$; and quartz is silicon dioxide, SiO_2.

Not only is light doubly refracted by calcite and quartz, but both rays are found to be plane-polarized. One ray, called the *ordinary ray,* is polarized with its vibrations in one plane; and the other ray, called the *extraordinary ray,* is polarized with its vibrations in a plane at right angles to the first. This polarization is illustrated in diagrams (c) and (d) by *dots* and *lines* and can be proven by a glass plate rotated as plate C in Fig. 45C, or with some other analyzing device like a *Nicol prism* or a *polarizing film.* These latter devices will be described in the next two sections.

Since the two opposite faces of a calcite crystal are always parallel to each other, the two refracted rays always emerge parallel to the incident light and are therefore parallel to each other. If the incident light falls perpendicularly upon the surface of the crystal, as in Fig. 45F, the extraordinary ray will be refracted away from the normal and will come out parallel to, but displaced from, the incident beam. The ordinary ray will pass straight through without deviation.

In general, the *O* ray obeys the ordinary laws of refraction, and in this way the

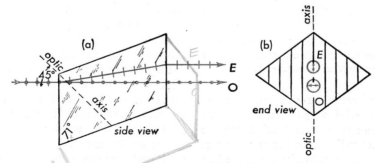

Fig. 45F *Double refraction in calcite. At normal incidence the O ray travels straight through and the E ray is refracted to one side.*

crystal acts like glass or water, whereas the E ray obeys no such simple law and behaves quite abnormally.

In other words, the O ray travels with the same velocity regardless of its direction through the crystal, whereas the velocity of the E ray is different in different directions. This is the origin of the designations ordinary and extraordinary.

One important property of calcite and quartz is that there is one and only one direction through either crystal in which there is no double refraction. This particular direction, called the *optic axis,* is shown by the dashed lines in Fig. 45E. The optic axis, it should be noted, is not a single line through a crystal, but a direction.

A plane passing through the crystal parallel to the optic axis and perpendicular to one face of the crystal is called a *principal section.* The plane of the page in Fig. 45F(a) is but one of any number of principal sections which, from the end view in diagram (b), appears as a vertical line. A useful rule always to be remembered is that the vibrations of the O ray are always perpendicular to the optic axis.

45.4. The Nicol Prism.
The Nicol prism is an optical device made from a calcite crystal and used in many optical instruments for producing and analyzing polarized light. Such a prism, as illustrated in Fig. 45G, is made by cutting a crystal along

Fig. 45G *Cross section and end view of a Nicol prism showing the elimination of the O ray by total reflection.*

a diagonal and cementing it back together again with a special cement, called *Canada balsam.* Canada balsam is used because it is a clear transparent substance whose reflective index is midway between that of the calcite for the O and E rays.

Optically the Canada balsam is more

dense than calcite for the E ray and less dense for the O ray. There exists, therefore, a critical angle of refraction for the one O ray (see Sec. 37.5), but not for the E ray. After both rays are refracted at the first crystal surface, the O ray is *totally reflected* by the first Canada balsam surface, as illustrated in the diagram, while the E ray passes on through to emerge parallel to the incident light. Starting with ordinary unpolarized light, a Nicol prism thus transmits plane polarized light only.

If two Nicols are lined up one behind the other as in Fig. 45H, they form an op-

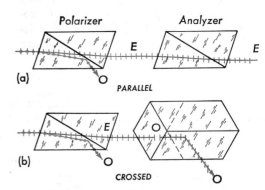

Fig. 45H   *Two Nicol prisms mounted as polarizer and analyzer. (a) Parallel Nicols. (b) Crossed Nicols.*

tical system frequently used in specially constructed microscopes for studying the optical properties of other crystals. The first Nicol which is used to produce plane-polarized light is called the *polarizer,* and the second which is used to test the light is called the *analyzer.*

In the parallel position, diagram (a), the polarized light from the polarizer passes on through the analyzer. Upon rotating the analyzer through 90°, as in diagram (b), no light is transmitted. For the same reason that the O vibrations in the original beam were totally reflected in the polarizer, the E vibrations are totally reflected as O vibrations in the analyzer.

Rotated another 90°, the light again gets through the analyzer just as in the parallel position in diagram (a). Still another 90°

finds the Nicols crossed again, with no light passing through.

45.5. Polarization by Selective Absorption.

When ordinary light enters a crystal of tourmaline, double refraction takes place in much the same way that it does in calcite, but with this difference: one ray, the so-called O ray, is entirely absorbed by the crystal, while the other ray, the E ray, passes on through. This phenomenon is called "selective absorption" because the crystal absorbs light waves vibrating in one plane and not those vibrating in the other.

Tourmaline crystals are therefore like Nicol prisms, for they take in ordinary light, dispose of the O vibrations, and transmit plane-polarized light as illustrated in Fig. 45I(a). When two such crystals are

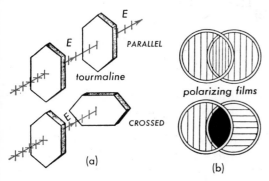

Fig. 45I *Diagrams illustrating the polarization of light by (a) tourmaline crystals, and (b) polarizing films.*

lined up parallel, with one behind the other, the plane-polarized light from the first crystal passes through the second with little loss in intensity. If either crystal is turned at 90° to the other, i.e., in the *cross position,* the light is completely absorbed and none passes through.

The behavior of tourmaline and similar optical substances is due to the molecular structure of the crystal. To draw an analogy, the regularly spaced molecules of a single crystal are like the regularly spaced trees in an orchard or grove. If one tries to run between the rows of trees carrying a very long pole held at right angles to the direction of motion, the pole must be held

in a vertical position. If it is held in the horizontal plane, the runner will be stopped.

The reason tourmaline is not used in optical instruments in place of Nicol prisms is that the crystals are yellow in color and do not transmit white light.

A more satisfactory substance for this purpose, which does transmit white light, is a relatively new manufactured material known as "Polaroid." This material is made in the form of very thin films, which have the general appearance of the more common substance "Cellophane," and is made from small needle-shaped crystals of an organic compound *iodosulphate of quinine.* Lined up parallel to each other and embedded in a *nitrocellulose mastic,* these crystals act like tourmaline by absorbing one component of polarization and transmitting the other. Two such films mounted separately in rings between thin glass plates are shown schematically in Fig. 45I. In the crossed position no light can pass through both films, whereas in the parallel position white light vibrating in the plane indicated by the parallel lines is transmitted. Many practical applications are being found for polarizing films of this kind, particularly wherever glaring light is not desired. The glaring light reflected at an angle from a table top, a book, a window pane, the water, or the road ahead when one is driving a car, is polarized and can be partly eliminated by polarizing films.

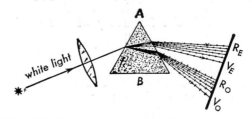

Fig. 45J *Refraction of white light by a prism cut from a calcite crystal.*

45.6. Dispersion by a Calcite Prism.

In Fig. 45J a prism is shown cut from a calcite crystal with the optic axis parallel to the refracting edge A. The optic axis, being perpendicular to the page, is represented by dots. (For the direction of the optic axis in calcite, see Fig. 45E.)

When white light is incident on one side of this prism, two completely separated spectra emerge from the other side. Not only is each spectrum complete in all its colors from red to violet but the light in each is plane-polarized. This can be demonstrated with an analyzing device like a Nicol prism, or polarizing film. By inserting the analyzer anywhere in the light beam and rotating it, one spectrum disappears first; then, 90° from it, the other fades and disappears while the first returns to full intensity.

The vibrations of all colors in the lower spectrum in Fig. 45J are perpendicular to the optic axis and are O vibrations. The upper spectrum with all vibrations parallel to the optic axis consists of E vibrations. If a prism were cut so that the refracted light as it travels through the crystal is parallel to the optic axis, only one spectrum is produced.

45.7. Scattering and the Blue Sky. The blue of the sky and the red of the sunset are due to a phenomenon called "scattering." When sunlight passes through the earth's atmosphere, much of the light is "picked" up by the air molecules and given out again in some other direction. The effect is quite similar to the action of water waves on floating objects. If, for example, the ripples from a stone dropped in a still pond of water encounter a small cork floating on the surface, the cork is set bobbing up and down with the frequency of the passing waves.

Light is pictured as acting in the same way on air molecules and fine dust particles. Once set into vibration by a light wave, a molecule or particle can send out the absorbed light again, sometimes in the same direction but generally in almost any other direction. This is illustrated schematically in Fig. 45K. Waves of light are shown being scattered at random in all directions.

Experiments show, in agreement with the theory of scattering, that the shortest waves are scattered more readily than longer

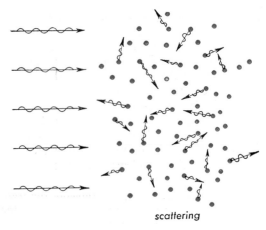

scattering

Fig. 45K *Light waves are scattered by air molecules.*

waves. To be more specific, the scattering is inversely proportional to the fourth power of the wavelength.

$$\text{scattering} \propto \frac{1}{\lambda^4} \qquad (45b)$$

According to this law the short waves of violet light are scattered ten times as readily as the longer waves of red light. The other colors are scattered by intermediate amounts. Thus when sunlight enters the earth's atmosphere, *violet* and *blue light* are scattered the most, followed by *green, yellow, orange,* and *red,* in the order named. For every ten violet waves ($\lambda = 0.00004$ cm) scattered from a beam, there is only one red wave ($\lambda = 0.00007$ cm).

violet	blue	green	yellow	orange	red
10	7	5	3	2	1

At noon on a clear day when the sun is directly overhead, as illustrated by an observer at A in Fig. 45L, the whole sky appears as *light blue.* This is the composite color of the mixture of colors scattered most effectively by the air molecules. As illustrated by the spectral color distribution in Fig. 42F, light blue of the color triangle is obtained by the added mixture of *violet, blue, green,* and *yellow.*

45.8. The Red Sunset. The occasional observation of an orange-red sunset is at-

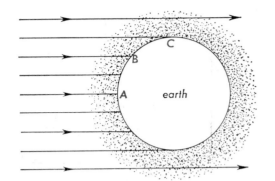

Fig. 45L *Schematic diagram showing the scattering of light by the air molecules of the earth's atmosphere.*

tributed to the *scattering of light* by fine dust and smoke particles near the earth's surface. This is illustrated in Fig. 45M. To an observer at *A*, it is noonday and the direct sunlight from overhead, seen only by looking directly at the sun itself, travels through a relatively short dust path. As a result, very little violet and blue are scattered away and the sun appears white.

As sunset approaches, however, the direct sunlight has to travel through an ever-increasing dust path. The result is that an hour or so before sundown, when the observer is at *B*, practically all of the blue and violet have been scattered out and, owing to the remaining colors, red, orange, yellow, and a little green, the sun appears yellow. At sunset, when the observer is at *C*, the direct rays must travel through so many

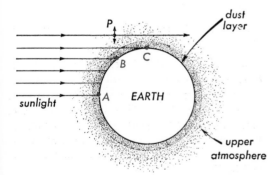

Fig. 45M *The scattering of light by a layer of dust near the earth's surface causes the sun to turn yellow, then orange, and finally red at sunset.*

miles of dust particles that all but red are completely scattered out and the sun appears red. At this same time the sky overhead is still light blue. If the dust blanket is too dense, even the red will be scattered appreciably from the direct sunlight and the deepening red sun will become lost from view before it reaches the horizon.

An excellent demonstration of scattering by fine particles is illustrated in Fig. 45N. A parallel beam of white light from a carbon arc and lens L_1 is sent through a water trough with glass sides. After passing through an iris diaphragm at the other end, a second lens L_2 forms an image of the circular opening on the screen. To produce the fine particles for scattering, about 40 gm of photographic fixing powder (hyposulfite of soda) are first dissolved in about 2 gal of water. Next, about 1 to 2 cm^3 of concentrated sulphuric acid are added and the two thoroughly mixed in the trough.*

As the microscopic sulfur particles begin to form, scattered blue light will outline the parallel beam through the trough. A little later, when more particles have formed, the entire body of water will appear light blue, due principally to multiple scattering. Light scattered out of the central beam of light is scattered again and again before emerging from the trough. At first the transmitted light which falls on the screen appears white. Later, as more scattering takes out the shorter wavelengths, this image representing the sun turns yellow, then orange, and finally red.

45.9. Polarization by Scattering. If the blue of the sky is observed through a Nicol prism or a piece of polaroid, the light is found to be partially plane-polarized. This polarization can also be seen in the scattering experiment described above. Observed through a polaroid film, the beam in the tank appears bright at one orientation of the polaroid and disappears with a 90° rotation.†

* The correct amount of acid to produce the best results is determined by trial. The first visible precipitate should appear after 2 or 3 min.

† For a more complete account of polarized light, see *Optics* by Jenkins and White, McGraw-Hill.

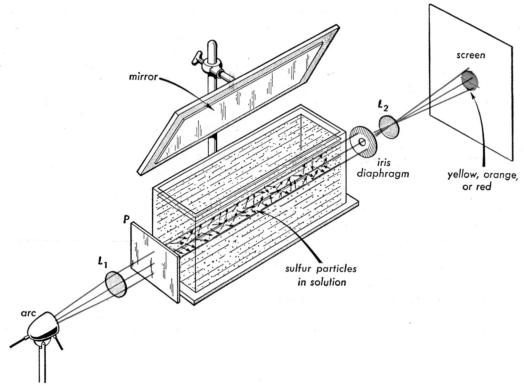

Fig. 45N *The sunset experiment. Demonstration of the scattering and polarization of light by small particles.*

PROBLEMS

1. Find the polarizing angle for diamond, with its refractive index of 2.41.

2. If the polarizing angle of a transparent plastic is found to be 55°, what is the refractive index? (*Ans.* 1.428.)

3. The polarizing angle for yellow light incident on a clear transparent solid is 57.8°. Calculate the refractive index and identify the material. See Table 38A.

4. Find the polarizing angle for a clear plastic with a refractive index of 1.418 for green light. (*Ans.* 54.8°.)

5. What is the polarizing angle for a dense flint glass having a refractive index of 1.720?

6. What is the polarizing angle for water, with its refractive index of 1.33? (*Ans.* 53.1°.)

7. Calculate the polarizing angle for blue light incident on crown glass. See Table 38A for index.

8. The polarizing angle for red light incident on a clear transparent material is 67° 28′. Calculate the refractive index and identify the material from Table 38A. (*Ans.* $\mu = 2.410$, diamond.)

9. What is the refractive index of flint glass if the polarizing angle is 59°?

10. If the refractive index for a plastic is 1.45, what is the angle of refraction for a ray of light incident at the polarizing angle? (*Ans.* 34.6°.)

11. The polarizing angle of a piece of glass, for green light, is 60°. Find the angle of minimum deviation for a 60° prism made of the same glass.

12. If the polarizing angle of a piece of clear plastic is 60°, find the angle of minimum deviation for a 50° prism made of the same plastic. (*Ans.* 44.2°.)

13. If the critical angle of a clear crystal for green light is 24.4°, calculate the polarizing angle.

14. The critical angle for violet light incident on a piece of glass is 36.1°. (a) Identify this glass in Table 38A, and (b) calculate its corresponding polarizing angle. (*Ans.* (a) dense flint, (b) 59.5°.)

15. Find the polarizing angle for the boundary separating water of index 1.33 from glass of index 1.52. Assume the incident ray to be in water.

16. Find the amount of light, relative to yellow light, scattered by each of the following wavelengths of light: ultraviolet light 2.0×10^{-5} cm, violet light 4.0×10^{-5} cm, yellow light 5.8×10^{-5} cm, red light 7.0×10^{-5} cm, and infrared light 10×10^{-5} cm. (*Ans.* 70, 4.4, 1.0, 0.47, and 0.11 times, respectively.)

17. Zinc sulfide deposited on a glass surface is a clear transparent material having a refractive index of 2.50. Calculate the polarizing angle for this medium.

18. A 60° calcite prism is cut with its faces parallel to the optic axis. Calculate the angle of minimum deviation for yellow light for each of the two polarized rays. The refractive index for calcite for the O ray is 1.658, and for the E ray, 1.486. (*Ans.* 52° and 36°.)

19. What is the ratio of the scattering of light waves between red light of wavelength 7×10^{-5} cm and violet light of wavelength 4×10^{-5} cm?

20. For every 200 waves of red light scattered by the air, how many waves of orange light will be scattered? Assume the wavelengths to be 7×10^{-5} cm and 6×10^{-5} cm, respectively. (*Ans.* 371.)

21. Calculate the ratio of the numbers of light rays scattered by the air for violet light ($\lambda = 4 \times 10^{-5}$ cm) and green light ($\lambda = 5 \times 10^{-5}$ cm).

22. Find the ratio of light waves scattered by fine particles between blue light ($\lambda = 4.3 \times 10^{-5}$) and red light ($\lambda = 7.0 \times 10^{-5}$ cm). (*Ans.* 7.0:1.)

Chapter 46

Relativity

The mention of the word "relativity" suggests the name of Albert Einstein,* the scientist to whom we are indebted for the now famous theory. To begin with, Einstein was a realist, and his theory rests upon physical facts which have been verified by repeated observations of well-planned experiments. Reference is made to the well-known Michelson-Morley experiment described in Chap. 44.

The Michelson-Morley experiment was performed (first in 1881) in the hope of detecting and measuring the earth's motion through space. The experimental fact that no fringe shift could be observed in the interference pattern of their apparatus led to the conclusion that either there is no such thing as an ether drift, or that the Michelson interferometer is incapable of detecting motion through an ether.

Relativity is divided into two parts. One part is called the *special, or restricted, theory of relativity,* and the other is called the *general theory.* The special theory, developed by Einstein in 1905, is thoroughly backed by numerous experimental observations of high precision and deals with observers and their reference frames moving with constant velocities. The mathematics of the special theory is simple enough, and we will consider several of the relationships that are necessary for the satisfactory explanations of certain atomic phenomena.

The general theory, proposed by Einstein in 1915, deals with motions of bodies in accelerated frames of reference. The mathematics of the general theory is quite difficult, and the experimental evidence for its validity is not as well founded as for the special theory.

46.1. The Lorentz-Fitzgerald Contraction. From the time Michelson and Morley announced the negative results of their ether-drift experiment, scientists tried to explain why the experiment failed. An ingenious explanation was first advanced by Fitzgerald in 1890. If objects moving through space have to push against the immovable ether, he suggested, they would be compressed in the direction of motion. This compression would, therefore, shorten the Michelson interferometer arms holding the mirrors and might exactly compensate for an existing ether drift.

Lorentz,* the famous Dutch physicist,

---

* Albert Einstein (1879-1955), German-Swiss physicist, was born of Jewish parents at Ulm, Württemberg, on March 14, 1879. His boyhood was spent in Munich where his father, a dealer in chemicals, had settled in 1880. When the family moved to Italy in 1894, young Albert went to Switzerland to study. There he worked his way through school, finally taking his Ph.D. degree at the University of Zurich in 1902. He was appointed extraordinary professor of theoretical physics at the University of Zurich in 1909, and in 1913 he was called to Berlin as director of the Kaiser-Wilhelm Institute for Physics. While at this post, he was elected a member of the Prussian Academy of Sciences and a member of the Royal Society of London. In 1921 he received the Nobel Prize in physics and, in 1925, the Copley Medal of the Royal Society. He is best known for his theory of relativity, the theory and explanation of Brownian motion, the theory of the photoelectric effect, and the quantum theory of radiant heat energy. Twice married, Einstein had several children. To his friends he was a quiet, sincere, and modest man who loved his pipe and violin, and disliked formality.

* Hendrik A. Lorentz (1853-1928), Dutch physicist, was born at Arnheim on July 18, 1853. He was educated at the University of Leyden, where he was appointed professor of theoretical physics at the age of 25. Those who knew him never lost the opportunity of mentioning his charming personality and kindly disposition. Of his numerous contributions to science he is best known for (1) a set of

studied this problem from an atomic point of view. All matter, he proposed, is made up of atoms, and atoms are made up of charged particles that produce electric and magnetic fields. These fields must exert forces on the electromagnetic ether, thus causing the atoms and molecules in moving matter to be pushed closer together. Starting with the well-known principles of electricity and magnetism, Lorentz derived the following formula for the length of any object:

$$l = l_0 \sqrt{1 - v^2/c^2} \qquad (46a)$$

where v is the velocity of the object through the ether, l_0 is its length when at rest in the ether, and c is the velocity of light. Note the resemblance of this equation to Eq. (12c). Suppose that an object is at rest, so that $v = 0$. Upon substitution of $v = 0$ in Eq. (46a), we find $l = l_0$, which says the object's length l will be just equal to its rest length l_0. If a rod were moving lengthwise with $\frac{3}{4}$ the speed of light, however, the substitution of $v = \frac{3}{4}c$ into the equation gives $l = 0.66\ l_0$. This indicates that the moving rod is only $\frac{2}{3}$ as long as when it is at rest. (See Fig. 46A.)

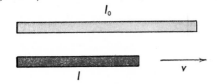

$$l_0$$

$$l \qquad\qquad v \longrightarrow$$

Fig. 46A   *Diagram of the Lorentz-Fitzgerald contraction.*

It is interesting to see what this equation reveals if a rod could move lengthwise with the speed of light, i.e., with $v = c$. The result is $l = 0$. This means that any object moving with the speed of light would be compressed to zero length. The velocity of light, therefore, becomes an upper limit for the velocity of any moving object.

four algebraic equations, known as the Lorentz transformation, which formed the basis of Einstein's special theory of relativity, and (2) for his theoretical explanation of the Zeeman Effect. In 1922 he was awarded, jointly with Zeeman, the Nobel Prize in physics.

The above formula, when applied to the cross arms of the interferometer used in the Michelson-Morley experiment (see Fig. 44K), shows that the arms are shortened by just the right amount to compensate for the expected drift. See Eq. (44f). This shortening of an object cannot be measured, for, if one attempts to measure the length of a moving object, the measuring stick must move with the same velocity, and an equal length of the stick shortens by the same amount.

46.2. Newtonian Mechanics. In the treatment of relative velocities in Chap. 12, it was explained that an *inertial frame of reference* is one in which Newton's laws of motion hold true. Such a frame is one that is not being accelerated, and the observer's reference frame is either at rest in that frame or is moving slowly in comparison with the speed of light and with constant velocity. If any reference frame is accelerated, Newton's laws of motion cannot be expected to hold, since a mass initially at rest in that frame would appear to accelerate without an applied force.

We also saw in Chap. 12 that, if any event occurring in one frame of reference is measured by an observer at rest in that frame, as well as by a moving observer in another frame, a set of equations could be written enabling either observer to determine the other's measurements. These transformation equations are very simple, and are the following:

$$x' = x - vt \qquad (46b)$$
$$t' = t \qquad (46c)$$
nonrelativistic

where x' and x are measured distances from any object point to each of the reference frame origins, and v is the relative velocity of the two frames. The distances and velocities are confined to one dimension only. If three dimensions are used, equations similar to Eq. (46b) can be written for y and z directions.

In setting up these transformation equations it is assumed that all observations and measurements are simultaneous, that is, that light travels with an infinite speed. This is the basis for writing Eq. (46c). Since light has a finite speed, however, it should be possible, by accurately observing an event from two different reference frames, to find that the above equations do not hold ex-

same value regardless of the motion of the source and the motion of the observer.

To see the meaning of this second statement, consider a reference frame and observer O at rest as shown in Fig. 46B. A

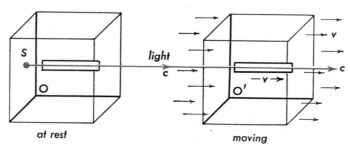

Fig. 46B   *The velocity of light is the same to all observers, that is, it is invariant.*

actly. *From the differences they should then be able to determine from the measured speed of light in each frame whether they are moving through the ether at different rates.* This was the purpose of the Michelson-Morley experiment, and it failed. Einstein interpreted this failure to mean that the velocity of light is *invariant.* What is meant by this is that no matter how a source of light moves or how an observer moves, he will always find the velocity of light in free space to be the same. This velocity we designate c.

46.3. Einstein's Special Theory of Relativity. Since the Michelson-Morley experiment fails to provide a fixed frame of reference in space, Einstein's theory assumes that all such experiments will fail, and that at relatively high speeds the laws of Newton are not valid. Einstein's special theory of relativity shows that the laws of physics can be restated so that they will apply to any frame of reference, and that at low relative velocities these laws reduce to Newton's laws of motion. The first postulate for setting up these equations is:

The laws of physics apply equally well for all observers as long as they are moving with constant velocities.

The second postulate follows from the assumption that the velocity of light is *invariant:*

The velocity of light in free space has the

source of light S is set up, and by means of an experiment like that of Fizeau, or Michelson (see Figs. 36I and 36J) the velocity of light is measured and found to be 3×10^8 m/sec. Another observer O', moving with a velocity v with respect to O, allows the light from the same source S to pass through his apparatus. Upon measuring the velocity of this same light in his frame, he too finds 3×10^8 m/sec.

For these two identical results to be consistent, Einstein derived new transformation equations. To do this he assumed that *distance* and *time* are relative, i.e., they are not *invariant.* His transformation equations may be written down and compared with the nonrelativistic equations as follows:

$x' = x - vt$	$x' = \gamma(x - vt)$ (46d)
$t' = t$	$t' = \gamma\left(t - \dfrac{vx}{c^2}\right)$ (46e)

nonrelativistic   *relativistic*

where γ is given by

$$\gamma = \frac{1}{\sqrt{1 - v^2/c^2}}$$ (46f)

Note the similarity of these two sets of equations. By setting $v = 0$ in Eq.(46f), we get $\gamma = 1$, and the relativistic equations reduce to the Newtonian forms. The value of

γ is just the ratio of the two *travel times* for the light paths in the Michelson-Morley experiment. See Eq.(44f).

Classical laws such as Newton's laws of motion can be used in most applications of kinematics and dynamics to the motions of macroscopic bodies; but at speeds above 10% the speed of light, the relativistic equations should be used.

Since these equations were first derived by Lorentz in 1895, their use in any problem is referred to as a *Lorentz transformation*. Lorentz arrived at the equations by assuming a contraction of moving objects in an ether, whereas Einstein in 1905 derived the equations by assuming only the speed of light as *invariant*.

46.4. Relativistic Velocity Transformation. Suppose the velocity of a body in an observer's frame of reference is u, and we wish to calculate the velocity u' of that same body as measured by an observer moving with a velocity v. For this calculation we use the velocity transformation equations, Eq.(12m). – P.90

$$u' = \frac{x'_2 - x'_1}{t'_2 - t'_1} \quad \text{and} \quad u = \frac{x_2 - x_1}{t_2 - t_1} \quad (46g)$$

We now make use of the relativistic transformation equations, Eqs.(46d) and (46f), and substitute unprimed terms for each primed term in the first relation. This gives

$$u' = \frac{\gamma(x_2 - vt_2) - \gamma(x_1 - vt_1)}{\gamma(t_2 - vx_2/c^2) - \gamma(t_1 - vx_1/c^2)} \quad (46h)$$

Upon canceling the γ's, collecting like terms, substituting from the right-hand equation of Eq.(46g), and simplifying, we obtain,*

$$\boxed{u' = \frac{u - v}{1 - uv/c^2}} \quad (46i)$$

relativistic

This is the velocity transformation equation in the theory of relativity. It shows that velocity, as in Newtonian mechanics, too, is not *invariant*. Different observers find different velocities.

$$u' = u - v \quad (46j)$$
nonrelativistic

Example 1. An observer on the earth (assumed to be an inertial frame of reference) sees a space ship A receding from him at 2×10^8 m/sec and overtaking a space ship B receding at 1.5×10^8 m/sec. Find the relative velocity of (a) space ship B as observed by A, (b) space ship A as observed by B, and (c) space ship B relative to space ship A as observed by O.

Solution. This example is shown schematically in Fig. 46C. The given quantities for (a) are $v = 2 \times 10^8$ m/sec; $u = 1.5 \times 10^8$ m/sec; and $c = 3 \times 10^8$ m/sec. Upon substitution in Eq.(46i) we obtain

Part (a)
$$u' = \frac{1.5 \times 10^8 \text{ m/sec} - 2.0 \times 10^8 \text{ m/sec}}{1 - 1.5 \times 10^8 \times 2.0 \times 10^8/(3 \times 10^8)^2}$$

$$u' = \frac{-0.5 \times 10^8}{1 - 3 \times 10^{16}/9 \times 10^{16}}$$
$$= -0.75 \times 10^8 \text{ m/sec}$$

For (b) we reverse the velocity symbols; $u = 2 \times 10^8$ m/sec and $v = 1.5 \times 10^8$ m/sec. Upon substitution in Eq.(46i), we obtain

Part (b)
$$u' = \frac{2.0 \times 10^8 - 1.5 \times 10^8}{1 - 2.0 \times 10^8 \times 1.5 \times 10^8/(3 \times 10^8)^2}$$

$$u' = \frac{0.5 \times 10^8}{1 - 3 \times 10^{16}/9 \times 10^{16}}$$
$$= +0.75 \times 10^8 \text{ m/sec}$$

For (c) we take just the difference between the two velocities observed by O.

$$u' = 1.5 \times 10^8 - 2.0 \times 10^8 = -0.5 \times 10^8 \text{ m/sec}$$

Example 2. Suppose space ship B in Example 1 (Fig. 46C) is replaced by a beam of light

* The algebraic steps from Eq. (46h) to Eq. (46i) are left as a student exercise.

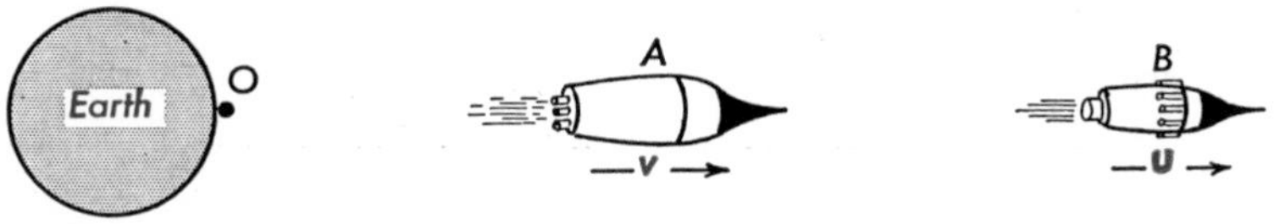

Fig. 46C Diagram of two space ships receding from the earth with constant velocities.

moving from left to right, which observer O measures and finds to be $c = 3 \times 10^8$ m/sec. What will the velocity of this same light be, as observed by space ship A?

Solution. The given quantities are $u = c$, $v = 2.0 \times 10^8$ m/sec, and $c = 3 \times 10^8$ m/sec. Upon first replacing u by c in Eq.(46i) and solving for u', we obtain

$$u' = \frac{u - v}{1 - uv/c^2} = \frac{c - v}{1 - cv/c^3} = \frac{c - v}{1 - v/c}$$
$$= \frac{c - v}{\frac{c - v}{c}} = c$$

Hence the observer in A finds the velocity of light to be c regardless of his velocity. Hence the velocity of light is the same to all observers; it is *invariant*.

46.5. Relativistic Mass. Einstein's special theory of relativity shows that, if the mass of an object is measured by two different observers, one moving with respect to the other, the results are different. Mass, therefore, is not invariant. Although the derivation will not be given here, the special theory gives, for the transformation equation,

$$m = \gamma m_0 \qquad (46k)$$

or

$$m = \frac{m_0}{\sqrt{1 - v^2/c^2}} \qquad (46l)$$

relativistic

where m_0 is the mass of an object at rest in the observer's reference frame, and m is its mass when it is moving with a velocity v. A schematic diagram of a practical situation is shown in Fig. 46D in which the rest mass m_0 is not moving with respect to you, the observer, while at the right the same mass m is shown moving with a velocity v.

Table 46A gives the values of the rela-

tivistic mass of objects for a large range of velocities.

At 10% the speed of light (18,600 mi/sec) the mass of a body is only $\frac{1}{2}$ of 1% greater than its rest mass. At 50% the speed of light the mass m has increased 15%, while

rest mass   moving mass

Fig. 46D *Schematic diagram illustrating the relativistic increase in mass, and the Lorentz-Fitzgerald contraction, due to motion.*

at 99.9% the speed of light, it has jumped to over 22 times its rest mass. These values are in excellent agreement with experiments on high-speed atomic particles, a subject that will be considered in detail in later chapters.

It is important to note that, as the speed of any given mass increases, the mass rises slowly at first, and then much more rapidly as it approaches the speed of light. No mass, however, can move with the speed of light, for by Eq.(46l) its mass would become infinite.

For low velocities v, Eqs.(46f) and (46l) are hard to evaluate, and the following approximation formula should be used:

$$\frac{1}{\sqrt{1 - v^2/c^2}} \cong 1 + \frac{1}{2}\frac{v^2}{c^2}$$

46.6. Einstein's Mass-Energy Relation. Just as sound, heat, and light are forms of energy, Einstein's special theory of relativity shows that mass is a form of energy. The expression giving the relation between mass

TABLE 46A. RELATIVISTIC MASS FOR DIFFERENT VELOCITIES

Velocity ratio v/c in per cent	1%	10%	50%	90%	99%	99.9%
Relative mass m/m_0	1.000	1.005	1.15	2.3	7.1	22.3

and energy is an equation familiar to everyone. It is

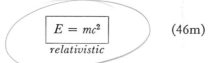

$$E = mc^2$$ (46m)

relativistic

where m is the mass, c is the velocity of light, and E is the energy equivalence of the mass. The validity of this equation is now well established by hundreds of experiments involving atomic nuclei as well as the general subject called *atomic energy*.

If an object has a rest mass of m_0, it has stored within it a total energy m_0c^2. If the same mass is moving with a velocity v, its mass has increased to m and the total stored energy is mc^2. These two masses are related by Eq.(46k).

When a force F is applied to accelerate a given mass, the amount of work done is given by

$$W = F \times s$$

As a result of this *work done,* the object,

whose rest mass is m_0, is moving with a velocity and has kinetic energy E_k.

$$F \times s = E_k$$ (46n)

Applying the law of conservation of energy, we can write

$$m_0c^2 + E_k = mc^2$$

Transposing, we obtain for the kinetic energy of a moving mass, the relation

$$E_k = mc^2 - m_0c^2$$ (46o)

Another form for this equation is obtained by substituting Eq.(46k) for m.

$$E_k = \frac{m_0c^2}{\sqrt{1 - v^2/c^2}} - m_0c^2$$ (46p)

or

$$E_k = m_0c^2 \left[\frac{1}{\sqrt{1 - v^2/c^2}} - 1 \right]$$ (46q)

In the abbreviated notation,

$$E_k = m_0c^2(\gamma - 1)$$ (46r)

PROBLEMS

(Assume the speed of light to be 3×10^8 m/sec, or 186,300 mi/sec, in all of the following problems.)

1. Find the length of a meter stick moving lengthwise at a speed of 2.7×10^8 m/sec. Assume a Lorentz-Fitzgerald contraction.

2. If a space ship 50 m long were to pass the earth traveling at 2.4×10^8 m/sec, what would be its apparent length, assuming, a Lorentz-Fitzgerald contraction? (*Ans.* 30 m.)

3. The brakeman on a freight train traveling 50 mi/hr is walking forward on top of one of the box cars at 4 mi/hr. A train just ahead of this one is traveling at 60 mi/hr. What is the velocity of the brakeman with respect to the engineer in the train ahead, to three significant figures, (a) in Newtonian mechanics, and (b) in special relativity?

4. A man on the ground observes a plane taking off on the airport runway at 120 m/sec. A car traveling 32 m/sec follows it down the runway. Find the relative velocity of the plane as seen by the driver of the car. (*Ans.* 88 m/sec.)

5. An observer on the earth sees one space ship traveling at 2.4×10^8 m/sec overtaking another space ship traveling at 1.8×10^8 m/sec. What is the relative velocity of (a) the second ship as seen by the first, (b) the first ship as seen by the second, and (c) the relative velocity as seen from the earth?

6. An observer on the earth sees a space ship, receding from the earth at 2.0×10^8 m/sec, launch a projectile ahead of it. As seen from the earth this projectile has a speed of 2.25×10^8 m/sec. What is the velocity of the projectile with respect to the space ship as seen from (a) the space ship, and (b) the earth? (*Ans.* (a) 0.5×10^8 m/sec, (b) 2.25×10^8 m/sec.)

7. An earth observer sees a space ship approaching the earth at $\frac{1}{3}$ the speed of light. It launches an exploration vehicle which from the earth appears to be approaching at $\frac{2}{5}$ the velocity of light. What is the velocity of the vehicle with respect to the space ship as seen from (a) the space ship, and (b) the earth?

8. Two space ships are observed from the earth to be approaching each other, each with

a velocity of $\frac{2}{3}$ the speed of light. With what velocity is each space ship approaching the other, as seen from either ship? (*Ans.* 2.77×10^8 m/sec, or $0.92\ c$.)

9. Atomic particles in the form of a beam have a velocity of 60% the speed of light. What is their relativistic mass as compared with their rest mass?

10. Atomic particles in the form of a beam have a velocity of 95% the speed of light. What is their relativistic mass compared with their rest mass? (*Ans.* $m/m_0 = 3.20$.)

11. An atomic particle has a rest mass of 1.7×10^{-25} Kg. Find its total mass energy when it is (a) at rest, and (b) when it has a velocity of $\frac{4}{5}$ the speed of light.

12. Two atomic particles, each with a rest mass of 2.0×10^{-25} Kg, approach each other in head-on collision. If each has an initial velocity of 2.0×10^8 m/sec, what is (a) the velocity of one atom as seen from the other, and (b) the relativistic mass of one as seen by the other? (*Ans.* (a) 2.77×10^8 m/sec, (b) 5.20×10^{-25} Kg.)

13. If an atomic mass of 1.5×10^{-25} Kg were converted into energy, and all of it imparted as kinetic energy to another atomic particle with a rest mass of 1.0×10^{-25} Kg, what would be the atom's velocity?

14. Starting with Eq.(46h), carry out the algebraic steps necessary to obtain Eq.(46i).

Chapter 47

Electricity at Rest

47.1. Electrification by Friction. It is impossible to say when electricity was first discovered. Records show that as early as 600 B.C. the attractive properties of amber were known. Thales of Miletus (640-546 B.C.), one of the "seven wise men" of ancient Greece, is credited with having observed the attraction of amber, when previously rubbed, for small fibrous materials and bits of straw. Amber was used by these people, even as it is now, for ornamental purposes. Just as the precious metals had their names of gold and silver, so amber had its name "electron."

Although the electrification of amber by friction was handed down from one writer to another, nothing new about the phenomenon was discovered for more than 2000 years. It was not until the beginning of the 17th century that Sir William Gilbert* announced the discovery that many substances could be electrified by friction. Gilbert named this effect "electric" after the word "electron." It is now well-estab-

* Sir William Gilbert (1540-1603), court physician to Queen Elizabeth and a noted philosopher and experimental physicist. In 1600 he published a book on magnetism, "De Magnete." This book was full of valuable facts and experiments on electricity and magnetism, and among other things contained many criticisms of his contemporaries, predecessors, and the early philosophers. In his preface he wrote: "Why should I submit this new philosophy to the judgment of men who have taken oaths to follow the opinions of others, to the most senseless corrupters of the arts, to lettered clowns, grammatists, sophists, spouters, and the wrong-headed rabble. To you alone true philosophers, ingenious minds, who not only in books but in things themselves look for knowledge, have I dedicated these foundations of magnetic science." So strongly does he advocate here, and carry out, himself, the experimental method, that he is to be classed as a scientist with his contemporary Galileo, "the father of modern physics."

lished that all bodies when rubbed together become electrified and that amber is just one of a number of substances which show the effect most strongly.

47.2. Electrostatic Attraction. The word "electrostatic" means electricity at rest, and the word "attraction" refers to the force exerted by one body upon another at a distance. To demonstrate electrostatic attraction, one often uses a rubber or amber rod and rubs it with a piece of flannel or fur. This electrifies the rod, so that, when the rod is held close to some small bits of paper, they jump up to the rod and hold fast.

The attraction of an electrified rubber rod for wood is illustrated in Fig. 47A. A

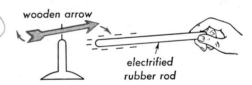

Fig. 47A *A rubber rod, electrified by rubbing against a piece of fur, attracts wood, as shown by the turning of the arrow.*

small arrow cut from a piece of dry wood is mounted so that it is free to turn as shown. When the electrified rubber rod is brought near the pointed end of the arrow it attracts the wood, turning the arrow until it points toward the rod. Brought near the opposite end, the wood is again attracted, turning the arrow to point away from the rubber rod.

An ordinary hard rubber comb when drawn through the hair becomes charged with electricity and will attract light objects in the same way. Sometimes the electrical charges produced in a comb are so great that tiny sparks can be seen to jump between the comb and hair. This is particularly noticeable in a darkened room. These sparks are the reason for the crackling noise so often heard when hair is being combed.

A spectacular effect is produced by bringing a charged rubber rod close to one side of a smoothly running stream of water from a faucet. As shown in Fig. 47B, the stream

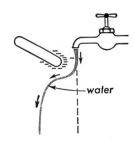

Fig. 47B *A thin stream of water is easily deflected by an electrified rod or comb.*

is diverted to one side and even into the horizontal before it falls again.

An ordinary sheet of writing paper, placed on the panel of a door or other similar flat surface and rubbed, will hold fast and remain there for some little time without falling down.

47.3. Electricity + and −. When two different substances are rubbed together and then separated, both are found to be electrified, one with one kind of electricity and the other with another. To illustrate this, one end of a rubber rod is charged by rubbing with fur and is then suspended in a small wire stirrup, as shown in Fig. 47C. When the electrified end of a similarly charged rod is brought close by, as shown in diagram (a), the suspended rod turns away, showing repulsion. If the fur is brought close by, in place of the rubber, the suspended rod is attracted and turns toward the fur. When a glass rod, previously rubbed with silk, is brought close by, as in diagram (b), there is attraction, and when the silk is brought up there is repulsion.

Since the fur, as well as the glass, attracts the electrified rubber rod, they each have the same kind of electrification: they are said to be *positively charged.* By similar notation the rubber and silk by their actions are said to be *negatively charged.* Positive charges are designated by a (+) sign and negative charges by a (−) sign.

Not only do the above experiments indicate the existence of two kinds of electrification, but they also demonstrate a rule concerning the action of one kind of electrification on another. Diagram (a), illustrating

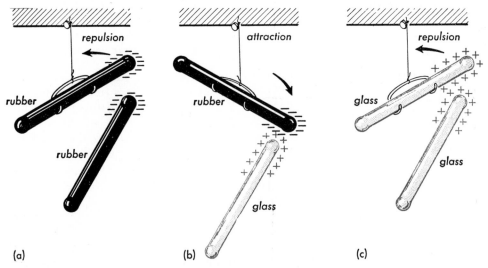

(a)   (b)   (c)

Fig. 47C *Like charges of electricity repel each other and unlike charges attract.*

a negatively charged rubber rod repelling a similar rod, shows that two negative charges repel each other. Diagram (b) shows that positive and negative charges attract each other, and diagram (c) that two positive charges repel each other. The general law can therefore be stated that:

Like charges repel and unlike charges attract.

47.4. Theory of Electrification. Historically there have been two outstanding theories of electrification: the one-fluid theory of Benjamin Franklin* and the two-fluid theory of Charles Du Fay. According to the two-fluid theory, all objects contain equal amounts of two fluids. When two different substances are rubbed together, one kind of fluid (positive) is spread over one object and the other kind of fluid (negative) over the other.

According to the one-fluid theory of Franklin, all bodies contain a certain specified amount of an "electric fire" or fluid to keep them in an uncharged or neutral state. When two objects are rubbed together, one accumulates an excess of fluid and becomes positively charged while the other loses fluid and becomes negatively charged. To Franklin we owe the terms "plus" and "minus," "positive" and "negative" electricity.

Both of these theories are in part correct, for now we know the mechanism by which bodies become electrified by friction. The modern theory is based upon the principle already put forward—that all substances are made of atoms and molecules. Each atom contains a nucleus having a known amount of positive charge (see Fig. 47D). This positive charge is due to the presence

* Benjamin Franklin (1706-1790). From printer's apprentice as a youth, he became a man of unusual powers, not only in politics and diplomacy but also in scientific research. His most famous scientific achievement was the discovery of the electrical nature of lightning. This he did by flying a kite into the clouds on a stormy day and noting the electrical sparks at the ground end of the kite string (a copper wire). Among his many practical applications of scientific discoveries, he invented the lightning rod and made the first pair of bifocal eyeglasses.

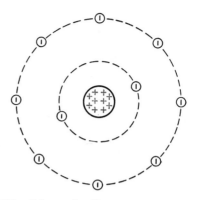

Fig. 47D *Schematic diagram of a neon atom showing its nucleus at the center with ten positive charges (called protons) surrounded on the outside by ten negative charges (called electrons).*

in the nucleus of a certain number of *protons.* All protons are alike and have the same mass and positive charge. Around every atomic nucleus there are a number of negatively charged particles, called *electrons.*

Normally each atom of a substance is electrically neutral; in other words, it has equal amounts of negative and positive charge. Since each electron has the same amount of charge as every other electron, and the same amount as every proton but of opposite sign, there are just as many protons in every nucleus as there are electrons around the outside. While protons are much smaller than electrons in size, they contain the bulk of the mass of every atom. One proton, for example, weighs nearly two thousand times as much as an electron. The electrons therefore are light particles or objects around a small but relatively heavy nucleus.

Individual atoms or large groups of atoms and molecules have an *affinity,* an *attraction,* for additional electrons over and above the exact number, which will just neutralize the positive charges of the nuclei. This attraction of the atoms for more than a sufficient number of electrons varies considerably from atom to atom and substance to substance. When, therefore, two different substances are brought into contact, the

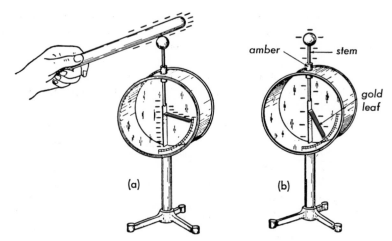

Fig. 47E *Diagram of an electroscope showing how such an instrument may be given a negative charge.*

substance with greater electron affinity seizes nearby electrons from the other, and thus acquires a net negative charge. Such is the case, for example, with rubber and amber when rubbed with fur. Having a strong affinity for electrons, both of these solids become strongly negative, whereas the fur becomes deficient of electrons and thereby positively charged.

47.5. The Electroscope. An electroscope is an instrument for measuring the electrical potential of a charged body. A thin strip of gold leaf is fastened to the side of a long narrow rod of metal and mounted in a metal and glass box (see Fig. 47E). The gold-leaf support, which will here be called the "stem," is insulated from the box with amber. When the metal knob N is touched

by a charged rubber rod, some of the charge flows onto and distributes itself over the gold leaf and support. Since like charges repel each other, the gold leaf is pushed out as shown in the diagram. When the source of charge is taken away the electroscope retains its acquired charge, which, distributing itself more or less uniformly over the stem, causes the leaf, as shown in diagram (b), to stand out at a somewhat smaller angle. The more charge given the electroscope, the higher the gold leaf is repelled.

If an electroscope is first charged negatively as shown in Fig. 47E(b), and then a negatively charged body is brought close to but not touching the knob, as shown in Fig. 47F(a), the gold leaf will rise as indi-

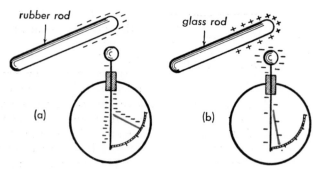

Fig. 47F *Brought near a negatively charged electroscope, (a) a negatively charged body causes the gold leaf to rise, and (b) a positively charged body causes the gold leaf to fall.*

cated. This happens because the electrons are repelled away from the knob to the far end of the stem, causing the gold leaf to rise still higher. As long as the two bodies do not touch each other, allowing more negatives to go to the electroscope, the gold

commonly called *insulators,* or *nonconductors.* Several examples of conductors and nonconductors are listed in Table 47A.

The property of electrical conduction is illustrated by an experiment in Fig. 47G. One end of a long thin copper wire is con-

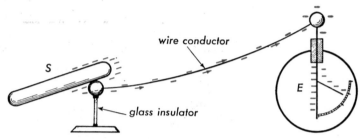

Fig. 47G *Experiment illustrating an electric current as the flow of electrons along a wire conductor.*

leaf will fall back to its original angle when the negatively charged rod is taken away.

If a positively charged body is brought up as shown in Fig. 47F(b), negatives from the stem and gold leaf are attracted to the knob, causing the gold leaf to fall. *Thus, with a negatively charged electroscope, a positive charge brought nearby causes the gold leaf to drop, and a negatively charged body causes it to rise.* If the electroscope is positively charged, the reverse action will take place: a positive charge causes it to rise and a negative causes it to fall.

47.6. Conductors and Insulators. Not all substances are good conductors of electricity. As a general rule, metals are good conductors whereas nonmetals are poor conductors. The poorest of conductors are

TABLE 47A. EXAMPLES OF SUBSTANCES THAT ARE GOOD ELECTRICAL CONDUCTORS AND OTHERS THAT ARE NONCONDUCTORS OR INSULATORS

Conductors	Nonconductors
Aluminum	Amber
Copper	Glass
Gold	Mica
Iron	Paper
Mercury	Porcelain
Nickel	Rubber
Platinum	Silk
Silver	Sulfur

nected to an electroscope and the other end to a small brass knob mounted on a glass pedestal. When a charged rubber rod is touched to the knob as shown, the gold leaf of the distant electroscope rises immediately. Electrons have been conducted along the wire. If a positively charged rod contacts the knob, electrons flow away from the electroscope, leaving the gold leaf with a positive charge.

If the copper wire in the above experiment is replaced by a nonconductor, like a silk thread, the electroscope cannot be charged by the rod contacting the distant knob. Poor conductors, such as glass and amber, are used to support metal parts of electrical apparatus for the purpose of insulating them from unnecessary losses of electricity. An electroscope, for example, will retain its electric charge well if the gold leaf and stem are insulated from the electroscope case with amber, as shown in Fig. 47E.

The difference between a conductor and an insulator, or dielectric, is that in a conductor there are free electrons, whereas in an insulator all of the electrons are tightly bound to their respective atoms. In an uncharged body, there are an equal number of positive and negative charges. In metals a few of the electrons are free to move from atom to atom; so that, when a negatively

charged rod is brought to the end of a conductor, it repels nearby free electrons in
the conductor, causing them to move. They
in turn repel free electrons in front of them,
thus giving rise to a flow of electrons all
along the conductor. Hence in Fig. 47G it
is not necessarily the electrons from the
charged rubber rod that actually reach the
electroscope leaf, but rather the electrons
from the end of the wire where it touches
the electroscope knob.

There are a large number of substances
that are neither good conductors of electricity nor good insulators. These substances are called *semi-conductors*. In them,
electrons are capable of being moved only
with some difficulty, i.e., with considerable
force.

47.7. The Law of Electrostatic Force. It
has already been demonstrated that like
charges repel and unlike charges attract.
Nothing that has thus far been said, however, has indicated just how strong the repulsion or attraction might be, nor how it
depends on the magnitude of the charges
and the distance between them.

The first quantitative measurements of
the force between two charged bodies were
made by Coulomb, a French scientist and
engineer, in 1780. He proved experimentally that:

*The force acting between two charges is
directly proportional to the product of the
two charges and inversely proportional to
the square of the distance between them.*

Symbolically this law is usually written
as an algebraic equation,

$$F = k \frac{QQ'}{d^2} \qquad (47a)$$

where F is the force, Q and Q' are the
charges, and d is the distance between them
(see Fig. 47H). The constant of proportionality, k, has a value that depends upon
the units of charge chosen.

In the electrostatic system of units, force
is measured in *dynes*, distance in *centimeters*, and *unit charge* is chosen so that
$k = 1$. Coulomb's law with $k = 1$ then de-

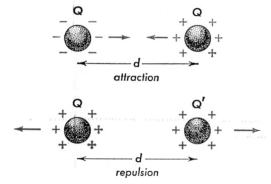

Fig. 47H *Coulomb's law. Two like charges repel each other, or two unlike charges attract
each other, with a force proportional to the
product of their charges and inversely proportional to the square of the distance between
them.*

fines unit charge, called the *electrostatic
unit* or the *statcoulomb*. *One electrostatic
unit or, one statcoulomb, is defined as that
charge which when placed one centimeter
from an equivalent charge exerts upon it
a force of one dyne.*

In the mks system, force is given in *newtons*, distance in *meters*, charge in *coulombs*, and $k = 9 \times 10^9$. It is customary to
define the coulomb (*abbr.* coul) in terms of
electric currents. (See Sec. 48.1.) *One coulomb is that quantity of electric charge
which, flowing by any point in a wire, in
one second produces a current of one ampere.* Experimental measurements give as
the best probable value: *1* coulomb =
2.9979 × 10⁹ statcoulombs. For most practical uses we will assume

1 coulomb = 3 × 10⁹ statcoulombs

Experiments described in later chapters
show that electrons are all alike and that
each carries a charge $e = 4.8022 \times 10^{-10}$
electrostatic units (4.8022×10^{-10} statcoulombs), or

$$e = 1.6019 \times 10^{-19} \text{ coulomb} \qquad (47b)$$

This means that, when a body has a unit
negative charge of one coulomb, it has an
excess of 6.24×10^{18} electrons and that a

body charged positively with one coulomb has a deficiency of 6.24×10^{18} electrons.

$$1 \text{ coulomb} = 6.24 \times 10^{18} \text{ electrons} \quad (47c)$$

Since the unit of charge in the mks system is measured in terms of electric currents, the numerical value of k in Eq.(47a) must be determined experimentally. The best value to date is $k = 8.9878 \times 10^9$. For most practical problems the approximation $k = 9 \times 10^9$ will be used.

$$k = 9 \times 10^9 \frac{\text{newton-meter}^2}{\text{coulomb}^2} \quad (47d)$$

To simplify some of the equations that are derived from Coulomb's law, it is convenient to introduce a new constant, ϵ_0, in place of k,

$$k = \frac{1}{4\pi\epsilon_0} \quad (47e)$$

and write Coulomb's law

$$F = \frac{1}{4\pi\epsilon_0} \cdot \frac{QQ'}{d^2} \quad (47f)$$

Using the numerical value of k from Eq.(47d) it follows that

$$\epsilon_0 = \frac{1}{4\pi \times 9 \times 10^9}$$

$$E_0 = 8.85 \times 10^{-12} \frac{\text{coulomb}^2}{\text{newton-meter}^2} \quad (47g)$$

This is the so-called rationalized mks system.*

Problem. A charge of $+25 \times 10^{-9}$ coulombs is located 6 cm from a charge of -72×10^{-9} coulombs. Calculate the force between them.

Solution. The given quantities are $Q = 25 \times 10^{-9}$ coulombs and $Q' = -72 \times 10^{-9}$ coulombs, $d = 0.06$ m. Substitution in Eq.(47a) gives

---

* Some books define ϵ_0 by the equation $\epsilon_0 = 1/k$ instead of $1/4\pi k$. Coulomb's law then becomes $F = QQ'/\epsilon_0 d^2$, where $\epsilon_0 = 1.11 \times 10^{-10}$. This is the so-called nonrationalized mks system. One must be careful in reading other texts to determine which system is being used.

$$F = 9 \times 10^9 \frac{\text{newton-m}^2}{\text{coulomb}^2}$$

$$\times \cdot \frac{(25 \times 10^{-9})(-72 \times 10^{-9}) \text{ coulomb}^2}{(0.06)^2 \text{ m}^2}$$

$$F = -4.50 \times 10^{-3} \text{ newton}$$

The minus sign indicates attraction.

47.8. Attraction of Neutral Bodies. An interesting demonstration of electrostatic attraction is shown in Fig. 47I. A tiny ball

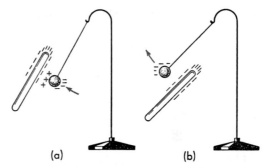

Fig. 47I (a) *A metallic-coated pith ball is attracted by a charged rod.* (b) *After contact, the pith ball is repelled.*

cut from the pithy core of a corn cob is coated with tin foil or metallic paint and suspended by a silk thread. When a charged rod is brought nearby as in (a), the pith ball is attracted to the rod and upon contact bounces away. As the rod is now moved toward the ball, it avoids the rod and keeps as far away as possible.

To explain this result, assume the rod to be negatively charged in the position shown in (a). Free electrons on the sphere are repelled to the opposite side, leaving an equal number of positives on the near side unneutralized. Attraction now takes place, because the positive charges are closest and the attractive force acting on them is greater than the repelling force on the negatives. When contact is made, negatives on the rod neutralize all the positives and the ball, with its negative charges, moves away by mutual repulsion.

47.9. Charging by Induction. To charge a body by induction is to give it a charge without touching it. One method of inducing a charge is illustrated in Fig. 47J. Two

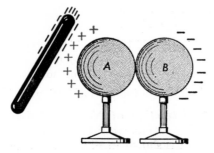

Fig. 47J   *Experiment showing how bodies may be charged by induction.*

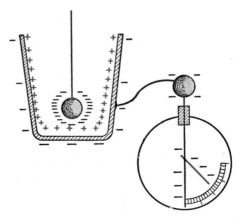

Fig. 47K   *Diagram illustrating Faraday's ice-pail experiment.*

metal spheres *A* and *B*, insulated by glass standards, are touching each other when a charged rubber rod is brought close to one of them. If sphere *B* is now moved away, and then the rod is removed from the vicinity, both spheres are found to be charged, sphere *A* positively and sphere *B* negatively.

The explanation is similar to that of the pith ball in the preceding section, the close proximity of the charged rod repels free electrons from sphere *A* to the far side of sphere *B* leaving unneutralized positives behind. Separated under these conditions, both spheres are left with their respective charges. This is called *charging by induction.*

47.10. Faraday Ice-Pail Experiment. The distribution of charge over a metallic conductor can in part be demonstrated by an experiment first performed by Michael Faraday in 1810. This demonstration,

known as *Faraday's ice-pail experiment,* involves a small metal ball, a hollow metal container like a tin pail, and an electroscope, as shown in Fig. 47K.

If the ball is charged from another source and then lowered into the pail, the leaf of the electroscope rises. Upon moving the ball around inside the pail, and even touching the inside surface with it, no change in the potential is shown by the electroscope leaf. After the ball has been removed, the inner surface of the pail and the ball are found to be completely free of charge.

To explain what happens, let the ball be charged negatively and lowered to the position shown. Free electrons in the metal pail are repelled to the outer surface and to the connecting electroscope, leaving posi-

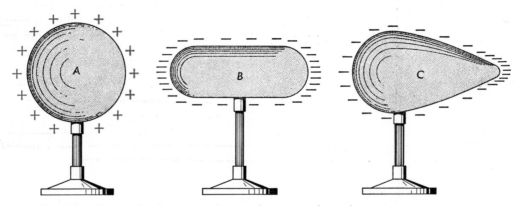

Fig. 47L   *Charge density on conductors is greatest in regions of greatest curvature.*

tives on the inside unneutralized. When the ball touches the pail, all negatives leave the ball and neutralize an equal number of positives. The fact that the electroscope leaf remains fixed when the ball is removed shows (1) that there is no redistribution of the negative charges on the outer pail surface, and (2) that the number of induced positives within the pail was equal to the number of negatives on the ball.

When static charges are acquired by a nonconductor like hard rubber, glass, or amber, they remain where they were first located. When a conductor like copper, silver, or gold acquires a charge, however, the charge quickly spreads over the entire surface. With a metallic sphere, whether solid or hollow, the charge spreads uniformly over the surface as shown in Fig. 47L. On other shaped conductors the charge distributes itself according to surface curvature, concentrating more at points and less where the walls are more nearly straight.

PROBLEMS

1. Two charges of -9×10^{-7} coul each are located 6 cm apart. What is the repelling force on each in newtons?

2. Two unlike charges of 20×10^{-8} coul are each located 30 cm apart. What is the attracting force on each in dynes? (*Ans.* 400 dynes.)

3. Two equal charges are located 12 cm apart and repel each other with a force of 0.36 newtons. Find the magnitude of each charge in (a) electrostatic units, and (b) coulombs.

4. Two small metal spheres 24 cm apart, and having equal negative charges, repel each other with a force of 1×10^{-3} newton. Find the total charge on the two bodies in coulombs. (*Ans.* 16×10^{-8} coul.)

5. A positive charge of 5×10^{-8} coul is located 5 cm from a negative charge of 10×10^{-8} coul. Calculate the force in newtons exerted by either charge upon the other.

6. A charge of -5×10^{-7} coul is located 20 cm from another charge of -5×10^{-7} coul. Calculate the force in newtons exerted by one charge upon the other. (*Ans.* 0.056 newtons.)

7. What charge Q placed 4 cm from a charge of 8×10^{-8} coul will produce a force of 0.015 newtons?

8. Four equal charges of $+8 \times 10^{-8}$ coul each are located at the corners of a square, 5 cm on each side. Calculate the resultant force on each charge, and show its direction on a diagram drawn to scale. (*Ans.* 0.0575 newtons.)

9. Two positive charges, $+5 \times 10^{-7}$ coul each, are located diagonally opposite each other on a square 5 cm on a side. Two negative charges, -5×10^{-7} coul each, are located at the other corners, respectively. Calculate the resultant force on each charge, and show this resultant on a diagram drawn to scale.

10. Three equal charges of $+8 \times 10^{-8}$ coul are each located at the corners of a right triangle whose sides are 10 cm, 24 cm, and 26 cm, respectively. Find the force exerted on the charge located at the 90° angle. (*Ans.* 5.82×10^{-3} newton at 9.8°.)

11. Four equal charges of $+6 \times 10^{-6}$ coul each are located at the corners of the square 4 cm on each side. Calculate the magnitude of the force on each charge, and show its direction on a diagram drawn to scale.

12. Two positive charges, 10×10^{-7} coul each, are located at diagonally opposite corners of a square 6 cm on a side. Two negative charges -10×10^{-7} coul each are located at the other corners, respectively. Calculate the resultant force on each charge, and show this resultant on a diagram drawn to scale. (*Ans.* 2.29 newtons diagonally inward on each.)

13. Three equal charges of $+8 \times 10^{-6}$ coul each are located at the corners of an equilateral triangle whose sides are 16 cm long. Calculate the resultant force on each charge.

Chapter 48

Electricity in Motion

When an electric charge is at rest it is spoken of as *static electricity,* but when it is in motion it is referred to as an *electric current.* In most cases, an electric current is described as a flow of electric charge along a conductor. Such is the case, for example, in the experiment of charging an electroscope from a distant point by means of a long copper wire and a charged rubber rod (see Fig. 47G). This experiment is explained by stating that electrons already in the wire are pushed along toward the electroscope by the repulsion of electrons from behind. No sooner does this current start, however, than the negative charge of the rod is dissipated and the current stops flowing.

48.1. Electron Current. To make an electron current flow continuously along a wire, a continuous supply of electrons must be available at one end and a continuous supply of positive charges at the other (see Fig.

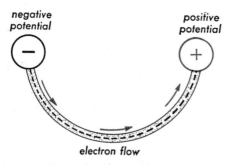

negative potential   positive potential

electron flow

Fig. 48A *Two terminals at different potentials and connected by a conductor give rise to an electron current.*

48A). This is like the flow of water through a pipe: to obtain a continuous flow, a continuous supply of water must be provided at one end and an opening for its escape

into some receptacle at the other. The continuous supply of positive charge at the one end of a wire offers a means of escape for the electrons. If this is not provided, electrons will accumulate at the end of the wire and their repulsion back along the wire will stop the current flow.

Many years ago, before it was known which of the electric charges, (+) or (−), moved through a wire, there seemed to be some evidence that it was the positive charge and not the negative. This notion became so thoroughly entrenched in the minds of those interested in electrical phenomena that in later years, when it was discovered that the negatives move in solid conductors and not the positives, it became difficult to change.

The convention that electric current flows from plus to minus is still to be found in many books and is used by some electrical engineers in designing electrical machines and appliances. The rapid growth and the importance of radio engineering and electronics, however, has brought about a change in this practice, and we shall hereafter in this text speak of current as one of electron flow from (−) to (+) and call it electron current.

There are two general methods by which a continuous supply of electrical charge is obtained: one is by means of *a battery* and the other by means of *an electric generator.* The battery is a device by which chemical energy is transformed into electrical energy; the generator is a device by which mechanical energy is transformed into electrical energy.

48.2. The Ampere. Electron current is measured in units called *amperes.* The ampere, named in honor of the French physicist Ampère,* is defined as *the flow of one coulomb per second.* In other words, one coulomb of electric charge flowing past any given point in one second constitutes a current of one ampere (*abbr.* amp).

$$1 \text{ ampere} = \frac{1 \text{ coulomb}}{1 \text{ second}}$$

If twice this quantity passes by in one second, the current is 2 amp. Thus electron current is analogous to the rate of flow of water through a pipe.

$$\text{current} = \frac{\text{quantity of charge}}{\text{time}}$$

$$I = \frac{Q}{t} \qquad (48a)$$

Remember that one coulomb = 6.24×10^{18} electrons (see Eq.(47C)); then a current of one ampere means a flow of 6.24×10^{18} electrons per second past any given point.

This enormous number does not mean that the electrons are moving with high speed through a conductor. Actually the number of moving charges is so large that their average velocity may be but a small fraction of a millimeter per second. When we picture a solid conductor as a crystal lattice, similar to those shown in Fig. 22F, the electrons are thought of as moving through the intervening spaces. This movement is not completely free, however, but is influenced by the repulsion and attraction of like and unlike charges.

48.3. Batteries. Batteries as continuous sources of electrical energy are the result of a long series of experiments which started with the discoveries of Alessandro Volta†

* André M. Ampère (1775-1836), French physicist and mathematician. Ampère began his career as professor of physics and chemistry at Bourg at the early age of 26. He later established the relation between electricity and magnetism, and helped to develop the subject he called electrodynamics. His only son, Jean J. Ampère, also became famous; he was a philologist, lecturer, and historian.

† Alessandro Volta (1745-1827), Italian scientist, and for more than 20 years professor of physics at Pavia. Traveling considerably throughout Europe, he became acquainted with many celebrities. In 1801 he was awarded the Copley medal of the

more than one hundred years ago. Today battery cells are manufactured in two common forms: (1) dry cells, as used in flashlights, portable radios, etc., and (2) wet cells, as used in automobiles, airplanes, boats, etc.

The voltaic cell, as shown in Fig. 48B, is

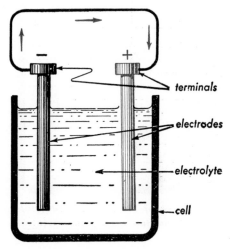

Fig. 48B *Diagram of a voltaic cell.*

composed of three parts, a pair of dissimilar metal plates called *electrodes,* a dilute acid solution called the *electrolyte,* and a nonconducting liquid container called the *cell.* While many different combinations of materials have been tried and used in such cells, zinc and carbon as electrodes, dilute sulfuric acid as the electrolyte, and a glass or hard rubber container as the cell, are the most common.

48.4. Electrolytic Dissociation. Individual molecules of sulfuric acid (H_2SO_4) are composed of seven atoms each: two hydrogen, one sulfur, and four oxygen atoms. When concentrated acid is poured into water to form a dilute solution, a small percentage of the molecules split up, that is, they *dissociate.* The two hydrogen atoms split off from the molecule, each leaving

Royal Society of London, and then was called to Paris and awarded a medal by Napoleon. In 1815 the Emperor of Austria made him director of the philosophical faculty of the University of Padua. A statue now stands in his memory at Como, his birthplace.

an electron behind with the remaining SO_4 molecule. Similarly some of the water molecules, each composed of two hydrogen atoms and one oxygen atom, dissociate by having one of the hydrogen atoms split off without an electron. (See Fig. 48C.)

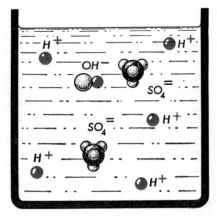

Fig. 48C *Some of the sulfuric acid molecules and water molecules in a dilute solution dissociate.*

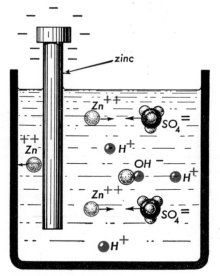

Fig. 48D *A zinc metal electrode in dilute sulfuric acid.*

Since each hydrogen atom leaves an electron behind, it has a net positive charge and is called a *positive ion*. Each remaining SO_4 fragment from the acid and OH fragment from the water has a surplus of negative charge and is called a *negative ion*.

If we now insert a zinc rod into this electrolyte, chemical action is initiated, whereby individual zinc atoms break off from the surface leaving two electrons behind. See Fig. 48D. Going into solution as doubly charged positive ions, they strongly attract SO_4^{--} ions. With each encounter of two such ions, combination takes place, resulting in the formation of neutral $ZnSO_4$ molecules.

$$Zn^{++} + SO_4^{--} = ZnSO_4$$

As more and more zinc ions go into solution, the negative charge on the zinc electrode increases and soon reaches a maximum.

Fig. 48E shows what happens around the carbon rod when the circuit is closed as in Fig. 48B. At this anode each

H^+ ion acquires an electron from the carbon, and two such particles form a neutral hydrogen molecule, H_2.

$$2(H^+) + 2(e^-) = H_2 \uparrow$$

Since hydrogen is a gas at normal temperatures, the accumulation of H_2 molecules results in the formation of bubbles of gas which rise to the surface. In giving up electrons, the carbon electrode acquires a positive charge and a certain definite positive potential.

48.5. The Cell Electromotive Force. If we examine both the zinc and carbon electrodes as shown in Fig. 48F we find each one maintains its appropriate potential. The positive electrode, called the *anode,* acquires a positive potential; and the negative electrode, called the *cathode,* acquires a negative potential.

With the voltmeter connected to the two terminals of the cell, the pointer indicates the *difference of potential* in volts, and this we call the *electromotive force (abbr. emf).*

Since the voltmeter completes the electric circuit between cathode and anode, a small electron current will flow from cathode to anode through the connecting wires and the voltmeter. Electrons leaving the

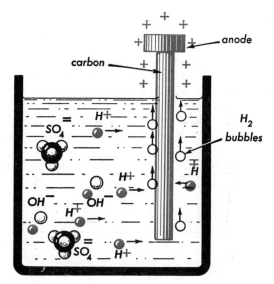

Fig. 48E   *A carbon rod in dilute sulfuric acid.*

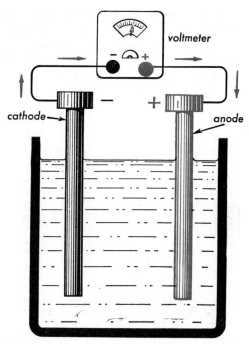

Fig. 48F   *The emf of a voltaic cell is measured with a voltmeter.*

zinc metal surface change the cathode potential, and electrons arriving at the carbon neutralize positives, thereby changing the anode potential. With the tendency of the potential difference to fall, chemical action takes place immediately and maintains a continuous supply of (+) and (−) charge at the terminals. Upon open circuit the terminals remain charged, but no current flows and no chemical action takes place.

48.6.   The Dry Cell. Probably the most common form of battery used today is composed of dry cells. While these cells are manufactured in different shapes and vary in size from $\frac{1}{8}$ in. to many inches, they all produce the same emf of 1.5 v between their two terminals.

One common form of dry cell is shown in Fig. 48G. The negative electrode is a zinc-coated metal container in which all chemical ingredients are sealed, and the positive electrode is a round carbon rod. In place of a liquid electrolyte we have a paste containing ammonium chloride, zinc chloride, and a little water. Surrounding the anode is a thin layer of powdered carbon and manganese dioxide.

When current is being supplied by the dry cell, zinc ions form at the cathode,

while ammonium ions gain electrons at the carbon rod, forming hydrogen and ammonia gas. The hydrogen reacts chemically with the manganese dioxide, and the ammonia gas with the zinc chloride. While the emf of all dry cells is 1.5 volts, the larger the cell, the greater is the current and the total electrical energy that it can supply.

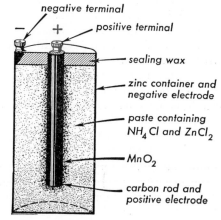

Fig. 48G   *Cross-section diagram of a dry cell or "flashlight" battery, showing the essential elements.*

48.7. Storage Batteries. When the electrical energy contained in a battery composed of dry cells has been exhausted, it is thrown away. A storage battery, on the other hand, is composed of what are called *wet cells;* when exhausted of its stored-up energy, such a battery can be rejuvenated or *recharged.*

The negative electrode of a storage cell, as shown in Fig. 48H, is composed of a set

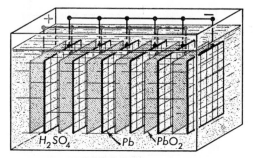

Fig. 48H *The cell of a storage battery has a number of plates.*

of parallel lead grills filled with *spongy lead* (Pb), while the positive electrode is another set of lead grills filled with porous *lead dioxide* (PbO_2).

When a current is supplied by the cell, PbO_2 in one set of grills, and Pb in the other, combine with the dissociated H+ and SO_4^{--} ions of the dielectric to form lead sulfate ($PbSO_4$) and water (H_2O). When the surfaces of all plates become coated with lead sulfate, they behave chemically alike, and no more current can be drawn from the cell.

To recharge a storage cell, the two terminals are connected to a direct current generator. The current flowing through the electrolyte reverses the chemical process, changing them back to their original form. Chemically, one writes

$$PbO_2 + Pb + 2H_2SO_4$$
$$\text{charge} \uparrow \quad \downarrow \text{ discharge} \qquad (48b)$$
$$2PbSO_4 + 2H_2O$$

Upon charging a cell, some of the dissociated water molecules of the electrolyte are converted into hydrogen gas at the cathode

and oxygen gas at the anode. These gases rise to the surface as bubbles and necessitate the occasional addition of water to the cell.

Regardless of the size, each such cell develops an emf of 2.2 volts. While many other kinds of storage cells have been developed, the lead battery is the most widely used in the United States.

48.8. The Battery. If two or more cells are connected together as shown in Fig. 48I, they form what is called a battery. In

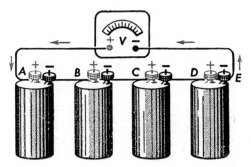

Fig. 48I *Four dry cells connected in series form a 6-volt battery.*

this diagram the battery is composed of four dry cells connected *in series*. By series connections it is meant that the (+) terminal of one cell is connected to the (−) terminal of the next.

The purpose in connecting two or more cells in series is to obtain a higher emf than that available with one cell alone. The potential difference between the extreme end terminals A and E of any battery is just the sum of those for the individual cells.

Each dry cell produces an emf of 1.5 volts, so that if the voltmeter is connected to two points, it will indicate 1.5 volts between A and B, 3.0 volts between A and C, 4.5 volts between A and D, and 6 volts between A and E.

The common flashlight contains several dry cells connected in series as shown in Fig. 48J. When new cells are inserted, they are all turned in the same direction so that the (+) terminal at the center of each cell makes good contact with the (−) case of the next cell. The closing of the switch shown in the figure applies the end termi-

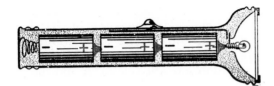

Fig. 48J   *Cross section of a 3-cell flashlight.*

nal voltage of 4.5 volts to the light bulb.

The storage battery commonly used in automobiles contains six wet cells of 2 volts each, connected in series as shown in Fig. 48K. Note how the heavy crossbars connect

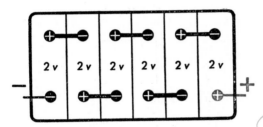

Fig. 48K   *Series connections for a 12-volt storage battery.*

the (−) terminal of any one cell with the (+) terminal of the next. With six cells in series the end terminals produce a resultant of 12 volts, hence its name of *twelve-volt battery.*

It is customary in circuit diagrams to represent battery cells as shown in Fig. 48L.

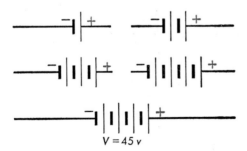

Fig. 48L   *Circuit diagrams indicating the cells of a battery.*

The (+) and (−) terminals of each cell are indicated by long and short lines, respectively. The first four diagrams shown represent one, two, three, and four cells, respec-

tively, connected in series. If many cells are to be represented, four or five can be drawn and the over-all terminal voltage written beneath it as shown by $V = 45$ volts.

48.9. Resistance. Every material object offers some resistance to the flow of an electron current through it. Good conductors like the metals, copper, silver, and aluminum, offer very little resistance, while nonconductors such as glass, wood, and paper offer a very high resistance.

The unit by which resistance is measured is called the *ohm,* in honor of the German physicist G. S. Ohm.* The standard international ohm is defined as the resistance offered to a steady electron current by a column of mercury 1 mm² in cross section and 106.3 cm long at a temperature of 0°C. An iron wire of these dimensions has a resistance of about $\frac{1}{10}$ of an ohm. In the mks system the unit of resistance is the *volt per ampere. One volt per ampere is called one ohm.*

There are several factors that determine the electric resistance of any wire: (1) the material of which it is composed, (2) the size of the wire, and (3) its temperature. If the length of a wire is doubled, its resistance is likewise doubled; if the cross-sectional area is doubled the resistance is halved. In more general terms, the resistance of a wire is proportional to its length and inversely proportional to its cross-sectional area. Symbolically,

$$R = \rho \frac{L}{A} \qquad (48c)$$

where R is the resistance, L the length, A

* George Simon Ohm (1787-1854), German physicist, was born at Erlavgen and educated at the university there. After teaching mathematics in Cologne for 16 years, and in Nuremberg for 16 more, he became professor of experimental physics in the high school at Munich. His writings were numerous and, but for one exception, were not of the first order. This single exception consists of a pamphlet on electric currents, the most important part of which is summarized in what is now called "Ohm's law." For this work he was awarded the Copley Medal of the Royal Society of London in 1841 and made a foreign member of the society one year later.

the cross-sectional area, and ρ the resistivity of the material in question. Resistivity is defined as the resistance of a wire 1 m long and 1 m² in cross section. Values of this constant are given for several common metals in Table 48A. The smaller the constant ρ, the better is the substance as a conductor.

TABLE 48A. RESISTIVITY OF METALS, ρ,
IN OHM METERS

Aluminum	$\rho = 3.2 \times 10^{-8}$
Bismuth	$\rho = 119 \times 10^{-8}$
Copper	$\rho = 1.72 \times 10^{-8}$
Iron	$\rho = 15 \times 10^{-8}$
Mercury	$\rho = 94.1 \times 10^{-8}$
Silver	$\rho = 1.05 \times 10^{-8}$
Tungsten	$\rho = 5.5 \times 10^{-8}$
Platinum	$\rho = 11 \times 10^{-8}$

To find the resistance of any sized wire made of one of these metals, the value of ρ is inserted in Eq.(48c) along with the length and cross-sectional area, and the value of R is calculated. To illustrate the method, consider the following:

Example. Find the resistance of a copper wire I mm² in cross section and 300 m long.

Solution. If we use Eq.(48c) and remember that there are 1000 mm in 1 m, we find that

$$R = 1.72 \times 10^{-8} \frac{300 \text{ m}}{1 \times 10^{-6} \text{ m}^2} = 5.16 \text{ ohms} \quad (48d)$$

The greater the resistivity of a wire, the poorer it is as an electrical conductor. Because of this, a term called the *conductivity* is sometimes used to specify the current-carrying ability of a material; it is defined as the reciprocal of the resistivity:

$$\sigma = 1/\rho.$$

What makes a material a good electrical conductor or not depends upon the number of free electrons within, and upon how easily these can move between the atoms from place to place. The free electrons in a metal behave a little like the molecules in a gas; they move about at random, with velocities that have a relatively high average value.

48.10. Ohm's Law. This is the well-known and fundamental law in electricity which makes it possible to determine the current flowing through a conductor when the resistance of the conductor and the potential difference applied to it are known. What Ohm discovered was that the ratio of the potential difference between the ends of a metallic conductor and the current flowing through the metallic conductor is a constant. The proportionality constant is called the electrical *resistance.*

$$\text{resistance} = \frac{\text{potential difference}}{\text{current}}$$

Symbolically, Ohm's law is often written

$$R = \frac{V}{I} \qquad (48e)$$

In electrical units,

$$1 \text{ ohm} = \frac{1 \text{ volt}}{1 \text{ amp}}$$

The law is of great importance because of its very general application to so many electrical phenomena. One of its simplest applications is illustrated in Fig. 48M. A dry cell is directly connected by wires to a small light bulb. The battery maintains a

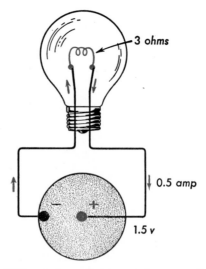

Fig. 48M   *A dry cell connected to a small light bulb.*

potential difference of 1.5 volts across the lamp. If the electron current flowing through the lamp is 0.5 amp, the resistance of the lamp is

$$R = \frac{1.5 \text{ volts}}{0.5 \text{ amp}} = 3 \text{ ohms}$$

Although the resistance as found here is assumed to be the resistance of the light bulb, it really includes the resistance of the connecting wires. In practice one usually uses wires of such low resistance that they can be neglected in most calculations. If they are not small, they cannot be neglected and must be added in as part of the R in Ohm's law.

Consider the illustration shown in Fig. 48N, where a battery of many cells main-

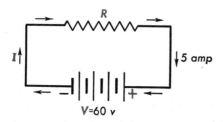

Fig. 48N   *Circuit diagram of a resistor R connected to a 60-volt battery.*

tains a potential difference of 60 volts across a circuit and a current of 5 amp through it. By Ohm's law the resistance of the circuit is given by Eq.(48e) as

$$R = \frac{V}{I} = \frac{60 \text{ volts}}{5 \text{ amp}} = 12 \text{ ohms}$$

Resistance in circuit diagrams is represented by a saw-toothed line as shown, and the word *ohm* is represented by the capital Greek letter omega, Ω. In Fig. 48N the resistance $R = 12\Omega$.

Resistance may be defined as the opposition offered to a flow of current through a circuit.

To determine the resistance of any electrical circuit it is common practice to use a voltmeter and an ammeter. The voltmeter is applied across the circuit to measure the potential difference, and the ammeter is connected in series to measure the current.

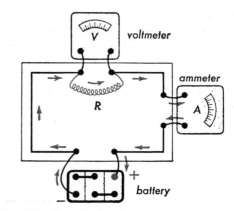

Fig. 48O   *Connector board for determining electrical resistance.*

Fig. 48O represents a connector board arranged for measurements of this kind. An appliance, or unknown resistor R, is connected between two terminals at the top, so the current supplied by the battery below must pass through it as well as the ammeter. The voltmeter is connected across R to measure the potential difference between its ends.

Suppose that three heating elements, commonly used as replacement elements for electrical kitchen utensils, are connected in turn to the two terminals at the top of the board and a 6-volt storage battery is applied to the terminals below. The voltage V and the current I from a sample set of measurements give the following results.

TABLE 48B.   RECORDED DATA

Element	Volts	Amperes
Toaster..................	6.1	2.3
Waffle iron..............	6.3	1.6
Iron....................	6.2	1.8

By Ohm's law, Eq.(48e), the resistance of each element can be calculated. This will be left as an exercise for the student.

When a switch is first closed to complete an electric circuit, there are essentially three velocities involved in the flow of an electron current: first, there is the electric impulse that travels along the wire with essentially the speed of light; second, the average random velocity of the electrons; and third, the *average drift velocity* of the electrons in the direction of the current, and this is relatively slow.

QUESTIONS

1. How are cells usually connected to form a battery? What determines the emf of a battery?

2. What is the voltage of a single dry cell? Of a single storage cell?

3. What is Ohm's law? In what units is each quantity measured?

4. What common electrical instruments are used to determine the factors in Ohm's law?

5. What is the equivalent resistance of two or more resistors connected in series?

6. What is the abbreviated notation for battery cells in series? How is a resistor shown in a circuit diagram?

7. Does the same current flow through each resistor in series connections?

8. If the resistance of a circuit and the applied voltage were known, how could you determine the current?

9. What inexpensive device would you propose to make as a project illustrating or making use of Ohm's law?

PROBLEMS

1. Make a diagram of a voltaic cell composed of zinc and carbon electrodes and dilute sulfuric acid in water as an electrolyte. Briefly explain what happens on a closed circuit.

2. Make a diagram of a dry cell showing the electrode and chemical materials used.

3. Make a diagram of a lead storage cell, label the essential elements, and write down the chemical reactions taking place on (a) charge and (b) discharge.

4. A 12-volt storage battery supplies a current of 48 amp when the starter in a car is turned on. What is the resistance of the starter motor? (*Ans.* 0.25 ohm.)

5. A battery of 5 dry cells is used in series in a flashlight having a bulb with a resistance of 22 ohm. What electron current flows when the light is turned on?

6. A storage battery of 12 cells is used in a boat. Each of two headlight bulbs has a resist-ance of 5.5 ohm. Find the current supplied to each bulb. (*Ans.* 4.36 amp.)

7. An electric light bulb connected to a house lighting circuit of 110 volts draws a current of 0.25 amp. (a) calculate the number of coul per sec flowing through the wire. (b) How many electrons per sec pass by any given point in the wire?

8. A wire 2 mm in diameter and 5 Km long is made of copper. What is its total resistance? (*Ans.* 27.4 ohm.)

9. The heater wire in a small stove is made of iron ribbon wire, 0.01 cm by 0.05 cm in cross section and 2 m long. Calculate its resistance.

10. A fine platinum wire 0.4 mm in diameter and 200 cm long is used as the sensitive element in an electrical resistance thermometer. Find the resistance. (*Ans.* 1.75 ohm.)

11. A battery of two dry cells in series is used in a flashlight having a bulb with a resistance of 25 ohm. Find the electron current when the light is turned on.

Chapter 49

Electrical Circuits and Kirchhoff's Laws

The fundamental relation concerned with electrical circuits is Ohm's law:

$$R = \frac{V}{I} \qquad (49a)$$

where R is the resistance of the circuit in ohms, V is the potential difference applied in volts, and I is the current in amperes.

Transforming this equation, one obtains two other useful forms of the same basic law.

$$I = \frac{V}{R} \qquad (49b)$$

$$V = IR \qquad (49c)$$

We will see in this chapter how these three forms of Ohm's law are applied to different kinds of electrical circuits involving *batteries* as sources of electromotive force and *resistors* as representatives of many of our everyday electrical appliances. The two common forms of electrical circuits involve resistors connected in series, resistors connected in parallel, and combinations of the two.

49.1. Resistors in Series. When several electrical devices are connected in series, the resistance R of the combination is equal to the sum of the resistances of the individuals. Symbolically,

$$R = R_1 + R_2 + R_3 + R_4 + \text{etc.} \qquad (49d)$$

This, *the law of series resistances,* is illustrated by an application of Ohm's law to the complete electric circuit in Fig. 49A. Three resistors $R_1 = 5$ ohm, $R_2 = 1$

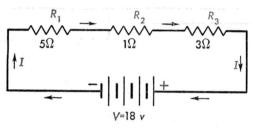

Fig. 49A *The same electron current flows through all resistors when connected in series.*

ohm, and $R_3 = 3$ ohm are connected in series with a battery capable of supplying a potential difference of 18 volts.

To calculate the current supplied by the battery, we first find the equivalent resistance of the entire series circuit. By Eq.(49d)

$$R = 5 + 1 + 3 = 9 \ \Omega$$

In other words, if the three resistors R_1, R_2, and R_3, are replaced by a single resistor R of 9 Ω, the electron current supplied by the battery will be the same. To find this current we note that the potential difference maintained by the battery $V = 18$ volts. Applying Ohm's law in the form of Eq. (49b), the electron current flowing through the circuit is

$$I = \frac{18 \text{ v}}{9 \ \Omega} = 2 \text{ amp}$$

This electron current of 2 amp flows through the high resistance as well as the low. Like water flowing through pipes of different sizes connected one after the other, just as much water passes through one pipe per second of time as through any other, and none can accumulate at any point.

405

A circuit diagram showing how an ammeter and a voltmeter are connected to a series circuit to measure current and voltage is given in Fig. 49B.

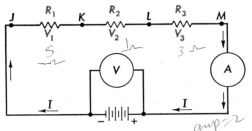

Fig. 49B *Circuit diagram of three resistors in series.*

If the two leads of the voltmeter are connected to the two points J and K, the potential difference across R_1 is measured. Knowing the resistance of R_1 and the current I through it, one can calculate this potential difference by using Eq.(49c).

$$V_1 = I_1 R_1$$
$$V_1 = 2 \text{ amp} \times 5 \text{ ohm} = 10 \text{ v}$$

Because the potential differs by 10 volts, from one side of the resistor to the other, this potential difference is commonly called the *IR drop*. In a similar way the *IR* drop across R_2 or R_3 can be measured by connecting the voltmeter to K and L, or L and M, or computed by means of Eq.(49c):

$$V_2 = 2 \text{ amp} \times 1 \text{ ohm} = 2 \text{ volts}$$
$$V_3 = 2 \text{ amp} \times 3 \text{ ohm} = 6 \text{ volts}$$

If we find the sum of all the *IR* drops around the circuit, we obtain

$$10 + 2 + 6 = 18 \text{ volts}$$

This is known as Kirchhoff's law and is written in the general form

$$\boxed{V = V_1 + V_2 + V_3 + \ldots} \quad \text{(49e)}$$

49.2. Parallel Circuits. A circuit diagram showing three resistors R_1, R_2, and R_3 connected in parallel is shown in Fig. 49C. The electron current I, leaving the battery at the lower left, divides at the first junction; part I_1 goes through R_1, and the remainder goes

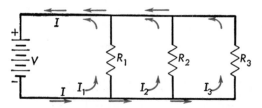

Fig. 49C *Parallel circuit for three resistors R_1, R_2, and R_3.*

on to the next junction. Part of this current I_2 goes through R_2, and the remainder goes on and through R_3. These three currents recombine at the top junctions and form, finally, the same total current I returning to the battery.

It is clear from this explanation that for any number of resistors in parallel

$$\boxed{I = I_1 + I_2 + I_3 + \text{etc.}} \quad \text{(49f)}$$

where I is the total current and I_1, I_2, I_3, etc., are the separate currents through the resistors. Eq.(49f) is the second of Kirchhoff's laws.

An excellent demonstration of Eq.(49f) is shown in Fig. 49D, where four ordinary

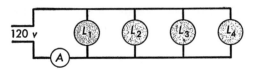

Fig. 49D *Parallel circuit of four light bulbs.*

tungsten filament light bulbs are connected in parallel to a house lighting circuit of 120 volts. The lamps may be the same or they may all be different.

Suppose the lamps are rated as 25, 50, 75, and 100 watts, respectively, and that we begin with all of the lamps sufficiently loose in their screw bases to be disconnected. Each lamp in turn should now be tightened in its socket, the ammeter current read and recorded, and then that lamp loosened again. Suppose these recorded currents are those shown at the left in Table 49A.

As the second step, tighten each lamp in turn without loosening any, and as each new lamp comes on, record the current.

These current totals could well appear like those shown at the right in Table 49A.

$I_1 = 0.24$ amp	$I_1 = 0.24$ amp
$I_2 = 0.44$ amp	$I_1 + I_2 = 0.68$ amp
$I_3 = 0.65$ amp	$I_1 + I_2 + I_3 = 1.33$ amp
$I_4 = 0.85$ amp	$I_1 + I_2 + I_3 + I_4 = 2.18$ amp

Such current sums in the second set of observations represent an experimental confirmation of Kirchhoff's law, as given by Eq.(49f).

49.3. Parallel Resistances. Another type of diagram frequently drawn for parallel circuits is shown in Fig. 49E. Three re-

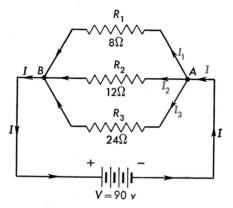

Fig. 49E   *Three resistors in parallel, illustrating Kirchhoff's law.*

sistors R_1, R_2, and R_3 are connected in parallel to a 90-volt battery. To find the total current through such a circuit, we proceed to find a single resistance R which, when substituted for the parallel combination of R_1, R_2, and R_3, will result in the same current. This equivalent resistance is given by *the law of parallel resistances,* as

$$\boxed{\frac{1}{R} = \frac{1}{R_1} + \frac{1}{R_2} + \frac{1}{R_3} + \text{etc.}} \quad (49g)$$

To illustrate its use, let $R_1 = 8\ \Omega$, $R_2 = 12\ \Omega$, and $R_3 = 24\ \Omega$, as shown in Fig. 49E. By direct substitution in Eq.(49g)

$$\frac{1}{R} = \frac{1}{8} + \frac{1}{12} + \frac{1}{24}$$

Since the common denominator is 24,

$$\frac{1}{R} = \frac{3}{24} + \frac{2}{24} + \frac{1}{24} = \frac{6}{24}$$

from which

$$R = \frac{24}{6} = 4\ \Omega$$

If we now imagine the parallel combination of three resistors replaced by a single resistor $R = 4\ \Omega$, the circuit will have the general form as Fig. 48N, and the current I will be given by Ohm's law as follows:

$$I = \frac{V}{R} = \frac{90 \text{ volts}}{4\ \Omega} = 22.5 \text{ amp}$$

This is the total current I supplied by the battery to the parallel circuit of Fig. 49E.

To find how this current divides at A into three parts I_1, I_2, and I_3, we note that the full 90 volts are directly applied to each resistor. Therefore, Ohm's law can be applied to each resistor separately as follows:

$$I_1 = \frac{90 \text{ volts}}{8\ \Omega} = 11.25 \text{ amp}$$

$$I_2 = \frac{90 \text{ volts}}{12\ \Omega} = 7.50 \text{ amp}$$

$$I_3 = \frac{90 \text{ volts}}{24\ \Omega} = 3.75 \text{ amp}$$

If we now apply Kirchhoff's law, Eq.(49f), we find

$$I = 11.25 + 7.50 + 3.75 = 22.5 \text{ amp}$$

and this is a check upon the previous total current. Note that the largest of the three currents, $I_1 = 11.25$ amp, flows through the smallest resistance, and the smallest current I_3 flows through the highest resistance.

Kirchhoff's law of currents is frequently stated as follows:

The sum of all the currents flowing into any junction point is equal to the sum of all the currents flowing out.

An inspection of junction A or junction B in Fig. 49E, will show how this definition gives us Eq.(49f).

Example. A battery supplies a potential difference of 180 volts to the ends of a circuit containing four resistors of 5, 6, 8, and 20 ohms

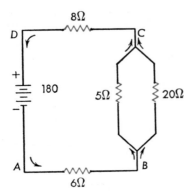

Fig. 49F *Series and parallel resistances in the same circuit.*

as shown in Fig. 49F. Calculate (a) the equivalent resistance of the 5- and 20-ohm parallel combination, (b) the electron current supplied by the battery, and (c) the electron current through each resistor.

Solution. (a) Apply the law of parallel resistances, Eq.(49g).

$$\frac{1}{R} = \frac{1}{5} + \frac{1}{20} = \frac{4}{20} + \frac{1}{20} = \frac{5}{20}$$

from which, by inverting, we obtain

$$R = 20/5 = 4 \text{ ohm}$$

(b) Since the parallel combination of 5 and 20 ohms is equivalent to 4 ohms, and it is in series with the other two of 6 and 8 ohms, respectively, the three are added by the law of series resistance, Eq.(49d),

$$R = 6 + 4 + 8 = 18 \text{ ohm}$$

Apply Ohm's law, Eq.(49b).

$$I = \frac{V}{R} = \frac{180 \text{ volts}}{18 \text{ ohm}} = 10 \text{ amp}$$

(c) The electron current of 10 amp flows through the 6-ohm resistor and divides at B of the parallel circuit. Combining again at C, the total electron current flows through the 8-ohm resistor. To find how the current divides in the parallel circuit, the IR drop across that circuit is found.

$$IR = 10 \text{ amp} \times 4 \text{ ohm} = 40 \text{ volts}$$

This value of 40 volts is the potential difference between B and C. If we apply Ohm's law to each of the two resistors separately, we obtain

$$I = \frac{40 \text{ volts}}{5 \text{ ohm}} = 8 \text{ amp} \quad \text{and} \quad I = \frac{40 \text{ volts}}{20 \text{ ohm}} = 2 \text{ amp}$$

Hence 8 amp flows through the 5-ohm resistor, and 2 amp through the 20-ohm resistor. Note that these currents are in inverse ratio to their resistances.

49.4. Internal Resistance. Although the terms *electromotive force* and *potential difference,* as applied to electrical circuits in general, are both measured in *volts,* there is a real distinction between them. This difference may be illustrated by a demonstration experiment shown by a circuit diagram in Fig. 49G.

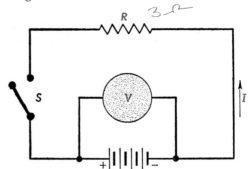

Fig. 49G *The measured voltage V changes when the switch is closed.*

A battery of four dry cells is connected to a resistor R of about 3 Ω. When the switch S is open, no current will flow around the circuit. The voltmeter, however, with its very high resistance of several thousand ohms will draw a negligibly small current from the battery, yet one that will indicate the electromotive force $\mathcal{E}$. For the four dry cells it would read 6.0 volts.

When the switch S is closed to complete the electric circuit, a current I of about 2 amp will flow around and through R, and the voltmeter will show a potential difference V between the battery terminals of about 5.4 volts.

The drop in battery voltage from 6.0 volts on open circuit to 5.4 volts on closed circuit is due to the *internal resistance* of battery cells. This internal resistance behaves as though it were in series with the battery and may be illustrated circuitwise as shown in Fig. 49H. The total resistance of this circuit is composed of the external resistance R in series with the battery's internal re-

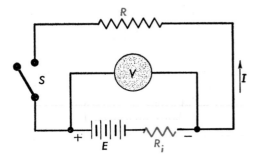

Fig. 49H *Batteries have an internal resistance R_1.*

rate method commonly employed for measuring resistance is known as the *Wheatstone bridge.* As shown in Fig. 49I this device consists of an electrical network of four re-

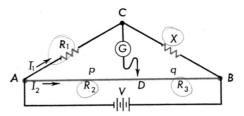

Fig. 49I *Slide-wire Wheatstone bridge.*

sistance R_i. When the switch is closed, the current I flowing through the circuit is given by Ohm's law as,

$$I = \frac{\mathcal{E}}{\mathcal{R}} \quad \mathcal{E} = 6 \text{ volts} \quad (49h)$$

where,

$$\mathcal{R} = R + R_i \quad (49i)$$

and $\mathcal{E}$ is the internal electromotive force of the battery ($\mathcal{E} = 6.0$ volts).

If the internal resistance $R_i = 0.3$ Ω, and $R = 2.7$ Ω, the total resistance $\mathcal{R} = 3.0$ Ω, and a current of 2 amp will flow through the circuit. The IR drop across R_i will be $2 \times 0.3 = 0.6$ volts, and the voltmeter will indicate $V = 5.4$ volts instead of the 6.0 volts it indicates on open circuit.

The emf $\mathcal{E}$ may be thought of as the driving force of the battery acting on the electrons in the circuit conductors. A voltmeter always measures the potential difference between the two points to which it is connected. This is true whether they are battery terminals or two points anywhere in the circuit. We see therefore that the effective V across a battery will depend upon the battery emf, the current being drawn from that battery, and the internal resistance.

Instead of applying Eq.(49h) to a circuit, it is customary to measure or specify V on closed circuit and then apply Ohm's law in the form

$$I = \frac{V}{R} \quad (49b)$$

where R is the external resistance only.

49.5. The Wheatstone Bridge. An accu-

sistors R_1, R_2, R_3, and X; a galvanometer G; and a battery V. By sliding the contact D along the straight resistance wire AB, a point is located where the galvanometer current is zero. Under these conditions the electron current I_1 must go on through R_1 and X, the current I_2 must go on through R_2 and R_3, and points C and D must be at the same potential. From the latter it is seen that the potential difference across R_1 must be the same as that across R_2, and the difference across X must be the same as that across R_3. Hence we can write

$$I_1 R_1 = I_2 R_2 \quad \text{and} \quad I_1 X = I_2 R_3$$

Dividing the second equation by the first, we obtain

$$\frac{I_1 X}{I_1 R_1} = \frac{I_2 R_3}{I_2 R_2} \quad \text{or} \quad X = R_1 \frac{R_3}{R_2} \quad (49j)$$

Since the resistors R_2 and R_3 are proportional to the wire lengths p and q, their ratio q/p can be substituted for R_3/R_2. Knowing the value of R_1 and measuring the lengths of p and q, we can calculate the unknown resistance X. In some arrangements the slide wire AB is done away with, and three adjustable resistance boxes are used for R_1, R_2, and R_3 as shown in Fig. 49J.

49.6. The Potential Divider. A potential divider is an electrical circuit constructed around a variable resistor or rheostat with one sliding contact. Connected to a battery as shown schematically in Fig. 49K, its purpose is to supply any desired potential dif-

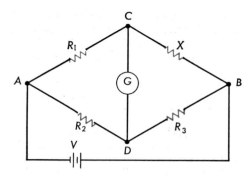

Fig. 49J   *Wheatstone bridge.*

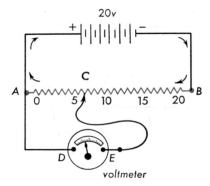

Fig. 49K   *Potential divider circuit for obtaining variable voltage.*

ference from zero up to the full voltage of the battery.

Suppose, as an illustration, that a battery supplies 20 volts to the extreme ends of a resistance wire AB and that a voltmeter V is connected to one end A and the sliding contact C. When the slider C is at A the voltmeter will read zero, but as it moves down toward B the reading will steadily rise. One-quarter of the way along, the voltmeter will read 5 volts; halfway along, 10 volts; three-quarters of the way, 15 volts; and finally at B it will read 20 volts. As a general rule the potential difference is directly proportional to the length of the resistance wire between A and C.

As a sample calculation, let the total resistance A to B in Fig. 49K be 100 ohm. By Ohm's law the current through AB will be

$$I = \frac{20 \text{ volts}}{100 \text{ ohm}} = 0.2 \text{ amp}$$

Let C be located three-quarters of the way along toward B so that the resistance A to C is $100 \times \frac{3}{4}$, or 75 ohm. The IR drop across this portion is, therefore,

$$IR = 0.2 \times 75 = 15 \text{ volts}$$

as read by the voltmeter.

PROBLEMS

1. A battery has an emf of 22 volts and an internal resistance of 0.5 Ω. What is the potential difference between the battery terminals when connected to an external resistance of 5 Ω?

2. A battery has an emf of 45 volts and an internal resistance of 1.0 Ω. (a) What current is supplied when it is connected to a 24 Ω resistor? (b) What is the potential difference across the battery? (c) What is the IR drop across the resistor? (*Ans.* (a) 1.8 amp, (b) 43.2 v, (c) 43.2 v.)

3. A battery has an emf of 26 volts and an internal resistance of 0.4 Ω. (a) Find the current supplied when the battery is connected to a 10-Ω appliance. (b) What is the IR drop within the battery? (c) What is the potential difference across the battery?

4. Two resistors of 6 Ω and 12 Ω, respectively,

are connected in parallel to a battery supplying a potential difference of 20 volts. Find (a) the equivalent resistance of the parallel circuit, (b) the total current, and (c) the current through each resistor. (*Ans.* (a) 4 ohm, (b) 5 amp, (c) 1.67 amp and 3.33 amp.)

5. Two resistors of 10 Ω and 30 Ω, respectively, are connected to a 45-volt battery. Find (a) the equivalent resistance of the parallel circuit, (b) the total battery current, and (c) the current through each resistor.

6. Three appliances of 6 Ω, 18 Ω, and 36 Ω, respectively, are connected in parallel to a 90-volt battery. Find (a) the equivalent resistance of the parallel circuit, (b) the total current supplied by the battery, and (c) the electron current through each appliance. (*Ans.* (a) 4 ohm, (b) 22.5 amp, (c) 2.5; 5; 15 amp.)

7. Three resistors of 3, 6, and 9 ohm, respectively, are connected in parallel. Calculate the equivalent resistance of the combination.

8. Two resistors, $R_1 = 8$ ohm and $R_2 = 32$ ohm, are connected in parallel, and then to a battery whose terminal voltage is 80 volts. Calculate (a) the equivalent resistance of the two parallel resistors, (b) the electron current supplied by the battery, and (c) the electron current flowing through R_1 and R_2 separately. (*Ans.* (a) 6.4 ohm, (b) 12.5 amp, (c) 10 amp, and 2.5 amp.)

9. Three resistors, $R_1 = 7$ ohm, $R_2 = 12$ ohm, and $R_3 = 8$ ohm, are connected in series, and then to a battery of ten dry cells. Calculate the electron current flowing.

10. Three resistors, $R_1 = 6$ ohm, $R_2 = 8$ ohm, and $R_3 = 24$ ohm, are connected in parallel. Find the equivalent resistance. (*Ans.* 3 ohm.)

11. Three hot plates of 4 Ω, 5 Ω, and 20 Ω, respectively, are connected in parallel to a 48-volt battery. Find (a) the circuit resistance, (b) the total current, and (c) the current through each hot plate.

12. Four appliances of 5 Ω, 6 Ω, 10 Ω, and 30 Ω, respectively, are connected in parallel to a house lighting circuit capable of maintaining $V = 120$ volts. Find (a) the equivalent resistance of the parallel circuit, (b) the total current supplied by the battery, and (c) the electron current through each appliance. (*Ans.* (a) 2 ohm, (b) 60 amp, (c) 4; 12; 20; 24 amp.)

13. Two resistors of 5 Ω and 20 Ω are connected in parallel. This parallel circuit is in series with an 8 Ω resistor, and the entire circuit is connected to a 60-v battery. Find the equivalent resistance of (a) the parallel combination and (b) the entire circuit. (c) Find the electron current through each resistor.

14. Two resistors, $R_1 = 15$ ohm and $R_2 = 24$ ohm, are connected in series to a battery whose voltage on open circuit is 120 volts. If the internal resistance of the battery is 1 ohm, find (a) the resistance of the circuit, (b) the electron current in the circuit, (c) the drop in potential across R_1 and R_2, and (d) the voltage across the battery. (*Ans.* (a) 40 ohm, (b) 3 amp, (c) 45 v and 72 v, (d) 117 v.)

15. Two resistors of 20 and 80 ohm, respectively, are connected in parallel, and the combination then connected to a 70-volt battery whose internal resistance is 1.5 ohm. Find (a) the resistance of the external circuit, (b) the electron current supplied by the battery, (c) the electron current through the external resistance, and (d) the voltage across the battery.

16. Two resistors, $R_1 = 12$ ohm and $R_2 = 24$ ohm, are connected in parallel. The combination is connected in series to a third resistor, $R_3 = 6$ ohm, and a 120-volt battery with an internal resistance of 1 ohm. Find (a) the current through the battery, (b) the drop in potential across the parallel circuit, (c) the current through each resistor, and (d) the voltage across the battery. (*Ans.* (a) 8 amp, (b) 64 v, (c) 5.33, 2.67, and 8 amp, (d) 112 v.)

17. Three resistors, $R_1 = 3$, $R_2 = 4$, and $R_3 = 12$ ohm, respectively, are connected in parallel. This combination is connected in series to two other resistors of $R_4 = 3$ and $R_5 = 5$ ohm, respectively, and to a 25-volt battery with an internal resistance of 0.5 ohm. Calculate (a) the equivalent resistance of the parallel combination, (b) the resistance of the entire circuit, (c) the current supplied by the battery, (d) the drop in potential across each resistor, and (e) the voltage across the battery.

18. Three light bulbs of 50 Ω, 75 Ω, and 150 Ω, respectively, are connected in parallel. This combination is connected in series with a 15-Ω appliance and the entire circuit is connected to a 120-volt line. Find the equivalent resistance of (a) the parallel combination, and (b) the entire circuit. (c) What current flows through each device? (*Ans.* (a) 25 ohm, (b) 40 ohm, (c) 0.5; 1.0; 1.5; 3.0 amp.)

19. An unknown resistor is connected to a Wheatstone bridge and the variable resistances adjusted until the galvanometer G shows no current. See Fig. 49J. The resistors R_1, R_2, and R_3 have values of 100, 650, and 2470 ohm, respectively. Find the unknown resistance.

20. An unknown resistor X is connected to a slide-wire Wheatstone bridge as shown in Fig. 49I. When the galvanometer G shows no current, $R_1 = 92$ ohm, the wire AB is 100 cm long, and the wire section AD is 65 cm. Find the resistance of X. (*Ans.* 49.5 ohm.)

Chapter 50

Electric Field, Potential, and Capacitance

50.1. Electric Potential. When a body has an excess of electrons (and is not close to other charged bodies), it has a *negative potential.* When it has a deficiency of electrons, it is said to have a *positive potential.* There are numerous exceptions to this, however, and it is customary to define positive potential and negative potential in a more general way. This is usually done as follows. If the connection of a body to the ground by an electrical conductor would cause electrons to flow onto the body from the ground, the body is at a *positive potential* (see diagram (a) in Fig. 50A). Con-

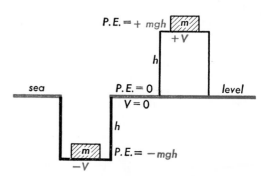

they were grounded, the flow of electrons *to* or *from* the ground brought them to *zero potential.* Electrical potential is analogous to the potential energy of a body in mechanics.

In mechanics, if a body is raised to a certain height *h* above sea level, its potential energy is positive, i.e., in returning to the ground it can perform an amount of work equal to *mgh.* See Fig. 50B. Con-

Fig. 50B *Electric potential in electricity is analogous to potential energy in mechanics.*

positive potential   negative potential

electrons

electrons

ground zero potential

(a)   (b)

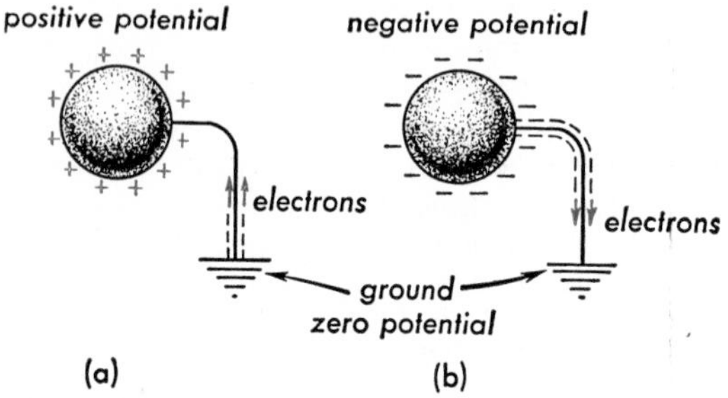

Fig. 50A *Showing the direction of the flow of electrons when a positively or negatively charged body is connected to the ground by a wire conductor.*

versely, if the connection of a body to the ground would cause electrons to flow off of the body into the ground, the body is at a negative potential (see diagram (b)).

In these definitions of positive and negative potential *it is assumed that the earth is at zero potential.* The bodies therefore had positive and negative potentials, respectively, before they were grounded, but after

versely, a body at a distance *h* below sea level has a negative potential energy *mgh*, for in lowering it to that point energy is given up. To raise it again, requires the expenditure of energy. Just as sea level is sometimes taken as the zero level of potential energy in mechanics, so the earth's potential is taken as the zero point of potential in electricity.

A quantitative definition of electric potential is usually given in terms of work or energy.

The electric potential V of a body is equal to the amount of work per unit posi-

tive charge done in carrying any charge Q from the ground up to the charged body.

$$V = \frac{W}{Q} \qquad (50a)$$

where W represents the work done and in the mks system is measured in *joules*. If the work done is large, the potential of the body is highly positive. If the work done is negative, i.e., if work is given up, the potential is negative. As a rule this energy is expressed in *volts*, and we speak of a potential of a body as being $+110$ volts, -2500 volts, etc.

It is also proper to speak of the potential of a point located anywhere in the free space around one or more charged bodies.

The electric potential at any point in an electric field is equal to the work per unit positive charge done in carrying any charge from the ground up to that point.

To give specific units to this definition, if the unit of charge is one coulomb and the work done is one joule, the potential is one volt.

$$1 \text{ volt} = 1 \frac{\text{joule}}{\text{coulomb}}$$

One one-thousandth of a volt is called a *millivolt* (abbr. mv), one-millionth of a volt a *microvolt* (abbr. μv), one thousand volts a *kilovolt* (abbr. Kv), and one million volts a *megavolt* (abbr. Mv).

The work per unit positive charge done in carrying a charge from the ground up to a point near a small body of charge Q is given by

$$V = k \frac{Q}{d} \qquad (50b)$$

where d, as shown in Fig. 50C, is the straight line distance from the center of the charged body to the unit test charge, and

$$k = 9 \times 10^9 \frac{\text{newton m}^2}{\text{coulombs}}$$

If the charge is located on a small spherical conductor of radius r, the potential at all points outside the sphere is the same as though the charge were concentrated at the center. At all points inside the sphere the

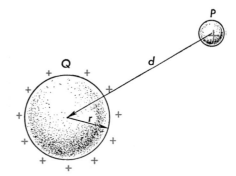

Fig. 50C *Potential near a charged spherical conductor.*

potential is the same as it is at the surface, namely

$$V = k \frac{Q}{r} \qquad (50c)$$

It will be noted from Eq.(50b) that as d is made larger and approaches infinity, V becomes smaller and approaches zero. Mathematically speaking, then, the ground referred to in the above definitions and statements, with its arbitrary assigned potential of zero, corresponds in Eq.(50b) to $d = \infty$.

Example 1. A spherical conductor of radius 1 cm has a charge of $+25 \times 10^{-10}$ coulombs. Calculate the potential at a point 10 cm from the center.

Solution. Apply Eq.(50b), and use mks units.

$$V = 9 \times 10^9 \frac{25 \times 10^{-10}}{0.10} = 225 \text{ volts}$$

50.2. Potential Difference. The potential of a body is defined as the work per unit positive charge done in carrying any charge from infinity to that body.

The difference of potential V between two bodies is defined as the work per unit positive charge done in carrying any charge from one of the bodies to the other.

For example, the potential difference between the two terminals of a car storage battery is 12 volts. This means that the work per unit positive charge done in carrying a charge from one terminal to the other is 12 joules per coulomb.

50.3. The Electric Field. In the space around a charged body is an invisible something called an *electric field*. This field is just another way of describing the action at a distance of one charge upon another.

The intensity of the electric field at any point in the neighborhood of a charged body is equal to the force per unit charge exerted on any charge placed at that point.

Since force is a vector quantity, an electric field has magnitude and direction. The field about a positive charge is therefore radially outward as shown in Fig. 50D(a).

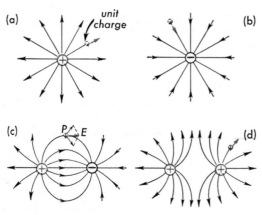

Fig. 50D   *Diagrams of the electric field around charged bodies.*

It is radially outward since a positive charge placed at any point is repelled along a line through the two charges. By a similar reasoning the field about a negative charge is radially inward as shown in diagram (b).

The electric field around two charged bodies is shown in diagrams (c) and (d). Each of these fields may be experimentally mapped by placing a positive charge at any one point and moving it always in the direction of the force F exerted on it. The lines traced out by such a charge are called *electric lines of force*. It is to be noted that as many lines as desired can be drawn and that no two lines ever cross. Furthermore, the lines themselves are imaginary and do not actually exist. They were first introduced by Michael Faraday about 1820 as an aid to the understanding of various electrical phenomena.

The direction of the lines of force is given by the arrowheads, and the relative magnitude of the field at any region is given by the relative number of the lines passing through that region. In agreement with Coulomb's law *the intensity of the field at any point near a single charged body is inversely proportional to the square of the distance away.*

Since E, the electric field intensity, is defined as the force per unit charge placed there, F/Q', Coulomb's law may be used to obtain a formula for the field intensity at any point near a small body of charge Q. Transposition of Q' to the other side in Eq.(47a) gives

$$E = \frac{E}{Q_1} \qquad \frac{F}{Q'} = k\frac{Q}{d^2}$$

or

$$\boxed{E = k\frac{Q}{d^2}} \qquad (50d)$$

The charge Q is in coulombs, the distance d to the field point is in *meters*, the field E at that point is in *newtons per coulomb*, and $k = 9 \times 10^9$ newton meters^2/coulomb^2. See Eq.(47d). Since E represents the force per unit charge, the force on any charge Q' placed at that point will be

$$F = Q' \times E \qquad (50e)$$

$$1 \text{ newton} = 1 \text{ coulomb} \times 1\,\frac{\text{newton}}{\text{coulomb}}$$

Example 2. A proton is an atomic particle having a mass of 1.672×10^{-27} Kg and a positive charge of 1.602×10^{-19} coulombs. Calculate the force on a proton in an electric field of 5000 newtons per coulomb, and compare this with its weight.

Solution. To find the electrical force, apply Eq.(50e).

$$F = Q'E = 1.602 \times 10^{-19} \times 5 \times 10^3$$
$$= 8.010 \times 10^{-16} \text{ newton}$$

To find the weight of a proton,

$$W = mg = 1.672 \times 10^{-27} \times 9.80$$
$$= 1.638 \times 10^{-26} \text{ newton}$$

A comparison of these two forces clearly indicates how negligibly small the gravitational force on atomic particles is when compared with the force due to electric fields commonly employed in the laboratory.

50.4. *Uniform Electric Field.* In many experimental studies of atomic structure, a great deal of knowledge can be obtained by observing the behavior of charged atomic particles traversing a uniform electric field. To obtain such a field, that is, a field constant in magnitude and direction over a specified volume of space, two flat metal plates are set up parallel to each other as shown in Fig. 50E.

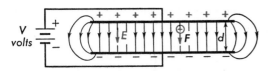

Fig. 50E   *The electric field between two parallel charged plates is uniform.*

When the terminals of a battery with a voltage V are connected to these plates, as indicated in the diagram, a uniform electric field E is produced between the plates. Outside of the plates and near the ends, the field is not uniform.

In mechanics, *work done* is defined as *force times distance, $W = F \times d$.* The electrical equivalent of this equation follows, therefore, by direct substitution of the equivalent electrical quantities for W and F. Since work done per unit charge is potential difference V, and the force per unit charge is the electric field intensity E, see Eqs.(50a) and (50e), the work equation $W = F \times d$ becomes

$$V = E \times d$$

or

$$E = \frac{V}{d} \qquad (50f)$$

between parallel plates

If V is in volts and d is in meters, E is in *volts/meter.*

$$1 \frac{\text{volt}}{\text{meter}} = 1 \frac{\text{newton}}{\text{coulomb}}$$

50.5. *The Capacitor.* A capacitor is an electrical device for storing quantities of electricity in much the same way that a reservoir is a container for storing water or a steel tank is a container for storing gas. The general form of a capacitor is that of two parallel conducting plates as shown in Fig. 50F.

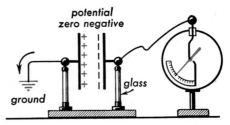

Fig. 50F   *Demonstration of the principles of a capacitor.*

Such plates are of relatively large area, close together, and contain between them a nonconducting medium called the *dielectric.* Common dielectrics are *air, glass, mica, oil,* and *waxed paper.*

Quantitatively, the capacitance of a capacitor is a measure of its ability to store-up electricity. To increase the capacitance of a capacitor, one or more of the following changes can be made: first, the area of the plates may be increased; second, the plates may be put closer together; and third, a more suitable dielectric may be inserted between the plates. If the plates of a capacitor are small in area and at the same time relatively far apart, the capacitance is small. If the area is large and the plates close together, the capacitance is large.

The principles of the capacitor are illustrated in Fig. 50F. One plate of this capacitor is grounded, and the other is insulated but connected to an electroscope or electrometer. If the right-hand plate is now given a negative charge as shown, electrons in the other plate are repelled into the ground, leaving that plate positively charged. If the insulated plate is given a positive charge (not shown), electrons from the ground are attracted to the other plate and it acquires a negative charge.

In either case the grounded plate is, by definition, at *ground potential,* or *zero potential.* The right-hand plate is at negative potential, since, if connected to the ground, its electrons would escape into the ground.

As shown in the diagram, however, the capacitor is charged.

If, while in the charged condition, the two plates of a capacitor are suddenly connected by a conductor, the negatives can flow through the conductor to the positives, thus neutralizing the charges. The capacitor has thus been discharged.

During the time a capacitor is being charged, the plates acquire a greater and greater difference of potential. If in Fig. 50F more electrons are added to the insulated plate, the potential difference is increased. The amount of charge stored-up in this way is limited only by the breakdown of the dielectric between the two plates. When the charge becomes too great, a spark will jump between the plates, thus discharging the capacitor.

Capacitance is not determined by the amount of charge a capacitor will hold before sparking occurs; it is defined as the amount of charge Q on one plate necessary to raise the potential V of that plate 1v above the other. Symbolically,

$$C = \frac{Q}{V} \qquad (50g)$$

The unit of capacitance, the *farad*, named in honor of Michael Faraday, is defined as the capacitance of a capacitor of such dimensions that *a charge of one coulomb will give the plates a difference of potential of one volt.*

$$1 \text{ farad} = \frac{1 \text{ coulomb}}{1 \text{ volt}} \qquad (50h)$$

Whether one plate of a 1-farad capacitor is grounded or not, the potential difference between the plates will be 1 volt when one plate has a positive charge of 1 coul and the other plate has a negative charge of 1 coul. Grounding simply brings that plate to zero potential without changing its charge.

A capacitance of 1 farad is very large and for practical purposes is not used. The *microfarad* is more convenient. The smaller unit is one-millionth of the farad and is abbreviated μf. In other words, 1,000,000

microfarads are equivalent to 1 farad. A still smaller unit, the *micromicrofarad*, is sometimes used. One micromicrofarad is one-millionth of 1 microfarad and is abbreviated $\mu\mu$f.

$$1 \ \mu f = 10^{-6} \text{ f} \qquad (50i)$$
$$1 \ \mu\mu f = 10^{-12} \text{ f} \qquad (50j)$$

The charging of a capacitor until the difference of potential is 1 volt is analogous to raising the level of water in a tank to 1 ft, whereas the charging of the same capacitor to the point where it sparks over is like filling the tank until water runs over the top. A large capacitance is like a tank of large cross-sectional area, and a small capacitance is like a tank of small area. It takes more charge to raise the potential of a large capacitance 1 volt, and it takes more water to raise the level in a large tank 1 ft.

Capacitors in common use today are of various kinds, sizes, and shapes. Perhaps the most common is the so-called "paper capacitor," used commonly in radios and the ignition system of automobiles. Two long strips of tin foil are glued to the two faces of a strip of thin paper. This paper is then soaked in paraffin or oil and rolled up with another paraffin-soaked strip of paper into a small compact unit. Each sheet of tin foil becomes one plate of the capacitor, and the paper becomes the dielectric separating them.

Another type of capacitor is the variable capacitor commonly used in tuning radios (see Fig. 50G). The capacitance of such a

Fig. 50G   *Variable capacitor commonly used in radio sets. (Courtesy, Hammarlund Manufacturing Co.)*

device can be varied in amount at will by the turning of a knob. The turning of a knob moves one set of plates between the other set, thus increasing or decreasing the effective plate area, and hence, the capacitance. The capacitance of such variable air capacitors is from zero to about 4000 $\mu\mu f$.

50.6. Calculation of Capacitance. A general formula for calculating the capacitance of a parallel plate capacitor is the following:

$$C = \epsilon \frac{A}{d} \qquad (50k)$$

where, as shown in Fig. 50H, A is the area of either of the parallel plates in m², d is the distance between them in m, ϵ a constant of the separating medium, and C is the capacitance in farads.

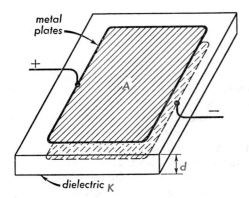

metal plates

dielectric K

Fig. 50H   *Diagram of the principal elements of a capacitor.*

The constant ϵ, called the *permittivity*, is the product of the constant $\epsilon_0 = 8.85 \times 10^{-12}$ and K the *dielectric constant*, or *dielectric coefficient*.

$$\epsilon = \epsilon_0 K \qquad (50l)$$

Values of the dielectric constant of a few substances are given in Table 50A.

In the mks system, permittivity has the units of farads/meter or, what is the equivalent, coulombs²/newton meter².

Example 3. Two rectangular sheets of tinfoil 20 cm × 25 cm are stuck to opposite sides of a thin sheet of mica 0.1 mm thick. Calculate the capacitance if the dielectric constant is 5.

Solution. The given quantities are $K = 5$,

$d = 1 \times 10^{-4}$ m, and $A = 0.20 \times 0.25 = 0.05$ m². By substituting in Eqs. (50k) and (50l), we obtain

$$C = 5 \times 8.85 \times 10^{-12} \frac{0.05}{1 \times 10^{-4}}$$

$$= 221 \times 10^{-10} \text{ farad} = 0.0221 \ \mu f$$

When capacitors are connected in parallel, as shown in Fig. 50I, their combined capacitance

parallel capacitors

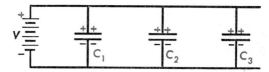

Fig. 50I   *Circuit diagram of parallel capacitors.*

is just the arithmetic sum of the individual capacities.

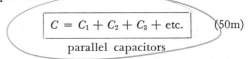

$$\boxed{C = C_1 + C_2 + C_3 + \text{etc.}} \qquad (50m)$$

parallel capacitors

When capacitors are connected in series, as shown in Fig. 50J, the combined capacitance

TABLE 50A. DIELECTRIC CONSTANTS

Dielectric	K
Vacuum	1.0000
Air	1.0006
Glass	5-10
Rubber	3-35
Mica	3-6
Glycerine	56
Petroleum	2
Water	81

series capacitors

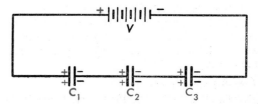

Fig. 50J   *Circuit diagram of series capacitors.*

is given by the reciprocal of the sum of the reciprocals.

$$\frac{1}{C} = \frac{1}{C_1} + \frac{1}{C_2} + \frac{1}{C_3} + \text{etc.} \qquad (50n)$$

series capacitors

The first formula is derived from the principle that capacitors in a parallel combination each have the same potential difference V given by $V = Q/C$, while $Q = Q_1 + Q_2 +$

$Q_3 +$ etc. The second of these formulas is derived from the principle that capacitors in a series combination acquire the same charge Q given by $Q = CV$, while $V = V_1 + V_2 + V_3 +$ etc.

It should be noted with care that these two formulas are just the reverse of those for series and parallel resistors.

PROBLEMS

1. If 2.4×10^{-5} joule of work is done in carrying a charge of 5×10^{-8} coul up to a charged body, what is its potential?

2. A charge of 8×10^{-7} coul is carried from a distant point up to a charged body. What is the potential of that body if the work done is 2×10^{-4} joule? (*Ans.* 250 v.)

3. A spherical conductor 2 cm in diameter has a charge of 5×10^{-9} coul. Calculate the potential of (a) a point 8 cm from the center and (b) the sphere.

4. A spherical conductor 3 cm in diameter has a charge of 2×10^{-9} coul. Calculate the potential of (a) the sphere and (b) a point 5 cm from the center. (*Ans.* (a) 1200 v, (b) 360 v.)

5. A metal sphere is suspended by a silk thread and charged negatively. In carrying a negative charge of 4×10^{-8} coul from a great distance to the metal sphere, an amount of work equal to 8×10^{-5} joule is done. What is the potential of the sphere?

6. A metal sphere is supported on the end of a thin glass rod and given a positive charge of 20×10^{-9} coul. What is the electric intensity at a distance of (a) 2 cm, (b) 5 cm, and (c) 10 cm from the center? (*Ans.* (a) 4.5×10^5 newtons/coul, (b) 7.2×10^4 newtons/coul, (c) 18.0×10^3 newtons/coul.)

7. Two insulated metal spheres 50 cm apart each have a charge of 5×10^{-8} coul. Calculate (a) the field intensity, and (b) the potential at a point 1.2 m from one charge and 1.3 m from the other.

8. A hollow metal ball 8 cm in diameter is given a charge of -4×10^{-8} coul. What is the potential at a point (a) 50 cm from the center, (b) on the surface of the ball, and (c) inside the ball? (*Ans.* (a) -720 v, (b) -9000 v, (c) -9000 v.)

9. Calculate the work done in carrying a charge of $+6 \times 10^{-8}$ coul from the ground to an insulated metal sphere, $r = 20$ cm, having a charge of $+4 \times 10^{-7}$ coul.

10. A metal sphere is suspended by a silk thread and charged positively. In carrying a plus charge of 2×10^{-8} coul from the ground to the metal sphere, an amount of work equal to 8×10^{-5} joule is done. What is the potential of the sphere with respect to the ground? (*Ans.* $+4000$ v.)

11. A potential difference of 5000 volts is applied to two parallel plates 2 cm apart. A small metal sphere with a charge of 1.8×10^{-10} coul is located midway between the plates. Find (a) the electric intensity between the plates, and (b) the force on the charged sphere.

12. Two flat metal plates 2 cm apart are connected to a 1000-volt battery. A proton with its positive charge of 1.6×10^{-19} coul is located between these plates. Find (a) the electric field intensity between the plates, and (b) the force on the proton in newtons. (*Ans.* (a) 50,000 v/m, (b) 8.0×10^{-15} newtons.)

13. Two flat metal plates 2 cm apart are connected to a 2000-volt source. A small charge Q of 5×10^{-9} coul is located in the field. Find (a) the electric field intensity, and (b) the force on the charge Q.

14. A battery of 8000 volts is applied to two parallel plates 5 mm apart. What is the force of an electron of charge 1.60×10^{-19} coul when it passes through the uniform electric field between the plates? (*Ans.* 2.56×10^{-13} newton.)

15. A 1000-volt battery is connected to a 10-μf capacitor. What is the charge on each plate?

16. A 250-volt battery is applied to a 6-μf capacitor. Find the charge on each plate. (*Ans.* 1.5×10^{-3} coul.)

17. Two sheets of tin foil 20 cm × 50 cm are glued to opposite faces of a glass plate 0.8 mm thick. Find its capacitance if the dielectric constant for glass is 5.

18. Two flat metal plates 40 cm × 100 cm are mounted parallel to each other and 1 cm apart. Find the capacitance when they are immersed in oil of dielectric constant 2. (*Ans.* 708 μμf.)

19. A parallel plate capacitor with air as a dielectric has a capacitance of 5 μf. What will be its capacitance if submerged in glycerine?

20. A parallel plate capacitor with glass as a dielectric has a capacitance of 0.05 μf. What will be its capacitance if the glass (dielectric constant 8) is replaced by mica (dielectric constant 3)? (*Ans.* 0.0188 μf.)

21. A capacitor is made up of 16 sheets of tin foil each 4 cm × 15 cm, separated by mica sheets 0.25 mm thick. Find the capacitance in μf if alternate sheets of tin foil are connected together. Dielectric constant of mica = 4.8.

22. Three capacitors 8, 12, and 24 μf, respectively, are connected in series. Find the capacitance of the system. (*Ans.* 4.0 μf.)

23. Three capacitors 4, 5, and 20 μf are connected in series to a 300-volt battery. Find (a) the capacitance and (b) the charge on each capacitor plate, and (c) the voltage across each capacitor.

24. Two capacitors of 5 μf and 20 μf, respectively, are connected in parallel, and the combination in series with a third capacitor of 10 μf. Find (a) the capacitance of the parallel circuit, (b) the total capacitance, and (c) the voltage across each capacitor, if the ends are connected to a 1000-volt battery. (*Ans.* (a) 25 μf, (b) 7.14 μf, (c) 286, 286, 714 v.)

25. Two sheets of tin foil 45 × 66 cm are glued to opposite faces of a glass plate 0.12 mm thick. Find its capacitance. Dielectric constant for glass = 5.7.

26. A capacitor is made up of 16 sheets of tin foil each 6 × 10 cm, separated by mica sheets 0.25 mm thick. Find the capacitance in μf if alternate sheets of tin foil are connected to-

gether. Dielectric constant of mica = 4.8. (*Ans.* 1.36 × 10⁻² μf.)

27. A variable air capacitor (see Fig. 50G) is made up of 15 semicircular duraluminum plates 8 cm in diameter. Find its maximum capacitance in μμf if alternate plates are connected together for the rotor, and the remaining plates for the stator. Assume the air gap between adjacent plates to be 0.5 mm.

28. Solve Prob. 27 if the capacitor is immersed in castor oil of dielectric constant 4.6. (*Ans.* 2860 μμf.)

29. Three capacitors, 4, 6, and 12 μf, respectively, are connected in series. Find (a) the capacitance of the combination, (b) the total charge stored by the combination when connected to a 250-volt source, and (c) the charge on each capacitor.

30. Three capacitors, 4, 5, and 20 μf, are connected in series to a 300-volt battery. Find (a) the capacitance of the combination, (b) the charge on each capacitor, and (c) the voltage across each capacitor. (*Ans.* (a) 2 μf, (b) 6 × 10⁻⁴ coul, (c) 150; 120; and 30 v.)

31. Two metal spheres 8 cm in diameter are to be charged by equal amounts, one plus and the other minus, until the potential difference between them is 1000 volts. How much charge should each one have?

32. An electronics technician has three capacitors, 3, 6, and 18 μf, respectively. How should these capacitors be connected to obtain a capacitance of (a) 1.8 μf, (b) 7.5 μf, and (c) 20 μf. (*Ans.* (a) All in series, (b) 18 and 6 in series, and the combination in parallel with the 3, (c) 3 and 6 in series, and this combination in parallel with 18.)

33. Find all capacitance values that can be obtained with the following capacitors: 4, 8, and 24 μf, respectively.

34. Starting with the formula $Q = CV$, and the left-hand diagram in Fig. 50I, derive the formula for the capacitance of capacitors connected in parallel.

35. Starting with the formula $Q = CV$, and the right-hand diagram in Fig. 50I, derive the formula for the capacitance of capacitors connected in series.

Chapter 51

Magnetism

Magnetism was known to the early Greek philosophers. According to one story Magnes, a shepherd, when on Mt. Ida on the island of Crete, was so strongly attracted to the ground by the tip of his staff and the nails in his shoes that he had difficulty in getting away. Upon digging into the ground to find the cause, he discovered a stone with the most amazing properties of attracting iron. This stone is now called lodestone or magnetite.

The idea that a lodestone can be used as a compass is a very old one. There is some evidence that the Chinese knew this as far back as A.D. 121. At any rate, a Chinese author, writing as early as the beginning of the 12th century, explains that a needle, when rubbed with lodestone and suspended free to turn, will point toward the south. This appears to be the first evidence that a piece of iron could be magnetized by a lodestone and used as a compass. The action of a lodestone or a bar magnet when suspended free to turn about a vertical axis is illustrated in Fig. 51A.

A compass as it is often made for demonstration purposes usually consists of a straight steel needle which has been magnetized and mounted free to turn on a sharp

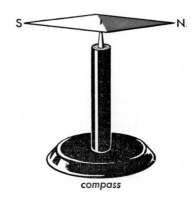

compass

Fig. 51B   *A compass needle is a magnet.*

pointed rod as shown in Fig. 51B. In the early days of the mariner's compass, it was common to float several small magnetic needles on water by mounting them on a block of wood or other light material. In more recent designs a compass needle with a jewel in its center is set upon the sharp point of a hard metal rod, much shorter than that shown in Fig. 51B, and placed in a small brass box with a glass top. Such compasses in appearance are familiar to everyone.

51.1. Magnets. Until recent years, magnets have been made of hardened steel and molded or rolled into many shapes. Perhaps the most common of these is the horseshoe magnet shown in Fig. 51C, or the straight bar magnet shown in Fig. 51D. The strongest magnets are now made of an alloy containing aluminum, cobalt, nickel, and iron. Small magnets of this alloy are strong enough to lift hundreds of times their own weight.

Pure iron (sometimes called soft iron), when magnetized, will not retain its magnetism and is therefore useless in making what are called permanent magnets. Soft iron is used, however, in the construction of

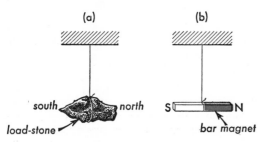

Fig. 51A   *Magnetized bodies, when free to turn, come to rest in a north-south direction.*

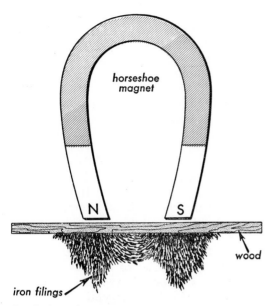

Fig. 51C   *The attraction of a magnet for iron acts through all substances.*

other words, magnetic attraction acts right through matter of all kinds. This can be demonstrated as shown in Fig. 51C by picking up iron filings on one side of a thin wooden board by holding a magnet close to the other side. If a sheet of copper, or brass, or, as a matter of fact, any substance, is placed over the magnet, the power of attraction is not destroyed. A small region of space can be partially shielded from magnetic fields if it is entirely surrounded by layers of soft iron.

While a few metals are known to be feebly attracted by a magnet, most substances like aluminum, copper, silver, gold, wood, glass, paper, etc., do not exhibit any noticeable effect. Of those weakly affected, nickel and cobalt are the most important. These two metals, as mentioned above, when alloyed together with other metals in the proper proportions, are found to exhibit stronger magnetic susceptibility than the best grades of iron or steel. As a pure element, however, iron is by far the most strongly magnetic.

electromagnets. These devices will be discussed and demonstrated in another chapter. Of the many practical applications of permanent magnets, the compass, the telephone receiver, and the radio loud-speaker are perhaps the most common.

51.2. The Power of Attraction. Nearly everyone has at sometime or another played with a small horseshoe magnet and discovered for himself that it attracted only things containing iron. Upon drawing the same magnet through the dry sand or dirt, you probably discovered that it will pick up small grains of iron ore.

If more extensive experiments are carried out, a magnet can be shown to attract magnetic substances at a distance even though matter lies in the intervening space. In

51.3. Magnetic Poles. When an ordinary straight bar magnet is dipped into a box of iron filings, the tiny bits of iron are observed to cling to the ends as shown in Fig. 51D. These preferred regions of attraction are called *magnetic poles*. If this same magnet is suspended by a thread as shown in Fig. 51A, it will come to rest in a position close to the north-south direction. The end toward the north is therefore called the *N* or *north-seeking pole,* and the other end the *S* or *south-seeking pole.*

That the *N* and *S* poles of a magnet are different may be shown by bringing the magnet close to a compass needle. Such an experiment is illustrated in Fig. 51E. When the *S* pole of the magnet is brought close to the *S* pole of the compass needle as in diagram (a), there is a force of repulsion acting, and the compass needle turns away as shown. A similar repulsion occurs between the two *N* poles as shown in diagram (b). If the *N* and *S* poles are brought near to each other, however, a very strong attraction arises and the compass needle turns toward the other, as shown in diagrams (c)

Fig. 51D   *The attraction of iron filings by a straight bar magnet shows greater attraction near the ends. These regions of greatest attraction are called* magnetic poles.

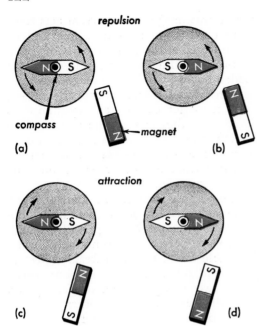

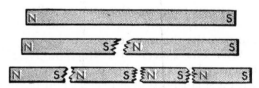

Fig. 51E *When the pole of one magnet is brought close to the pole of another magnet, like poles are found to repel each other and unlike poles to attract.*

and (d). These experiments show, therefore, that *two kinds of magnetic poles exist* and that *like poles repel and unlike poles attract.*

Permanent magnets can now be made so strong that one magnet can be lifted by the repulsion of another. This is illustrated in Fig. 51F. Unless guide rods of glass or some other substance are used, however, the floating bar will move to one side and then fall. In other words, the forces of repulsion are such that the upper bar is not in stable equilibrium. If the floating magnet is turned end for end, opposite poles become adjacent and the two magnets at-

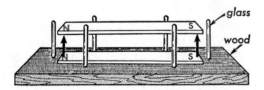

Fig. 51F *One magnet may be suspended in mid-air by the strong repulsion of like poles of another magnet.*

tract each other. Although the forces may be great enough, no one has ever succeeded in floating a magnet in mid-air by means of permanent magnets, against the pull of gravity without guide rods.

It should be pointed out that each magnetic pole in a magnetized body is not confined to a single point but extends over a finite region. From a distance, however, each polar region acts as though it were concentrated at a point, similar to that of the center of mass in mechanics.

51.4. Poles Exist in Pairs. If a magnet is broken in the middle in an attempt to separate the poles, one finds new poles formed at the broken ends. If one of these pieces is again broken, each piece is again found to contain two poles of opposite kind. As long as this process is repeated, the same result is obtained—a magnetic pole of one kind is always accompanied by a pole of opposite polarity. This is conveniently illustrated by magnetizing a hack-saw blade and breaking it successively into smaller and smaller pieces as shown in Fig. 51G.

Fig. 51G *The poles of a magnet cannot exist alone. When a bar magnet is broken, poles appear on either side of the break, such that each piece has two opposite poles.*

Each time a piece is broken, each fragment, upon being tested with a compass, is found to have an N pole on one side and an S pole on the other. A hack-saw blade is readily magnetized by stroking it from one end to the other with one of the poles of a magnet.

It is possible to magnetize a bar of steel so that it has three or more polar regions. This is illustrated in Fig. 51H where a hack-saw blade has been magnetized with an N pole at each end and an S polar region in the center. The combined strength of the N poles is seen by the quantity of iron

Fig. 51H *Diagram of a bar magnet with iron filings showing three polar regions.*

filings to be equal to the S pole strength in the center. We might say, therefore, that the magnet has four poles: an N pole at either end and two S poles at the center.

51.5. The Magnetic Field. In the space surrounding every magnet, there exists what is called a magnetic field. Although this field cannot be seen, it can be demonstrated and mapped out in the following way.

If a very small compass is placed at some point near the N pole of a straight bar magnet, and then moved always in the direction the compass is pointing, the center of the compass will trace out a smooth line called a magnetic line of force. Starting at various points, many such lines may be drawn as shown in Fig. 51I. Each line

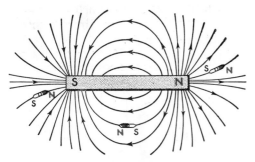

Fig. 51I *Diagram of the magnetic field and magnetic lines of force about a straight bar magnet, as obtained with a small compass needle.*

starts at some point near the N pole and ends at a corresponding point near the S pole.

These magnetic *lines of force,* as they are called, do not really exist; they are but useful devices that may be used in describing the many different magnetic phenomena to be taken up in later chapters. It should be noted that, where the magnet exerts its strongest attraction near

the poles, the lines are closest together and that each line points away from the N pole and toward the S pole. This latter is an arbitrary assignment, being the direction indicated by the N pole of the compass.

A close examination of the iron filings clinging to a magnet (see Figs. 51D and 51H) shows that each tiny needle-like piece of iron lines up in the direction of the magnetic lines of force. The reason for this is that each filing has become magnetized by the magnet, and having its own N and S poles, acts like a compass. An excellent demonstration of the field and its direction can be performed by laying a plate of glass or a sheet of paper over a magnet and then sprinkling iron filings over the top. By gently tapping the glass or paper, the filings turn and line up as shown in the photographic reproduction given in Fig. 51J.

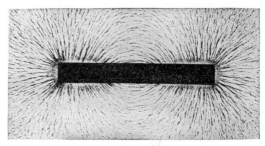

Fig. 51J *Photograph of the iron filings lined up by the magnetic field of a permanent straight bar magnet.*

51.6. The Field about Separated Magnets. When two magnets are brought close together as shown in Fig. 51K, the mutual action of the two is such as to produce a complicated magnetic field. This is illustrated by compass-made drawings at the top and by photographic reproductions of the iron-filing method of observation at the bottom.

A simplified explanation of many electric and magnetic phenomena can be given by assuming that these imaginary *lines of force* are endowed with certain real but simple properties. Lengthwise along the lines they act as though they were stretched rubber bands under constant tension, whereas sideways they act as if they repelled each other.

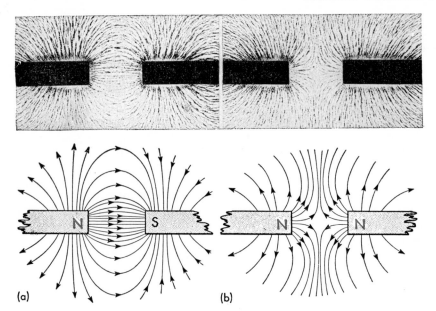

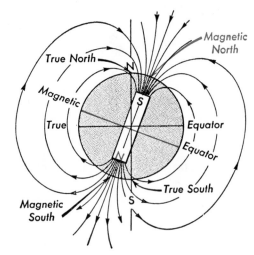

Fig. 51K *Diagrams and photographs illustrating the magnetic fields around pairs of magnetic poles.*

Both of these properties are illustrated in Fig. 51K. When the two poles are of different polarity as in diagram (a), the lines of force acting like stretched rubber bands tend to pull the poles together. In diagram (b) where the poles are alike, the lines repel each other, pushing the poles apart.

51.7. The Earth's Magnetic Field. To Sir William Gilbert we owe the view that the earth is a great magnet. To prove his theory, Gilbert shaped a lodestone into a sphere and demonstrated that a small compass placed at any spot of the globe always pointed, as it does on the earth, toward the North Pole.

The earth, therefore, has been schematically pictured in Fig. 51L as a large magnetized sphere of iron, or as though it contained a huge permanent magnet. Since the magnetic axis is at an angle with the polar axis, the earth's magnetic poles are not at the *true North* and *true South Poles*. The true North and true South Poles are points located on the earth's rotational axis.

The *North Magnetic Pole* is located in far northern Canada, while the *South Magnetic Pole* is located almost diametrically opposite in the Southern Hemisphere. As

for polarity, the North Magnetic Pole is an *S* pole and the South Magnetic Pole is an *N* pole. This becomes apparent from the magnetic lines of force which always start from an *N* pole and are directed toward, and end, at an *S* pole.

Although the cause for the earth's mag-

Fig. 51L *Schematic diagram illustrating the earth as a huge magnet surrounded by a magnetic field extending far out into space.*

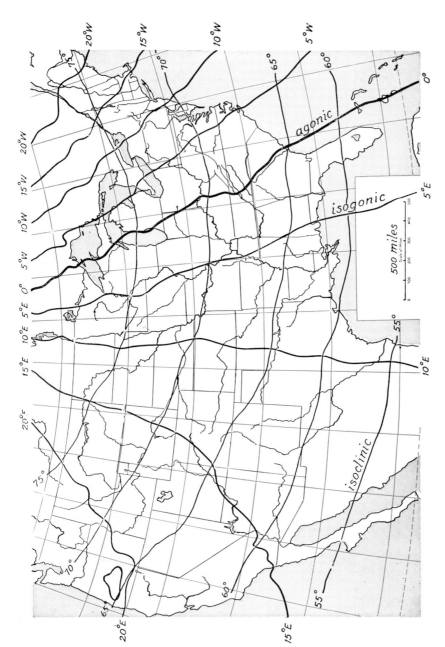

Fig. 51M *A magnetic map of the United States for the year 1954 showing the
declination of a compass from true north and the angle of dip of a dip needle.
Such maps are drawn from data asembled by the U.S. Coast and Geodetic Survey.*

netism is not completely understood, several reasonable theories have been proposed. The earth is known to contain large iron ore deposits, some of these deposits being almost pure iron. One theory proposes that, during the ages past, all these iron deposits gradually became magnetized, in very nearly the same direction, and that together they act like one huge permanent magnet. Another theory, and a very plausible one, is that the magnetism is due to large electric currents which are known to be flowing around the earth, not only in the earth's crust but also in the air above. These earth currents seem to be connected in some direct way with the earth's rotation. This appears to be corroborated by the fact that the earth is magnetized in a direction almost parallel to the earth's polar axis.

51.8. Magnetic Declination. Since the earth's magnetic and polar axes do not coincide, a compass needle does not in general point toward True North. Because of the influence of the irregular iron deposits near the earth's surface, the magnetic field is not as regular as it is pictured in Fig. 51L and a compass needle may deviate considerably from magnetic north. The angle that a compass needle deviates from True North is called the *angle of declination*.

A map showing the angle of declination for the United States during the year 1954 is shown in Fig. 51M. The more or less vertical set of irregular lines are lines of equal declination and are called *isogonic lines*. At every point along the line marked 20°E, for example, a compass needle actually points 20° east of True North. In the region of San Francisco the declination is seen to be about 18°E, while in the region of New York it is about 11°W. The line through points where a compass points True North, 0°, is named the *agonic line*.

51.9. Magnetic Dip. If a compass needle is mounted free to turn about a horizontal axis as shown in Fig. 51N, it will not come to rest in a horizontal position but will dip down at some angle with the horizontal as shown. This direction, called the *dip*, is the angle the earth's field makes with

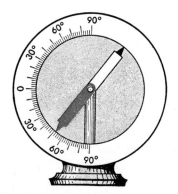

Fig. 51N   *A magnetic dip needle.*

the earth's surface at the point in question. Referring to Fig. 51L it is seen that in the far north and south the angle of dip is quite large, whereas near the equator it is quite small. Fig. 51O indicates the approxi-

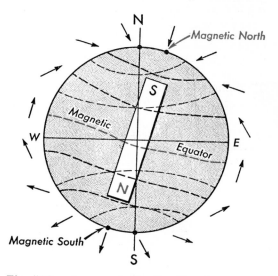

Fig. 51O   *Arrows show the direction a dip needle takes at different parts of the earth's surface.*

mate dip at different latitudes for one cross section of the entire globe.

At a region on the Boothia Peninsula just north of Hudson Bay and 20° from True North, a dip needle points straight down, perpendicular to the earth's surface, and locates the North Magnetic Pole. At a region about 18° from the true South Pole a dip needle points straight up, at

90° from the horizontal, and locates the South Magnetic Pole.

On maps of terrestrial magnetism, all points that have equal dip angles are connected by a line called an *isoclinic* line. Such lines for different angles form a set of nearly parallel lines as shown on the map of the United States in Fig. 51M.

In San Francisco the earth's magnetic induction B (see Sec. 51.13) is about 5.4×10^{-5} webers/meter^2 (*abbr.* w/m^2), or 0.54 gauss (see Eq.(53h)) and the angle of dip about 62°. This gives a horizontal component of 0.25×10^{-4} webers/meter^2 or 0.25 gauss.

Careful and accurate measurements of the *declination* and *dip* show that the earth's magnetic field is continually changing. Although these changes are extremely small, they are somewhat periodic and at times quite erratic.

51.10. Magnetization. When a strong magnet is brought close to a piece of soft iron, the iron takes on all the properties of a new but somewhat weaker magnet. This phenomenon, called *magnetization,* is illustrated in Fig. 51P(a). As long as the

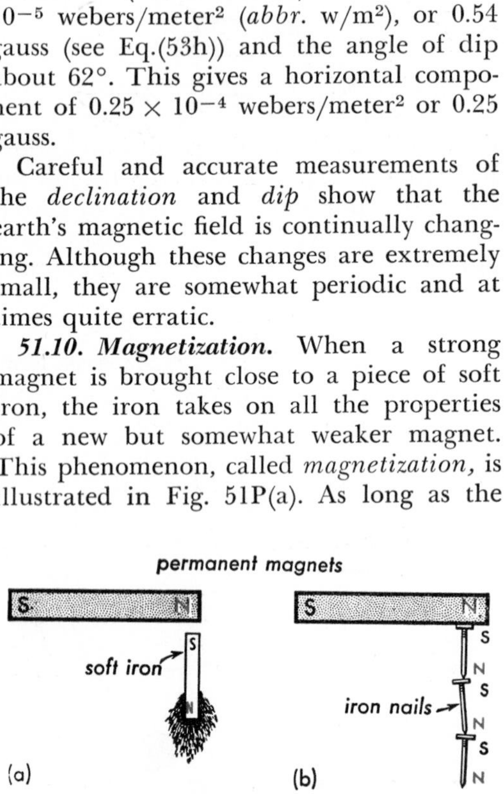

permanent magnets

(a)   (b)

Fig. 51P   *Soft iron may be magnetized by induction at a distance or by contact.*

permanent magnet is held close to the soft iron bar, the iron filings cling to the end as shown. When the permanent magnet is removed, however, the soft iron immediately loses its magnetism and the iron filings drop off.

When a piece of iron is magnetized, a pole of opposite sign is created at the points of closest approach as shown in the diagrams. If a common iron nail is brought up to the N pole of a permanent magnet,

it will become magnetized with a S pole at the point of contact and an N pole at the other end, as shown in diagram (b). Having two poles, the nail is thus magnetized and will attract another nail and magnetize it in the same way. With a good strong magnet this process can be repeated by adding one nail after the other.

It is now clear how iron filings line up with the lines of force of a magnet. Each filing becomes magnetized and, like a small compass, turns parallel to the field in which it is located.

51.11. Molecular Theory of Ferromagnetism. The modern theory of magnetism, which is now quite firmly established as being correct, is that a piece of iron consists of myriads of tiny elementary magnets. These tiny ultramicroscopic magnets may consist of individual atoms and molecules themselves, or of groups of atoms aligned to form small elementary iron crystals. How single atoms can act as magnets will be explained later. Before a piece of iron or steel has been magnetized, these elementary magnets may be thought of as being oriented more or less at random throughout the metal as shown in Fig. 51Q(a).

During the time a piece of iron is being magnetized, the elementary magnets are turned around and lined up parallel to each other and to the magnetizing field. This is shown by the schematic representation in diagram (b). Lined up in this way, the small N and S poles are adjacent to each other and cancel each other's effect on external objects. At one end there are many free N poles, and at the opposite end an equal number of free S poles.

When a magnet is broken at any point, *free S poles* are exposed at one side of the break and *free N poles* at the other. It is therefore clear why poles always exist in pairs and that, no matter how many times a magnet is broken, each piece will contain an N at one end and an S pole at the other.

When soft iron is magnetized by induction and the permanent magnet is taken away, the elementary magnets return to their original random orientations, but, when hardened steel becomes magnetized,

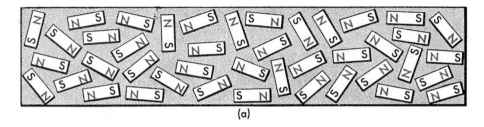

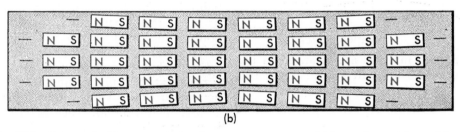

Fig. 51Q *Schematic diagrams of the elementary magnets within a piece of iron: (a) un-magnetized, and (b) magnetized.*

they remain lined up after the magnetizing field is taken away.

51.12. Coulomb's Law for Magnetic Poles. For a study of the law of force between magnetic poles, specially designed magnets have been used. The necessity for this is realized when it is remembered that single magnetic poles cannot be isolated by

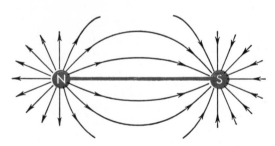

Fig. 51R *Map of the magnetic field around a special type of permanent magnet.*

breaking a magnet in two. The special magnets consist of thin steel rods about 18 in. long, with a small steel ball on either end. When magnetized the N and S poles become concentrated in the steel balls as shown in Fig. 51R.

As used in the Hibbert balance* shown

* Magnetic balance made by W. G. Pye & Co., Cambridge, England.

in Fig. 51S, one magnet is balanced on a special set of scales and another is held tightly in an adjustable clamp stand. If the two adjacent poles, when they are brought together, are alike, the repulsion will throw the one magnet off balance. The weight that must then be added to the left-hand side to restore balance again is a direct

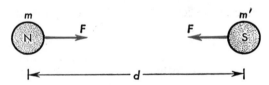

Fig. 51S *The Hibbert magnetic balance.*

measure of the force of repulsion. Carrying out experiments of a similar nature, Coulomb was the first to find that *the force acting between two magnetic poles is inversely proportional to the square of the distance between them.* Having discovered this relation, he compared the pole strengths of different magnets with each other and found that *the force between two poles is proportional to the product of the pole strengths.* Combining these two relations, Coulomb proposed as a general law for magnetic poles,

$$F = \kappa \frac{mm'}{d^2} \qquad (51a)$$

where F is the force, m and m' are the strengths of the poles, and d is the distance between them. In the rationalized mks system used in this text, F is in *newtons*; m and m' are in *ampere meters* (*abbr.* amp-m); and κ, the proportionality constant, is

$$\kappa = 10^{-7} \frac{weber}{ampere\,meter} \qquad (51b)$$

When two magnets are arranged in the configuration shown in Fig. 51T, the two

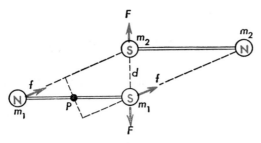

Fig. 51T *Geometry of the forces and torques involved in the Hibbert balance.*

poles nearest each other will exert by far the strongest forces on each other. These forces, represented by F in the diagram, are an *action* and *reaction* pair.

To measure the force F exerted on the lower S pole, the lower magnet is initially balanced carefully on a pivot P at its center of mass. Under these conditions the two attractive forces f, due to the poles of the upper magnet, will cancel out since they exert equal and opposite torques.

If the magnets are long and the distance d relatively small, the force of repulsion between the extreme end poles will be exceedingly small. To a first approximation, this force and the torque it exerts can be neglected.

51.13. Magnetic Induction B. It is quite common practice to refer to the strength or the intensity of a magnetic field as the *magnetic induction*.

The magnetic induction B at any point in space may be defined as the force per

unit *N-pole acting on any pole placed at that point.*

Algebraically,

$$B = \frac{F}{m'} \qquad (51c)$$

Suppose, for example, that when a unit pole of *1 ampere meter* is placed at a given point in space it experiences a force of *5 newtons*. The magnetic induction B at that point is then said to have a magnitude of *5 newtons/ampere meter* (*abbr.* amp-m). If a pole with a strength of m'' ampere meters is placed at this same point where the magnetic induction is known to be B newtons/ampere meter, the force acting on the pole in newtons is

$$F = m''B \qquad (51d)$$

From the above definition that $B = F/m'$, and Coulomb's law, a relation for the magnetic induction at any point near a single pole of strength m may be obtained. When m' is transposed to the left side of Eq.(51a),

$$\frac{F}{m'} = \kappa \frac{m}{d^2}$$

or

$$B = \kappa \frac{m}{d^2} \qquad (51e)$$

where d is the distance from the field producing pole m to the point in question.

While the magnetic induction B, as given by Eq.(51c), is in *newtons/ampere meter*, B will be found by Eq.(51e) to be in *webers/meter²* (*abbr.* w/m²). The two relations are consistent since

$$1 \frac{newton}{ampere\,meter} = 1 \frac{weber}{meter^2} \qquad (51f)$$

The preferred units of B are *webers/meter²*. (See Sec. 53.1 and Eq.(53h).)

The direction of the magnetic field at any point is the direction of the force acting on an N pole placed at that point. This is another way of determining or plotting magnetic lines of force. As illustrated in Fig. 51U, an N pole placed in a position

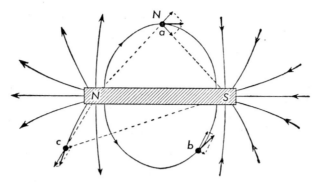

Fig. 51U   *The force acting on a unit N pole placed in a magnetic field gives the magnitude and direction of the magnetic field at that point.*

(a), equidistant from the two poles of the magnet, is repelled by the N pole with the same force that it is attracted by the S pole. The resultant of these two forces is the horizontal force to the right and parallel to the magnet. If an S pole were located at the same point, the resultant force would be just oppositely directed. It is therefore clear why a compass placed at (a) turns parallel to the magnet, and why at other points like (b) it turns in another direction. Forces acting on each pole of the compass needle turn it into the equilibrium positions found and plotted as the magnetic field in Fig. 51I.

Example 1. Calculate the magnetic induction B at a point 8 cm from an N pole of 48 ampere meters.

Solution. By making direct substitutions of the given quantities into Eq.(51e), we obtain

$$B = 10^{-7} \frac{\text{weber}}{\text{ampere meter}} \times \frac{48 \text{ ampere meters}}{64 \times 10^{-4} \text{ meter}^2}$$

$$= 7.5 \times 10^{-4} \frac{\text{weber}}{\text{meter}^2}$$

The direction of B is outward, away from N.

PROBLEMS

1. Two magnetic poles of equal strength are located 2 cm apart. Each exerts a force of 0.004 newton on the other. Calculate the pole strength.

2. Two magnetic S poles of equal strength exert a force of 0.04 newton on each other when they are located 8 cm apart. Find the pole strength. (*Ans.* 50.6 amp-m.)

3. Three N poles of 4 ampere meters each are located at the corners of an equilateral triangle 5 cm on a side. Find the resultant force on each pole.

4. Three S poles of 2 ampere meters each are located at three corners of a right triangle whose sides are 6 cm, 8 cm, and 10 cm, respectively. Find the force in dynes on the pole at the 90° corner. (*Ans.* 12.8 dynes.)

5. Find the magnitude of the magnetic induction at a point (a) 2 cm from an N pole of 4 amp-m, (b) 10 cm from an S pole of 3.2 amp-m, and (c) 1 m from an S pole of 0.8 amp-m.

6. A straight bar magnet has two poles of 40 amp-m each, with centers 8 cm apart. Calculate the magnetic induction at a point in line with the two poles, (a) 3 cm beyond the N pole, and (b) 12 cm beyond the S pole. (*Ans.* (a) 4.11×10^{-3} w/m², directed away from the magnet; (b) 1.78×10^{-4} w/m², directed toward the magnet.

7. A straight bar magnet has two poles of 50 amp-m each, spaced 10 cm apart. Find the magnetic induction at a point in line with the two poles, (a) 5 cm from the S pole, and (b) 10 cm from the N pole.

8. A straight bar magnet has two poles, 20 cm apart, each with a strength of 15 amp-m. Calculate the magnitude of the magnetic in-

duction at a point 12 cm from the N pole and 16 cm from the S pole. (*Ans.* 1.19×10^{-4} w/m².)

9. Two S poles of 16 amp-m and two N poles of 40 amp-m are placed at each of the corners of a square 10 cm on a side. With like poles diagonally opposite each other, what are the forces between (a) one S pole and the other S pole, (b) one N pole and the other N pole, and (c) one N pole and one S pole? What is the resultant force on (d) each S pole, and (e) each N pole?

10. Two N poles of 25 amp-m and two S poles of 15 amp-m are placed at each of the corners of a square 5 cm on a side. With unlike poles diagonally opposite each other, what is the magnitude of the magnetic induction (a) at the center of the square, and (b) at the center of the side between the two S poles? (*Ans.* (a) 4.53×10^{-3} w/m², (b) 1.43×10^{-4} w/m².)

11. A straight bar magnet has two poles, each of 16 amp m and located 10 cm apart. Find the magnitude of the magnetic induction at a point in line with the poles at a distance beyond the N pole of 1, 5, 10, 15, and 20 cm. Plot a graph of B vs x, where x is the distance from the center of the magnet.

12. Solve Prob. 11 if the line along which the chosen field points are located passes through the center of the magnet perpendicular to the magnet axis, and the distances are 0, 5, 10, 15, and 20 cm, as measured outward from the magnet center. (*Ans.* 12.8×10^{-4}, 4.52×10^{-4}, 1.14×10^{-4}, 0.404×10^{-4}, 0.183×10^{-4} w/m².)

13. Find the magnetic induction at a point on one side of the square in Prob. 10, midway between an S and an N pole.

14. Find the force exerted on an S pole of 50 amp-m when it is placed in a field where the magnetic induction is 4.8×10^{-3} w/m². (*Ans.* 0.240 newton.)

15. Calculate the force in dynes exerted on an N pole of 8 amp-m when placed in a field where the magnetic induction is 6.5×10^{-4} w/m².

16. When an N pole of 50 amp-m is placed 5 cm from another pole of unknown strength, it experiences an attractive force of 2 newtons. Find (a) the magnetic induction at the point in question, and (b) the strength of the unknown pole. (*Ans.* (a) 0.040 w/m², (b) 1000 amp-m; S.)

Chapter 52

Effects of Electric Currents

Everyone is more or less familiar with the electrical appliances of the modern household: the electric lights, electric toaster, iron, refrigerator, vacuum cleaner, washing machine, etc. All of these devices depend for their operation upon one or more of four general effects produced by electric currents; these are (1) *the heating effect,* (2) *the magnetic effect,* (3) *the mechanical effect,* and (4) *the chemical effect.* It is the purpose of this chapter to consider the first three of these different phenomena and to take up in some detail the important principles involved.

52.1. Electric Energy. When the householder pays his monthly electricity bill, he pays according to the amount of electric energy consumed. To calculate electric energy, a general formula involving *current, voltage,* and *time* is usually employed. A battery or generator, in supplying current to any electric system, maintains a constant difference of potential between two ends of the circuit.

Consider the two terminals of a battery as shown in Fig. 52A and the mechanical

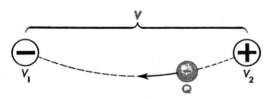

Fig. 52A   *The work done per unit charge in carrying any charge Q from one terminal to the other is called the difference of potential V.*

work that would be required to move a negative charge from the (+) terminal to the (−) terminal. The amount of work done per unit charge in carrying any charge

Q from one terminal to the other is called the *difference of potential.* Symbolically,

$$V = \frac{W}{Q} \qquad (52a)$$

where V is in volts, W in joules, and Q in coulombs.

If, instead of carrying a charge from one terminal to the other and thereby doing work, we connect the two terminals with a conductor, a current I will flow and the battery will be doing work for us in creating heat. By definition, *the current I is defined as the amount of charge Q flowing per second of time.*

$$I = \frac{Q}{t} \qquad (52b)$$

If we solve this equation for Q,

$$Q = It$$

and substitute It for Q in Eq.(52a), we obtain

$$V = \frac{W}{It}$$

Upon transposing, we find

$$\boxed{W = VIt} \qquad (52c)$$

joules = volts × amperes × seconds

If V is in volts, I is in amperes, and t is in seconds, the energy W is in joules. (1 joule = 10^7 ergs.) Since by Ohm's law, $I = V/R$, direct substitution for I or for V gives two other useful forms of the same equation.

$$W = I^2Rt \qquad W = \frac{V^2}{R}t \qquad (52d)$$

52.2. Electric Power. Power is defined in mechanics, as well as in electricity, as the rate at which energy is developed or expended. $P = W/t$. Dividing each of the above energy equations by t, we find that

$$P = I^2R \qquad P = V^2/R$$

and

$$\boxed{P = VI} \qquad (52e)$$

where P is in watts. These are practical equations since with most electrical equipment the *voltage, current,* and *resistance* are usually known from voltmeter and ammeter readings. The last equation is well worth memorizing: *"Power in watts is equal to potential difference in volts times current in amperes."* The other two follow by a direct substitution from Ohm's law.

Energy as expressed in Eq.(52c) is power VI multiplied by the time t. *Power in kilowatts multiplied by the time in hours gives the energy in kilowatt-hours.* The kilowatt-hour is the unit of electric energy by which all electric energy is calculated and paid for (1 kilowatt = 1000 watts). The watt-hour meter placed on the premises of every consumer is a slowly revolving motor, having a low resistance winding which is in series with the line and which therefore conducts the current in the line, and a high resistance winding which is across the line and which therefore conducts a small current proportional to V. The time factor t is accounted for by the automatic recording of the total number of rotations of the armature by a small clocklike mechanism with dials and pointers.

Example 1. Two resistors of 3 ohms and 5 ohms, respectively, are connected in series with a battery of 20-volt terminal voltage (see Fig. 52B). Calculate (a) the electron current through the circuit, (b) the potential difference across each resistor, (c) the power consumed by each resistor, (d) the total energy consumed in 2 hr of operation, and (e) the total cost of operation for 40 hr at 3 cents per kw-hr.

Solution. Connected in series, the two resistors $R_1 = 3$ ohm and $R_2 = 5$ ohm have a total resistance of $R = 8$ ohm.

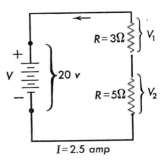

Fig. 52B *The power consumed by any resistance is given by the voltage across it multiplied by the current.*

(a) If we apply Ohm's law, the electron current through the circuit is found to be

$$I = V/R = 20/8 = 2.5 \text{ amp}$$

(b) The drop in potential across any resistor is given by IR.

$$V_1 = I_1R_1 = 2.5 \times 3 = 7.5 \text{ volts}$$
$$V_2 = I_2R_2 = 2.5 \times 5 = 12.5 \text{ volts}$$

(c) The power consumed is given by VI, the potential drop across each resistor multiplied by the electron current through it.

$$P_1 = V_1I = 7.5 \times 2.5 = 18.75 \text{ watts}$$
$$P_2 = V_2I = 12.5 \times 2.5 = 31.25 \text{ watts}$$

(d) The power supplied by the battery is VI, the voltage across its terminals multiplied by the total electron current in amperes.

$$P = VI = 20 \times 2.5 = 50 \text{ watts}$$

in agreement with the sum of the two values in (c).

To find the energy, multiply by the time in seconds.

$$W = 50 \text{ watts} \times 7200 \text{ sec} = 360,000 \text{ joules}$$

(e) The power 50 watts should next be expressed in kilowatts and multiplied by the time in hours, to give

$$W = 0.05 \text{ kw} \times 40 \text{ hr} = 2 \text{ kw-hr}$$

At 3 cents per kw-hr, the total cost will be 6 cents.

52.3. The Heating Effect of an Electric Current. When an electron current is sent through a wire, heat is generated and the temperature of the wire rises. If the current is increased, the rate at which heat is generated increases rapidly until the wire itself glows a deep red. A still further increase in current will heat the wire to a yellow or white heat. Beyond this point, if it has not already done so, the wire will reach a temperature where it will melt and become a liquid.

Whether a wire is only warmed by an electron current or heated to incandescence depends upon a number of factors, the two principal ones being the current and the resistance. Experiment shows that the energy expended in a wire is given by Eq.(52c).

$$W = VIt$$

where V is in volts, I is in amperes, and t is in seconds. Electrical energy, like mechanical energy, is measured in joules. Heat energy is measured in calories.

By the law of conservation of energy, each calorie of heat produced will require the expenditure of a definite amount of electrical energy. As an equation we can therefore write

$$W \propto H$$

or

$$W = JH \qquad (52f)$$

where J is a proportionality constant and, as in mechanics, is found to have the value

$$J = 4.18 \frac{\text{joules}}{\text{calorie}} \qquad (52g)$$

If we solve Eq.(52f) for H, we obtain

$$H = \frac{1}{J} W$$

and substituting W from Eq.(52c),

$$H = \frac{1}{J} VIt$$

or

$$H = 0.24 \; VIt$$

If Ohm's law is introduced in the form $V = IR$, we can substitute IR for V and obtain

$$\boxed{H = 0.24 \; I^2Rt} \qquad (52h)$$

This is known as *Joule's law*.

Example 2. If the heating element of an electric toaster has a resistance of 22 ohms and is connected to an ordinary house lighting circuit of 110 volts, how much heat will be generated in 1 min?

Solution. From Ohm's law, $I = V/R$, the electron current is first calculated.

$$I = 110/22 = 5 \text{ amp}$$

We can now make use of Joule's law by substituting in Eq.(52h).

$$\text{heat} = 0.24 \times (5)^2 \times 22 \times 60 = 7920 \text{ calories}$$

For some electric appliances, heating is a desired effect, while in others it is a source of trouble and even danger. In an electric iron, hot plate, or toaster, for example, heat is the main objective of the device. In such appliances a relatively large current of several amperes is sent through a coil or element of special wire having a resistance of several ohms. As a rule the wire is of some alloy, such as nichrome, and of such a size that the heat developed will not raise the temperature higher than red hot. Diagrams of typical heating elements used in three different household appliances are shown in Fig 52C.

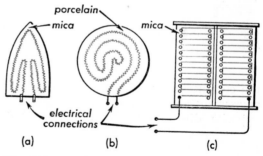

porcelain
mica   *mica*

electrical connections

(a)   (b)   (c)

Fig. 52C *Diagrams of the heating elements of various electrical appliances found in many modern homes: (a) electric iron, (b) electric stove, and (c) electric toaster.*

52.4. Magnetic Effect, Oersted's Experiment. The first discovery of any connection between electricity and magnetism was made by Oersted * in 1820. Often, during

* Hans Christian Oersted (1777-1851), Danish scientist. Born the son of an apothecary, Oersted spent part of his boyhood teaching himself arithmetic. At the age of 12, he assisted his father in

his lectures at the University of Copenhagen, Oersted had demonstrated the nonexistence of a connection between electricity and magnetism. His usual procedure was to place a current-carrying wire at right angles to, and directly over, a compass needle to show that there was no effect of one on the other. On one occasion, at the end of his lecture, when several members of the audience came up to meet him at the lecture room desk, he placed the wire parallel to the compass needle and, not the least expecting it, saw the needle move to one side (see Fig. 52D). Upon his reversing

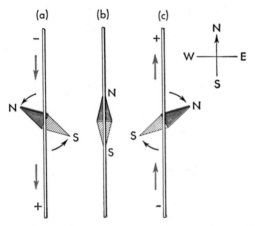

Fig. 52D *Diagram of Oersted's experiment illustrating the effect of an electron current upon a compass needle.*

the current in the wire, the needle, to his amazement and perplexity, deviated in the opposite direction. Thus this great discovery was made quite by accident, but, as Lagrange once said of Newton on a similar occasion, "such accidents come only to those who deserve them."

his shop and there became interested in chemistry. Passing the entrance examinations at the University of Copenhagen at the age of 17, he entered the medical school, and graduated six years later with his doctorate in medicine. At age 29 he returned to the university, this time as professor of physics. It was at one of his demonstration lectures on chemistry and metaphysics that he discovered the magnetic effect bearing his name. The discovery not only brought him many endowments and prizes, but also made him one of the most eminent personalities in his own country.

52.5. The Left-Hand Rule. Oersted's experiment is interpreted as demonstrating that *around every wire carrying an electric current there is a magnetic field.* The direction of this field at every point, like that around a bar magnet, can be mapped by means of a small compass or by iron filings. If a wire is mounted vertically through a hole in a plate of glass or other suitable nonconductor, and then iron filings are sprinkled on the plate, there will be a lining-up of the filings parallel to the magnetic field. The result shows that the magnetic lines of force or *lines of induction* are concentric circles whose planes are at right angles to the current. This is illustrated by the circles in Fig. 52E.

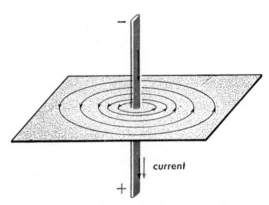

Fig. 52E *Experiment demonstrating the magnetic field about a straight wire carrying an electron current.*

The left-hand rule used in electromagnetism can always be relied upon to give the direction of the magnetic field due to an electron current in a wire. Derived from experiment, the rule states:

If the current-carrying wire were to be grasped with the left hand, the thumb pointing in the direction of the electron current, (−) to (+), the fingers will point in the direction of the magnetic induction.

In other books, using the older convention that current in a wire is from + to −, the *right-hand rule* is used to give the magnetic field the same direction that it has here.

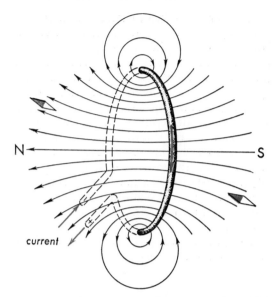

current

Fig. 52F *Diagram of the magnetic field through and around a single loop of wire carrying an electron current.*

52.6. Magnetic Properties of a Solenoid.

Not long after the announcement of Oersted's discovery of the magnetic effect of a current-carrying wire, Ampère found that a loop or coil of wire acted as a magnet. This is illustrated by a single loop of wire in Fig. 52F, and by a coil of several turns of wire in Fig. 52G. A coil of wire of this kind is sometimes referred to as *solenoid*, or as a *helix*. In either case, the magnetic lines of force are such that one side or end of the coil acts like an *N* magnetic pole

and the other side or end like an *S* magnetic pole.

At all points in the region around a coil of wire carrying a current, the direction of the magnetic field, as shown by a compass, can be predicted by the left-hand rule. Inside each loop or turn of wire, the lines point in one direction, whereas outside they are oppositely directed.

Outside the coil, the lines go from *N* to *S* in quite the same way they do about a permanent bar magnet, whereas inside they go from *S* to *N*.

Not only does one coil of wire act like a magnet but two coils may be used to demonstrate the repulsion and attraction of like and unlike poles.

Another left-hand rule which must not be confused with the one in the preceding section, but which follows directly from it, is the following: *If the solenoid were to be grasped with the fingers pointing in the direction of the electron current, around the coil from (−) to (+), the thumb would point in the direction of the internal field as well as the N pole.*

52.7. The Electromagnet.

Five years after Oersted's discovery and Ampère's demonstration of the magnetic properties of a solenoid, William Sturgeon filled the center of a coil of wire with soft iron and thereby produced a powerful magnet. This is illustrated in Fig. 52H. As long as the electron current continues to flow, the addition of the iron core produces a magnet hundreds

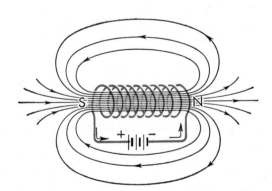

Fig. 52G *Diagram of the magnetic field around a solenoid carrying an electron current.*

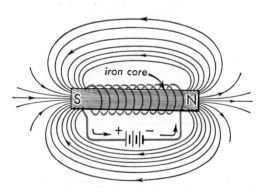

Fig. 52H *Diagram of an electromagnet and the field surrounding it when a current flows through the coil.*

of times stronger than does the solenoid alone. A nearby compass needle, if set oscillating, will demonstrate this effect by vibrating quickly with the iron core in place, and slowly with it removed.

Again, with the iron core in the solenoid, a nearby rod of soft iron, magnetized by induction as shown in Fig. 51P, will attract iron filings much more strongly than when the iron core is removed.

52.8. Mechanical Effects of Electric Currents. In 1821, Michael Faraday discovered that, when a wire carrying a current is placed in the field of a magnet, a mechanical force is exerted on the wire. This is the principle upon which the modern electric motor is based.

A demonstration of Faraday's discovery is shown in Fig. 52I, where a flexible cop-

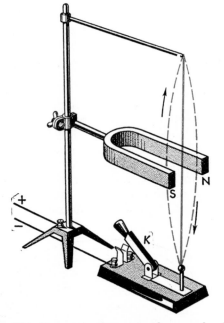

Fig. 52I *Demonstration of the mechanical effect of an electron current in a magnetic field.*

per wire about one meter long is suspended from a support. A U-shaped magnet straddles the wire somewhere near the middle.

Upon closing the switch K, an electron current flows up through the wire and the wire moves to the left. If the battery con-

nections are reversed, thereby reversing the electron current, the deflection of the wire will be to the right.

If the magnet is turned over, thereby interchanging N and S poles, the deflection of the wire will again reverse. In other words, the reversing of either the magnetic field or the direction of the electron current will reverse the direction of the force acting on the wire. The reversal of both will make it the same.

The existence of a mechanical force may be demonstrated by another simple experiment as shown in Fig. 52J. Two parallel

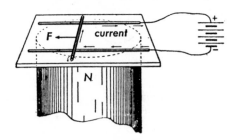

Fig. 52J *An experimental arrangement for demonstrating that a wire carrying a current in a magnetic field experiences a force tending to move it across the field at right angles to the current, and at right angles to the field.*

brass bars fastened to a board are placed over the N pole of a magnet and then connected to a battery. When a round metal rod is laid across the bars, thus allowing an electron current to flow in the direction shown, the rod experiences a force and rolls to the left. A reversal of either the electron current or the polarity of the magnet will cause the rod to roll to the right. A reversal of both will cause it to roll to the left.

It should be emphasized here that this force is exerted on the electrons, the moving charges in the wire, and that they, being confined to the wire, cause it to move. An electron at rest in a magnetic field experiences no force from the magnet. An electron moving across magnetic lines of force experiences a force at right angles to both the field and the direction of motion.

52.9. Interaction Between Magnetic Fields. To gain some understanding of this

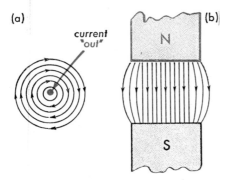

Fig. 52K *Magnetic fields (a) due to an electron current and (b) due to magnetic poles.*

mysterious invisible force acting on a current-carrying wire in a magnetic field, consider the diagrams in Fig. 52K.

The circles in diagram (a) represent the circular magnetic lines of force around a straight wire carrying a current. The directions of the arrows are given by the left-hand rule, shown here for an electron current up and out of the page.

The lines of force in diagram (b) represent the magnetic field between two opposite poles of a magnet.

If we now place the current-carrying wire between the poles of the magnet, the two fields interact on each other. The interaction is such that a newly formed field like that shown at the right in Fig. 52L is obtained. Imagining that the magnetic lines of force act like stretched rubber bands, one can predict from this diagram that the wire should experience a force F to the left.

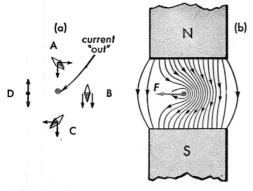

Fig. 52L *Diagrams of two interacting magnetic fields.*

To understand how such a field can arise out of two interacting symmetrical fields, it should be remembered that the field direction at any point is that taken by a small magnetic dipole placed there. Consider as examples the points A, B, C, and D of diagram (a). At A the field due to the current in the wire is to the right, and that due to the magnet poles is down. If the two fields exert equal torques on the tiny compass needle, it will point along a direction halfway between the two.

At B the field due to the wire is down, and so is the field due to the magnet. A compass at this point would point down. At C the fields are again at right angles, and the compass points down and to the left. At D the fields are oppositely directed and, if they are equal in magnitude, cancel each other's effect. This process repeated for many other points will lead to the field shown in diagram (b).

It is important to note that the direction of the current I in the wire, the direction of the magnetic field B at the wire due to the magnet, and the direction of the force F acting on the wire are all at right angles to each other. Furthermore, the direction of the force F can be quickly ascertained by applying the left-hand rule to the electron current in the wire. If the wire were to be grasped with the left hand, the thumb pointing in the direction of the electron current (− to +), the force is toward the weakened field, that is, toward the region where the fingers are oppositely directed to the field of the magnet.

52.10. The Electric Motor. An electric motor is a device by which electrical energy in the form an an electron current is transformed into mechanical energy. The principle of the motor is illustrated in Fig. 52M. A wire carrying an electron current is bent into a loop and placed between two magnetic poles as shown in Fig. 52N. In this horizontal position, the resultant magnetic field is warped, which forces one wire down and the other up. Mounted free to turn about an axis, the loop rotates until it is in a vertical plane. At this point, the current in the loop is reversed in direction by

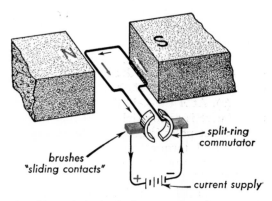

Fig. 52M *Principal elements for demonstrating the principles of an electric motor.*

means of *sliding contacts* and a *split ring commutator.* The reversal of the electron current reverses the forces so that the side of the loop which was previously pushed up is now pushed down, and the side previously pushed down is now pushed up. The loop therefore rotates through half a turn more, where the current again reverses. A repetition of this reversing process at each half turn gives rise to a continuous rotation, the left side of the coil or loop always moving down and the right side always moving up.

52.11. Ammeters and Voltmeters. Electrical instruments designed to measure an electric current are called *ammeters,* and those designed to measure potential difference are called *voltmeters.* The principle upon which both of these devices operate is essentially the same as that of the electric motor as shown in Fig. 52M. They differ

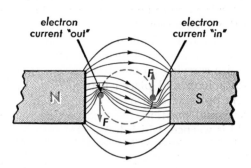

Fig. 52N *Magnetic field lines in an electric motor with two poles.*

from the motor, however, in the delicateness of their construction and the restrained motion of the rotating armature.

A coil of fine copper wire is so mounted between the two poles of a permanent magnet that its rotation, as shown in Fig. 52O, is restrained by a hairspring. The

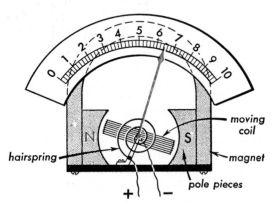

Fig. 52O *Diagram of the essential parts of an ammeter or voltmeter.*

farther the coil is turned from its equilibrium or zero position, the greater is the restoring force. To this coil is fastened a long pointer, at the end of which is a fixed scale reading amperes if it is an ammeter, or volts if it is a voltmeter. Upon increasing the current through the moving coil of an ammeter or voltmeter, the resultant magnetic field between the coil and the magnet is distorted more and more. The resulting increase in force therefore turns the coil through a greater and greater angle, reaching a point where it is just balanced by the restoring force of the hairspring.

Photographs of two small panel instruments are shown in Fig. 52P. The two connections, necessary in each instrument, are on the back and are not shown. On each instrument they lead to the moving coil by means of flexible connections near or through the armature pivots.

Whenever an ammeter or voltmeter is connected to a circuit to measure electron current or potential difference, the ammeter must be connected in series and the voltmeter in parallel. As illustrated in Fig. 52Q, the ammeter is so connected that all

Fig. 52P *Photographs of the front face of a typical voltmeter and ammeter. The two electrical connections to each of these panel-type instruments are on the back and are not shown.* (Courtesy, General Electric Co.)

of the electron current passes through it. To prevent a change in the electron current when such an insertion is made, all ammeters must have a low resistance. Most

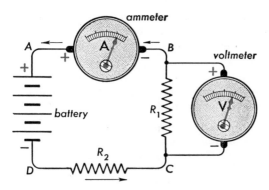

Fig. 52Q *Circuit diagram showing the connections for an ammeter and voltmeter.*

ammeters therefore have a low resistance wire, called a *shunt,* connected across the armature coil.

A voltmeter, on the other hand, is con-nected across that part of the circuit for which a measurement of the potential difference is required. If the potential difference between the ends of the resistance R_1 is wanted, the voltmeter is connected as shown. If the potential difference across R_2 is desired, the voltmeter connections are made at C and D, whereas, if the potential difference maintained by the battery is desired, the connections are made at A and D. In order that the connection of a voltmeter to a circuit does not change the electron current in the circuit, the voltmeter must have a high resistance. If the armature coil does not have a large resistance of its own, additional resistance is added in series.

Very delicate ammeters are often used for measuring very small currents. A meter whose scale is calibrated to read thousandths of an ampere is called a *milliammeter.* One whose scale is calibrated in millionths of an ampere is called a *microammeter* or *galvanometer.*

PROBLEMS

1. Two resistors of 4 ohm and 12 ohm, respectively, are connected in parallel, and then to a 120-volt line. Find (a) the electron current through each resistor, (b) the power consumed by each resistor, (c) the energy consumed by each resistor in 10 min, and (d) the total cost of operation for 3 hr at 1½ cents per kw-hr.

2. During a one-month period, an electric refrigerator, connected to the ordinary house lighting circuit of 120 volts, ran for an accumulated time of 180 hr. (a) If the electron current drawn is 3.5 amp, what is the total amount of energy consumed? (b) At the rate of 2 cents per kw-hr what was the total cost of running? (*Ans.* (a) 2.72×10^8 joules, (b) $1.51.)

3. A television receiver draws 2.4 amp from

the 110-volt line in a house wiring system. Find the total cost of running a total time of 100 hr at the rate of 1.8 cents per kw-hr.

4. Three resistors of 8, 12, and 20 ohm, respectively, are connected in series to a 120-volt line. Calculate (a) the electron current through the circuit, (b) the power consumed by each resistor, (c) the total energy consumed by each resistor in 10 min, and (d) the cost of operation for 10 h as 1.25 cents per Kw-hr. (*Ans.* (a) 2 amp, (b) 72, 108, 180 watts, (c) 43,200, 64,800, 108,000 joules, (d) 4.5 cents.)

5. An electric toaster draws a current of 4 amp when connected to the house-lighting circuit of 120 volts. How many calories of heat are produced in 1 min?

6. The heating element of an electric heater draws a current of 10 amp when connected to 110 volts. How many calories of heat are produced in 1 hr? (*Ans.* 950,000 cal.)

7. An electric toaster with a resistance of 25 ohm draws a current of 5 amp when connected to a house-lighting circuit. If it takes 2 min running to make dark toast, how many calories are required?

8. The heating element of an electric stove connected to a 220-volt line draws an electron current of 5 amp. Find the amount of heat produced in 10 min. (*Ans.* 158,000 cal.)

9. An electric iron having a resistance of 15 ohm is connected to a 110-volt supply. Find the heat developed in 5 min.

10. Calculate the heat developed by an electric soldering iron in 10 min if it draws 3.5 amp on a 120-volt line. (*Ans.* 60,500 cal.)

11. A teakettle containing 1 gallon of water (3785 cm³) at a temperature of 10°C is heated on an electric stove. If the heating element draws an electron current of 8 amp from a 220-volt line, and one-half of the heat generated goes to heat the water, how long will it take for the water to reach the boiling point?

12. An electric coffee pot containing 1000 cm³ of water at 15°C is connected to a 110-volt line. If the electron current drawn is 4.5 amp and 65% of the heat developed goes into the water, how hot will the water be in 8 min? (*Ans.* 52.1°C.)

13. Three resistors, 5 Ω, 8 Ω, and 12 Ω, respectively, are connected in series to a battery. If

these resistors are immersed in a glass containing 500 cm³ of water and a current of 5 amp sent through them, how long will it take to raise the water from 25°C to the boiling point of 100°C?

14. An electric iron having a resistance of 18 ohm is connected to a 120-volt supply. Find the heat developed in 10 min. (*Ans.* 115,000 cal.)

15. Calculate the heat developed by a 200-watt electric soldering iron in 10 min.

16. A boiler containing 5 gallons of water (3875 cm³/gal) at a temperature of 25°C is heated on an electric stove. If the heating element draws an electron current of 10 amp from a 220-volt line, and 70% of the heat generated goes to heat the water, how long will it take for the water to reach the boiling point? (*Ans.* 6 min 33 sec.)

17. An electric coffee pot containing 1000 cm³ of water at 15°C is connected to a 110-volt line. If the electron current drawn is 4.5 amp and 65% of the heat developed goes into the water, how hot will the water be in 8 min?

18. The heating element of an electric stove when connected to a 110-volt line draws an electron current of 12 amp. Find the amount of heat produced in 30 min. (*Ans.* 5.72 × 10⁵ cal.)

19. A voltmeter having a resistance of 100 Ω shows a full scale reading when 5 volts is applied to its terminals. What resistance connected to this instrument will give it a full scale reading when connected to 120 volts?

20. A voltmeter with a resistance of 200 Ω shows a full scale reading when 1 volt is applied to its terminals. What resistance connected to this instrument will give it a full scale reading of (a) 5 volts, (b) 50 volts, and (c) 150 volts? (*Ans.* 800 Ω, 9800 Ω, 29,800 Ω.)

21. A voltmeter with a resistance of 5000 Ω shows a full scale reading at 25 volts. What resistance should be connected to this instrument to have it give a full scale reading of 500 volts?

22. If the voltmeter in Prob. 19 is used as a milliammeter, what current will give a full scale deflection? (*Ans.* 0.005 amp.)

23. What shunt resistance across the voltmeter in Prob. 21 will make it into an ammeter with a full scale deflection for 5 amp?

24. What shunt resistance across the voltmeter in Prob. 20 will make it into an ammeter with a full scale deflection for 5 amp? (*Ans.* 0.200 Ω.)

25. What shunt resistance across the voltmeter in Prob. 21 will make it into an ammeter with a full scale deflection of 25 amp?

26. A voltmeter having a resistance of 500 ohm shows a full scale reading when an electron current of 10 milliamperes flows through it. What shunt resistance across this instrument will enable it to be used as an ammeter indicating 5 amp on full scale deflection? (*Ans.* 1.00 Ω.)

27. A voltmeter having a resistance of 800 ohm shows a full scale reading at 120 volts. What resistance should be connected to this instrument to have it give a full scale reading of 600 volts?

28. A voltmeter having a resistance of 500 ohm shows a full scale reading when an electron current of 10 milliamperes flows through it. What shunt resistance across this instrument will enable it to be used as an ammeter indicating 15 amp on full scale deflection? (*Ans.* 0.333 ohm.)

29. What shunt resistance across the voltmeter in Prob. 21 will make an ammeter of it with a full scale deflection reading 10 amp?

Chapter 53

Magnetic Induction

We have seen in the preceding lessons how an electron current gives rise to a magnetic field surrounding the conductor, and also how a current-carrying wire placed in a magnetic field experiences an unbalanced force tending to move it across the field. The mathematical formulation of the principles involved in these magnetic and mechanical effects depends primarily upon a quantitative account of the magnetic field strength.

The strength of the magnetic field at any point in and around any electrical equipment is represented by the letter B and is called the *magnetic induction*. As a simple illustration, the magnetic induction around a long, straight wire is everywhere perpendicular to the wire, and the magnetic lines of force representing B are drawn as concentric circles as shown in Fig. 53A. While the direction of B, as represented by the arrowheads, is given by the left-hand rule,

the magnitude of B at any point is given by *Ampère's theorem,* a fundamental principle connecting electric currents with the magnetic fields they produce.

53.1. Ampère's Theorem. Consider a wire of any shape carrying an electron current. The current in each small part of the wire contributes to the magnetic induction

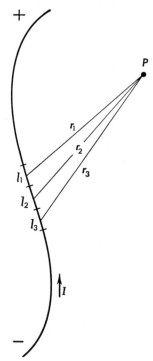

Fig. 53B *The magnetic induction at a point P is due to all current elements of the conductor.*

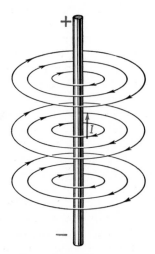

Fig. 53A *The magnetic field around a long, straight conductor.*

at all points around the wire. In Fig. 53B, for example, the small element of wire of length l_1 at a distance r_1 from any chosen point P produces its own magnetic induction contribution at P which, by the left-hand rule for electron currents, is "out" from the page. Similarly, the small element of wire l_2, at a distance r_2 from the same point P, produces another contribution at P which is out from the page. The resultant magnetic induction at P is, therefore, the vector sum of the contributions from all elements of the wire.

The magnitude of the magnetic induction due to a small current element was first proposed by Biot and Savart in 1820, and later formulated by Ampère, to be given by

$$B = \kappa \frac{Il \sin \theta}{r^2} \qquad (53a)$$

where, as shown in Fig. 53C, B is the magnetic induction at a point P, l is the length

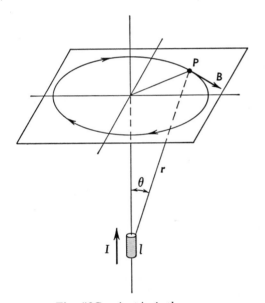

Fig. 53C *Ampère's theorem.*

of a current element of the wire, r is the distance from l to P, θ is the angle between r and l, and κ is a proportionality constant. This equation is usually called *Ampère's theorem.*

The magnitude of the constant κ, like the constant k in Coulomb's law, depends on the choice of units for the other factors. In applying Ampère's theorem to straight wires and circular coils of various kinds,

the factor 4π enters so frequently into the formulas that it is convenient to express κ in terms of another constant μ_0, as follows,

$$\kappa = \frac{\mu_0}{4\pi}$$

This is analogous to replacing k in Coulomb's law for electric charges by $\frac{1}{4\pi\epsilon_0}$. See Eq.(47f).

Ampère's theorem, therefore, becomes

$$B = \frac{\mu_0}{4\pi} \cdot \frac{Il \sin \theta}{r^2} \qquad (53b)$$

If I is in amperes, and r and l are in meters, B is in webers/meter^2 and the constant

$$\mu_0 = 4\pi\kappa = 12.57 \times 10^{-7}$$
$$\text{webers/ampere meter} \qquad (53c)$$

or

$$\kappa = \mu_0 = 10^{-7} \text{ webers/ampere meter} \qquad (53d)$$

From a study of Eq.(53a) and Fig. 53C, it seems reasonable that doubling the electron current I, or doubling the length of the element l, would double the magnetic induction. It is also reasonable by comparison with the field around magnetic poles, and Coulomb's law, that the magnetic induction should vary inversely as the square of the distance r. That the magnetic induction varies as $\sin \theta$, however, was first proved experimentally by Ampère.

To obtain the resultant value of B at any specified point near a current-carrying wire, the contributions from all small elements l of the entire circuit must be added together. To do this, a summation process, the *integral calculus*, is usually required. With the calculus, many different calculations are readily carried out, but without it they are, except for the following simple case, difficult.

53.2. The Magnetic Induction at the Center of a Circular Turn.
Consider a circular loop of wire, as shown in Fig. 53D, where each small element l of the wire is perpendicular to the radial distance r, and equidistant from the center P. Since $\theta =$

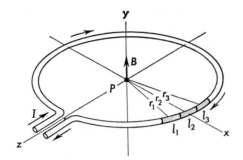

Fig. 53D *Ampère's theorem applied to a single loop of wire.*

90°, and $\sin \theta = 1$, Eq.(53b) becomes the same for each element l_1.

$$B_1 = \frac{\mu_0}{4\pi} \cdot \frac{Il_1}{r_1^2}, \qquad B_2 = \frac{\mu_0}{4\pi} \cdot \frac{Il_2}{r_2^2}$$

$$B_3 = \frac{\mu_0}{4\pi} \cdot \frac{Il_3}{r_3^2}, \text{ etc.}$$

If we sum up the mutually parallel contributions from all elements of the wire, the resultant magnitude of B becomes

$$B = \frac{\mu_0}{4\pi} \left(\frac{Il_1}{r^2} + \frac{Il_2}{r^2} + \frac{Il_3}{r^2} + \cdots \right)$$

or $\qquad B = \frac{\mu_0 I}{4\pi r^2} (l_1 + l_2 + l_3 + \cdots)$

Since the sum $l_1 + l_2 + l_3 + \ldots$ must equal the circumference of the wire loop, the above parenthesis can be replaced by $2\pi r$.

$$\boxed{B = \mu_0 \frac{I}{2r}} \qquad (53e)$$

for single turn

where $\mu_0 = 12.57 \times 10^{-7}$ weber/ampere meter, I is in amperes, r is in meters, and B is in webers/meter². Note that B is the magnetic induction at the center only and that its direction is perpendicular to the plane of the loop. For the general shape of the field, see Fig. 52F.

If, instead of a single loop of wire, the coil has a number of turns, N, each turn contributes the same field at the center, and the resultant magnetic induction will be given by

$$\boxed{B = \mu_0 \frac{NI}{2r}} \qquad (53f)$$

for flat coil

where N is the number of turns.

53.3. The Magnetic Induction Inside a Solenoid. The general shape of the field in a solenoid is shown in Figs. 52G and 53E.

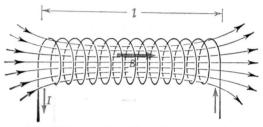

Fig. 53E *A solenoid of N turns of wire.*

When Ampère's theorem is applied to such a coil, the magnetic induction B at the center is found to be given by

$$\boxed{B = \mu_0 \frac{NI}{l}} \qquad (53g)$$

for solenoid

where l is the length of the solenoid in meters, N is the number of turns, I is the electron current in amperes, and B is the magnetic induction in webers/meter². If the solenoid is long compared to its diameter, the magnetic induction along the center axis will be fairly uniform.

In the *cgs* system, magnetic induction is measured in *maxwells/centimeter²*, or *gauss*.

$$1 \text{ weber/meter}^2 = 10^4 \text{ maxwells/cm}^2$$
$$= 10^4 \text{ gauss} \qquad (53h)$$

53.4. Field near a Straight Conductor. The magnetic induction around a straight wire is shown in Fig. 52E to be everywhere perpendicular to the wire, and the lines of force to be concentric circles. The magnitude of the induction at any point P, close to a long, straight wire, is found from Ampère's theorem to be given by

$$B = \mu_0 \frac{I}{2\pi r} \tag{53i}$$

for straight wire

where, as shown in Fig. 53F, r is the per-pendicular distance to the point P in meters, and I is the electron current in amperes.

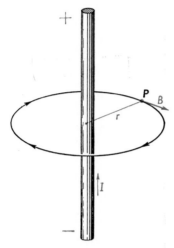

Fig. 53F *Magnetic induction* B *around a straight conductor carrying an electron current.*

53.5. Force on a Moving Charge.

In Sec. 52.8 it was shown how a current-carrying wire, when placed in a magnetic field, ex-periences a mechanical force tending to move it across the field. This mechanical force is due directly to the force exerted by the magnetic induction upon the individ-

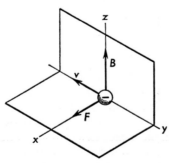

Fig. 53G *Force on a negative charge moving across a magnetic field.*

ual moving electrons within the conductor. (See Fig. 53G.)

A charge Q, moving with a velocity v, through a magnetic field at right angles to B, experiences a force F given by

$$F = QvB \tag{53j}$$

In the *mks* system, F is in *newtons*, B is in *webers/meter²*, v is in *meters/sec*, and Q is in *coulombs*. The vectors B, v, and F are all mutually perpendicular to each other.

If the velocity vector v makes an angle θ with B, as indicated in Fig. 53H, the mag-

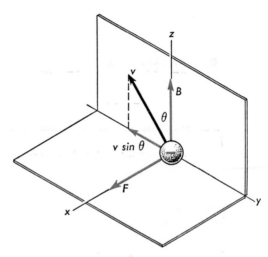

Fig. 53H *Force on a negative charge moving at an angle to a magnetic field.*

nitude of the force F is proportional to the component of the velocity perpendicular to B.

$$F = QvB \sin \theta \tag{53k}$$

If the charge Q in Fig. 53H is positive, the force F is opposite in direction to the one shown. When a charged particle moves parallel to the field, that is, along the mag-netic lines, $\sin \theta = 0$, there is no force.

53.6. Force on a Current-Carrying Wire.

To find the force on a current-carrying wire in a magnetic field we make use of the above Eq.(53j), $F = QvB$. (See Fig. 53I.) A single moving charge Q constitutes a cur-rent $I = Q/t$. Moving with a velocity v it will, in a time t, travel a distance $l = vt$.

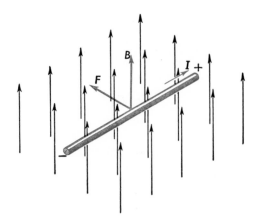

Fig. 53I *The force on a current-carrying wire in a magnetic field.*

Substituting for Q and v in Eq.(53j), we obtain

$$F = It \times \frac{l}{t} \times B \qquad \text{or} \qquad F = IlB \quad (53l)$$

In the *mks* system, F is in *newtons*, B is in *webers/meter²*, I is in *amperes*, and l is in *meters*. In the *cgs* system, F is in *dynes*, B is in *maxwells/cm²*, I is in *abamperes*, and l is in *cm*. 1 *abampere* = 10 *amperes*, and 1 *maxwell/cm² = 1 gauss*.

Like a moving charge in Fig. 53H, a current-carrying wire that makes an angle θ with the field experiences a force proportional to $\sin \theta$.

$$F = IlB \sin \theta \qquad (53m)$$

Example. A wire 40 cm long and carrying an electron current of 2.5 amperes is located in a uniform magnetic field in which $B = 10^{-2}$ weber/meter². Calculate the force on the wire when it makes an angle of 60° with the field direction.

Solution. Since θ is measured from the direction of B, $\theta = 60°$, and substitution in Eq.(53m) gives

$F = 10^{-2} \times 2.5 \times 0.40 \times 0.866$
$\qquad = 8.66 \times 10^{-3}$ newton

53.7. Total Magnetic Flux and Flux Density. In Chap. 51 the magnetic field over a region of space is graphically represented by what are called *lines of force*. In order to specify the *strength* or *intensity* of

a magnetic field at any point in space, the vector quantity, called *magnetic induction B*, is there defined. (See Sec. 51.13.) Since lines of force are frequently used as graphical representations of the variations in the magnetic induction from point to point, they are also called *lines of induction*.

The direction of the magnetic induction B at any point is tangent to the line of induction passing through that point, and its magnitude is given by the number of lines per unit area. The unit area is so chosen that it includes the point in question and is everywhere perpendicular to all lines passing through it.

In the *mks* system, a line of induction is called a *weber*, while in the *cgs* system a line of induction is called a *maxwell*.

The total number of lines of induction passing through a surface is called the magnetic flux and is represented by ϕ. In a region where the field is uniform and the surface area A is normal to the lines of induction,

$$\phi = BA \qquad (53n)$$

53.8. Magnetic Intensity and Permeability. Consider a long solenoid bent into the form of a ring. Such a coil with closely spaced windings is often called a Rowland ring, after H. A. Rowland who first made use of it in his work on electricity and magnetism. When an electron current is sent through a Rowland ring, the magnetic lines of induction B are continuous, and confined entirely within the space enclosed by the winding. If l is the circumference of the ring, the magnetic induction inside is given by Eq.(53g):

$$B_0 = \mu_0 \frac{NI}{l} \qquad (53o)$$

When as in Fig. 53J the same wire is wound on a ring of ferromagnetic material like iron, the internal field is greatly increased. (See Fig. 52H.) This large increase in B, over and above the field there previously, is to be ascribed to an additional field B_1 set up by the thousands of tiny elementary magnets that turn to line up with the magnetizing field B_0.

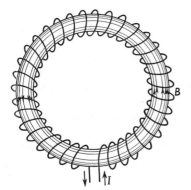

Fig. 53J *Toroidal solenoid, or "Rowland ring."*

$$B = \mu_0 \frac{NI}{l} + \chi \frac{NI}{l} = (\mu_0 + \chi) \frac{NI}{l}$$

Here we introduce and define the *magnetic intensity* H as

$$H = \frac{NI}{l} \qquad (53q)$$

and the *permeability* as

$$\mu = (\mu_0 + \chi)$$

Finally we may write,

$$\boxed{B = \mu H} \qquad (53r)$$

or

$$\mu = \frac{B}{H}$$

It is now known that the magnetic properties of these tiny magnets are in reality due to the spinning of electrons in the iron atoms themselves. Furthermore, the field produced by these spinning negative charges is similar to the field produced by a flow of electrons in a coil of wire. Since the field B_1, set up by the elementary magnets, is proportional to the magnetizing field, we may write,

$$B_1 = \chi \frac{NI}{l} \qquad (53p)$$

The proportionality constant χ is called the *magnetic susceptibility.*

The resultant *flux density, B,* is therefore the sum of the two fields B_0 and B_1.

The permeability of iron, or any other ferromagnetic material, does not have a fixed value, but varies with different specimens and with the magnetic intensity H. For a vacuum, and practically so for air, χ in Eq.(53p) is 0, and $\mu = \mu_0$. For iron, on the other hand, μ may go as high as 7×10^{-3} webers/ampere-meter, and permalloy (Ni 78.5%, Fe 21.5%) as high as 7×10^{-2} w/amp-m.

Fig. 53K shows a typical magnetization curve for silicon steel, a relatively common material used in motors, transformers, and other electrical equipment. As characteristic of all magnetic substances, the curve rises

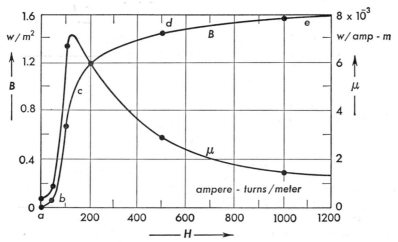

Fig. 53K *Typical magnetization and permeability curves. (For silicon steel.)*

slowly at first (*a* to *b*), then rapidly and uniformly (*b* to *c*), and finally turns over and flattens out (*d* to *e*). The flattened section represents a saturation condition in which B rises very little as H is increased. In other words, when the tiny elementary magnets are all lined up, B increases only by the amount H contributes by the electron current in the winding.

A table of the important magnetic properties of silicon steel follows.

53.9. Magnetic Moments. When a bar magnet is located in a uniform magnetic field as shown in Fig. 53L, it is acted upon by a torque which tends to line it up with the field. The force acting on each pole is given by Eq.(51d):

$$F = mB \qquad (53s)$$

where m is the pole strength in *ampere meters*. Assuming the distance between pole centers to be l, each of these oppositely di-

TABLE 53A. MAGNETIC CONSTANTS OF SILICON STEEL

H $\left(\dfrac{\text{amp-turns}}{\text{m}}\right)$	$\mu_0 H$ $\left(\dfrac{\text{webers}}{\text{m}^2}\right)$	μ $\left(\dfrac{\text{webers}}{\text{amp-m}}\right)$	B $\left(\dfrac{\text{webers}}{\text{m}^2}\right)$	$\dfrac{\mu}{\mu_0}$
0	0	3100×10^{-7}	0	250
50	0.000063	8600×10^{-7}	0.043	680
100	0.00013	67000×10^{-7}	0.67	5300
200	0.00025	60000×10^{-7}	1.20	4700
500	0.00063	28800×10^{-7}	1.44	2300
1000	0.0013	15800×10^{-7}	1.58	1250
10000	0.013	1720×10^{-7}	1.72	137

It will be seen that, when H is small (between 0 and 200 amp-turns/m), μ is very large, and practically all of the field is due to the magnetization of the iron. Beyond an H of about 1000 amp-turns/m, the permeability decreases to a relatively low value.

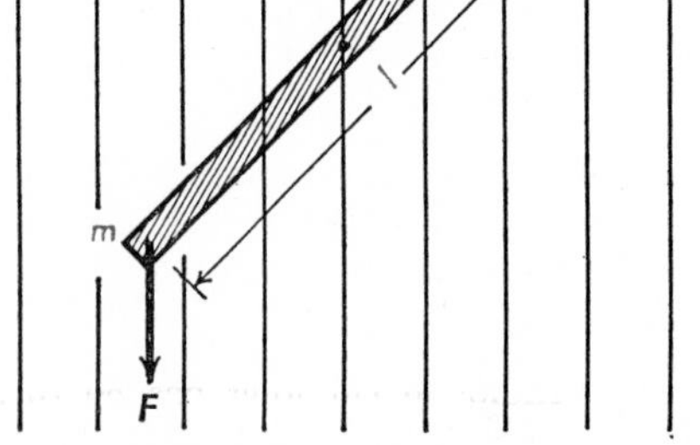

rected forces has a lever arm $d = \frac{1}{2}l \sin \theta$. The total torque L is equal to $2(F \times d)$.

$$L = 2(mB \times \tfrac{1}{2}l \sin \theta)$$
$$L = mlB \sin \theta$$

The product ml is a property of the magnet alone, and by analogy with *mass moment* and *force moment* in mechanics it is called the *magnetic moment*.

$$M = ml \qquad (53t)$$

The torque may therefore be written simply as

$$L = MB \sin \theta \qquad (53u)$$

When the magnet is at right angles to B,

$$L = MB \qquad (53v)$$

If a current-carrying loop of wire is located in a magnetic field as shown in Fig. 53M, it too is acted upon by a torque, tending to line its axis up with the field B. This torque is given by Eq.(53u), where the magnetic moment is given by the very simple relation

$$M = IA \qquad (53w)$$

Fig. 53L   *A bar magnet in a magnetic field is acted upon by a torque.*

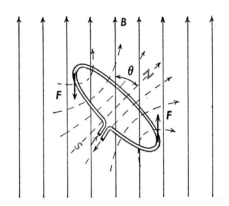

Fig. 53M   *A current-carrying loop of wire in a magnetic field is acted upon by a torque.*

where I is the current in amperes, and A is the loop area in meters². If the flat coil has a number of turns N, the equation is multiplied by N, so that $M = NIA$.

Because the magnetic field set up by a current loop is similar to the field around a straight bar magnet, the quantity M is frequently called the *magnetic dipole moment*.

The magnetic properties of all substances are due entirely to the motions of electrons within the atoms, and magnets of all kinds are the result of the lining-up of electron current loops, or spinning electrons. Each tiny elementary magnet has a magnetic moment M, and can be thought of as a magnet, as given by Eq.(53t), or as a current loop as given by Eq.(53w).

PROBLEMS

1. Calculate the magnetic induction at a distance of 1 cm from a long straight wire carrying an electron current of 100 amp.

2. Two long, straight, parallel wires 4 cm apart each carry an electron current of 100 amp. Calculate the magnetic induction at a point between the wires, 1 cm from one and 3 cm from the other, when the currents are (a) in the same direction, and (b) in opposite directions. (*Ans.* (a) 13.3×10^{-4} w/m², (b) 26.7×10^{-4} w/m².)

3. A wire 50 ft long is wound into a flat coil 2 in. in diameter. If an electron current of 10 amp flows through the coil, what is the magnetic induction at the center?

4. Two long, straight, parallel wires 6 cm apart each carry an electron current of 40 amp. Calculate the magnetic induction at a point between the wires, 2 cm from one and 4 cm from the other, when the currents are (a) in the same direction, and (b) in opposite directions. (*Ans.* (a) 2.0×10^{-4} w/m², (b) 6.0×10^{-4} w/m².)

5. A wire 100 ft long is wound into a flat coil 2 in. in diameter. If an electron current of 5 amp flows through the coil, what is the magnetic induction at the center?

6. A flat coil of 50 turns has a diameter of 4 in. and carries an electron current of 15 amp. Find the magnetic induction at the center. (*Ans.* 9.28×10^{-3} w/m².)

7. If the magnetic induction at the center of a solenoid 25 cm long is to be 2×10^{-2} w/m² when an electron current of 6 amp is flowing through it, how many turns must it have?

8. A flat coil of 50 turns has a diameter of 4 in. and carries an electron current of 7 amp. Find the magnetic induction at the center. (*Ans.* 4.33×10^{-3} w/m².)

9. If the magnetic induction at the center of a solenoid 50 cm long is to be 2×10^{-2} w/m² when an electron current of 6 amp is flowing through it, how many turns must it have?

10. A solenoid 60 cm long has 1000 turns of wire. What electron current is required to produce a magnetic induction of 2×10^{-2} w/m² at its center? (*Ans.* 9.55 amp.)

11. A straight wire 6 in. long and carrying an electron current of 25 amp is placed in a field where the magnetic induction is 1 w/m². If the wire and the field are perpendicular to each other, find the force on the wire.

12. A solenoid 50 cm long has 70 turns of wire. What electron current is required to produce a magnetic induction of 4×10^{-4} w/m² at its center? (*Ans.* 2.27 amp.)

13. A solenoid 30 cm long has 50 turns of wire and carries an electron current of 1.2 amp. (a) Calculate the flux density at the center. (b) What will be the flux density when a bar of

silicon steel is inserted as a core? (c) What is the permeability? (See Fig. 53K for part (c).)

14. A flat coil of 14 turns and radius 20 cm carries a current of 16 amp. Find the magnetic induction at its center in gauss. (*Ans.* 7.05 gauss.)

15. A solenoid 50 cm long carries an electron current of 8.5 amp. How many turns are required if the magnetic induction at the center is to be 100 gauss?

16. A copper wire 250 ft long is wound into a solenoid 6 in. in diameter and 60 in. long. (a) What is the magnetic induction at the center if an electron current of 0.48 amp flows through the wire? If a silicon steel core is inserted, (b) what is the permeability, and (c) what will be the flux density? (*Ans.* (a) 6.28×10^{-5} w/m^2, (b) 8.60×10^{-4} w/amp-m, (c) 0.043 w/m^2.)

17. A straight wire 6 in. long and carrying an electron current of 15 amp is placed in a field where the magnetic induction is 1 w/m^2. If the wire and the field are perpendicular to each other, find the force on the wire.

18. An electron moves with $\frac{1}{25}$ the velocity of light through a magnetic field where the magnetic induction is 5×10^{-4} w/m^2. If the electron's path is perpendicular to the magnetic induction, (a) what force acts on the electron, and (b) what is the radius of the circular path? See Appendix VIII. (*Ans.* (a) 9.6×10^{-16} newtons, (b) 13.5 cm.)

19. Solve Prob. 18 if the velocity is $\frac{1}{100}$ the velocity of light and the magnetic induction is 3.5×10^{-5} w/m^2.

20. An electron current of 50 amp flows through a straight wire 150 cm long. If this wire is placed in a field of 2×10^{-2} w/m^2 making an angle of 90° with the field direction, what is the force on the wire? (*Ans.* 0.15 neuton.)

21. An electron with its charge of 1.6×10^{-19} coulomb moves with $\frac{1}{10}$ the speed of light across a magnetic field of 0.01 w/m^2. Find the magnitude of the mechanical force acting on the electron.

22. A bar magnet 12 cm long with magnetic pole strengths of 16 amp-m is placed in a uniform magnetic field of 5×10^{-2} w/m^2. Find (a) the magnetic moment, and (b) the maximum torque acting on the magnet. (*Ans.* (a) 1.92 amp-m^2, (b) 0.096 newton m.)

23. A bar magnet 8 cm long is placed in a uniform magnetic field of 500 gauss, at right angles to B. If the measured torque acting on the magnet is found to be 0.005 newton meters, find (a) the magnetic moment of the magnet, and (b) the pole strength.

24. A single loop of wire 6 cm in diameter carries a current of 5 amp. If this loop is located in a uniform magnetic field of 5×10^{-3} w/m^2 with the plane of the loop parallel to B, find (a) the magnetic moment of the loop, and (b) the torque acting on the loop. (*Ans.* (a) 0.0143 amp-m^2. (b) 6.85×10^{-5} newton m.)

25. A circular coil of 25 turns, 20 cm in diameter, and carrying a current of 2 amp, is placed in a uniform magnetic field. If the maximum torque exerted upon it is 0.45 newton meters, what is (a) the magnetic moment of the coil, and (b) the magnetic induction B?

Chapter 54

Induced Electric Currents

54.1. Induced Electric Currents. The discovery of induced electric currents goes back more than one hundred years to 1831 and the well-planned experiments of Michael Faraday.* A straight bar magnet plunged into a coil of wire was found to produce an electric current. The experiment is illustrated in Fig. 54A. As the *N* pole of the magnet is plunged into the coil, a galvanometer needle deflects to the *right;* when it is withdrawn, the needle deflects to the *left,* indicating a current in the opposite

* Michael Faraday (1791-1867), English experimental physicist. Born the son of a blacksmith, Faraday's early life was spent earning his living as a bookbinder's apprentice. Taking time from his work to read some of the books passing through his hands, Faraday became intensely interested in science and developed a passionate desire to make science his life work. His chance finally came when he was made a valet and assistant to the great English scientist Sir Humphrey Davy of the Royal Institute. As a young man he openly proclaimed that women were nothing in his life, and even wrote and published a poem in criticism of falling in love. At the age of twenty-nine, he saw, fell desperately in love with, and married Sarah Barnhard who became a devoted and inspiring companion for the nearly fifty remaining years of his life. Four months after his marriage, he made the famous discovery of the motion of a wire carrying a current in the field of a magnet. Since a current-carrying wire would move in a magnetic field, should not the reverse be true and a magnet be made to produce current in a wire? For days he experimented with magnets and coils of wire until, in desperation, he plunged a magnet down into a coil and observed that a current was generated in the coil. Why had he not discovered this before? The motion was the connecting link he had failed to realize. For this discovery the whole scientific world sought to honor him. So many universities gave him honorary degrees that he soon had to turn down such honors. He refused the presidency of both the Royal Institute and the Royal Society of London, and also refused to be knighted. Like all great scientists, he loved his work more than these honors.

direction. If the *S* pole is moved down into the coil, the needle deflects to the *left;* as it is withdrawn, the deflection is to the *right.*

The relative motion of the coil and magnet is what produces the current; and it

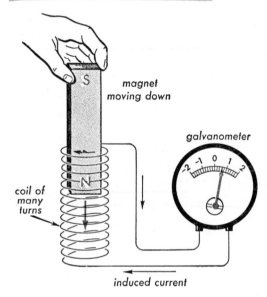

magnet moving down

galvanometer

coil of many turns

induced current

Fig. 54A *Diagram of Faraday's experimental discovery of induced electric currents.*

makes no difference whether the coil alone moves, whether the magnet alone moves, or whether they both move. In each case, when the relative motion ceases, the current stops. A somewhat "old-fashioned" way of describing the action is to say that only when a wire is cutting the line of force is there an induced emf. A somewhat more acceptable statement at the present time is that only when the total magnetic flux linking a closed electrical circuit is changing is there an induced emf. To demonstrate this concept, a simple experiment like that shown in Fig. 54B may be performed.

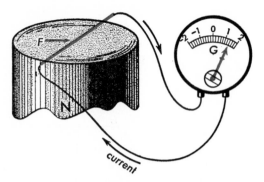

Fig. 54B *Experimental arrangement for demonstrating induced electron currents.*

A flexible wire connected to an ammeter, and held in the hands, is moved in various ways across the pole of a magnet. When a straight section of the wire is held over the N pole and moved to the right, an electron current flows in the direction shown by the arrows. If the wire is moved in the opposite direction, the induced emf and current reverses direction. If the wire is moved vertically upward or downward, parallel to the magnetic induction, no current flows. In other words, *there is an induced emf only when the total number of lines of induction through the closed circuit is changing.*

The fact that a current is produced means that electrical energy has been created. It has been created at the expense of mechanical work, for, in moving the wire across the field, a force F had to be exerted for a distance s. The faster the wire moves, and the stronger the field through which it moves, the greater is the required force and the greater is the induced emf and the resultant electron current. If the wire stops moving in mid-field, the emf drops to zero. These are the essential principles of the electric generator.

The *left-hand rule* may be used to predict the direction of the induced emf in any section of wire. Imagine grasping the wire in the left hand, with the fingers pointing in the direction of the magnetic induction immediately in front of the wire. Then, as the wire moves through the magnetic field, the thumb will point in the direction of the induced emf.

54.2. Induced Electromotive Force. It was shown in Sec. 53.5 how an electric charge Q, moving with a constant velocity v through a magnetic field where the flux density is B, experiences a force F upon it, given by

$$F = QvB \qquad (54a)$$

where F, B, and v are all mutually perpendicular to each other.

When a single wire is made to cross magnetic lines of induction, as shown in Fig. 54C, every atomic charge within the metal

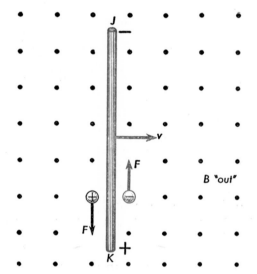

Fig. 54C *Forces on the charges in a conductor moving through a magnetic field.*

experiences a force upon it, parallel to the conductor. The direction of the force on the + charges is from J to K, while the force on the − charges is from K to J. Since only the electrons are free to move in a metallic conductor, the negative charges migrate along the wire, building up a negative potential at one end and a positive potential at the other.

Consider the straight conductor sliding along a U-shaped conductor to form a closed circuit as shown in Fig. 54D. The potential difference, created between the ends, forces electrons through and around the circuit in the direction indicated. In other words, the moving conductor becomes the source of an *electromotive force.*

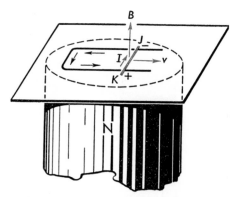

Fig. 54D *A current is induced by the motion of a conductor.*

The electromotive force developed within a moving conductor of length l is defined as the work per unit charge done in carrying any charge from one end to the other. From mechanics, we draw upon the principle that work done W is equal to *force times distance* moved. With the force given by Eq.(54a) and the distance moved by l, the work done on a charge Q is

$$W = QvBl$$

If we now divide both sides of the equation by Q, the work per unit charge becomes

$$\mathcal{E} = vlB \qquad (54b)$$

where $\mathcal{E}$ is the emf, or work per unit charge done on the charges in this section of the moving conductor.

In the mks system, B is in webers/meter², v is in meters/second, l is in meters, and $\mathcal{E}$ is in volts. It should be pointed out that it makes no difference in the above treatment whether the wire moves through a stationary magnetic field or whether the field moves across a stationary conductor. It is the relative motion giving rise to the crossing of lines of induction that produces the emf.

54.3. Faraday's Law. Faraday's law states that *the electromotive force generated in a conductor is equal to the rate of change of magnetic flux through the circuit.* For example, as the magnet in Fig. 54A is plunged

down into the coil, the number of lines of induction threading through the coil increases, and an induced electron current results. When the magnet is removed, the total flux linking the coil decreases, and again an electron current flows.

Consider again a U-shaped conductor with a slide wire moving with a velocity v across a uniform magnetic field B, as shown in Fig. 54E. At one instant, the total flux

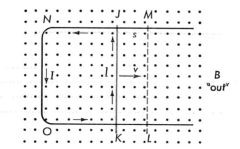

Fig. 54E. *The change of magnetic flux through a circuit.*

ϕ_1 linking the circuit $JKON$ is BA_1 (see Eq.(53n)). In time t, the wire reaches the position ML where the total flux ϕ_2 linking the circuit $MLON$ has increased to BA_2. The change in flux, therefore, is $\phi_2 - \phi_1 = B(A_2 - A_1)$, where the change in area, $A_2 - A_1 = l \times s$. Hence $\phi_2 - \phi_1 = sBl$. Dividing both sides by t, we get

$$\phi = BA$$

$$\frac{\phi_2 - \phi_1}{t} = \frac{s}{t}Bl = vBl = \mathcal{E} \qquad (54c)$$

Hence, the electromotive force $\mathcal{E}$ is given by

$$\mathcal{E} = \frac{\phi_2 - \phi_1}{t} \qquad (54d)$$

Here we have derived Faraday's law from Eq.(53n), for the particular case in which there is relative motion between a conductor and a magnetic field. However, the law is equally valid for the case in which the change in flux, $\phi_2 - \phi_1$, is due to a change in the strength of the magnetic field without any relative motion between conductor and flux. If it were not equally valid for this second case, the law of conservation of energy would be violated.

Since Eq.(54d) represents the flux change in a single turn of wire of area A, then an equal flux change in a coil of N turns of wire will induce an over-all emf N times as great. In the mks system, ϕ_2 and ϕ_1 are in webers, t is in seconds, and $\mathcal{E}$ is in volts. (Note: Eq.(54d) gives the *average* emf.)

54.4. The Electric Generator. An electric generator is constructed in the same way as an electric motor, with a rotating armature containing coils of wire, pole pieces, field windings, brushes, and a commutator. Instead of supplying an electron current to obtain mechanical rotation, mechanical work is done to turn the armature, thus producing an electron current.

If, in the construction of a generator, two solid rings are used as a commutator, as shown in Fig. 54F, the current delivered to

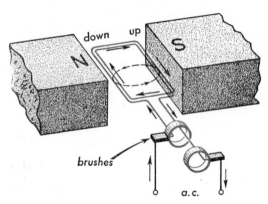

Fig. 54F   *Illustration of the principles of the electric generator.*

the brushes flows first in one direction, then in the other. The reversal of current with each half-turn of the armature is due to the fact that each wire moves up across the field at one instant and down at the next. At one instant, the one terminal is positive and the other negative; at the next instant the first terminal is negative and the second positive. This periodically reversing emf produces what is called an *alternating* emf.

If a direct current is desired, the commutator of the generator must be of the split-ring type illustrated in Fig. 54G. It

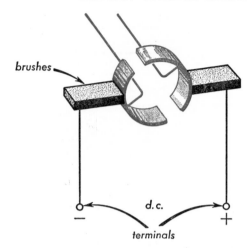

Fig.   54G   *Split-ring commutator for a direct-current generator.*

can be seen with this arrangement that one brush is at all times in contact with wires moving up across the field, while the other is in contact with wires moving down across the field. This produces a uni-directional electron current and the whole machine is called a *direct-current* (d.c.) *generator*.

It is important to note that a generator does not make electricity. The electricity, or electric charge, is always in the wire, and a generator sets it into motion. A generator produces an electron current.

54.5. Direct and Alternating Currents. The difference between a direct and an alternating current is that a direct current always flows in one direction, while an alternating current reverses its direction periodically. To send a direct current through an electric circuit, a source capable of developing a constant electromotive force is necessary. For this purpose, a battery or direct current generator is used.

To send an alternating current through a circuit, on the other hand, a source capable of reversing its emf is required. To do this, an alternating current generator is generally used.

Graphical representations of both direct and alternating currents are given in Figs. 54H and 54I for purposes of comparison. The lower curves in each figure permit a comparison of the *electron currents* through

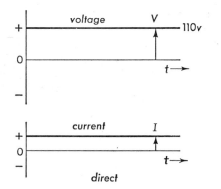

Fig. 54H *Graphs of 110-volt direct voltage and current.*

a circuit while the upper curves permit a comparison of the *emf,* or *voltage,* of the source. The horizontal scale on all diagrams represents the *time.*

Within the short time of one second, the generators in most power plants reverse the emf many times. For example, the power supplied to private homes and public buildings in nearly all cities in the United States is in the form of alternating current at 25, 50, or 60 cycles per second, and 110 or 220 volts.

A 60-cycle, 110-volt alternating emf, for example, is one in which the potential difference reverses direction 120 times per second. The rating of 110 volts specifies an effective voltage called the *root mean square* emf and not the so-called *peak* emf of 155 volts.

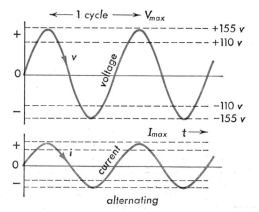

Fig. 54I *Graphs of 110-volt alternating voltage and current.*

The magnitude of the emf induced in a coil rotating at uniform speed, as shown in Fig. 54F, may be computed either from the vertical velocities of the wires forming the sides of the coil or by the rate of change of flux through the coil. In either case,

$$\mathcal{E} = NBA\omega \sin \omega t \qquad (54e)$$

where N is the number of turns in the coil, B is the magnetic induction in *webers/meter*^{2}, A is the coil area in *meters*^{2}, ω is the angular speed in *radians/second,* and t is the time in *seconds.* If f represents the *frequency of rotation,*

$$\omega = 2\pi f \qquad (54f)$$

The top curve in Fig. 54I represents the electromotive force $\mathcal{E}$, or the output emf V, at any instant, where V_{max} and I_{max} are constants and represent the amplitude or *peak emf* and *peak current,* respectively. From Eq.(54e), the emf is a maximum when the plane of the coil is parallel to the field and zero when it is perpendicular to the field. In the parallel position the coil sides are cutting across the lines of induction, while in the perpendicular position they are moving along the lines of induction. Eq.(54e) is a maximum when sin $\omega t = 1$. This gives

$$\mathcal{E}_{max} = NBA\omega \qquad (54g)$$

Example. A rectangular coil of wire having 60 turns with dimensions of 10 cm × 20 cm is set rotating at a constant speed of 1800 rpm in a uniform magnetic field of flux density $B = 0.5$ w/m^2. The axis of the coil is perpendicular to the field. Find the maximum emf produced.

Solution. Since ω is $2\pi f$, $\omega = 2\pi \times 1800/60 = 188.5$ rad/sec. Direct substitution in Eq.(54g) gives

$$\mathcal{E}_{max} = 60 \times 0.5 \text{ w/m}^2 \times 0.10\text{m}$$
$$\times 0.20\text{m} \times 188.5 \text{ rad/sec}$$
$$\mathcal{E}_{max} = 113 \text{ w/sec} = 113 \text{ volts}$$

Since the power dissipated as heat in any resistor at any instant is I^2R, where I is the magnitude of the current at that instant, the average power dissipated when an alternating current flows through the resistor is the average of I^2R (not the square of the average I) *over* each cycle. Since the average

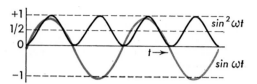

Fig. 54J   *The average value of sin² θ is ½.*

of $\sin^2 \omega t$, as ωt varies from 0 to 2π, is $\frac{1}{2}$ (see Fig. 54J), the average value of I^2 is $\frac{1}{2}(I_{max})^2$. Calling the square root of this average I_{rms},

$$I_{rms} = 0.707 \, I_{max} \qquad (54h)$$

In a similar averaging process the *root mean square emf* is given by

$$V_{rms} = 0.707 \, V_{max} \qquad (54i)$$

For an rms value of 110 volts, the maximum is 155 volts.

If an alternating current is applied to cir-

cuits containing inductance and capacitance, Ohm's law, as it is used with resistance and direct current, does not apply. In such instances, the current and voltage are not in phase with each other, that is, they do not rise to a maximum at the same time or fall to zero at the same time, and more complicated formulas must be used. Such circuits will be treated in Chap. 56.

Alternating current circuits for which the direct current relations of Ohm's law do hold true are those in which all of the circuit elements are pure resistances. Most electric lights and many heating units are of this class. In applying Ohm's law to pure resistance circuits, it is common practice to use the rms voltage V_{rms} and calculate the *rms* current I_{rms}. These values can be used in Eqs.(52c), (52d), and (52e) to calculate energy or power.

PROBLEMS

1. A wire 20 cm long moves with a speed of 25 m/sec through a uniform magnetic field where the magnetic induction is 0.3 w/m². If the wire, field, and motion are all mutually perpendicular, what emf is produced in the wire?

2. A wire 10 meters long is located in the wing of an airplane making 720 Km/hr. If the magnetic induction due to the earth's field has a value of 5×10^{-4} w/m², what is the maximum possible induced emf? (*Ans.* 1.0 v.)

3. A wire 50 cm long moves with a speed of 5 m/sec through a uniform magnetic field where the flux density is 0.2 w/m². If the wire, field, and motion are all mutually perpendicular to each other, what emf is induced in the wire?

4. A wire 8 m long is located in the wing of an airplane flying at 600 Km/hr. If the magnetic induction of the earth's field has a value of 5.4×10^{-5} w/m² and makes an angle of 90° with the airplane's direction of motion, find the emf. Assume the wire to be perpendicular to the Bv-plane. (*Ans.* 0.072 v.)

5. A wire 1 meter long moves with a speed of 15 m/sec through a uniform magnetic field where the flux density B is 0.2 w/m². If the wire, field, and motion are all perpendicular to each other, what emf is produced in the wire?

6. A wire 20 cm long is moved with a speed of 4 m/sec through a uniform magnetic field where the magnetic induction B is 0.25 w/m². Find the emf produced in the wire. (*Ans.* 0.20 v.)

7. A U-shaped conductor 20 cm wide (see Fig. 54E) is located in a uniform magnetic field where the magnetic induction is 4×10^{-3} w/m². If a straight rod across the loop moves with a speed of 5 m/sec, find (a) the magnitude of the emf, and (b) the rate of change of the flux linking the circuit.

8. A U-shaped conductor 25 cm wide (see Fig. 54E) is located in a uniform magnetic field where the magnetic induction is 1200 gauss. Find (a) the magnitude of the emf induced in a rod sliding along the loop at 1.5 m/sec, and (b) the rate of change of flux. (*Ans.* (a) 45 mv, (b) 0.045 w/sec.)

9. A flat rectangular loop of wire, 5 cm by 20 cm, is located in a uniform magnetic field where the magnetic induction is 5×10^{-2} w/m² with its plane perpendicular to the flux lines. If the loop is turned to a position where its plane is parallel to the field, in 0.01 sec, what rms emf is induced in the loop? Use Eq.(54d).

10. A flat rectangular coil, 8 cm by 12 cm, contains 50 turns of wire. Located in the earth's

magnetic field where the magnetic induction is 5.4×10^{-5} w/m², the coil is turned from a position where its plane is parallel to the field to where it is perpendicular to the field, in 0.02 sec. What average emf is induced? Use Eq (54d). (*Ans.* 1.30×10^{-3} v.)

11. A flat rectangular coil, 10 cm by 20 cm, and containing 50 turns of wire, is rotating at the constant speed of 3000 rpm in a magnetic field where the magnetic induction is 0.2 w/m². Calculate (a) the maximum emf produced, and (b) the root mean square voltage.

12. A flat circular coil 12 cm in diameter, containing 150 turns of wire, is rotating at 1800 rpm in a magnetic field where the magnetic induction is 0.25 w/m². Find (a) the maximum emf developed, and (b) the root mean square voltage. (*Ans.* (a) 79.9 v, (b) 56.5 v.)

13. A flat rectangular coil, 30 cm by 20 cm, and containing 150 turns of wire, is rotating at the constant speed of 4800 rpm in a magnetic field where the magnetic induction is 0.2 w/m². Calculate (a) the maximum voltage, and (b) the root mean square voltage.

14. A flat circular coil 20 cm in diameter and containing 100 turns of wire is rotating at 2400 rpm in a magnetic field where $B = 0.25$ w/m². Find (a) the maximum emf produced, and (b) the root mean square voltage. (*Ans.* (a) 197.4 v, (b) 139.6 v.)

15. A rectangular coil of 100 turns is 20 cm wide and 40 cm long. What is the speed at which this coil should rotate in the earth's magnetic field ($B = 5 \times 10^{-4}$ w/m²) to produce a peak emf of 1.5 volts?

16. A flat circular coil of 50 turns is 20 cm in diameter. If this coil is to be rotated in a uniform magnetic field to produce a root mean square voltage of 100 volts at 1000 cycles/sec, what must be the value of the magnetic induction? (*Ans.* 1.43×10^{-2} w/m².)

17. An a.c. generator whose terminal root mean square emf is 110 volts is connected to a resistance of 20 ohm. If the internal resistance of the generator is 2.5 ohm, what is the peak electron current?

18. A resistance of 12 ohm is connected to an a.c. generator whose internal resistance is 1.2 ohm. If the rms current in the circuit is 8.5 amp, find the peak emf of the generator on open circuit. (*Ans.* 158 v.)

19. An electric toaster with a resistance of 16 ohm is connected to a 220-volt a.c. line. Find (a) the peak voltage, and (b) the peak electron current.

20. An electric iron with a resistance of 15 ohm is connected to a 220-volt a.c. line. Find (a) the peak voltage, and (b) the peak electron current. (*Ans.* (a) 311 v, (b) 20.7 amp.)

21. Two resistances of 5 and 20 ohm, respectively, are connected in parallel, and the combination in series with a resistance of 8 ohm. The ends of this circuit are connected to a generator supplying an rms emf of 28 volts a.c. at its terminals. Find (a) the peak voltage across the 8-ohm resistance, and (b) the peak electron current through each resistance.

22. A rectangular coil of 200 turns is 10 cm wide and 20 cm long. What is the minimum speed at which this coil can be rotated in the earth's field to generate a peak voltage of 0.10 volt? Assume the magnetic induction to be 5.0×10^{-5} w/m². (*Ans.* 79.6 cycles/sec.)

23. A flat circular coil of 10 turns is 20 cm in diameter. If this coil is located in a uniform magnetic field where $B = 0.2$ w/m², how fast must it rotate about a diameter to generate an rms emf of 28 volts?

24. A flat circular coil of 20 turns is 10 cm in diameter. If an rms voltage of 50 volts and 1000 cycles/sec are to be obtained by rotating this coil in a uniform magnetic field, what must be the value of the magnetic induction? (*Ans.* 7.16×10^{-2} w/m².)

Chapter 55

Transformers

Because of the widespread use of transformers in long-distance power transmission as well as in telephones, radio transmitters and receivers, television, etc., it is of interest to consider the elementary principles upon which these instruments operate. A transformer is an electrical device by which the electromotive force of a source of alternating current may be increased or decreased.

55.1. The Primary Circuit. To study the actions and principles of a transformer, we must return to the *solenoid,* or *electromagnet,* treated in Sec. 52.7. Before an electron current is started through the coil of an electromagnet, no magnetic field whatever exists. This is illustrated by diagram (a) in Fig. 55A. When the switch *S* is first closed, completing the electric circuit, the electron current does not rise immediately to its full value but requires a certain amount of time to "build up" (see Fig. 55B). Starting at zero at the time the switch is closed, the current increases rapidly at first, then more slowly, and finally reaches its full value, the value given by Ohm's law.

During the time the electron current is increasing, the magnetic induction *B,* in and around the solenoid, is increasing as shown in diagram (b) of Fig. 55A. This field continues to grow in strength until the current reaches its maximum value, whereupon both the current and the field become constant. In most circuits, this whole process requires but a small fraction of a second. A constant current is indicative, therefore, of a constant unchanging magnetic field as shown in diagram (c).

When the switch is opened, the current will not stop instantly, nor will the surrounding field vanish instantly. The current will decrease with time, as shown in the graph of Fig. 55B, and the magnetic induction will decrease accordingly as shown in Fig. 55A(d). When the current reaches zero, the field will once more vanish simultaneously as in diagram (a). Thus, by opening and closing a switch, a magnetic field of increasing and decreasing strength is produced.

55.2. The Secondary Circuit. If a loop of wire is placed around an electromagnet, as shown in Fig. 55C, and the switch in the circuit is closed and opened as described in the preceding section, an electromotive force, and hence an electron current, will be induced in the loop. Immediately after the switch has been closed and the current and magnetic induction begin to rise, the total flux through the loop increases so that we obtain an induced emf. An induced emf means that, if the loop ends are connected together, or to something else, to form a closed circuit, a current will flow in the loop as shown by the arrows in the diagram.

When the electromagnet current reaches a steady state, the field becomes constant. This means that the total flux through the loop is no longer changing and the loop current has dropped to zero.

If the switch *S* is opened at this time, allowing the electromagnet current to decrease, the magnetic induction will decrease, and the total flux through the loop will fall. This decreasing flux, linking the loop circuit, induces an electron current opposite in direction to that shown in the diagram. When the current in the electromagnet winding drops to zero, the field vanishes and so does the induced emf. The properly timed closing and opening of a switch can, therefore, induce in a loop of wire one complete cycle of an alternating current.

To increase the emf in the outside circuit, many loops of wire are usually em-

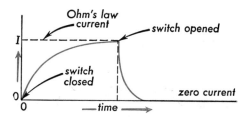

Fig. 55B   *Current-time graph for an electromagnet as illustrated in Fig. 55A.*

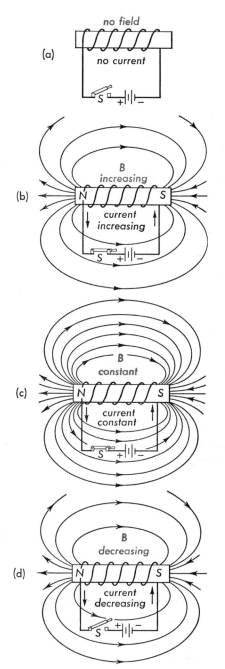

ployed. Such an arrangement is similar to that shown in Fig. 55D and is called an *open-core transformer.* The inside winding is called the *primary* and the outside winding is called the *secondary.* As the magnetic induction increases, the total flux through each loop of the secondary increases, and approximately the same emf is induced in each turn of the coil. Since the turns are all in series with each other, the total emf between the outside ends is the sum of the individual emf's for each turn.

It is customary for both the primary and secondary windings of a transformer to be wound with well-insulated copper wire and for both windings to be electrically insulated from each other.

55.3. The Induction Coil. When the primary terminals of an open-core transformer are connected to a battery as a source of

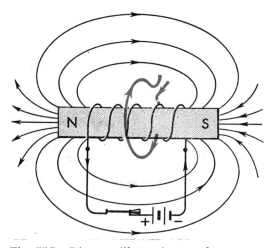

Fig. 55A   *Schematic diagrams of the changing magnetic field around an electromagnet when the current is increasing, constant, and decreasing.*

Fig. 55C   *Diagram illustrating an electron current induced in a loop of wire placed in the changing field of an electromagnet.*

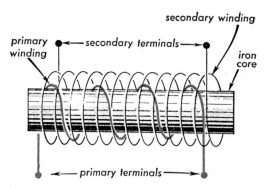

Fig. 55D   *Diagram of an open-core transformer.*

emf, a current in the secondary is induced only at the instant the circuit is closed and again when it is opened. To derive an alternating current from the secondary winding, the primary circuit must be opened and closed continually. When this is done, the field will increase and decrease periodically and the secondary will have induced in it, to deliver through the secondary terminals, an alternating current.

An induction coil is an open-core type of transformer with a few turns of large wire in the primary, many turns of fine wire in the secondary, and an automatic circuit *interrupter,* or *vibrator,* as shown in Fig. 55E. When the switch is closed and a current is started through the primary winding *PP,* the iron core becomes magnetized and attracts the iron knob *B.* Mounted on a strip of spring steel *L,* the vibrator bends to the left, breaking the primary circuit at the point *C.* When the current stops and the core loses its magnetism, the vibrator springs back to the right, making contact again. Proper adjustment of the thumbscrew *T* will cause the iron knob *B* to vibrate back and forth periodically, making and breaking the electric circuit. Each time the circuit is made the magnetic field grows, inducing a current in the secondary winding in one direction; and each time it is broken the field falls, inducing an oppositely directed current. Since each vibration of the knob *B* completes one cycle of an alternating current, the frequency of the vibrator determines the frequency of the alternating current delivered at the secondary terminals.

If, as is usually the case, the number of

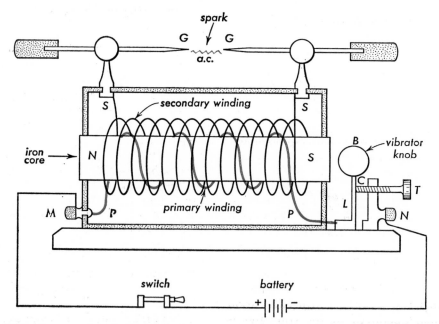

Fig. 55E   *Cross-section diagram of a laboratory induction coil capable of producing high-voltage sparks at the expense of a small battery.*

turns of wire in the secondary greatly exceeds the number of turns in the primary, the average voltage of the secondary will be many times higher than the direct current voltage impressed on the primary, and a spark will jump across the gap *GG*.

Perhaps the best example of a *vibrator type of induction coil* being used today is the automobile radio. Here a very small induction coil about 1 in. in diameter and 3 in. long is employed. The function of the coil is to take current from the 6- or 12-volt storage battery, with which every car is equipped, and to deliver at the secondary terminals an alternating emf of from 200 to 300 volts. This alternating current is then changed into direct current by a single radio tube, called *a rectifier,* and a system of coils and condensers called *a filter system.* Thus the constant high voltage necessary for the proper operation of the radio receiver is obtained in the roundabout way of first transforming constant low voltage into high voltage alternating emf and then rectifying it to a constant high voltage.

A similar induction coil without a vibrator, called *a spark-coil* or *auto-transformer,* is used in the ignition system of an automobile. Generally, such coils are about 2 in. in diameter and 4 in. long, and are wound on an open core as shown in Fig. 55D. The primary winding of such coils contains about 100 turns of heavy copper wire, and the secondary winding several thousand. The primary is connected to the 6- or 12-volt storage battery by wires through the timing system, the purpose of which is to open and close the circuit periodically with the motion of each cylinder of the motor. Each time the circuit is closed and opened, a high voltage induced in the secondary winding is connected to, and is discharged as a spark across, the terminals of one of the motor's spark plugs. The term "auto-transformer" applies to a transformer in which one end of the primary winding is connected by a wire directly to one end of the secondary. This common junction has little effect upon the normal operation of the coil, and is usually connected to the ground. On an au-

tomobile, the ground connection is made to the metal frame of the car.

55.4. The Closed-Core Transformer. A transformer, like an induction coil, has *a primary winding, a secondary winding,* and *an iron core.* The principal difference between the two is that a transformer does not have a vibrator and it operates on an alternating current supply.

Historically, the first closed-core transformer was made by Michael Faraday in 1831. Two coils of wire, one acting as a primary and the other as a secondary, were wound around opposite sides of an iron ring as shown in Fig. 55F. When a current

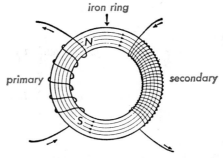

Fig. 55F *Diagram of the first closed-core transformer. (Designed by Michael Faraday.)*

is started in the primary winding, the magnetic field set up is confined almost entirely to the iron core. In other words, the lines of induction that develop in the primary, as a result of the growing primary current, also thread through the secondary, inducing an electromotive force and current. The iron acts like a good conductor of magnetic lines of induction, guiding them through the secondary winding.

When an alternating current is connected to the primary of a transformer, no vibrator is required to start and stop the current; the current rises and falls periodically, satisfying the conditions for a changing magnetic field and induced currents.

Most modern transformers are of the closed-core type, as illustrated in Figs. 55G and 55H.

55.5 Step-Up and Step-Down Transformer. Nearly all transformers come under

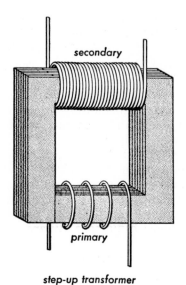

step-up transformer

Fig. 55G   *A step-up transformer with a closed core.*

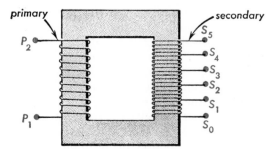

Fig. 55H   *Transformer with a tapped secondary.*

one of the two following classes: (a) *step-up*, or (b) *step-down transformers.* As shown in Fig. 55G, the step-up transformer is one in which the secondary winding has more turns of wire than in the primary. In the step-down transformer the reverse is true. The importance of this distinction is based upon the general and well-established principle that the ratio of the number of turns of wire in the primary and secondary windings is the same as the ratio of the respective voltages in each. This may be stated as an equation.

$$\frac{\text{number of primary turns}}{\text{number of secondary turns}} = \frac{\text{primary voltage}}{\text{secondary voltage}} \quad (55a)$$

Thus, if a transformer has 100 turns in the primary and 100,000 turns in the secondary, the voltage delivered at the secondary terminals will be 1000 times the voltage impressed upon the primary. If this same transformer were connected to the ordinary house lighting circuit of 110 volts a.c., the voltage at the secondary terminals would be 110,000 volts a.c.

The step-down transformer is just the reverse of this: the secondary voltage is lower than the primary voltage. As an illustration, suppose the primary of a transformer has 2000 turns of fine wire and the secondary has 100 turns. Having a turn-ratio of 20:1, this transformer when connected to the 110-volt a.c. line will deliver at its secondary a difference of potential of $\frac{1}{20}$ of 110 volts, or 5.5 volts. Such transformers are used in electric welding, for the ringing of doorbells, for the operation of toy electric trains, for lighting the filaments in radio tubes, etc.

Another type of transformer in common use has a tapped secondary. A tapped secondary is one in which different secondary voltages can be obtained by making connections to different numbers of secondary turns as shown in Fig. 55H. If secondary connections are made to S_0 and S_1, a relatively low voltage is obtained. If the upper connection is shifted to S_2, S_3, etc., more and more secondary turns are included, and the secondary voltage is proportionally larger. The effect is similar in many ways to the potential divider.

A type of transformer in widespread use

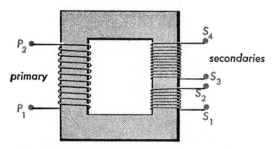

Fig. 55I   *Transformer with two secondaries.*

today has two or more independent secondary windings. See Fig. 55I. Electrically insulated from each other, these secondaries produce their own voltage as given by Eq.(55a).

Transformers used in the construction of modern radio and television receivers and transmitters are of the shell type shown in Fig. 55J.

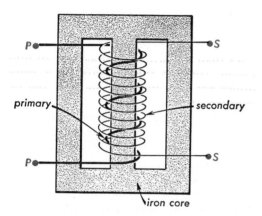

Fig. 55J *Shell-type transformer.*

55.6. Power. The increase in voltage of an alternating current by means of a step-up transformer appears at first sight to be a violation of the law of conservation of energy, i.e., it appears as though a large amount of energy could be obtained at the expenditure of a smaller amount. This is really not the case, for, when the voltage is increased, the current is simultaneously decreased by the same proportion.

When, for example, a transformer is used to step up the voltage to 100 times that supplied to the primary, the current in the secondary becomes only $\frac{1}{100}$ of the current in the primary. Therefore the power $(V_p I_p)$ supplied at the primary is just equal to that delivered at the secondary $(V_s I_s)$. In general, when the voltage is stepped up by a transformer, the current is stepped down by the same proportion.

In practice this is not exactly true, because a transformer is not quite 100% efficient. A small amount of electrical energy is continually expended, principally in the form of heat. In a well-designed transformer, such losses do not exceed 2 or 3%; so that a transformer is often considered to be almost 100% efficient.

55.7. Power Transmission. In the transmission of electrical energy over wires for long distances, transformers are practically indispensable. At the power house in the distant mountains, for example, electric current is generated by huge alternating current generators at the relatively low voltage of several thousand volts. If an attempt were made to transmit this electrical energy, at a voltage of say 2200 volts, over many miles of wire cable to a distant city, the current would be so large that nearly all of the energy would be consumed in heating the power line. The heat generated, it should be remembered (see Eq.(52h), is proportional to the square of the current (heat $= 0.24 I^2 R t$).

To avoid large heat losses, transformers at the power house (see Fig. 55K) step the voltage up to some 220,000 volts before switching the current onto the power line. Since the voltage in the case cited is increased one-hundred fold, the current drops by the same proportion to one-hundredth. Since the square of $\frac{1}{100}$ is $\frac{1}{10,000}$, the heat loss along the transmission line is only one ten thousandth of what it would have been had the transformer not been used.

At the city end of the power line, a transformer substation steps the voltage down to something like its original value of 2200 volts. From there, branch lines distribute the power to various sections of the city where smaller transformers, one near each group of several houses, steps it down again to the relatively safe voltage of 110 to 220 volts.

An experimental transformer for studying the relations between primary and secondary voltages, power input and power output, etc., is shown in Fig. 55L. It consists of a closed-core transformer with one side of the core removable and a set of several coils with different numbers of turns.

Although coils with any desired number of turns may be used, typical ones for a laboratory experiment would have 350, 250,

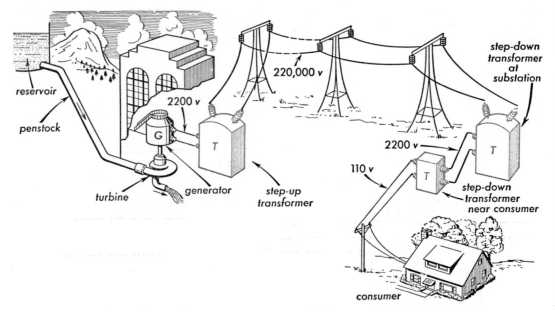

Fig. 55K   *Illustration of the use of transformers in the transmission of electrical energy from the power house in the mountains to the consumer in the distant city.*

250, 200, 150, 100, and 50 turns, respectively. In addition to these, a special coil of 100 turns with taps at every twentieth turn, and a tube with two separate windings of 200 turns and 20 turns, respectively, would be useful. The auxiliary equipment needed

is shown in Fig. 55M, and consists of an a.c. voltmeter reading up to 150 volts, a potential divider of several hundred ohms, a double-pole-single-throw switch, and a double-pole-double-throw switch.

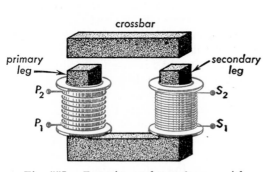

Fig. 55L   *Experimental transformer with changeable coils.*

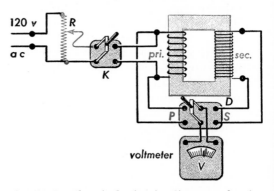

Fig. 55M   *Electrical circuit diagram showing connections for transformer experiment.*

PROBLEMS

1. The secondary of a step-down transformer has 25 turns of wire, and the primary is connected to a 110-volt a.c. line. If the secondary is to deliver 2.5 volts at its output terminals, how many turns should the primary have?

2. The primary of a step-down transformer has 300 turns and is connected to a 120-volt a.c. line. If the secondary is to supply 5 volts at its terminals and an electron current of 3.5 amp, find (a) the number of turns in the secondary,

and (b) the electron current in the primary. (*Ans.* (a) 12.5 turns, (b) ~~0.0582 amp.~~)

3. A step-up transformer with 175 turns in the primary is connected to a 120-volt a.c. line. The secondary delivers 10,000 volts at its terminals and a current of 40 milliamp. (a) How many turns are in the secondary? (b) What is the current in the primary? (c) What power is drawn from the line?

4. The primary of a step-up transformer is connected to a 110-volt a.c. line. The secondary with 8600 turns delivers 10,000 volts and a current of 20 milliamp. Calculate (a) the number of turns in the primary and (b) the current drawn from the line. (*Ans.* (a) 94.6 turns, (b) 1.82 amp.)

5. One end of a power transmission line of 6 ohm is connected to a 220-volt line and the other end to a load resistance of 16 ohm. Find the power consumed by (a) the line, and (b) the load. (Each of the two wires is 3 ohm.)

6. If by means of transformers the source voltage in Prob. 5 is stepped up to 2200 volts, and then down to 160 volts at the load, find the power consumed by (a) the line, and (b) the load. Assume both transformers to be 100% efficient. (*Ans.* (a) 3.17 watts, (b) 1600 watts.)

7. A step-up transformer has 125 turns in the primary coil and 25,000 turns in the secondary coil. If the primary is connected to a 220-volt a.c. line, find the voltage delivered at the secondary terminals.

8. The primary of a step-up transformer having 520 turns is connected to a house lighting circuit of 120 volts a.c. If the secondary is to deliver 2500 volts, how many turns must it have? (*Ans.* 10,830.)

9. The secondary of a step-down transformer has 50 turns of wire, and the primary is connected to a 110-volt a.c. line. If the secondary is to deliver 2.5 volts at its output terminals, how many turns should the primary have?

10. The primary of a step-down transformer has 450 turns and is connected to a 110-volt a.c. line. If the secondary is to supply 2 volts at its terminals and an electron current of 50 amp, find (a) the number of turns in the secondary, and (b) the electron current in the primary. (*Ans.* (a) 8.18 turns, (b) 0.909 amp.)

11. A step-up transformer with 160 turns in the primary is connected to a 120 volt a.c. line. The secondary delivers 10,000 volts at its terminals and a current of 50 milliamp. (a) How many turns are in the secondary? (b) What is the current in the primary? (c) What power is drawn from the line?

12. The primary of a step-up transformer is connected to a 208-volt a.c. line. The secondary with 12,000 turns delivers 8000 volts and a current of 20 milliamp. Calculate (a) the number of turns in the primary, and (b) the current drawn from the line. (c) What is the power? (*Ans.* (a) 312, (b) 0.769 amp, (c) 160 watts.)

13. A step-down transformer with 1200 turns in the primary is connected to a 115-volt a.c. line. If the transformer is to have three separate secondaries to give 2.5, 5.0, and 7.5 volts, respectively, how many turns should each have?

Chapter 56

Alternating Currents

56.1. Self-Induction. When a battery is first connected to the ends of a long straight copper wire, the electron current rises quickly to the value given by Ohm's law. When the same wire is wound into a coil or solenoid, however, the current rises more slowly as shown by curve (b) in Fig. 56A. If an iron core is inserted to make the solenoid an electromagnet, the current rises much more slowly, as shown in curve (c).

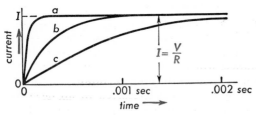

Fig. 56A *Current-time graph for a long copper wire in the form of (a) a straight wire, (b) a coil, and (c) a coil with an iron core.*

The cause of this lagging of the current is an emf induced in the wire which is opposed in direction to the rising current. This *back emf,* as it is sometimes called, is extremely small if the wire is straight, is large if it is a coil, and still larger if a soft-iron core is inserted. To explain the existence of a back emf, consider a small section of one turn of wire in a solenoid of many turns. As the current rises in this section, the growing magnetic induction which develops around it threads through the neighboring loops of wire, inducing in them an emf. These induced emf's and their corresponding currents run counter to the impressed emf and current. This property is called *self-induction.*

The unit by which one measures the self-induction of a coil is called the *henry* in honor of the American scientist, Joseph Henry.*

A coil having an inductance of one henry is one in which a change in the current of one ampere per second produces a back emf of one volt.

A coil with a large number of turns is one that has a large inductance L, whereas one with but a few turns has a small inductance. The higher the inductance, the more slowly does the current rise or fall within the coil.

The establishment of a steady current in an inductance requires work, since the back emf's must be overcome. Not all of the electrical energy expended in reaching the steady current state is lost. Some is stored up in the form of a magnetic field. When the source emf is disconnected from the circuit, the magnetic induction decreases, thereby inducing an oppositely directed emf and corresponding current.

Two experiments demonstrating the property of self-induction are illustrated in

* Joseph Henry (1797-1878), American physicist and scientific administrator, was born in Albany, New York, in 1797. He attended a country school, but quit at the age of thirteen. Later he attended the Albany Academy. Becoming interested in electricity and magnetism, he invented the magnetic telegraph and the electric relay, and discovered the phenomenon of self-induction. In 1832 he became professor of natural philosophy at Princeton, and in 1842 was elected by Congress as first secretary of the Smithsonian Institution in Washington, D.C. In this capacity, he founded the U. S. Weather Bureau and inaugurated the idea of distributing scientific publications to libraries and scientific bodies all over the world. He was the principal figure in the organization of the National Academy of Sciences, of which he was the second president. By general consent, Henry was the foremost American physicist of his time.

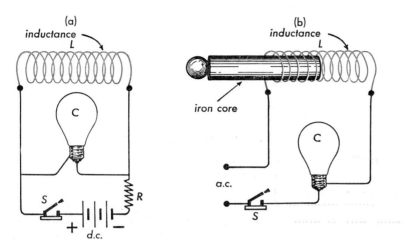

(a) inductance L

(b) inductance L

iron core

C

a.c.

S

S

R

d.c.

Fig. 56B *Two experiments illustrating the self-induction of a coil of wire. The circuit (b) is commonly used as a dimmer for electric lights.*

Fig. 56B. In diagram (a), a solenoid of many turns of wire is connected in parallel with an electric light to a 110-volt battery *B*. When the switch *S* is closed, the light flashes bright for an instant and then becomes dim. When the switch is opened, the light again flashes bright for a moment and then goes out. When the switch is closed, the back emf in the inductance prevents the current from building up rapidly through the inductance. The inductance therefore acts as though it had a very high resistance so that practically all of the current goes through *C*. When the current becomes steady, there is no back emf in *L*, and part of the current flows through *C* and part through *L*. When the switch is opened, the magnetic field falls off, inducing a current in *L*. This current flowing through the lamp *C* causes it to light up momentarily to full brightness.

The second experiment, as illustrated in diagram (b), demonstrates an increase in the self-induction of a coil due to a soft-iron core. Connected to an alternating emf, the light is bright when the iron core is out and dim when it is in place inside the solenoid. When the iron is inside, the back emf induced in the coil at each rise and fall of the current is very much greater than before, since the waxing and waning magnetic field is strengthened by its pres-

ence. The increased inductance therefore prevents the current's reaching a very high value before the current stops again and reverses its direction. The effect on the brightness of the lamp is the same as if the inductance were replaced by a variable resistance whose value is greatest when the iron core is inside the solenoid.

When a current is started in an electromagnet, the tiny elementary magnets within the iron core (these are the elementary magnets referred to in Sec. 51.11) turn around from their random orientations and line up with each other to make a single magnet of the entire core. In turning around, the field of each elementary magnet threads through the coil windings, inducing an emf opposing the rising current. This is another way of accounting for the back emf of self-induction.

56.2. Calculation of Inductance. In many instances, the inductance of a solenoid can be calculated from its geometry. For a long solenoid of uniform cross section, or a Rowland ring as shown in Fig. 53J, the inductance *L*, in *henries*, is given by

$$L = \mu \frac{N^2 A \ (m^2)}{l \ (m)} \tag{56a}$$

where *N* is the number of turns of wire, *A* is the cross-sectional area of the core in *square meters*, μ is the permeability of the core in *webers/ampere-meter,* and l is the length of the coil in meters.

Example. A round bar 4 cm in diameter and 20 cm long is wrapped with one layer of copper wire to form a solenoid. The coil has 200 turns, and the permeability of the iron is 2×10^{-3} w/amp-m. Find the inductance.

Solution. The given quantities are just those occurring on the right in Eq.(56a). $N = 200$, $\mu = 2 \times 10^{-3}$, $l = 0.20$ m, and $A = \pi r^2 = 0.00126$ m².

$$L = \frac{2 \times 10^{-3} \times (200)^2 \times 0.00126}{0.2} = 0.504 \text{ henry}$$

Without the iron core, the solenoid above would have a very much smaller inductance. For an air core, μ would be equal to $\mu_0 = 12.57 \times 10^{-7}$, and the inductance would be only 0.316 millihenry. *The millihenry (abbr. mh) is a smaller unit of inductance and is equal to one-thousandth of a henry; while a still smaller unit, the microhenry (abbr. μh) is equal to one-millionth of a henry.*

It should be noted that, if the core is air or a vacuum, L is a constant independent of the electron current and magnetizing field H. If the core is a ferromagnetic material, however, L will vary because the permeability varies.

56.3. Time Constants. When a capacitance C is connected in series with a resistance R and a battery emf V (see Fig. 56C), an electron current flows for a short period of time because it takes time for the plates of the capacitor to acquire their

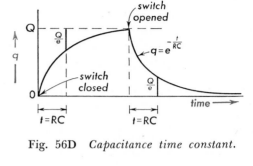

Fig. 56D   *Capacitance time constant.*

full charge Q. The rate at which a capacitor charges up is shown graphically in Fig. 56D. If now the switch S is opened, disconnecting the battery, and then the switch K is closed, the capacitor will discharge, and again an electron current will flow through R.

The time taken for the charge on the capacitor to reach within $\frac{1}{e}$ th of its full charge Q while charging, and the time taken to drop to $\frac{1}{e}$ th of its full charge while discharging, is called the circuit *time constant.*

$$\boxed{\text{time constant} = RC} \qquad (56b)$$

The constant e equals 2.718, ($1/e = 0.369$), and is the base of natural logarithms. The greater the resistance and the larger the capacitance, the greater is the time required to charge or discharge a capacitor.

When an inductance L is connected in series with a resistance R and a battery of

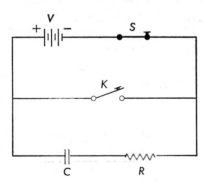

Fig. 56C   *Series circuit containing capacitance and resistance.*

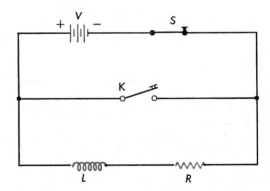

Fig. 56E   *Series circuit containing inductance and resistance.*

emf V (see Fig. 56E), it takes time for the electron current I and the accompanying magnetic field to build up to a steady state. When the switch S is opened and the switch K closed, the field decreases and the electron current falls, approaching zero as t approaches infinity. The time constant of the circuit, that is, the time for the electron current to rise to within $\frac{1}{e}$-th of its final value (see Fig. 56F), is given by

$$\text{time constant} = \frac{L}{R} \qquad (56c)$$

56.4. Stored Electrical Energy. When a capacitor like that shown in Fig. 56C is fully charged, electrical energy is stored in

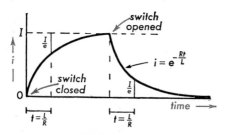

Fig. 56F *Inductance time constant.*

the form of an electric field. If W represents the stored energy in *joules,*

$$W = \tfrac{1}{2}CV^2 \qquad (56d)$$

where C is in farads and V is in volts.

Similarly, when a steady electron current is maintained in an inductance L, as shown in Fig. 56E, electrical energy is stored up in the surrounding magnetic field to the amount,

$$W = \tfrac{1}{2}LI^2 \qquad (56e)$$

where L is in *henries,* I is in *amperes,* and W is in *joules.*

56.5. Inductive and Capacitive React-ance. All electrical devices connected to a source of alternating emf contain a certain amount of *resistance, inductance,* and *ca-pacitance.* If the total inductance and ca-pacitance of the circuit are small compared

with the resistance, Ohm's law can be ap-plied to find the current in the various parts.

If the inductance and capacitance are not relatively small, they will introduce phase differences, or time lags, between current and voltage, so that Ohm's law will not ap-ply in the ordinary way. Such a circuit is shown schematically in Fig. 56G.

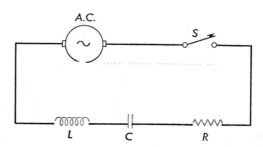

Fig. 56G *Series circuit containing inductance, capacitance, and resistance.*

Since an emf suddenly applied to an in-ductance requires a certain time for the electron current to build up to a fixed value (see Fig. 56A), the application of an *alter-nating* emf finds the current lagging behind the voltage in its rapid changes and re-versals. Furthermore, if the frequency is very high there is not enough time for the electron current to rise very far from zero toward its Ohm's law value.

Because the inductance effect reduces the electron current, it may be thought of as something analogous to a resistance. The measure of this effect is called *inductive re-actance,* to distinguish it from a true re-sistance where electrical energy is converted into heat.

$$X_L = 2\pi f L \text{ ohm} \qquad (56f)$$
inductive reactance

where f is the frequency or cycles per sec-ond.

When a capacitor is inserted into a *d.c. circuit,* the plates charge up, and the elec-tron current drops to zero. The capacitor thereafter acts as though it were an infinite resistance. Connected to an alternating emf, however, it may act quite differently. As the frequency f rises in an *a.c. circuit, the resistive effect of a capacitor decreases.* The reversing of the emf reverses the flow of electrons to and from the plates of the capacitor, and the alternating flow of charge constitutes an *alternating current.* Because a capacitor differs from a pure resistance, in that it stores electrostatic energy, its resistive effect is called *capacitive reactance.*

$$X_C = \frac{1}{2\pi f C} \qquad (56g)$$

capacitive reactance

56.6. *A.C. Series Circuit.* When an inductance L, capacitance C, and a resistance R, are connected in series to an a.c. generator as shown in Fig. 56G, the electron current in the circuit can be determined by the following equation,

$$I = \frac{V}{\sqrt{R^2 + (X_L - X_C)^2}} \qquad (56h)$$

where I and V are the electron current and voltage, respectively. The quantity $X_L - X_C$ in this equation is often called the *reactance* and is represented by X,

$$X = X_L - X_C, \quad \text{so that} \quad I = \frac{V}{\sqrt{R^2 + X^2}}$$

The whole denominator is called the *impedance* and is represented by Z.

$$Z = \sqrt{R^2 + (X_L - X_C)^2}$$

and

$$I = \frac{V}{Z} \qquad (56i)$$

Note the identical form of this last equation to Ohm's law for direct currents. The resistance R in Ohm's law has here been replaced by the impedance Z.

The relations between R, X_L, and X_C and the resultant impedance Z of a series circuit containing them may be represented graphically by treating all quantities as vectors. As shown in Fig. 56H, the resistance R is represented by a vector along the x-axis, the reactances X_L and X_C by vectors up and down on the y-axis, and the impedance Z as the vector resultant of X and

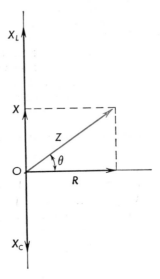

Fig. 56H   *Impedance diagram for a.c. circuit.*

R. In practice, R includes the resistance of the inductance winding as well as all the connecting wires of the circuit.

56.7. *Phase Relations Between I and V.* The effect of an inductance and a capacitance on an *a.c. series circuit* is such as to alter the phase of the electron current I with respect to the applied alternating emf or voltage. If the inductive reactance X_L is greater than the capacitive reactance X_C, the electron current will lag behind the impressed voltage; while if X_C is greater than X_L the electron current will lead the impressed voltage.

The amount the electron current lags or leads is given by the phase angle θ, where θ is given by

$$\tan \theta = \frac{X}{R} \qquad (56j)$$

In Fig. 56H, θ is seen to be the angle between Z and R. In one complete cycle of either the current or voltage, the phase angle has changed by 2π radians, so that a phase lag of 45° means that the electron current is $\frac{1}{8}$ of a cycle behind the voltage. A graphical representation of this example is given in Fig. 56I.

56.8. *Power Factor.* With direct current circuits, the power is given by the product

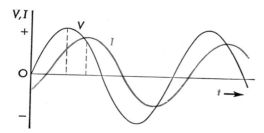

Fig. 56I   *Graph showing current lagging 45°
behind voltage.*

$V \times I$, and is measured in *volt-amperes*, or *watts*. In alternating current circuits, the instantaneous rate at which energy is supplied is equal to the product of the instantaneous voltage and the instantaneous current. Since both of these are sometimes zero, it is clear that the power consumption varies over each cycle and that some sort of average power must be taken.

The average power supplied to any a.c. circuit is equal to the rms voltage times the rms electron current multiplied by the cosine of the angle of lag.

$$\boxed{P = VI \cos \theta} \qquad (56k)$$

The quantity $\cos \theta$ is called the *power factor*. A low power factor in *a.c. circuits* is to be avoided, since, for a given supply voltage V, a large current would be needed to transmit appreciable electrical energy. The I^2R heat losses in the lines should be held to a minimum by making the power factor as near unity as possible. This means that θ should be as near zero as possible, thus allowing the smallest current for the power delivered.

Examination of the impedance diagram, Fig. 56H, will show that a circuit containing a relatively large inductive reactance should contain an equally large capacitive reactance to make $\theta = 0$, and the power factor $\cos \theta = 1$.

Example. A 60-ohm resistor is connected in series with a 0.25-henry inductor, a 50-μf capacitor, and an a.c. generator delivering 110 volts (rms) at 60 cycles. Find (a) the reactance, (b) the impedance, (c) the electron current in the circuit, (d) the power factor, and (e) the power.

Solution. By direct substitution in Eqs.(56f), (56g), (56h), and (56i),

$$X_L = 2\pi f L = 2\pi \times 60 \times 0.25 = 94.25 \text{ ohms}$$
$$X_C = 1/(2\pi f C) = 1/(2\pi \times 60 \times 50 \times 10^{-6})$$
$$= 53.05 \text{ ohms}$$

(a) $X = X_L - X_C = 94.25 - 53.05 = 41.20 \text{ ohms}$

$$Z = \sqrt{R^2 + X^2} = \sqrt{(60)^2 + (41.2)^2}$$
$$= 72.8 \text{ ohms}$$

(c) $I = V/Z = 110/72.8 = 1.51 \text{ amps}$

Fig. 56H is drawn to scale as a graphical solution for part of this problem. By direct substitution in Eq.(56j),

(d) $\tan \theta = \dfrac{X}{R} = \dfrac{41.2}{60} = 0.687 \quad \text{or} \quad \theta = 34.5°$

$\cos \theta = 0.824 = \text{power factor}$

By Eq.(56k),

(e) $P = VI \cos \theta = 110 \times 1.51 \times 0.824$
$$= 137 \text{ watts}$$

The power expended in a circuit containing inductance and capacitance cannot be measured with a voltmeter and ammeter. To measure power, one uses a *wattmeter*. Such an instrument takes the emf, current, and power factor into account and reads the power directly. By reading a wattmeter, an ammeter, and a voltmeter, the power factor of a circuit can be determined by Eq.(56k).

$$\text{power factor} = \cos \theta = \frac{P}{VI} \qquad (56l)$$

56.9. Lenz's Law. When a conductor moves through a magnetic field, the induced current in the wire is in such a direction that its own magnetic field generated by that current acts on the original magnetic field in a way opposing the motion. Stated for the first time by H. Lenz in 1833, this is known as Lenz's law. The action of the two magnetic fields upon each other is always such as to oppose the motion or any change in conditions already existing, for if they assisted the change we would have perpetual motion and a violation of the law of conservation of energy.

If the N pole of a straight bar magnet is approaching a solenoid (see Fig. 54A), the induced electron current in the coil is in such a direction as to produce an N pole at the nearest face of the coil. The two N poles therefore repel each other, tending to stop the motion. To keep the current flowing, a force F must continually be supplied to the moving magnet. It is this force F, moving through a given distance, that determines the amount of mechanical work done in producing a given current. If now the N pole is withdrawn from the solenoid, the induced current in the coil reverses in direction and produces an S pole at the nearest face. The opposite poles therefore attract each other, tending to stop the motion. Again, to keep the current flowing, a force F must be continually supplied; thus work is done.

There are numerous ways of demonstrating Lenz's law. One common experiment is to move a flat copper or aluminum plate rapidly through a strong magnetic field as shown in Fig. 56J. As each part of the plate

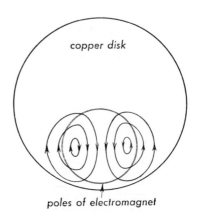

Fig. 56K   *Eddy currents in a moving plate conductor.*

the hand, the sensation is that of movement through thick molasses.

If the solid disk is replaced by a slotted disk, as shown in Fig. 56L(a), strong currents are induced in the vertical bars as they enter the field, and the disk stops quickly. If the slots are open at one end as in diagram (b), each bar is an open circuit and no large induced currents can be produced. Consequently, the disk is not strongly retarded but swings through the magnetic field rather freely.

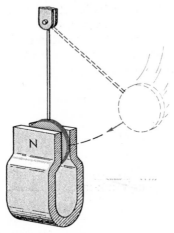

Fig. 56J   *Induced currents in the copper-disk pendulum quickly stop it from swinging through.*

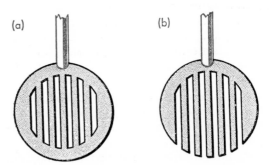

Fig. 56L   *Slotted copper disks for the demonstration of induced eddy currents.*

enters the field, a strong opposing force tends to stop it. What happens electrically is that strong eddy currents of electricity are produced in the metal as shown in Fig. 56K. The magnetic field arising from these eddy currents opposes the field through which it is moving. If the plate is held in

Another interesting demonstration is illustrated in Fig. 56M. A coil of wire with an extra long iron core is set on end, and a solid metal ring or band slipped over the top as shown. At the instant an alternating emf is applied to the coil, the metal ring is thrown upward several feet into the air.

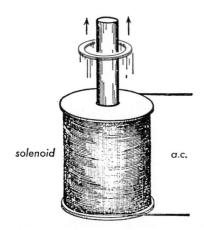

solenoid   a.c.

Fig. 56M *A metal ring is flipped up in the air by means of induced currents. A demonstration of Lenz's law.*

The explanation is not difficult since the arrangement is quite the same as a *step-down transformer;* the solenoid acts as a primary of many turns and the ring acts as a secondary of only one turn. As the current first starts to flow in one direction in the primary, the expanding magnetic field induces an oppositely directed current in the ring. The field set up by the ring current therefore opposes the field of the primary, and the repulsion of like poles pushes the ring upward. When the primary current reverses, the secondary current also reverses, and again there is a repulsion. To demonstrate the existence of a large current, the ring, if held down over the core, will soon become hot.

56.10. Levitation. The phenomenon known as "levitation" is another illustration of Lenz's law. A metal bowl *B*, as in Fig. 56N(a), is supported in stable equilibrium in mid-air just above an electromagnet *M* of special design. Top and side views of the iron core and coil windings are shown in diagrams (b) and (c). Excited by an alternating current, the raised iron knobs, labeled *N* and *S*, reverse their polarity periodically with the current. As the electron current builds up in the direction indicated in diagram (b), the magnetic induction grows. With the aluminum bowl in place as in diagram (c), the growing field

induces strong eddy currents in the aluminum conductor. These currents in turn give rise to opposing fields. Since the primary field being created by an alternating current increases and decreases rapidly, the bowl always experiences an upward force.

Should the bowl move to one side, as for example to the left in diagram (c), the changing field at *A* will induce stronger electron currents on that side of the bowl

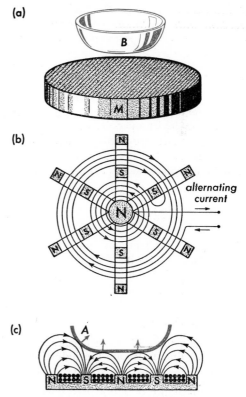

(a)

(b)

alternating current

(c)

Fig. 56N *A metal bowl is suspended in mid-air.*

and give rise to an increased repulsion, pushing the bowl back toward the center as indicated. The strong induced currents give rise to so much heat that the bowl soon becomes hot.

Because the coil windings of a levitator have a relatively large inductive reactance, a fairly large capacitance must be inserted in the a.c. circuit to raise the power factor close to unity, and thereby keep the cur-

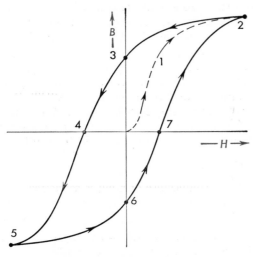

Fig. 56O   *Hysteresis loop.*

shown how a rising electron current in a coil containing iron gives rise to a magnetization curve as shown in Fig. 53K. When an alternating current is applied to such an inductance, thereby reversing the magnetizing field *H* with each half cycle, the magnetization *B* lags behind as shown in Fig. 56O. As the elementary magnets within the iron try to line up with *H*, first one way and then the other, the tendency to turn around gives rise to mechanical stresses in the iron; these in turn produce heating. This wasted energy due to the cyclic magnetization is given by the area within the *hysteresis loop* in Fig. 56O and is called *hysteresis loss.*

Hysteresis losses are not to be confused with other losses due to eddy currents set up in the iron core (see Fig. 56K). To reduce these eddy currents to a minimum, thereby reducing heat losses, the iron core is laminated, that is, built up of layers of thin iron sheets.

rent in the levitator coils at a maximum and the current supplied by the source at a minimum.

56.11. Hysteresis. In Sec. 53.8, it was

PROBLEMS

1. An electron current of 5 amp flows through an inductance of 2.5 μh. How much energy is stored in the surrounding magnetic field?

2. What steady electron current will store up 6 joules of energy in an inductance of 50 mh? (*Ans.* 15.5 amp.)

3. An inductance of 60 μh is connected to a 60-cycle a.c. line. Calculate the inductive reactance.

4. A capacitance of 120 μf is connected to a 50-cycle a.c. line. Find the capacitive reactance. (*Ans.* 26.5 ohm.)

5. A capacitor of 6 μf is connected in series with a 5×10^4 ohm resistor. Calculate the time constant of this combination.

6. What resistance connected in series with a capacitance of 20 μf will give the combination a time constant of 1 sec? (*Ans.* 50,000 ohm.)

7. What resistance connected in series with an inductance of 6 mh will give the combination a time constant of 0.25 sec?

8. An inductor of 50 μh is connected in series with a 600-ohm resistor. Find the time constant. (*Ans.* 8.33×10^{-8} sec.)

9. An oscillator coil is wound on a glass tube 4 cm in diameter and 20 cm long. How many turns of copper wire must it have to give it an inductance of 250 μh?

10. A round iron bar 2 cm in diameter and 10 cm long is wound with copper wire to form a solenoid. If the iron has a permeability of 16×10^{-4} w/amp-m, and the inductance is 0.25 h, how many turns of wire does it have? (*Ans.* 221 turns.)

11. A solenoid 2.0 cm in diameter and 50 cm long has 420 turns of wire. Find its inductance when it has (a) an air core, and (b) an iron core of permeability 2.5×10^{-3} w/amp-m.

12. A solenoid 6 cm in diameter and 50 cm long has 2000 turns of fine wire. Calculate its inductance when it has (a) an air core, and (b) an iron core of permeability 6×10^{-3} w/amp-m. (*Ans.* (a) 28.4 mh, (b) 135.7 h.)

13. A capacitance of 3 μf is connected to a d.c. voltage supply of 10,000 volts. Find (a) the

stored charge, and (b) the stored electrical energy.

$$C = \frac{Q}{v}$$

14. A capacitance of 25 μf has a charge of 5×10^{-2} coul. Calculate (a) the potential difference across the terminals, and (b) the stored electrical energy. (*Ans.* (a) 2000 v, (b) 50 joules.)

15. An inductance of 25 μh is connected to a 1000-cycle a.c. line. Calculate the inductive reactance.

16. A capacitance of 250 μf is connected to a 60-cycle a.c. line. Find the capacitive reactance. (*Ans.* 10.6 Ω.)

17. A 60-ohm resistor is connected in series with a 0.25-henry inductor, a 50-μf capacitor, and an a.c. generator delivering 110 volts (rms) at 60 cycles. Find (a) the reactance, (b) the impedance, (c) the electron current in the circuit, (d) the power factor, and (e) the power.

18. An inductance of 60 mh is connected in series with a resistance of 90 ohm, a capacitance of 50 μf, and a generator delivering a 60-cycle rms voltage of 30 volts at its terminals. Find (a) the reactance, (b) the impedance, (c) the rms current, (d) the phase angle, (e) the power factor, and (f) the useful power developed. (*Ans.* (a) $- 30.4$ Ω, (b) 95 Ω, (c) 0.316 amp, (d) $- 18.7$ deg, (e) 0.947, (f) 8.98 watts.)

19. A capacitance of 15 μf, in series with a resistance of 100 ohm is connected to a 400-cycle generator supplying an rms voltage of 27 volts at its output terminals. Calculate (a) the capacitive reactance, (b) the impedance, (c) the rms electron current in the circuit, and (d) the power factor.

20. An inductance of 20 mh, in series with a resistance of 60 ohm is connected to a 600-cycle generator supplying an rms voltage of 48 volts at its output terminals. Calculate (a) the inductive reactance, (b) the impedance, (c) the rms electron current, and (d) the power factor. (*Ans.* (a) 75.4 ohm, (b) 96.4 ohm, (c) 0.498 amp, (d) 0.622.)

21. A 0.5-h inductor is connected in series with a 0.4-μf capacitor and a 500-cycle generator delivering an rms voltage of 1000 volts at its output terminals. If the resistance of the circuit

is 1000 ohm, find (a) the reactance, (b) the impedance, (c) the rms electron current, (d) the power factor, and (e) the power expended.

22. A 5.0-μf capacitor is connected in series with a 0.06-h inductor and a 400-cycle generator delivering an rms voltage of 30 volts at its terminals. If the resistance of the circuit is 90 ohm, find (a) the reactance, (b) the impedance, (c) the rms electron current, (d) the power factor, (e) the power expended. (*Ans.* (a) 71.2 ohm, (b) 114.8 ohm, (c) 0.261 amp, (d) 0.784, (e) 6.14 watts.)

23. An inductance of 5 mh is connected to a 1000-cycle/sec a.c. line. Calculate the inductive reactance.

24. An inductance of 240 μh is connected to a 500-cycle/sec a.c. line. Calculate the inductive reactance. (*Ans.* 0.75 ohm.)

25. A capacitance of 180 μf is connected to a 500-cycle/sec a.c. line. Find the capacitive reactance.

26. If a capacitor, when connected to a 60-cycle/sec line, has a capacitive reactance of 40 ohm, what is its capacitance? (*Ans.* 66.2 μf.)

27. An inductance of 40 mh, in series with a resistance of 10 ohm, is connected to a 60-cycle/sec generator supplying an rms voltage of 120 volts at its output terminals. Calculate (a) the inductive reactance, (b) the impedance, (c) the rms electron current, and (d) the power factor.

28. A capacitance of 60 μf, in series with a resistance of 50 ohm, is connected to a 60-cycle/sec generator supplying an rms voltage of 120 volts at its output terminals. Calculate (a) the capacitive reactance, (b) the impedance, (c) the rms electron current in the circuit, and (d) the power factor. (*Ans.* (a) 44.2 ohm, (b) 66.7 ohm, (c) 1.80 amp, (d) 0.75.)

29. A 125-μf capacitor is connected in series with a 50-mh inductor and a 60-cycle/sec generator delivering an rms voltage of 120 volts at its terminals. If the resistance of the circuit is 10 ohm, find (a) the reactance, (b) the impedance, (c) the rms electron current, (d) the power factor, and (e) the power expended.

$$\mu f = 10^{-6}$$

Chapter 57

The Discovery of the Electron

Historically, a study of electrical discharges through gases and the discovery of the electron mark the beginning of a new branch of physical science called *"modern physics."* Modern physics, dealing principally with atoms, molecules, and the structure of matter, has developed at such a tremendous rate within the past three-score years that it now occupies the center of attention of many leading scientists the world over. It is not exaggeration to state that recent discoveries in atomic physics have had and will continue to have a tremendous influence on the development of civilization. Because the subject of atomic physics is relatively new, it is logical to treat the subject matter associated with each major discovery in a more or less chronological order.

57.1. Electrical Discharge Through a Gas. In 1853, an obscure French scientist by the name of <u>Masson</u> sent the first electric spark from a high-voltage induction coil through a partially evacuated glass vessel and discovered that, instead of the typical spark observed in air, the tube was filled with a bright glow. Several years later, Heinrich Geissler, a German glass blower in Tübingen, developed and began to manufacture gaseous discharge tubes. These tubes, made in diverse sizes, shapes, and colors of glass, and resembling the modern neon and argon signs used in advertising, attracted the attention of physicists in the leading scientific institutions and universities of the world. They purchased many of these "Geissler tubes" and used them for study and lecture demonstrations.

In 1869, W. Hittorf of Munster, with improved vacuum pumps, observed a dark region near one electrode of the electrical discharge that grew in size as the exhaustion was continued. This is but one of a number of phases of the study of electrical discharge through gases that were observed and studied a few years later by Sir William Crookes.*

In Fig. 57A, a long glass tube about 4 cm in diameter and 150 cm long is shown connected to a mercury diffusion pump and a mechanical vacuum pump. The purpose of the pumps is to enable one to observe continuously the changes in the electrical discharge as the air is slowly removed from the tube. The purpose of the *trap* is to freeze out any mercury vapor and to prevent it from reaching the discharge. High voltage from an induction coil is shown connected to the two electrodes, one at either end of the tube.

Although an induction coil does not deliver direct current, its characteristics are such that the potentials are higher on half of the alternations than they are on the other, and the two electrodes act nearly the same as if a high-voltage direct current were used. The negative electrode under

* Sir William Crookes (1832-1919), English physicist and chemist. At the age of 22 he became an assistant at the Radcliff Observatory in Oxford. He was knighted in 1897, received the Order of Merit in 1910, and was president of the Royal Society from 1913 to 1915. He invented and made the first focusing type of X-ray tube. His experiments with electrical discharges through rarefied gases led to his discovery of the dark space that now bears his name.

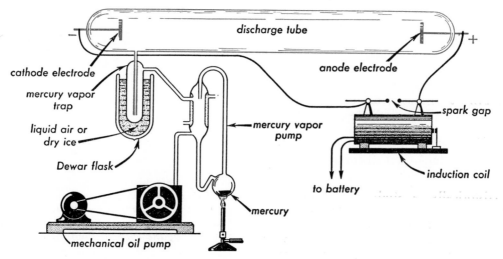

Fig. 57A *Diagram of a gaseous discharge tube, showing the electrical connections as well as the vacuum pumps and accessories.*

these circumstances is called the *cathode,* and the positive electrode the *anode.*

As the long tube is slowly pumped out, an emf of 10,000 to 15,000 volts will produce the first discharge when the pressure has dropped to about $\frac{1}{100}$ of an atmosphere, i.e., at a barometric pressure of about 10 mm of mercury. This first discharge, as illustrated in diagram (a) of Fig. 57B, consists of long, thin, bluish-colored streamers. As the gas pressure drops to about 5 mm of mercury, sometimes called a Geissler-tube

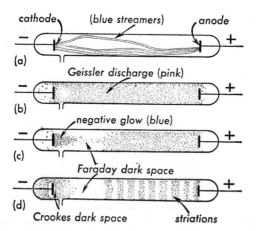

Fig. 57B *Sketches of the general appearance of a high-voltage electric discharge through rarefied air at various stages of evacuation.*

vacuum, the discharge changes to pink and, at the same time, widens until it fills the whole tube as shown in diagram (b). At a still lower pressure of about 2 mm, a dark region called the *Faraday dark space* appears in the region of the cathode, which divides the bright discharge into two parts, a long pinkish section called the *positive column* and a short bluish section called the *negative glow.* As the pressure drops still further, the Faraday dark space grows in size and the negative glow moves away from the cathode, producing another dark space between it and the cathode. With the appearance of this second dark region, called the *Crookes dark space,* the positive column divides into a number of equally spaced layers, called "striations."

As the pumping proceeds, the striations and the negative glow grow fainter, and the Crookes dark space widens, until finally, at a pressure of about 0.01 mm, it fills the whole tube. At this point a new feature appears: the whole glass tube itself glows with a faint greenish light.

57.2. Cathode Rays. The green glow in the final stage of the gaseous discharge just described was soon found to be a *fluorescence of the glass produced by invisible rays emanating from the cathode itself.* These *cathode rays,* as they are called, believed by Sir William Crookes to be an "ultra gaseous state" and by Johann W. Hittorf to be a "fourth state" of matter, were discovered to be tiny corpuscles which we now call *electrons*. In the relatively free space of a highly evacuated tube, cathode particles, torn loose from the atoms of the cathode, stream down the length of the tube and seldom collide with a gas molecule until they hit the glass walls.

The first important discovery concerning the nature of cathode rays was that they travel in straight lines. This was first revealed by Hittorf, in 1869, by casting shadows of objects placed inside the discharge tube. Hittorf's discovery is usually demonstrated by a tube of special design, as shown in Fig. 57C.

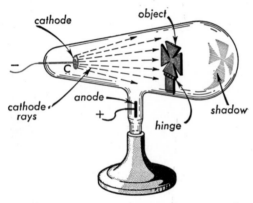

Fig. 57C *A Crookes' discharge tube for demonstrating that cathode rays travel in straight lines.*

Where the rays strike the walls of the tube, the glass fluoresces green, while in the shadow it remains dark. Under continuous bombardment of the walls by cathode rays, the fluorescence grows fainter because of a fatigue effect of the glass. This effect is demonstrated by tipping the object down on its hinge, thus permitting the rays to strike the fresh glass surface. Where the shadow appeared previously, a bright green image of the object is clearly visible.

That *cathode rays have momentum and energy* was first demonstrated in 1870, by Crookes, who used a tube of special design as illustrated in Fig. 57D. Leaving the

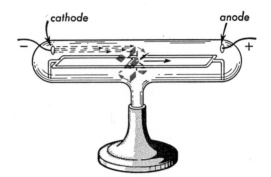

Fig. 57D *Demonstration of experiment showing that cathode rays have momentum and energy. Cathode rays striking the vanes of a small pinwheel cause it to roll from one end of the tube to the other.*

cathode and acquiring a high speed on their way toward the anode, the rays strike the mica vanes of a small pinwheel and exert a force, causing it to turn and thus roll along a double track toward the anode. When it reaches the end of the track, a reversal of the potential, making the right-hand electrode the cathode, will send it rolling back toward the anode, now at the left. From this experiment Crookes concluded that cathode particles have *momentum,* and that they therefore have *mass, velocity,* and *kinetic energy* $\frac{1}{2}mv^2$.

That *cathode rays are negatively charged particles* was first discovered in Paris, in 1895, by Jean Perrin. A discharge tube of special design usually used to demonstrate this property is illustrated in Fig. 57E. A beam of cathode rays is narrowed down to

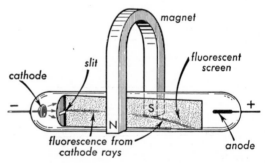

Fig. 57E *The bending of a beam of cathode rays in the field of a magnet demonstrates that cathode rays are negatively charged particles.*

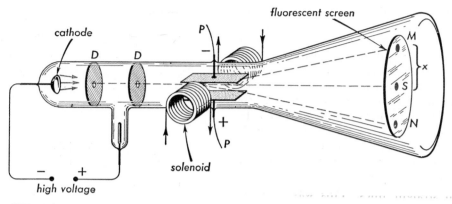

Fig. 57F *Diagram of discharge tube used by J. J. Thomson to measure the velocity of cathode rays.*

a thin pencil or ribbon of rays by a narrow slit near the cathode. The path of the rays is made visible by allowing them to strike a long strip of metal painted with zinc sulfide, a fluorescent paint. By placing a horseshoe magnet over the outside of the tube, as illustrated, the path of the cathode rays is bent down. If the polarity of the magnet is reversed, the path is bent up. The bending shows that they are charged, and the direction of bending shows the kind of charge. Being charged, a stream of particles is like an electron current. From the direction of the magnetic field and the current, and by application of the left-hand rule (see Sec. 52.5), the charge is found to be *negative*. (Remember that the left-hand rule applies to a current from (−) to (+).)

The penetrating power of cathode rays was first demonstrated by Heinrich Hertz and his assistant, P. Lenard, by passing cathode rays through thin aluminum foils. Out in the air, the rays were found to retain sufficient power to cause fluorescence and phosphorescence.

57.3. J. J. Thomson's Experiments.
When, in 1895, it was discovered that cathode rays were negatively charged particles, the question immediately arose as to whether or not they were all alike. It was clear from the beginning that two things would have to be done: (1) measure the amount of charge on the particles and (2) measure the mass of the particles.

Although the first attempts to measure the electronic charge and mass were not entirely successful, J. J. Thomson* did succeed, in 1897, in determining the velocity of the rays and in measuring the ratio between their charge and mass.

The discharge tube designed for these experiments is shown in Fig. 57F. Cathode rays, originating at the left-hand electrode and limited to a thin pencil of rays by pinholes in diaphragms *DD*, are made to pass between two parallel metal plates and the magnetic field of two external solenoids to a fluorescent screen at the far end.

When the two metal plates *P* are connected to a high potential, the particles experience a downward force, and their path curves to strike the screen at *N*. Without a charge on the plates, the beam passes straight through undeviated and strikes the screen at *S*.

When the magnetic field alone is applied, so that the magnetic lines are perpendicular to the plane of the page, the path of the

* Sir Joseph John Thomson (1856-1940), English physicist, educated at Owens College, Manchester, and at Trinity College, Cambridge. He was appointed Cavendish professor at Cambridge in 1884, and professor of physics at the Royal Institution, London, in 1905. He was awarded the Nobel Prize in physics in 1906, was knighted in 1908, and elected to the presidency of the Royal Society in 1915. He became master of Trinity College in 1918 and helped to develop at Cambridge a great research laboratory attracting scientific workers from all over the world.

rays curves upward to strike the fluorescent screen at some point M. If both the electric field and the magnetic field are applied simultaneously, a proper adjustment of the strength of either field can be made, so that the deflection downward by the one is exactly counteracted by the deflection of the other upward. When this condition is attained, a measurement of the magnetic induction B and the electric intensity E permits a calculation of the velocity of cathode rays.

Deflection in an Electric Field. In Chap. 50, Eq.(50e), on the theory of electricity it is shown that if e is the charge on a body located in an electric field of strength E, the force exerted on the particle is given by

$$F_E = eE \tag{57a}$$

As a charged particle like an electron enters the electric field between two charged plates (shown in Fig. 57G), this force acts

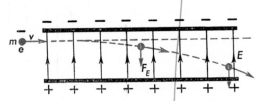

Fig. 57G *Electrons in a uniform electric field E follow a parabolic path.*

straight downward, parallel to the field lines at all points. The net result is that the particle traverses a parabolic path in much the same way that a projectile follows a parabolic path in the earth's gravitational field.

Deflection in a Magnetic Field. In Chap. 53, Eq.(53j), it is shown that if e is the charge on a body moving through a magnetic field B, the force acting upon it is given by

$$F_B = evB \tag{57b}$$

Since this force is always at right angles to both the magnetic induction and the direction of motion, the particle will traverse a circular path. (See Fig. 57H.) By counterbalancing the two forces F_E and E_B, i.e., by making them equal in magnitude and op-

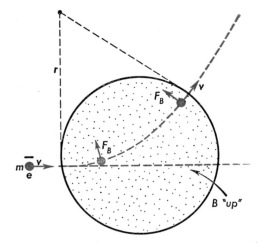

Fig. 57H *Electrons in a uniform magnetic field B follow a circular path.*

posite in direction, the two relations can be set equal to each other.

$$eE = evB \tag{57c}$$

By canceling the charge e on both sides of this equation, we obtain

$$E = vB$$

from which

$$v = \frac{E}{B} \tag{57d}$$

where E is in volts per meter, B is in webers per meter², and v is in meters per second. If we insert the known values of E and B, *the velocity v can be calculated*. The results show that cathode rays generally travel with a speed of several thousand miles per second, about $\frac{1}{5}$ *the velocity of light*. Furthermore, the velocity is not always the same but depends upon the voltage applied between the anode and cathode. By increasing this voltage, the velocity of the rays is increased.

It is of interest to point out here that tubes used for scanning and observing moving pictures by modern television receivers are quite similar in shape and principle to J. J. Thomson's cathode-ray tube of Fig. 57F.

57.4. *The Ratio of Charge to Mass, e/m.*
The next step taken by Thomson was to measure the deflection of the cathode beam

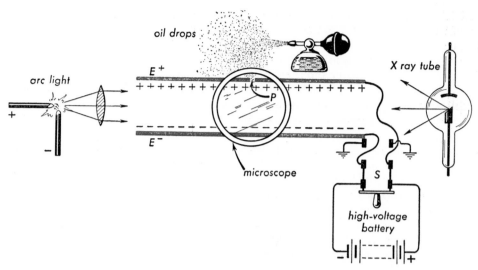

Fig. 57I *Schematic diagram of Millikan's oil-drop experiment. From this experiment the charge of the electron was determined.*

produced by a magnetic field alone and, from this, to calculate the ratio between the charge e and the mass m of the electron. To do this, he reasoned that, if a charged particle moving through a uniform magnetic field has a force exerted on it at right angles to its direction of motion, causing it to move in the arc of a circle, the force is of the nature of a centripetal force. Calling F_B a centripetal force (see Eq.(14h))

$$F_B = m \frac{v^2}{r}$$

and from Eq.(57b) we obtain

$$Bev = m \frac{v^2}{r} \quad (57e)$$

centripetal force

Transposition of m to the left side, and B and v to the right side, in the second equation results in

$$\frac{e}{m} = \frac{v}{Br}$$

where r is the radius of the circular arc in meters through which the particles are deviated; v is the velocity of the particles in meters per second, as measured in the last section; m is the particle mass in kilograms; and B is the magnetic induction in webers per meter². With all of these known, the value of e/m can be calculated. It is found to be

$$e/m = 1.7589 \times 10^{11} \frac{\text{coul}}{\text{Kg}} \quad (57f)$$

Such a large number means that the mass of a cathode ray particle in Kg is extremely small, compared with the charge it carries in coulombs. If now it were possible by some experiment to measure the charge e alone, the value could be substituted in Eq.(57f) and the mass m calculated.

57.5. Millikan's Oil-Drop Experiment. Millikan* began his experiments on the electronic charge e in 1906. His apparatus is illustrated by the simple diagram in Fig. 57I. Minute oil drops from an atomizer are

* Robert Andrews Millikan (1868-1953), American physicist, educated at Oberlin College and Columbia University, for 25 years professor of physics at the University of Chicago and for 30 years president of the Norman Bridge Laboratory at the California Institute of Technology in Pasadena. He served during World War I in the research division of the Signal Corps with the rank of lieutenant colonel. His principal contributions to science have been his measurement of the charge on the electron, his photoelectric determination of the energy in a light quantum, and his precision study of cosmic rays. He was the second American to be awarded the Nobel Prize in physics (1923). He has also been awarded the Edison Medal, the Hughes Medal of the Royal Society, the Faraday Medal, and the Mattenci Medal.

sprayed into the region just over the top of one of two circular metal plates, E^+ and E^-. Shown in cross section, the upper plate is pierced with a tiny pinhole P through which an occasional oil drop from the cloud will fall. Once between the plates, such a drop, illuminated by an arc light from the side, is observed by means of a low-powered microscope.

With the switch S in the "up" position, the capacitor plates are grounded so that they are not charged. Under these conditions, the oil drop falling under the pull of gravity has a constant velocity. This *terminal velocity*, as it is called, is reached by the drop before it enters the field of view and is of such a value that the downward pull of gravity, F_G, in Fig. 57J(a), is

pel the drop up across the field of view. The drop will move upward with a constant velocity if F_E is greater than the gravitational force F_G. Again using the stop watch, this time to measure the velocity of rise, we can calculate the upward force F_E. Knowing the force, and the voltage on the capacitor plates, we can compute the charge on the drop.

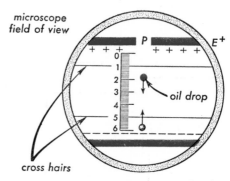

Fig. 57K *Microscope field of view showing oil drop.*

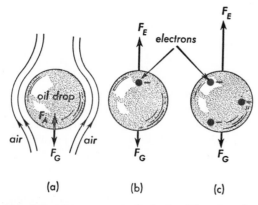

Fig. 57J *Diagrams of oil drop with extra electronic charges.*

exactly equalized by the upward resisting force of the air. By measuring this velocity of fall, the force F_G can be calculated and from it the mass of the oil drop determined. The velocity of the drop can be determined by using a stop watch to measure the time required for the drop to fall the distance between the two cross hairs illustrated in Fig. 57K.

As the drop nears the bottom plate, the switch S is thrown "down," charging the two parallel plates positive and negative. If now the drop has a negative charge, as illustrated in diagram (b), there will be an upward electrostatic force F_E, acting to pro-

As the drop nears the top plate, the switch S is thrown "up" and the plates are again grounded. Under these conditions the drop falls again, under the pull of gravity alone. Upon nearing the bottom plate, the switch is again thrown "down" and the drop rises once more. When this process is repeated, a single drop may be made to move up and down many times across the field of view. Each time it falls, the velocity is measured and the mass computed, while each time it rises the velocity is measured and the charge computed.

Millikan found that, if X rays were allowed to pass through the apparatus while an oil drop was being observed, the charge on the drop could be increased or decreased almost at will. One time, on rising, the velocity would be low due to a small charge (see diagram (b) in Fig. 57J), while the next time the velocity would be high due to a larger charge, as in diagram (c). Regardless of the amount of charge, the rate of fall for a given drop will always be the same, because the total mass of a number of electrons is so small compared with the mass of the oil drop that their added mass is not perceptible.

Millikan, and numerous other experimenters who have repeated these experiments, have found that the charge on a drop is never less than a certain minimum value, and is always some integral multiple of this value. In other words, any one electron is like every other electron, each carrying this minimum charge called e.

$$\boxed{e = -1.6019 \times 10^{-19} \text{ coul}} \quad (57g)$$

This is the most recent and probable value of the electronic charge.

57.6. The Mass of the Electron. From Millikan's determination of the charge on the electron and Thomson's measurement of e/m, the mass of the electron can be calculated by dividing one value by the other. Using the most accurately known values for both e and e/m, we obtain

$$m = \frac{e}{e/m} = \frac{1.6019 \times 10^{-19} \text{ coul}}{1.7589 \times 10^{11} \text{ coul/Kg}}$$
$$= 9.1072 \times 10^{-31} \text{ Kg}$$

that is,

$$m = 9.1072 \times 10^{-31} \text{ Kg} \quad (57h)$$

This mass is unbelievably small; its value has been determined many times and by many experimenters, and yet it is always the same.*

* For a more complete and elementary treatment of these early experiments, see *Electrons + and −*, by R. A. Millikan, Univ. Chicago Press.

PROBLEMS

1. Electrons with a velocity of $\frac{1}{10}$ the velocity of light enter a uniform magnetic field at right angles to the magnetic induction. What will be the radius of their circular path if $B = 2.0 \times 10^{-3}$ w/m²?

2. Electrons entering a uniform magnetic field where $B = 50$ gauss, in a direction at right angles to the lines of induction, have a velocity of 4.8×10^9 cm/sec. Calculate the radius of their circular path. See Eq.(53h). (*Ans.* 5.46 cm.)

3. Two flat parallel metal plates 20 cm long and 4 cm apart (see Fig. 50E) are connected to a 50-volt battery. If electrons enter this field with a velocity of 2×10^9 cm/sec, how far will they be deviated from their original straight line path by the time they reach the other end?

4. In J. J. Thomson's experiment shown in Fig. 57F, a magnetic induction field of 2.4×10^{-3} w/m² is employed. If electrons entering this field have a velocity of 3.4×10^9 cm/sec, what potential difference applied to the parallel plates will keep their path straight? Assume the plates to be 0.8 cm apart. See Eq.(50f). (*Ans.* 6528 volts.)

5. Electrons, moving in a uniform magnetic field where $B = 10$ gauss, follow a circular path of 46.5 cm radius. Calculate their velocity. See Eq.(53h).

6. Electrons, moving in a uniform magnetic field $B = 6 \times 10^{-4}$ w/m², follow a circular path of 20 cm radius. Find the velocity. (*Ans.* 2.11×10^7 m/sec.)

7. If one gram of free electrons could be bound together on the moon and another gram of electrons on the earth, what would be their force of repulsion? Earth-moon distance is 239,000 mi.

8. Make a diagram and briefly explain the experiment by which J. J. Thomson measured the velocity of electrons.

9. Make several diagrams showing the main features of an electrical discharge through a gas-filled tube as the pressure is lowered.

10. Diagram, and briefly explain, the three experiments given in this chapter to demonstrate that cathode rays (a) travel in straight lines, (b) have momentum and energy, and (c) are negatively charged particles.

11. Explain, and give a diagram of, Millikan's oil-drop experiment. What conclusions were reached by Millikan in this experiment?

12. Electrons are injected with a speed of 2×10^7 m/sec into a uniform magnetic field at right angles to the lines of force. If the magnetic induction is 2×10^{-3} w/m², find the diameter of the circular path. (*Ans.* 11.36 cm.)

13. If a beam of electrons, moving with a speed of 3×10^7 m/sec, enters a uniform magnetic field at right angles to the lines of force

and describes a circular path with a 10-cm radius, calculate the magnetic induction.

14. A 300-volt battery is connected to two
flat, parallel metal plates 8 cm long and 1.5 cm
apart. If electrons enter this field from one end,
moving with a constant velocity of 4×10^7
m/sec, how far will they be deviated from their
original straight line path by the time they
reach the other end? (*Ans.* 0.702 cm.)

15. Electrons are injected with a speed of
5×10^6 m/sec into a uniform magnetic field at
right angles to the lines of induction. If the
flux density is 2×10^{-3} w/m², find the diameter of their circular path.

16. If a beam of electrons with a speed of
3×10^7 m/sec enters a uniform magnetic field
at right angles to B and describes a circular
path of 10 cm radius, what is the value of B?
(*Ans.* 1.70×10^{-3} w/m².)

Chapter 58

Atoms and the Periodic Table

Although no one has ever seen an atom, there is no doubt in the mind of the true scientist that such particles really exist. To the physicists and chemists who have built up and established the present-day theories of the structure of matter, atoms are as real as any material objects large enough to be seen with the eyes or to be felt with the hands. Their reality is evidenced by hundreds of experiments that can be planned and executed in the research laboratory.

As the subject of atomic physics is developed in this and the following chapters, it will become more and more apparent that, although a physicist requires an extremely imaginative mind, the accumulated knowledge of atoms, their structure, and their behavior under a multitude of conditions, are based upon exact results of experiments performed with the greatest of accuracy and precision.

58.1. The Discovery of Positive Rays. During the latter part of the 19th century, when many physicists were investigating the various properties of cathode rays, Goldstein designed a special discharge tube; with it he discovered new rays called *canal rays.* The name "canal rays" is derived from the fact that the rays, traveling in straight lines through a vacuum tube in the opposite direction to cathode rays, pass through and emerge from a canal or hole in the cathode. A tube designed to illustrate this is shown in Fig. 58A.

Shortly after the measurement of the electronic charge by J. J. Thomson in 1896, W. Wien deflected a beam of canal rays in a magnetic field and came to the conclusion that the rays consisted of positively charged particles. Due to this and other experiments, canal rays have become more commonly known as *positive rays.*

Since the time of Goldstein's discovery, positive rays have been found to be charged atoms of different weights. The origin of the charge carried by such atoms is ex-

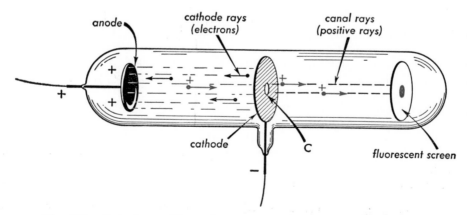

Fig. 58A *Experiment illustrating canal rays discovered by Goldstein.*

plained briefly as follows. As the electrons from the cathode stream down the tube toward the anode, they occasionally collide with the atoms and molecules of the small quantity of remaining gas, knocking electrons from them. This process, called *ionization*, is illustrated by a schematic diagram of a single oxygen atom in Fig. 58B. Before

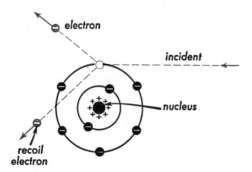

Fig. 58B *Schematic diagram of an oxygen atom in the process of becoming ionized by a collision with a high-speed electron.*

the collision, the atom as a whole, with its eight electrons and eight equal positive charges on the nucleus, has no net charge. After one of the electrons is removed by collision, it has but seven electrons and therefore a net positive charge equivalent in amount to the charge of one electron.

Since the atom is now positively charged, the anode repels and the cathode attracts such atoms, accelerating them toward the cathode. There exists, therefore, between the anode and cathode, two streams of particles: electrons moving toward the anode, and positively charged atoms or molecules moving toward the cathode.

Of the many particles striking the cathode in Fig. 58A, the ones moving toward the small opening C, constituting the observed canal rays, pass straight through to the fluorescent screen. As each atom or molecule strikes the screen, a tiny flash of light is produced. These tiny flashes, which can be seen individually in the field of view of a microscope, are called *scintillations*.

Any process by which an electron is removed from an atom or molecule is called

ionization, and the resulting charged particle is called a *positive ion*. The amount of charge carried by an electron is a unit called *the electronic charge.*

58.2. The Thomson Mass Spectrograph.

Ever since the time canal rays were shown to be positively charged atoms or molecules of the gas contained within the discharged tube, physicists have tried to determine with ever-increasing accuracy the mass and charge of the individual ray particles. Although the charge and mass of every electron were known from Thomson's and Millikan's experiments to be the same as those for every other electron, it could be postulated that the mass of the positive rays should be different for the atoms of different chemical elements. The further postulation could be made that if each positive ion were produced by the removal of one electron from a neutral atom, all positive ions should have the same net charge. This, in part, is anticipating what is now known.

In 1911, J. J. Thomson developed a method of measuring the relative masses of different atoms and molecules by deflecting positive rays in a magnetic and an electric field. The apparatus he developed for doing this is shown schematically in Fig. 58C; it is called *Thomson's mass spectrograph.*

The entire spectrograph, enclosed in an airtight glass chamber, is first thoroughly evacuated; then a small quantity of the gas, the masses of whose atoms are to be measured, is admitted to the bulb at the left. When a high voltage is applied to this chamber, electrons from the cathode ionize the atoms and molecules in the region between the anode *A* and the cathode *C*. Traveling to the right, many of these positively charged particles pass through the narrow hole in the cathode, thus forming a very narrow pencil of rays. Leaving the cathode with a constant velocity, they then pass between the poles of an electromagnet and the parallel plates of a capacitor, and thence to a fluorescent screen at the far end of the chamber.

The two parellel plates, when charged, exert an upward force on the particles, de-

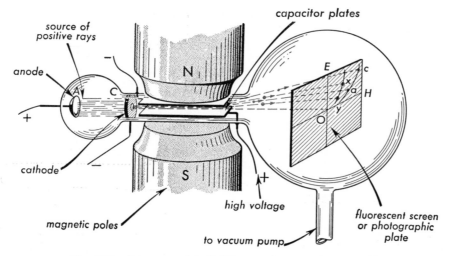

Fig. 58C *Diagram of J. J. Thomson's mass spectrograph.*

flecting them from the point O toward E. The magnetic field, on the other hand, with its magnetic lines vertically downward and in the plane of the page, exerts a force at right angles to this, deflecting the particles "into" the page from the point O toward H.

Suppose now that the apparatus contains a pure gas like helium, all of the atoms of which have exactly the same mass. Of these atoms, the ones that are ionized in a region near the cathode C cannot attain a very high velocity before reaching the cathode. Since these atoms remain longer in the deflecting fields, their paths are bent considerably up and back to a point such as c on the screen. Particles ionized near the anode A, on the other hand, attain a high velocity upon reaching the cathode and, being under the influence of the deflecting fields for a shorter time, have their paths bent only a little, to a point like a on the screen. Since the velocities of the particles vary considerably, a bright streak or line of fluorescence will appear on the screen. From a calculation of the forces exerted by both fields, it is found that the line on the screen should have the shape of a parabola.

If the gas in the apparatus is not pure but contains two kinds of atoms, the positive ions passing through the cathode will have two different masses. Although each ion will contain the same positive charge, and will therefore experience the same electric and magnetic forces when passing through the fields, the heavier particles will not be deflected as much as the lighter ones. The net result is that the heavier particles form one parabolic curve like xy, and the lighter particles another curve like ac.

By substituting a photographic plate for the fluorescent screen and exposing it to the rays for several minutes, photographs like those reproduced in Fig. 58D are obtained. The continual bombardment of the photographic plate by atoms and molecules has the same effect as does light, and images are produced upon development. The upper half of each picture is taken with the connections as shown in Fig. 58C, and the lower half by reversing the polarity of the electromagnet and exposing for an equal length of time.

When photograph (a) was taken, the spectrograph contained *hydrogen, oxygen,* and *mercury,* and the magnetic field was relatively weak. From the known strengths of both the electric and magnetic fields, and the assumption that each atom carries a unit positive charge, the mass of the atoms producing each parabola can be calculated. The results of these calculations show that the two largest parabolas are due to ionized

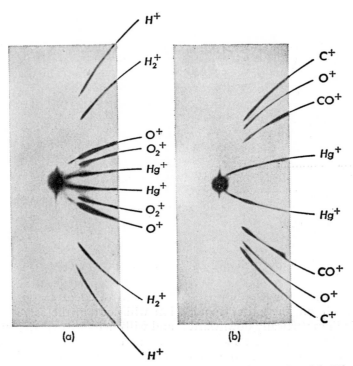

Fig. 58D *Reproductions of the photographs of parabolas made with Thomson's mass spectrograph.*

hydrogen atoms (H+) of mass 1, and ionized hydrogen molecules (H₂+) of mass 2. The next three are due to ionized atoms (O+) of mass 16, ionized oxygen molecules of mass 32, and ionized mercury atoms (Hg+) with a mass of approximately 200.

When photograph (b) was taken, the mass spectrograph contained carbon monoxide gas and mercury vapor, and the magnetic field was relatively strong. Upon calculating the masses of the particles producing the different parabolas, the four intense lines were identified as due to ionized carbon atoms (C+) of mass 12, ionized oxygen atoms (O+) of mass 16, ionized carbon monoxide molecules (CO+) of mass 28, and ionized mercury atoms (Hg+) of mass about 200. The three faint parabolas which show in the original photograph but probably not in the reproduction, are due to doubly ionized atoms of *carbon, oxygen,* and *mercury.*

A doubly ionized atom or molecule is one that has lost two electrons in place of one and, having a net positive charge of two

units, is designated by two (+) signs as superscripts. Since the particles have double charges, the electric and magnetic forces exerted on them are double those for singly ionized atoms and they produce larger parabolas, because they undergo greater deflections.

The principal conclusion to be drawn from Thomson's experiments is: *Positive rays or canal rays are charged atoms or molecules of whatever gas is present in the apparatus.*

It is significant to point out that, while Thomson found many atoms could be doubly and some even triply ionized, hydrogen could never be found more than singly ionized and helium more than doubly ionized. The reason for this, as will be seen later, is that neutral hydrogen atoms have but one electron and neutral helium atoms but two. All other elements have more than two electrons.

58.3. The Periodic Table of Elements. From present-day knowledge of physics, chemistry, and astronomy, it is quite certain that the entire universe is made up of 80 to 90 stable elements. By an element is meant a substance composed of atoms having identical chemical properties. All but two or three of these elements have been found in the earth's crust, some of them in much greater abundance than others. Silicon and iron are examples of abundant elements, whereas platinum is an example of a rare element.

Long before the Thomson mass spectrograph had been devised and used to measure the relative masses of atoms, the chemist had arranged all of the elements in a table according to their atomic weights. The most common form of this arrangement is given in Appendix IX. Divided as they are into eight separate groups, all elements in the same column have similar chemical properties. In Group I, for example, the elements Li, Na, K, Rb, and Cs, known as the *alkali metals,* have one set of chemical properties, whereas the elements Be, Mg, Ca, Sr, and Ba in Group II, known as the *alkaline earths,* have another set of chemical properties. The largest group of elements having similar chemical properties are the fourteen rare earth elements listed by themselves at the bottom of the table.

The names of the elements are all indicated by one-letter and two-letter symbols. (The full names are given in the second column of Appendix VI.) The number preceding each abbreviation is the order number of that element and is called *the atomic number.* The average weight of atoms of that element called *the atomic weight,* is given in the last column.

The atomic weights of all elements are based upon the weight of oxygen, 16. This is purely an arbitrary selection of a unit of weight but one which has considerable significance when it is noted that the weights of the first 25 elements, with the exception of chlorine (Cl), atomic number 17, are very close to whole numbers. This suggests the possibility that the weights of all atoms are really whole number units of the unit of weight, the hydrogen atom, and that those weights of an element which differ considerably from whole numbers are incorrectly

determined values. On the strength of this, Prout was the first to propose the hypothesis that all elements are made of hydrogen atoms as building stones. These suppositions, as will be seen later, are only partly true.

58.4. Thomson's Discovery of Isotopes.

In 1912, Thomson, in comparing the mass of the neon atom with the known masses of other elements, discovered two parabolas for neon in place of one. Upon computing the masses of the particles involved, the stronger of two parabolas was found to be due to particles of mass 20 and the other, a fainter parabola, to particles of mass 22.

Since the atomic weight of neon was then known to be 20.2, Thomson expressed the belief that neon is composed of two kinds of atoms, 90% of which have a mass of 20 and the other 10% a mass of 22. Because these two kinds of atoms exist as a mixture and cannot be separated chemically, their atomic weight, when measured by chemical methods, is found to be their average value, 20.2.

The discovery of two kinds of neon atoms, identical chemically but differing in atomic weight, suggested the possibility that all other elements whose atomic weights were not whole numbers might also be mixtures of atoms that do have whole number weights. Not only has this been confirmed by experiment, but a large majority of the elements have been found to be mixtures of from two to ten different kinds of atoms.

To all atoms of different weight belonging to the same element, Soddy gave the name *isotopes.* The external structures of all isotopes of a given element are identical. The two atoms, Ne-20 and Ne-22, shown in

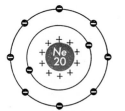 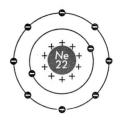

Fig. 58E *Schematic diagrams of the two different kinds of neon atoms, one of mass 20 and the other of mass 22. The external electron structures of two such isotopes are identical.*

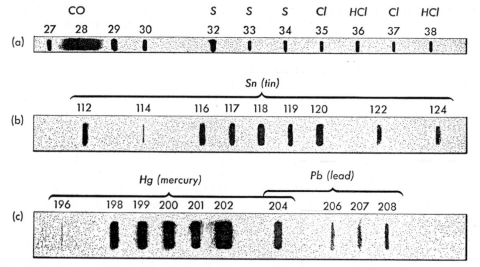

Fig. 58F *Reproductions of photographs taken with a mass spectrograph, illustrating the linear shift of atoms differing by one unit of mass. (a) Carbon monoxide, sulfur, chlorine, and HCl lines. (b) and (c) Isotopes of mercury, tin, and lead.*

Fig. 58E, are neon isotopes. Each of these neutral atoms, before it is ionized to become a positive ray, has ten external electrons and ten positive charges on the nucleus. They differ only in the weight of the nucleus.

Atoms having different weights but belonging to the same chemical element have the same atomic number and are called isotopes.

58.5. Aston's Mass Measurements. Immediately following World War I, in 1919, F. W. Aston* developed a new and improved type of mass spectrograph, employing both the electric and magnetic fields. The chief improvement of this device over Thomson's mass spectrograph was the "focusing" of the rays of different velocities to the same point on the screen or photo-

---

* Francis William Aston (1877-1945), British scientist, born in Birmingham and educated at Malvern College and Cambridge University. He became assistant lecturer in physics at the Birmingham University in 1909, and received the Mackenzie Davidson Medal of the Röntgen Society in 1920. In 1922, he was awarded the Hughes Medal of the Royal Society and the coveted Nobel Prize in chemistry for his work on atomic mass measurements. He has written an authoritative book entitled *Isotopes*, in which a full account of his work is given.

graphic plate. This had two important effects: (1) it made it possible to observe rare isotopes which might otherwise escape detection, and (2) it produced sharper images of the different masses on the photographic plate, so that their masses could be more accurately measured.

An Aston mass spectrogram is reproduced at the top of Fig. 58F. In taking this particular photograph, Aston had introduced into his apparatus, among other things, a little *hydrochloric acid* (HCl), *carbon monoxide* (CO), and *sulfur dioxide* (SO_2). Being close together in the periodic table, these elements furnish an excellent demonstration of the linear shift of atoms and molecules, differing in mass by one unit. It is found from this, and other photographs, that sulfur has three isotopes with masses 32, 33, and 34, and that chlorine has two isotopes of mass 35 and 37.

Since the atomic weight of chlorine is 35.46, then for every atom of mass 37 in a given quantity of chlorine gas there are four of mass 35. Mixed together in these proportions, they give an average mass of 35.4.

The photographic lines corresponding to masses 28, 36, and 38 are due to diatomic molecules CO and HCl, each molecule having the combined weight of its constituent atoms. Since there are two relatively abundant chlorine isotopes, there are two kinds of HCl molecules. One type, H^1Cl^{35}, has a mass of 36; and the other type, H^1Cl^{37}, a mass of 38.

A CO molecule of the type producing the strong line at mass 28 in Fig. 58F(a) is shown schematically in Fig. 58G. Since the mole-

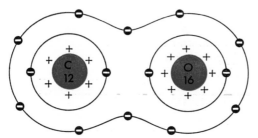

Fig. 58G *Schematic diagram of a diatomic molecule, carbon monoxide (CO).*

cule is neutral, there are just as many electrons surrounding the two bound atoms as there are positive charges on the nuclei (six on the carbon nucleus and eight on the oxygen nucleus). When the molecule becomes ionized and is moving through the apparatus as a positive ray, it contains one less electron than the number shown. Since the mass of the electrons is negligibly small, the mass of the molecule is 12 + 16 or 28 mass units.

So successful was Aston with his mass measurements and his determination of isotopes of different elements that he attempted an investigation of the entire periodic table. All of the known elements are listed in Appendix VI, with all of their observed isotopes. In each case, the most abundant isotope is given in heavy type, while the very rare isotopes, i.e., those present to less than 1%, are given in parentheses. Where more than one isotope is given in heavy type, the isotopes occur with almost equal abundance. The masses given in italics represent unstable atoms which are responsible for *radioactivity,* the subject of Chap. 69. Recent developments in mass spectroscopy have made it possible to detect exceptionally rare isotopes. In neon, for ex-

ample, an isotope of mass number 21 has been found, making three in all, with relative abundances as follows:

Isotope	Ne-20	Ne-21	Ne-22
Abundance, %	90.4	0.6	9.0

In a pure carbon monoxide gas, all of the molecules are diatomic and alike in every respect except for mass. Since there are two carbon isotopes, 12 and 13, and three oxygen isotopes, 16, 17, and 18 (see Appendix VI), there are six different combinations of atoms to form molecules. These are $C^{12}O^{16}$, $C^{12}O^{17}$, $C^{12}O^{18}$, $C^{13}O^{16}$, $C^{13}O^{17}$, and $C^{13}O^{18}$. The relative abundances of all but the C^{12} and O^{16} isotopes are so small, however, that more than 90% of the molecules in a given quantity of gas are of the type $C^{12}O^{16}$, with a mass of 28.

58.6. Isobars. Another mass spectrograph of remarkably high precision was devised in 1933 by an American physicist, K. T. Bainbridge.

Two photographs taken with this instrument are shown in Fig. 58F. The middle picture (b) shows the many isotopes of tin, and the lower plate (c) the isotopes of mercury and lead. The rare lead isotope 204 falls on top of the strong mercury isotope 204. Such coincidences are called *isobars.*

Atoms having the same mass but belonging to different chemical elements are called isobars.

The first pair of isobars, see Appendix VI, occurs in argon and calcium. The principal isotope of argon, atomic number 18, has a mass of 40, as does also the principal isotope of calcium, atomic number 20. Other examples are Cr54 and Fe54, Ge76 and Se76, Rb87 and Sr87, Zn92 and Mo92. The isobars Hg204 and Pb204 are illustrated in Fig. 58F(c).

58.7. Unit Mass and the Hydrogen Atom. Until 1927, all oxygen atoms were thought to have the same mass and were arbitrarily chosen to be the standard by which all atomic masses were measured. At this time Giauque and Johnson discovered the existence of two rare oxygen isotopes with masses 17 and 18. So rare are these heavier particles that in every ten thousand oxygen atoms only sixteen of them have a mass of 18, and only three a mass of 17.

The arbitrary choice of unit atomic mass is therefore taken to be $\frac{1}{16}$ of the mass of the oxygen isotope 16. On this basis, very accurate mass spectrographic measurements give, for the mass of the hydrogen atom 1.008, a value nearly 1% higher than unity. This apparent discrepancy is real, however, and, as we shall see in a later chapter on nuclear disintegration, it plays an important role as a source of *atomic energy* in the sun and stars.

To compare the masses of atoms with the mass of an electron, it is convenient to know the mass of the atom in kilograms. This mass can be calculated by knowing its equivalence in atomic mass units, *unit atomic mass being defined as $\frac{1}{16}$ the mass of an oxygen 16 atom*. This unit mass is found by experiment to be

$$M = 1.660 \times 10^{-27} \text{ Kg} \qquad (58a)$$

This number multiplied by the "atomic weight" of any atom will give its mass in kilograms.

Compared with the mass of the electron, namely,

$$m = 9.1072 \times 10^{-31} \text{ Kg} \qquad (58b)$$

an atom of unit mass would be 1824 times as heavy. The hydrogen atom is slightly heavier than one unit mass and is about 1840 times as heavy as the electron. This latter number is convenient to remember, for it is often quoted to illustrate the enormous difference between the mass of the nucleus of a hydrogen atom and the mass of its one and only electron.

Atomic number is defined as that number ascribed to an element specifying its position in the periodic table of elements. (See column 1, Appendix VI.)

Mass number is defined as that whole number nearest the actual mass of an isotope measured in atomic mass units. (See column 4, Appendix VI.)

Atomic weight is defined as the average weight of all the isotopes of an element, weighted according to relative abundance and expressed in atomic mass units.

QUESTIONS

1. Who discovered isotopes? What are isotopes?

2. What is meant by (a) atomic number, (b) mass number, and (c) atomic weight?

3. How do isotopes of any given element differ from each other?

4. What is meant by relative abundance?

5. What are isobars? Give an example.

6. How much greater is the mass of a hydrogen atom than the mass of an electron?

7. What do the more or less equal spacings of the mass spectrograms shown in Fig. 58F suggest regarding the relative masses of atoms?

PROBLEMS

1. The atomic weight of aluminum is 26.97. Find the mass in grams of one aluminum atom.

2. If the atomic weight of gold is 197.2, how many atoms are there in 1 gm of gold metal? (*Ans.* 3.05×10^{21} atoms.)

3. The atomic weight of manganese is 54.94. How many atoms are there in 1 gm of manganese metal?

4. If the atomic weights of silicon and oxygen

are 28.06 and 16.00, respectively, find the mass in grams of a silicon dioxide molecule. (See Fig. 22A.) (*Ans.* 9.96×10^{-23} gm.)

5. The atomic weights of hydrogen, carbon, and oxygen, are 1.01, 12.00, and 16.00, respectively. How many ethyl alcohol molecules are there in 1 gm of ethyl alcohol? (See Fig. 22A.)

6. Define or briefly explain the meaning of the following: (a) isotopes, (b) isobars, (c) posi-

tive rays, (d) atomic weight, and (e) unit atomic mass.

7. Name five members of each of the following classifications: (a) alkali metals, and (b) alkaline earths. (See Appendix VI.)

8. What chemical element has the greatest number of isotopes? (See Appendix VI.)

9. Make a list of elements having (a) atoms of one mass only, and (b) only two isotopes. (See Appendix VI.)

10. Carbon has two isotopes, 12 and 13, while oxygen has three, 16, 17, and 18. Find the mass in kilograms for each of the six possible CO molecules. (*Ans.* $C^{12}O^{16} = 4.65$, $C^{12}O^{17} = 4.81$, $C^{12}O^{18} = 4.98$, $C^{13}O^{16} = 4.81$, $C^{13}O^{17} = 4.98$, $C^{13}O^{18} = 5.15 \times 10^{-26}$ Kg.)

11. Nitrogen has two isotopes, 14 and 15. Calculate the mass in kilograms for each of the three possible kinds of diatomic molecules.

12. The two stable isotopes of copper have masses of 63 and 65 atomic mass units. The normal mixture of these atoms has an atomic weight of 63.57. What percentage of any given amount of the normal metal is composed of Cu^{63} atoms? (*Ans.* 71.5%.)

13. The fifth element in the periodic table, boron, has two stable isotopes with masses of 10 and 11 atomic mass units, respectively. The normal mixture of these atoms has an atomic weight of 10.82. Calculate the percentage of any given amount of the normal boron composed of B^{10} atoms.

Nucleus = 1840 x as heavy as e^-

Chapter 59

Light Sources
and Their Spectra

59.1. The Spectrum. When a block of metal like iron or copper is heated slowly to incandescence, the first noticeable change in its appearance occurs at a temperature of about 1000°K. At this temperature, the metal appears with a dull red glow. As the temperature continues to rise, the color changes slowly to orange, then to yellow, and finally to white.

If the metal, as it is slowly being heated, is observed through a prism, the first appearance of visible light will be found at the extreme red end of the spectrum. As the temperature rises, the light spreads slowly out across the spectrum until, at white heat, the entire band of visible colors from red to violet is seen. At the orange stage where the temperature is about

1500°K, the pure spectrum colors contain red, orange, and yellow; when the yellow stage is reached where the temperature is about 2000°K, the spectral green is included. When the white stage is reached at about 3000°K, and the spectrum is complete, a further rise in temperature continues to increase the intensity of each color without a noticeable change in color.

What the prism has done in such an experiment is to separate all of the light waves according to their wavelengths, the longest waves of red light at the one side, the shortest waves of violet light at the other, and the intermediate waves at their proper places in between. The fact that the color is continuous from red through violet is characteristic of the spectrum of all solids

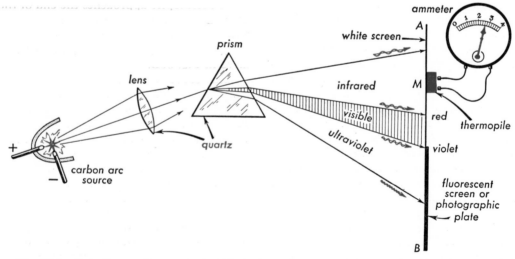

Fig. 59A *Experiment demonstrating the existence of the ultraviolet and infrared rays beyond the visible spectrum.*

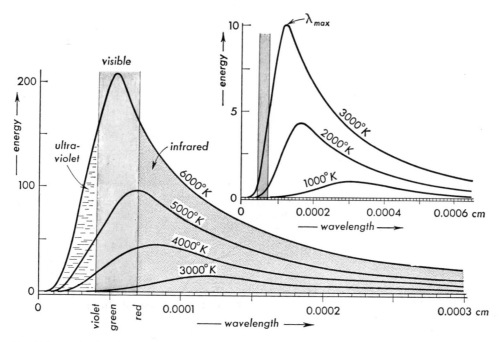

Fig. 59B *Distribution of the energy emitted by a hot solid at different temperatures.*

and liquids; this means that there is a continuous set of different wavelengths present.

To demonstrate the existence of an ultraviolet and infrared spectrum, an experiment of the type illustrated in Fig. 59A may be performed. The visible light from a carbon arc lamp is made to pass through a quartz lens and prism to be focused on a nearby screen.

If, at the violet end of the spectrum, the screen is painted with luminous paint, a bright fluorescence will be observed for a short distance beyond the visible violet. When the screen is replaced by a photographic plate, the exposed and developed picture will again show the extension of the spectrum into the ultraviolet.

To detect the presence of the infrared radiations, a thermopile* is conveniently used, as shown at the top of the screen. Connected to an ammeter, a thermopile measures the amount of light energy falling upon its front face. If the thermopile is first placed to receive violet light, and then

* For the principles of the thermopile, see Sec. 27.3.

slowly moved across the visible spectrum out into the infrared region beyond, the ammeter will show a steady rise in current. The current will continue to rise until a maximum is reached at a point in the region of M, and then it will drop off slowly as the thermopile approaches the end of the screen at A. A graph of the energy from the carbon arc source, for the different parts along the screen, is shown by the 3000°K curve in Fig. 59B.

Each curve represents the amount of energy given out over the entire spectrum by a solid at different temperatures. Studying these curves, one will observe that, at low temperatures, very little light is emitted in the visible spectrum. At 1000°K, only the visible red is seen and even that is very faint. At 2000°K, the brightness of the red not only increases, but the other colors, orange, yellow, and green, appear. At 3000°K, the temperature of a low-current carbon arc or tungsten filament light, all of the visible spectrum is emitted, but the maximum radiation is in the infrared. At 6000°K, the temperature of the surface of

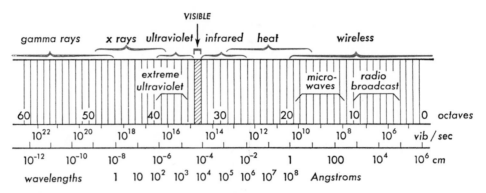

Fig. 59C *Complete wavelength and frequency chart of the electromagnetic spectrum as it is now known.*

the sun, the maximum energy is radiated in the green of the visible spectrum, with an appreciable amount of ultraviolet light on the one side and the infrared on the other. Thus the visible spectrum, as seen by the human eye, is but a small band out of all the waves emitted by a body as hot as the sun.

It is an interesting fact that the maximum energy radiated by a hot body shifts to shorter and shorter waves as the temperature rises. To be more exact, if the temperature of a body is doubled, the radiated energy maximum, λ_{max}, shifts to $\frac{1}{2}$ the wavelength. If the temperature is tripled, the energy maximum shifts to $\frac{1}{3}$ the wavelength, etc. This is known as Wien's* displacement law, and is written as an algebraic equation

$$\lambda_{max} T = C \qquad (59a)$$

where C is a constant, found by experiment to have a value of 0.2897 cm degrees, T is the absolute temperature, and λ_{max} the wavelength in cm at which the maximum energy is radiated. By substituting the constant C in Eq.(59a), the wavelength maximum radiated by a hot body can be calculated for any temperature.

---

* Wilhelm Wien (1864-1928), German physicist, chiefly known for important discoveries with cathode rays, canal rays, and the radiation of light. He was awarded the Nobel Prize in physics in 1911 for his discovery of the displacement law of heat radiation named in his honor.

The total energy radiated by a hot solid body is proportional to the fourth power of the absolute temperature. This law, known as the *Stefan-Bolzmann law,* is treated in Sec. 28.5.

59.2. The Complete Spectrum. *Visible, ultraviolet,* and *infrared* light waves do not represent all of the known kinds of electromagnetic radiation. A complete chart of the known spectrum is shown in Fig. 59C. Beyond the visible and infrared toward longer wavelengths, we find the *heat waves* and the *wireless waves,* while beyond the ultraviolet toward shorter wavelengths we find the *x rays* and the *gamma rays.*

In spite of the tremendous expanse of wavelengths ranging all the way from the longest wireless waves several miles in length to γ-ray waves one-million-millionth of a centimeter in length, all electromagnetic waves travel with the same velocity in vacuum: 186,300 mi/sec, or 3×10^{10} cm/sec.

Although their velocities in a vacuum are all the same, the properties of the various waves differ considerably. One striking illustration of these differences is found in the response of the human eye. Of the entire spectrum, only one very narrow band of waves can be seen, all the rest being invisible. Another illustration is the passage of light waves through the atmosphere. With the exception of the band of waves known as the extreme ultraviolet, the air is fairly transparent to all electromagnetic waves. To waves of the extreme ultraviolet,

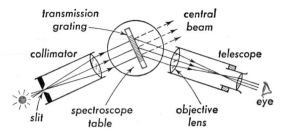

Fig. 59D *Diagram of a diffraction-grating spectroscope used in observing the visible spectrum.*

the air is quite opaque. *Fog is opaque to all but the wireless waves.*

59.3. The Angstrom as a Unit of Length. Because the wavelengths of light are so very small, the physicist has adopted a smaller unit of length than the centimeter or millimeter. This unit is called the angstrom (*abbr.* A or Å), after the Swedish scientist by that name. In 1868 Angstrom published a map of the visible spectrum of the sun, and on this map he labeled the wavelengths in ten-millionths of a millimeter. Since that time, light waves have been specified in these units.

In one centimeter, there are 100,000,000 angstroms.

$$1 \text{ cm} = 10^8 \text{ A}$$

In light, the velocity c in a vacuum is given by

$$c = \nu\lambda \qquad (59b)$$

where ν is the vibration frequency and λ is the wavelength. From this we see that the longer the wavelength, the lower is the frequency; and the shorter the wavelength, the higher is the frequency. It is common practice among physicists to designate the wavelength of light waves by the Greek letter λ (*lambda*) and the frequency by the Greek letter ν (nu).

59.4. Diffraction-Grating Instruments. As already explained in Sec. 43.7, and illustrated in Figs. 43Q and 43R, a diffraction grating is a device capable of separating white light into a spectrum. The essential difference between this spectrum and the one from a prism is that the diffraction

grating produces several images of the same spectrum, whereas a prism confines all of the light to one.

A glass transmission grating is shown in Fig. 59D mounted on the center table of a laboratory spectroscope. As the telescope is rotated to a position on either side of the central beam, the various colors and wavelengths emitted by the source can be observed in the *first order spectrum,* the *second order spectrum,* etc. (see Figs. 43O and 43Q).

Transmission gratings were first made by Fraunhofer, a German physicist, in 1819, and the first reflection gratings were made by H. A. Rowland,* an American physicist, in 1882. Although Rowland's first gratings were ruled on flat surfaces, his best ones were ruled upon the polished surfaces of concave mirrors.

59.5. Classification of Spectra. A spectrum may be defined as a wavelength analysis of a source of light. As illustrated in Sec. 59.1, such an analysis is usually made with a prism spectrograph or a diffraction grating. Different sources produce different wavelengths of light and hence reveal different spectra. All spectra may be grouped into four main classes:

(*a*) *Continuous emission spectra*
(*b*) *Line emission spectra*
(*c*) *Continuous absorption spectra*
(*d*) *Line absorption spectra*

* Henry A. Rowland (1848-1901), American physicist, is noted principally for his ruling of the first high quality diffraction gratings and his publication of a large and detailed photograph of the sun's spectrum. He was the recipient of many honors, including the Rumford Medal and the Draper Medal.

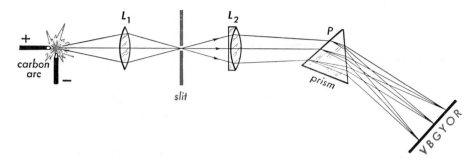

Fig. 59F *Experimental arrangement used in demonstrating spectrum lines in emission.*

The first of these, *continuous emission spectra,* has already been treated in detail in Sec. 59.1. There it was demonstrated that, when light from a hot *solid* like the tungsten filament of an electric light, or the positive carbon of an arc, is sent through a prism, a continuous band of color from red to violet is observed (see color plate, Fig. 59E). The intensity of such a spectrum depends upon the temperature and upon the hot body itself. All hot solids raised to the same temperature give very nearly the same continuous emission spectrum.

59.6. Line Emission Spectra. When the slit of a spectrograph is illuminated by the light from a mercury arc, a sodium lamp, or a neon discharge tube, a number of bright lines appear on the photographic plate in place of a continuous spectrum.

It is important to realize that line spectra derive their name from the fact that a slit is used whose image constitutes a line. If a small circular opening were used in place

of a slit, a disk image would appear in the place of each line.

The most intense sources of spectrum lines are obtained from metallic arcs and sparks. The flame of a carbon arc may be used for demonstration purposes by previously soaking the *positive carbon rod* in various chemicals. (An experimental arrangement for projecting the spectrum on a large screen is shown in Fig. 59F.) Common salt water (sodium chloride in solution) gives a brilliant yellow line characteristic of sodium. Solutions of strontium or calcium chloride will show other strong spectrum lines in the red, green, and blue.

While a continuous emission spectrum arises from hot solids, *a line spectrum always arises from a gas at high temperatures.* It is the gas flame of the carbon arc that gives rise to the line emission spectrum in the above experiment.

59.7. Continuous Absorption Spectra. Continuous absorption spectra are usually

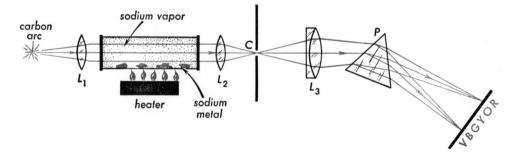

Fig. 59G *Experimental arrangement for demonstrating the line absorption spectrum of sodium vapor.*

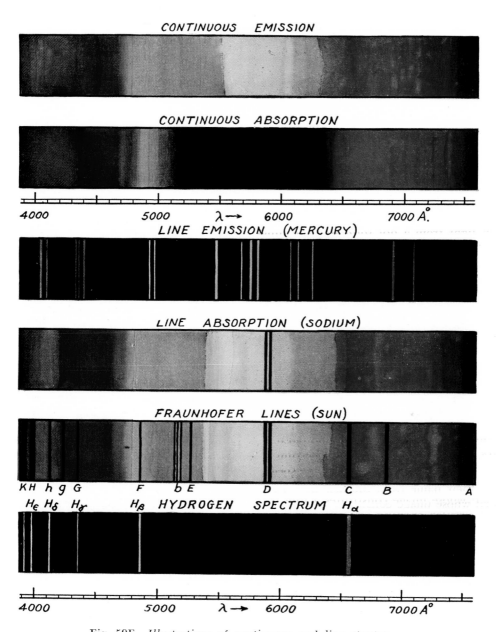

CONTINUOUS EMISSION

CONTINUOUS ABSORPTION

4000 5000 λ⟶ 6000 7000 A°.

LINE EMISSION (MERCURY)

LINE ABSORPTION (SODIUM)

FRAUNHOFER LINES (SUN)

KH h g G   F   b E   D   C   B   A
H_ε H_δ H_γ   H_β HYDROGEN   SPECTRUM   H_α

4000 5000 λ⟶ 6000 7000 A°

Fig. 59E   *Illustrations of continuous and line spectra.*

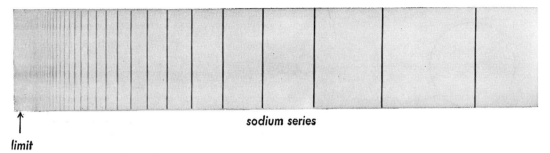

sodium series

↑

limit

Fig. 59H   *Absorption spectrum of sodium vapor. The principal series of sodium.* (After Jenkins.)

produced by passing a continuous emission spectrum through matter in the solid or liquid state. Good demonstrations can be performed by allowing white light to pass through colored glass. When the light is later dispersed by a prism, the missing colors will in general cover a wide band of wavelengths. The same experiment was described in Chapter 42 to demonstrate *body color* and *color mixing*.

59.8. Line Absorption Spectra. Line spectra in absorption are produced by sending continuous white light through a gas. Experimentally, the gas or vapor is inserted in the path of the light as shown in Fig. 59G. Light from a carbon arc, after passing as a parallel beam through a glass tube containing sodium vapor, is brought to a focus at the slit *C*. From there the light passes through a lens L_3 and a prism *P* to form a spectrum on the observing screen.

Sodium is chosen as an example for demonstration purposes because of its convenience. The vapor is produced by inserting a small amount of metallic sodium in a partially evacuated glass tube and heating it with a small gas burner. As the metal vaporizes, filling the tube with sodium vapor, a dark line will appear in the yellow region of the spectrum (see color plate, Fig. 59E).

If a photograph is taken of this absorption, and the photographic plate is long enough to extend into the ultraviolet, many absorption lines as shown in Fig. 59H are detected. A systematic array of absorption lines like this occur only with a few elements, principally with the alkali metals, lithium, sodium, potassium, rubidium, and caesium. All elements in the gaseous state, however, give rise to a number of absorption lines, usually in the ultraviolet region of the spectrum.

59.9. The Sun's Spectrum. The solar spectrum, consisting of a bright colored continuous spectrum interspersed by thousands of dark lines, was first observed by Wollaston in 1802, and independently discovered and studied by Fraunhofer in 1817. Fraunhofer mapped out several hundred of these lines and labeled eight of the most prominent lines by the first letters of the alphabet.

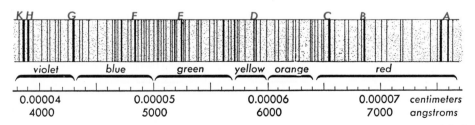

Fig. 59I   *Diagram of the solar spectrum indicating the most prominent lines labeled as they first were by Fraunhofer with the first letters of the alphabet.*

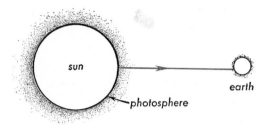

Fig. 59J *Light from the sun must pass through the solar atmosphere and the earth's atmosphere before reaching an observer on the earth's surface.*

The strongest of these lines, now called Fraunhofer lines, are illustrated in Fig. 59I.

In 1882, the American physicist, H. A. Rowland, ruled the first diffraction grating and, from photographs made with it, published a large map of the sun's spectrum. These lines are explained as being due to the absorption of light by the solar atmosphere. The surface of the sun at a temperature of 6000°K emits light of all wavelengths, i.e., a continuous emission spectrum. As this light passes out through the cooler gas layers of the solar atmosphere (see Fig. 59J), certain wavelengths are absorbed. Because the absorbing medium is in the gaseous state, the atoms and molecules there do not absorb all wavelengths equally, but rather they absorb principally those wavelengths they would emit if heated to a high temperature. Thus the atoms of one chemical element with their own characteristic frequencies absorb certain wavelengths, whereas the atoms of other elements absorb certain other wavelengths.

Before the sunlight reaches the earth's surface where it can be examined by an observer with a spectroscope, it must again pass through absorbing gases, this time the earth's atmosphere. Here, too, certain wavelengths are partially absorbed, producing other dark lines.

That the missing wavelengths correspond to definite chemical elements is illustrated by diagram in Fig. 59K. The center strip (b) represents a small section of the visible spectrum as obtained with sunlight entering the slit of a spectroscope. The upper and lower strips, (a) and (c), represent the bright line spectrum observed when an iron arc and a calcium arc are successively placed in front of the same slit. Where each calcium line occurs in the laboratory source, an absorption line is found in the sun's spectrum. The same is true for each iron line. The remaining lines, not matched by an iron or calcium line, are due to other elements.

It has been possible by spectrum photographs of this kind to identify about $\frac{2}{3}$ of the known chemical elements as existing on the sun. The reason why not all 90 or more elements are found is that some are too rare to produce absorption, whereas with others existing within the sun in large enough quantities the temperature is either too high or too low to bring out their lines.

Eight prominent Fraunhofer lines labeled in Fig. 59I have been identified as follows:

A, oxygen . . . . $\lambda = 7594 \times 10^{-10}$ m
B, oxygen . . . . $\lambda = 6870 \times 10^{-10}$ m
C, hydrogen . . . . $\lambda = 6562 \times 10^{-10}$ m
D, sodium . . . . $\lambda = 5893 \times 10^{-10}$ m
E, iron . . . . $\lambda = 5270 \times 10^{-10}$ m
F, hydrogen . . . . $\lambda = 4861 \times 10^{-10}$ m
G, iron . . . . $\lambda = 4308 \times 10^{-10}$ m
H, calcium . . . . $\lambda = 3968 \times 10^{-10}$ m

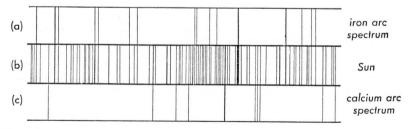

Fig. 59K *Schematic diagram illustrating the comparison of laboratory spectra from different elements with the many-line spectrum of the sun.*

59.10. The Balmer Series of Hydrogen. The first successful attempt to obtain a formula that represents the hydrogen series was made by Balmer, in 1885. Since that time, these lines have become known as the Balmer series of hydrogen. Balmer's formula is written

$$\lambda = B\left[\frac{n^2 \times m^2}{n^2 - m^2}\right] \qquad (59c)$$

where λ = wavelength in meters.

$B = 9.1127 \times 10^{-8}$ m

$m = 2$

$n = 3, 4, 5, 6, 7, \ldots$

If the number 3 is substituted for n in the above formula, the wavelength λ of the first line of the series is calculated. Likewise, if the number 4 is substituted in its place, the wavelength of the second line can be calculated, etc. When these calculations are carried out, the following wavelengths are obtained for the first four lines:

	Calculated	*Measured*
$H_\alpha = \frac{36}{5}B =$	6561.1×10^{-10}m	6562.1×10^{-10}m
$H_\beta = \frac{64}{12}B =$	4860.8×10^{-10}m	4860.7×10^{-10}m
$H_\gamma = \frac{100}{21}B =$	4339.4×10^{-10}m	4340.1×10^{-10}m
$H_\delta = \frac{144}{32}B =$	4100.7×10^{-10}m	4101.3×10^{-10}m

These wavelengths, as well as those calculated for other lines of the series, agree exactly with the measured values. Balmer did not derive his formula from any theory, but simply formulated it from the measured wavelength for each series line. The meaning of those whole numbers m and n is given in Sec. 60.4.

PROBLEMS

1. At what wavelength will the maximum energy be radiated by a solid piece of metal heated to a temperature of 2800°C?

2. Find the wavelength at which the maximum energy is radiated from a block of black carbon at a temperature of 227°C. What kind of light is it? (*Ans.* 5.79×10^4 A. Infrared.)

3. The wavelength range of the light of the visible spectrum extends from 4000 A in the violet to 7500 A in the red. What are these same wavelength limits in centimeters?

4. X rays from a certain X-ray source have a wavelength of 0.18 A. What is the wavelength in meters? (*Ans.* 1.8×10^{-9} m.)

5. Find the frequency of violet light of wavelength 4200 A.

6. What is the frequency of X rays if the wavelength is 0.40 A? (*Ans.* 7.5×10^{18} vib/sec.)

7. Calculate the wavelength maximum for light radiated by a body at 20 million degrees absolute. To what kind of light is this equivalent?

8. Calculate to five figures the wavelength of the tenth line of the Balmer series of hydrogen. (*Ans.* 3749.2 A.)

9. Briefly describe an experiment arrangement by which a line emission spectrum is produced.

10. Briefly describe an experimental arrangement by which a line absorption spectrum is produced.

11. Find the wavelength of the tenth line of the Balmer series of hydrogen.

12. Calculate the wavelength of the eighth line of the Balmer series of hydrogen. (*Ans.* 3796.9 A.)

13. Determine the wavelength of the series limit of the Balmer series of hydrogen. (Note $n = \infty$.)

14. From what kind of source does one obtain the most intense line emission spectrum?

15. How can one produce a line absorption spectrum in the laboratory?

Chapter 60

The Structure of Atoms

60.1. The Thomson Atom. Early in the 20th century, while Einstein was working out his special theory of relativity, J. J. Thomson proposed a type of electron shell structure for all atoms. His model structures were worked out by mathematics from Coulomb's law for charged particles and soon became known as the *"plum-pudding atom."*

Thomson visualized all of the positive charge of an atom as being spread out uniformly throughout a sphere about 10^{-8} cm in diameter, with the electrons as smaller particles distributed in shells somewhat as shown in Fig. 60A. While the net force

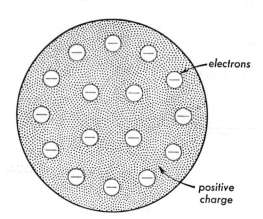

Fig. 60A *Diagram of the Thomson atom model.*

exerted by the positively charged sphere on each electron is toward the center of the sphere, the electrons mutually repel each other and form shells.

An excellent demonstration of the tendency to form rings for a two-dimensional model is shown in Fig. 60B. A glass dish 15 to 20 cm in diameter is wound with about 30 turns of No. 14 insulated copper wire. The most common steel sewing needles are then mounted in small corks (8 mm diameter and 8 mm long) as shown at the left, and magnetized by stroking from top to bottom with the *N* pole of a strong Alnico magnet.

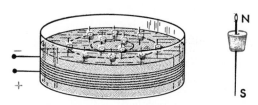

Fig. 60B *Floating needles in a magnetic field demonstrating the electron shell structure of the Thomson atom.*

With water in the dish, and a current of 1 to 2 amp through the coil, a single needle is placed upright in the water. Released, it will migrate to the center where the magnetic field is strongest. The addition of needles, one after another, near the edge of the dish, will result in the formation of geometrically symmetrical patterns and rings.

An increase or decrease in current will cause any given pattern to shrink or expand, corresponding to a greater or lesser positive charge. The stability of such ring patterns undoubtedly influenced the later extension by Bohr and Stoner of the quantized orbit model of the hydrogen atom to all atoms.

60.2. Bohr's Theory of the Hydrogen Atom. In 1913 Niels Bohr* proposed a the-

* Niels Bohr (1885-   ), Danish physicist, was born at Copenhagen, the son of Christian Bohr, professor of physiology at the University of Copenhagen. After taking his Ph.D. degree at Copenhagen in 1911, he studied for one year under J. J. Thomson at Cambridge, and one year under Ernest Ruth-

ory of the hydrogen atom that marked the beginning of a new era in the history of physics. With his theory, Bohr gave not only a satisfactory explanation of the Balmer series of hydrogen but a model for the structure of all other atoms as well.

Starting with what should be the simplest of all atoms, Bohr assumed that a hydrogen atom, $Z = 1$, consists of a nucleus with one positive charge $+e$ and a single electron of charge $-e$ revolving around it in a circular orbit of radius r (see Fig. 60C). Because it is

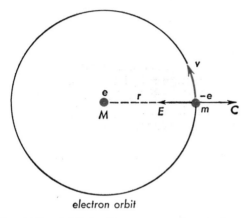

electron orbit

Fig. 60C *Orbital diagram of the hydrogen atom according to the Bohr theory.*

1840 times heavier than the electron, the nucleus could be assumed at rest.

To keep the electron in its orbit and prevent it from spiraling in toward the nucleus, or away from it to escape, Bohr next assumed that the inward centripetal force is due to, and therefore is, the inward electrostatic force E. From Eq.(14h), the centripetal force is mv^2/r, and from Coulomb's law, Eq.(47a), the electrostatic force is kee/r^2. Equating these two, we obtain

------

erford at Manchester. Returning to Copenhagen in 1913, with the results of the Rutherford scattering experiments fresh in his mind, he worked out and published his now famous theory of the hydrogen atom. In 1920, Bohr was appointed head of the institute for theoretical physics at the University of Copenhagen. In 1921 he was awarded the Hughes Medal of the Royal Society, and in 1922 the Nobel Prize in physics. Today he is the most honored Danish scientist and the father of a fine family.

$$m \frac{v^2}{r} = k \frac{ee}{r^2} \qquad (60a)$$

In the mks system of units,

m is in Kg
v is in m/sec
e is in coulombs
r is in meters
$k = 9 \times 10^9$

At this point Bohr introduced his second assumption, *the quantum hypothesis*. The electron, he assumed, cannot move in any sized orbit, stable under the conditions of the equation above, but in just certain *definite and discrete orbits*. The sizes of these orbits are governed by Eq.(60a) and the rule that the *angular momentum of the electron in its orbit is equal to an integer n times a constant h divided by* 2π.

$$mvr = n \frac{h}{2\pi} \qquad (60b)$$

$$n = 1, 2, 3, 4, 5, \cdots\cdots$$

In this equation n is called the principal *quantum number* and, because it can take whole number values only, it fixes the sizes of the allowed orbits. To find the radii of these "Bohr circular orbits," Eq.(60b) is solved for v, then squared and substituted in Eq.(60a) to give

$$r = \frac{n^2 h^2}{4\pi^2 m e^2 k} \qquad (60c)$$

If we put into this equation the known values of the constants e, m, h, and k,

$e = -1.60 \times 10^{-19}$ coul
$m = 9.10 \times 10^{-31}$ Kg
$h = 6.62 \times 10^{-34}$ joule sec
$k = 9 \times 10^9$ newton m^2/coul^2

the orbits shown in Fig. 60D are calculated. The innermost orbit, with $n = 1$, has a radius $r = 0.528 \times 10^{-10}$ m, or 0.528 A, and a diameter of 1.06 A.

1 meter $= 10^{10}$ angstroms

The second orbit is four times larger,

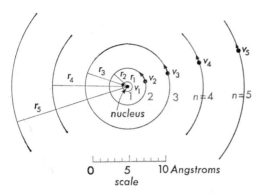

Fig. 60D *Scale diagram of the Bohr circular orbits of hydrogen.*

and the third is nine times, etc. The constant *h* is *Planck's constant*.

The velocity of the electron, when it is in any one orbit, can be determined from Eqs.(60b) and (60c). By substituting the value of *r* from Eq.(60c) in Eq.(60b) and solving for the velocity *v*, we obtain

$$v = k \frac{2\pi e^2}{nh} \qquad (60d)$$

In the innermost orbit, $n = 1$, the velocity v is $\frac{1}{137}$ the velocity of light. In the second orbit the speed is only $\frac{1}{2}$ as great, and in the third only $\frac{1}{3}$ as great, etc. With such small orbits and such high velocities, the number of revolutions per second becomes very high.

Since the circumference of any circular orbit is $2\pi r$, the frequency with which an electron goes around each orbit is given by

$$f = \frac{v}{2\pi r} \qquad (60e)$$

In the second Bohr circular orbit, the frequency is calculated to be 10^{15} rps. This, by comparison with the frequency of vibration of visible light waves, is of the same order of magnitude.

It should be noted that the one and only electron in each hydrogen atom can occupy only one orbit at any one time. If the electron changes its orbit, it must move to one of the allowed orbits and never stop in between.

60.3. Electron Jumps. Bohr's third and final assumption regarding the hydrogen atom concerns the emission of light. Bohr postulated that light is not emitted by an electron when it is moving in one of its fixed orbits, but only when the electron jumps from one orbit to another, as illustrated in Fig. 60E. Bohr said that the frequency of this light is not determined by the frequency of revolution but by the difference in energy between the initial and final orbit,

$$\boxed{E_2 - E_1 = h\nu} \qquad (60f)$$

where E_2 is the energy of the *initial orbit*, E_1 the energy of the *final orbit*, h is Planck's constant, and ν is the frequency of the light.

To illustrate this, let E_1, E_2, E_3, E_4, etc., represent the total energy of the electron when it is in the orbits $n = 1, 2, 3, 4$, etc., respectively. When, for example, the electron is in orbit $n = 3$ where its energy is E_3, and it jumps to orbit $n = 2$ where the energy is E_2 (see Fig. 60E), the energy differ-

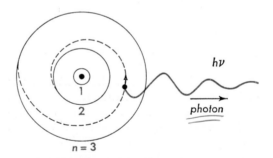

Fig. 60E *Schematic diagram of Bohr's quantum hypothesis of the radiation of light from a hydrogen atom.*

ence $E_3 - E_2$ is ejected from the atom in the form of a light wave of energy $h\nu$ called a *photon*. Here, then, is the origin of light waves from within the atom.

60.4. Bohr's Success. The success of Bohr's theory is not to be attributed so much to the mechanical picture or model of the atom just proposed, but rather to the development of an equation that agrees exactly with experimental observations.

By combining the equations presented in the preceding section, Bohr derived an equation for the frequency ν of the light waves emitted by hydrogen atoms. This equation is

$$\nu = 3.28965 \times 10^{15} \left(\frac{1}{n_1^2} - \frac{1}{n_2^2} \right) \quad (60g)$$

where n_1 and n_2 represent the *principal quantum numbers* of two orbits.

If we introduce the wave equation, valid for all waves,

$$c = \nu\lambda \quad (60h)$$

and replace ν by c/λ, where c is the speed of light, Eq.(60g) can be written

$$\boxed{\lambda = 9.1127 \times 10^{-8} \left(\frac{n_2^2 \times n_1^2}{n_2^2 - n_1^2} \right)} \quad (60i)$$

where λ is the wavelength of the light in *meters*, n_2 is the quantum number of any orbit of the hydrogen atom in which an electron is confined, and n_1 is the quantum number of the orbit to which the electron jumps to emit light of wavelength λ.

Bohr found that, if in Eq.(60i) he placed $n_1 = 2$ and $n_2 = 3$, the calculated wavelength, $\lambda = 0.00000065647$ m, is obtained, which is extremely close to the measured wavelength of the red spectrum line of hydrogen. (See p. 501.) If he placed $n_1 = 2$ and $n_2 = 4$, the calculated wavelength agreed exactly with the measured wavelength of the blue-green spectrum line of hydrogen.

In fact, the entire series of lines in the hydrogen spectrum are exactly represented by Eq.(60i), by setting $n_1 = 2$ and $n_2 = 3$, 4, 5, 6, etc. This series of lines, so prominently displayed by the sun and stars, as well as by any hydrogen discharge tube in the laboratory, is known as the *Balmer series*. (See Sec. 59.10.)

These quantum number changes correspond, as shown in Fig. 60F, to an electron jumping from any outer orbit n to the next to the smallest orbit $n = 2$. In any high-voltage electrical discharge in a glass tube containing hydrogen gas, many thousands of atoms may each have their one and only

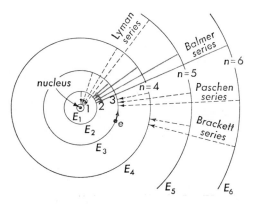

Fig. 60F *Diagram of the Bohr circular orbits of hydrogen showing the various electron jumps that give rise to the emission of light waves of different frequency.*

electron jumping from orbit 3 to 2, while in many other atoms the electron may be jumping from other orbits to $n = 2$. Hence, upon observing the light through a spectroscope, one may observe the entire Balmer series of lines.

60.5. Bohr's Predicted Series. Bohr's orbital model of the hydrogen atom not only accounts for the Balmer series of hydrogen, but also for many other observed lines as well.

By substituting $n_1 = 1$ and $n_2 = 2$, 3, 4, etc., in Eq.(60i), one obtains a series of spectrum lines in the ultraviolet region of the spectrum. These lines were first photographed by T. Lyman of Harvard University, and the wavelengths are found to check exactly with calculations. This series, now called the Lyman series, which can only be photographed in a vacuum spectrograph, is reproduced in Fig. 60G. On the orbital picture of Fig. 60F, the Lyman series of lines arises from electron jumps from any outer orbit directly to the innermost orbit, the *normal state*.

If, in Eq.(60i), n_1 is set equal to 3 and n_2 to 4, 5, 6, etc., the calculated frequencies predict spectrum lines in the infrared spectrum. These lines were first looked for and observed, exactly as predicted, by F. Paschen; the series is now known by his name. Another series of lines arising from electron jumps, ending on orbit $n = 4$, was

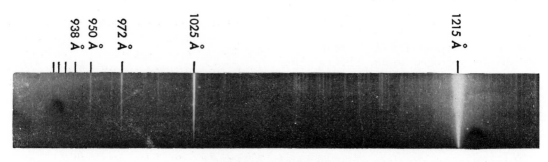

Lyman series of hydrogen

Fig. 60G *Photograph of the extreme ultraviolet series of hydrogen, predicted by Bohr's theory and first observed by Lyman.*

predicted and observed in the far infrared by Brackett.

60.6. Normal and Excited Atoms. When the single electron of a hydrogen atom is in the innermost orbit, $n = 1$, the atom is said to be in its normal state. As the name implies, this is the condition of most free hydrogen atoms in a gas under normal room temperature and pressure. If an electrical discharge is sent through a vessel containing hydrogen gas, cathode rays (electrons) moving at high speed make frequent collisions with electrons, knocking some of them out of the atom completely and some of them into one of the outer allowed orbits, $n = 2, 3, 4$, etc.

When the electron is completely removed from the atom, the atom is said to be *ionized;* whereas when it is forced into an outer orbit, the atom is said to be *excited.* Once in an excited state, an atom will not remain that way long, for the electron under the attraction by the nucleus will jump to an inner orbit. By jumping to an inner orbit, the electron loses all or part of the energy it had gained.

When an electron is in an excited state, it does not necessarily return to the innermost orbit by a single jump, but may return by several jumps, thereby emitting several different light waves, or quanta.

60.7. Energy Levels. By combining Bohr's equations, Eq.(60a) and Eq.(60b), the energy of an electron in a circular orbit of the hydrogen atom can be calculated. The total energy is just the sum of the kinetic energy $\frac{1}{2}mv^2$, and the potential energy.

$$\text{total } E = \text{K.E.} + \text{P.E.} \qquad (60j)$$

To find the potential energy of the electron in its orbit we use Eq.(50b). By this equation we see that the potential V, at any point at a distance r from the nuclear charge $+e$, is given by

$$V = k\frac{e}{r}$$

Since V is the work done per unit charge in bringing any charge up to a distance r, one must multiply by the electron's charge $-e$ to obtain as the stored potential energy, $-Ve$.

The two forms of stored energy are, therefore,

$$\text{P.E.} = -k\frac{ee}{r}$$

and

$$\text{K.E.} = +\frac{1}{2}mv^2$$

Substituting Eq.(60d) for v, and Eq.(60c) for r, and substituting in Eq.(60j), one obtains, as Bohr did,

$$\text{total } E = -\frac{2\pi^2me^4k^2}{n^2h^2} \qquad (60k)$$

The minus sign signifies that one must do work on the electron to remove it from the atom.

With the exception of the principal quantum number n, all quantities in this equation are the same for all orbits. We can therefore write

$$E = -\frac{1}{n^2}R \qquad (60l)$$

where R is constant and equal to

$$R = \frac{2\pi^2 m e^4 k^2}{h^2}$$

which, upon substitution of the known values of all the constants, gives

$$R = 2.1790 \times 10^{-18}\ \text{joules} \qquad (60m)$$

Eq.(60l) is an important equation in atomic structure, for it gives the energy of the electron when it occupies any one of the different orbits of the hydrogen atom. Instead of drawing orbits to the scale of their radius as in Fig. 60D, it is customary to draw horizontal lines to an energy scale, as shown in Fig. 60H. This is called an *energy level diagram*. The various electron jumps between the allowed orbits of Fig. 60F now become vertical arrows between the energy levels.

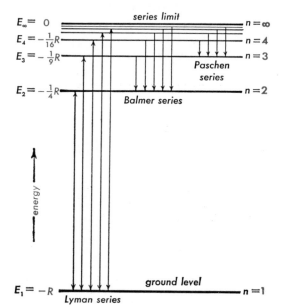

Fig. 60H *Energy level diagram for the hydrogen atom. Vertical arrows represent electron jumps.*

The importance of this kind of diagram is to be attributed to Bohr's third relation, Eq.(60f), where the energy $h\nu$ of each radiated light wave is just equal to the difference between two energies. The energy of each radiated photon is, therefore, proportional to the length of its corresponding arrow.

The first line of the Balmer series $\lambda = 6561A$, the red line in Figs. 59E and 66B, corresponds to the short arrow, $n = 3$ to $n = 2$. The second line of the same series is the blue-green line $\lambda = 4861A$, and corresponds to the slightly longer arrow, $n = 4$ to $n = 2$, etc.

When an electrical discharge is sent through hydrogen gas, each atom, by collision with other atoms, has its only electron excited to an upper level, and then that electron jumps down again from one level to another, giving rise to the emission of light waves. If, as another experiment, a whole continuous spectrum of light waves is sent through a tube containing hydrogen gas, the hydrogen atoms will be in the ground level, $n = 1$, and by *resonance* may absorb frequencies corresponding to any one of the Lyman series. In absorbing one of these frequencies, the electron of that atom will jump to an upper energy level. The arrowheads at the top of these vertical lines, correspond, therefore, to resonance absorption. Those same excited electrons can then return by downward jumps, emitting light, and stopping finally on the ground level.

Resonance absorption is the explanation of the dark lines of the sodium spectrum shown in Fig. 59H and the solar spectrum in Fig. 59E.

60.8 Bohr-Stoner Scheme of the Building-Up of Atoms. Bohr and Stoner proposed an extension of the orbital model of hydrogen to include all of the chemical elements. As shown by the examples in Fig. 60I, each atom is composed of a positively charged nucleus with a number of electrons around it.

Although the nucleus is a relatively small particle less than 10^{-12} cm in diameter, it contains almost the entire mass of the atom, a mass equal in *atomic mass units* to the *atomic weight.*

The positive charge carried by the nucleus is equal numerically to the atomic number, and it determines the number of electrons located in orbits outside.

A helium atom, atomic number $Z = 2$, has two positive charges on the nucleus and two electrons outside. A lithium atom, atomic number $Z = 3$, contains three positive charges on the nucleus and three electrons outside. A mercury atom, atomic number 80, contains 80 positive charges on the nucleus and 80 electrons outside.

The orbits to which the electrons are confined are the Bohr orbits of hydrogen with $n = 1$, 2, 3, etc., and are called electron shells. Going from element to element in the atomic table, starting with hydrogen, electrons are added one after the other, filling one shell and then another. A shell is filled only when it contains a number of electrons given by $2n^2$. To illustrate this, the first shell $n = 1$ is filled when it has 2 electrons, the second shell $n = 2$ when it has 8 electrons, the third shell $n = 3$ when it has 18 electrons, etc. $2 \times 1^2 = 2$, $2 \times 2^2 = 8$, $2 \times 3^2 = 18$, etc.

quantum number	$n=1$	$n=2$	$n=3$	$n=4$
number of electrons	2	8	18	32

Among the heavier elements there are several departures from the order in which the shells are filled. Although these departures are not important from the present standpoint, their nature is illustrated by the mercury atom, Fig. 60I. The four inner shells, $n = 1$, 2, 3, and 4, are entirely filled with 2, 8, 18, and 32 electrons, respectively, while the fifth shell contains only 18 electrons and the sixth shell 2 electrons. The reasons for such departures are now well understood and are indicative of the chemical behavior of the heavy elements.

It is important to note that, as the nuclear charge increases and additional electrons are added in outer shells, the inner shells, under the stronger attraction of the nucleus, shrink in size. The net result of this shrinkage is that the heaviest elements in the periodic table are not much larger in diameter than the lighter elements. The schematic diagrams in Fig. 60I are drawn approximately to the same scale.

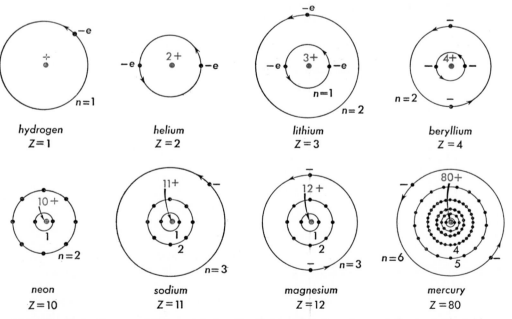

Fig. 60I   *Bohr-Stoner orbital models for the light and heavy atoms of the periodic table.*

The experimental confirmation of these upper limits to the allowed number of electrons in each shell is now considered one of the most fundamental principles of nature. A sound theoretical explanation of this principle of atomic structure was first given by W. Pauli, in 1925, and is commonly referred to as the *Pauli exclusion principle*.

60.9. Elliptical Orbits. Within but a few months after Bohr (in Denmark) published a report telling of his phenomenal success in explaining the hydrogen spectrum with circular orbits, Sommerfeld (in Germany) extended the theory to include elliptical orbits as well. Because these orbits played such an important role in later developments in atomic structure, they deserve some attention here.

The net result of Sommerfeld's theory showed that the electron in any one of the allowed energy levels of a hydrogen atom may move in any one of a number of orbits. For each energy level $n = 1$, $n = 2$, $n = 3$, etc., as shown in Fig. 60H, there are n possible orbits.

Diagrams of the allowed orbits for the first three energy levels are shown in Fig. 60J. For $n = 3$, for example, there are three orbits, with designations $l = 2$, $l = 1$, and $l = 0$. The diameter of the circular orbit is given by Bohr's theory, and this is just equal to the major axes of the two elliptical orbits. The minor axes are $\frac{2}{3}$ and $\frac{1}{3}$ of the major axis.

It is common practice to assign letters to the l-values as follows.

$l = 0$	$l = 1$	$l = 2$	$l = 3$	$l = 4$ *orbits*
s	p	d	f	g

According to this system, the circular orbit with $n = 3$ and $l = 2$ is designated $3d$, while the elliptical orbit $n = 2$ and $l = 0$ is designated $2s$, etc. n is the *principal quantum number* and l is the *orbital quantum number*. All orbits having the same value of n have the same total energy, the energy given by Bohr's equation for circular orbits, Eq.(60l).

Each of the allowed orbits of the Bohr-Sommerfeld model of the hydrogen atom becomes a subshell into which electrons are added to build up the elements of the periodic table in the Bohr-Stoner scheme. These subshells are tabulated as follows:

Subshells

n \ l	0	1	2	3	4
1	$1s^2$				
2	$2s^2$	$2p^6$			
3	$3s^2$	$3p^6$	$3d^{10}$		
4	$4s^2$	$4p^6$	$4d^{10}$	$4f^{14}$	
5	$5s^2$	$5p^6$	$5d^{10}$	$5f^{14}$	$6g^{18}$

(*Shells*)

The maximum number of electrons allowed in any one subshell is given by the relation

$$2(2l + 1)$$

This is called the *Pauli exclusion principle,* each subshell being filled when it contains the following number of electrons.

$l = 0$	1	2	3	4
Subshell s	p	d	f	g
Number of electrons 2	6	10	14	18

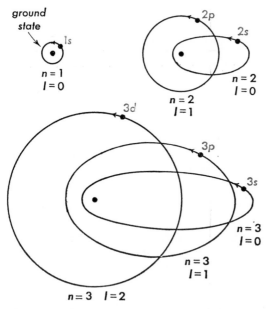

Fig. 60J *Electron orbitals for the hydrogen atom according to the Bohr-Sommerfeld theory.*

An orbital diagram of an argon atom is given in Fig. 60K. The electron configuration is given below, the exponents specifying the total number of electrons in that subshell. Because such elliptical orbits are not easily drawn, it is customary to group all subshells of the same n-value together and show them in rings as in Fig. 60I.

A complete table of subshell build-up of all the known elements is given in Appendix IX. The rules for the filling of subshells, and ones that hold throughout the periodic table are the following:

1. *Subshells are grouped under like values of $n + l$.*
2. *Groups are filled in the order of increasing $n + l$.*
3. *Within each $n + l$ group, subshells are filled in the order of decreasing l-values.*

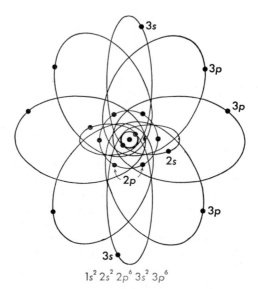

$$1s^2\,2s^2\,2p^6\,3s^2\,3p^6$$

Fig. 60K   *Electron configuration for an argon atom. $Z = 18$.*

PROBLEMS

1. **Find** the diameter of the first four circular orbits of hydrogen according to the Bohr theory.

2. What would be the approximate quantum number n for a circular orbit of hydrogen 0.0001 mm in diameter? This would be just big enough to see under a microscope. (*Ans.* $n = 31$.)

3. Calculate the wavelength of the third line of the Balmer series of hydrogen.

4. Find the wavelengths of the fourth and fifth lines of the Balmer series of hydrogen. (*Ans.* 4100.7A; 3969.1A.)

5. Compute the wavelengths of the first three lines of the Lyman series of hydrogen.

6. Find the wavelengths of the first three lines of the Paschen series of hydrogen. (*Ans.* 1.8756×10^{-4} cm; 1.2822×10^{-4}; 1.0941×10^{-4}.)

7. Make a diagram of a zinc atom (atomic number 30) according to the Bohr-Stoner scheme.

8. Make a diagram of a krypton atom (atomic number 36) according to the Bohr-Stoner scheme. (*Ans.* 2, 8, 18, 8.)

9. Calculate the wavelengths of the 4th and 5th spectrum lines of the Paschen series of hydrogen. See Eq.(59c).

10. Calculate the wavelength of the second spectrum line of the Brackett series of hydrogen. See Eq.(59c). (*Ans.* 26,245A.)

11. Find the radius of the twenty-fifth orbit of the electron in a hydrogen atom.

12. Make a diagram of a zinc atom according to the Bohr-Stoner scheme.

13. Make a diagram of a krypton atom, showing the number of electrons in each shell according to the Bohr-Stoner scheme.

14. Determine the wavelength of the fourth line of the Brackett series of hydrogen. (*Ans.* 19,440A.)

15. What would be the approximate quantum number n for a circular orbit of hydrogen 1 mm in diameter?

16. (a) Solve Eq.(60a) for r as the only unknown. (b) Solve Eq.(60b) for r as the only unknown.

17. Set the right-hand sides of the equations obtained in Prob. 16 equal to each other, and solve for v as the unknown quantity.

18. Using Eq.(60d) for v and the known values of e, m, h, and k, calculate the electrons' velocity in the first Bohr circular orbit. (*Ans.* 2.19×10^6 m/sec.)

Chapter 61

The Photoelectric Effect — *Nobel Prize (Einstein)*

The photoelectric effect was discovered by Heinrich Hertz, in 1887, when he observed that ultraviolet light, falling on the electrodes of a spark gap, caused a high-voltage discharge to jump greater distances than when it was left in the dark. One year later, Hallwachs made the important observation that ultraviolet light falling on a negatively charged body caused it to lose its charge, whereas a positively charged body was not affected. Ten years later J. J. Thomson and P. Lenard showed independently that the action of the light was to cause the emission of free negative charges from the metal surface. Although these negative charges are no different from all other electrons, it is customary to refer to them as "photoelectrons."

61.1. Photoelectrons. The photoelectric effect, in its simplest form, is demonstrated in Fig. 61A. Light from a carbon arc is focused by means of a quartz lens onto a freshly polished plate of zinc metal. When the plate is charged negatively, and the

light is turned on, the gold leaf of the attached electroscope slowly falls. It falls because the electrons, under the action of the light, leave the zinc plate at the illuminated spot P. When the plate is positively charged, the gold leaf does not fall, showing that the plate retains its charge. The same result of no discharge is observed if the zinc plate is negatively charged and a sheet of glass is inserted, as shown in the figure. When the glass is removed, the gold leaf again falls. Since common glass transmits visible and infrared light, but not ultraviolet, we conclude from the latter result that electrons are liberated only by ultraviolet light. This is also generally true for nearly all of the known metals.

A few elements, namely the alkali metals, *lithium, sodium, potassium, rubidium,* and *caesium,* are exceptions to this, for they will eject photoelectrons when visible light falls on them. For this reason the *alkali metals* are often used in the manufacture of photoelectric cells.

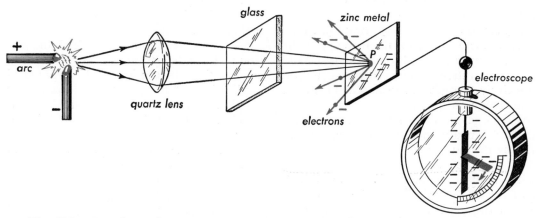

Fig. 61A *Experimental arrangement for demonstrating the photoelectric effect. When the glass plate is inserted, the effect stops.*

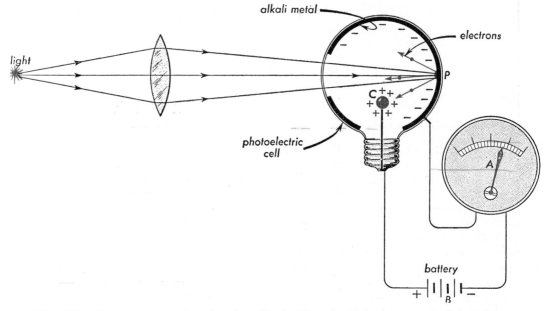

Fig. 61B *Diagram of a photoelectric cell, showing the light beam and electrical connections necessary for its operation.*

61.2. The Photoelectric Cell. Photoelectric cells are usually made by depositing a thin layer of an alkali metal on the inner surface of a small vacuum tube (see Fig. 61B). If the cell is to operate in ultraviolet light, it is made of quartz, whereas if it is to be used in visible light it is made of common glass. The cell must be thoroughly evacuated, as the oxygen content of the air will combine chemically with the active metal layer, contaminating its surface and making it insensitive to visible light. A small section of the cell is always left clear to serve as a window for the incoming light. Photoelectrons, upon leaving the metal surface, are attracted and collected by the positively charged electrode C. The negative charge on the metal film and the positive charge on the central collector electrode are maintained at a constant potential by the battery B.

A beam of light shining through the window of a photoelectric cell acts like a switch that completes an electric circuit. When the light strikes the metal P, there is a flow of electrons to the collector C, thus causing a current to flow around the circuit. This current can be measured by means of an ammeter at A. If the intensity of the light increases, the number of photoelectrons increases and the current therefore rises. When the light is shut off, the photoelectric action ceases and the current stops. If the metal film is positively charged, the cell becomes inactive to light, since electrons attempting to leave the plate are held back by electrostatic attraction. All of these factors are readily demonstrated by a simple electrical circuit arranged as shown in Fig. 61B.

61.3. Practical Applications. Talking motion pictures, television, and burglar alarms are but three of the hundreds of practical applications of the photoelectric cell. The simplest of these is the burglar alarm, in which a beam of infrared light (invisible to the eye) is projected across the room into a photoelectric cell connected as shown in Fig. 61B. When an intruder walks through the beam, thus interrupting the light for an instant, the photoelectric current ceases momentarily. An electric relay in place of the ammeter at A in the circuit moves, causing another electric circuit to be completed and thereby ringing an electric bell.

During the filming of talking motion pictures, a "sound track" is produced photographically on the side of the master motion picture film. Such sound tracks are shown in Fig. 61C. In strip (a), which is

two other types of sound track used in other patented recording systems.

When a sound film is projected on the screen in the theater (see Fig. 61D), the

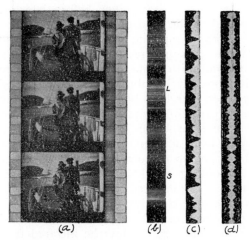

Fig. 61C (a) Section of a moving picture film from Metro-Goldwyn-Mayer's "Spawn of the North," showing the single variable density sound track. (b) Enlarged section of sound track from (a). (c) Section of a unilateral variable area sound track. (d) Section of a bilateral variable area sound track.

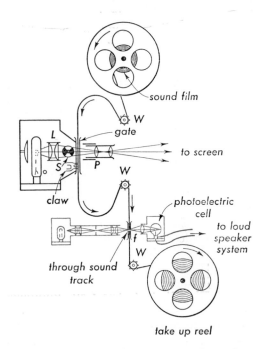

Fig. 61D Cross section of a motion picture projector with sound attachment.

just a sample of one of the several kinds of sound tracks, the sound vibrations on the stage are converted into electrical vibrations by the stage microphone and then carried over wires to the camera taking the pictures. There the electrical impulses are made to move one of the jaws of a narrow slit through which a beam of light passes to the edge of the film. Loud sounds open the slit wide with each vibration, allowing a large amount of light through.

When the film is developed and positives are made for distribution, the loud sounds show up as periodic bands with considerable contrast as at L in strip (b). The latter strip is an enlarged section of the *single variable density* sound track seen on the right in photograph (a). Weaker sounds produce bands with less contrast as at S. Strips (c) and (d) are enlarged sections of

film for the pictures themselves must of necessity move intermittently through the projection system P of the projection machine. As the film moves downward, each picture (frame) stops momentarily in front of the condensing lenses L and then moves on for the next frame. While the film is moving, the light is cut off by a rotating shutter S, and while it is at rest the light passes through to the screen. Thus the continuous motion seen on the screen is the result of a number of still pictures projected one after the other in rapid succession. To make this motion seem smooth, and not jumpy, it is standard practice to project 24 frames each second.

To produce the sound, a small subsidiary beam of light, shown in detail in Fig. 61E, shines through the sound track at a point 25 frames farther along on the film

$$h\nu - (h\nu_0) = KE_{max}$$

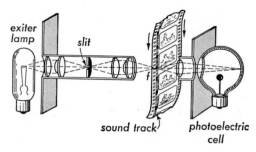

Fig. 61E *Detail of sound "pick-up" system of a moving picture projector showing the exciter lamp, sound track, and photoelectric cell.*

where the motion is no longer intermittent, but smooth. As the sound track moves through the focus line *f* of the subsidiary light at constant speed, the transmitted light falling on the photoelectric cell fluctuates exactly as the sound track interrupts it. The photoelectric cell then changes the fluctuating light beam into a fluctuating electric current with the same variations. When transmitted to the radio amplifier and loudspeaker, the fluctuating current is changed into sound vibrations. Thus, sound vibrations have been carried over a light beam from the photographic film to the photoelectric cell and then by means of a loud-speaker system reproduced as sound.

61.4. Sound over a Light Beam. The sending of voice and musical sounds for several miles over a light beam is readily accomplished with a suitable light source as transmitter and a photoelectric cell as a receiver. A convenient laboratory demonstration can be made by using a small ¼-watt neon glow lamp as a source of light, as shown in Fig. 61F.

Sound waves entering the microphone *M* produce electric current fluctuations which, after being strengthened by a two-

stage amplifier, cause the intensity of the neon glow lamp *N* to fluctuate accordingly. Made into a parallel beam by a lens L_1, the light travels across the room to a second lens L_2 and a photoelectric cell, where the light is changed back into a varying electric current. This faint signal is then amplified by a two-stage amplifier before it is delivered to the loudspeaker.

If the microphone is replaced by a phonograph "pick-up," records can be played at the transmitter end, and excellent reproduction can be obtained from the loudspeaker. The light beam can be made completely invisible by placing an infrared filter in the light beam at *F*. Talking several miles over a beam of invisible light was developed to quite a high state of perfection during World War II. One system employs the infrared light from a glow discharge tube containing caesium, while several others, modulated by mechanically vibrating mirrors, employ the infrared from a tungsten filament lamp. Another system employs the invisible ultraviolet light from a glow discharge tube containing gallium.

61.5. Velocity of Photoelectrons. The first measurements of the velocity of photoelectrons led to the very startling discovery that the velocity does not increase as the intensity of the light increases. Increasing the intensity of the light increases the number of photoelectrons, but not their velocity. This discovery, as we shall see later, has had far-reaching implications in its result, for it has played an important role in the development of our modern concepts of light and atomic structure.

Lenard's experiments, performed as far back as 1902, showed, that to increase the velocity of photoelectrons one must increase the frequency of the light, i.e., use

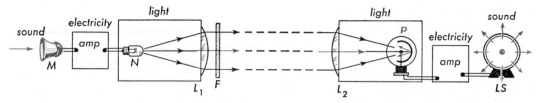

Fig. 61F *Voice and musical sounds can be sent long distances over a beam of light.*

shorter wavelengths. The shorter the wavelength of the light used, the higher are the velocities of the electrons.

61.6. Einstein's Photoelectric Equation. Following an earlier idea of Planck's that light waves consist of tiny bundles of energy called *photons* or *quanta*, Einstein proposed an explanation of the photoelectric effect as early as 1905. His ideas were expressed in one simple relation, an algebraic equation, destined to become famous in the annals of physics. Two Nobel Prizes, one to Einstein in 1921 and one to Millikan in 1923, have been granted on this, the photoelectric equation,

$$h\nu = W + \tfrac{1}{2}mv^2 \qquad (61a)$$

The first term, $h\nu$, represents the total energy content of a single quantum of light incident on a metal surface, as shown in Fig. 61G. The letter h is a constant, called

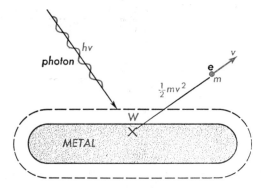

Fig. 61G *A light quantum (photon) of energy hν, incident on a metal surface, ejects an electron with a velocity v given by Einstein's equation.*

Planck's constant of action, which has the same value for all light waves regardless of the frequency ν. At or beneath the surface of the metal, this *light quantum*, better known as a *photon*, is completely absorbed and, in disappearing, imparts its total energy to a single electron. Part of this energy W is consumed in getting the electron free from the atoms and away from the metal surface; the remainder is used in giving the electron a kinetic energy $\tfrac{1}{2}mv^2$,

and therefore a velocity. For some metals like platinum, the energy required to pull an electron away from the surface is large, whereas for other metals like the alkalies it is quite small. W is called the *work function* of the metal.

61.7. Millikan's Measurements of h. The letter h in Einstein's photoelectric equation is important because it is fundamental to the structure of all matter and is therefore *a universal constant*. Having first been introduced by Planck in 1901, the name *Planck's constant* has become firmly attached to this symbol h. The first experimental confirmation of Einstein's photoelectric equation came in 1912 when A. L. Hughes, and independently O. W. Richardson and K. T. Compton, observed that the energy of photoelectrons increased proportionately with the frequency. The constant of proportionality they found to be approximately equal to a constant, Planck's constant h.

Subsequently, Millikan carried out extensive experiments which established the photoelectric equation so accurately that his work is now considered to give one of the most trustworthy values for h.

To do this, it was necessary to measure the three factors, v, W, and $\tfrac{1}{2}mv^2$, and calculate h as the unknown quantity in Eq.(61a). The most recent value obtained for this universal constant is

$$\text{Planck's Constant}$$
$$h = 6.62 \times 10^{-34} \text{ joule sec} \qquad (61b)$$

Since the frequency of visible light is about 6×10^{14} vib/sec, the energy in a single photon or quantum of visible light is the product of these two numbers or 3.972×10^{-19} joules. In other words, it would take about 2.5×10^{18} photons to do one joule of work.

It should be pointed out in passing that the photon, in ejecting an electron from a metal surface as in the photoelectric effect, disappears completely, i.e., it is annihilated. This is exactly the reverse of the process of the production of X rays, where a high-speed electron, upon hitting a metal target and being suddenly stopped, creates and emits a photon of high frequency.

61.8. The Photoelectric Threshold. The photoelectric threshold, ν_0, is defined as the frequency of light which, falling on a surface, is just able to liberate electrons without giving them any additional kinetic energy. For such a frequency, the kinetic energy $\frac{1}{2}mv^2$ in Einstein's equation is zero and the energy of the photon, $h\nu_0 = W$. Eq.(61a) can therefore be written in the form

$$h\nu = h\nu_0 + \tfrac{1}{2}mv^2 \qquad (61b)$$

The meaning of ν_0 in this new equation is quite clear: For frequencies lower than ν_0, electrons are not liberated, whereas for frequencies greater than ν_0 they are ejected with a determined velocity.

The photoelectric threshold for most metals lies in the ultraviolet where the frequencies are relatively high. For the alkali metals the threshold lies in the visible and near infrared spectrum. In other words, it takes photons of less energy to free electrons from the alkali metals than it does to free them from most other metals.

61.9. Secondary Electrons. When electrons strike the surface of a metal plate, they knock additional electrons free from the surface. These are called *secondary electrons* and the process is called *secondary emission* (see Fig. 61H). As the speed of a

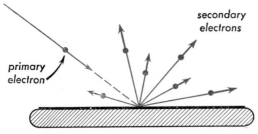

Fig. 61H *The impact of a single electron liberates additional electrons from a metal surface.*

primary or incident electron increases from zero to a few hundred volts, the number of secondaries increases toward a definite maximum. For most metal surfaces, this maximum is in the neighborhood of two, while for certain alkali metal films it may be as great as eight or ten. In general, it is greatest for surfaces having a *low work function*.

61.10. Photo-Multiplier Tubes. The process of secondary electron emission is widely used in a special type of photoelectric cell used most effectively in detecting faint light. A cross-section diagram of such a photo-multiplier tube is given in Fig. 61I.

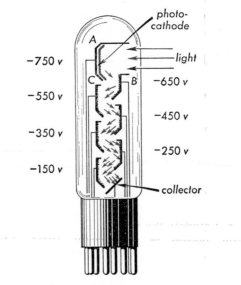

Fig. 61I *Photo-multiplier tube with six stages. Cesium-oxide, silver-coated photo-cathode.*

The number of photoelectrons from the photo-cathode A is proportional to the intensity of the incident light. These are attracted toward the next plate B, more positive by 100 volts, where upon impact additional electrons are liberated. Attracted to the next more positive plate C, still more electrons are liberated. By the time the collector plate has been reached, a small avalanche of electrons has developed, and a correspondingly large charge and current are led off through that electrode to a suitable recording device.

If each electron on impact releases n secondaries, then, in a tube with k stages, the number arriving at the collector would be n^k. For example, if $n = 6$, and if $k = 5$, then $n^k = 7776$ electrons. This is an enormous gain over the signal obtained from a standard photo tube. Photo-multiplier tubes have been used most successfully with faint light, not only with visible light but with infrared and ultraviolet as well.

PROBLEMS

1. Find the energy equivalent to a light wave of wavelength 5×10^{-7} m. Such light is in the green region of the visible spectrum.

2. Calculate the energy in joules of ultraviolet light of wavelength 3×10^{-7} m. (*Ans.* 6.62×10^{-19} joules.)

3. If X rays with a wavelength of 5.0×10^{-10} m fall on a metal plate, what would be the maximum velocity of the photoelectrons emitted? (Assume the work function to be negligibly small, $W = 0$.)

4. Assuming the work function of sodium to be negligibly small, what will be the velocity of photoelectrons emitted as the result of incident light of wavelength 3×10^{-8} m? This is ultraviolet light. (*Ans.* 3.81×10^6 m/sec.)

5. Find the energy equivalent to a γ-ray whose wavelength is 1×10^{-3}A.

6. Calculate the energy in joules of a visible light photon of Wavelength 7500A. (*Ans.* 2.65×10^{-19} joules.)

7. If the photoelectric threshold of metallic copper is at $\lambda = 3200$A, and ultraviolet light of wavelength 2536A falls on it, find (a) the maximum kinetic energy of the photoelectrons ejected, (b) the maximum velocity of the photoelectrons, and (c) the value of the work function in joules.

8. If light of wavelength 6000A falls on a metal surface and emits photoelectrons with a velocity of 2.5×10^7 cm/sec, what is the wavelength of the photoelectric threshold? (*Ans.* 6550 A.)

9. If X rays with a wavelength of 0.42A fall on a metal plate, what would be the maximum velocity of the photoelectrons emitted? The work function can be assumed to be negligibly small.

10. Find the over-all gain of a ten-stage, photo-multiplier tube if the average number of secondary electrons produced by each primary electron is six. (*Ans.* 60.4×10^6.)

11. A six-stage, photo-multiplier tube has an over-all gain of 15,625. Find the average number of secondary electrons produced by each primary electron.

12. Make a diagram showing how a photoelectric cell could be used to count the number of cars passing a given point on a highway in a single day.

13. When X rays with a wavelength of 1.5A fall on a copper plate, what would be the maximum velocity of the photoelectrons emitted? Assume the work function to be negligible.

Chapter 62

X Rays

One of the most interesting episodes in the history of modern science began with the accidental discovery of X rays by Wilhelm Röntgen* in 1895. While studying the green fluorescent stage of an electrical discharge in a Crookes tube, Röntgen observed the bright fluorescence of some nearby crystals of barium platino-cyanide. Even though the discharge tube was in a darkened room, and entirely surrounded with black paper to prevent the escape of visible light, a distant screen covered with crystals would fluoresce brightly when the discharge was turned on. Röntgen reasoned, therefore, that some kind of invisible, yet penetrating, rays of an unknown kind were being given out by the discharge tube. These rays he called *X rays,* the letter *X* meaning, as it so often does in algebra, an unknown.

In the short series of experiments that followed his discovery, Röntgen found that the unknown rays were coming from the glass walls of the tube itself and, in particular, from the region where the most intense part of the cathode ray beam was striking the glass. So great was the importance of this discovery that, within but a few weeks

* Wilhelm Konrad von Röntgen (1845-1923). Born at Lennep on March 27, 1845, Röntgen received his education in Holland and Switzerland. His scientific career began at the age of 25 when he became an assistant in the physics laboratory at Würzburg, Germany. After a teaching period extending over a period of 25 years, which carried him to the University of Strasbourg, then to Hohenheim, back to Strasbourg, then to Giessen, and finally to Würzburg again, he discovered X rays in his laboratory at Würzburg in 1895. For this discovery, he received the Rumford Medal of the Royal Society in 1896 and the first Nobel Prize in physics in 1901. Röntgen also conducted researches in light, heat, and elasticity, but none of these works compares in importance with his discovery of X rays.

of Röntgen's announcement, X rays were being used as an aid in surgical operations in Vienna. This, along with other practical applications and uses that can be made of a single scientific discovery, is a good example of the role played by modern science in the rapid advancement of civilization.

62.1. X-ray Tubes. The Crookes tube with which Röntgen made his discovery bears very little resemblance to the modern X-ray tube. In form it had somewhat the appearance of the tube shown in Fig. 57F. Within a short period of time after Röntgen's discovery, quite a number of noteworthy improvements upon tube design were made. The first important contribution in this direction came immediately after the discovery that it is the sudden stopping of electrons that gives rise to X rays.

In X-ray tubes of early design, the electrons from the cathode were not allowed to strike the glass walls, but were directed toward the anode as a target, as shown in Fig. 62A. By curving the cathode like a concave mirror, it was found that it was possible to focus the electrons on one spot on the target, thus making of that spot a localized source of X rays. Radiating out-

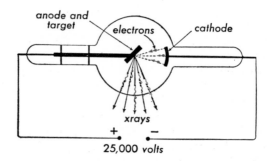

Fig. 62A *Diagram of early form of* X-ray tube.

ward in all possible directions, these "Röntgen rays," as they are sometimes called, have no difficulty in passing through the glass walls of the tube.

The biggest improvement in X-ray tube design was made by Coolidge, an American physicist, in 1913. In the Coolidge tube, now a commercial product (see Fig. 62B),

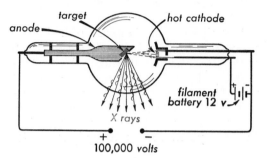

Fig. 62B *Diagram of a Coolidge X-ray tube employing a hot cathode.*

a tungsten wire filament is placed at the center of the cathode and heated to incandescence by a storage battery or low-voltage transformer. This filament, being a copious source of electrons, gives rise at the target to a far more intense source of X rays than was previously possible with a cold cathode. Under the terrific bombardment of the target by so many electrons, most metals will melt. To overcome this difficulty, a metal with a high melting point, like tungsten or molybdenum, is imbedded in the face of a solid copper anode to become the target. Copper, being a good heat conductor, helps to dissipate the heat.

The early sources of high voltage applied to the anode and cathode of X-ray tubes were supplied by induction coils of various descriptions. Although some of these sources are still in use, they have been almost entirely supplanted by a more efficient high-voltage transformer. The emf generated by these transformers varies between 50,000 and 2,000,000 volts. The normal emf used for surgical work is about 100,000 volts, whereas for the treatment of diseases the higher emf's are employed. The high-voltage alternating emf supplied by a transformer is not applied directly to the

X-ray tube, but is first changed into direct current by means of rectifier tubes.

62.2. Penetration of X Rays. Four useful and important properties of X rays are their ability (1) to penetrate solid matter, (2) to cause certain chemical compounds to fluoresce, (3) to ionize atoms, and (4) to affect a photographic plate. The penetration of X rays depends upon two things: first, the voltage applied between the anode and cathodes of the X-ray tube; and second, the density of the substance through which the rays must travel. The higher the voltage applied to the tube, the greater is the penetration. *X rays of great penetrating power are called hard X rays, whereas those having little penetrating power are called soft X rays.*

The relation between density and penetration may be illustrated in several ways. When X rays are sent through a block of wood containing nails, or a closed leather purse containing coins, a clear and well-defined image of the nails, or coins, can be formed and observed on a fluorescent screen. The experimental arrangement is the same as that shown in Fig. 62C. When

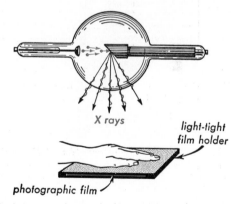

Fig. 62C *Arrangement for taking X-ray photographs of the bones of the hand.*

X rays are sent through the hand or any part of the body to obtain photographs of the bones, it is the difference in penetration between the flesh and the bones that permits a picture to be made. Materials like paper, wood, flesh, etc., composed principally of light chemical elements like those at the beginning of the periodic table, are readily penetrated by X rays. In other words, they are poor absorbers of X rays. For materials like brass, steel, bone, gold, etc., composed partly of heavy elements, like those farther along and near the end of the periodic table, the penetration of X rays is very poor. Hence, heavy elements, or dense substances, are good absorbers.

The bones of the body, which contain large amounts of calcium, are relatively good absorbers of X rays, whereas the soft tissue, composed principally of much lighter elements—hydrogen, oxygen, carbon, and nitrogen—are poor absorbers. This explains the general appearance of X-ray photographs. X-ray pictures like the ones in Fig. 62D are similar to shadows

areas becomes transparent upon development.

Where only flesh is traversed, the X rays penetrate through to the photographic film, causing it to develop out black. The bones therefore appear white against a darker background. If this "negative film," as it is called, is printed on paper as in Fig. 62D, it becomes a "positive" with the bones appearing black.

If the photographic film is placed farther away from the hand than shown in the diagram, the shadow picture will be larger and less distinct. The best pictures are obtained by placing the film as close in contact with the object to be photographed as is physically possible. Whenever a film is being exposed for an X-ray picture, it is

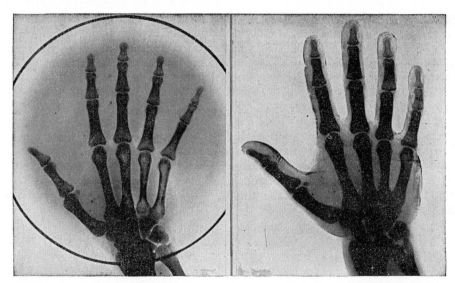

Fig. 62D *X-ray photographs of the wrist bones of the hand. (a) With hand in water. (b) With lead-oxide ointment spread on hand.* (Courtesy, Stamford Research Laboratories, American Cyanamid Co.)

cast by the objects being photographed. The focus point on the X-ray target, being bombarded by high-speed electrons, acts as a point source of rays. These rays spread out in straight lines as shown in Fig. 62C. On passing through the hand to the photographic film, more X rays are absorbed by the bones than by the flesh. The shadow cast by the bones is therefore lacking in X rays, and the photographic film for these

mounted in a black paper envelope or thin aluminum box. This prevents visible light from reaching the film but allows the X rays to pass through.

62.3. Ionizing Power. As X rays pass through matter in the solid, liquid, or gaseous state, they are found to *ionize* atoms and molecules. This can be shown by charging a gold-leaf electroscope positively or negatively and placing it some 10 to 15 ft

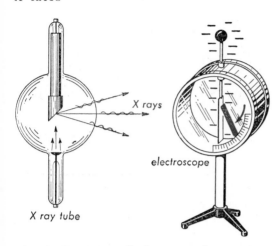

X rays

electroscope

X ray tube

Fig. 62E *X rays discharge an electroscope.*

away from an X-ray tube. When the X-ray tube is turned on (see Fig. 62E), the gold leaf falls, showing discharge.

The explanation of this experiment is as follows: X rays pass through the electroscope and ionize the air by removing electrons from many of the oxygen and nitrogen molecules. Leaving these particular molecules with a net positive charge, the freed electrons move about until they are picked up by other neutral molecules, thus giving them a net negative charge. The result is that the passage of X rays through matter produces both *positively charged* and *negatively charged ions.* If the electroscope is negatively charged, it attracts the positively charged ions to the gold leaf, neutralizing the charge and repelling the negatively charged ions to the "grounded" walls where they, too, become neutralized. If the electroscope is positively charged, it attracts the negative ions to it, again neutralizing the charge. The positive ions in this case are repelled to the walls. In either case, whether the electroscope is positively or negatively charged, the gold leaf falls, showing discharge.

It is the ionization of atoms and molecules in a substance that limits the penetrating power of X rays. Heavy elements contain more electrons than light elements, thus placing more electrons in the path of the X rays to stop them. The stopping power of a thin sheet of lead, for example, is equivalent to the stopping power of a sheet of aluminum several times thicker. Lead atoms each contain 82 electrons, whereas aluminum atoms each contain only 13.

62.4. Practical Applications. During the first few weeks following Röntgen's discovery of X rays, reports from all over the world were received by the editors of scientific journals telling of how the new rays could be put to practical use. A few examples of the first applications were (1) the location of a bullet in a patient's leg, (2) the observation and photography of the healing of a broken bone, (3) the detection of contraband in baggage, (4) the distinction between artificial and real gems, (5) the detection of pearls in oysters, and (6) the examination of the contents in parcel post. In 1897 Dr. Morton exhibited in New York an X-ray picture of the entire skeleton of a living and fully clothed adult.

The biological effects became important when it was found that X rays killed off some forms of animal tissue more rapidly than others. This made them a possible means of cure for certain skin diseases. In particular, the application to the treatment of well-known forms of cancerous growths in animals and human beings has yielded amazing results, and oftentimes a cure. When an internal cancer is treated by sending a beam of X rays directly through the body, the cancerous tissue as well as the normal tissue is slowly killed off. It is principally because the normal tissue grows in again more rapidly than the cancerous tissue that it is possible to bring about a cure. Periodic radiation allows the normal tissue to build up in the intervals.

Although only certain diseases can be successfully treated by X rays, a great deal of research work is still being carried on with extremely high voltage X rays in the hope of discovering new and more effective medical aids. It is generally believed that the killing-off of cell tissue by X rays is due in part to ionization and in part to the formation of free radicals of the molecules within the individual cells.

The importance of X rays in some phases of the field of engineering cannot be over-estimated. This can be appreciated when it is realized that metal castings or welded joints sometimes contain internal flaws or blowholes that otherwise escape detection. Because of the disastrous results that might occur by the insertion of defective castings or welded joints into a bridge or building, many such metal parts are examined by X rays before they are used.

62.5. X Rays Are Waves. Not long after Röntgen's discovery of X rays, there arose in scientific circles two schools of thought concerning the nature of these penetrating rays. One school held to the belief that X rays are high-speed particles like cathode rays, but more penetrating; and the other school held to the idea that they are electromagnetic waves of extremely high frequency. Although many experiments were performed to test these two hypotheses, several years passed before the wave theory was proven to be correct.

The crucial experiment came in 1912 when Von Laue* suggested to his associates, W. Friedrich and P. Knipping, that they try diffracting X rays by sending them through a thin crystal. Believing that the ultramicroscopic structure of a crystal is a three-dimensional array of regularly spaced atoms, Von Laue reasoned that the equally spaced layers of the atoms would act like a diffraction grating. (For details of the action of a diffraction grating on light waves, see Sec. 43.7.)

The experiment, as it was performed, is shown diagrammatically in Fig. 62F. X rays

---

* Max von Laue (1879-   ). Born near Coblenz, Germany, in 1879, young Max was educated in the German universities of Strasbourg, Göttingen, and Munich. Following this, his teaching and research work carried him to the university at Munich, Zurich, Frankfort on the Main, and finally Berlin. Since he was interested in theoretical physics, his early attentions were confined to various phases of Einstein's theory of relativity, and to Bohr's quantum theory of atomic structure. His chief contribution to physics, however, was the instigation and supervision of experiments leading to the diffraction of X rays by crystals. For this work, which proved the wave nature of X rays, he was granted the Nobel Prize in 1914.

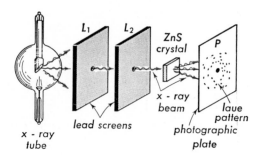

Fig. 62F *Experimental demonstration of the wave property of X rays. Diffracted by the atoms in a crystal, a Laue pattern is photographed.*

from a cold cathode X-ray tube, and limited to a narrow pencil of rays by a pinhole in each of the two lead screens L_1 and L_2, are shown passing through a thin crystal to a photographic film or plate at P. In addition to the central beam, the major part of which goes straight through to produce a blackened spot at the center of the film, there are many other weaker beams emerging in different directions to produce other spots on the same film. The pattern of spots obtained in this way is always quite symmetrical, and is referred to as a *Laue pattern*.

Photographs of two Laue patterns obtained with single crystals are reproduced in Fig. 62G. The small number of spots in

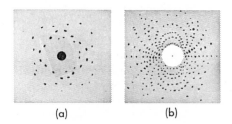

(a)   (b)

Fig. 62G *X-ray diffraction patterns from crystals: (a) Zinc sulfide crystal (face-centered cubic crystal), (b) Sugar crystal (a complex crystal structure).*

(a) is indicative of a relatively simple crystal structure for zinc sulfide, ZnS, and the large number of spots signifies a relatively complex crystal structure for sugar, $C_{12}H_{22}O_{11}$. While the picture for sugar was being taken, the central beam was masked off by a small lead disk placed just in front of the film to prevent excessive blackening. Simple Laue patterns in general arise from simple crystal structures. Common salt is an example of a simple crystal, containing (see Fig. 22G) sodium ion (Na)$^+$ and chlorine ions (Cl)$^-$ in equal numbers arranged in a three-dimensional cubic lattice. Fig. 62H

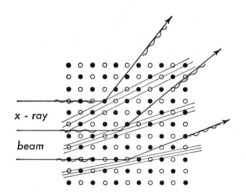

x - ray

beam

Fig. 62H *Illustration of the reflection of X rays from the various atomic planes in a cubic crystal lattice.*

is a cross section through such a crystal, showing the alternation of ions in two of the three directions. Here, in this two-dimensional array, the origin of the different spots on a Laue pattern is illustrated.

Each spot arises from the reflection of some of the incident X rays from one of the various sets of parallel crystal planes, three of which are shown by the sets of parallel lines. Always, the rays obey the law of reflection that the angle of incidence equals the angle of reflection. While the reflection planes shown in the diagram are all perpendicular to the plane of the page, there are many other planes in a three-dimensional lattice to reflect the rays off in other directions.

The success of the Laue experiment proves the correctness of two postulates: (1) that X rays are light rays of very short wavelength, and (2) that the ions of a crystal are arranged in a regular three-dimensional lattice. These are the results for which Von Laue was granted the Nobel Prize in physics in 1914. As a direct result of the Laue experiment, two new and important fields of experimental physics were opened up: (1) the study and measurement of X-ray wavelengths, and (2) the study of crystal structures by their action on X rays.

62.6. The X-ray Spectrograph. No sooner had Von Laue, Friedrich, and Knipping announced the results of their experiments than many investigators began a study of the various phases of *X-ray diffraction* by crystals. The most outstanding of these experiments are those of W. H. Bragg* and his son, W. L. Bragg; they also developed the X-ray spectrometer and spectrograph.

A diagram of an X-ray spectrograph is shown in Fig. 62I. Instead of having pinhole screens, as in Fig. 62F, and sending a narrow pencil of rays through a crystal, the early spectrographs used screens with narrow slits and reflected the rays from one face of a crystal. The crystal is not fixed tightly in place but can be turned back and forth about a pivot C at the center of the front face. As this rocking motion takes place, the crystal acts somewhat like a mirror and causes the reflected X-ray beam to sweep back and forth along the photographic film from one end to the other. After the photographic film has been exposed to the rays for some time, and then developed, it is found to have the general appearance of the reproduction in Fig. 62J. This unusually clear photograph was originally taken by de Broglie who used an X-ray tube containing a tungsten-metal anode target. Instead of a general blackening from end to end, the film shows *bands* and *lines,* indicating that at certain orientation angles of the crystal the reflected rays were unusually intense, while at others

* Sir William Henry Bragg (1862-   ), British physicist and professor at the University of London. Bragg's researches on radioactive phenomena brought him early recognition from scientific societies at home and abroad. Joint work with his son, William Lawrence Bragg (1890-   ), on the arrangement of ions in crystals, and the development of the X-ray spectograph are his greatest scientific contributions. In 1915, father and son were jointly granted the Nobel Prize in physics, as well as the Barnard Gold Medal from Columbia University.

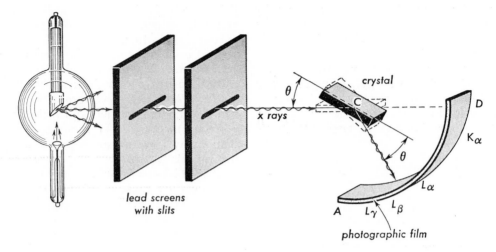

Fig. 62I   *Schematic diagram of a Bragg X-ray crystal spectrograph.*

there were apparently none. The lines, which are particularly noticeable at points marked $K\alpha$, $L\alpha$, $L\beta$, and $L\gamma$, are called *X-ray spectrum lines.*

The origin and interpretation of these

at such an angle θ that the crests of the waves reflected from adjacent atomic layers move off together. This occurs when the additional distance traveled by ray (2), *AMB* in the diagram, is exactly one whole

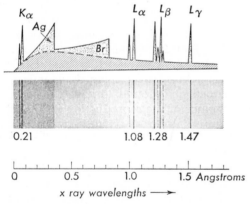

Fig. 62J   *X-ray spectrogram taken with an X-ray tube containing a tungsten metal target.*
(After de Broglie.)

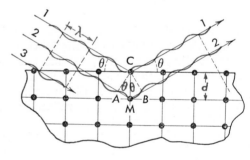

Fig. 62K   *Illustration of the Bragg rule of reflection for X rays from the surface layers of a crystal.*

spectrum lines are illustrated by a detailed diagram in Fig. 62K. To reflect X rays of one given wavelength from a crystal, a certain relation must exist between the direction of the incident rays and the distance d between surface layers of the crystal. This relation, known as *the Bragg rule,* requires the waves to be incident on the crystal face,

wavelength greater than that traveled by the ray (1) next above it. When the angle is adjusted so that this is true, other rays like (3), belonging to the same wave train as (1) and (2), will be reflected from the third crystal layer to be "in step" with the others.

Suppose now that the X-ray tube in Fig. 62I emits X rays of only one wavelength; then, as the crystal rocks back and forth, there will be no reflection except at one particular angle θ, and this will occur where the conditions of Bragg's rule are satisfied. At this particular position on the photographic plate, a single dark line will appear. If now the distance d between crystal layers is known, and the angle θ for the X-ray line measured, the wavelength of the X rays can be calculated. One wavelength, it will be noted in Fig. 62K, is equal to twice the length of the side AM of the right triangle AMC. Thus, with one side and two angles of a triangle known, either of the other sides can be calculated. Bragg's rule therefore becomes

$$2d \sin \theta = \lambda \qquad (62a)$$

In the case of a sodium chloride crystal, NaCl, the atomic spacing is 2.81A, or 2.81×10^{-10} m.

Since several spectrum lines appear in the photograph in Fig. 62J, there are several different wavelengths emitted by the same X-ray tube. The two fluted appearing bands between the K and L X-ray lines are not of interest here because they appear on all X-ray spectrograms; they are due to the strong absorption of X rays of many other wavelengths by the silver and bromine atoms in the photographic plate itself. Had the original photographic film been exposed for a much longer time, the spectrogram would have shown a general blackening over the whole plate. This blackening, illustrated by the shaded area in the curve above, is due to X rays of all different wavelengths being emitted by the X-ray tube; it is these which, although not very intense, strongly affect the photographic plate at the two bands, Ag and Br.

62.7. The Origin of X Rays. X rays, like visible light, originate from the jumping of an electron from one orbit to another. When high-speed electrons from the cathode of an X-ray tube strike the target, they ionize many of the atoms comprising the surface layers of the metal.

Due to their very high speeds (about $\frac{1}{10}$ the velocity of light), the electrons penetrate the atoms and remove an electron from the inner shells by collision. This is illustrated in Fig. 62L where an electron is

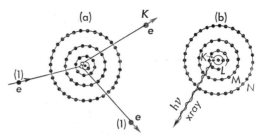

Fig. 62L *Schematic diagram illustrating (a) the ionization of an atom by a high-speed electron, and (b) the subsequent jumping of an inner electron with the simultaneous emission of an X ray.*

knocked out of the K-shell. The designations K, L, M, N, O, P, etc., for the various electron shells originated with the X-ray spectroscopist and are identical with the quantum numbers $n = 1, 2, 3, 4, 5, 6$, etc. When an electron is missing in the innermost K-shell, a nearby electron from the next shell beyond jumps into the vacant space, simultaneously emitting a photon of energy $h\nu$. Such X rays, arising from millions of atoms, produce the K-lines shown in Fig. 62J.

Since the L-shell now has one less electron, an M electron can jump into the L-shell vacancy, with the consequent emission of another but different X-ray frequency. These are the L-lines in Fig. 62J. The jumping process continues until the outermost shell is reached, where an electron jumping in gives rise to visible light. Thus we see how it is possible for a single atom to emit X rays of different wavelengths.

The continuous X-ray spectrum, illustrated by the shaded area under the curve in Fig. 62J, is due to another phenomenon often referred to as "Bremsstrahlung." These radiations are due to the slowing down of high-speed electrons as they pass close to the nuclei of the atoms within the target of the X-ray tube. The process is illustrated in Fig. 62M. As the electron passes through the atom, it is attracted by the positive charge of the nucleus and deflected in its path.

During the deflection of the electron in

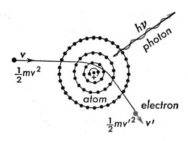

Fig. 62M *Diagram illustrating the production of a photon by a high-speed electron as it passes through an atom close to the nucleus. ("Bremsstrahlung.")*

the strong electric field of the nucleus, a light wave of energy is $h\nu$ is emitted. Since the law of conservation of momentum must hold for such a collision, the electron is deflected off to one side of the atom, and the photon off to the other. Since the law of conservation of energy must hold, some

of the energy of the incoming electron $\frac{1}{2}mv^2$ is given up to the newly created photon $h\nu$, and the remainder $\frac{1}{2}mv'^2$ is retained by the electron. Thus the electron is slowed down to a velocity v' by the encounter. The closer the electron comes to the nucleus, the greater is its loss in velocity and energy, and the greater is the frequency and energy of the radiated photon. By the conservation of energy,

$$\frac{1}{2}mv^2 - \frac{1}{2}mv'^2 = h\nu \qquad (62b)$$

The highest frequency that is possible is one in which the electron is completely stopped by the atom. In this special case,

$$\frac{1}{2}mv^2 = h\nu_{\max} \qquad (62c)$$

For a more complete treatment of X rays, see *X-Rays* by A. H. Compton and S. K. Allison, Van Nostrand, Princeton.

QUESTIONS

1. What contribution did Coolidge make to the design and construction of X-ray tubes?

2. What are hard X rays? What are soft X rays? How is hardness or softness related to X-ray wavelengths?

3. How is X-ray absorption related to the periodic table of elements?

4. Which of the following materials is the best absorber of X rays: (a) beryllium, (b) magnesium, (c) calcium, (d) copper, (e) gold, (f) lead, or (g) uranium?

5. What is the process of ionization by X rays? What happens to the liberated free electrons?

6. Why does the skin show so clearly in the X-ray photograph in Fig. 62D(b)?

7. If a small child swallowed a safety pin, why would an X-ray photograph clearly show the location of the pin?

8. How is the penetrating power of X rays related to the voltage applied to the tube?

9. Briefly explain why an X-ray photograph of the hand shows the bones more clearly than the flesh surrounding them.

10. An X-ray photograph of a closed leather purse will readily show silver coins or other metal articles inside. Explain.

11. How and by whom were X rays discovered?

12. Diagram a modern X-ray tube of the type developed by Coolidge.

PROBLEMS

1. X rays sent through a Bragg crystal spectrometer using a rock salt crystal are reflected at an angle of 20.5°. What is the wavelength of the X rays?

2. X rays sent through a Bragg crystal spec-

trometer show three spectrum lines at 4.28°, 5.92°, and 7.56°, respectively. If the crystal used is rock salt, what are the wavelengths of the X rays? (*Ans.* 0.498A, 0.579A, 0.740A.)

3. X rays of wavelength 1.45×10^{-8}cm are

diffracted by a Bragg crystal spectrograph at an angle of 12.4°. Find the effective spacing of the atomic layers in the crystal.

4. X rays having a wavelength of 0.36×10^{-8} cm are diffracted at an angle of 4.8° in a Bragg crystal spectograph. Find the effective spacing of the atomic layers in the crystal. (*Ans.* 2.15A.)

5. When a molybdenum target is used in an X-ray tube, the two shortest wavelengths emitted are found with a Bragg crystal spectrograph to be diffracted at angles of 6°24′ and 7°15′, respectively. Find their wavelengths. Assume a crystal spacing of 2.81×10^{-8}cm.

6. When a tungsten target is used in an X-ray tube, the two shortest wavelengths emitted are found with a Bragg crystal spectograph to be diffracted at angles of 2°47′, and 3°16′, respectively. Find their wavelengths. Assume a crystal spacing of 2.81×10^{-8}cm. (*Ans.* 0.273A and 0.320A.)

Chapter 63

Electromagnetic Waves and Vacuum Tubes

There is little doubt that *radio, radar,* and *television* are among the greatest miracles of modern science. Traveling with the speed of light, code signals, the human voice, and music can be heard around the world within the very second they are produced in the broadcasting studio. Through television, world events can be observed in full color at the same moment they occur hundreds of miles away.

The more we learn of the fundamental principles of radio and its operation, the more amazing does their reality become. It is the purpose of this chapter to introduce some of the earlier fundamental principles of wireless telegraphy in the approximate chronological order in which they were discovered and developed, and in so doing gain some familiarity with *electromagnetic waves.*

63.1. The Leyden Jar. A cross section of a "Leyden jar" of the type invented by the Dutch scientist Musschenbroek in 1746 is shown in Fig. 63A. Two metallic conductors forming the plates of a capacitor are separated by a glass bottle as a dielectric insulator. When such a capacitor is connected to a source of high potential, one plate will become positively charged and the other will be negative. If the source voltage is high enough, an electric spark will jump between the terminals indicating a sudden discharge of the capacitor, and an electron current will surge first one way and then the other around the circuit.

This oscillatory current was first postulated by Joseph Henry, then derived from theory by Lord Kelvin, and later proven experimentally by Fedderson. Fedderson,

looking at a capacitor discharge with a rotating mirror, observed that each initial breakdown spark was followed by a succession of fainter sparks. The initial spark ionizes the air, making of it a good conductor and, of the entire system *ABCDEFGA*, a complete electrical circuit.

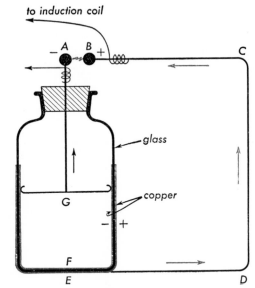

Fig. 63A *The discharge of a Leyden jar is oscillatory.*

63.2. The Oscillatory Circuit. The Leyden jar circuit in Fig. 63A contains, in addition to a *capacitance,* an *inductance* as well. The single loop *FGABCD* and *E* forms practically one turn of a coil. An inductance and capacitance, connected as shown in simplest, schematic form in Fig. 63B, form the necessary elements of all oscillating circuits.

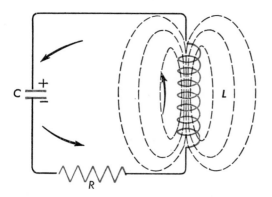

Fig. 63B *Schematic diagram of an oscillating circuit.*

If, initially, the capacitance is charged as indicated, the surplus electrons on the plate below cause a surge of negative charge counterclockwise around the circuit to neutralize the positives and, in so doing, set up a magnetic field in and around the inductance. When the positives become neutralized and the electron current tends to cease, the magnetic flux linking the circuit decreases and keeps the current flowing in the same direction. Once this field has vanished and the current has ceased, the capacitance is found to be in a charged condition, the upper plate negative and the lower plate positive.

Having reversed the charge on the capacitance, the above process will repeat itself, this time the electron current surging clockwise around the circuit. Thus the current rushes first in one direction, then the other,

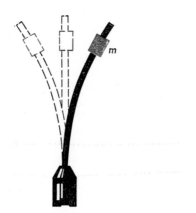

Fig. 63C *A vibrating spring is like an electrical oscillating circuit.*

oscillating back and forth in an electrical way just as any spring pulled to one side and released vibrates in a mechanical way (see Fig. 63C).

When a straight spring is pulled to one side and released, the kinetic energy it gains upon straightening keeps the spring moving, and it bends to the other side. Just as the vibration amplitude of the spring slowly decreases because of *friction,* so also does the current in the electrical circuit decrease because of *electrical resistance.* A graph showing how current slowly dies out in an electric circuit is given in Fig. 63D. These

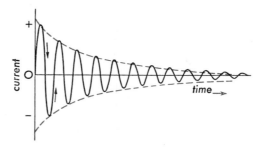

Fig. 63D *Graph of the damped oscillations of an electrical circuit.*

are called *damped vibrations,* or *damped oscillations.* If the resistance of the circuit is high, the damping is high and the current quickly dies out after but few oscillations. If the resistance is low, however, the damping is small, the amplitude decreases slowly, and there are many oscillations.

To calculate the frequency of an oscillating circuit, either of the following formulas may be used:

$$T = 2\pi\sqrt{LC} \qquad \boxed{f = \frac{1}{2\pi\sqrt{LC}}} \quad (63a)$$

where L is the inductance in henries, C is the capacitance in farads, T is the time for one complete oscillation in seconds, and f is the number of oscillations per second. T is the period and f the frequency. The formula at the left is to be compared with the analogous formula for the period of a vibrating spring.

$$T = 2\pi\sqrt{m/k} \qquad (63b)$$

The mass m for the spring is analogous to the inductance L for the circuit, and the stiffness $1/k$ is analogous to the capacitance C. An increase of the inductance L, or capacitance C, or both, increases the period and decreases the frequency of the oscillating circuit.

Example. A Leyden jar with a small capacitance of 0.01 μf is connected to a single turn of wire (about 6 in. in diameter) having an inductance of 1 microhenry. Calculate the natural frequency of the circuit.

Solution. Since 1 henry $= 10^6$ microhenries and 1 farad $= 10^6$ microfarads, direct substitution for L and C in Eq.(63a) gives

$$f = \frac{1}{2\pi\sqrt{LC}} = \frac{1}{2\pi\sqrt{1 \times 10^{-6}\,h \times 1 \times 10^{-8}\,f}}$$
$$= 1{,}590{,}000 \text{ cyc/sec}$$

or   1.59 megacycles/sec.

63.3. Maxwell's Electromagnetic Wave Theory.

In 1856, James Clerk Maxwell wrote his now famous theoretical paper on electromagnetic waves. In this scientific publication, he proposed the possible existence of electromagnetic waves and at the same time postulated that, if such waves could ever be produced, they would travel through free space with the speed of light.

Light itself, said Maxwell, is propagated as an electromagnetic wave, and electrically produced waves should differ from light only in their wavelength and frequency. Because Maxwell gave no clues as to how such waves might be generated or detected, their real existence was not discovered until 32 years later when Heinrich Hertz made his important discovery.

63.4. Hertzian Waves.

In 1888, a young German scientist, Heinrich Hertz,* began

* Heinrich Rudolf Hertz (1857-1894). German physicist born at Hamburg, February 22, 1857. He studied physics under Helmholtz in Berlin, at whose suggestion he first became interested in Maxwell's electromagnetic theory. His researches with electromagnetic waves which made his name famous were carried out at Karlsruhe Polytechnic between 1885 and 1889. As professor of physics at the University of Bonn, after 1889, he experimented with electrical discharges through gases and narrowly missed the

a series of experiments in which he not only produced and detected electromagnetic waves, but also demonstrated their properties of reflection, refraction, and interference. One of his experimental arrangements is diagramed in Fig. 63E.

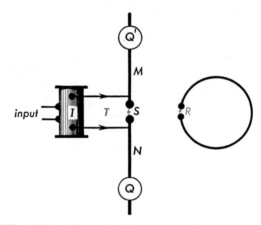

Fig. 63E *Schematic diagram of the apparatus with which Hertz produced and detected the first radio waves.*

The transmitter consists of two spheres QQ' located near the ends of two straight rods MN separated by a spark gap S. With the two rods connected to an induction coil I, sparks jump across the gap S, giving rise to oscillating currents in MN. That such a generator is an oscillating circuit can be seen from the fact that the spheres QQ' form the plates of a capacitor and the rods form the inductance.

The receiver, or detector, consists of a single loop of wire with a tiny spark gap at R. This circuit, too, is an oscillating circuit with the spark gap as a capacitance C and the loop as an inductance L. Tuning the transmitter frequency to that of the receiver is accomplished by sliding the spheres Q along the rods MN, resonance being indicated by the appearance of sparks at R.

With apparatus of this general type, Hertz was able to transmit signals a distance of several hundred feet. He found that large metal plates would reflect the

discovery of X rays described by Roentgen a few years later. By his premature death, science lost one of its most promising disciples.

radiation, and that at normal incidence the reflected waves would interfere with those coming up to set up standing waves with nodes and loops. As the receiver was moved slowly away from the reflector, nodes and loops were located by the appearance of sparks only at equally spaced intervals.

With a large prism of paraffin he demonstrated refraction, and with a lens made of pitch he focused the waves as a glass lens focuses visible light.

63.5. Electromagnetic Waves. To visualize the production of waves by a Hertzian oscillator, consider the schematic diagram in Fig. 63F. Let the rods MN and spheres

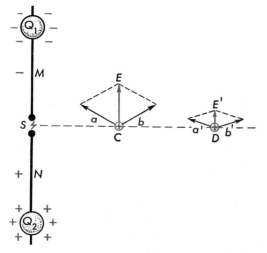

Fig. 63F *Hertzian dipole.*

Q_1 and Q_2 be charged initially as indicated, and consider the electrostatic action of the charges on a small charge C located some distance away. The negative charge Q_1 attracts C with a force a and the positive charge Q_2 repels it with a force b. Since by symmetry these two forces are of equal magnitude, their resultant CE is parallel to MN. If the isolated charge is farther away as at D, the resultant force is also parallel to MN, but weaker. In other words, the electric field E at points C and D is up and parallel to MN, decreasing in intensity as the distance from the transmitter increases.

Suppose that a spark jumps the gap S and oscillation sets in. One-half cycle after

the condition shown in Fig. 63F, electrons have surged across the gap, charging Q_1 positively and Q_2 negatively. With reversed charges the resultant force on C and D will be down instead of up. Thus it is seen how oscillations in the transmitter, which constitute a surging of electrons back and forth between M and N, give rise to a periodically reversing electric field at distant points.

In addition to an electric field at C and D, the surging electrons in MN give rise to a magnetic field as well. When the electron current is down (using the conventional left-hand rule), the magnetic induction B at C or D is perpendicular to and into the plane of the page, and when the electron current is up the magnetic intensity is out from the page. The surging of the charges therefore gives rise to a periodically reversing magnetic intensity, the direction of which is at right angles to the electric intensity at the same points.

According to Maxwell's theory, the E and B fields do not appear instantly at distant points; time is required for their propagation. The speed of propagation, according to Maxwell (and this has been confirmed by numerous experiments) is the same as the speed of light. The changing E and B fields at C therefore lag behind the oscillating charges in MN, and those at D lag behind still farther.

Figure 63G is a graph of the instantaneous

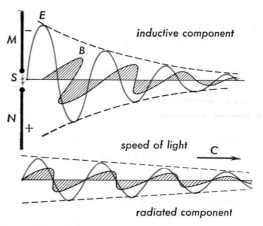

Fig. 63G *Graph of the electromagnetic waves emitted by a Hertzian dipole.*

values of the electric and magnetic fields as they vary with distance from the transmitter. At certain points the fields are a maximum and at other points they are zero. As time goes on, these electric and magnetic waves move away from the transmitter with a speed of 186,300 mi/sec.

The mathematical theory of electromagnetic radiations shows that, close to the transmitter, the E and B fields, called the *inductive components,* are 90° out of phase and that their magnitudes fall off very rapidly with distance. Farther out, however, the two get in step with each other and their amplitudes fall off more slowly, as shown in the diagram. The latter are called the *radiated components* and are the ones detected at great distances.

Suppose now that a series of sparks is made to occur in the gap S of a transmitter as in Fig. 63H. Each spark will give rise to

Fig. 63H   *Damped electromagnetic waves from a Hertzian oscillator.*

a damped oscillation in MN which in turn sends out a damped electromagnetic wave. The succession of sparks sends out a train of such waves which, as they leave the antenna, decrease rapidly in magnitude at first, then more slowly as they get farther away. Only the electric component of such waves is shown in the diagram.

If an electrical conductor is located at some distant point, the free electrons within it will, as such waves go by, experience up and down forces tending to set them in oscillation. If the conductor is an oscillating circuit whose natural frequency is that of the passing waves, resonance will occur and large currents will be set up.

63.6. Air-Core Inductances and Transformers. When a high-frequency alternating current is sent through a solenoid with an iron core or the primary of an iron-core transformer, the back emf is so large that

the current as well as the magnetic induction cannot build up to any appreciable value before it reverses in direction. This is made evident by curve (c) in Fig. 56A which shows how the iron core tends to hold the current back. The result is that in one ten-thousandth of a second or less the current hardly gets started in one direction before it stops and reverses. Eq.(56f) shows that a high frequency emf impressed upon a large inductance gives rise to a very large inductive reactance.

In an iron-core transformer the back emf in the primary winding so retards the building up of strong fields that little or no induced currents can be "drawn" from the secondary. To overcome this difficulty, the iron core is done away with, so that we have what is called an *air-core transformer.* In the absence of any iron, the current in the coil may, as illustrated by curve (b) in Fig. 56A, rise to an appreciable value each time it changes in direction. The rapidly increasing and diminishing flux that links both circuits induces a current in the secondary of exactly the same frequency.

Air-core transformers, consisting of nothing more than two coils of a few turns each, a primary winding and a secondary winding, are used extensively in radio and television transmitters and receivers. In these instances the alternating currents with frequencies of thousands and even millions of cycles per second are usually referred to as *radio frequencies,* and the transformers are referred to as *radio frequency transformers.*

63.7. The Vacuum Tube Rectifier. While the great American inventor, Thomas A. Edison, was striving by a process of trial and error to produce a satisfactory electric light bulb, he made an accidental discovery, the importance of which was first recognized and used successfully by Sir John Fleming. Now called a vacuum tube rectifier or diode, the Fleming valve is used in nearly every radio and television transmitter and receiver to change alternating current into direct current.

The Fleming valve, as shown in Fig. 63I, consists of a highly evacuated glass bulb containing a wire filament that is heated

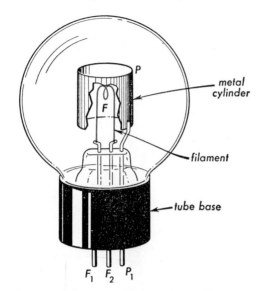

Fig. 63I *Diagram of a Fleming valve, or rectifier tube. Such tubes are now called diodes.*

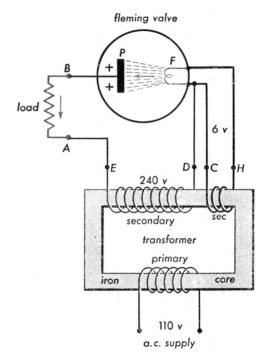

Fig. 63J *Circuit diagram of a Fleming valve rectifier.*

electrically to incandescence. Surrounding the filament and connected to the outside through the tube base and a prong, P_1, is a cylindrical metal plate P. When the filament is heated to incandescence, it gives off large quantities of electrons in much the same way that water, when heated to the boiling point, gives off steam. The emission of electrons by a hot body is called *thermionic emission* and is due to the high temperature and not to the electric current. Heating a metal by any other means will produce the same effect. Electrons emitted from hot metal surfaces are called *thermoelectrons*.

The principal action of the *filament F* and *plate P* is explained by means of a typical electric circuit shown schematically in Fig. 63J. The circuit consists of a *transformer* having *two secondary windings*, a *Fleming valve*, and a *load*. The latter, shown as a resistance, represents any electrical device requiring unidirectional current for its operation. With an alternating current of 110 volts supplied to the primary, a high voltage, 240 volts for example, is delivered by one secondary to the terminals *ED* and a low voltage of 5 volts alternating current is delivered by the other

secondary to the terminals *CH*. The latter, called the *filament winding*, is for the purpose of heating the filament.

When for a fraction of a second the plate *P* of the tube is positively charged and the filament *F* is negatively charged, the electrons from *F* are attracted to the plate *P* and constitute a current flowing across the vacuum space *PF* and through the load from *B* to *A*. One-half cycle later, when the potential is reversed and *P* becomes negatively charged and *F* positively charged, the electrons from *F* are repelled by *P* and very little current flows.

The emfs in each part of the rectifier circuit are shown by graphs in Fig. 63K. The primary emf of 110 volts is shown in (a), the secondary emf of 240 volts in (b), and the *rectified* or *pulsating emf* through the load *AB* in (c).

63.8. Full-Wave Rectifier. A full-wave rectifier tube, sometimes called a *duo-diode*, is essentially a double Fleming valve with two plates and two filaments. (See Fig. 63L.) The two prongs F_1 and F_2 in the base are

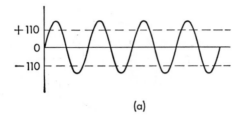

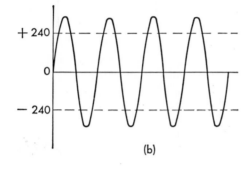

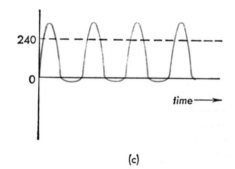

(c)

Fig. 63K *Alternating current as rectified by a Fleming valve or diode.*

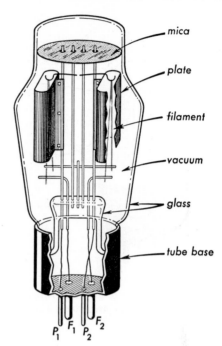

Fig. 63L *Drawing of a full-wave rectifier tube.*

when P_1 is + and P_2 is −, electrons from the filament are attracted to P_1, and, when a moment later P_1 is − and P_2 is +, electrons from the filament are attracted to P_2.

In the first instance a current flows around the circuit $F_1P_1GEABHJF_1$, and in the second it flows around the circuit $F_2P_2DEABHCF_2$. In each case the current has gone through the load AB in the same direction and has pulsating characteristics as shown in Fig. 63N.

If such a pulsating current were used to supply the direct current needed in every radio receiver, a loud objectionable hum with a frequency of 120 cycles would be heard. To make this current a steady smooth direct current, as illustrated by the straight line in the same graph, and thus eliminate the hum, a *filter circuit* as shown in Fig. 63O is used. The terminals A and B are connected to, and replace, the load A and B in Fig. 63M. K is an iron-core inductance and C_1 and C are capacitors of large capacity.

As the current through $AaLbB$ starts to flow, the capacitors become charged, as

connected to both filaments in series, while the prongs P_1 and P_2 are connected one to each plate.

A schematic diagram of a rectifier circuit employing such a tube is shown in Fig. 63M. Here an iron-core transformer with one primary and two secondary windings is used, differing from the single phase rectifier in Fig. 63J in that the center of each secondary winding is now connected to the load. CHJ is the filament winding and supplies current to both filaments (shown as one bent wire) while GED is the high-voltage winding. The latter supplies an alternating potential to the plates so that,

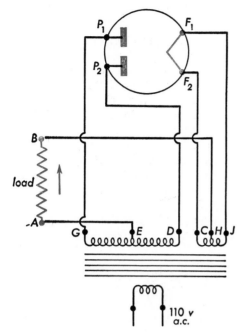

Fig. 63M *Diagram for a full-wave rectifier circuit.*

shown, and a magnetic field is created around K. This has a retarding action which prevents the current from reaching its otherwise peak value. When a moment later the filament-to-plate current drops to near zero, the capacitors discharge and the field around K collapses, thus sending a current through AB. This process is repeated with each pulse of electrons from either plate of the tube, and the current through ab remains steady. Large capacities and large self-inductance deliver more constant voltage.

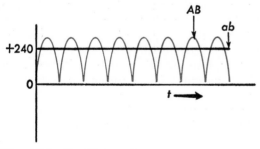

Fig. 63N *Rectified voltage from a full-wave rectifier circuit.*

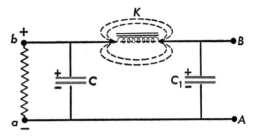

Fig. 63O *Electrical filter circuit for "smoothing out" pulsating direct current.*

63.9. De Forest's Audion.

Although the Fleming valve was originally developed for the purpose of detecting wireless waves, its operation as such did not prove to be very satisfactory until, in 1906, De Forest* invented the *audion*. By inserting a grid wire between the *plate* and *filament* of a Fleming valve, he created a device capable not only of detecting wireless waves, but

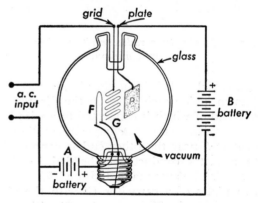

Fig. 63P *Diagram of the De Forest audion.*

of amplifying the signals as well. The purpose of the grid (see Fig. 63P) is to control the flow of electrons from the hot filament F to the plate P.

* Lee De Forest (1873-1961), American scientist; Ph.D. from Yale University, 1899. His most famous invention was the audion, considered by many to be the most important invention ever made in radio. He designed and installed the first five high-power radio stations for the U. S. Navy. After 1921 he devoted his time to the development of talking motion picture film. He was awarded gold medals at the St. Louis exposition in 1904, the Panama Pacific Exposition in San Francisco in 1915, and the Institute of France in 1923. He received the Cresson Medal of the Franklin Institute in 1921 for his important contributions to wireless.

A circuit diagram showing how the audion may be used as a one-tube receiver of radio waves is given in Fig. 63Q. The filament F is heated by a 6-volt battery A, and the plate P is maintained at a positive potential of 45 volts or more by the *B-battery*. The capacitor C and inductance L form an *oscillation circuit,* the natural frequency of which may be varied by changing the capacity of C. The arrow indicates a capacitor of variable capacitance.

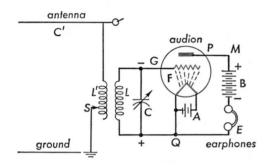

Fig. 63Q *One-tube radio receiver using a De Forest audion.*

Co-axial with L is another inductance L' (shown beside each other in the diagram), one end of which is connected to a wire in the air called the *antenna,* and a sliding contact S near the other end is connected to a metal conductor embedded in the ground. The antenna and ground form the two plates of a capacitor C' with the air as a dielectric. This capacity C' with the variable inductance L' forms a second oscillation circuit whose natural frequency is varied by the sliding contact S.

By varying the frequency of the $L'C'$ circuit until it matches the frequency of any passing wave (shown as damped wireless waves in Fig. 63H), an oscillating current and magnetic field occur in L'. By tuning the LC circuit to this same frequency, resonance is set up and the oscillating current imposes alternate $(+)$ and $(-)$ charges on the grid G. During the time the grid G is negative, electrons from the

filament are repelled and are unable to reach the plate P. When the grid is positive, however, the electrons from the filament are accelerated toward the plate and constitute a flow of current clockwise around the circuit $PMEQFP$.

Not only does the grid act as a rectifier valve and let the electron current flow in one direction only, from filament to plate, but it acts as an amplifier, allowing large currents from the high voltage B-battery to flow through when it is slightly positive, and practically no current when it is slightly negative.

Voltage graphs for the two parts of the receiver circuit are given in Fig. 63R. Dia-

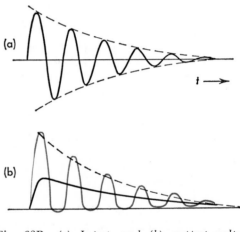

Fig. 63R *(a) Input, and (b) output voltage curves for De Forest audion used in wireless receiver, Fig. 63Q.*

gram (a) represents the oscillating potentials in the LC circuit connected to the grid, and diagram (b) the current through the plate and earphones. Since the frequency of this rectified current is far too rapid for the electromagnets in the earphones, their metal diaphragms over the pole tips move up and down with the heavy dotted line in (b), which is heard as a single audible click. A succession of damped waves is then heard as a noise, with each damped wave producing a single vibration of the receiver diaphragms.

QUESTIONS

1. What is an oscillatory circuit? What are its three principal elements?

2. Upon what does the natural frequency of a circuit depend? What is the formula for the frequency?

3. What is electrical resonance? Under what conditions does it arise?

4. What are Hertzian waves? What is a Hertzian dipole?

5. What are electromagnetic waves? What is their nature? With what speed do they travel?

6. What are damped oscillations? How can damping be reduced?

7. Draw from memory a schematic wiring diagram of a full-wave rectifier showing the vacuum tube, transformer, and load.

8. Make a schematic diagram of a full-wave rectifier and filter circuit consisting of a transformer, vacuum tube, choke coil, two capacitors, and a load.

9. Draw from memory a wiring diagram of a one-tube radio receiver as shown in Fig. 63Q, but using a cathode type of vacuum tube in place of a De Forest audion.

PROBLEMS

1. Calculate the frequency and period of an oscillating circuit containing two 3-μf capacitors and an inductance of 3.4 μh if all three are connected in parallel.

2. What inductance connected to a capacitor of 0.05 μf will give the circuit a natural frequency of 6 megacycles/sec? (*Ans.* 0.0141 μh.)

3. What capacitance, if connected in parallel to an inductance of 6 μh, will give an oscillating circuit a frequency of 250 kilocycles/sec?

4. Determine the frequency of an oscillating circuit composed of two capacitors and one inductor, all connected in parallel: $C_1 = 5$ μf, $C_2 = 25$ μf, and $L = 10$ μh. (*Ans.* 9.19 Kc/sec.)

5. Two capacitors of 10 μf each are first connected in series and then the combination connected across an inductor of 2μh. Calculate the period of the oscillating circuit.

6. Calculate all of the possible frequencies that can be obtained by combining two or more of the following to form an oscillating circuit: $C_1 = 2$ μf, $C_2 = 4$ μf, $L = 8$ μh. (*Ans.* 39.8, 28.1, 23.0, 48.8 Kc/sec.)

7. A 5-mh inductor is connected in parallel with a 50-μf capacitor. What is the natural frequency of this circuit?

8. A 60-μh inductor is connected across a 75-μf capacitor. What is the frequency of

the fifth harmonic of the oscillating circuit thus formed? (*Ans.* 11.86 Kc/sec.)

9. What capacitance connected in parallel to an inductance of 0.5 μh will produce an oscillating circuit with a fundamental frequency of 1 megacycle/sec?

10. What inductance connected in parallel to a capacitance of 20 μf will produce an oscillating circuit with a fundamental frequency of 30 kilocycles/sec? (*Ans.* 1.41 μh.)

11. Calculate the frequency of an oscillating circuit composed of a 1-μf capacitor and a 1-μh inductor.

12. What capacitance in parallel with an inductance of 0.1 μh will have a frequency of 1 megacycle/sec? (*Ans.* 0.253 μf.)

13. A capacitance of 0.1 μf is connected to an inductance of 8×10^{-8} henry. Find (a) the frequency and (b) the wavelength of the electromagnetic waves emitted.

14. What capacitance should be used with an inductance of 0.09 μh to produce electromagnetic waves having a wavelength of 10 cm? (*Ans.* 0.0313 $\mu\mu$f.)

15. What inductance should be used with a capacitance of 0.04 μf to produce electromagnetic waves of wavelength 1 meter?

Chapter 64

Vacuum Tubes and Transistors

64.1. Modern Vacuum Tubes. Every radio enthusiast today knows that there are hundreds of different kinds of radio tubes. Some contain two filaments and two plates, while others contain as many as three or four separate grids. Although a treatment of such complex tubes is out of place here, the fundamental principles of all of them are little different from De Forest's audion. One important difference, however, is illustrated in Fig. 64A, and that is the employment in some tubes of a cathode in place of a filament as a source of thermal electrons.

A fine tungsten wire filament is threaded through two small holes running lengthwise through a porcelain-like insulating rod. Fitting snugly around this rod is the cathode, a metal cylinder coated on the outside with a thin layer of thorium, strontium, or caesium oxide. These particular oxides are copious emitters of electrons when heated to a dull red heat. Insulated from the cathode, the filament as a source of heat can be, and generally is, connected directly to an appropriate transformer winding.

A schematic diagram of the cathode type of tube containing one plate and one grid is given in Fig. 64B. A circuit diagram showing the electrical connections and instruments needed to measure the *grid-volt-*

mica, plate, grid, cathode, tungsten filament, glass stem, vacuum, tube base

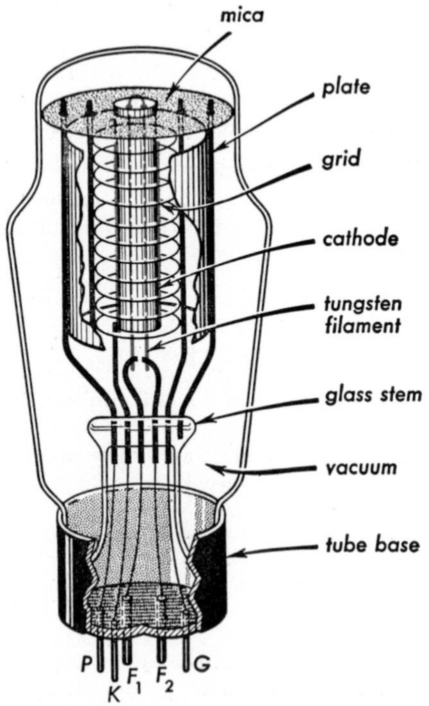

Fig. 64A *Modern radio tube with a cesium-coated cathode as a source of thermal electrons. The filament serves only to heat the cathode.*

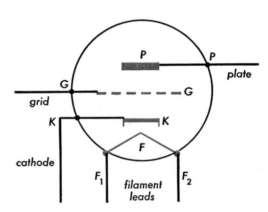

Fig. 64B *Schematic diagram of a cathode type of radio tube.*

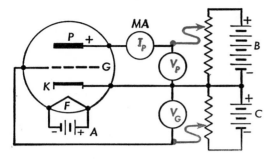

Fig. 64C *Circuit diagram for determining the characteristics of a triode vacuum tube.*

age vs. the *plate-current* curve for vacuum tubes in general is given in Fig. 64C. A variable voltage is applied to the plate *P* by a *B*-battery through a potential divider, and a variable voltage is applied to the grid *G* by a *C*-battery which is connected to another potential divider. The various applied grid potentials are read from the voltmeter V_G and the corresponding plate current is read from a milliammeter *MA*.

Four characteristic curves taken with the above circuit connections are reproduced in Fig. 64D, one for each of four plate voltages, 50, 100, 150, and 200 volts, respectively.

The flattening-out of all the curves at the top indicates that, when the grid is

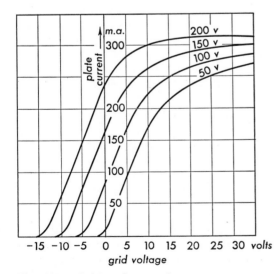

Fig. 64D *Grid voltage—plate current curves for normal grid-controlled vacuum tube.*

highly positive, practically all of the electrons leaving the filament get to the plate and no further increase in plate current can occur. Should the cathode be heated to a higher temperature, however, more electrons will be emitted and the saturation current will occur at higher plate currents than those shown. The foot of each curve, near -2, -6, -11, and -16 volts, indicates what negative voltage on the grid will stop all electrons and prevent them from reaching the plate. The higher the $+$ potential on the plate, the more negative must be the grid to stop the electrons.

64.2. Vacuum Tube Oscillator. To broadcast the human voice by radio, a generator of alternating current of extremely high frequency and constant amplitude is required. In commercial broadcasting stations and amateur transmitters, this function is performed by a vacuum tube and circuit of relatively simple design.

One type of oscillator circuit is shown in Fig. 64E. When the switch *S* is closed, con-

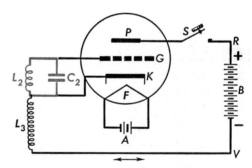

Fig. 64E *Vacuum tube oscillator circuit for generating radio waves of constant amplitude.*

necting the *B*-battery to the plate of the tube, an electron current from the cathode *K* to the plate *P* starts a current in the circuit $PRVL_3K$. This growing current in L_3 creates an expanding magnetic field, which cutting across L_2 induces a current in the grid circuit in such a direction that the grid becomes negative. A negative charge on the grid, as shown by the characteristic curves in Fig. 64D, causes the plate current to decrease. This decreasing current causes the field about L_3 to collapse, thus inducing a reversed current in the grid circuit and therefore a positive charge on the grid. Such a charge increases the plate current, and the above process is repeated.

If the two circuits, L_2C_2 and $PRVL_3$, are properly tuned by adjusting C_2, resonance will occur and energy from the B-battery will be continuously supplied to keep the oscillations going with constant amplitude. The graph of the continuous oscillations shown in Fig. 64F represents the voltage

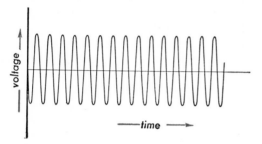

Fig. 64F *Continuous oscillations in a vacuum tube oscillator circuit like that shown in Fig. 64E.*

across L_3 as it varies in time. The L_2C_2 circuit controls the frequency by controlling the grid potential while the large voltage and current fluctuations take place in the L_3 circuit.

64.3. Radio Transmitter. To use an oscillating tube circuit, of the kind described above, as part of a radio transmitter, the high-frequency oscillations in the L_2C_2 circuit must be modified by sound waves and then applied to an antenna and ground system, for broadcasting as electromagnetic waves. A simplified circuit diagram showing one of the many ways of doing this is given in Fig. 64G. There are three parts to

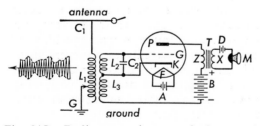

Fig. 64G *Radio transmitter employing a microphone and only one tube as an oscillator.*

this particular "hook up": (1) *the microphone circuit* containing a battery D and a transformer T, (2) *the oscillator circuit* in the middle, and (3) *the antenna circuit* C_1L_1G at the left.

By talking or singing into the microphone, the diaphragm inside moves back and forth with the sound vibrations, thus altering the steady current previously flowing around the circuit DMX. An illustration of the pulsating current is shown in Fig. 64H(a). Current pulsations in X, the

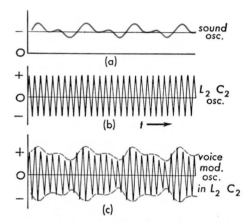

Fig. 64H *Graphs of (a) sound waves, (b) continuous oscillations in L_2C_2 and (c) voice-modulated oscillations in L_2C_2.*

transformer primary, cause similar pulsations in Z, the secondary circuit carrying the plate current. The effect of the relatively low frequency audio currents on the high-frequency oscillations already there is to alter their amplitude as shown in diagram (c).

Through the *coupling* of L_3 with L_1, the modulated oscillations are induced in the antenna circuit by resonance, and are radiated as electromagnetic waves of the same frequency and form. The continuous wave produced by the radio-frequency oscillations alone is called the *carrier wave,* and the alteration of its amplitude by *audio-frequencies* is called *modulation.* Although radio transmitters with one vacuum tube have been used by radio amateurs, it is customary to find transmitters with half a dozen or more tubes. The principal function of additional tubes, in receivers as well as transmitters, is to amplify currents wherever they are needed, thereby providing greater transmitting range and clearer reception.

64.4. Vacuum Tube Amplifier. One of the most important functions of the vacuum tube is its use as an *amplifier* of radio frequency or audio frequency currents, as shown in Fig. 64I. The *input* resistor repre-

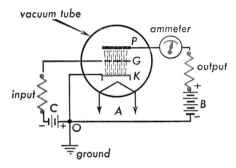

Fig. 64I *Amplifier circuit with one vacuum tube.*

sents some part of any circuit in which a weak but varying current is flowing; the *output* resistor represents another circuit to which a stronger current of the same form is delivered. In some cases these are resistors as shown, but in others they are the primary and secondary windings of separate transformers. The source of the additional energy is the *B*-battery plate supply.

In amplifying any given signal current, a faithful reproduction of the *wave form* must be carried out, otherwise *distortion* will result; musical sounds from a radio will be harsh or pictures from a television receiver will be blurred. To amplify without distortion, a tube must be used that has a long straight section in its *characteristic curve* (see Fig. 64D), and it should be operated at the center of this straight portion. Such an operation is shown by the graph in Fig. 64J. To make the tube operate at *M*, a small battery, called a *C*-battery or *C*-bias, is inserted in the grid circuit to maintain the grid at a negative potential. For the curve and tube shown, this requires −5 volts, while for other types of tubes it

might well require greater or smaller potentials.

When no input signal potentials are imposed, the grid is held at −5 volts and a steady current of 15 milliamperes flows through the plate and output circuit. If now an alternating current like a radio frequency of constant amplitude is impressed across the input terminals, the grid potential will rise and fall in the same way, and an undistorted but amplified current will flow in the plate and output circuit. The time variations in grid potential are shown in Fig. 64J, and the corresponding

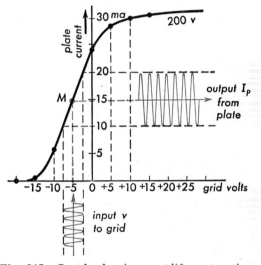

Fig. 64J *Graph showing amplifier operation.*

plate current oscillations at the right and center. If the input radio frequency is voice-modulated, the amplified current will also be voice-modulated without distortion. It should be noted that, if the impressed grid voltage variations are too large, say −20 to +10 volts, the amplified currents will reach the curved portions of the curve above and below, and *distortion* of the *wave form* will result. As long as the tube is operated on the straight portion of the curve, the plate current is directly proportional to the impressed grid potential, and faithful amplification takes place.

64.5. Semi-Conductors. In Chap. 47 we were introduced to the fact that certain metals are good conductors of electricity, while other materials like ceramics are insulators, that is, poor conductors of electricity. Since the resistance range between these two groups of materials is about a million million fold, a lot of materials lie in between. These materials are called *semi-conductors*.

Of the hundreds of semi-conductors known to science, certain ones are of considerable importance. Typical examples are the crystalline forms of several elements listed in the fourth column of the periodic table (see Appendix X). Two important ones are *silicon* and *germanium*. In Fig. 64K is a diagram of a small germanium

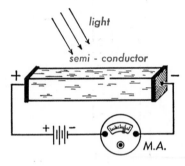

Fig. 64K *Circuit diagram for demonstrating the photoconductivity of a semi-conductor like germanium or silicon.*

crystal about 5 mm square and 2 cm long, which is connected to a battery and a milliammeter by wires, completing an electric circuit. When light is allowed to fall on the crystal, its electrical resistance decreases and the current rises. This response to light is instantaneous and is called *photoconductivity*.

If the germanium crystal is heated, the current again rises, indicating a decrease in electrical resistance. This *heating effect* is not instantaneous, however, since it takes a long time for the current to return to its original value, that is, for the temperature of the crystal to return to room temperature. The resistance of metallic conductors behaves in just the opposite way; their resistance increases with a rise in temperature.

In order to explain the light and heat effects described above, we must refer to the crystal lattice of semi-conductors. Silicon and germanium atoms each have what the chemists call four *valence electrons,* that is, four electrons that enter into the chemical binding in solids. The crystal pattern of atoms in both crystals is a tetrahedral structure, as shown in Fig. 64L, each atom shar-

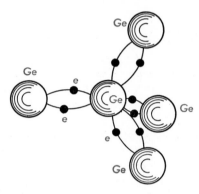

Fig. 64L *Each atom in a germanium crystal is bound at the center of a tetrahedron formed by its four nearest neighbors.*

ing one of its electrons with each neighbor, the neighbor in turn sharing one of its four with it. Such a sharing of electrons between two atoms is called a *covalent bond*.

Because of the difficulty of drawing a three-dimensional tetrahedral lattice structure, it is convenient to flatten the diagram out and represent the bonding as a square lattice, as shown in Fig. 64M.

At temperatures close to absolute zero, all electrons in a crystal are tied up strongly by these chemical bonds. When the crystal is raised to room temperature, however, the thermal motions of the atoms are sufficient to break some of the bonds and free some of the electrons to wander throughout the crystal. Where an electron has broken free, as shown at the upper right and lower left in Fig. 64M, a hole has been created. Since that part of the crystal was neutral beforehand, it now lacks an electron, and the vacant hole is equivalent to a net positive charge.

Due also to thermal agitation, a *bound*

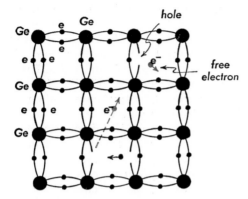

Fig. 64M *Schematic diagram of the covalent bonding of atoms in a germanium crystal. Thermal agitation breaks some bonds and liberates electrons.*

electron next to a hole can move across to fill the gap, the net motion of the negative charge from one bonded position to another being in effect equivalent to the motion of a hole in the opposite direction. The motion of a hole is, therefore, equivalent to the motion or a positive charge. This action is shown at the lower center in Fig. 64M.

64.6. P-Type and N-Type Crystals. Most crystals like silicon and germanium are not pure, but contain small quantities of other elements. If crystals are formed with arsenic as an impurity, the arsenic atoms, with five electrons each, provide a crystal lattice with extra electrons. Such a crystal as shown in Fig. 64N is therefore one in which there is

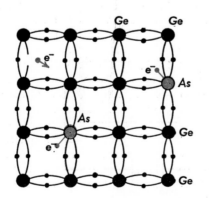

Fig. 64N *N-type crystal lattice with arsenic atoms as an impurity.*

one unbound electron from each arsenic atom. Due to thermal agitation, additional electrons are shaken loose and an equal number of holes thereby created. With more free electrons (*N*-carriers) than holes (*P*-carriers), the application of a potential across such a crystal finds more negatives moving than positives. For this reason, this lattice with a surplus of *N*-carriers is called an *N*-type crystal.

If crystals are grown with aluminum as an impurity (see Fig. 64O), the aluminum

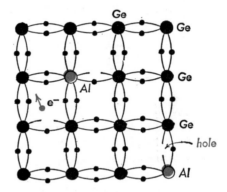

Fig. 64O *P-type crystal lattice with aluminum atoms as an impurity.*

atoms, with only three valence electrons each, form a crystal lattice with an electron deficiency, that is, with holes. Such a crystal at room temperature has more holes than free electrons; it is called a *P*-type crystal. Neither of these crystals, by itself, has a net charge. The surplus of free negatives in an *N*-type crystal is compensated for by the positive charges on the arsenic nuclei, while the surplus of holes in the *N*-type crystal is compensated for by the deficiency in positive nuclear charge of the aluminum nuclei.

When light falls on a crystal as in Fig. 64K, the light is absorbed within a few atomic layers. The absorbed energy breaks some of the electron bonds and creates holes. This process is called *photoionization*. The potentials applied at the ends of the crystal cause the electrons to move to the left, and the holes to the right. This flow of charge constitutes a current.

64.7. PN-Junction. When two semi-conductors of the *P* and *N* types are brought into contact as shown in Fig. 64P, they form what is called a *PN*-junction. In the region

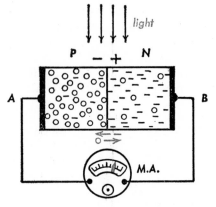

Fig. 64P   *PN-junction of semi-conductors. The principle of the "solar battery."*

of contact, the free electrons in the *N*-crystal diffuse into holes across the boundary, thereby setting up a potential difference between the otherwise neutral crystals. Since electrons have left the *N*-crystal, that side acquires a positive potential, while the *P*-crystal having some holes filled acquires a negative potential.

If the junction is maintained at constant temperature in a darkened room, no current will be observed through the milliammeter. The reason for this is that reverse potentials are set up between the crystal ends and the metallic electrodes, so that no

potential difference exists between *A* and *B*.

If we now shine light on the *PN*-junction, the light is absorbed, freeing additional electrons and creating holes. Due to the potential difference in the region close to the junction, electrons move to the right, holes to the left, and we have a current. Such a current is readily demonstrated by a milliammeter *MA*; this is the principle of the so-called *solar battery*.

Since the *ionization* process arising from the absorption of light occurs only in the surface layers of atoms, solar batteries are made with very thin crystals deposited on some insulating material.

64.8. PN-Junction Rectifier. When a single semi-conductor is maintained at room temperature, the thermal agitation finds the atoms, as well as the free electrons and holes, vibrating at random. This random motion does not give rise to any net current flow in any direction. To produce a current, a battery is applied to the ends as shown in Fig. 64K. Because the crystal is a relatively poor conductor, the charge migration, called a *drift current,* is slow. If we now have two crystals forming a *PN*-junction as shown in Fig. 64Q, there are two ways we can apply voltage to produce a current. If the *P*-crystal is made positive as shown at the left in Fig. 64Q, the force is such as to pull electrons to the right and holes to the left. Both of these constitute current flow, but notice, holes are being pulled from where there are lots of holes, and electrons from where there are lots of

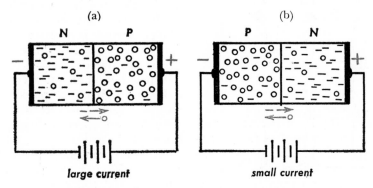

Fig. 64Q   *NP- and PN-junctions have a rectifying action.*

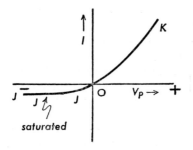

Fig. 64R *Characteristic curve for a PN-junction.*

electrons, and so we obtain a large current.

If we reverse the voltage as in diagram (b), we will be trying to pull holes from where there are very few, and electrons from where there are very few, and we will obtain a relatively small current. So if we now apply different voltages across a PN-junction and measure the current flow, we can plot the results and obtain a graph of the type shown in Fig. 64R. In one direction we get current flow and in the other direction we get very little. This is why a PN-junction acts like a Fleming valve, a rectifier of alternating currents—a large current flows when P is positive and a very small current when P is negative.

64.9. Transistors. A transistor as shown in Fig. 64S is composed of three semi-con-

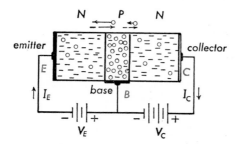

Fig. 64S *Circuit diagram for an NPN-transistor.*

ductor elements, two of the N-type crystals and one of the P-type crystals. This combination is referred to as an NPN-transistor. We can also have a PNP-type of transistor.

Suppose we now apply a potential V_E

across the first junction of the NPN-transistor and a potential V_C across the second junction as shown in the diagram. Due to the electric field across the first junction, electrons from the emitter E move to the right, and the positive holes from the base B move to the left. Operating in the K region of Fig. 64R, a small voltage V_E will give rise to a relatively large current across this junction. In the region close to the junction, electrons will be filling up holes.

With a reverse electric field on the second junction, electrons from the base B try to move to the right, and holes from the collector C to the left. Operating in the J-region of Fig. 64R (the *saturated* condition), little or no transport of charge takes place. An increase of V_C even to a large value will not change this nonconducting condition.

By making the center element of the transistor very thin, an entirely different behavior of charge transfer occurs. The electrons migrating across the first junction have little time to find a hole and be neutralized. Most of them cross over into the collector crystal where there are relatively few holes. Hence the current flow across the two junctions is approximately the same. Since a few electrons do recombine with holes in the center element, however, the current I_C is not quite as large as the current I_E, so that the ratio is slightly less than unity.

$$I_C = \alpha I_E$$

A typical value of α would be 0.90, or 90%.

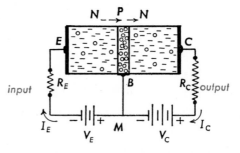

Fig. 64T *Transister amplifier circuit diagram.*

64.10. Transistor Amplifier. An amplifier circuit using a transistor in place of a vacuum tube is shown in Fig. 64T. Since the current I_C is very nearly equal to the current I_E, little electron current flows through BM. With the input resistance R_E small, and the output resistance R_C large, the nearly equal currents through them signify a small $I_E R_E$ drop across the input and a large $I_C R_C$ drop across the output. Hence, there is a voltage gain and, therefore, a power gain.

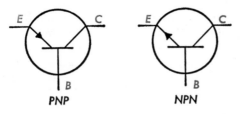

Fig. 64U *Schematic diagrams of transistors. Arrows are opposite to electron flow.*

The ratio of the output power $I_C{}^2 R_C$ to the input power $I_E{}^2 R_E$ is called the *power gain.*

$$A = \frac{I_C{}^2 R_C}{I_E{}^2 R_E}$$

A typical power gain would be $A = 40$.

If we now apply a weak alternating current as an *input* power, the a.c. *output* power in the collector circuit could be 40 times larger.

64.11. Transistor Oscillator. Simple schematic diagrams of transistors, as used in circuit diagrams, are shown in Fig. 64U. The arrow inside the circle indicates the direction of the holes or + current, and specifies the direction of the voltages that are to be applied.

Figure 64V shows a simple oscillator circuit employing a *PNP*-transistor instead of

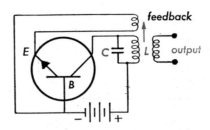

Fig. 64V *Oscillator circuit using an NPN-transistor.*

a vacuum tube. The oscillation frequency is determined by *L* and *C* in the collector circuit, and feedback of a weak oscillating signal to the emitter is accomplished by the small coil *F* which picks up induced voltages from *L*.

QUESTIONS

1. Diagram the circuit of a vacuum tube oscillator for generating high radio frequencies of constant amplitude.

2. Draw from memory an amplifier circuit with one vacuum tube.

3. Make from memory a drawing of a radio transmitter employing a microphone and one vacuum tube.

4. (a) What is a semi-conductor? (b) What is a *P*-type crystal? (c) What is a *PN*-junction?

5. (a) What is a solar battery? (b) What are the principles of the solar battery?

6. (a) What is a transistor? (b) What is a *PNP*-transistor?

7. Explain the photoconductivity of a semiconductor like germanium.

8. Since an *N*-type semi-conductor crystal has more free electrons than holes, why is it electrically uncharged?

9. Since a *P*-type semi-conductor crystal has more holes than free electrons, why is it electrically uncharged?

10. Make a circuit diagram of a transistor amplifier using a *PNP*-transistor. Show the + and − terminals of both batteries.

11. Make a diagram showing what instruments you would connect to a *PNP*-transistor to obtain readings for plotting a curve like Fig. 64R. How would you obtain different voltages, and read the currents?

Chapter 65

Electron Optics

There exists a remarkable similarity between optical systems of prisms and lenses, as they act upon light rays, and electric and magnetic fields as they act upon streams of electrons. It is the purpose of this chapter to consider some of these similarities and to treat several practical applications of *electron optics*. To begin with, it is convenient to present one of the standard methods of producing a beam of electrons, and to give the formula for calculating electron velocity.

65.1. An Electron Accelerator. A schematic diagram of an electron accelerator is shown in Fig. 65A. The source of electrons

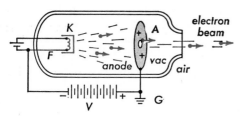

Fig. 65A *Electrons are accelerated by an applied potential V.*

is a caesium-oxide-coated cathode K, heated by a filament F. The cathode and filament are connected to the negative terminal, and the circular disk at the center to the positive terminal of a high-voltage battery V. Starting from rest at the cathode, the electrons are accelerated along the electric lines of force, acquiring at the anode A a velocity v.

By connecting the (+) terminal to the ground, the anode is brought to the potential of the surrounding walls of the room and the electrons are not attracted back toward A, but continue on with con-

stant velocity. With a thin aluminum foil at the end and a high applied voltage V, electrons may be projected into the air beyond.

One of the results of J. J. Thomson's experiments with cathode rays was the discovery that the velocity of electrons depends upon the potential applied between the anode and the cathode. The higher the voltage, the higher is the electron velocity. Since the energy required to carry an electric charge Q through a difference of potential V is given by $Q \times V$ (see Eq. (50a)), the kinetic energy acquired by an electron of charge e falling through a difference of potential V will be $V \times e$. If we equate this product to the kinetic energy $\frac{1}{2}mv^2$,

$$Ve = \tfrac{1}{2}m_0v^2 \qquad (65a)$$

where V is the applied accelerating potential in volts, m_0 is the rest mass of the electron in Kg, v the velocity in meters per second, and e the charge on the particle in coulombs.

Example. Calculate the velocity of electrons accelerated by a potential of 10,000 volts. (The electronic charge $e = 1.60 \times 10^{-19}$ coul, and $m = 9_0 \times 10^{-31}$ Kg.)

Solution. Direct substitution in the above equation gives

$$10,000 \times 1.6 \times 10^{-19} = \tfrac{1}{2}(9 \times 10^{-31}) \times v^2$$

from which

$$v = \sqrt{\frac{10,000 \times 1.6 \times 10^{-19} \times 2}{9 \times 10^{-31}}}$$
$$= 0.6 \times 10^8 \text{ m/sec}$$

This is just $\frac{1}{5}$ the velocity of light. (Velocity of light $c = 3 \times 10^8$ m/sec.)

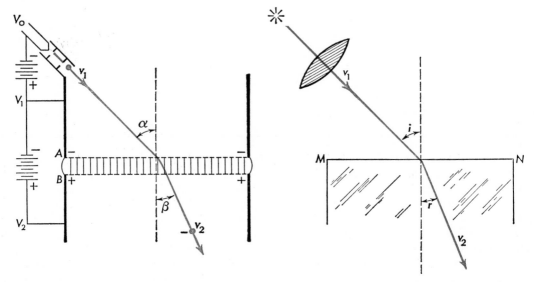

Fig. 65B *The bending of light in refraction is analogous to the bending of the path of an electron.*

Instead of calculating the velocity of electrons in meters per second, it is customary to refer to their kinetic energy in terms of the applied voltage. For example, in the problem above the energy gained by the electrons is said to be 10,000 *electron volts (abbr.* 10,000 ev, or 10 Kev). They are also sometimes referred to as 10,000 volt electrons.

If voltages greater than 255,000 volts are used in Eq.(65a), the calculated velocities will be greater than the velocity of light. Consequently, for voltages of about 20,000 volts or more, the relativistic formula should be used. From the formula for the kinetic energy of a high-speed mass Eq. (46r), we obtain

$$Ve = m_0c^2(\gamma - 1) \qquad (65b)$$

where
$$\gamma = \frac{1}{\sqrt{1 - v^2/c^2}} \qquad (65c)$$

65.2. Refraction of Electrons. When a moving electron, entering an electric field, makes an angle with the electric lines of force, it is bent in its path according to *Bethe's law of refraction* (see Fig. 65B). A correlation of this law with Snell's law in optics (see Eq.(37b)) is indicated by the following parallel equations.

Snell's law	*Bethe's law*	
$\dfrac{\sin i}{\sin r} = \dfrac{v_1}{v_2}$	$\dfrac{\sin \alpha}{\sin \beta} = \dfrac{v_2}{v_1}$	(65d)

Note the reverse order of the velocities v_1 and v_2. When a ray of light enters a more dense medium, it is slowed down and at the same time bent toward the normal. Electrons, on the other hand, are deflected toward the normal when, in crossing a potential layer, they are speeded up. If the grid potentials are reversed, the electrons will be retarded in crossing the potential layer and they will be deflected away from the normal. In other words, *reverse the direction of the electrons, keeping their speed the same, and they will retrace their paths exactly.* Such a behavior is analogous to the very useful principle in geometrical optics that *all light rays are retraceable.*

To carry the refraction analogy a little further, consider the bending of electron paths by electrically charged bodies as shown in Fig. 65C. Attraction by the positively charged wire and repulsion by the negative produce a prism-like action in case (a). A negatively charged metal ring produces a converging lens-like action in case (b); a positively charged ring produces a diverging lens action in case (c).

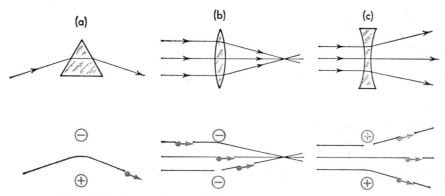

(a) (b) (c)

Fig. 65C *Comparison of light optics with electron optics.*

Since, by Eq.(65a), $v^2 \propto V$ and $v \propto \sqrt{V}$, the velocities v_1 and v_2 in Bethe's law of electron refraction may be replaced by $\sqrt{V_1}$ and $\sqrt{V_2}$, respectively, giving

$$\frac{\sin \alpha}{\sin \beta} = \frac{\sqrt{V_2}}{\sqrt{V_1}} \qquad (65e)$$

V_1 and V_2 are the potentials of the two grids A and B in Fig. 65B, taken with respect to the cathode source of electrons in the electron gun as zero.

65.3. Electron Lenses. An electron lens, known as a double-aperture system, is shown in Fig. 65D; it is to be compared in

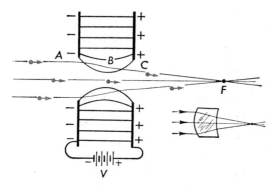

Fig. 65D *Double-aperture electron lens and its optical analogue.*

its action to parallel rays of light incident on a converging glass lens as shown at the lower right. While both are converging systems, the essential difference between

the two is that, whereas light rays are bent only at the two surfaces, electrons are refracted continuously as they pass through the potential layers.

The focal length of a glass lens is fixed in value by the radius of curvature of its two faces and the refractive index for the light used, but the focal length of an electron lens can be varied at will by altering v, the velocity of the electrons, and V, the voltage applied to the system. In this respect, the latter can be compared to the crystalline lens of the eye where the focal length can be changed by altering the lens curvature.

In the diagram, refraction for the upper path is greatest near A and, although it changes sign at some point near B, the gain in velocity due to the electric field produces a lesser deviation over the second half of the path, thereby causing convergence. If the electrons are reversed in direction on the right, they will retrace their paths and emerge parallel at the left. If the electric field is reversed in direction, however, the electron paths will not be the same but the system will still act as a converging lens.

A second type of electron lens, known as a double-cylinder system, is shown in Fig. 65E. In passing through the potential gap, the electric field has a converging action for the first half of the distance and a diverging action during the second half. Because they spend a greater time in the first half of the converging field, and the

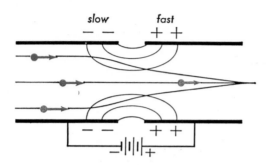

Fig. 65E *Symmetrical electron lens.*

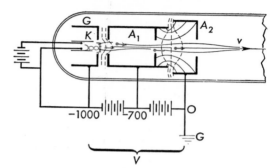

Fig. 65G *Electron gun.*

force on a charged particle is independent of velocity, the impulse (force × time) is greater for the convergence interval than it is for the divergence interval.

By making the second cylinder larger than the first, as in Fig. 65F, the electric

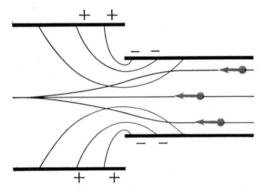

Fig. 65F *Asymmetrical electron lens.*

lines of force spread out more in the second cylinder. Such spreading weakens the field in the larger cylinder and reduces the divergent action to bring the electrons to a shorter focus.

65.4. An Electron Gun. A narrow beam of high-speed electrons, all having as nearly as possible the same velocity, has many practical applications in the field of electronics and atomic research. A device for producing such beams is called an "electron gun" (see Fig. 65G).

Electrons from a small filament-heated cathode K are accelerated by a difference of potential V applied to the cylinders of an electrostatic lens system, A_1 and A_2. The

purpose of the guard ring maintained at the potential of the cathode is to improve the properties of the lens action of the first aperture and thereby collect a maximum number of emitted electrons into the collimated beam.

The function of the second lens is to converge the bundle toward a focus and then introduce enough divergence to straighten the beam out into a narrow pencil. The velocity of the emergent beam is given by Eq.(65a) where V is the over-all voltage from cathode K to anode A_2.

65.5. The Cathode-Ray Oscilloscope. One of the simplest applications of an electron gun is to be found in every *cathode-ray oscilloscope*, an instrument whose purpose is to reveal the detailed variations in rapidly changing electric currents, potentials, or pulses (see Fig. 65H). In appearance this device looks like J. J. Thomson's cathode-ray tube (see Fig. 57F), and is actually the important element in one type of television receiver.

A cathode-ray oscilloscope is a vacuum tube containing *an electron gun* at one end, two pairs of *deflector plates* (or magnetic coils) near the middle and a *fluorescent screen* at the other end. When an alternating potential is pplied to the *x-plates,* the electron beam bends back and forth from side to side and, when applied to the *y-plates,* it bends up and down. The luminous spot produced where the beam strikes the fluorescent screen traces out a horizontal line in the first instance and a vertical line in the second.

It is customary to apply a *saw-tooth po-*

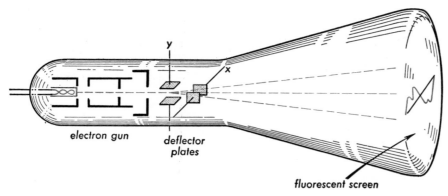

y

x

electron gun   deflector
                       plates

fluorescent screen

Fig. 65H   *Cathode-ray oscilloscope.*

tential to the x-plates (see Fig. 651(a)) and the unknown potential to be studied, (b), to the y-plates. The saw-tooth potential supplied by a special radio tube circuit, called a "sweep circuit," causes the beam spot to move from left to right across the screen at constant speed and then jump quickly back from right to left to repeat the motion, (c). When the vertical deflections occur at the same time, the spot draws

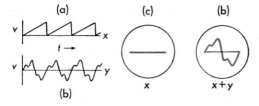

(a)   (c)   (b)

v

t →

v

(b)

Fig. 65I   *Potentials applied to a cathode-ray tube, and graphs appearing on fluorescent screen.*

out a graph of the varying potential as in diagram (d). By varying the sweep circuit frequency until it matches the frequency of the studied signal, repeated graphs will be drawn out, one on top of the other, and persistence of vision and the fluorescent screen will present a stationary graph.

Green fluorescent screens are used for visual observation since the eye is most sensitive to this color; blue screens are used for photographic purposes since films and plates are most sensitive to blue.

The oscilloscope has many practical applications, and is to be found in every re-

search laboratory as well as in every radio and television and repair shop. Its principal function is to analyze, or diagnose, rapidly changing potentials whose frequencies may be as low as a fraction of a cycle per second or as high as thousands of megacycles per second. Periodic or transient potentials as small as a fraction of a microvolt may also be studied by first amplifying them with standard vacuum tube circuits. (See Sec. 64.4.)

Another valuable feature of the oscilloscope is its ability to measure time intervals between electrical impulses less than a microsecond apart. One microsecond is equal to one-millionth of a second.

65.6. Infrared Telescope. A telescope for seeing objects illuminated in the dark by infrared light is diagramed in Fig. 65J. An image of the object to be observed is focused on the photo-cathode of the vacuum tube by means of an ordinary glass lens L. The caesium-oxide-coated cathode under infrared illumination emits photoelectrons which, accelerated to the right by $A_1 A_2 A_3$ and A_4, are brought to a focus on the green fluorescent screen at the right. The visible light they produce there by their impact is then observed by means of a magnifying eyepiece.

Electron focusing is accomplished by varying the potential applied to the second anode A_2; the infrared light image is focused by moving the lens L; and the visible light image is focused by moving the eyepiece.

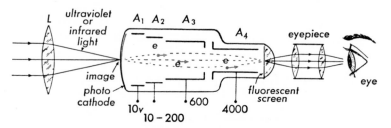

Fig. 65J *Ultraviolet and infrared telescope employing an electron-image tube.*

65.7. Magnetic Lenses. When electrons cross a magnetic field, and their paths make an angle with the magnetic lines, they are deflected in spiral-like paths which, if properly controlled, may bring them to a focus. Such focusing properties of magnetic fields, illustrated by the cross section of a flat coil in Fig. 65K, were first demonstrated and proved mathematically by Busch in 1926. It can be shown that the focal length of such a lens, the magnetic field strength, and the electron velocity fit into well-known formulas in optics.

By encasing a flat coil in a hollow iron ring, the magnetic field becomes more concentrated and the refraction of electrons becomes more abrupt as they pass through the field. As a consequence the refraction more nearly resembles that of optical lenses. Still greater concentration is brought about by providing a small narrow gap on the inside of the iron casing, as shown in the diagram.

If electron paths diverge too far from the principal axis of a coil lens, aberrations of the kind described for light in Chap. 39 arise. For this reason *diaphragms* are often used to confine electron beams to the center of the coil, as an *iris diaphragm* is used to confine light rays to the center of a lens.

65.8. Electron Microscope. The electron microscope, like the optical microscope, is an instrument used principally in the research laboratory for magnifying small objects to such an extent that their minutest parts may be observed and studied in detail. The importance of this device in the field of medical research cannot be overestimated. To illustrate, many viruses known to medical science as being responsible for certain human diseases lie beyond the range of the optical microscope. With the electron microscope, magnifications of from 10 to 100 times that of the finest optical microscopes make many of these viruses, and some of their detailed structure, visible

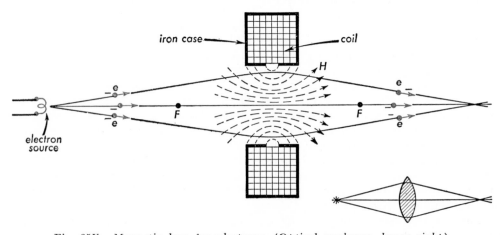

Fig. 65K *Magnetic lens for electrons. (Optical analogue, lower right.)*

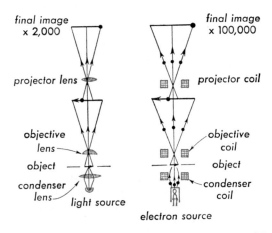

final image
× 2,000

projector lens

objective
lens

object

condenser
lens

light source

final image
× 100,000

projector coil

objective
coil

object

condenser
coil

electron source

Fig. 65L *Optical microscope compared with electron microscope.*

to the eye. While the highest magnification obtained with the best optical microscope is about 2000×, electron microscopes have already been made that give magnifications as high as 100,000×.

A schematic diagram of an electron microscope employing magnetic lenses is shown in Fig. 65L. At the bottom, a source of electrons is concentrated on the object (small arrow) by a condenser coil. Passing through or around the object, these electrons focus a magnified image of the object just below the projector coil. Only a small

Electrons, like light waves, are stopped by metallic films; only when they are extremely thin can transmitted rays be employed. For opaque objects the light, or electrons, may be reflected from the surface and only surface structures may be observed.*

65.9. The Electrocardiograph. When two small metal electrodes are placed at random on the skin of the human body, small and continuously changing potential differences are found to exist between them. When these varying potentials are carefully measured and compared with muscular activity, many of them can be correlated directly with certain activities of the body organs.

Each muscular action within the body is preceded and accompanied by an electrical impulse, the magnitude of which depends upon many factors. Such impulses accompanying the beating of the heart, for example, are exceedingly large (of the order of one millivolt); they are of such importance to the medical profession that special instruments have been devised and successively used to graphically record their intricate and minute variations. Such an instrument is called an *electrocardiograph.*

A schematic wiring diagram of one type of electrocardiograph is shown in Fig. 65M.

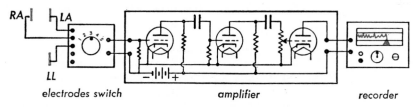

RA LA

LL

electrodes switch   amplifier   recorder

Fig. 65M *Schematic diagram for an electrocardiograph used by physicians and surgeons.*

central section of these electrons pass into the projector coil, to be brought to focus in a further magnified image at the top. There the image of only a small section of the object can be seen directly on a fluorescent screen or can be photographed with ordinary photographic plates. Figure 22H shows reproductions of photomicrographs taken in this way.

RA, *LA*, and *LL* represent three metal electrodes that are taped to the patient's *right arm*, *left arm*, and *left leg*, respectively. Varying potentials created between any pair of electrodes are selected by the switch box *S* and, after being amplified,

* For a more complete treatment of electron optics, see *Electron Optics*, by V. K. Zworykin and others, John Wiley and Sons.

are applied to the vertical deflector plates of an oscilloscope or to the ink stylus of a recorder. The latter instrument draws out the potential changes on a moving strip of paper to make what is called an *electro-cardiogram*.

Small sections of electrocardiograms are shown in Fig. 65N. Curve (a) is characteris-

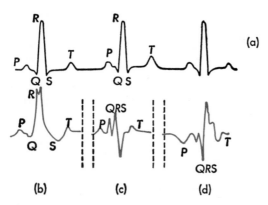

Fig. 65N (a) *Electrocardiogram of a normal heart.* (b), (c), *and* (d): *Waves showing three types of abnormalities.*

tic of a normal heart action. After a relaxation period, *T—P*, an electrical pulse *P*, associated with the activity of the right and left atrium, is recorded. This activity stimulates the right and left ventricles (see Fig. 26H, and their response results in the *QRS* section of the curve. Between *S* and *T*, both ventricles are still activated, the pulse *T* indicating a restoration to the relaxed condition.

Although an electrocardiogram is only a record of a series of complex electrical events, it does indicate the time relations and magnitudes of certain muscular activity. In (b), (c), and (d), single-period sections of abnormal electrocardiograms are shown as samples of the thousands of different curves found in practice. If, as an illustration, the electrical conduction to one ventricle is poor, the *QRS* section of the curve is delayed as well as modified. If, on the other hand, there is a larger than normal heart muscle, the *QRS* curve widens, etc.

65.10. Electroencephalography. When small metal electrodes are placed on a patient's scalp, potentials of the order of from one to fifty microvolts are found to exist between any given pair. The predominant frequencies of these varying potentials are lower than 100 cycles per second. They are called "brain waves." Instruments used to record these waves are essentially the same as those used in electrocardiography, and are called *electro-encephalographs*. (See Fig. 65M.)

At the present time it is common practice to use a dozen or more electrodes on one patient in order to localize with precision tumors and other abnormalities. Potential waves from any three or more selected points are often recorded simultaneously to provide additional information by correlation. Reproductions of two electroencephalograms (*abbr. EEG*), are shown in Fig. 65O. It will be noted that there is a

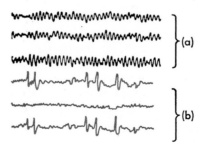

Fig. 65O *Electroencephalograms* (*EEG*): (a) *normal,* (b) *epileptic seizure.*

marked difference between (a) the waves from a normal patient's record, and (b) those from a patient in epileptic seizure.

When EEG recordings are analyzed into their component waves, as is done with complex sound waves, various frequencies can be identified and associated with recognized abnormalities. Very low frequencies up to about 8 cyc/sec are called *delta waves;* those around 10 cyc/sec, *alpha waves;* and those in the range 10 to 60 cyc/sec, *beta waves*. Of the many brain disorders detectable from EEG records, the most familiar are: *epilepsy; cerebral thrombosis; encephalitis* and *meningitis;* and *brain tumor*.

QUESTIONS

1. What is Bethe's law? In what way is it like Snell's law in optics? In what way is it different?

2. What kind of electric field will deviate an electron beam the way a glass prism deviates a light beam?

3. What are electron lenses? How are they made?

4. What is an electron gun? What can it be used for? Does it employ electron lenses?

5. What is a cathode ray oscilloscope? What is its purpose?

PROBLEMS

1. Make a diagram of an electron gun, using two hollow tubes of different diameter. Show the electric field and electron paths. Reverse the potentials, and assume a parallel beam again coming in from the left.

2. Make a diagram of an electron gun. Label the principal elements. Briefly describe its action.

3. Make a diagram of a cathode ray oscilloscope. Label the principal parts. Briefly describe its action.

4. Make a diagram of your idea of an electron microscope. Label the principal elements.

5. What voltage applied to an electron gun will give electrons a velocity of 3×10^7 cm/sec?

6. If 5000 volts are applied to an electron gun, what will be the velocity of the electrons? (*Ans.* 4.19×10^7 m/sec.)

7. Make a table of electron velocities for the following accelerating voltages: $V = 10, 50, 100, 200, 500,$ and 1000 volts.

8. What voltage applied to an electron gun will produce electrons having a speed of 2000 mi/hr? (*Ans.* 2.25×10^{-6} v.)

9. The moon weighs 1.62×10^{23} lb, is 239,000 mi from the earth's center, and makes one trip around the earth in its orbit in about 28 days. Find (a) the moon's velocity in mi/sec, and (b) its apparent increase in mass due to this motion. See end of Sec. 46.5.

10. A meteorite with a 400 Kg rest mass passes the earth with a speed of 295,000 Km/sec. What is its apparent mass? (*Ans.* 2200 Kg.)

11. Electrons accelerated by a potential $V_1 = 1000$ volts enter an electric field between two grids as shown in Fig. 65B. If the angle of incidence is 35°, and the potential across the grids is 500 volts, find the angle of refraction.

12. If in Prob. 11 the voltage across the grids is reversed, find the angle of refraction. (*Ans.* 54.3°.)

13. Electrons accelerated by a potential of 300 volts enter an electric field as shown in Fig. 65B. If the angle of incidence is 45°, and the angle of refraction is 32°, find the potential difference between the grids.

14. If the angles are reversed in Prob. 13, find the potential difference between the grids. (*Ans.* 131 v.)

15. Electrons from an electron gun enter a uniform magnetic field perpendicular to the lines of induction. If their circular path has a diameter of 20 cm, and a potential of 200 volts is applied to the gun, find the magnetic induction B.

16. Electrons are to be accelerated by an electron gun and then allowed to enter a uniform magnetic field. If the magnetic induction is 8×10^{-4} weber/m², and the circular path is to have a radius of 5 cm, what voltage should be applied to the gun? (*Ans.* 140.5 v.)

17. Electrons accelerated by a potential $V = 500$ volts enter a uniform magnetic field in which the magnetic induction is 4×10^{-4} weber/m². Moving at right angles to the field, what is the radius of their circular path?

18. Calculate the velocity of electrons accelerated by a potential of 500,000 volts. (*Ans.* 2.59×10^8 m/sec.)

Chapter 66

Spinning Electrons

With the development of the Bohr-Som-merfeld theory of the hydrogen atom in 1913, and its extension to the building-up of the electron structure of all atoms of the periodic table, within but a few years three new but important discoveries followed: (1) the discovery of the spinning electron, (2) the quantization of orbital electrons in a magnetic field, and (3) the direct experimental evidence for the existence of electron shells.

66.1. Orbital Mechanical Moment. The foundations of our present day concepts of atomic structure were introduced into modern science when Bohr first proposed his theory of the hydrogen atom. (See Chap. 60.) According to Bohr's theory, the hydrogen atom is composed of a proton as a nucleus with a single electron revolving around it in a circular orbit. The quantum theory was introduced when Bohr assumed (see Eq.(60b)) that the orbital angular momentum p_l of the electron must always be a whole number multiple of a unit of angular momentum, $\dfrac{h}{2\pi}$

$$p_l = n \frac{h}{2\pi} \qquad n = 1, 2, 3, 4, \ldots$$

where n is the *principal quantum number* and h is *Planck's constant.*

$$h = 6.6238 \times 10^{-34} \text{ joule sec}$$

With the introduction of elliptical orbits as allowed states for the electron, a new quantum number l was introduced. This new quantum number, too, has integral values only, and is assigned letters as follows:

$$l = 0 \quad 1 \quad 2 \quad 3 \quad 4 \quad 5 \quad 6 \quad 7 \ldots$$
$$\quad s \quad p \quad d \quad f \quad g \quad h \quad i \quad j \ldots$$

In this newer notation, the orbital angular momentum is given by

$$p_l = l \frac{h}{2\pi} \qquad (66a)$$

The angular momentum p_l is frequently called the *mechanical moment,* and unit angular momentum $h/2\pi$ is frequently abbreviated $\hbar$.

$$\hbar = \frac{h}{2\pi} \qquad (66b)$$

where $\hbar = 1.054 \times 10^{-34}$ joule sec

The mechanical moment of an s-electron orbit is 0; of a p-electron orbit, $1\hbar$; of a d-electron orbit, $2\hbar$, of an f-electron orbit, $3\hbar$, etc.

66.2. Orbital Magnetic Moment. Since an electron has a negative charge, its orbital motion, like that of a current in a loop of wire, sets up a magnetic field. The direction of this field, as shown in Fig. 66A, is given by the *left-hand rule.* Since angu-

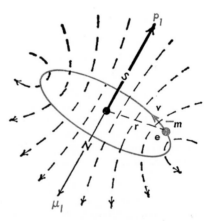

Fig. 66A *An orbital electron produces a magnetic field.*

556

lar momentum is a vector quantity (see Sec. 21.5) p_l is shown pointing up along its axis of rotation. The direction of this mechanical moment is given by the *right-hand rule.*

The magnetic field produced by the orbital electron is quite similar to the field around a bar magnet, and is therefore specified as a magnetic dipole moment. This magnetic moment μ_l is given by

$$\frac{\mu_l}{p_l} = \frac{e}{2m} \tag{66c}$$

where e and m are the charge and mass of the electron.

The left-hand term μ_l/p_l is called the *gyromagnetic ratio.* It is the ratio between

which evaluated is equal to

$$\mu_B = 9.273 \times 10^{-24} \text{ ampere meters}^2 \tag{66f}$$

The magnetic moment for a p-electron orbit is one Bohr magneton, for a d-electron orbit is two Bohr magnetons, etc. An s-electron orbit with $l = 0$, has no mechanical moment and no magnetic moment.

66.3. Spectral Series. When the spectra of most of the elements in the periodic table are examined, they are found to be complex arrays of hundreds of lines spaced in what appear to be random patterns. (See Fig. 66B(a).) A few of the elements, however, give rise to a much simpler looking spectrum, the lines arranging themselves into series like those in Figs. 66B(b),

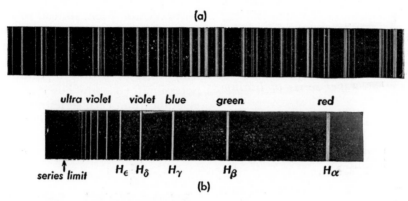

Fig. 66B (a) *Small section of the spectrum of titanium, Z = 22.* (b) *Photograph of the Balmer series of hydrogen, Z = 1.*

the magnetic moment and the mechanical moment. By substituting p_l from Eq.(66a), we obtain

$$\mu_l = l\hbar \frac{e}{2m} \tag{66d}$$

All symbols on the right, except l, are fixed atomic constants, and together they form a unit of magnetic moment called the *Bohr magneton.* The Bohr magneton is given by

$$\mu_B = \hbar \frac{e}{2m} \tag{66e}$$

59E(f), and 60G. In addition to hydrogen, the elements revealing such simple spectral series are the elements in the first column of the periodic table (Appendix X).

	Li	Na	K	Rb	Cs	Fr
$Z =$	3	11	19	37	55	87

The spectrum arising from each of these, the alkali metals, is composed of several spectral series in different wavelength regions, but having the same general appearance as shown in Fig. 59H. If the wavelengths of any one of these series are measured, and the frequencies are calculated and plotted, one obtains a graph of the kind shown in Fig. 66C.

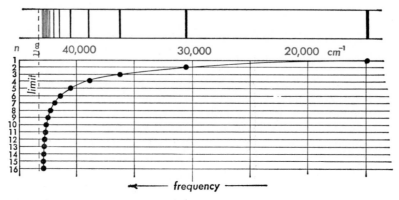

Fig. 66C   *Frequency plot of the principal series in the spectrum of lithium, Z = 3.*

The first successful attempt to fit all such lines of a series into one general formula was made by Rydberg* in 1896. His formula is,

$$\nu_n = \nu_\infty - \frac{\Re}{(n+\mu)^2} \qquad (66g)$$

where, for the *principal series of lithium*, shown in Fig. 66C,

$$\Re = 109,722 \text{ cm}^{-1}$$
$$\nu_\infty = 43,488 \text{ cm}^{-1}$$
$$\mu = 0.9596$$
$$n = 1, 2, 3, 4, \ldots$$

ν_n is the frequency of the different lines n, and ν_∞ is the frequency of the series limit.

By substituting $n = 1$ in Eq.(66g), one obtains the frequency of the first line of the lithium series, $\nu_n = 14,915$ cm^{-1}, corresponding to $\lambda = 6705$A. By substituting $n = 2$, one obtains the frequency of the second line of the series, etc.

The principal success of the Rydberg formula is remarkable because it fits all series in all spectra by changing the constants ν_∞ and μ. $\Re$ remains the same for all series in all elements. Because the actual frequencies of visible light waves are so extremely high, it is customary to divide them all by the speed of light. ($c = 3 \times 10^{10}$ cm/sec.) Such frequencies are then

* The Rydberg constant $\Re$ used here can be obtained by dividing the value of R given in Eq. (60m) by Planck's constant h and the speed of light c.

called *wave numbers*. The frequency of a spectrum line in wave numbers is therefore just equal to the number of wavelengths in a distance of 1 cm, instead of the number in 3×10^{10} cm. Frequencies, in wave numbers, have the units of 1/cm, (cm^{-1}).

66.4. The Spinning Electron. If the spectrum lines of hydrogen, lithium, sodium, potassium, etc., are observed under high magnification, each series member is found to be a double line. (See Fig. 66D.) These

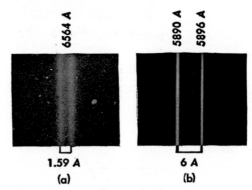

Fig. 66D   *Highly magnified photographs, showing the doublet structure of (a) the first member of the Balmer series of hydrogen (the red line), and (b) the first member of the principal series of sodium (the yellow line).*

closely spaced doublets arise from the fact that all electrons are spinning. The single electron in the hydrogen atom, which is responsible for the observed spectrum, is spinning around its own axis as it moves in an

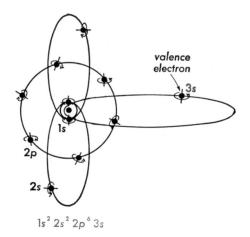

$1s^2 \, 2s^2 \, 2p^6 \, 3s$

Fig. 66E *Atomic model of sodium showing the spinning of all electrons. Z = 11.*

in 1925, to explain the double-line structure in the spectra of the alkali metals. Each electron, whether it is bound to an atom or a crystal, or is alone in free space, has an angular momentum. The spin angular momentum is given by

$$p_s = s\hbar \qquad (66h)$$

where s is the spin quantum number and has the value $\frac{1}{2}$.

$$s = \tfrac{1}{2} \text{ only} \qquad (66i)$$

Since an electron always has a negative charge, its spinning around its own mechanical axis generates a magnetic field like that shown in Fig. 66F. This field is similar to the field around a bar magnet and may be specified by its equivalent *magnetic moment*. The magnetic moment μ_s of a spinning electron is given by

$$\frac{\mu_s}{p_s} = 2\frac{e}{2m} \qquad (66j)$$

and is oppositely directed to its mechanical moment. Note that the *gyromagnetic ratio* is twice that for an electron orbit. Eq.(66c).

By substituting the value of p_s from Eq.(66h) in this formula, we obtain

$$\boxed{\mu_s = \hbar\,\frac{e}{2m}} \qquad (66k)$$

Since this is the same as Eq.(66e), we see

orbit around the nucleus. Similarly, the single-valence electron in all sodium atoms is spinning as shown in Fig. 66E.

Electrons in any completed (closed) subshell pair off with axes parallel but with opposite spin and orbit directions. Hence, in sodium: $Z = 11$, the one-valence electron $3s$ is unpaired, and its spin constitutes the resultant spin of the entire electronic system. Furthermore, it is the jumping of this valence electron from one orbit to another that is responsible for the observed spectrum.

The spinning of electrons in atoms was first proposed by Goudsmit and Uhlenbeck,

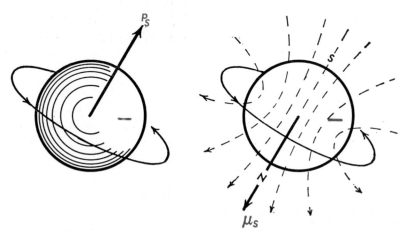

Fig. 66F *A spinning electron has a mechanical moment p_s and a magnetic moment μ_s.*

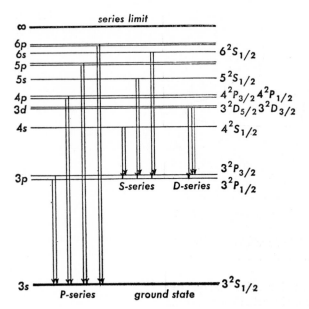

Fig. 66G   *Energy level diagram for the sodium atom, Z = 11.*

that while *a spinning electron has a mechanical moment of $\frac{1}{2}\hbar$, it has a magnetic moment of one Bohr magneton.*

66.5. Electron Spin-Orbit Interaction. The fact that the spectrum lines in the Balmer series of hydrogen, and those in the series of the alkali metals, are doublets, is interpreted to mean that each of the energy levels of these atoms is double. (See Fig. 66G for the energy level diagram of sodium.)

The doubling of energy levels in atoms having one valence electron, is due to the interaction between the magnetic field of the electron orbit, and the magnetic field of the electron spin. We have seen in Sec. 53.9 that a bar magnetic located in a magnetic field has a torque exerted on it which tends to line it up parallel to the field. A spinning electron in a magnetic field behaves in exactly the same way; there is a torque acting upon it, trying to turn its axis parallel to B. Due to the mechanical properties of a revolving mass, the electron precesses around B in much the same way that a mechanical top precesses in a gravitational field. (See Figs. 21G and 21H.)

A schematic diagram of the precession of

a spinning electron is given in Fig. 66H. Such a motion is called a *Larmor precession,* and its frequency f is given by

$$f = \frac{e}{4\pi m} B \qquad (661)$$

A good demonstration of this precession can be made by a gyroscope of the kind

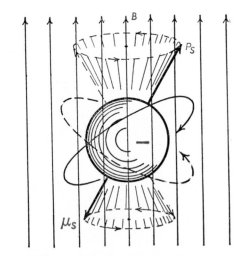

Fig. 66H   *A spinning electron in a magnetic field precesses around an axis, parallel to the magnetic induction B.*

Fig. 66I *A spinning ball gyroscope with a bar magnet on its axis will precess in a magnetic field.*

shown in Fig. 66I. A nonconducting sphere, mounted free to turn in ball-bearings, is mounted in double gimbel rings and placed directly over the center of an electromagnet as shown. When the ball is set spinning in the position shown, and the magnetic field is turned on, the ball will retain its inclination angle as it precesses around the vertical axis. By reversing the magnetic field the precession will reverse direction.

Owing to orbital motion, as well as the positive charge on the nucleus, every electron in an atom is subjected to a magnetic field. To see how this field comes about, consider the simple case of a hydrogen atom with its one electron in an orbit around a positive charge. If we imagine ourselves riding around with the electron, looking out at the nucleus, we see this positive charge

as though it were moving in an orbit around us. This moving charge gives rise to a magnetic field at the electron of the form shown in Fig. 66J. In this field the electron carries out a Larmor precession.

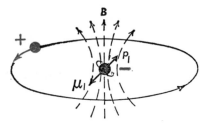

Fig. 66J *The magnetic field at an electron in an atom is due to the positively charged nucleus that appears to be going around it in an orbit.*

Since an electron has a spin angular momentum $s\hbar$, as well as an orbital angular momentum $l\hbar$, the total angular momentum of the atom will be the vector sum of the two, and its magnitude will depend upon their relative orientations. If we represent $l\hbar$ and $s\hbar$ by vectors as shown in Fig. 66K,

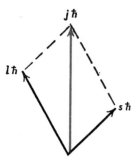

Fig. 66K *Angular momentum vectors for electron spin and orbital motions.*

their vector sum $j\hbar$ will represent the total angular momentum. j is called the *total quantum number.*

The quantum theory requires that all possible vector sums for these two quantities differ from each other by $\hbar$. For each value of the orbital quantum number l, there are two possibilities, either $\quad\quad j\hbar = l\hbar + s\hbar$

or $\quad\quad\quad j\hbar = l\hbar - s\hbar$ $\quad$ (66m)

Since all angular moments have the common factor $\hbar$, the quantum numbers l, s, and j, may be used as vectors, and we can write,

$$j = l + s \quad \text{and} \quad j = l - s \quad (66n)$$

For a d-electron, for example, $l = 2$ and $s = \frac{1}{2}$,

$$j = 2 + \tfrac{1}{2} = \tfrac{5}{2} \quad \text{and} \quad j = 2 - \tfrac{1}{2} = \tfrac{3}{2}$$

All values of l, except $l = 0$, will give two j-values (see Fig. 66L), and these will always

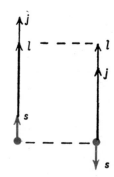

Fig. 66L *Angular momentum vectors for the two allowed states of an orbital electron.*

be half-integral. Since the total energy of the atom with l and s parallel will be different from when they are oppositely directed, all levels but s will be double.

Note in Fig. 66G that capital letters S, P, and D designate l values for levels, their subscripts designate j values, and the superscripts that they belong to a system of doublets. The two transitions from $3^2P_{3/2}$ to $3^2S_{1/2}$ and $3^2P_{1/2}$ to $3^2S_{1/2}$ correspond to the two yellow lines in the sodium spectrum (see Fig. 66D) and are the first member of the P-series, shown at the right in Fig. 59H.

66.6. Space Quantization and the Zeeman Effect. When hydrogen atoms are located in a magnetic field B, the quantum theory requires that their electrons take on certain specified directions. These directions are determined as follows: The projection of the total angular momentum $j\hbar$ on the field direction B (see Fig. 66M) must take on

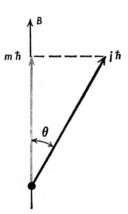

Fig. 66M *Orientation diagram of an atom in an external magnetic field B.*

values differing from each other by $\hbar$. As an equation

$$j\hbar \cos \theta = m\hbar \quad (66o)$$

where m is the *magnetic quantum number*, and is given by

$$m = \pm\tfrac{1}{2}, \pm\tfrac{3}{2}, \pm\tfrac{5}{2}, \ldots \pm j \quad (66p)$$

If, for example, the total quantum number $j = \frac{5}{2}$, the allowed orientations of j are six in number, and are specified by

$$m = \tfrac{5}{2}, \tfrac{3}{2}, \tfrac{1}{2}, -\tfrac{1}{2}, -\tfrac{3}{2}, -\tfrac{5}{2} \quad (66q)$$

These six orientations are shown in Fig. 66N, and the process is referred to as *space*

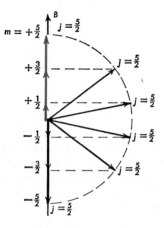

Fig. 66N *Vector diagram representing space quantization of an atom in a magnetic field B.*

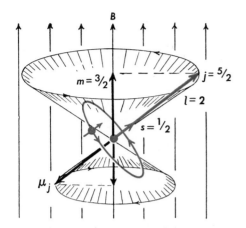

Fig. 66O *An electron spin and orbit precess together as a unit around the magnetic field direction B.*

quantization. The minus values indicate only that the component of $j\hbar$ is opposite in direction to the field B.

A diagram of the precession of an atom in a magnetic field, when the electron is in a state $l = 2$, $s = \frac{1}{2}$, $j = \frac{5}{2}$, and $m = \frac{3}{2}$, is shown in Fig. 66O. Because the energy of the atom differs slightly between the different orientations of the electron, energy levels as well as spectrum lines will be split into a number of equally spaced components. To observe this phenomenon, the light source must be placed in a strong and uniform magnetic field, and the light observed with a spectrograph. The phenomenon, called the Zeeman effect, is observed in the spectra of all elements. Some line patterns contain but a few lines, while others contain many. Typical Zeeman patterns, as seen under high magnification, are reproduced in Fig. 66P.

66.7. Pauli Exclusion Principle. We have now seen that four quantum numbers are required to specify the state of an electron in an atom. These are:

$$
\begin{array}{ll}
n & \text{principal quantum number} \\
l & \text{orbital quantum number} \\
j & \text{total quantum number} \\
m & \text{magnetic quantum number}
\end{array}
\quad (66r)
$$

According to the Pauli exclusion principle, no two electrons in the same atom can have all four quantum numbers alike. They may have three alike but at least one must be different.

Consider, for example, the number of electrons that can have $n = 3$ and $l = 2$. Such electrons are designated $3d$. The two j-values possible are $j = l + s$ and $j = l - s$, i.e., $j = \frac{5}{2}$ and $j = \frac{3}{2}$. (See Eq.(66n).) For $j = \frac{5}{2}$ there are six possible values of m, and for $j = \frac{3}{2}$ there are four possible values of m. Together, these are:

$$
\begin{array}{l}
j = \frac{5}{2},\ m = \frac{5}{2},\ \frac{3}{2},\ \frac{1}{2},\ -\frac{1}{2},\ -\frac{3}{2},\ -\frac{5}{2} \\
j = \frac{3}{2},\ m = \quad\ \ \frac{3}{2},\ \frac{1}{2},\ -\frac{1}{2},\ -\frac{3}{2}
\end{array}
\quad (66s)
$$

or ten possibilities in all. Note that this is just the number of electrons that fills an $l = 2$ subshell in the building up of elements in the periodic table. In a similar way, an s-subshell can have two electrons, a p-subshell 6, and an f-subshell 14.

66.8. Elastic and Inelastic Impacts. When an electron collides with a neutral atom in a rarefied gas, the collision is either *elastic* or *inelastic*. An elastic collision is one in which the law of conservation of momentum and conservation of mechanical energy are both upheld. In other words, the atomic particles behave as though they were perfectly elastic spheres; the total energy and

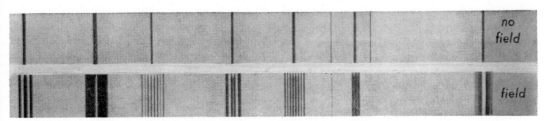

Fig. 66P *Small section of the spectrum of rhodium, $Z = 45$. (Upper) Ordinary lines with no magnetic field. (Lower) Zeeman patterns when light source is in strong magnetic field of 7.0 webers/meter^2. (After Harrison and Bitter.)*

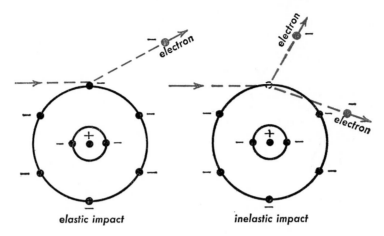

elastic impact   inelastic impact

Fig. 66Q   *Schematic diagrams showing elastic and inelastic impacts.*

total momentum before impact is equal to the total energy and momentum after impact. (See Fig. 66Q.)

An inelastic collision is one in which the impinging electron, in striking a neutral atom, hits one of the electrons and either knocks it into one of the outer orbits (energy levels), or knocks it completely out of the atom. In the first instance, we say the atom has been *excited,* and in the second case it has been *ionized.* In either case it is usually a valence electron that is involved.

To raise an electron from its normal state to an excited state, or to remove it from the atom, requires the expenditure of energy; this is supplied by the impinging electron. As a consequence, some of the total energy before collision is used for excitation or ionization, and what is left is divided between the two particles. Because the masses of atoms are thousands of times that of the electron, nearly all kinetic energy before impact, and after, is confined to the electron. The recoil velocity and kinetic energy of an atom that has been hit by a moving electron is relatively small.

66.9. Franck-Hertz Experiments. One of the most direct proofs of the existence of energy levels or electron shells within an atom is to be found in the Franck-Hertz experiments. These experiments make it possible to measure the energy necessary to raise an electron from the ground state in

an atom to an outer orbit, or state, or to remove it from the atom entirely.

In the Franck and Hertz experiments, a vapor like sodium or mercury is bombarded with electrons of known velocity. A diagram of the apparatus in its simplest form is given in Fig. 66R. Electrons from a hot

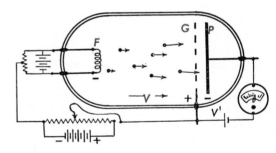

Fig. 66R   *Diagram of the Franck and Hertz experiment.*

filament F are accelerated toward a grid G by applying a voltage V between them. An opposing voltage V', much smaller than V, is applied between the grid G and the plate P. If sodium atoms are to be used, the gas pressure is reduced to where the mean distance between atomic collisions (the mean free path) is considerably smaller than the filament-to-grid distance, and somewhat greater than the grid-to-plate distance.

If an electron starts from rest at the filament and reaches the grid G without hitting a sodium atom, its velocity v is given by the equation

$$Ve = \tfrac{1}{2}mv^2 \qquad (66t)$$

where V is in volts, e is in coulombs, m is in Kg, and v is in m/sec. In order for an electron to collide inelastically with an atom, it must have sufficient kinetic energy $\tfrac{1}{2}mv^2$ to raise the valence electron from its

$$V = 2.1 \text{ volts}$$

This means that electrons accelerated by a potential difference of 2.1 volts or more, upon collision with a normal sodium atom, can knock the single valence electron from its 3s-orbit into the 3p-orbit. In so doing the electron gives up kinetic energy equivalent to 2.1 electron volts, and slows down accordingly.

The curve reproduced in Fig. 66S, show-

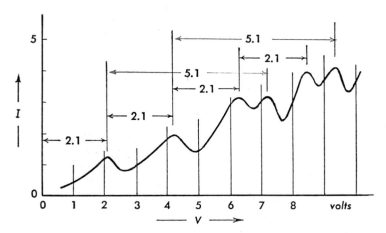

Fig. 66S   *Critical potential curve for sodium atoms showing the excitation potential of 2.1 volts and the ionization potential of 5.1 volts.*

ground level to the first excited level. To find how much energy this is, consider the example of sodium, $Z = 11$, in which the first energy state above the ground state is responsible for the yellow light we observe in any sodium arc light or lamp. This light arises from the jump of the valence electron from a 3p-orbit, into the ground state, a 3s-orbit. (See Fig. 66G.) This light of wavelength $\lambda = 5.893 \times 10^{-7}$ m has a frequency $\nu = 5.091 \times 10^{14}$ vib/sec, and each photon an energy $h\nu = 3.359 \times 10^{-19}$ joules.

To find the voltage equivalent of this energy, we write

$$Ve = h\nu$$

and substituting the electronic charge $e = 1.601 \times 10^{-19}$ coulombs and $h = 6.6238 \times 10^{-34}$, we obtain

ing the variation in plate current with the accelerating voltage V, is characteristic of the Franck and Hertz experiment with sodium. As V starts from zero and is slowly increased, the speed and number of electrons reaching the grid G increase and the plate current rises. When the velocity has increased sufficiently to excite sodium atoms, however, inelastic collisions occur. With a further increase in V, more electrons reach the critical velocity, are stopped by inelastic collision, and, not being able to reach the plate P, cause a drop in the current. This drop in current continues until the critical speed is attained far enough in front of the grid to collide inelastically again and reach the plate. The current, therefore, rises again and continues to rise until the electrons, after one inelastic collision, attain the critical speed and make a second inelastic collision.

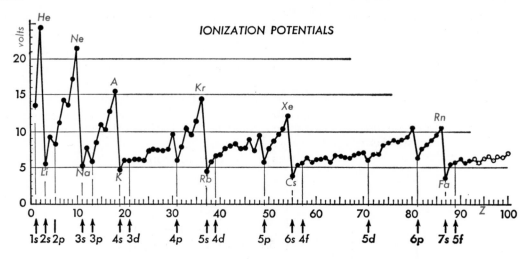

Fig. 66T *Ionization potentials of the elements.*

The double peaks in Fig. 66S show that, not only have collisions occurred in which the valence electron has been excited, but also collisions in which the electron is completely removed from the atom. Complete ejection of the electron from sodium requires an electron velocity equivalent to $V = 5.1$ volts. This then is the ionization potential of sodium, which in Fig. 66G is equivalent to raising the valence electron from its *ground state* to the *series limit*.

66.10. Ionization Potentials. The ionization potential of an element is defined as the energy in electron volts required to remove the most loosely bound electron from the normal atom. The *electron volt* is defined as the energy equivalent to the kinetic energy of an electron accelerated through a potential difference of 1 volt. Using Eq.(66h), the energy of $1ev$ is 1.60×10^{-19} joules.

A graph of the ionization potentials of the elements of the periodic table is given in Fig. 66T. It is clearly seen that the alkali metals, Li, Na, K, Rb, Cs, and Fr, have low values, about 5 volts, while the inert gases, He, Ne, A, Kr, Xe, and Rn, have the highest values. The inert gases represent those atoms in which all the electron subshells are complete. The adding of one more proton to the nucleus, and the addition of one more electron to the outer structure to make the next atom, an alkali metal, requires that electron to go into a new subshell, an outer orbit. Such an electron, being on the average farther away from the nucleus, requires less energy to remove it from the atom. As protons are added to the nucleus, and electrons are added in this same subshell, the binding of the electrons grows stronger and stronger.

A direct correlation between the low ionization potentials of the alkali metals and the beginning of new subshells, as shown by the arrows at the bottom of Fig. 66T, leads to the building-up of the periodic table as given in Appendix IX.*

* For a more complete account of atomic structure, see *Introduction to Atomic Spectra* by H. E. White, McGraw-Hill, New York.

QUESTIONS AND PROBLEMS

1. What is the atomic unit of angular momentum? What is the unit of magnetic moment?

2. What is the Rydberg formula? What is *Larmor precession?*

3. What is a total quantum number? What

is the Pauli exclusion principle? What are the four quantum numbers involved in the Pauli exclusion principle?

4. What is the Zeeman effect? What is space quantization?

5. What was the Franck-Hertz experiment?

6. What is an excitation potential? What is an ionization potential?

7. The Sharp Series of spectrum lines of lithium has a series limit at 28573 cm^{-1}. If the series constant $\mu = 0.5884$, what is (a) the frequency, and (b) the wavelength, of the second line of the series?

8. Using the Rydberg formula, calculate (a) the frequency, and (b) the wavelength of the second member of the principal series of lithium. (*Ans.* (a) 30952 cm^{-1}, (b) 3231 A.)

9. Make a space quantization diagram for the electronic state, $l = 3$, $s = 1/2$, $j = 7/2$.

10. Calculate the excitation potential for the first line of the principal series of lithium.* (*Note:* The energy level diagram for lithium is quite similar to that for sodium, Fig. 66G.) (*Ans.* 1.84 volts.)

11. Calculate the ionization potential for lithium.* (*Note:* The limit of the principal series represents the valence electron at infinity.)

* Frequency in wave numbers, cm^{-1}, when multiplied by the speed of light, $c = 3 \times 10^{10}$ cm/sec, gives the true frequency ν.

Chapter 67

Radio, Radar, TV, and Microwaves

This chapter is concerned with electromagnetic waves at the long wavelength end of the electromagnetic spectrum. The basic relation involved is the well-known wave equation

$$c = \nu\lambda \qquad (1)$$

where ν is the frequency, λ the wavelength, and c the speed of the waves. In a vacuum, c is the same for all electromagnetic waves and is equal to the speed of light

$$c = 3 \times 10^8 \frac{m}{\text{sec}} \qquad (2)$$

A chart of the complete electromagnetic spectrum extending from the shortest known waves, the γ rays, to the longest known waves of radio is given in Fig. 67A. The long wavelength end of this chart is seen to be divided into equally spaced bands with the designations shown in Table 67A.

The SHF and EHF bands are frequently referred to as *microwaves*.

$$1000 \frac{\text{cycles}}{\text{sec}} = 1 \frac{\text{kilocycle}}{\text{sec}} = 1 \text{ Kc}$$

$$1{,}000{,}000 \frac{\text{cycles}}{\text{sec}} = 1 \frac{\text{megacycle}}{\text{sec}} = 1 \text{ Mc}$$

67.1. Long-Distance Reception. It has long been known that certain bands of radio waves travel farther at night than they do in the daytime. During daylight hours programs heard on standard broadcast bands, 550 to 1500 kilocycles/sec, are generally received at distances up to 10 to 100 mi. At night, however, signals can be heard at 10 to 100 times these distances, but with intensities often varying in an erratic manner. Such nocturnal variations are due to changing atmospheric conditions and are known as "fading." Fading is more pronounced at greater distances but improves considerably after the first hour or two after sundown, only to become worse again shortly before sunrise.

Short radio waves in the range 1.5 to 40 megacycles travel great distances day or night but are strongly susceptible to chang-

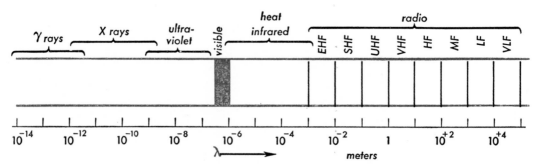

Fig. 67A *Electromagnetic spectrum showing wavelengths of radio bands.*

TABLE 67A. RADIO WAVE BANDS

Band Designation		ν	λ
VLF	very low frequency	3 Kc	100 Km
LF	low frequency	30 Kc	10 Km
MF	medium frequency	300 Kc	1 Km
HF	high frequency	3,000 Kc	100 m
VHF	very high frequency	30 Mc	10 m
UHF	ultra high frequency	300 Mc	1 m
SHF	super high frequency	3,000 Mc	10 cm
EHF	extremely high frequency	30,000 Mc	1 cm
		300,000 Mc	0.1 cm

ing atmospheric conditions. One time of day, for example, communications between two greatly distant stations may be carried on over 20 m waves but not over 40 m waves. Later during the day the reverse may be true.

It is now known that the great distances spanned by radio are due to the reflection (actually refraction) of waves by a layer of electrically charged atoms and molecules in the upper atmosphere. The possible existence of such a layer was first postulated by O. Heaviside and A. E. Kennelly in 1902 to account for the propagation of waves around the earth's curved surface. The existence of such a layer was first demonstrated experimentally in 1925 by G. Breit, M. Tuve, and others, and its elevation shown to vary from 50 to 150 mi.

As illustrated in Fig. 67B, waves radiated upward from a transmitter T are bent back toward the earth where they are again reflected upward. The diagram indicates how the entire earth's surface might be covered with radio waves, the intensity of which should decrease with distance from the transmitter. At short distances of only a few miles a "ground wave," T to G in the figure, is heard as a strong steady signal day and night.

For some reason the Kennelly-Heaviside layer does not reflect the ultra-high frequency waves used in *television* and *radar*. For this reason both are restricted to short-range operation, the waves traveling only in straight lines like visible light. To receive radar or television signals, therefore, the receiver antenna must be within sight of the transmitting antenna, and to cover a large area the transmitting antenna should be located high in the air atop a building, hill, or mountain peak.

67.2. The Scanning Process in Television. For years the sending of pictures by wire or radio has been an everyday occurrence. The fundamental principle involved in this process, and illustrated in Fig. 67C, is known as *scanning*. Every picture to be transmitted is scanned by an *exploring spot* which, starting at the top, moves in straight lines over the entire picture. The spot first moves from A to B, then from C to D, then

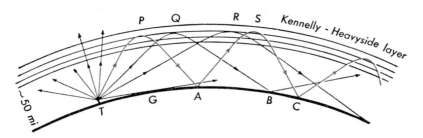

Fig. 67B *Radio waves are refracted (reflected) by the ionized gas layers high in the earth's atmosphere.*

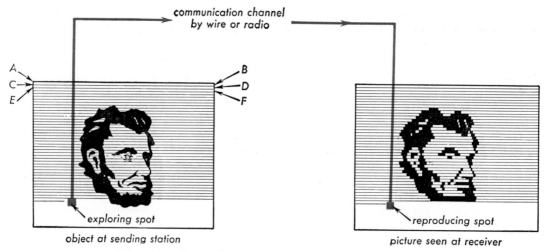

Fig. 67C *Illustration of the process of picture scanning.*

E to *F*, etc., until the entire picture has been covered. Each time the spot reaches the right-hand side, it jumps back to the left and starts on the next line.

The exploring spot in any scanning device is so constructed that it generates an electric current proportional to the brightness of its instantaneous position. Such a pulsating current, called the *video signal,* is transmitted over wires or radio waves to the receiving station. There in a specially designed instrument a *reproducing spot,* whose brightness is proportional to the video signal amplitude, moves over a viewing screen in a path similar to that of the exploring spot. In this way the reproducing spot reconstructs the original picture.

It will be realized that the smaller the scanning and reproducing spots and the greater the number of lines, the better will be the details of the scanned picture being reproduced at the receiving end. The diagram shown here includes only 50 lines per picture as compared with 525 lines used in some standard (black and white) broadcasts.

If a single picture is to be sent by wire, as is generally the case in the *telephotographic newspaper service,* the scanning process requires from 10 to 20 min. In television, however, it is standard practice to scan and transmit 30 distinct and separate pictures every second of time. At the receiving station these pictures are rapidly flashed one after the other upon a viewing screen. All are still pictures differing progressively one from the next so that, due to persistence of vision, the motions seem smooth and continuous, just as with moving pictures.

To avoid spurious shadows and images, the process of *interlacing* is employed. By this process each picture is scanned twice, first by running the exploring spot over the odd numbered lines 1, 3, 5, 7, etc., and then over the even numbered lines 2, 4, 6, 8, etc.

In many respects the apparatus used in television differs very little from that used in radio broadcasting. The varying current from the exploring element of a scanning device, called a *televisor,* takes the place of the voice currents from a microphone. In other words, instead of modulating the carrier wave of a radio transmitter with the voice currents due to sound waves, it is modulated with the *video current* from the light of a picture image in a televisor. Except for the *televisor tube* used in the transmitter, and a similar device called a *kinescope* used in the receiver, television equipment consists of numerous electrical circuits containing radio tubes or transistors similar to those in any radio receiving set.*

* *Television,* by V. K. Zworykin and G. A. Morton, Wiley, New York.

67.3. Radar. Radar is one of the most important electronic developments of World War II and may be defined as the art of determining by means of *radio echoes* the presence, distance, direction, and velocity of distant aircraft, ships, land masses, cities, and other objects. RADAR derives its name from the longer title "RAdio Detection And Ranging."

Basically, a complete radar station consists of a *transmitter,* a *receiver,* and an *indicator.* As shown by a schematic diagram in Fig. 67D, the transmitter sends out high-

always made whereby the power from the transmitter is blocked out of the receiver. In most radar equipment this is accomplished by means of intermittent transmission, commonly called the *pulsed system.* According to this system, the transmitter is turned *on* for only a fraction of a second to send out a train of waves while the receiver is made very insensitive. When the transmitter goes *off,* the receiver is turned *on* to full sensitivity to receive the faint echo signal returning. When the receiver goes *off,* the transmitter comes *on* again to

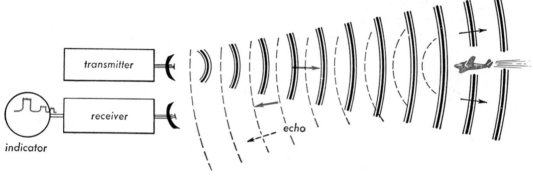

Fig. 67D   *Illustration of the principles of radar detecting and ranging.*

frequency radio waves which, traveling outward with the velocity of light, are reflected from a distant object. That small portion of the reflected waves returning toward the station is picked up and amplified by the receiver. The signal is then fed into any one of a number of indicating devices, some of which are so complete as to give continuously the instantaneous *distance, direction,* and *relative velocity* of the object. With one type of air-borne unit, ground objects can be observed on the screen of a kinescope even though fog or clouds intervene. Such systems are extremely useful in reducing the flying hazards that are always present during inclement weather.

The wavelengths of the waves used in radar are in the *microwave* region of the electromagnetic spectrum. They have wave lengths in the range of 1 cm to 10 cm.

The Pulsed System. Since a powerful transmitter must operate side by side with a supersensitive receiver, some provision is

send out another wave train and repeat the above process hundreds of times per second.

A graph of the received pulses from an object 9 mi away is shown in Fig. 67E. Since

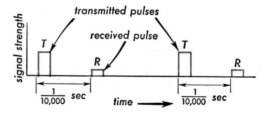

Fig. 67E   *Graph of transmitted pulses showing received pulse, or echo, from an object 9 mi distant.*

the velocity of radio waves is 186,300 mi/sec, the same as light, the time interval between each transmitted pulse T and its echo R returning is a direct measure of the distance. If a frequency of 30,000 megacycles is used, the wavelength is 1 cm and each pulse will contain thousands of waves.

Rectified by the receiver, an entire wave train appears as a voltage pulse as in the graph.

One type of *indicator* used for determining this time interval is a *cathode-ray oscilloscope,* or *kinescope,* of the type shown in Fig. 65H. While the scanning spot is kept at constant intensity, a saw-tooth potential is applied to the horizontal sweep to make it move with constant speed across the fluorescent screen.

Electrical circuits are so arranged that the spot starts at the left just prior to the transmitter's emission of a pulse. When, a fraction of a second later, a pulse is initiated, a small part of the energy is applied as a vertical deflection of the spot, thereby producing a trace T as shown in Fig. 67F.

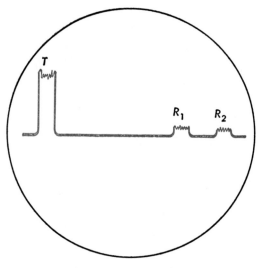

Fig. 67F   *Trace of spot on cathode-ray tube as used in radar ranging.*

When the returning echo signal arrives at the receiver, it too is applied as a vertical deflection, and a peak like the one at R_1 is produced. Upon reaching the right-hand end of the screen, the spot is extinguished and returned to the left, where it is again turned on and the above process repeated. As the spot retraces the same line many times every second, persistence of vision gives rise to the appearance of a steady trace.

If several different objects reflect waves of sufficient intensity to be picked up by the receiver, several peaks R_1, R_2, etc., will be seen on the indicator screen. In radar parlance, each such peak on the trace is called a *pip,* and its distance along the horizontal line from T is a direct measure of the time required for the signal to go out and return and is therefore a measure of the range of the object that caused it. Various methods of accurately measuring the distance interval have been developed.

If an object is coming toward or receding from a radar station, the frequency of the waves reflected from it will be increased or decreased respectively as in the Doppler effect. Hence by measuring the frequency change between the waves going out and those coming back, the velocity of approach or recession becomes known.

67.4. Wave Guides. The term "wave guide" is generally applied to a special class of metallic conductors having the property of conducting high-frequency oscillations from one place to another. To be more specific, it is a radio transmission line by which power generated at an oscillator can be transmitted to some utility point with little or no loss along the line.

Two types of wave guide commonly used at present are shown in Fig. 67G. The first,

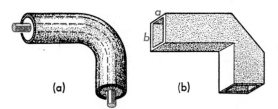

Fig. 67G   *Wave guides commonly used in radar and television transmission lines: (a) coaxial cable, and (b) hollow conductor.*

called a *coaxial cable* or *concentric line,* consists of a wire conductor insulated from, and running lengthwise through, the center of a tubular conductor. Power from any high-frequency source, when connected to the central wire and tubular sheath, is propagated as waves through the dielectric between the two conductors.

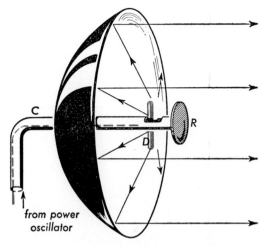

from power
oscillator

Fig. 67H *Radar antenna system for producing a parallel beam.*

The second is a hollow rectangular pipe called a *wave guide.* Power introduced as electromagnetic waves at one end is guided by the conducting walls to the other end. Each conductor is shown with a 90° bend to show that waves can be guided around corners.

While there is no limit to the frequency transmitted by coaxial lines, there is a

Since wave guides are comparable in cross section to the waves they propagate, and a coaxial cable will transmit any frequency no matter how low, the latter is generally used for waves longer than 10 cm, whereas hollow pipes are used with waves shorter than 10 cm. The power capacity of a hollow pipe, transmitting at its dominant mode, is greater than a coaxial cable of the same size.

Fig. 67H shows an arrangement in which the high-frequency oscillations from an oscillator tube source (not shown) are fed through a coaxial cable C to a single dipole, or Hertzian doublet, D. Radiated waves from the doublet are reflected into a parallel beam by the mirror. Since the overall length of a dipole must be equal to $\frac{1}{2}$ a wavelength, the two small rods for 10 cm waves would each be 2.5 cm, or 1 in., long.

67.5. Scanning. In a majority of radar installations the receiver uses the same antenna as the transmitter, thereby requiring a rapid switching mechanism that connects the transmitter to the antenna, when a pulse is to be radiated, and then to the receiver to pick up a possible echo signal (see Fig. 67I). Such dual use of one antenna

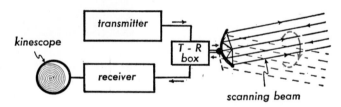

Fig. 67I *Block diagram indicating a T-R box for alternately connecting the antenna reflector to the transmitter and receiver. Conical, or spiral scanning, is also indicated.*

lower limit for hollow wave guides. This lower limit, called the *cut-off frequency* or critical frequency, is the limiting case of a so-called *dominant mode* of vibration inside the guide and is analogous in some respects to the *fundamental vibration* of a given air column in sound. The dominant mode occurs in a rectangular pipe when the wider of the two dimensions b is $\frac{1}{2}$ a wavelength. The narrow dimension of the latter is not critical, but in practice is made to be about $\frac{1}{2}b$.

saves space and weight and eliminates the mechanical difficulty of making two directive antennas point in exactly the same direction while they are moved about.

In certain types of radar installation the transmitter beam is made to sweep back and forth across the ground or sky with a scanning motion similar to that used in television. In one system a spiral scanning motion adapts itself to total coverage of a given area. When the beam crosses the path of any reflecting object, an echo signal returns to the receiver where it is amplified and applied to the cathode beam of a kinescope. As the transmitter beam carries out its scanning motion, the cathode ray spot on the kinescope is made to traverse a similar path. At that instant, when an echo signal returns, the spot brightens, and its location on the screen locates the relative position of the object in the scanning field.

Because the reflector is rotated mechanically, the radar scanning speed is considerably slower than in television. Its usefulness, however, is unquestionable, for high above the clouds in a plane it is possible to observe the positions and shapes of many landmarks on the ground below.

67.6. Diathermy. It has long been known that, if the human body is subjected to direct or low frequency alternating currents of any appreciable magnitude and duration, detrimental and all too often lethal effects will result. It was in 1890 that the French physicist d'Arsonval, and a year later Nikola Tesla, discovered that relatively large alternating currents with a frequency of 10 kilocycles/sec or more could be carried by the body without detrimental effects of any kind. Today it is common practice in the well-equipped hospital to deliberately use very high frequency currents to produce beneficial, internal, heating effects in various parts of the body. This practice is called *diathermy*.

In recent machines, continuous high voltage with frequencies of from 25 to 100 megacycles per sec are produced by vacuum tubes and oscillator circuits, and the disagreeable electrodes and needles used some years ago have been replaced by a flexible insulated wire that can be wound lightly around an extremity, or wound into a flat coil and laid upon a pad against the body area to be heated. A high-frequency current sent through such a coil produces an oscillating magnetic field of the same frequency. When the coil is close to the body, these fields induce localized eddy currents of the same frequency within the body tissue and these in turn are dissipated as localized heat.

A photograph of an up-to-date microwave diathermy generator, designed to operate at a frequency of 2450 Mc is shown in Fig. 67J. Since it is in the wavelength range as employed in radar, energy in the

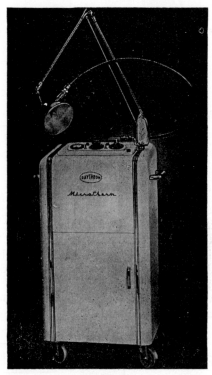

Fig. 67J *The "Microtherm," a generator used in microwave therapy.* (Courtesy, Raytheon Manufacturing Co.)

form of microwaves is guided and directed by reflectors to the exact region to be heated. In penetrating the body, these waves set molecules into oscillation and bring about a more uniform heating of the fatty and vascular tissues. The localization of such heat is particularly effective in the treatment of *sprains, bruises, neuritis, arthritis,* and *congestion of all kinds.* In spite of claims to the contrary, experimental evidence and theory agree that the only effect these high frequencies have upon the body is a heating effect and that no organ responds to a particular range.

QUESTIONS AND PROBLEMS

1. What is RADAR? What do the letters stand for?

2. What is a pulsed radar system? Why is the operation intermittent?

3. How is the distance of an object determined? How is the velocity of a moving object determined?

4. What is a wave guide? How many kinds are there?

5. What is the process called scanning? What is a video signal?

6. What is meant by "interlacing"?

7. Make a diagram from memory showing the principles of a black-and-white television receiver tube. Label each essential part and briefly explain how it works.

8. Make from memory a wavelength and frequency chart showing the bands used for (a) standard radio broadcasts, (b) short wave radio, (c) frequency modulation broadcasts, (d) television, and (e) radar.

9. Radar waves of frequency 6×10^3 Mc/sec are reflected from a paraboloidal metal reflector. Calculate the over-all length of the dipole used at its focal plane.

10. The dipole of a radar transmitter has an over-all length of 3.0 cm. Calculate the frequency in Mc/sec. (*Ans.* 5000 Mc/sec.)

11. A television transmitter broadcasts on a frequency of 82 Mc/sec. Find the length of the dipole of the transmitting antenna.

12. A television receiver uses a straight dipole with an over-all length of 1.8 m. What is its natural frequency? (*Ans.* 83.3 Mc/sec.)

Chapter 68

Photon Collisions and Atomic Waves

In the preceding chapters we have seen that light waves consist of small finite bundles of energy, called *quanta* or *photons,* and that they too, like atomic particles, may be made to collide with atoms of one kind or another. This was the case both in the *photoelectric effect* (Chap. 61) and in the production of X rays (Chap. 62). The first part of the present chapter deals with the *corpuscular nature of light,* and the last part with the *wave nature of atomic particles.*

This last statement suggests a sort of "Dr. Jekyll and Mr. Hyde" existence for light waves as well as for atoms. Under some conditions, light and atoms may both act as though they were waves, whereas under other conditions they may both act like small particles.

68.1. Photoelectric Effect with X Rays. When a beam of X rays is allowed to shine on the surface of a thin sheet of metal, like gold, several different phenomena may be observed to take place. Acting like waves, the X rays may be scattered at different angles to produce a diffraction pattern (see Fig. 62F), or, acting like particles, they may collide with atoms and eject electrons as in the photoelectric effect (see Chap. 61).

Even though a beam of X rays may contain waves all of the same frequency, not all of the ejected photoelectrons acquire the same velocity, but are divided into several well-defined groups. These different groups are illustrated schematically by the lengths of the arrows in Fig. 68A.

Careful measurements of the velocities of the photoelectrons, first made by Robinson and his collaborators in 1914, have shown that each velocity group is to be associated with the various shells of electrons within the atoms. The slowest electrons, all with the same velocity v_K, are ejected from the K-shell, the next faster group with a veloc-

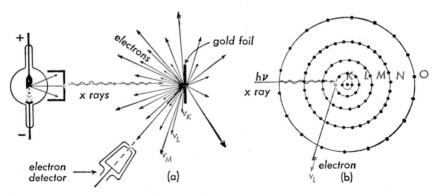

Fig. 68A (a) *Photoelectric effect produced with X rays gives rise to electrons with several different velocities. (b) Detail of an X ray ejecting an L electron from a heavy atom.*

576

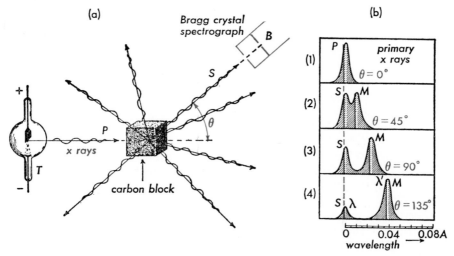

Fig. 68B *The Compton effect. (a) Schematic diagram of Compton's experiment. (b) Graphs of the X-ray spectrum lines observed with a Bragg crystal spectrograph.*

ity v_L from the L-shell, the next group with a velocity v_M from the M-shell, etc.

The closer an electron is to the nucleus (see diagram (b)), the greater is the attracting force and the greater is the force and energy necessary to liberate it from the atom. The velocity of the electrons in each group is given by Einstein's photoelectric equation,

$$hv = W + \tfrac{1}{2}mv^2 \qquad (68a)$$

where W, the work function, is the energy necessary to free an electron from any one of the different electron shells (see Sec. 61.6).

While all of the incident X-ray photons have the same energy hv, more energy W will be used in liberating a K electron than there will be in liberating an L electron. This being the case, a photon liberating a K electron will have less energy left over for the electron than would another photon liberating an L electron from a similar atom. This experiment shows as well as one could wish that electrons exist in shells within the atom.

It should be pointed out that the energy W, used up in ejecting a photoelectron, is not lost by the atom but is later given out again in the form of X rays of various frequencies. In atoms where a K electron has been ejected, an L electron may jump into

the vacated K-shell, with the simultaneous emission of a K X ray. This may be followed immediately by an M electron's jumping into the vacated L-shell and the emission of an L X ray.

68.2. The Compton Effect. While making a spectroscopic study of scattered X rays in 1923, A. H. Compton* discovered a new phenomenon, now known as the Compton effect. After considerable controversy with other experimenters, Compton proved quite conclusively that an X ray may collide with an electron and bounce off with reduced energy in another direction. This is analogous to the collision of two billiard balls.

Compton's historic experiment is illustrated schematically in Fig. 68B. X rays from a tube T were made to strike one face of a small carbon block and scatter out in various directions. With an X-ray spectro-

* Arthur H. Compton (1892-1962), American physicist, born in Wooster, Ohio, on September 10, 1892. He received the degree of Doctor of Philosophy at Princeton University in St. Louis, Mo., in 1920. In 1923 he discovered the change in wavelength of X rays when scattered by carbon, the phenomenon now known as the Compton effect. In recognition of this important discovery, in 1927 he was awarded the Nobel Prize in physics jointly with C. T. R. Wilson, of England. He is now the President of Washington University, St. Louis, Missouri.

graph at one side of the block he measured the wavelength of the X rays S scattered in a direction θ. These wavelengths he then compared with those of the incident beam P.

The comparisons are illustrated by graphs in diagram (b). The top curve (1) represents the wavelength λ of the X rays in the beam P, before striking the block. The other three curves, (2), (3), and (4), represent the two wavelengths λ and λ', observed when the spectrograph is located at the angles $\theta = 45°$, $\theta = 90°$, and $\theta = 135°$, respectively. These graphs show that some of the scattered X rays have changed their wavelengths whereas others have not. They further show the important result that as the angle increases, the change in wavelength of the modified rays M increases.

To explain the modified wavelengths M, Compton invoked the quantum theory of light and proposed that a single X ray photon, acting as a material particle, may collide with a free electron and recoil off as though it were a perfectly elastic sphere (Fig. 68C(a)). Applying the law of conservation of energy to the collision, Compton

assumed that the energy $\frac{1}{2}mv^2$ imparted to the recoiling electron must be supplied by the incident X-ray quantum $h\nu$. Having lost energy, the X ray moves off in some new direction with a lower frequency ν' and energy $h\nu'$. By applying conservation of energy, we obtain

$$h\nu = h\nu' + \tfrac{1}{2}mv^2 \qquad (68b)$$

Since in most cases the velocity of the recoiling electron is so near the velocity of light c, the relativistic equations must be applied. Using Eq.(46r) for the kinetic energy of a moving mass, we write

$$\boxed{h\nu = h\nu' + m_0c^2(\gamma - 1)} \qquad (68c)$$

where

$$\gamma = \frac{1}{\sqrt{1 - v^2/c^2}} \qquad (68d)$$

and m_0 is the *rest mass* of the electron.

As with two perfectly elastic balls, Compton also applied the law of conservation of momentum and derived an equation from which he could calculate the change in wavelength λ' of the scattered X ray.

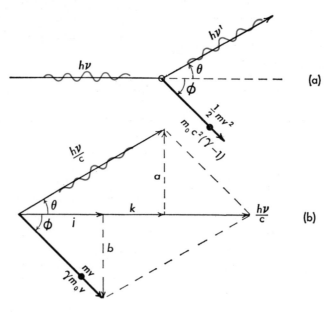

Fig. 68C *Vector diagrams for the collision between an X-ray photon and a free electron. The Compton effect.*

These calculated changes were found to agree exactly with those observed by the experiment.

The fact that a beam of light has the equivalence of a momentum mv, and can exert a pressure on a wall on which it falls, has long been known. According to the quantum theory the momentum of a single photon is given by the energy $h\nu$ divided by the velocity of light c,

$$\text{momentum of a photon} = \frac{h\nu}{c} \quad (68e)$$

Compton's experiment is considered a proof of this equation.

Since momentum is a vector quantity, we construct a vector diagram as shown in Fig. 68C(b). The momentum of the X ray before impact is $h\nu/c$, while its momentum after impact is $h\nu'/c$, and the momentum of the electron is mv.

For electrons close to the speed of light the momentum mv is written in the relativistic form $\gamma m_0 v$. (See Eq.(46k).) By resolving the two momenta into two components, we obtain a and k as components of $h\nu'/c$, and b and j as components of $\gamma m_0 v$.

Conservation of momentum requires the vector sum of j plus k to equal the initial momentum $h\nu/c$, and the vectors a and b to cancel each other. As equations,

$$\frac{h\nu}{c} = \frac{h\nu'}{c} \cos \theta + \gamma m_0 v \cos \phi \quad (68f)$$

and $$\frac{h\nu'}{c} \sin \theta = \gamma m_0 v \sin \phi \quad (68g)$$

By combining Eqs.(68c), (68f), and (68g), and changing from frequencies ν and ν' to wavelengths by λ and λ', respectively, Compton derived the equation

$$\lambda' - \lambda = \frac{h}{m_0 c}(1 - \cos \theta) \quad (68h)$$

The quantity $h/m_0 c$ is called the *Compton wavelength,* and is equal to 2.43×10^{-12} meters. For those X rays that are scattered at an angle of $90°$, the observed

or calculated change in wavelength is just this amount and is the same for all X-ray wavelengths incident on the scatterer.

Compton's success is to be attributed to the exact agreement he found between the wavelength shift calculated from his application of the quantum theory and the values measured by experiment.

The first discoveries of the recoil electrons from the Compton effect were made by C. T. R. Wilson, and by Bothe and Becker. The existence of these collision products is readily shown by sending a beam of X rays through a Wilson cloud chamber just prior to its expansion. (Fig. 68D).

When an X ray collides with a free electron the Compton effect can be expected, since the recoiling photon and electron are able to conserve energy and momentum. But when an X ray collides with an electron bound to an atom, the photoelectric effect

Fig. 68D *Recoil electrons from X rays passing through the air in a Wilson cloud chamber. The Compton effect* (after C. T. R. Wilson).

takes place, since the atom can now recoil and conserve energy and momentum with the electron.

68.3. De Broglie's Electron Waves.

In 1924 De Broglie, a French theoretical physicist, derived an equation predicting that all atomic particles have associated with them waves of a definite wavelength. In other words, a beam of electrons or atoms should, under the proper experimental conditions, act like a train of light waves or a beam of photons. The wavelength of these waves, as predicted by De Broglie, depends upon the mass and velocity of the particles according to the following relations:

$$\boxed{\lambda = \frac{h}{mv}} \qquad (68i)$$

This is known as *De Broglie's wave equation*. For an electron moving at high speed, the denominator mv is large and the wavelength is small. In other words, the faster an electron moves, the shorter is the wavelength associated with it. (See Fig. 68E.)

Fig. 68E   *Schematic diagram of a De Broglie wave.*

To acquire some concept of the relative wavelengths of electrons moving with different velocities, several values have been computed from De Broglie's equation (see Table 68A). The velocities are listed in miles per second in column 2 and in per cent of the velocity of light in column 3. The potentials listed in column 1 are the voltages required by Eq.(65a) to give an electron any one of the velocities listed in columns 2 and 3. It will be noted that the wavelengths at the bottom correspond closely to those for X rays and γ rays.

68.4. The Davisson-Germer Experiment. The first experimental proof of the wave nature of atomic particles was demonstrated in 1927 by two American physicists, C. J. Davisson and his collaborator, L. H.

Germer. Their experiment is illustrated schematically in Fig. 68F. Electrons from a hot filament F are accelerated toward an anode P where, upon passing through a system of pinholes, they emerge as a nar-

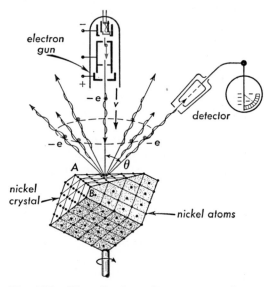

Fig. 68F   *The Davisson-Germer experiment. Electrons striking the surface layers of a crystal are diffracted at different angles just as if they were waves with a very short wavelength.*

row beam as indicated. This source acts as an "electron gun" from which electrons of any desired velocity may be obtained by applying the proper potential V.

Upon striking one of the polished faces of a nickel crystal, the electrons, acting

TABLE 68A. WAVELENGTHS ASSOCIATED WITH ELECTRONS MOVING WITH DIFFERENT VELOCITIES ACCORDING TO DE BROGLIE'S WAVE EQUATION

$V \left(\begin{array}{c}\text{applied}\\\text{voltage}\end{array}\right)$	$v \left(\begin{array}{c}\text{velocity}\\\text{in mi/sec}\end{array}\right)$	$\dfrac{v}{c} \left(\begin{array}{c}\text{velocity}\\\text{in per cent}\end{array}\right)$	$\lambda \left(\begin{array}{c}\text{wavelength}\\\text{in angstroms}\end{array}\right)$
1	370	0.20	12.23
10	1,100	0.62	3.87
100	3,700	1.98	1.22
1,000	18,000	6.26	0.38
10,000	36,000	19.50*	0.12
100,000	100,000	54.80*	0.03
1,000,000	175,000	94.10*	0.01

* These values take into account the increase in mass of the electron due to the theory of relativity. (See Eq.(65b).

like waves, are diffracted off in certain preferred directions. These preferred directions are located by means of a detector in which the electrons are collected and their accumulated charge measured. The detector is mounted so that it may be turned to any angle θ, and the crystal is mounted so it may be turned about an axis parallel to the incident beam.

With the electron-beam incident perpendicular to the crystal surface shown in Fig. 68F, the preferred direction of diffraction for 54-volt electrons was found to be 50°. Under these conditions the surface rows of atoms parallel to AB act like the rulings of a diffraction grating, producing the first-order spectrum of 54-volt electrons at $\theta = 50°$. This is illustrated in a cross-section detail in Fig. 68G. The waves reflected from

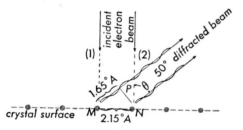

Fig. 68G *Diagram of electron diffraction from the surface layer of a nickel crystal. The regular spacing of the atoms acts like a diffraction grating.*

one row of atoms M must travel one whole wavelength farther than the waves from the adjacent row N.

68.5. Electron Diffraction Patterns. Experiments analogous to von Laue's X-ray diffraction experiments (see Fig. 62F) were first performed in 1928 by the English physicist, G. P. Thomson, and independently by the Japanese physicist, Kikuchi. A schematic diagram of their experimental apparatus is given in Fig. 68H. Electrons of

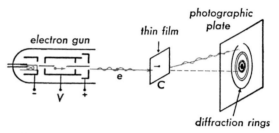

Fig. 68H *Experimental arrangement for observing the diffraction of electron waves by thin films or crystals.*

known velocity from an "electron gun" are projected at the front face of a thin metal film or crystal at C. A short distance farther on, the diffracted electrons strike a photographic plate where they produce patterns of the type reproduced in Fig. 68I.

Kikuchi's photograph (b) was made by projecting 68,000-volt electrons through a thin mica crystal. In this instance we have the exact analogue to the X-ray diffraction patterns of Friedrich, Knipping, and von Laue (see Figs. 62F and 62G). The electrons, in passing through the crystal, are diffracted by the atom centers in such a way

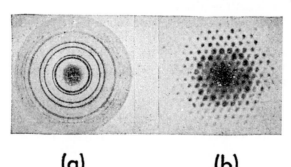

(a)   (b)

Fig. 68I *Photographs of electron diffraction patterns demonstrating the wave nature of electrons. (a) 36,000 volt electrons from a thin silver foil (after G. P. Thomson). (b) 68,000 volt electrons from a thin mica crystal (after Kikuchi).*

that the various crystal planes act like mirrors to reflect them the same as they do with X rays of an equivalent wavelength. Because high-speed electrons had to be used to penetrate the crystal, the diffraction spots are closer together; the reason for this is that the equivalent electron wavelength, $\lambda = 0.047\text{A}$, is about $\frac{1}{50}$ of the crystal spacing.

68.6. Electron Waves within the Atom.

The most recent development in the theory of atomic structure shows that the Bohr picture of the atom with sharply defined electron orbits is not correct. The new theory does not discard the Bohr theory entirely, but only modifies it to the extent that the electron does not behave as though it were a particle. The electron behaves as if it were made up of waves (sometimes called De Broglie waves) of the type described in the previous sections.

The new theory of the hydrogen atom was worked out independently by the two German theoretical physicists, W. Heisenberg and E. Schrödinger, in 1925, and was later modified and improved by the English theoretical physicist, P. Dirac, in 1928.* Schrödinger, making use of De Broglie's idea of electron waves, pictures the single electron in the hydrogen atom as moving around the nucleus as a kind of *wave packet*. This wave packet, as it is called, is formed in somewhat the same way that standing waves are set up and maintained in sound waves.

To set up these standing waves, according to Schrödinger, the length of the path of an electron around the hydrogen nucleus must be a whole number of wavelengths. Since the circumference of a circle is $2\pi r$, and the De Broglie wavelength $\lambda = h/mv$, the conditions to be satisfied by the new theory are

$$n\frac{h}{mv} = 2\pi r \qquad (68j)$$

* For their contributions to the new theory of atomic structure, Heisenberg was granted the Nobel Prize in physics for the year 1932, while Schrödinger and Dirac were jointly granted the prize one year later.

where $n = 1, 2, 3$, etc. This is exactly the condition proposed by Bohr in his orbital theory presented in Eq.(60b), since transposing the momentum to the other side of the equation gives $2\pi mvr = nh$. It is not surprising, therefore, that the new theory also gives exactly the Bohr equation, Eq. (60g), for the frequencies of the hydrogen spectrum.

One method of representing the electron in the atom is to picture an electron wave as one having a considerable length, so that it extends to standing waves. These may be illustrated schematically as shown in Fig. 68J. In the first figure there are

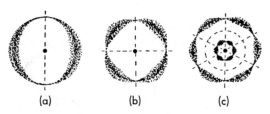

(a)   (b)   (c)

Fig. 68J *Schematic diagram of the waves of the orbital electron in a hydrogen atom.*

two radial nodes; in the second, four radial nodes; and in the third, six radial nodes and one spherical node. In this representation the electron is not thought of as a particle located at some point within the atom but as though its mass and charge were spread out symmetrically throughout the space immediately surrounding the nucleus of the atom. It is interesting to point out that, while the Bohr circular orbits were confined to a plane, the wave model allows the electron distribution to be three-dimensional.

Even though the new theory of the hydrogen atom is an improvement upon the older Bohr orbit theory, and gives a more satisfactory explanation of all known phenomena, it is more difficult to form a mental picture of what an atom might look like. Indeed, the modern theoretical physicist goes so far as to say that the question, "What does an atom look like?" has no meaning, much less an answer. There are others, however, who still maintain that only those things that can be pictured are the things that are understood and that all mental thought processes are made in terms of things we detect by sight or touch. For this reason an interpretation is often given to the theory and its resultant equations that the amplitude of the electron waves within an atom represents the distribution of the electronic charge and mass. At the nodes where the motion is practically zero, there is assumed to be little or no charge, while at the antinodes there is a maximum amount of charge.

Photographs representing a few of the possible states of the single electron in hydrogen are shown in Fig. 68K. These are

three-dimensional distributions can be visualized by imagining each figure to be rotating about a vertical axis, as illustrated by the white line in the second figure. This particular figure in three dimensions would have a shape similar to a smoke ring.

68.7. The New Atomic Picture. Although the Bohr atom has been replaced by the more satisfactory model of a *nucleus surrounded by electron waves,* it is still customary, for convenience only, to talk about electron *shells* and *orbits.* The reason for this is that there is a close analogy between the old and the new models. When the Bohr-Stoner scheme of the building-up of the elements is extended to the new theory

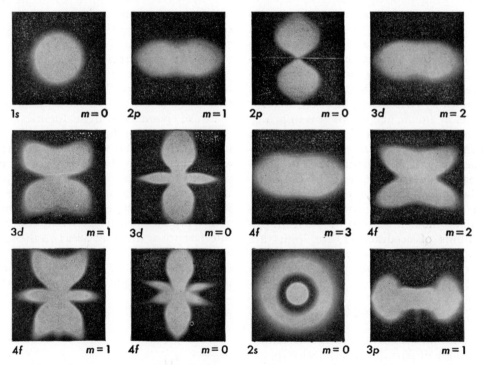

1s	m = 0	2p	m = 1	2p	m = 0	3d	m = 2
3d	m = 1	3d	m = 0	4f	m = 3	4f	m = 2
4f	m = 1	4f	m = 0	2s	m = 0	3p	m = 1

Fig. 68K   *Electron wave density figures representing the single electron states of the hydrogen atom.*

not pictures of real atoms but are made to represent them. They are made by photographing a specially designed mechanical top. Where the electronic charge density is large, the figure is white; where it is practically zero at the nodes, it is dark. The

of electron waves, the electrons are found to distribute their charge in such a way that something analogous to shells is formed.

This is illustrated by the graph for a rubidium atom, atomic number 37, in Fig.

68M. The shaded area above represents the distribution of the charge of 37 electrons on the new theory, and the lower orbital model represents the electron shells on the old theory. The new model is represented by a graph because it is spherically symmetrical in space, while the old model is represented by orbits because it is confined to one plane. Proceeding out from the several maxima at distances corresponding nucleus it is seen that the charge rises to closely to the discrete *K, L, M, N,* and *O* shells of the orbital model. In other words, the new atom also has a shell-like structure.

68.8. Heisenberg's Uncertainty Principle. The quantum theory description of a light beam as being made up of discrete packages of energy *hν*, called photons, would seem to rest upon our ability to determine for a given photon both the *position* and the *momentum* that it possesses at a given instant. These are usually thought of as measurable quantities of a material particle. It was shown by Heisenberg, however, that for particles of atomic magnitude it is in principle impossible to determine both position and momentum simultaneously with perfect accuracy. If an experiment is designed to measure one of them exactly, the other will become uncertain, and vice versa.

An experiment can measure both position and momentum but only within certain limits of accuracy. These limits are specified by the *uncertainty principle* (sometimes called the *principle of indeterminacy*) according to which

$$\Delta x \cdot \Delta p \cong h \qquad (68k)$$

Here Δx and Δp represent the variations of the value of position and the corresponding momentum of a particle which must be expected if we try to measure both at once, i.e., the uncertainties of these quantities.

The uncertainty principle is applicable to photons, as well as to all material particles from electrons up to sizable bodies dealt with in ordinary mechanics. For the latter, the very small magnitude of *h* renders Δx and Δp entirely negligible compared to the ordinary experimental errors encountered in the measuring of its position *x* and its momentum *p*.

When *p* is very small, as it is for an electron or a photon, the uncertainty may become a large percent of the momentum itself, or else the uncertainty in the position is relatively large.

According to Bohr the uncertainty principle of Heisenberg's provides complementary descriptions of the same phenomenon. That is, to obtain the complete picture of any event we need both the wave and corpuscular properties of matter, but because of the uncertainty principle it is impossible to design an experiment that will show both of them in all detail at the same time. Any one experiment will reveal the details of either the wave or corpuscular character, according to the purpose for which the experiment is designed.

The interference fringes in Young's double-slit experiment, shown in Fig. 43J, constitute one of the simplest manifestations of the wave character of light. Identical fringe patterns, however, can be obtained by sending a beam of electrons or protons through the same slits. On the wave theory a small part of the incident wave goes through one slit and another small part goes through the other, and these when they come together produce constructive and destructive interference at different areas on the screen. See Fig. 68L.

If on the corpuscular theory, however, a photon *hν*, or a particle *m*, goes through

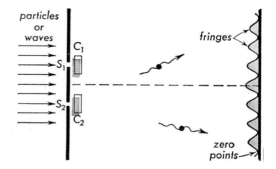

Fig. 68L *Young's double-slit experiment modified to demonstrate both wave and corpuscular properties of matter.*

one slit, how can it be effected by the other slit, and hence go to one of the appropriate fringe areas on the screen, and never to one of the zero points?

To answer this question let us suppose small sensitive detectors, such as scintillation counters (see Figs. 71G and 71H), are placed behind the two slits as shown in Fig. 68L. These detectors C_1 and C_2 can register each photon or particle that goes through one slit or the other. But, in so doing, the fringe pattern will have been destroyed because of the deflections suffered by the corpuscles in producing scintillations. Because of a change in direction the momentum p is changed so that its new momentum is uncertain.

Hence, when we use slit detectors to make Δx small, we introduce a large change in momentum p, and destroy the fringe pattern. When we do without the slit counters to restore the fringe pattern making Δp small, Δx becomes large because we do not know what slit the corpuscle went through.

Some philosophers regard the uncertainty principle as one of the profound principles of nature. Physicists, on the other hand, are inclined to believe it to be an expression of our inability thus far to formulate a better theory of radiation and matter.

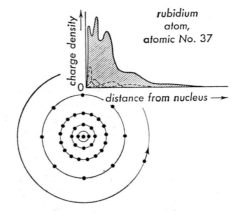

Fig. 68M *Diagrams comparing the new and the old theories of atomic structure, according to wave mechanics and the Bohr-Stoner model.*

PROBLEMS

1. Calculate the momentum of an X ray having a wavelength of 1×10^{-10} meter.

2. What would be the De Broglie wavelength of a 2000-Kg car moving along the highway at 30 m/sec? (*Ans.* 1.1×10^{-38} m.)

3. Find the wavelength associated with an electron moving with $\frac{1}{10}$ the velocity of light.

4. Calculate the wavelength associated with a proton moving with $\frac{1}{20}$ the velocity of light. (*Ans.* 2.64×10^{-14} m.)

5. Find the wavelength of an α-particle accelerated by a potential difference of 10,000 volts.

6. The equivalent wavelength of a moving electron is 0.25×10^{-10} m. What voltage applied between two grids will bring it to rest? (*Ans.* 2400 volts.)

7. If 2000 volts are applied to an electron gun, what is the equivalent wavelength of the electrons?

8. The electron beam in a television receiver tube is accelerated by 12,000 volts. What is the

De Broglie wavelength of the electrons? (*Ans.* 0.112 A.)

9. Briefly explain the Davisson-Germer experiment. What was observed and what were the conclusions?

10. If the electron beam in a TV picture tube is accelerated by 10,000 volts, what is the De Broglie wavelength? (*Ans.* 1.23×10^{-11} m.)

11. Calculate the momentum of each photon in a beam of visible green light, $\lambda = 5000$ A.

12. Find the momentum of each photon in a beam of violet light, $\lambda = 4000$ A. (*Ans.* 1.66×10^{-27} Kg m/sec.)

13. Find the speed of an electron whose wavelength is equivalent to 1 A.

14. X rays of wavelength 0.82 A fall on a metal plate. Find the wavelength associated with the photoelectrons emitted. Neglect the work function of the metal. (*Ans.* 0.0997 A.)

Chapter 69

Radioactivity

Radioactivity may be defined as a spontaneous disintegration of the nucleus of one or more atoms. The phenomenon was discovered originally by Becquerel * in 1896 and is confined almost entirely to the heaviest elements in the periodic table, elements 83 to 102. What Becquerel discovered was that uranium, element 92, gave out some kind of rays that would penetrate through several thicknesses of thick black paper and affect a photographic plate on the other side. When the same phenomenon was confirmed several months later by Pierre and Marie Curie,† these rays became known as Becquerel rays.

* Antoine Henri Becquerel (1852-1908), French physicist. Born in Paris on December 15, 1852, Antoine succeeded to his father's chair at the Museum of Natural History in 1892. In 1896 he discovered radioactivity, the phenomenon for which he is most famous. The invisible but penetrating rays emitted by uranium and other radioactive elements are now called Becquerel rays. For these researches he was granted the Nobel Prize in physics in 1903.

† Pierre Curie (1859-1906) and Marie Curie (1867-1936), French physicists. Pierre Curie was educated at the Sorbonne where he later became professor of physics. Although he experimented on piezoelectricity and other subjects, he is chiefly noted for his work on radioactivity performed jointly with his wife, Marie Sklodowska, whom he married in 1895. Marie was born in Poland on November 7, 1867, where she received her early scientific training from her father. Becoming involved in a student's revolutionary organization, she left Poland for Paris where she took a degree at the university. Two years after the discovery of radioactivity by Becquerel, Pierre and Madame Curie isolated polonium and radium from pitchblende by a long and laborious physical-chemical process. In 1903 they were awarded the Davy Medal of the Royal Society, and (jointly with Becquerel) the Nobel Prize in physics. Professor Curie, who was elected to the Academy of Sciences in 1905, was run over and killed by a carriage in 1906. Succeeding him as professor at the university, Madame Curie in 1911 was awarded the Nobel Prize in chemistry. She has the unique distinction of having had a share in the awards of two Nobel Prizes.

69.1. Discovery of Radium. Unlike the discovery of many new phenomena, the discovery of radium by Pierre and Madame Curie in 1898 was brought about intentionally by a set of carefully planned experiments. Having found that pitchblende was active in emitting Becquerel rays, the Curies chemically treated a ton of this ore in the hope of isolating from it the substance or element responsible for the activity. The first concentrated radioactive substance isolated was called *polonium* by Madame Curie, a name chosen in honor of her native country, Poland. Five months later came the isolation of a minute quantity of *radium,* a substance that was a powerful source of Becquerel rays. Continued experiments by the Curies, and others, soon led to the isolation of many other substances now recognized as radioactive elements. Some of the more common of these are *ionium, radon,* and *thorium.*

69.2. The Properties of Becquerel Rays. It is to the experimental genius of Rutherford ‡ that we owe the complete unraveling of the mystery surrounding the nature of Becquerel rays. As the result of an extensive series of experiments, Rutherford and his coworkers discovered that these penetrating rays are of three quite different

‡ Lord Rutherford (1871-1937), British physicist, was born in New Zealand where he attended the university. In 1898 he became Macdonald professor of physics at McGill University, Montreal, Canada, and in 1907 professor of physics at Manchester University. In 1919 he became professor and director of experimental physics at the University of Cambridge, and in addition held a professorship at the Royal Institution in London. He is most famous for his brilliant researches establishing the existence and nature of radioactive transformations and the electrical structure of the atom. For this work and until the time of his death in 1937 he was acclaimed by many as the greatest living experimental physicist. He was awarded the Nobel Prize in chemistry in 1908, and was knighted in 1914.

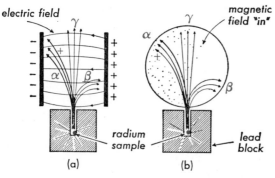

Fig. 69A *The bending of Becquerel rays in (a) an electric field, and (b) a magnetic field.*

kinds. A simplified experiment demonstrating this is illustrated in Fig. 69A. A small sample of radium is dropped to the bottom of a small drill hole made in a block of lead. This produces a narrow beam of rays emerging from the top of the block, since those rays entering the walls of the lead are absorbed before reaching the surface. When electrically charged plates are placed at the side of this beam as shown in diagram (a), the paths of some rays are bent to the left, some to the right, and some are not bent at all. A magnetic field as shown in diagram (b) exhibits the same effect. Those paths bending to the left indicate positively charged particles called α *rays* or α particles, those bending to the right indicate negatively charged particles called β *rays* or β *particles,* and those going straight ahead indicate no charge and are called γ *rays* or photons.

Rutherford, by a series of experiments, was able to show that each α ray is in reality a *doubly ionized helium atom,* i.e., a helium atom with both of its electrons removed. Such a particle is nothing more than a bare helium nucleus with double the positive charge of a hydrogen nucleus or proton, and a mass number or atomic weight four times as great. The β *rays* he found are ordinary electrons with a mass of 1/1836 the mass of a *proton* or 1/7360 the mass of an α *particle,* while γ *rays* are electromagnetic waves of about the same or a little higher frequency than X rays. Although γ rays all travel with exactly the

velocity of X rays and visible light, α rays are ejected with a speed of from $\frac{1}{10}$ to $\frac{1}{100}$ the velocity of light. β particles move faster than α particles, some of them traveling with 99% the velocity of light.

69.3. Identification of Alpha Particles. The first conclusive evidence that alpha particles are helium nuclei was obtained by Rutherford and Royds in England in 1909. A special glass tube as shown in Fig. 69B,

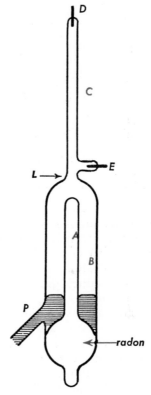

Fig. 69B *Special discharge tube used in proof that alpha particles are helium nuclei.*

was used for this purpose. A thin-walled glass tube *A* containing radon gas, was sealed inside a thick-walled tube *B* containing mercury. At the top was a glass capillary tube *C* with two metal electrodes *D* and *E* sealed through the glass as shown.

Tubes *B* and *C* were evacuated through the side tube *P*, and then mercury raised to the level shown. After maintaining this condition for some time, some of the alpha rays emitted by the radon gas atoms passed through the thin glass walls of tube *A* to be collected in tube *B*. Here these particles acquire electrons and become neutral atoms. After standing for six days the mercury was raised to the level *L*, forcing the helium into the capillary. A high voltage was applied to the electrodes, and the light from the discharge was observed with a spectroscope. The line spectrum observed was found to be identical with that obtained when a discharge was sent through another tube containing regular helium gas.

69.4. Ionizing Power. When Becquerel rays penetrate matter in the gaseous, liquid, or solid state, they do not continue to move indefinitely, but are brought to rest slowly by ionizing atoms all along their path. Being ejected from their radioactive source with tremendously high speeds, all three types of rays collide with electrons and knock them free from atoms. They are, therefore, *ionizing agents*. The relative number of ionized atoms created along the path of an *α* particle, however, is much greater than the number created by a *β* particle or *γ* ray. If, in traveling the same distance in a given material, a *γ* ray produces one ionized atom, a *β* particle will, on the average, produce approximately 100, and an *α* particle will produce about 10,000. Thus *α* particles are powerful ionizing agents, while *γ* rays are not.

As stated above, an *α* particle, ejected from a radioactive atom, is but a nucleus of a helium atom and lacks the two electrons necessary to make of it a neutral atom. As this particle speeds through matter, it picks up and loses electrons at a rapid rate. No sooner does an electron become attached than it is swept off again by other atoms. Finally, upon coming to rest, however, each *α* particle collects and retains two electrons, becoming a *normal helium atom*.

69.5. Penetrating Power. At each collision with an atom, Becquerel rays lose, on the average, only a small part of their initial energy. Usually an *α* particle or *β* particle will make several thousand colli-

sions before being brought to rest. At each collision, some of the kinetic energy is expended in ionizing the atom encountered while giving that same atom a certain amount of kinetic energy. Since *α* particles produce the greatest number of ions in a given path, they penetrate the shortest distance and therefore have the poorest penetrating power. The penetrating powers of the three kinds of rays are roughly inversely proportional to their ionizing power.

	α	*β*	*γ*
Relative ionizing power......	10,000	100	1
Relative penetrating power....	1	100	10,000

69.6. Methods of Detecting Becquerel Rays. There are several well-known methods for detecting and measuring radioactivity; the most common of these are

electroscopes	*Geiger-Mueller counters*
electrometers	*scintillation counters*
cloud chambers	*ionization chambers*
bubble chambers	*photographic emulsions*

We have already seen how X rays passing through an electroscope cause the charge to disappear and the gold leaf to fall. This same action may be demonstrated with *α*, *β*, and *γ* rays. The stronger the source of rays or the nearer the sample is brought to the electroscope, the more rapid is the discharge. Experiments show that, if the walls of the electroscope are too thick, only the *γ* rays get through to produce ionization on the inside. For this reason specially designed electroscopes made with thin windows of light material like aluminum are used for measuring *α* and *β* rays.

The Braun type of electrometer is conveniently used for demonstration purposes. This device uses a lightweight metal pointer, pivoted a trifle above its center of gravity, and insulated from its ring support by a nonconductor *I* as shown in Fig. 69C. In principle, the electrometer operates exactly like an electroscope; when charged positively or negatively, the needle rises and the pointer indicates the acquired potential on a scale.

If a radioactive source is brought close

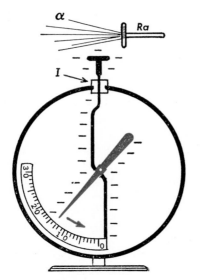

Fig. 69C *Diagram of a Braun-type electro-meter—used here to detect radioactivity.*

to the knob or terminal of a charged elec-trometer, the needle slowly returns to the vertical, or no charge, position. The α particles produce many ions in the air close to the source; oppositely charged ions are drawn toward the knob and there neu-tralize the charge.

69.7. The Wilson Cloud Chamber. In 1912 C. T. R. Wilson devised a method by which one may actually observe the paths

of α and β particles. As will be seen in the following chapters, this method is used ex-tensively in modern atomic physics as a means of studying many different atomic processes. The device by which this is ac-complished consists of an expansion cham-ber in which water vapor is made to con-dense upon ions produced by the high-speed particles that have previously passed through it.

To begin with, the conditions under which water in the vapor state will con-dense into fogdrops are quite critical. These conditions are: *first,* there must be water vapor present; *second,* there must be dust particles or ions on which the drops can form; *and third,* the temperature and pressure must be brought to a definite value. That water drops will condense only upon ions or dust particles can be demon-strated with an ordinary glass jar contain-ing a little water as shown in Fig. 69D. If allowed to stand for a short period of time, some of the water will evaporate and fill the bottle with vapor. Ions are next formed in the bottle by momentarily in-serting a small gas flame as shown in dia-gram (a). Compressed air is then injected into the bottle through a tube, so that when the stopper is quickly removed the sudden expansion will produce a dense fog

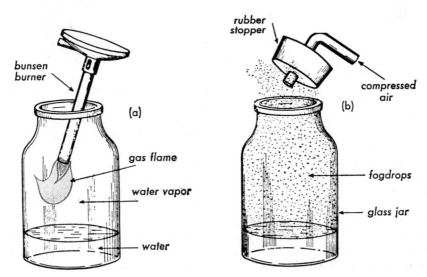

Fig. 69D *Experiment demonstrating the formation of fogdrops on ions in a glass jar.*

as shown in diagram (b). If the flame is not first inserted to produce ions, no appreciable fog can be formed.

The purpose of the compressed air and subsequent expansion of the chamber is to lower the temperature, thus causing the air to become super-saturated with water vapor. Under these conditions the vapor will condense on all ionized molecules present.

When an α or β particle "shoots" through the air, positive and negative ions are formed all along its path. The removal, by collision, of each electron from a neutral atom or molecule leaves a positively charged ion. The electron that attaches almost immediately to another neutral atom or molecule forms a negatively charged ion. If immediately after an α particle has gone through a cloud chamber an expansion takes place, fogdrops will form on the newly created ions, revealing clearly the path the particle has taken. As illustrated by the photographs in Fig. 69E, such α-ray

Gamma rays are never observed in a cloud chamber, since they produce so few ions. In passing through several feet of air a single γ ray will, on the average, produce only one or two ions. This is not enough to produce a recognizable cloud track. If a very strong source of γ rays is available, however, their presence can be observed in a cloud chamber by the chance collisions some of them have made with electrons. These recoiling electrons, are called "Compton electrons" and were explained in Sec. 68.2, and shown in Fig. 68D.

A diagram of a simple type of Wilson cloud chamber is shown in Fig. 69F. The

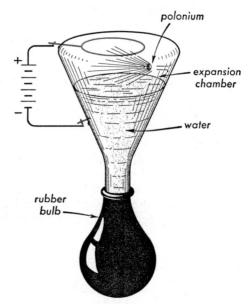

Fig. 69F   *Diagram of a small laboratory type of Wilson cloud chamber.*

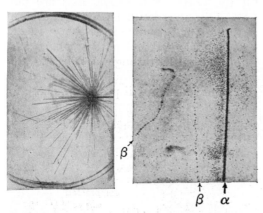

Fig. 69E   *(a) α-ray tracks from radium as seen in a Wilson cloud chamber. (b) One α-ray and two β-ray tracks. (After C. T. R. Wilson, Proceedings of the Royal Society of London, Vol. 87, 1912, p. 292.*

tracks are straight and quite dense, whereas the β-ray tracks are crooked and sparsely lined with drops. The β rays, being very light particles, are easily deflected by collision, while the relatively heavy α particles "plow" right through thousands of atoms with only an occasional deflection.

arrangement is made from an ordinary flat-bottomed flask with a rubber bulb attached to the neck. A tiny deposit of radium or polonium is inserted in the end of a thin-walled glass tube as indicated. When the rubber bulb is squeezed to compress the air in the top, and then released to cause an expansion, fogdrops will form on the ions created by the α particles. The battery and the wires leading to the wire ring in the top of the chamber and the water below are for the purpose of quickly re-

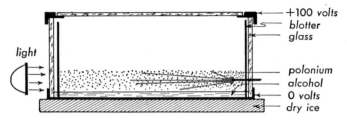

Fig. 69G *Cross-section diagram of a diffusion cloud chamber.*

moving ions previously formed in the chamber. This clears the field of view for newly formed tracks.

Another type of cloud chamber, one that is readily made in any laboratory workshop, is shown in Fig. 69G. This is the so-called *diffusion cloud chamber,* a device that is continuously sensitive to track formation. A glass cylinder separates and insulates a shallow metal pan below from a metal ring and glass disk above. The bottom pan contains alcohol and rests on a slab of "dry ice" (solid CO_2).

A blotter, extending 80% of the way around the walls, rests with its lower edge in the alcohol. Evaporated alcohol around the warm upper edge of the blotter mixes with the air and slowly settles as it cools. In the dotted region, alcohol vapor is saturated and small droplets will form on any ions present. Alpha particles shooting out through this space create positive and negative ions, and hence tracks are observed.

A potential of 100 volts or so between the bottom pan and the top ring will clear the field of ions, so that newly formed tracks are not masked by a dense fog of droplets. A strong source of light shining through the 20% open space through the blotter wall illuminates the tracks, thus making them visible.

69.8 Range. The range of an α particle is defined as the distance such a particle will travel through dry air at normal atmospheric pressure. In a partial vacuum where there are fewer air molecules per centimeter to bump into, the distance traveled before coming to rest will be greater, whereas in air under higher than normal atmospheric pressure there are more molecules per centimeter and the distance will

be diminished. Experiments show that some radioactive elements eject α particles with a higher speed than others. The higher the initial speed, the greater is the range. The range of the α particles from *radium* is 3.39 cm, whereas the range of those from *thorium C'* is 8.62 cm.

The ranges of α particles in general have been determined in three different ways: *first,* by the Wilson cloud chamber, *second,* by the number of ions produced along the path, and *third* by scintillations produced on a fluorescent screen.

In the Wilson cloud chamber photograph of Fig. 69H, α particles of two different ranges are observed. The radioactive sample used to obtain this picture was a mixture of *thorium C* and *thorium C'*. The shorter tracks with a 4.79 cm range are

Fig. 69H *Wilson cloud-chamber tracks from thorium C and C'.* (After Rutherford, Chadwick, and Ellis; coutesy of Cambridge University Press.)

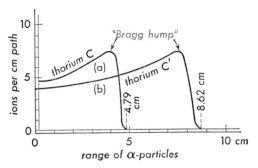

Fig. 69I *Graphs of the relative number of ions produced at various points along the path of an α particle (a) from thorium* C, *and (b) from thorium* C′.

due to the α particles from *thorium C* which disintegrate to become *thorium C″*, and the longer tracks of 8.62 cm range are due to the α particles from *thorium C′* which disintegrate to become lead (see the last chart in Appendix VI).

This is the well-known method of counting fogdrops. An enlarged photograph of a cloud track, as reproduced in Fig. 69J, reveals the individual fogdrops separated sufficiently to enable the number of drops per centimeter of path to be counted. In measurements of this kind, it is assumed that each ion produces one fogdrop.

The third method used in measuring the range is illustrated in Fig. 69K. When each α particle strikes a fluorescent screen, a tiny flash of light is produced. These flashes, called *scintillations,* are observed by means of a microscope. When the sample is moved farther and farther away, by pulling the rod *R* back, a point is reached where scintillations are no longer observed. The distance *d,* where the α particles just fail to reach the screen, is a direct measure of the range.

69.9. Range of Alpha Particles—Experiment. A simple laboratory experiment for

Fig. 69J *Enlarged photograph of a cloud chamber track showing individual fogdrops.*
(After Brode.)

When one measures the number of ions produced along the path of an α particle, curves similar to those shown in Fig. 69I are obtained. At the end of each track the number is seen to reach a maximum and then drop to zero within a very short distance. This maximum on the graph is called the "Bragg hump" in honor of W. H. Bragg, who discovered the phenomenon. The maximum number of ions is therefore produced just before the particles are stopped, i.e., where they are moving at relatively low speeds. The point at which the ion density drops rapidly to zero gives the range as shown in the figure. Although the experimental method by which ion density is usually determined will not be presented here, another method will be.

measuring the range of α particles is shown in Fig. 69L. It involves the use of a radioactive source obtained from any physics supply house, a Braun-type electrometer,

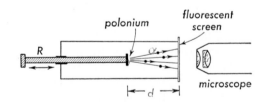

Fig. 69K *Experimental method of measuring the range of α particles.*

and an ionization chamber made from ordinary sheet metal. The ionization chamber, about the size of the most common tin can, has a hole in the bottom and a sliding disk plunger for a top. The radio-active source on the Braun electrometer, and a small metal clamp is used to ground the needle to the frame when it swings

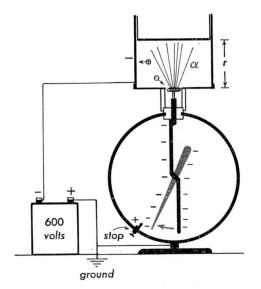

Fig. 69L *An experimental arrangement for measuring the range of α particles.*

about 3 cm from its zero position. A 600-volt radio battery of small capacity is a convenient source of high potential.

The plunger distance r is first set at about 8 cm. In this position the needle rises

steadily, hits the clamp C, and quickly drops back to zero. The needle rises again and drops back quickly at a regular rate, due to the continual collection of charge from the ions in the chamber above. With a stop watch the time t required for any given number n of discharges of the needle is recorded. The plunger is then lowered 5 mm and the discharge time again measured. This process is repeated for distances diminishing by 5-mm steps, and the discharge rate determined.

The quantity n/t for each setting of the plunger distance r is a direct measure of the ion current, that is, to the number of ions produced per second. If n/t is plotted against r, a curve similar to that shown in Fig. 69M is obtained. The drop in ion current at distances less than the *range* is due to the fact that α particles hit the plunger before they reach the end of their range in air and are prevented from creating their full quota of ions. The leveling-off of the current at larger values of r signifies that all α particles reach the end of their range in air and create their full ion quota. From the intersection of the dotted lines the α-particle range is found to be approximately 3.3 cm, in good agreement with the accurately known value of 3.39 cm.

The ranges of α particles from some of the natural radioactive elements are given in Chap. 70, Tables 70A and 70B.

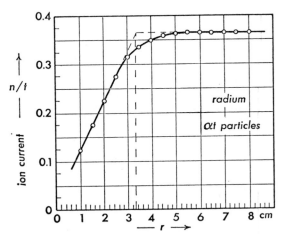

Fig. 69M *Graph of the ion current from the α particle range experiment. (See Fig. 69L.)*

QUESTIONS

1. Who discovered radioactivity? What were the circumstances?

2. Who discovered radium, polonium, and thorium?

3. What names are given to the different radioactive rays? Who unraveled this mystery?

4. What are α rays, β rays, and γ rays?

5. What are the relative ionizing powers and penetrating powers of the different rays?

6. What is a Wilson cloud chamber? How does it work?

7. What kinds of particles do not leave tracks in a Wilson cloud chamber? Why not?

8. Define or briefly explain each of the following: (a) scintillations, (b) the Bragg hump, (c) penetrating power, (d) ionizing power, and (e) an ionized atom.

9. What is meant by the range of an α particle?

10. From your knowledge of atomic structure explain how an α particle loses energy as it passes through matter, such as a gas.

11. Draw a graph showing how the specific ionization along the path of a α particle varies with distance. Indicate the range of the particle on the plot.

12. Why does the α particle-range graph of Fig. 69M round off at the top instead of showing a sharp break in the curve?

13. What effect do the β and γ rays from the radium source described in Sec. 69.9, have upon the measured ion current and the α-particle range measurements?

14. What is the purpose of the "dry ice" in the operation of a diffusion cloud chamber? (See Fig. 69G.)

Chapter 70

Disintegration and Transmutation

70.1. Transmutation by Spontaneous Disintegration. A careful study of radio-activity indicates that α, β, and γ rays originate from within the nucleus of the atom. When a radium atom disintegrates by ejecting an α particle, the nucleus loses a net positive charge of 2. Since the number of positive charges on the nucleus determines the exact number of electrons outside of the atom, and this in turn determines the chemical nature of an atom, the loss of an α particle, with two positive charges, leaves a new chemical element. Thus a *radium atom,* for example, in disintegrating, changes into a new atom called *radon.* We say that there has been a *transmutation.* Not only does a nucleus lose a double charge by emitting an α particle and thereby *drops down two places in atomic number,* but it also loses a weight of four units and thus *drops down four units in atomic weight,* or four atomic mass units.

It is common practice among physicists to designate all atomic nuclei in an abbreviated form. The nucleus of radium, for example, is written $_{88}Ra^{226}$. The subscript to the left of the chemical symbol gives the *atomic number,* i.e., the number of positive charges on the nucleus, and the superscript on the right gives the atomic *mass number,* or weight.

The disintegration of radioactive nuclei may be written in the form of simple equations, as follows:

For radium $\quad _{88}Ra^{226} \rightarrow {}_{86}Rn^{222} + \alpha \quad$ (70a)

or $\qquad\qquad _{88}Ra^{226} \rightarrow {}_{86}Rn^{222} + {}_2He^4 \quad$ (70b)

As another example,

for polonium

$$_{84}Po^{210} \rightarrow {}_{82}Pb^{206} + {}_2He^4 \qquad (70c)$$

When a nucleus like *radium B* disintegrates by ejecting a β particle (an electron) to become *radium C,* the nuclear positive charge *increases by one unit.* Such a transmutation yields a new element one atomic number higher in the chemical table. Since an electron weighs only 1/1836 part of a hydrogen atom or proton, the change in mass due to a β particle leaving a nucleus is too small to change the atomic mass number. Although the loss in weight is measurable, it changes the atomic weight so slightly that for most purposes of discussion it can be, and is, neglected.

For radium B

$$_{82}RaB^{214} \rightarrow {}_{83}RaC^{214} + {}_{-1}e^0 + \gamma \text{ ray} \quad (70d)$$

In each equation the sum of the subscripts on the right side of the equation is equal to the subscript on the left. The same is true for the superscripts. The designation $_2He^4$ represents the α particle, and $_{-1}e^0$ represents the β particle. In nearly all radioactive disintegrations where a β particle is emitted, one finds a γ ray also. In such cases, as shown by the example in Eq.(70c), *radium B* ejects a β particle and a γ ray to become *radium C,* a nucleus higher in atomic number by unity, but with the same mass number.

A γ ray, like the β ray particle, changes the weight of a nucleus by a negligible amount, and, since it has no charge, it does not alter either the atomic number or the mass number.

70.2. Half-life. *The half-life of a radioactive element is the time required for half of a given quantity of that element to disintegrate into a new element.* For example, it takes 1600 years for $\frac{1}{2}$ of a given quantity of radium to change into radon. In another 1600 years, $\frac{1}{2}$ of the remainder will have disintegrated, leaving $\frac{1}{4}$ of the original amount. The half-life of radium is therefore said to be 1600 years.

The rate at which a given quantity of a radioactive element disintegrates, that is, *decays*, is found by observing the activity of a given sample over a period of time and plotting a graph of the type shown in Fig. 70A. Here, for *polonium*, the activity drops

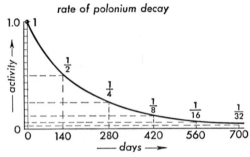

rate of polonium decay

Fig. 70A *Decay curve for the radioactive element, polonium. Polonium has a half-life of 140 days.*

to $\frac{1}{2}$ of its original value in 140 days. In another 140 days it again drops to half value, etc. The term activity may be defined as the number of rays given off per second of time, or as the number of ionized atoms produced each second by the rays.

The only difference between the decay curve of one element and that of another is the horizontal time scale to which they are plotted. To turn Fig. 70A into a decay curve for radium, the times 140, 280, 420 days, etc., need only be changed to read 1600, 3200, 4800 years, etc., respectively. Since, therefore, all radioactive decay curves follow the same law, one does not have to wait for half of a given sample to disintegrate to be able to calculate how

long it will be before half will have changed. This would require too many years of waiting for some elements.

A decay curve for the radioactivity of any given substance is best shown on what is called a *semi-log graph*. Such a graph involves the use of cross-section paper in which the spacings on the horizontal scale are uniform, while on the vertical scale they are proportional to the logarithms of numbers. Such cross-section paper can be purchased, or made by using the B or C scale on the slipstick of a slide rule.

In Fig. 70B, the fractions $\frac{1}{1}$, $\frac{1}{2}$, $\frac{1}{4}$, $\frac{1}{8}$, $\frac{1}{16}$, etc., are plotted on semi-log graph paper with the polonium *time scale* plotted horizontally. Note that a straight line is the result. If a semi-log graph is plotted for the activity of any other radioactive element, it too will be a straight line, but with a different slope.

Suppose that for a given sample of radioactive material the initial number of particles given off per minute is N_0. After a time t, the number of atoms yet to disintegrate will have decreased and the reduced number of particles given off per minute will be N. Hence, the ratio N/N_0 will decrease with time t. If the logarithm of the inverse ratio N_0/N is plotted against t, as shown by the dotted line in Fig. 70B, it too will produce a straight line. The latter shows that the log N_0/N is proportional to t. We can therefore write

$$\log_e \frac{N_0}{N} = \lambda t \qquad (70e)$$

where λ is the proportionality constant and is called the *decay constant*.

To find the half life of an element from the semi-log graph we find the point where $N = \frac{1}{2}N_0$, and call the corresponding time t, the *half-life* T. For this graph point, Eq.(70e) gives

$$\log_e \frac{N_0}{\frac{1}{2}N_0} = \lambda T \qquad (70f)$$

or $$\log_e 2 = \lambda T \qquad (70g)$$

Looking up the Naperian logarithm of 2, we find 0.693. Hence,

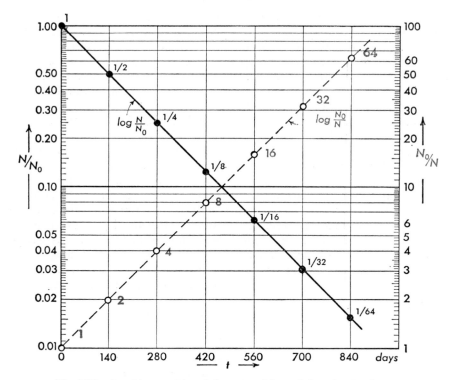

Fig. 70B *Semi-log graphs of the α particle activity of polonium.*

$$0.693 = \lambda T \qquad (70h)$$

or

$$\boxed{T = \frac{0.693}{\lambda}} \qquad (70i)$$

This is the relation between the decay constant λ and the half-life T of any element.

Example 1. A count-rate meter is used to measure the activity of a given sample. At one instant the meter shows 4750 counts per minute (*abbr.* C/M). Five minutes later it shows 2700 C/M. Find (a) the decay constant, and (b) the half-life.

Solution. To find the decay constant λ, use Eq.(70e). We first find

$$\frac{N_0}{N} = \frac{4750}{2700} = 1.760$$

From Appendix IV, we find,

$$\log_{10} 1.760 = 0.2455$$

Multiplying this by 2.3026, we obtain,

$$\log_e 1.760 = 0.5653$$

Using Eq.(70e), we obtain

(a) $\qquad \lambda = \dfrac{0.5653}{5 \text{ min}} = 0.1131 \text{ min}^{-1}$

Substituting in Eq.(70i), we obtain for the half-life:

$$T = \frac{0.693}{0.1119} = 6.1 \text{ min}$$

The mean life is defined as the average time an atom or particle exists in a particular form, and is given by the reciprocal of the decay constant.

$$\tau = \frac{1}{\lambda}$$

As shown by Eq.(70i) the half life T is just slightly over $\frac{2}{3}$ rds the mean life τ.

$$T = 0.693\tau$$

70.3. Radioactive Series. It was Rutherford and his colleagues who discovered that, when one radioactive atom disintegrates by ejecting an α or β particle, the remaining atom is still radioactive and may sooner or later eject another particle to become a still different atom. This process they found to continue through a series of elements, ending up finally with a type of atom that is stable and not radioactive. It is now known that nearly all natural disintegration processes, occurring among the heaviest elements of the periodic table, finally end up with *stable lead atoms,* atomic number 82.

There are at least four known radioactive series or chains of elements, one starting with uranium-238, a second with thorium-232, a third with uranium-235, and a fourth with plutonium-241. The first and fourth of these series are given in Tables 70A and 70B. All four series are given in a graphical tabulation in Appendix VI.

come 91. This increase of one positive change is attributed to the loss of one negative charge. These processes of successive disintegration continue until *lead,* a *stable* atom, is the end result.

As explained in Sec. 58.4, all atoms with the same atomic number but different mass number are called isotopes of the same element. For example, $_{82}RaB^{214}$, $_{82}ThB^{212}$, $_{82}AcB^{211}$, $_{82}RaD^{210}$, $_{82}Pb^{209}$, $_{82}Pb^{208}$, $_{82}Pb^{207}$, and $_{82}Pb^{206}$ are isotopes of the same chemical element, lead (see Appendix VI). Even though the first five of these are radioactive, i.e., unstable, the other three are stable. Chemically they behave exactly alike and are separated only with difficulty. The isotopes 214, 210, and 206 belong to the uranium-238 series, 212, and 208 to the thorium series, 211 and 207 to the ura-

TABLE 70A. RADIOACTIVE SERIES OF ELEMENTS
URANIUM 238 SERIES

Element	Symbol	Atomic Number	Mass Number	Particle Ejected	Range in Air	Half-life
Uranium I.........	UI	92	238	α	2.70 cm	2×10^9 yr
Uranium X_1........	UX_1	90	234	β	....	24.5 days
Uranium X_2........	UX_2	91	234	β	....	1.14 min
Uranium II........	UII	92	234	α	3.28	3×10^5 yr
Ionium...........	Io	90	230	α	3.19	83,000 yr
Radium..........	Ra	88	226	α	3.39	1600 yr
Radon..........	Rn	86	222	α	4.12	3.82 days
Radium A.........	RaA	84	218	α	4.72	3.05 min
Radium B.........	RaB	82	214	β	....	26.8 min
Radium C.........	RaC	83	214	α, β	....	19.7 min
Radium C'.........	RaC'	84	214	α	6.97	10^{-6} sec
Radium C''........	RaC''	81	210	β	....	1.32 min
Radium D.........	RaD	82	210	β	....	22 yr
Radium E.........	RaE	83	210	β	....	5 days
Polonium..........	Po	84	210	α	3.92	140 days
Lead.............	Pb	82	206	stable	....	infinite

When a uranium atom of mass number 238 and atomic number 92 disintegrates by ejecting an α particle, the remainder is a new atom, *uranium X_1,* of mass number 234 and atomic number 90. When a uranium X_1 atom disintegrates by ejecting a β particle to become *uranium X_2,* the mass number remains unchanged at 234, while the atomic number increases by one to be-

nium-235 series, and 209 to the neptunium series.

70.4. Daughter Products. When an element disintegrates by emitting α or β rays, it creates a new chemical element. Such "offspring" atoms are referred to as the *daughter element,* an element which itself may or may not be radioactive. Consider as an example the radioactive element

TABLE 70B. NEPTUNIUM SERIES†

Element	Symbol	Atomic Number	Mass Number	Particle Ejected	Range in Air	Half-life
Plutonium.........	Pu	94	241	β	..	...
Americium.........	Am	95	241	α	4.1*	500 yr
Neptunium.........	Np	93	237	α	3.3*	2.25×10^6 yr
Protoactinium......	Pa	91	233	β	..	27.4 da
Uranium..........	U	92	233	α	3.3*	1.63×10^5 yr*
Thorium...........	Th	90	229	α	3.3	7×10^3 yr
Radium............	Ra	88	225	β	..	14.8 da
Actinium..........	Ac	89	225	α	4.4	10 da
Francium..........	Fa	87	221	α	5.0	4.8 min
Astatine...........	At	85	217	α	5.8	0.018 sec
Bismuth...........	Bi	83	213	$\beta(94\%)$ $\alpha(4\%)$	4.6	47 min
Polonium..........	Po	84	213	α	7.7	10^{-6} sec
Lead..............	Pb	82	209	β	..	3.3 hr
Bismuth...........	Bi	83	209	stable	..	infinite

† See F. Hagemann, L. I. Katzin, M. H. Studier, A. Ghiorso, and G. T. Seaborg. *Physical Review*, vol. 72, 252, August, 1947.

* See *Radioactivity and Nuclear Physics* by J. M. Cork, D. Van Nostrand, Princeton.

radon, $Z = 86$. Of the several known isotopes of this element (see Appendix VI), isotope 220 is a derivative of the thorium series beginning with $_{90}Th^{232}$.

Thoron-220 is a gas and is α-active, that is, it disintegrates by giving off α particles. The daughter product, polonium-216, called ThA, is α-active, and has an extremely short half-life of 0.158 sec. The daughter product of this element, however, has the relatively long half-life of 10.6 hours. The reactions involved here are as follows.

$$_{86}Tn^{220} \rightarrow {}_{84}ThA^{216} + {}_2He^4 \quad (T = 54.5 \text{ sec})$$
$$_{84}ThA^{216} \rightarrow {}_{82}ThB^{212} + {}_2He^4 \quad (T = 0.158 \text{ sec})$$
$$_{82}ThB^{212} \rightarrow {}_{83}ThC^{212} + {}_{-1}e^0 \quad (T = 10.6 \text{ hr})$$

If a given quantity of thoron gas is confined to a closed vessel, the Tn nuclei that disintegrate will tend to accumulate as ThA. Not much of this daughter product can accumulate, however, since with the short half-life of 0.158 sec, most of the nuclei quickly disintegrate into ThB. In the period of ten to fifteen minutes, few of these ThB disintegrate, and they do accumulate. A graph of this decrease of parent element Tn and the accumulation of

daughter element, ThA, and its daughter element, ThB, is shown in Fig. 70C.

70.5. Half-Life Experiment. A relatively simple experiment for measuring the half-life of a radioactive element is shown in Fig. 70D. Thoron gas $_{86}Tn^{220}$ from a small glass vessel A, injected into an ionization chamber C, is detected by the ion current I as it flows through the electrometer E into the ground G.

Immediately upon squeezing the rubber bulb B and injecting the thoron, the electroscope needle rises and falls, discharging intermittently through the stop S. The time t is recorded from a seconds clock each time a discharge occurs, and these are recorded against the discharge number n. A typical set of recorded times are plotted in Fig. 70E. The leveling-out of the graph after some time signifies that little thoron gas is left, and a reasonable horizontal line is drawn at $n = 14$ as the last discharge that could be obtained. Coming down, therefore, to the point $N = 7$, where the activity was at half value, the time $t = 56$ sec is read from the graph as the half-life of $_{86}Tn^{220}$.

The decay curve of Fig. 70E can be

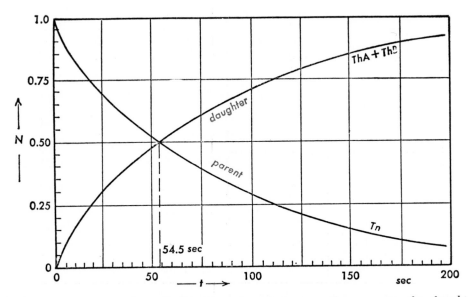

Fig. 70C *Decay curve for $_{86}Tn^{220}$ (thoron) and the growth curve for the daughter products,* $_{84}ThA^{216} + _{82}ThB^{212}$.

plotted as a semi-log graph by plotting the difference between the line $N = 14$ and the curve value at each 10-second interval, and plotting these as shown in Fig. 70F. When the best possible straight line is drawn through the points, the half-value point comes at $t = 56$ sec.

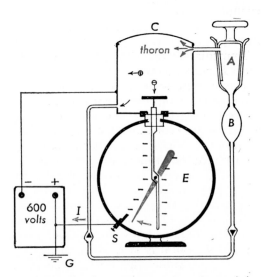

Fig. 70D *Simple apparatus for determining the half-life of a radioactive gas like throron,* $_{86}Tn^{220}$.

Mathematically, this value can be computed from the graph and Eq.(70e) as follows: At time $t = 0$ we obtain $N_0 = 14$. Choosing any other point far down on the graph, such as the one at $t = 150$ sec, we find $N = 2.2$. Dividing one value by the other gives $N_0/N = 6.36$. Looking up this number in a table of Naperian logarithms, we find $\log_e 6.36 = 1.850$. (Ordinary $\log_{10}$ tables can be used if the logarithm obtained is multiplied by 2.30258.) Substitution of this value in Eq.(70e), along with $t = 150$ sec, gives as the value for the decay constant:

$$\lambda = \frac{1.850}{150} = 0.0123$$

When this is substituted in Eq.(70i), we obtain

$$T = \frac{0.693}{0.0123} = 56.3 \text{ sec}$$

as the half-life.

70.6. Different Forms of Energy. Einstein, in working out the theory of relativity, arrived at a number of simple equations concerning the nature of the physical world. One of these equations, having to do with the increase in mass of a moving

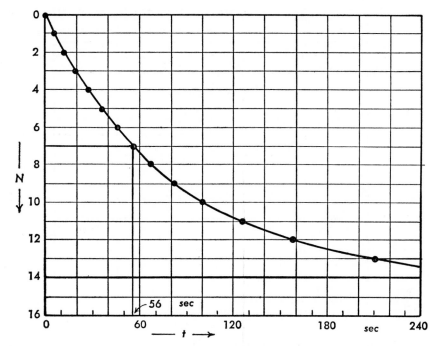

Fig. 70E *Experimental decay curve for thoron ($_{86}Tn^{220}$), obtained using the apparatus shown in Fig. 70D.*

object, was presented in Sec. 46.6. It is important at this point to consider this mass-energy equation again.

$$E = mc^2 \qquad (70j)$$

where m is the mass, c is the velocity of light, and E is the energy equivalence.

From this relation we can predict that mass can be turned into energy, or energy into mass. In other words, mass is a form of energy, for if a quantity of mass m could be annihilated, a definite amount of energy E would become available in some other form. To illustrate this, suppose that a 1-gm mass could be completely annihilated and the liberated energy given to some other body in the form of kinetic energy.

$$E = 1 \times 10^{-3} \text{ Kg} \times 9 \times 10^{16} \text{ m}^2/\text{sec}^2$$
$$= 9 \times 10^{13} \text{ joules}$$

In the English system of units this is equivalent to 7×10^{13} ft-lb, or enough energy to propel the largest battleship around the world.

The annihilation of mass then is a source of undreamed-of energy. In the following chapters we will see that disintegration is one means whereby mass can be annihilated or created through planned laboratory experiments.

In the following chapters we will see that if an atom, a part of an atom, or an electron is annihilated, the energy may either be transformed into kinetic energy and given to another atomic particle in the form of a velocity, or it may appear as a γ ray of specified frequency ν and energy $h\nu$. To find the equivalence between mass energy, γ ray energy, and kinetic energy, all of the following quantities are equated to each other.

$$\boxed{E = mc^2 = h\nu = \tfrac{1}{2}m_0 v^2 = Ve} \qquad (70k)$$

It is customary among physicists to express each of these energies in terms of V in volts. Thus one speaks of a one-million volt γ ray, a three-million volt electron, or a 12.5-million volt proton, etc. This terminology is used for convenience only, and

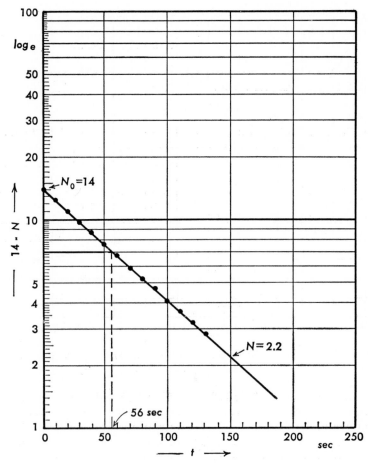

Fig. 70F *Semi-log graph for finding the half-life of thoron, $_{86}Tn^{220}$.*

denotes the value of V in the above equation which, with the electronic charge substituted for e, gives the energy of the γ ray photon, or the energy of the moving atomic particle. For all energies, m in the second term is the relativistic mass given by Eq.(46l), and the fourth term is the kinetic energy of any particle whose rest mass is m_0. At very high velocities the fourth term must be replaced by the relativistic kinetic energy $m_0c^2(\gamma - 1)$. (See Eq.(46r).)

When an atomic nucleus ejects an α or β particle, the mass of that nucleus diminishes not only by the rest mass of the ejected particle, but by an amount called the *annihilation energy*. A small part of the nuclear mass is annihilated and given to the ejected particle as kinetic energy. While the anni-

hilated mass varies from isotope to isotope, it is usually less than 1% of one atomic mass unit.

As a convenient figure to use in disintegration problems, we will calculate the energy equivalent to the annihilation of unit atomic mass, namely, 1.66×10^{-27} Kg. Using the second and last terms of Eq.(70k), we find

$$\boxed{Ve = mc^2} \qquad (70l)$$

$$V = \frac{1.66 \times 10^{-27} \times 9 \times 10^{16}}{1.60 \times 10^{-19}}$$
$$= 931{,}000{,}000 \text{ volts}$$

The annihilation energy of 1 amu = 931 million electron volts, abbreviated

$$1 \text{ amu} = 931 \text{ Mev} \qquad (70m)$$

When a γ ray is ejected from a nucleus, it carries wit it an energy $h\nu$. This energy may be expressed by (a), the mass equivalence as given by the second and third terms of Eq.(70k), or by the voltage equivalence as given by the third and fifth terms. It is customary to use the latter relation, and write

$$\boxed{Ve = h\nu} \qquad (70n)$$

Example 2. A γ ray has a wavelength of 4.5 $\times 10^{-13}$ m. Find its energy equivalence in million electron volts.

Solution. Using the wave equation $c = \nu\lambda$, and substituting c/λ for ν in Eq.(70n), we obtain

$$V = \frac{hc}{e\lambda}$$

Substituting, we find that

$$V = \frac{6.62 \times 10^{-34} \times 3 \times 10^8}{1.60 \times 10^{-19} \times 4.5 \times 10^{-13}}$$
$$= 2.75 \times 10^6 \text{ volts}$$

It is common practice to express the initial energy of α particles by specifying either their range in air or their energy equivalence in Mev. This applies to other high-speed particles as well, particles such as protons and deuterons which are the nuclei of the two hydrogen isotopes. A graph like the one shown in Fig. 70G is useful for converting the observed range of an α particle to its equivalent energy in Mev, or vice versa.

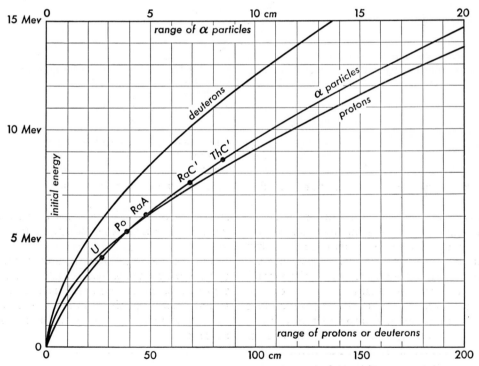

Fig. 70G *Graphs giving the range of protons, deuterons, and α particles for different initial energies in million electron volts.*

QUESTIONS AND PROBLEMS

1. What is spontaneous disintegration?

2. What is transmutation? What change takes place in the nucleus of an atom when an α particle is emitted? What change takes place when a β particle is emitted?

3. What is meant by the half-life of a radio-active isotope?

4. What is meant by the range of radioactive rays? Which of the three kinds of rays should have the greatest range?

5. What is the abbreviated designation for atomic nuclei?

6. Write down the nuclear reaction, in the abbreviated form, for the emission of an α particle by an ionium nucleus (atomic number 90). See Appendix VI.

7. Write down the nuclear reaction for the emission of an α particle by radium A (atomic number 84). See Appendix VI.

8. Write down the nuclear reaction for α particle emission by uranium-238. (See Appendix VI.)

9. Write the nuclear reaction for the emission of a β particle by actinium-227. (See Appendix VI.)

10. Write the nuclear reaction for the emission of a β particle by radium B. (See Appendix VI.)

11. If the activity of a radioactive sample drops to $\frac{1}{8}$ of its initial value in 2 hr and 15 min, what is its half-life?

12. If the activity of a radioactive sample drops to $\frac{1}{32}$ of its initial value in 7.5 hr, find its half-life. (*Ans.* 1.5 hr.)

13. How long will it take a sample of radon to decrease to 10% if its half-life is 3.82 days? Find your answer by plotting a decay curve.

14. How long will it take a sample of radium D to decrease to 10% if its half-life is 22 years? (*Ans.* 73.1 yr.)

15. If the activity of a radioactive sample drops to $\frac{1}{16}$ of its initial value in 10 hr and 40 min, find its half-life.

16. The activity of a radioactive sample drops to $\frac{1}{32}$ of its initial value in 54 hr. Find its half-life. (*Ans.* 10.8 hr.)

17. How long will it take for the activity of a sample of radon 222 to decrease to 1%? Determine your answer by graphing the time decay curve.

18. How long will it take for the activity of a sample of francium-221 to decrease to $\frac{1}{10}$ of 1%? (*Ans.* 8.0 hr.)

19. What radioactive atoms are isotopes of bismuth? (See Appendix VI.) Give symbols, atomic numbers, and mass numbers.

20. If 5 lb of lead could be completely annihilated, how many joules would be produced? (*Ans.* 20.4×10^{16} joules.)

21. Calculate the mass equivalent to an energy of (a) 15 Mev, (b) 24 Mev, and (c) 3.5 Mev.

22. If the following masses could be annihilated, how much energy, in Mev, is created? (a) 0.0216 atomic mass unit, (b) 0.0589 atomic mass unit. (*Ans.* (a) 20.1, (b) 54.8.)

23. At one instant a count-rate meter shows a radioactive sample emitting 2040 counts per minute. Ten minutes later the activity has dropped to 1630 counts per min. Find (a) the decay constant, and (b) the half-life.

24. In recording the activity of a given radioactive sample, a count-rate meter indicates 6520 counts per minute. Two minutes later the meter shows the activity has dropped to 4840 counts per min. Calculate (a) the decay constant, and (b) the half-life. (*Ans.* (a) 0.149 min^{-1}, (b) 4.65 min.)

Chapter 71

Beta and Gamma Rays

Beta rays emitted by the natural radio-active elements have been studied by many people. It was Becquerel who first found them to be comparable to cathode rays. Today we know them as electrons. One of the greatest mysteries of atomic physics has been the origin of these particles. The great mass of experimental evidence shows that most of them come from the nucleus, yet they do not exist in the same form inside any of the known nuclei. Furthermore, unlike α particles and γ rays, they do not emerge from the nuclei with the same energy and range, but with a wide band of velocities.

71.1. Beta Ray Spectrograph. This is an instrument by which one can experimentally determine the velocity of β particles from a radioactive source. Fig. 71A is a dia-

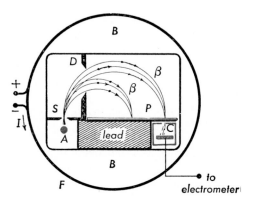

Fig. 71A *Diagram of a beta-ray spectrograph.*

gram of one such instrument, developed in principle by Robinson in England. Beta particles from a small radioactive source A, consisting of a fine wire with a deposit of material on its surface, are allowed to pass through a slit S. With the entire vacuum

tube located in a uniform magnetic field, the β particles follow circular paths and are brought to focus on a photographic plate P or at the open slit of an ionization chamber C. Each of the three semicircular paths in any one group shown in the diagram has the same radius and diameter. The focusing action indicated can best be demonstrated by using a compass and drawing several semicircles with the same radius, but slightly displaced centers. The velocity of any group of electrons is given by Eq.(57e), as

$$Bev = \frac{mv^2}{r} \qquad (71a)$$

where r is the path radius, B the magnetic induction, and e, m, and v the electrons charge, mass, and velocity, respectively.

If the field B is constant, and a photographic plate P is located as shown in the figure, its development after a time t will result in a photograph like the drawing in Fig. 71B. In addition to a darkened back-

Fig. 71B *Diagram of a beta-ray spectrogram.*

ground all along the plate, one finds several lines parallel to the slit. The background indicates β particles present with all different velocities, while the lines signify groups with discrete and definite velocities. Not all spectrograms with such a continuous background contain these lines, however.

In some β ray spectrographs, the β parti-

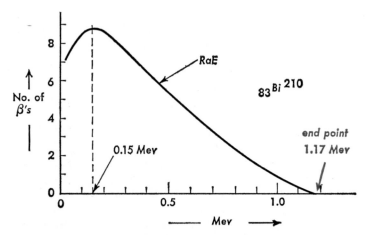

Fig. 71C   *Graph of beta-ray energies from RaE.*

cles are collected in an ionization chamber C as shown in Fig. 71A. Different velocities are determined by slowly and continuously changing the magnetic induction B. This is accomplished by changing the current I in the field coils F. If measurements of electrometer current are recorded for different values of B, a graph similar to that shown in Fig. 71C can be plotted.

The measured ion current is plotted as the number of β particles, and the coil current I is plotted as the energy the particles would have to enter the slit at C. This curve, made using Ra E as a source, which is the radioactive bismuth isotope $_{83}Bi^{210}$, shows β particles with a maximum energy at 0.15 Mev, and an *end-point* energy of 1.17 Mev. The end-point, or cut-off, at the high-energy end of this curve, signifies a velocity limit or maximum. As shown by Table 71A, such end-point energies have different values for different isotopes.

71.2. The Neutrino Postulate. In 1931 Pauli, of Germany, suggested that in β-ray emission all nuclei of the same isotope emit the same amount of energy, and that this is the *end-point energy* shown in Fig. 71C. (See also Table 71A.) To account for the observed fact that some β particles emerge with much less energy than others, he made the following postulate. The emission of a β particle by any nucleus is accompanied by a companion particle having a variable energy E. While the β particle is an ordinary negatively charged electron, the companion particle, now called a *neutrino,* has no charge. In some respects a neutrino is

TABLE 71A. END-POINT ENERGIES FOR β RAYS.

Isotope	Designation	End Point E	Half-life
$_{82}Pb^{214}$	Ra B	0.72 Mev	26.8 m
$_{83}Bi^{210}$	Ra E	1.17 Mev	4.8 d
$_{87}Fr^{223}$	Ac K	1.20 Mev	21.0 m
$_{88}Ra^{225}$	—	0.320 Mev	15 d
$_{89}Ac^{228}$	Ms Th$_2$	1.55 Mev	6.1 h
$_{90}Th^{231}$	UY	0.21 Mev	25.6 y
$_{90}Th^{234}$	UX$_1$	0.193 Mev	24 d

like a photon; it has no rest mass, it has energy E, and it travels with the speed of light c. Hence, the reaction for β-emission by a nucleus like $_{83}Bi^{210}$, can be written

$$_{83}Bi^{210} \rightarrow {}_{84}Po^{210} + \beta^- + \nu \qquad (71b)$$

where ν represents the neutrino.

The neutrino postulate has served another important function in atomic processes; it permits the retention of the law of conservation of momentum. All even-numbered nuclei, *even A,* are known to have an angular momentum given by an integral quantum number, $I = 0, 1, 2, 3, 4, \ldots$, all odd-numbered nuclei, odd-A, are known to have an angular momentum given by a half-integral quantum number, $I = \frac{1}{2}, \frac{3}{2}, \frac{5}{2}, \frac{7}{2}, \ldots$. Furthermore, all electrons are known to have a spin angular momentum given by a half-integral quantum number, $s = \frac{1}{2}$. By assigning the neutrino a spin angular momentum equal in magnitude to that of the electron, the two spins can either cancel each other as shown in Fig. 71D, or

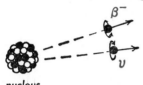

nucleus

Fig. 71D *Each beta particle from a nucleus is accompanied by a neutrino.*

add together, thus keeping the nuclear spin integral or half-integral valued as the case may be.

Only recently have experiments been performed that appear to establish the existence of these phantom particles, neutrinos. Since nuclei are composed of neutrons and protons, the two ejected particles are created by the nucleus, a neutron transforming into a proton as it emits an electron of mass m_0, charge $-e$, and spin $\frac{1}{2}\hbar$, and a neutrino of energy E, no charge, and spin $\frac{1}{2}\hbar$. (See Eq.(66b).)

71.3. Conservation of Nuclear Energy. The simultaneous emission of a β particle and a neutrino from the nucleus of an atom requires energy. Not only does the disintegrating nucleus give up the mass of the two particles, but some additional mass which it converts into kinetic energy. By adding up all this energy in the form of mass, the total loss in the mass of an atom can be calculated.

Consider as an example the β-emission of $_{83}Bi^{210}$ as represented by Eq.(71b). The masses of the two atoms involved are known to be

$$_{83}Bi^{210} \quad 210.04951 \text{ amu}$$
$$_{84}Po^{210} \quad \underline{210.04826} \text{ amu}$$
$$\Delta m = 0.00125 \text{ amu}$$

To convert this mass into Mev, we multiply Δm by the value 931 Mev given by Eq.(70m), which gives

$$E = 1.16 \text{ Mev}$$

This is just the end-point energy derived from experiment and shown in Fig. 71C. The mass of the ejected electron need not be included here since the two masses above are for the neutral atoms. $_{83}Bi^{210}$ has 83 orbital electrons included in its mass of 210.04951 amu, while $_{84}Po^{210}$ includes 84 electrons. When $_{83}Bi^{210}$ ejects an electron from the nucleus, the daughter product $_{84}Po^{210}$ picks up a stray electron to become a neutral atom.

71.4. Gamma Rays. For many radioactive elements the emission of an α or β particle from a nucleus is immediately followed by the emission of a γ ray. It has been shown by crystal diffraction spectrographs that γ rays are electromagnetic waves and that they consist of sharp lines of discrete wavelengths. Just as visible light, and ultraviolet and infrared radiation as well as X rays are known to be emitted from the outer structure of the atom by an electron's jumping from one energy level to another, so γ rays are believed to arise from a transition of a nucleon from one energy state to another within the nucleus. (Neutrons and protons combined are called *nucleons*.)

There is good evidence that γ rays are emitted by the daughter element, that is, that they are preceded by particle emission. A good example is to be found in the case of Ra D. This nucleus is the lead isotope $_{82}Pb^{210}$, and with a half-life of 22 years it emits a β particle. The reaction is

$$_{82}Pb^{210} \rightarrow {}_{83}Bi^{210} + \beta^- + \nu + \gamma \text{ ray} \quad (71c)$$

These emissions are represented on a nuclear energy level diagram in Fig. 71E. When a $_{82}Pb^{210}$ nucleus emits a β particle and a neutrino, the end-point energy is found to be 18,000 electron volts (*abbr.* 18 Kev). This leaves a $_{83}Bi^{210}$ nucleus in what is called an *excited state* or energy level. A transition down to the ground level is accompanied by the emission of a γ ray with an energy $h\nu$. This energy is equiva-

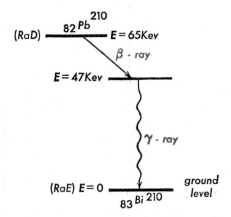

Fig. 71E *Energy level diagram illustrating β-ray emission followed by γ-ray emission.*

lent to 47 Kev. Although it is not shown in this diagram, this nucleus, too, is radioactive and emits another β ray to become $_{84}Po^{210}$. (See Eq.(71b).)

71.5. Internal Conversion. When a γ ray is emitted by a disintegrating nucleus, it must of necessity pass some of the outer electrons on its way out of the atom. Upon passing close to one of the electrons, a photoelectric action may occur, whereby the γ ray is absorbed and an electron is emitted. Energetically this process must follow the photoelectric Eq.(61a),

$$hv = W + \tfrac{1}{2}mv^2 \qquad (71d)$$

Part of the γ ray energy hv is used to pull the electron away from the atom, and the remainder is imparted to it as kinetic energy. As a rule this kinetic energy is relatively large, and $\tfrac{1}{2}mv^2$ must be replaced by the relativistic form $m_0c^2(\gamma - 1)$. (See Eq. (65b).)

Since the energy required to remove an electron from an atom will differ from one shell to another, the electrons can be expected to have any one of several discrete energies. The definite sharp lines shown in Fig. 71B supply the evidence for this assumption. Furthermore, the experimentally determined energies check exactly with those determined from X rays as shown in Fig. 68A. The process just described is illustrated schematically in Fig. 71F, and is called internal conversion (*abbr.* IC).

If by internal conversion an electron is ejected from the innermost *K*-shell, leaving a vacancy there, another electron from the *L*-shell or *M*-shell falls in to take its place and, in so doing, emits an X ray. Confirmation of such a process is assured since the measured wavelengths of such X rays are identical with those emitted by the same element in an X-ray tube.

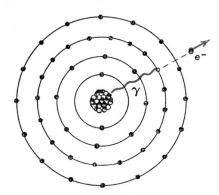

Fig. 71F *Orbital electron ejected by a γ-ray from the same atom's nucleus. Internal conversion.*

71.6. Scintillation Counters. A scintillation counter is a sensitive device used in nuclear physics studies for the detection and measurement of high-energy atomic radiation. In principle it is based upon the earliest discoveries in radioactivity that α particles upon striking a fluorescent material, like zinc sulfide, produce a tiny flash of light. (See Sec. 69.8.) These flashes, called *scintillations,* can be seen by the dark adapted eye, or they can be detected by a photomultiplier tube and amplified.

It is now well known that when high-energy-charged atomic particles pass through certain transparent materials, fluorescent light is produced all along the path. (See Fig. 71G.) As the fast moving particle collides with atoms and molecules, electrons are raised to excited energy levels, and in returning to their ground states, emit light. For many crystals and plastics this *fluorescent light* is blue or violet in color, while for others it is ultraviolet or infrared.

A typical scintillation counter tube is shown in Fig. 71H. A block of fluorescent

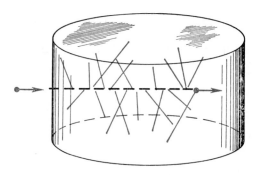

Fig. 71G *Diagram of the fluorescent light developed by an atomic particle traversing a transparent crystal or plastic fluor.*

material is mounted on the flat end of a special photomultiplier tube and then encased in a thin-walled, light-tight aluminum shield. When a particle traverses the fluor, the light ejects electrons from the photocathode by the photoelectric effect. The charge multiplication built up by the eight or more dynodes makes a sizeable voltage pulse that activates some electronic counting device. (See Fig. 71I.)

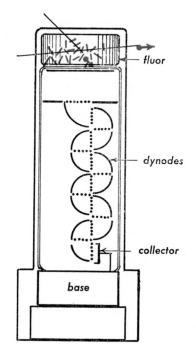

Fig. 71H *Scintillation detector tube using a photomultiplier tube with a fluorescent block.*

When γ rays are to be detected, the fluorescent materials frequently used are crystals of sodium iodide, NaI, and caesium iodide, CsI. For high energy β rays, such plastics as polystyrene, impregnated with anthracene, are used. These are inexpensive and very effective and can be quite large in size. For α particles with their relatively low penetrating power, a thin layer of zinc sulfide deposited on the photomultiplier tube or a plastic surface is commonly used.

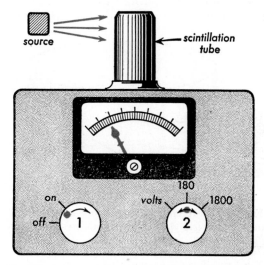

Fig. 71I *One type of scintillation counter with a count-rate meter, two ranges, and an on-off switch.*

The principal advantages of scintillation counters over other detectors of nuclear radiation are: (1) they operate in air or in a vacuum; (2) they deliver an electrical impulse which is proportioned to the energy lost by the traversing particle; and (3) they can count at amazingly high speeds.

While the duration of a single pulse from a NaI crystal counter will last about one microsecond, the pulse time from an anthracene counter can be as short as one thousandth of a microsecond (10^{-9} sec).

71.7. Cerenkov Radiation. In 1934 Cerenkov, in Russia, discovered that fast moving electrons, such as β particles from radioactive materials, will produce light within a transparent medium if their velocity is greater than the speed of light in that medium. In a medium like glass or plastic, the speed of light is about $\frac{2}{3}$ to $\frac{3}{4}$ the speed of light in a vacuum, yet many β particles are ejected at speeds greater than this and some of them close to $c = 3 \times 10^8$ m/sec.

The phenomenon of Cerenkov radiation is analogous to (a) the production of the V-shaped wave from a ship, the ship traveling through water at a speed greater than the wave velocity; or (b) the shock waves from a missile traveling through the air at a speed greater than sound. (See Fig. 11O.)

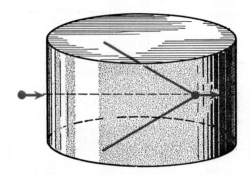

Fig. 71J *The conical wave from a high-speed atomic particle in a transparent medium; Cerenkov radiation.*

In Fig. 71J a particle is shown generating a conical wave as it travels with a velocity V through a medium of refractive index μ. While the conical wave front makes an angle ϕ with the particle's direction, the light travels outward at right angles to the wave front.

The principle of Cerenkov radiation is frequently used to detect high-energy atomic particles. A Cerenkov counter has the same general construction as shown in Fig. 71H, except that the fluor is replaced by a transparent medium, liquid or solid, and with a refractive index specified for the particular particle speeds to be detected.

71.8. Semiconductor Detectors. Recent experiments show that semiconducting materials like those used in transistors are useful detectors of α rays and other heavy atomic particles. (See Fig. 64A.) One type of semiconductor detector used is shown in Fig. 71K. A thin layer of gold metal is

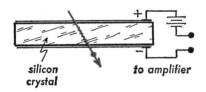

Fig. 71K *Semiconductor detector using silicon.*

deposited on the two surfaces of a thin wafer of very pure silicon, and the two conducting surfaces connected to a 1 to 20 volt battery and amplifier. When a charged particle enters the crystal, free electrons and holes develop, increasing its conductivity. The sudden current pulse thereby created is amplified and then measured or counted.

71.9. Radiation Absorption. As high-energy-charged particles travel through matter in the solid, liquid, or gaseous state, their energy is gradually dissipated in a number of different ways, principally by the excitation and ionization of atoms and molecules. Gamma rays on the other hand, have a far greater range because they have no electric charge. Unless their energy is over 1 Mev, their absorption is due to the photoelectric effect or the Compton effect. In either case, ions are formed in the process, and, in relation to those produced by charged particles, are far apart.

A diagram representing the absorption of γ rays is given in Fig. 71L. If I_0 repre-

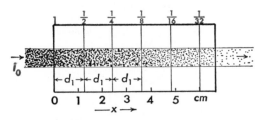

Fig. 71L *Diagram illustrating the absorption of γ rays by matter.*

sents the intensity of the beam as it enters the medium, there will be some depth d_1 at which the intensity will have dropped to $\frac{1}{2}I_0$. Imagine now that we divide the medium into layers, each of thickness d_1. The beam intensity $\frac{1}{2}I_0$ entering the second layer will be reduced to $\frac{1}{2}$ of this initial value and emerge to enter the third layer with an intensity $\frac{1}{4}I_0$. Upon traversing the third layer, the entering beam $\frac{1}{4}I_0$ will be reduced to half value, or to $\frac{1}{8}I_0$, etc.

If we now plot a graph of the beam intensity I against the number of absorbing layers, or the depth x, we obtain the curve shown in Fig. 71M. While the absorption

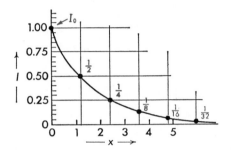

Fig. 71M *Absorption curve for γ rays.*

curves for different γ ray energies, and different absorbers, are not identical, they are alike in that they follow the same law. Just as in the case of the half-lives of radioactive isotopes (see Fig. 70B), if we plot the absorption on a semi-log graph, we obtain a straight line. From this straight line we can write

$$\log_e \frac{I_0}{I} = \mu x \qquad (71e)$$

The proportionality constant μ is often called the *absorption coefficient* and represents the fraction of the beam absorbed from the beam per centimeter path. The calculation of μ can be made from the experimental data by selecting any two values of I from the straight-line section of such a semi-log graph.

71.10. Radiation Absorption. If a beam of β and γ rays, emitted by a radioactive source, are allowed to enter an absorbing medium, the β rays are absorbed within a much shorter distance than are the γ rays. A schematic diagram of the relative absorptions is shown in Fig. 71N.

Suppose we perform an experiment, using a small sample of radium as a ra-

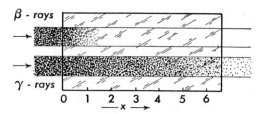

Fig. 71N *Schematic diagram showing the relative absorption of β and γ rays.*

diation source, a scintillation counter as a detector, and aluminum or lead sheets as absorbers. (See Fig. 71O.) Radiation from a radium source S, in passing through absorbers at A, enters the fluor block C, and the signal developed is amplified by the photomultiplier tube PM.

The number of counts per minute (C/M), detected by the scintillation counter, is shown here being recorded with an electronic amplifier called a *scaler*.

The five circles represent the end view of electronic tubes, each having ten small pins. Only one pin at a time in each tube will glow orange-red in color, the light arising from a neon gas discharge around it. Each pulse from the scintillator will cause the glow to jump to the next pin clockwise in tube "1." When the tenth pulse arrives and the glow jumps from pin 9 to 0, the glow in the next tube "10" will jump from pin 0 to pin 1. The next time around for tube "1," the glow in tube "10" will jump to 2, thus indicating a total count of 20. This process continues, thus activating the third tube for hundreds, the fourth for thousands, etc. The reading showing in the diagram is 12,631.

By depressing the "Reset" switch, all five tubes return to their zero positions. To determine the number of counts per minute from any setting, the "Count" switch is raised at the same time the button on a stop-watch is pressed. At the end of one minute, by the watch, the "Count" switch is depressed, stopping the counting process. The total counts are then read directly from the tubes.

Such scalers as these are usually equipped with a dual-purpose milliammeter as shown

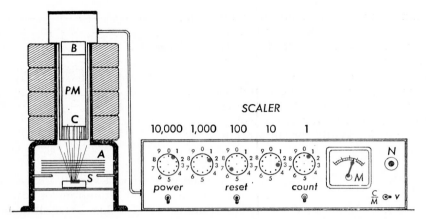

Fig. 71O *Scintillation tube with scaler counter for radiation absorption measurements.*

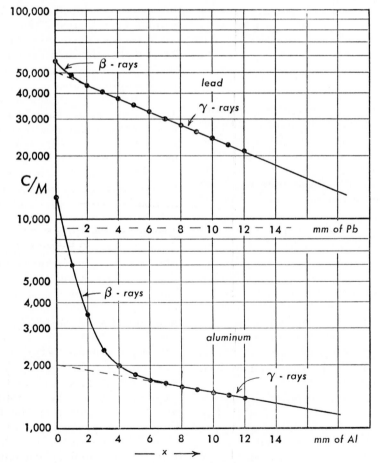

Fig. 71P *Semi-log graphs of β ray and γ ray absorption by lead (Pb) and aluminum (Al).*

at the right. When the accompanying switch is thrown to the *V* position, the knob *N* can be turned to adjust and set the total voltage applied to the photomultiplier tube. When it is thrown to the C/M position, the meter pointer will read directly the counts per minute. As one observes this meter for a fixed set of counting conditions, the pointer will fluctuate about some median position, and the observer must estimate the average value. It is for this reason that, for accuracy, the tube readings are preferred.

With no absorbers in place, and the source far removed from the scintillation counter, stray radiation from nearby objects and cosmic rays can and should always be measured and recorded as "background C/M." After the source is inserted in the holder, absorbers are inserted one at a time between the source and the counter, and the C/M determined for each. The results of this experiment, using first a series of lead absorbers and then a series of aluminum absorbers, are shown on a semi-log graph in Fig. 71P.

Since β rays from a radioactive source have a range of velocities, the upper part of each graph is curved. At the point where each curve straightens out, the β rays are completely absorbed and only the more penetrating γ rays are left. The straight section signifies that γ ray absorption follows Eq.(71e), and that absorption coefficients can be determined for both lead and aluminum.

PROBLEMS

(*Note:* Refer to Appendix IX for all problems.)

1. Write down the reaction for the disintegration of RaD. (See Table 71A.)

2. Write down the reaction for the disintegration of AcK. (See Table 71A.)

3. Atoms of $MsTh_2$ emit β particles with an end-point energy of 1.55 Mev. (a) Write down the reaction, and (b) find the loss in nuclear mass due to this particle and the neutrino. (See Table 71A.)

4. Atoms of UY emit β particles with an end-point energy of 1.20 Mev. (a) Write down the reaction, and (b) find the loss in nuclear mass due to the emission of this particle and the neutrino. (See Table 71A.) (*Ans.* (b) 0.00023 amu.)

5. Atoms of Ra D have a mass of 210.04958 amu, and emit β particles followed by a γ ray as shown in Fig. 71E. (a) Write down the reaction, and (b) what is the atomic mass of the daughter product? (See Table 71A.)

6. An electron has a kinetic energy equivalent of 2 Mev. What is its velocity relative to the velocity of light, v/c? (See Eq. 65b). (*Ans.* 97.9%.)

7. An electron has a velocity of 99.5% the speed of light, ($v/c = 0.995$). Calculate its equivalent energy in Mev.

8. Calculate the absorption coefficient of aluminum for γ rays as given by the experimental graph in Fig. 71P. (*Ans.* 0.032 mm^{-1}.)

9. Calculate the absorption coefficient of lead for γ rays as given by the experimental graph in Fig. 71P.

10. Atoms of the radioactive isotope $_{90}Th^{234}$ have a mass of 234.11650, and a half-life of 24 days. Sixty-five percent of these nuclei emit β particles with an energy of 193 Kev, while 35% emit 100 Kev β particles, followed by a γ ray. Either way they become the same daughter element $_{91}Pa^{234}$. (a) Make a single energy level diagram for these changes. (b) Write down the two different reactions. (c) Find the γ ray energy in amu. (d) What is the mass of the daughter atom? (*Ans.* (c) 0.0010 amu. (b) 234.11629 amu.)

11. Atoms of the radioactive isotope $_{88}Ra^{225}$ have a mass of 225.09344 amu and a half-life of 15 days. Sixty-three percent of these nuclei emit a β particle with an energy of 280 Kev, followed by a γ ray, while 37% emit a 320 Kev β particle with no γ ray. Either way they become the same daughter element $_{89}Ac^{225}$. (a) Make a single energy level diagram for these two disintegration modes. (b) Write down the two reactions. (c) Find the γ-ray energy in amu. (d) What is the mass of the daughter atom?

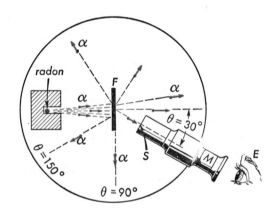

Chapter 72

Atomic Collisions and Nuclear Disintegration

The continual search of the scientists for some knowledge of the ultimate particles into which all matter may be subdivided has led within the last 60 years to the discovery of still smaller particles than molecules and atoms: protons, neutrons, mesons, neutrinos, etc. These discoveries are but the first steps toward solving the age-old mystery of why all solids, large or small, do not fall apart.

72.1. Rutherford's Scattering Experiments. As early as 1903, P. Leonard sent cathode rays through thin films of metal and measured their penetration and absorption in matter. He concluded from his experiments that the mass associated with solid matter is not distributed uniformly throughout the body, but is concentrated upon myriads of tiny isolated centers which he called *dynamids*. It was for these experiments that he was awarded the Nobel Prize in physics in 1905.

During the following decade Sir Ernest Rutherford, and his collaborators H. Geiger and E. Marsden, performed a series of ingenious experiments on the scattering of α particles, the results of which implied that the positive charge and mass of every atom is confined to a particle smaller than 10^{-12} cm in diameter. Historically this marks the beginning of the idea of a nuclear atom proposed formally by Niels Bohr several years later. A schematic diagram of the scattering experiments is given in Fig. 72A.

High-speed α particles from the radioactive element radon, confined to a narrow beam by a hole in a lead block L, were made to strike a very thin gold foil F. While most of the α particles go straight

through the foil as if there were nothing there, some of them collide with atoms of the foil and bounce off at some angle. The latter phenomenon is known as *Rutherford scattering*.

Fig. 72A *Diagram of the Rutherford scattering experiments.*

The observations and measurements made in the experiment consisted of counting the number of particles scattered off at different angles θ. This was done by the scintillation method of observation. Each α particle striking the fluorescent screen S produces a tiny flash of light, called a *scintillation,* and is observed as such by the microscope M. With the microscope fixed in one position the number of scintillations observed within a period of several minutes was counted, then the microscope was turned to another angle, and the number again counted for an equal period of time.

In the schematic diagram of Fig. 72B, α particles are shown passing through a foil

614

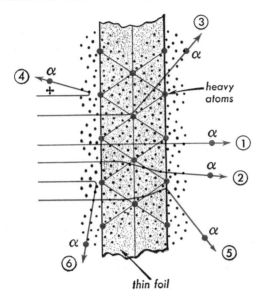

Fig. 72B *Schematic diagram of α particles being scattered by the atomic nuclei in a thin metallic film.*

three atomic layers thick. Although the nuclear atom was not known at the time the experiments were performed, each atom is drawn in the figure with the positively charged nucleus at the center and surrounded by a number of electrons. Since most of the film is *free space,* the majority of the α particles go through with little or no deflection as indicated by ray (1). Other α's like (2) passing relatively close to an atom nucleus are deflected at an angle of a few degrees. Occasionally, however, an almost *head-on collision* occurs as shown by (4) and the incoming α particle is turned back toward the source.

As an α particle approaches an atom, as represented by ray (6) in diagram (b), it is repelled by the heavy positively charged nucleus and deflected in such a way as to make it follow a curved path. The magnitude of the repulsive force is at all times given by Coulomb's law, see Eq.(47a).

$$F = k\frac{QQ'}{r^2} \qquad (72a)$$

Whatever the force of repulsion may be at one distance r, it becomes four times as great at $\frac{1}{2}$ the distance, nine times as great

at $\frac{1}{3}$ the distance, sixteen times as great at $\frac{1}{4}$ the distance, etc. We see, therefore, that at very close range the mutual repulsion of the two particles increases very rapidly and finally becomes so great that the lighter α particle is turned away. The repelling force, still acting, gives the particle a push, causing it to recede with the same velocity as that with which it approached. The actual trajectory is in every case a hyperbolic orbit with the nucleus at the focus. (See Fig. 72C.)

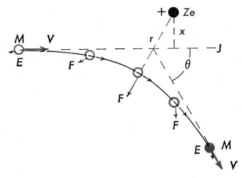

Fig. 72C *Diagram of the deflection of an α particle by a nucleus. Rutherford scattering.*

72.2. The Rutherford Scattering Experiments. To see how the principles of mechanics, and Coulomb's law, Eq.(72a), are applied to the deflection of α particles passing by an atomic nucleus, we refer to Fig. 72C. The α particle of mass M, charge E, moving with a velocity V along the line MJ would, in the absence of Coulomb's law, pass within a distance x of a relatively heavy nucleus of charge Ze. Due to the mutual repulsion of the two positive charges, the force F, given by

$$F = k\frac{Ze \cdot E}{r^2} \qquad (72b)$$

and acting on the α particle at all points, gives rise to a hyperbolic trajectory as shown.

Approaching along one asymptote, and receding along the other, the α particle is deflected through a total rangle θ.

By applying these principles to find the numbers of particles scattered at different angles Rutherford obtained the following formula:

$$N = N_0 \frac{nt(Ze)^2 E^2}{2^4 r^2 (\frac{1}{2}MV^2)^2 \sin^4 \frac{1}{2}\theta} \quad (72c)$$

N = number of α's striking the screen
n = number of atoms per unit volume
t = foil thickness
$\frac{1}{2}MV^2$ = kinetic energy of α particle
θ = angle scattered
N_0 = number of α's striking the foil

While this formula looks quite complicated, it can be separated into parts as follows:

1. foil thickness $\quad N \propto t$
2. kinetic energy $\quad N \propto 1/(\frac{1}{2}MV^2)^2$
3. scattering angle $\quad N \propto 1/\sin^4 \frac{1}{2}\theta$ $\quad (72d)$
4. nuclear charge $\quad N \propto (Ze)^2$

Repeated experiments with different films made of light and heavy elements, like copper, silver, and gold, showed that the relative number of the wide-angled deflections increases with atomic weight. From all of these results and numerous calculations, Rutherford came to the following conclusions:

1. An increase in film thickness t increases proportionately the number of target nuclei to be hit, and hence the number of particles scattered out.

2. The greater the energy or velocity of the incident particle, the smaller will be the angle through which it will be deflected.

3. A single impact can deflect a particle through a large angle and by head-on collision reverse its direction.

4. Increased deflections resulting from foils of increasing atomic number Z are the result of stronger Coulomb forces arising from increased nuclear charge Ze.

5. Deflections resulting from nuclear collisions are perfectly elastic, and obey the laws of conservation of mechanical energy and momentum.

6. That all of the positive charge of an atom is confined to a particle smaller than 10^{-12} cm in diameter.

7. That practically all of the weight of an atom is confined to this same particle.

8. That the amount of positive charge in atomic units is approximately equal to $\frac{1}{2}$ the atomic weight.

Although an α particle (mass number, 4) is light compared with an atom of a metal like gold (mass number, 197), it is 7000 times heavier than a single electron. For this reason the electrons surrounding the atomic nucleus are pushed to either side as the α particle goes speeding through, and they have little effect upon the shape of the trajectory.

A graph representing the force of repulsion between an α particle and a positively charged nucleus is illustrated in Fig. 72D.

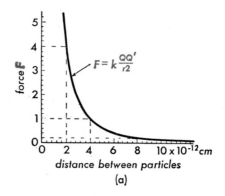

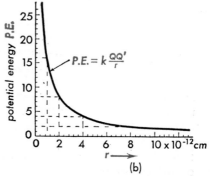

Fig. 72D *Graphs representing the repulsion between a positively charged nucleus and an α particle. (a) Coulomb's law giving the repelling force F, and (b) the potential curve giving the energy.*

Diagram (a) shows the rapid increase in force as the distance decreases, while diagram (b) shows the rapid rise in potential energy. The potential energy between electric charges is analogous to the potential energy of points in the gravitational field of a mass. (See Sec. 18.6.) In gravitation fields, magnetic fields, and electric fields, the force per unit mass, pole strength, and charge, respectively, is inversely proportional to the square of the distance r, whereas the respective potential energies are inversely proportional to the distance. For the potential energy of a charge Q' in an electric field, we have

$$\text{potential energy P.E.} = k\frac{QQ'}{r} \quad (72e)$$

The reason for giving this equation, and the potential energy curve in Fig. 72C, is that an interesting mechanical model for demonstrating Rutherford scattering can be derived from it. Such a model is illustrated in Fig. 72E, where the circular peak at the right represents the nucleus of an atom and has a form generated by rotating curve (b) of Fig. 72D, about its vertical axis at $r = 0$.

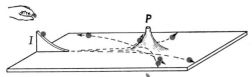

Fig. 72E *Mechanical model of an atomic nucleus for demonstrating Rutherford scattering.*

Marbles, representing α particles, roll down a chute and along a practically level plane where they approach the potential hill. Approaching the hill at various angles, the marbles roll up to a certain height and then off to one side or the other. The paths they follow, if watched from above, are *hyperbolic* in shape. Approaching the hill in a head-on collision, the ball rolls up to a certain point, stops, then rolls back again.

Thus the potential energy of the α particle close to the nucleus is analogous to the potential energy of a marble on the hillside, and the electrostatic force of repulsion is analogous to the component of the downward pull of gravity.

72.3. Elastic Collisions Between Atoms. Collisions between free atomic particles were first studied by Rutherford with apparatus as shown in Fig. 72F. A long glass tube, containing a small sample of radioactive material R, was first thoroughly evacuated by means of a vacuum pump and then filled with a gas of known constitution. Alpha particles from the radioactive source were then permitted to travel through the gas to the other end of the tube where, upon passing through a thin aluminum foil to a fluorescent screen S, they could be observed as scintillations in the field of view of a microscope M. This is exactly the arrangement used by Rutherford in measuring the range of α particles from different radioactive elements (see Fig. 69K).

With air in the tube T and *radium C'* as a source of α particles, scintillations could be observed with the screen as far back as 7 cm. With hydrogen in the tube it was found that the distance d could be greatly increased. Inserting thicker and thicker aluminum foils between F and S in front of the fluorescent screen, the range of the particles was calculated to be equivalent to 28 cm of air. The conclusion Rutherford drew from this result was that an α particle occasionally collides with a hydrogen atom, much the same as a large ball collides with a lighter one, imparting to it a greater velocity and hence a greater penetrating

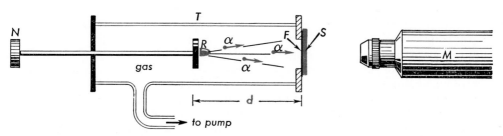

Fig. 72F *Rutherford's apparatus used in observing atomic collisions between α particles from radium and the atoms of a gas like hydrogen, helium, nitrogen, oxygen, etc.*

(a)   (b)   (c)

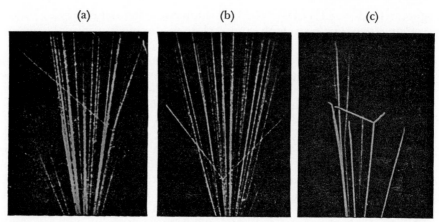

Fig. 72G *Wilson cloud chamber photographs of collisions between α particles and*
(a) an hydrogen atom, (b) a helium atom, and (c) an oxygen atom. (After Rutherford,
Chadwick, and Ellis.)

power. Of the many recoil hydrogen atoms from collisions with α particles, some of them undergo "head-on" collisions and go shooting off in a forward direction with over half again (more accurately 1.6 times) the speed of the incident α particle.

The enormous increase in range is due principally to a higher velocity. Each hydrogen nucleus, called a *proton*, is stripped of its orbital electron, and, with but a single positive charge, produces fewer ions per centimeter path than an α particle with its double positive charge. Curiously enought, protons or α particles having the same velocity would have about the same range. The reason for this is that, whereas an α particle has double the charge of a proton and produces more ions per centimeter of its path, which tends to slow it down more rapidly, it also has four times the mass and therefore four times the energy. The range curves in Fig. 70G show that for *protons* and α *particles* with the same kinetic energy, the protons have about ten times the greater range.

A more convincing study of such atomic collisions can be made with a Wilson cloud chamber. Out of thousands of cloud chamber photographs of the ion tracks made by α particles from radioactive elements, one occasionally observes forked tracks of the type reproduced in Fig. 72G. When each of these pictures was taken, the cloud

chamber contained different gases. For photograph (a) the cloud chamber contained hydrogen, for (b) it contained helium, and for (c) it contained oxygen. Schematic diagrams of these same collisions are illustrated in Fig. 72H. Note in (b) that the angle be-

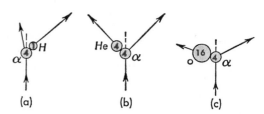

Fig. 72H *Diagrams of collisions between α particles and other nuclei of different mass.*

tween the two recoiling particles is 90°, a right angle.

Most elastic collisions between atoms are not "head-on" collisions, but ones in which the incident particle strikes the other a glancing blow. When an α particle having a mass of 4 units collides with a hydrogen atom of 1 unit, the α particle is deviated only a little from its path, whereas the hydrogen atom nearly always recoils off at quite a large angle. This is in agreement with the laws of conservation of energy and momentum applied to two perfectly elastic spheres.

When an α particle collides with a helium

atom, both particles have the same mass of 4 units each, and the two always glance off at right angles to each other. The laws of mechanics show that for a "head-on" collision between perfectly elastic spheres of equal mass, one moving and one at rest, the incident particle is stopped by the collision and the second body goes on in the forward direction with all of the velocity.

When an α particle collides with an oxygen atom having a mass of 16 units, the oxygen atom recoils to one side with a relatively low velocity, and the α particle glances off to the other side with a high or low velocity depending upon the angle of recoil. The oxygen atom with its greater mass and charge ionizes more particles per centimeter path and therefore leaves a heavier track.

It should be pointed out that atomic collisions involving such high velocities take place between the heavy nuclei of the atoms and are little affected by the light orbital electrons. If a nucleus is hit hard by a collision, it will be partially or wholly denuded of its electrons. When it comes to rest, it will soon pick up enough electrons to make it a neutral atom again.

72.4. The Discovery of Nuclear Disintegration. Upon repeating the range experiments illustrated in Fig. 72F, with a heavy gas in the tube T, Rutherford made a new and startling discovery in 1919. When nitrogen gas (atomic weight, 14) was admitted to the tube, scintillations could be observed at a distance of 40 cm or more from the source. No such long-range particles had ever been observed before. What were these long-range particles? They could not be electrons or γ rays, for these are not capable of producing visible scintillations. Rutherford allowed the new rays to pass through a magnetic field and discovered from their deflection that they had the mass and charge of protons. In other words, the long-range particles were hydrogen nuclei.

Rutherford was not long in coming forward with the correct explanation of the phenomenon. An α particle, near the beginning of its range where its velocity is high, may make a "head-on" collision with a nitrogen nucleus and be captured. This capture is then followed immediately by a disintegration in which a proton is ejected with high speed. The process is illustrated in Fig. 72I, and the transformation can be

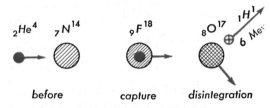

before   capture   disintegration

Fig. 72I   *The disintegration of a nitrogen nucleus by a high-speed α particle.*

represented by the following simple reaction.

$$_2He^4 + {_7}N^{14} = (_9F^{18}) = {_8}O^{17} + {_1}H^1 \qquad (72f)$$

When the α particle, with a charge of $+2$ and mass 4, collides with the nitrogen nucleus with a charge of $+7$ and mass 14, they form a single particle with a charge of $+9$ and mass 18. Since an atom with a nuclear charge of $+9$ would be expected to have all the chemical properties of *fluorine,* atomic number 9, the newly formed nucleus is labeled $_9F^{18}$.

An examination of the table of isotopes, however (see Appendix VI), shows that no such isotope exists in nature. The reason becomes apparent when it is realized that such a combination of particles is not stable. A fluorine nucleus of mass 18 is unstable and disintegrates by discharging a proton, a particle with a charge of $+1$ and a mass of 1. This leaves behind a residual nucleus with a charge of $+8$, and a mass of 17. Under atomic number 8 in the same Table VI, an oxygen isotope of mass 17 is seen to have been found in nature.

Thus the above disintegration process started with two stable nuclei, *helium* and *nitrogen,* and out of them were created two new stable nuclei, *oxygen* and *hydrogen.* This is called a *transmutation* of elements. Because the intermediate step indicates but a momentary existence of a fluorine nucleus, $_9F^{18}$, this step is often omitted from

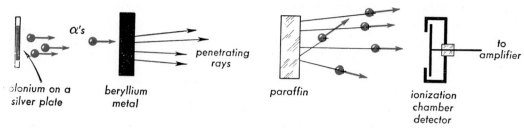

Fig. 72J *The experiment by which Chadwick discovered the neutron. The penetrating
rays are neutrons and α particles.*

any discussion of the above process and the disintegration reaction simply written

$$_2He^4 + {_7}N^{14} = {_8}O^{17} + {_1}H^1$$

Such transformation reactions are like equations and must balance: first, the total amount of charge must remain the same, and second, the mass numbers must balance. The first of these is accomplished by having the sum of the subscripts on one side of the reaction equal to the sum of the subscripts on the other side, and the second by having the sum of the superscripts the same on both sides. In every known atom the subscript, representing the nuclear charge, is the sole factor determining the chemical element to which the atom belongs.

72.5. Chadwick's Identification of the Neutron.

In 1932 Chadwick, in England, performed an experiment for which he was later awarded the Nobel Prize in physics in 1935. As diagramed in Fig. 72J his experiment consisted of bombarding a beryllium target with α particles. Penetrating particles emerging from the beryllium were permitted to impinge upon a block of paraffin from which protons were found to emerge with high speed. From energy calculations he was able to show that the penetrating rays were uncharged particles with the mass of protons; these he called *neutrons*. The disintegration taking place in the metal target is the following (see Fig. 72K):

$$_2He^4 + {_4}Be^9 = {_6}C^{12} + {_0}n^1 \qquad (72g)$$

The α particle, $_2He^4$, makes a collision and unites with a beryllium nucleus, $_4Be^9$, causing a disintegration; whereupon a neutron, $_0n^1$, is expelled with high velocity. The residual particle with a charge of +6 and

mass of 12 units is a stable carbon nucleus such as found in nature.

The penetrating rays from the beryllium block in Fig. 72J are mostly neutrons which, in bombarding the paraffin block, collide

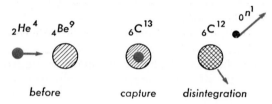

Fig. 72K *The neutron process discovered by Chadwick. See Fig. 72J.*

elastically with hydrogen atoms, knocking them out on the other side. An elastic "head-on" collision between two particles of the same weight, like a neutron and proton, finds the entire velocity of one transferred to the other; the neutron is stopped and the proton goes on. The protons, having a positive charge, can be observed by their tracks in a Wilson cloud chamber, whereas neutrons cannot.

The reason fast neutrons have such a high penetrating power is that they are not slowed down by ionizing atoms as they pass close by them. A proton, electron, or α particle has a charge and can ionize atoms by attracting or repelling electrons from a distance, but a neutron without a charge cannot do this. It must make a direct collision with another particle to be slowed down or stopped.

Neutrons can now be produced in such intense beams that they are often used in place of X rays wherever radiations of high penetrating power are desired.

72.6. The Nucleus Contains Neutrons and Protons.

Since the time of Chadwick's identification of the neutron as an elementary particle, our ideas concerning the nucleus of the atom have had to be modified. We now believe that the nucleus contains but two kinds of particles, neutrons and protons. Each neutron has a mass of one unit and no charge, whereas each proton has a mass of one unit and a positive charge of one unit. This differs from the older idea that the nucleus contains protons equal in number to the atomic weight and enough electrons to neutralize the surplus charge in excess of the amount specified by the atomic number.

TABLE 72A. SHOWING THE NUMBER OF NEUTRONS AND PROTONS IN THE NUCLEI OF A FEW ELEMENTS

Atom	Protons	Neutrons
$_1H^1$	1	0
$_1H^2$	1	1
$_2He^4$	2	2
$_3Li^6$	3	3
$_3Li^7$	3	4
$_4Be^9$	4	5
$_4Be^{10}$	4	6
$_5B^{11}$	5	6
$_7N^{13}$	7	6
$_8O^{16}$	8	8
$_{11}Na^{23}$	11	12
$_{29}Cu^{65}$	29	36
$_{80}Hg^{200}$	80	120
$_{92}U^{238}$	92	146

Since only the proton has a charge, any given nucleus of atomic number Z and mass number M is now believed to have Z protons and $M-Z$ neutrons, and in a neutral atom the number of protons believed to be equal to the number of orbital electrons. The nuclear particles of a few of the elements of the periodic table are given in Table 72A, as examples.

Schematic diagrams of the nucleus of five different atoms are given in Fig. 72L.

72.7. Atomic Masses Are Not Whole Numbers.

When an α particle collides with the nucleus of an atom and produces a disintegration as shown in Fig. 72I, the

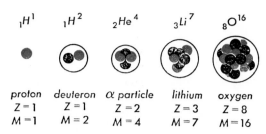

$_1H^1$	$_1H^2$	$_2He^4$	$_3Li^7$	$_8O^{16}$
proton	deuteron	α particle	lithium	oxygen
$Z=1$	$Z=1$	$Z=2$	$Z=3$	$Z=8$
$M=1$	$M=2$	$M=4$	$M=7$	$M=16$

Fig. 72L *Diagrams showing the number of protons and neutrons in the nuclei of hydrogen, deuterium, helium, lithium, and oxygen.*

total energy before collision must be equal to the total energy after collision. To verify this, all forms of energy involved in the process must be included: (1) *the kinetic energy of all particles,* (2) *the energy of a γ ray if one is involved,* and (3) *the mass-energy.* The latter is necessary since disintegration experiments show that the total mass of the two colliding particles is not in general equal to the total mass after disintegration. To test this change, it is necessary that we know the exact masses of all atoms individually.

Recent mass spectographic measurements by Aston, Bainbridge, and others (see Chap. 58) show that the masses of atoms are not exactly whole number values as previously suspected and given in Appendix VI. A list of the most recent mass determinations of some of the lighter elements of the periodic table is given in Appendix VII. These values are all based upon the oxygen isotope 16 as having a mass of exactly 16.0000.

72.8. Conservation of Energy in Nuclear Disintegrations.

To illustrate the law of conservation of energy as it applies to nuclear disintegrations, consider Rutherford's first experiment, shown in Figs. 72F and 72I, where α particles from *radium C'* passing through nitrogen gas make collisions with, and disintegrate, nitrogen nuclei. The total energy of any two particles before impact will be the sum of the masses of the two nuclei, $_2He^4 + _7N^{14}$, plus their kinetic energy E_1. The total energy after impact will be the sum of the masses of the two nuclei, $_8O^{17}$ and $_1H^1$, plus their kinetic energy E_2. If we insert accurately known masses, the reaction becomes

$$_2\text{He}^{4.00387} + _7\text{N}^{14.00751} + E_1 =$$
$$_8\text{O}^{17.00453} + _1\text{H}^{1.00814} + E_2 \quad (72h)$$

It is customary to express the energies E_1 and E_2 in *mass units* or in million electron volts, Mev. Now the kinetic energy before impact is confined to the α particle from radium C', which has been measured and found to be equivalent to 7.7 Mev. Dividing this value by 931, from Eq.(70k), gives the equivalent of 0.00827 mass unit. Adding mass-energy for both sides of Eq.(72g), we must obtain the same total.

$$
\begin{array}{llll}
_2\text{He}^4 = & 4.00387 & _8\text{O}^{17} = & 17.00453 \\
_7\text{N}^{14} = & 14.00751 & _1\text{H}^1 = & 1.00814 \quad (72i) \\
E_1 = & \underline{0.00827} & E_2 = & \underline{\quad ? \quad} \\
\text{Total} & 18.01965 & & 18.01965
\end{array}
$$

Simple addition and subtraction show that, to give the proper sum for the right-hand column, E_2 must be equal to 0.00698 mass unit. Multiplying by 931 gives, this time, 6.50 Mev as the energy liberated. This is the liberated energy utilized in the "explosion" which drives the proton and oxygen nuclei apart.

In general, when an atomic nucleus disintegrates by splitting up into two particles, the annihilation energy is divided between them. Experiments show that this division takes place according to the ordinary laws of mechanics, that *the kinetic energies of the two particles are approximately inversely proportional to their respective masses.*

When, in the above example, the avail-able energy is divided between an oxygen nucleus of mass 17 and a proton of mass 1, the $_8\text{O}^{17}$ nucleus acquires an energy of 0.36 Mev, and the proton an energy of 6.18 Mev. A proton with this kinetic energy and velocity has a range of 49 cm in air. Recent repetitions of Rutherford's experiment give measured ranges of 48 cm and an energy of 6 Mev, in good agreement with the calculation.

Graphs showing the ranges of protons, deuterons, and α particles for different energies are drawn in Fig. 70G.

72.9. The Cockcroft-Walton Experiment. Believing that the disintegration of atomic nuclei might be accomplished by using other than α particles as projectiles, Rutherford instigated in 1930 the construction of a high-voltage, direct-current generator at the Cavendish laboratory. The purpose of this *million-volt* source of potential was to accelerate hydrogen nuclei, *protons,* to high speeds and then cause them to strike known substances. In this way he hoped to produce new and various kinds of disintegrations.

Becoming impatient with the relatively slow progress of the project, however, Rutherford suggested to Cockcroft and Walton that lower voltages be tried in the meantime to see if, by chance, disintegrations might occur. In 1932 Cockcroft and Walton announced that they had successfully disintegrated lithium atoms with protons accelerated by relatively low voltages. Their apparatus is schematically represented in Fig. 72M.

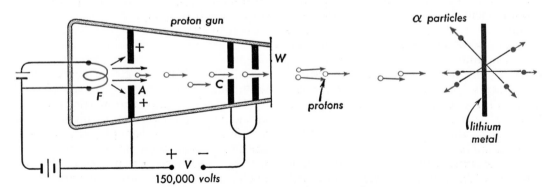

Fig. 72M *Schematic diagram of the Cockcroft-Walton experiment. Lithium is disintegrated by 150,000-volt protons.*

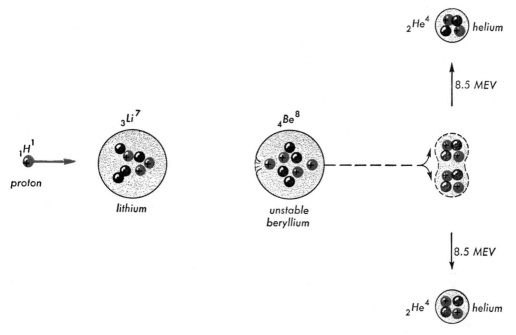

Fig. 72N *Disintegration of a lithium nucleus by a proton of 0.15 Mev energy. The Cockcroft-Walton experiment.*

Electrons from a hot filament F, passing through hydrogen gas in the region of A, ionize many hydrogen atoms. These protons with their positive charge are then accelerated toward the other end of the tube by a potential V of 150,000 volts. Upon passing through the opening C and a window W, they emerge from the acceleration chamber as a narrow beam of protons.

This tube, acting as a "proton gun," is aimed at a target consisting of lithium metal. Cockcroft and Walton observed and measured α particles emanating from the metal with a range of 8 cm, an energy equivalent to 8.5 Mev. Considering the relatively low energy of the bombarding protons of only 0.15 Mev, this is a tremendous release in atomic energy. The transmutation taking place here is written as follows:

$$_1H^1 + {_3}Li^7 + E_1 = {_2}He^4 + {_2}He^4 + E_2 \quad (72j)$$

This reaction, illustrated in Fig. 72N, shows a proton, $_1H^1$, of energy $E_1 = 0.15$ Mev, entering a lithium nucleus, $_3Li^7$, to form a new but unstable beryllium nu-

cleus, $_4Be^8$. Being unstable, this compact structure of eight particles splits up into two α particles which are driven apart with great violence. Since the measured energy of each α particle is equivalent to 8.5 Mev, each disintegration involves the liberation of 17.0 Mev energy. The source of energy is to be found in the annihilation of a part of the total atomic mass.

The loss in mass can be calculated from the table of atomic weights, given in Appendix VII. List the involved masses in two columns and add.

$_1H^1 = 1.00814$	
$_3Li^7 = 7.01822$	$_2He^4 = 4.00387$
$E_1 = \underline{0.00016}$	$_2He^4 = \underline{4.00387}$
8.02652	8.00774

E_1 is the mass equivalent to the energy of the incident proton and is obtained by dividing 0.15 Mev by 931 (see Eq.(70j)). The difference between the two sums, $8.02652 - 8.00774 = 0.01878$ mass unit, represents the loss in mass by the disintegration. When multiplied by 931, this gives 17.48 Mev as the liberated energy, a value in good agreement with the experimentally determined value of 17.0 Mev.

It might be thought that such a disintegration as the one described above could be used as a source of energy, but as yet it has not been feasible to do so. While each nuclear collision and disintegration liberates at least one hundred times as much energy as that supplied to the proton, it takes many particles to make a few collisions. In other words, only a small percentage of the proton bullets hit the tiny nuclear targets as they pass through matter. Most of them are slowed down by electron collisions and the ionization of atoms. To a proton bullet the lithium nuclei, as targets in the lithium metal, present an area millions of times smaller than the space between them.

QUESTIONS AND PROBLEMS

1. If, in Rutherford's scattering experiments, the number of α particles observed at an angle $\theta = 60°$ is 20 per minute, how many per minute should be observed at 30° and 150°?

2. When the scintillation microscope used in a Rutherford scattering experiment is set at an angle, $\theta = 30°$, the number of α particles observed is 3000 per hour. How many per hour should be observed at 60° and at 150°? (*Ans.* 216, and 16.)

3. If, in Rutherford's experiments, scintillations are observed at an angle of 30° for an aluminum foil, 250 α particles are counted in 1 min. How many counts per minute would be observed if the aluminum foil were replaced by foils of equal thickness made of (a) copper, (b) silver, and (c) gold?

4. Complete the following disintegration reactions:

$_1H^2 + _8O^{16} \rightarrow + _2He^4$ $_1H^2 + _5B^{10} \rightarrow + _0n^1$

$_2He^4 + _{13}Al^{27} \rightarrow + _1H^1$ $_1H^1 + _3Li^6 \rightarrow + _2He^3$

(*Ans.* $_7N^{14}$, $_{14}Si^{30}$, $_6C^{11}$, $_2He^4$.)

5. From the known masses of the atoms in the reactions of Prob. 4, find the energy liberated by each disintegration in Mev. Assume the incident energy of the lighter nucleus in each reaction to be 20 Mev.

6. From the graphs plotted in Fig. 70G, write down the ranges of the following particles: (a) 10 Mev protons, (b) 13 Mev protons, (c) 12 Mev α particles, (d) 10 Mev deuterons, and (e) 8 Mev α particles. (*Ans.* (a) 116 cm, (b) 182 cm, (c) 14.1 cm, (d) 67 cm, (e) 7.3 cm.)

7. If the following mass is annihilated, and 90% of its goes into kinetic energy of an α particle, find the range of the particle in air at normal atmospheric pressure: (a) 0.0123 amu, and (b) 0.0039 amu.

8. Briefly explain the experiment by which Chadwick discovered the neutron. Make a diagram.

9. Give a brief description of the Rutherford experiment in which the first nuclear disintegrations were discovered.

10. Make a table of the following atoms giving the number of protons and neutrons in each nucleus: Ba^{138}, Ca^{44}, Fe^{56}, I^{127}, and Au^{197}.

11. The range of protons in air is found to have the following values: (a) 5 cm, (b) 12 cm, (c) 75 cm, and (d) 200 cm. Find their energies in Mev.

12. Deuterons from a radioactive source are found to have three definite ranges: (a) 10 cm, (b) 75 cm, and (c) 115 cm. Determine their energies from Fig. 70G. (*Ans.* (a) 3.4 Mev, (b) 10.7 Mev, (c) 13.5 Mev.)

13. Alpha particles from a radioactive material are found to have three ranges: (a) 2.5 cm, (b) 7.2 cm, and (c) 17.0 cm. Find their energies using Fig. 70G.

14. In a nuclear disintegration process, a mass of 0.00820 amu is annihilated and 95% of the liberated energy is imparted as kinetic energy to an alpha particle. Find (a) its energy in Mev, and (b) its range. (*Ans.* (a) 7.23 Mev, (b) 6.2 cm.)

Chapter 73

Cosmic Rays

73.1. Early Experiments. It has long been known that a charged electroscope, if left standing for some little time, will discharge regardless of how well the gold leaf is insulated. Realizing that the rays from radioactive materials can be stopped by a sufficient thickness of heavy matter, Rutherford and Cooke (in Canada, 1903) surrounded an electroscope with a thick wall of brick and found very little decrease in the rate of discharge. McLennan and his co-workers (also in Canada) lowered an electroscope into a lake, hoping that the thick layer of water would screen off the rays. This experiment, like the other, failed. In 1910 Glockel, with an electroscope, rose nearly 3 mi in a balloon in order to get away from the ground radiation, but to his astonishment he found that the rate of discharge did not decrease, but increased, the higher he went. The same effect was observed by Hess (in Austria, 1911) and Kolhörster (in Germany, 1914). Rising to heights as great as $5\frac{1}{2}$ mi, both of these observers independently found that the intensity of these unknown radiations became greater the higher they went. Because in one of his scientific publications concerning these results Hess suggested the possibility that some kind of penetrating rays were entering the earth's atmosphere from outer space, he is usually credited with the discovery of cosmic rays. For this reason he was granted the Nobel Prize in physics for the year 1936.

73.2. Millikan and Bowen's Discovery. Soon after World War I (1922), R. A. Millikan, with the help of I. S. Bowen, constructed several small, self-recording string electroscopes. Making use of their war time experiences with sounding balloons, they sent these electroscopes high into the strato-

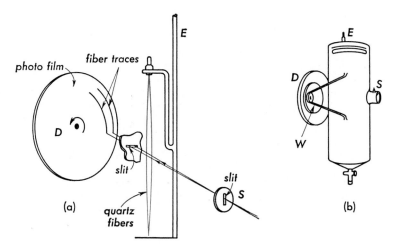

Fig. 73A *Diagrams of one of the sensitive electroscopes sent up into the stratosphere by Millikan and Bowen to measure cosmic rays. (a) Schematic diagram, (b) scale drawing of entire instrument 6 in. high.*

sphere by fastening each one to two sounding balloons. As shown in Fig. 73A, the string electroscope *E* consists of two gold-covered quartz fibers insulated and mounted with their ends together. When they are charged, the fibers spread apart due to mutual repulsion, and as they discharge they slowly come together.

Daylight, passing through a narrow vertical slit *S* in the instrument case, casts a shadow of the center section of the fibers on a rotating disk *D* which contains a photographic film. As the film turns slowly and the fibers come together, they leave a double trace, as indicated in the diagram. On the same film, a small oil manometer recorded the height of ascent and a small thermometer recorded the temperature. The film was driven by a watch *W*, the whole apparatus weighing only 7 oz. On one of the best record flights, only one of the balloons burst at a height of 10 mi and the other brought the instruments safely to earth. Like the earlier results obtained by other experimenters, Millikan and Bowen found the ionization to increase with increasing altitude. After extending the observations of previous workers to higher altitudes, Millikan and Bowen became convinced, and announced their belief, that the rays were coming from interstellar space.

73.3. The Penetration of Cosmic Rays. In order to determine the nature of the new rays, Millikan and his co-workers, Otis, Cameron, and Bowen, in the fall of 1922, began an extensive study of the penetrating power of cosmic rays. Since cosmic rays penetrate our atmosphere of many miles of air, how far might they penetrate beyond?

Self-recording electroscopes were lowered to various depths in snow-fed lakes as illustrated schematically in Fig. 73B. Measurements taken at Arrowhead Lake in Southern California (at an elevation of 5100 ft) agreed approximately with those taken at Muir Lake near Mt. Whitney (at an elevation of 11,800 ft), provided one took into account the increased air path for the lower elevation. The extra mile and a quarter of air is equivalent in weight to 6 ft of water. As cosmic rays penetrate deeper and deeper below the surface of water, their number decreases, until at a depth of 100 ft the intensity is reduced to about one-ten-thousandth of that at the surface. With very sensitive electroscopes, cosmic radiation ca-

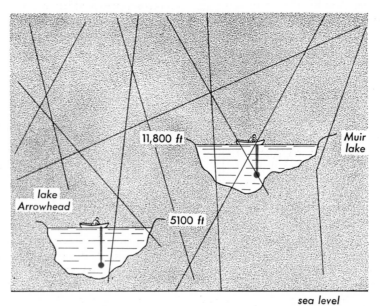

Fig. 73B   *Illustrating the lowering of self-recording electroscropes into deep, snow-fed lakes to measure the absorption of cosmic rays by the water.*

pable of penetrating 2000 ft of water has more recently been detected. This is a far greater penetrating power than that possessed by any known X rays or γ rays from radioactivity.

73.4. The Geiger-Mueller Tube Counter.

There are at least eight methods of observing and measuring cosmic rays. These are (a) *Geiger-Mueller tube counters,* (b) *Wilson cloud chambers,* (c) *ionization chambers,* (d) *photographic emulsions,* (e) *scintillation counters,* (f) *bubble chambers,* (g) *electroscopes, and* (h) *semiconductors.*

The Geiger-Mueller tube, named after its inventors, is one of the simplest electrical instruments ever designed (see Fig. 73C).

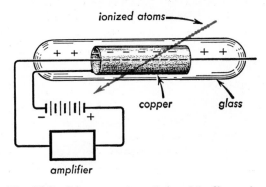

Fig. 73C *Diagram of a Geiger-Mueller tube.*

It consists of an open-ended copper cylinder from 1 to 25 in. long, fitted inside a thin-walled glass cylinder with a fine tungsten wire stretched along the middle. After the tube has been partially evacuated (a pressure of from 5 to 10 cm of mercury is convenient), a potential of about 1000 volts is applied, the positive to the center wire and the negative to the cylinder.

When a single cosmic ray or high-speed particle from a radioactive source goes through a Geiger-Mueller tube, ions are created by the freeing of electrons from air molecules. These freed electrons are attracted by the positively charged wire and move toward it, acquiring within a very short distance a high velocity of their own. Because of this velocity they, too, can ionize other atoms, thus freeing more electrons. This multiplication of charges re-

peats itself in rapid succession, producing within a very short interval of time an *avalanche of electrons toward the central wire.* This sudden surge of charge is equivalent to the flow of a small current impulse along the electrical circuit. When this current has been intensified by an amplifier, it may be made to operate an electric switch, a radio loud-speaker, or any kind of electrical device.

Quite frequently, the impulses of a Geiger-Mueller tube are made to operate a small counting device. Each cosmic ray particle passing through the tube is therefore counted automatically. The number of counts received per second depends upon the size of the counter tube. An average-sized tube 1 in. in diameter and several inches long, at sea level, gives from 50 to 100 counts per minute.

A common form of Geiger counter is shown in Fig. 73D. It consists of a G-M

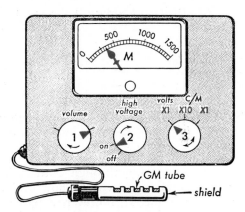

Fig. 73D *Geiger counter instrument complete with G-M tube and counting-rate meter.*

counter tube about 10 cm long connected to a box containing vacuum tube circuits, a small loud-speaker, and a counting-rate meter M.

Dial (1) operates the speaker and permits the individual ray pulses to be heard. Dial (2) turns on the vacuum tubes as in any radio or TV receiver, and turning it clockwise increases the voltage supplied to the G-M tube. Dial (3) has three position points to which it can be turned. The position marked volts connects the meter M so that it shows the voltage on the G-M tube. When in the X 1 position, under C/M, the meter M directly reads counts per minute, and in the X 10 position the meter reading should be multiplied by 10.

73.5. Directional Effects. To observe the direction of the greatest cosmic ray intensity, a cosmic ray telescope is used. Such a telescope is made by connecting two or more Geiger-Mueller tubes *in coincidence,* and mounting them on a common support some distance apart. Tubes in coincidence are so connected electrically that a current will flow in the accompanying electric circuit only when both tubes discharge at the same time. When one tube is set above the other, as shown in Fig. 73E (a), a single

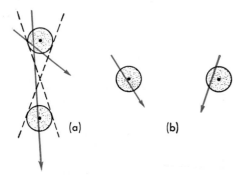

Fig. 73E *Diagram of two Geiger counters. Connected in coincidence, they form a cosmic-ray telescope.*

cosmic ray, on going through both cylinders, will cause a current to flow and a count to be made. If, however, a particle goes through one and not the other, no count is recorded. Experiments at sea level show that, when the telescope is mounted in the horizontal position (b), few counts are made, whereas when it is mounted in a vertical direction many more counts are recorded. The interpretation to be made, therefore, is that cosmic rays come principally from overhead.

As a verification of the telescope method, a Wilson cloud chamber is frequently inserted between two Geiger counter tubes as shown in Fig. 73F, and a photograph of each cosmic ray is taken. Thousands of such photographs are made automatically by

Fig. 73F *With a Wilson cloud chamber mounted between two Geiger tubes connected in coincidence, the cosmic rays are made to take their own picture. (After Brode.)*

having a single cosmic ray take its own picture. This is accomplished by allowing the sudden electric current from the counter tubes, produced by a ray in transit, to open and close a camera shutter, to cause the cloud chamber to expand, and to flash a light, illuminating the fog track that forms.

In the reproduction of Fig. 73F, either one of the two cosmic rays would have tripped the electrical devices and taken the picture. It should be noted that both rays passed right through a 0.5-in. lead plate

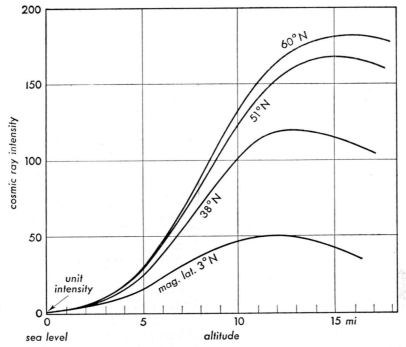

Fig. 73G *The intensity of cosmic rays increases with altitude up to a height of 10 to 15 mi, and then decreases.*

without being deviated. Cloud chamber pictures are not photographs of cosmic rays, but of the path traversed by the rays.

73.6. The Altitude Effect. The results of airplane and balloon flights into the stratosphere have shown that the intensity of cosmic rays increases up to a height of from 12 to 15 mi, and then decreases again. In 1935 Stevens and Anderson,* for example, rose to a height of nearly 14 mi carrying with them, among other scientific instruments, Geiger-Mueller tube counters. With these instruments they measured the cosmic-ray intensity at various altitudes on both their ascent and descent.

The compiled experimental results of various observers taken at different elevations are illustrated by the curves in Fig. 73G. Near the city of Omaha, at a latitude of 51°N, the maximum is found at a height of 15 mi where an intensity 170 times as great as that at sea level has been measured.

* Capt. A. W. Stevens and O. A. Anderson, *National Geographic Magazine*, Vol. LXIX, 1936, p. 693.

From that altitude to the highest points that observations have been made, about 17 mi, there is a gradual decrease in total intensity.

The four different curves in the figure show, from altitude measurements made by observers all over the world, that in nearing the magnetic equator the cosmic-ray intensity decreases at high altitudes, as well as at sea level.

73.7. Primaries and Secondaries. Experimental observations show that the cosmic rays entering our atmosphere are almost entirely composed of positively charged atomic nuclei. About two-thirds of these so-called *primary cosmic rays* are protons, and the other third (by mass) are about 90% α particles and 10% heavier nuclei like carbon, nitrogen, oxygen, iron, etc.

Upon entering the atmosphere, a high-energy primary particle soon collides with another atomic nucleus, splitting one or both particles into a number of smaller nuclear fragments, each one of which carries away some of the primary's energy.

These high-speed particles in turn collide with other nuclei, further dividing their energy to produce other high-speed particles. All of these rays, with the exception of the primary particle, are called *secondary cosmic rays.*

One of the results of cosmic-ray collision processes is the creation of very high-frequency and highly penetrating gamma rays. These photons, too, are included in the classification, *Secondary Cosmic Rays.*

At a height of some 15 mi, about ten to fifteen times as many secondary cosmic rays exist as have entered the atmosphere as primaries. At this level, where more than $\frac{9}{10}$ of the earth's atmosphere still lies below, as many rays are observed moving in a horizontal direction as in the vertical. From the diagram presented in Fig. 73H it be-

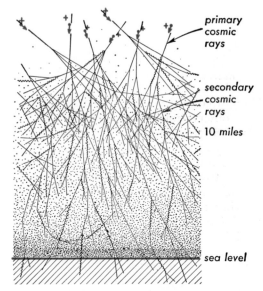

Fig. 73H *Schematic illustration of secondary cosmic rays produced from primaries entering the earth's atmosphere.*

comes quite clear why the primaries are difficult to distinguish from the far greater number of secondaries.

At lower altitudes the total intensity decreases, since many of the secondaries produced above are stopped by collision. In other words, so much energy is lost by successive collisions that the energy is gradu-

ally absorbed as heat motion by the air molecules. By the time sea level is reached, the remaining rays consist principally of a few high-speed secondaries and primaries. Even at sea level, some of these rays have enough energy left to penetrate several hundred, and even several thousand feet of earth and water.

It should be borne in mind that, between collisions of the type indicated in Fig. 73H, each cosmic-ray particle is continually being slowed down as it "plows through" thousands of air molecules, knocking electrons free to produce ions. These are the ions on which fogdrops form, revealing the path in a cloud chamber.

Although γ rays also lose energy by collisions with atoms to produce Compton electrons, the γ rays themselves do not leave visible tracks in a Wilson cloud chamber. The reason for this is that collisions are few and far between, and the resulting fogdrops are too far apart.

73.8. The Latitude Effect. By the year 1930, studies of cosmic-ray intensities by Millikan indicated that the number of cosmic rays arriving at the earth's surface was constant at all latitudes. This led him to the conclusion that the primary cosmic radiation entering the atmosphere must be γ rays of very high energy. He reasoned that, if they were charged atomic particles, they would be deflected by the earth's magnetic field, and fewer would reach the earth near the magnetic equator.

In 1931 the Dutch physicist, Clay, sailing from Amsterdam in the northern hemi-

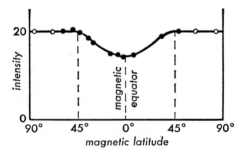

Fig. 73I *Graph of the cosmic-ray intensity at various latitudes of the earth's surface.*

sphere to Batavia, Dutch Guiana, in the southern hemisphere, carried Geiger counters with him aboard ship. Measuring the cosmic-ray intensity daily enroute, he obtained the results shown by the graph in Fig. 73I. The curve shows that as one proceeds from magnetic north to magnetic south, at sea level, the cosmic-ray intensity remains quite constant, until a magnetic latitude of about 42° is reached. In this region the intensity begins to drop appreciably, reaches a minimum at the equator, and rises again to symmetrical intensities in the southern hemisphere.

73.9. Effect of the Earth's Magnetic Field. The decrease in cosmic-ray intensity at the earth's magnetic equator (see Fig. 73I) is now explained as being due to the

Because of these forces, many charged particles from the sun and outer space are trapped by the field in two belts. The recent discovery of these belts by Van Allen and his colleagues at State University of Iowa was made from instruments carried into space by American earth-circling satellites. These belts surround the earth, except at the regions of the magnetic poles, the outer one being caused largely by the slower particles, protons and electrons, from the sun. The inner Van Allen belt is formed by more energetic particles from outer space, and is centered about 2500 mi above the magnetic equator.

If the primary energy is very large, little deflection will occur, and particles like *a* and *b* will reach our atmosphere and per-

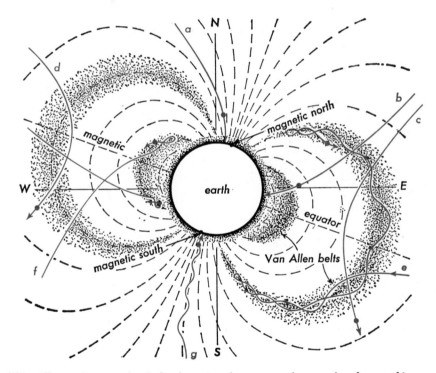

Fig. 73J *Illustration of the behavior of primary cosmic rays in the earth's magnetic field. The shaded arches are the Van Allen belts.*

earth's magnetic field. This is illustrated in Fig. 73J. The paths of all charged particles crossing the earth's magnetic field are bent by a force that is perpendicular to the direction of the field.

haps the ground. At somewhat lower energies they will be deflected back into space as *c* and *d*. At still lower energies they may follow paths like *e*, *f*, and *g*.

Particle *e* spirals around the field lines

and follows them in toward the earth. As the field gets stronger, a point is reached where the particle is turned back, and spiraling around the field lines approaches the earth again on the other side. Such particles running back and forth are trapped; they account for the large number of ionized particles that form the Van Allen belts.

Slow particles, such as *g*, entering the earth's field parallel to the lines of force from far away, will be guided by the field and reach the earth's surface. A day or two after an active display of solar flares, so many particles become trapped in the outer Van Allen belt that they spill out

ered by Anderson in 1932 by photographing the tracks of cosmic rays in a Wilson cloud chamber. Under the influence of a strong magnetic field applied perpendicular to the face of the cloud chamber, positively charged particles should bend to the right and negatively charged particles should bend to the left. In order to be certain that those bent one way were not all coming from above, and those bent the other way were particles of the same kind and charge coming from below, Anderson inserted a block of lead in the chamber to slow down the particles. Under these conditions photographs similar to the one shown in (a) of Fig. 73K were obtained.

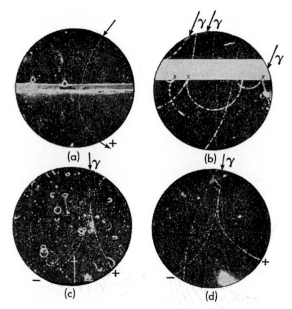

Fig. 73K   *Wilson cloud chamber photographs of pair production. X ray coming close to the nucleus of an atom produces a pair of electrons, one positive and one negative (a) Discovery of a positron (after Anderson), (b) three pairs of electrons produced by X rays (after Anderson), (c) pair produced in air by X rays (after Lauritson and Fowler), (d) pair produced in air by X rays from thorium C″ (after Simons and Zuber).*

into the earth's atmosphere, creating auroras. Since particles with only the highest of energies can get down to the earth's atmosphere near the magnetic equator, the cosmic ray latitude effect is well understood.

73.10. Discovery of the Positron. The positron, or positive electron, was discov-

Here Anderson could be quite certain, from the curvature of the track on each side of the lead, that the particle entered from the side shown above, for in passing through the lead plate it could only have been slowed down and not speeded up. Knowing the direction of motion, the direction of the field, and the direction of bending, Anderson concluded that such a particle had a positive charge. Comparing the track with well-known electron tracks and α particle tracks, he concluded that the new particle had about the same mass as the electron. Later experiments continued to give more positive proof of the existence of a positive electron. Now, very strong beams of positrons can be produced in the laboratory.

It should be pointed out here that near sea level most cosmic rays come from above, whereas a few come from other angles and the horizontal, and some even from below.

73.11. Creation of Electron Pairs. Soon after Anderson's discovery of the positron, several theoretical physicists attempted to calculate the conditions under which a positron might exist in nature. An extension of the quantum theory of the electron, proposed earlier by P. Dirac, led them to the prediction that if a high-energy photon, i.e., a high-frequency γ ray, were to come close enough to the nucleus of an atom, the electric field of the nucleus would be strong enough to annihilate the γ ray and create in its place a *pair of particles, an electron and a positron.* These two particles, the theory predicts, should have the same mass, and equal but opposite charges. A schematic diagram of pair production is given in Fig. 73L.

Blackett, Anderson, and others, looking for such pairs in a cloud chamber, soon found them exactly as predicted. Gamma rays from a radioactive element like *thorium C″*, in passing through matter, were observed to produce pairs of electrons. Three photographs of such incidents are shown in Fig. 73K. In (b) three different pairs are seen emerging from the points marked X on the lower side of a lead plate, and in (c) and (d) a pair is seen having been produced apparently in mid-air. As usual the γ rays that produced these pairs do not show up in the cloud chamber.

When an electron pair is created, *conservation of energy and momentum* requires the two particles to move almost straight forward. Without a magnetic field

applied to the cloud chamber, the particles travel side by side in almost parallel paths, but with a magnetic field the path of the positron bends to one side and that of the electron to the other.

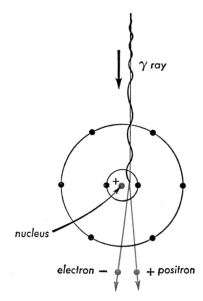

Fig. 73L *Schematic diagram of pair production.*

The reason positrons were not discovered earlier in the history of physics is that they do not exist long in the free state. As soon as a positron meets with an electron, the two are annihilated.

Experiments indicate that all electrons and positrons spin around an axis through their center of mass. There is good evidence that, when a positron and an electron come close together, they frequently combine by revolving around each other like a double-star, with their spin axes parallel to one another. As such a pair they are called *positronium.* Positronium is very short lived, for soon the two particles disintegrate completely; in their place γ rays are created. If the particles were spinning in the same direction, they would disintegrate into three γ rays of different energies, whereas, if they were spinning in opposite directions, they would produce two γ rays. Conservation of energy and momentum requires each of these latter rays to have an energy of $\frac{1}{2}$ Mev. (See Eq.(701).)

73.12. Cosmic-Ray Showers. Out of hundreds and hundreds of cloud chamber photographs of cosmic rays, the experimenter is occasionally rewarded with a picture of a cosmic-ray shower. Instead of one or two tracks in the picture, in this instance one finds anywhere from half a dozen or more to several hundred. As shown by the photographs in Fig. 73M most of the tracks

where atoms are packed very close together, carries out the multiple collision process illustrated in Fig. 73H. Here, within a short distance of 1 or 2 cm of lead, enough atoms are encountered to yield many secondaries. These secondaries, emerging from the lower face of the metal, result in the observed photographs. In a thin sheet of metal, relatively small showers are usually found, whereas with a thick metal block showers of many tracks are occasion-

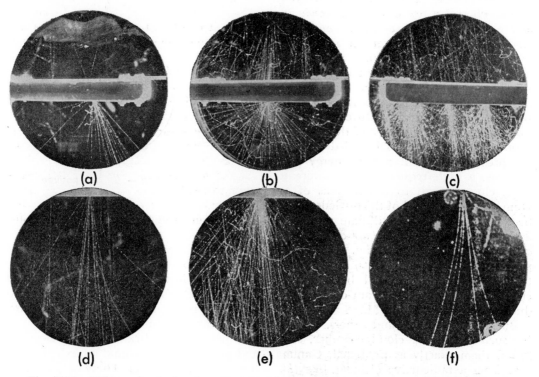

Fig. 73M *Wilson cloud chamber photographs of cosmic-ray showers.* (The first three photographs are reproduced through the courtesy of R. B. Brode and the last three through the courtesy of C. D. Anderson and the Physical Review.)

of a shower seem to come from one localized region, usually within a solid piece of matter like a lead plate or the wall of the cloud chamber.

An extensive study of showers by both the experimental and theoretical physicists has led to the conclusion that each shower is produced by a single, high-energy cosmic ray. A charged particle of very high energy upon entering a solid block of matter,

ally photographed. The first five photographs in Fig. 73M were taken without a magnetic field so that the tracks are all straight, while the last photo was taken with a magnetic field. The bending of three tracks to the right and three to the left indicates equal numbers of both positrons and electrons.

In photograph (a), a single high-speed particle is seen to enter the lead plate from above and to produce some twenty or more secondary particles, each with enough energy to get through and into the air space below. In (b), two small showers of particles enter the top surface of the lead plate, whereas a single larger shower emerges from the bottom. Apparently one or two of the particles at the center of the one shower above have the necessary high energy to produce the lower shower, whereas the others of lower energy are stopped by the lead. Note particularly the fanning out of the rays below. In (c) a small shower of very high-energy particles enters the chamber from above, having been produced far above the cloud chamber in a shower-producing process, probably by a single particle of extremely high energy. As some of these secondaries pass through the lead, each produces a shower of its own.

Direct evidence that some showers originate with a single high-energy particle is shown in Fig. 73N. Here, in a cloud chamber with five equally spaced lead plates, a relatively large shower is seen to have grown from but one or possibly two particles at the top. Not only does this avalanche grow in numbers with each traversal of a lead plate, but the relatively small spread of the tracks indicates how nearly each new particle recoils along with the others in the forward direction. In this picture, one observes in the small space of several inches the process that, in Fig. 73H, requires several miles of air.

73.13. Mesons. The presence in cosmic rays of charged particles having a mass several hundred times that of an electron, yet considerably lighter than a proton, was discovered by Anderson and Nedermeyer in 1938. These particles, now called *mesons,* are of several kinds, and experimental data taken in balloons and airplanes show that most of them are produced high in the atmosphere by the collisions of primary cosmic rays with air nuclei.

In these collisions positively and negatively charged π mesons are produced along with neutral π mesons, protons, and neutrons as shown in Fig. 73O. The π mesons,

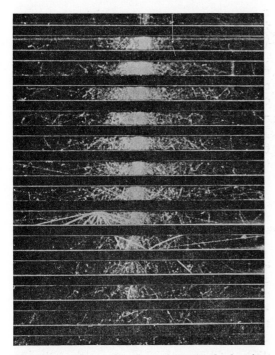

Fig. 73N   *Cloud chamber photograph showing cascade shower of cosmic rays developed in 13 lead plates, each 1.3 cm thick. (Courtesy, Wm. B. Fretter.)*

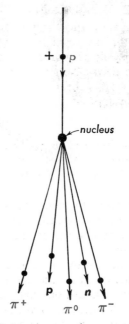

Fig. 73O   *Primary cosmic ray produces mesons by nuclear collision.*

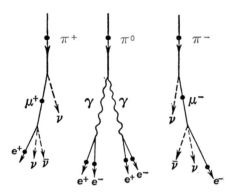

Fig. 73P   *π mesons disintegrate into μ mesons,*
γ rays, electrons, and neutrinos.

exist in atomic nuclei and to consist of protons, and neutrons.

The possible existence of, and the spontaneous disintegration of, mesons was first predicted by Yukawa* in 1935, and first photographed by Williams and Roberts in 1940. All charged π mesons seem to have a half-life of 2×10^{-8} sec, and each one decays into a charged μ particle called a *muon*, and a lightweight neutral particle called a neutrino. The charged muon in turn decays, with a half-life of 2×10^{-6} sec, into an electron and two neutrinos, as shown in Fig. 73P and Fig. 73Q. The neutrino ν_0 is an uncharged particle, postulated first by Pauli in order to explain nuclear phenomena in keeping with the fundamental laws of the conservation of energy and of momentum. (See Sec. 71.2.)

each with a mass of about 275 m_e, along with other nucleons, recoil forward with speeds close to that of light. (m_e = mass of an electron.) The term nucleons is here applied to only those particles believed to

* Yukawa, *Proceedings Physical and Math. Society,* Japan, 17, 48 (1935).

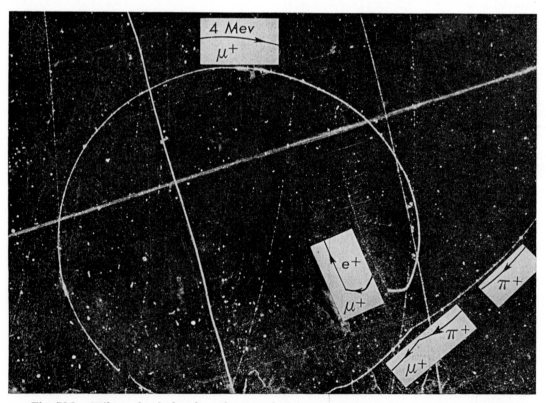

Fig. 73Q   *Wilson cloud chamber photographed in a magnetic field of 8000 gauss showing decay of π meson into a μ meson and the μ meson into a positron.* (Courtesy, W. Powell.)

The uncharged π mesons are very unstable. With a half-life of less than 10^{-14} sec, they decay into two γ rays. In the upper atmosphere these γ rays create cascade showers of electrons by electron pair-production and bremsstrahlung. See Fig. 73N. Many

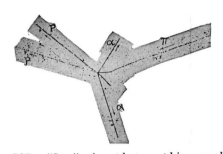

Fig. 73R *"Star" in photographic emulsion showing the explosion of a nucleus resulting from the capture of a slow π meson.* (Courtesy, C. F. Powell's laboratory, University of Bristol, England.)

of the charged μ mesons, with their mass of about 210 m_e, traverse the atmosphere before decaying, and reach the surface of the earth. At sea level the charged cosmic rays are nearly 70% μ mesons and 29% electrons and positrons, with about 1%

heavier particles like protons, deuterons, α particles, etc.

In traversing solid matter, negatively charged π mesons frequently slow down to such a speed that, upon an encounter with a nucleus, they are attracted by the $+$ charge and captured. In this process the meson mass is transformed into energy exciting the nucleus to such a state that it literally explodes by shooting out a number of heavier particles like protons, deuterons, α particles, etc. Fig. 73R shows such a "star" event in a photographic emulsion.

Recent studies of cosmic ray tracks made in photographic emulsions and cloud chambers indicate the presence of particles with various other masses and charges (to be discussed in Chap. 80).

Most recent cosmic ray observations at high altitudes and at sea level show the following:

Primaries		Sea Level	
H	89%	μ mesons	70%
He	9%	e^+ and e^-	29%
Li, Be, B	0.5%	heavier particles	1%
C, N, O	0.5%		
Ne, Mg, Si	0.1%		
Fe	0.03%		

QUESTIONS

1. Make a diagram of a Geiger-Mueller tube counter, and briefly explain how it is able to be used to detect atomic particles of high energy.

2. Who was awarded the Nobel Prize in physics for the discovery of cosmic rays? What was his experimental observation?

3. How does the intensity of cosmic rays vary with altitude?

4. Explain why the intensity of cosmic rays is a minimum near the equator. Make a diagram.

5. How was the positron discovered, and by whom?

6. Under what conditions are electron pairs created?

7. What is a cosmic ray telescope, and how is it made?

8. What are primary cosmic rays, and of what are they composed?

9. What are secondary cosmic rays, and of what are they composed?

10. Make a list of all the atomic particles found in cosmic rays.

Atomic Accelerators

74.1. The Lawrence Cyclotron. At the time Cockcroft and Walton were performing their first disintegration experiments (see Fig. 72M), E. O. Lawrence,* an American physicist, was developing a new type of atomic accelerator which soon attracted the attention of the leading physicists the world over. So successful was this "atomic machine gun" in producing high-speed atomic projectiles for disintegration experiments that a new and larger cyclotron was soon constructed and put into operation. Now a cyclotron of considerable size occupies a most prominent position in many of the leading physics laboratories of the world.

One of the cyclotrons located at the University of California, called the "sixty-inch," is an instrument capable of producing intense beams of protons, deuterons or α particles having energies of 10, 20, and 40 Mev,

* Ernest O. Lawrence (1901-   ), American experimental physicist. Deriving his early education in South Dakota, Lawrence obtained the A.B. degree at the University of South Dakota in 1922, the master's degree at Minnesota in 1923, and the Ph.D. at Yale University in 1925. After two years as National Research Fellow he became, at the early age of 26, Assistant Professor of Physics at Yale University. The following year he was appointed Associate Professor of Physics at the University of California, and in 1930 was made full Professor. Having built up the Radiation Laboratory at the same institution, he became its Director in 1936. In 1937 he was awarded the Comstock Prize of the National Academy of Sciences, the Cresson Medal of the Franklin Institute, and the Hughes Medal of the Royal Society of London. Lawrence is a member of the National Academy of Sciences and is noted principally for his invention and development of the cyclotron and its application to the production of induced radioactivity. It is for these discoveries that he was granted the Nobel Prize in 1939. During World War II he directed one of the main research projects leading to the isolation of uranium-235 used in atomic bombs.

respectively. The purpose of these high-speed particles, as is the case with all such instruments, is to subject various known substances to bombardment and thus produce disintegrations and transmutations of all kinds.

Although the operation of a large cyclotron requires an elaborate outlay of apparatus and equipment, the principles upon which it operates are quite simple. As a means of explaining these principles, cross-section diagrams of a cyclotron are shown in Figs. 74A and 74B.

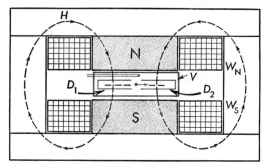

Fig. 74A *Cross-section diagram of a cyclotron.*

The very heart of the instrument consists of two short, hollow, half cylinders, D_1 and D_2, mounted inside of a vacuum chamber V, between the poles of a powerful electromagnet, and connected on the outside to the two terminals of a high-frequency alternating current generator. It is interesting to point out that this generator is really a short-wave radio transmitter supplying energy to the "dees" (D_1 and D_2) instead of to the antenna. When a trace of hydrogen gas is admitted to the evacuated chamber, the hot-wire filament F ionizes some of the hydrogen atoms, thereby pro-

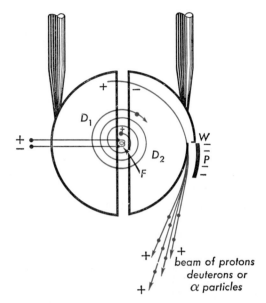

Fig.74B *Detailed diagram of the "dees" of a cyclotron.*

stance is to be bombarded is then placed in this beam, and the disintegrated fragments are studied by means of various detective devices.

The fundamental principle that makes the cyclotron work at all is the fact that *the time required for a charged particle to make one complete turn within the dees is the same for all speeds*. The faster a particle travels the larger is the circle it must traverse, thus keeping the time constant. Hence, with a constant frequency of the alternating current supply, some particles may be just starting their acceleration near the center while others farther out have already acquired higher speeds. The result is a more or less continuous stream of protons emerging from the window W.

If the alternating current voltage applied between the *dees* of the cyclotron is 200,000 volts, with each half turn a particle obtains an added velocity equivalent to 200,000 volts. If a proton makes 25 complete revolutions before leaving the chamber at W, it will have acquired a velocity equivalent to 200,000 times 25 times 2, or 10,000,000 volts. Here, then, is a beam of 10 Mev protons acquired by the application of a potential only $\frac{1}{50}$ as great.

When hydrogen in the evacuated chamber of the 60-in. cyclotron is replaced by *deuterium* and the magnetic field strength is doubled, a beam of high-energy deuterons is obtained. Having twice the mass but the same charge as protons, these particles acquire twice as much energy. If helium gas is used in place of deuterium, many of the atoms become doubly ionized at the source and after acceleration emerge from the cyclotron window with an energy of about 40 Mev. By increasing or decreasing the frequency of the potential applied to the dees, and properly adjusting the magnetic field, protons, deuterons, or α particles of 10, 20, and 40 Mev, respectively, can be produced.

Some of the details of the cyclotron shown in Fig. 74A are as follows: The dimension, 60 in., refers to the diameter of the poles of the cyclotron magnet; this in turn limits the size of the dees and therefore the maximum energy available in the

ducing the protons to be used as atomic bullets. At the particular instant when D_1 is charged positively and D_2 is charged negatively, a proton in the neighborhood of F will be accelerated toward D_2. Moving through the strong magnetic field of the huge magnet, this positively charged particle traverses a circular path as shown in the diagram. If, after making a half turn, the potential is reversed so that D_1 becomes negatively charged and D_2 positively charged, the proton will be attracted by one and repelled by the other, causing it to increase its speed. With added speed it therefore moves in the arc of a larger circle as shown. After this second half turn, the potential again reverses, making D_1 positive and D_2 negative, and again the proton speeds up. Thus, as the potential reverses periodically, the proton travels faster and faster, moving in ever-expanding circles, until, reaching the outer edge, it passes through a narrow open window W.

Upon leaving W all protons must pass close to a negatively charged plate P where, by attraction, their paths are straightened out and they become a separated beam of projectiles. Whatever subform of atomic projectiles. Most of the instrument's total weight of 200 tons lies in the solid iron core and the pole pieces located inside the field windings. The latter, consisting of many turns of thick copper wire, are encased in tanks W_S and W_N through which cooling fluid is continually circulated.

A photograph of an 11-Mev deuteron beam from the Harvard University cyclotron is shown in Fig. 74C. From the point where the particles emerge from the cyclotron window at the left center to where they come to rest in mid-air at the lower

find the time required for any charged particle to make one complete circle the formula $s = vt$ from mechanics is employed. The distance traveled in one turn is represented by s, and T represents the time.

$$T = \frac{s}{v} = \frac{2\pi r}{v} \qquad \text{(74b)}$$

By solving Eq.(74a) for v, and substituting Eq.(74b), we obtain

$$v = \frac{Ber}{m} \qquad \text{and} \qquad T = \frac{2\pi}{B} \cdot \frac{m}{e} \qquad \text{(74c)}$$

The right-hand equation shows that the

Fig. 74C *Photograph by Paul Donaldson of an 11-Mev deuteron beam from the Harvard cyclotron.* (Courtesy, Harvard University Press and A. K. Solomon.)

right, they ionize the air molecules and atoms, causing them to emit visible light.

74.2. Theory of the Cyclotron. The theory of the cyclotron involves simple classical laws describing the motion of a charged particle in a uniform magnetic field. By Eq.(57e), the force on a particle in a magnetic field is given by Bev, and this is equal to the centripetal force mv^2/r.

$$Bev = \frac{mv^2}{r} \qquad \text{(74a)}$$

Here e is the charge on the particle in coulombs, m is its mass in kilograms, v is its velocity in meters per second, and r is the radius of its circular path in meters. To

period T is independent of r and v and, for like particles (that is, the same e and m), varies with the magnetic induction B. The alternating potential E applied to the cyclotron dees must therefore match in frequency the particles' motion due to the field B. It is customary in practice to apply a fixed frequency to the dees and adjust the current in the magnetic field coils until resonance occurs. In the 60-in. cyclotron, $B = 1.6$ webers/meter² or 16,000 gauss.

74.3. The Van de Graaff Generator. This machine, developed in 1931 by R. Van de Graaff at Princeton University, employs the principle of the electrostatic generator discovered many years ago. A typical installa-

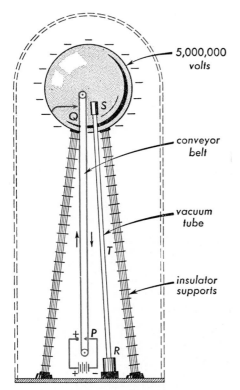

Fig. 74D   *Diagram of a Van de Graaff generator of high voltage.*

surrounding air and through the insulators becomes equally fast.

Atomic particles to be accelerated are generated inside a vacuum tube source S inside the sphere. Starting at the top of a long straight vacuum tube T, electrons are accelerated downward toward ground potential, where, acquiring the full energy of the available voltage, they are allowed to bombard whatever target is being studied. Where installations are designed for accelerating protons, deuterons, or α particles, the battery potential is reversed and the sphere acquires a high positive potential.

74.4. The Betatron. The *betatron,* invented in 1941 by D. W. Kerst at the University of Illinois, is an electron accelerator capable of producing electron beams of high energy as well as X rays of extremely high penetrating power. This ingenious device differs from the cyclotron in at least two fundamental respects: first, the electrons are accelerated by a rapidly changing magnetic field, and, second, the circular orbit of the particles has a constant radius.

A cross-section diagram of a 20 Mev betatron is shown in Fig. 74E. A glass vacuum tube in the shape of a *doughnut,* and con-

tion, as shown in Fig. 74D, consists of a large hollow sphere, supported on insulating columns and charged by a belt conveying electrical charges from a battery at ground potential and depositing it inside the sphere. The fabric conveyor belt, a foot or more in width, and running over well-aligned rollers, travels about 60 mi/hr.

As the belt passes between the metallic surface and row of needle points at P, electrons from the points jump toward the positive electrode and are caught by the belt. Upon entering the sphere at the top, the electrons jump to the needle points Q where they go quickly to the outside surface of the sphere. The "spraying" of electrons *to* and *from* the points is assured by keeping the battery potential high (about 50,000 volts) to maintain a "brush discharge." As more and more electrons arrive at the sphere, its negative potential rises higher and higher until leakage into the

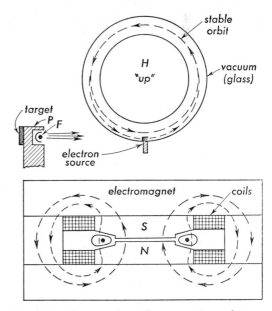

Fig. 74E   *Cross-section diagrams of an electron accelerator, called a betatron.*

Fig. 74F   Photograph of the 184-in., 4000-ton, synchro-cyclotron at the University of California.

taining an *electron gun,* is mounted between the poles of an electromagnet. An alternating current (180 cycles/sec) applied to the coils causes some of the magnetic lines of force to pass through the vacuum tube at the electron orbit and the remainder through the orbit center, as shown below. Electrons are injected only at the beginning of each quarter cycle when the field begins to increase in the "up" direction. The increasing field through the center of the orbit gives rise to an electromotive force, tangent to the orbit, speeding up the electrons; whereas the increasing field at the orbit is just sufficient to increase the centripetal force and keep the electrons from spiraling outward. The stability of such an orbit is brought about by properly shaping the pole faces of the magnet, adjusting the frequency and strength of the magnetic field, and injecting the electrons

energy, and impinging upon a target, give rise to X rays capable of penetrating many feet of solid iron and lead.

74.5. The Synchro-Cyclotron. The firm belief that new and fundamental discoveries in nuclear physics can be made with atomic projectiles having greater and greater energies has led scientists and engineers in various institutions to combine their efforts in groups to design and construct larger and larger atomic accelerators. One such instrument is the synchro-cyclotron shown in Fig. 74F.

The fundamental differences between this and the orthodox cyclotron are the use of one dee in place of two and the use of an applied alternating-current potential whose frequency is made to rise and fall periodically instead of remaining constant. The principles of operation are illustrated in Fig. 74G. Starting at the center, protons,

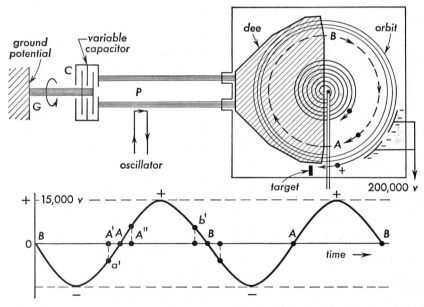

Fig. 74G *Illustration of "phase stability" as it applies to the synchro-cyclotron.*

at the proper voltage at the appropriate time.

During World War II, a 350-ton betatron was constructed by the General Electric Company and put into use as a source of extremely penetrating X rays. In this instrument electrons accelerated to 100 Mev

deuterons, or α particles are made to move in circles of increasing radius, the acceleration taking place as they enter and leave the lips of the dee. At the outer edge they are deflected out of the field, as in the cyclotron, or allowed to strike a suitable target inside the vacuum chamber.

The theory of the synchro-cyclotron* is based upon "phase stability," a principle fundamental to nearly all high-energy accelerators. This relatively new idea can be derived from the well-founded theory that, as a particle is accelerated and approaches the speed of light, continued acceleration increases the mass, while the speed approaches a nearly constant value. In other words, as more and more energy is given to a particle, more and more of it is stored as *increased mass* and less and less as *increased speed*.

To apply this principle to an accelerator like the synchro-cyclotron, consider the conditions that exist when a positively charged particle in a uniform magnetic field is moving with constant speed in an orbit of constant radius and at the same time in synchronism with an applied high-frequency potential. Such an orbit is represented by the dotted circle in Fig. 74G, with the particle entering and leaving the lips of the dee at A and B when the potential (see graph below) is zero. By Eq.(74a), $Bev = mv^2/r$. Since, from mechanics, angular velocity $\omega = v/r$, and the frequency of revolution $f = \omega/2\pi$, direct substitution in Eq.(74a) gives $m = Be/2\pi f$. Multiplying both sides of this equation by the square of the speed of light c^2 gives

$$mc^2 = \frac{Bec^2}{2\pi f}$$

where mc^2 represents the total energy E of the particle,

$$E = \frac{Bec^2}{2\pi f} \qquad (74d)$$

It may be seen from these equations that mc^2 includes the *rest mass* m_0c^2 of the particle, and that to increase E the magnetic induction can be *increased* as in the betatron and synchrotron (see Sec. 74.6), or *the frequency can be decreased* as in the synchro-cyclotron.

Returning now to the high-speed but

* The theory of phase stability of atomic accelerators of high energy was first developed in 1945 by V. Veksler (*Journal of Physics*, USSR, Vol. 9, p. 153 (1945)), and independently by E. M. McMillan (*Physical Review*, Vol. 68, p. 143 (1945)).

stationary orbit AB in Fig. 74G, assume that a particle is a little early in entering the dee. Arriving there, as shown by A' in the graph below, the dee has a negative potential a' and the particle is accelerated by attraction. Being accelerated, the mass increases with little increase in speed. Due principally to increased mass the particle now describes a larger circle, and the next time around it has dropped back to arrive more nearly at the time of *zero potential*. Hence, if the magnetic induction B were to be increased or the frequency f were to be decreased, the particle might be made to continually enter and leave the dee ahead of the zero phase and receive acceleration each time around.

If a particle gets behind the zero phase (A to A'' in the graph), it will not be accelerated and, moving with more nearly constant or diminished speed, will permit a decreasing frequency of an applied potential to catch up and get ahead again. Hence phase stability is assured and acceleration will occur as the particle spirals outward with increasing energy.

In the 184-in. synchro-cyclotron, the high-frequency potential is applied to the dee stem at P (see Fig. 74G), and the variable condenser C, composed of a fast rotating set of "fan blades" passing between a set of stationary blades, varies the frequency up an down through relatively wide limits. In producing 200 Mev deuterons, the frequency of the dee potential rises and falls 120 times/sec between the limits of 12.5 and 8.5 megacycles/sec.

The positive ions are pulsed into the center of the dee when the frequency is 11.3 megacycles, and they arrive at the outer edge when it has dropped to about 9.6 megacycles. Having made 10,000 turns around the chamber in a period of only one-thousandth of a second, the deuterons have an energy of 200 Mev. The target, located inside the vacuum chamber, is therefore bombarded by pulses coming at the rate of 120 per sec.

A drop from 11.3 to 9.6 megacycles decreases f (see Eq. 74d) by about 15%, thereby increasing a deuteron's energy E

and mass m by 15%, or 0.3 atomic mass unit (*abbr.* amu). Such an increase, by Eq. (70m), is equivalent to 200 Mev.

74.6. The Synchrotron. This device is an electron accelerator employing the principles of the *cyclotron,* and *phase stability.* A cut-away diagram of such an instrument is shown in Fig. 74H. As in the betatron,

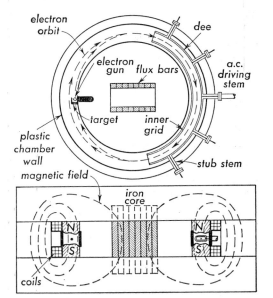

Fig. 74H   *Cross-section diagrams of a 300-Mev synchrotron.*

electrons are injected into a doughnut-shaped vacuum chamber by an electron gun. Operating first as a betatron, the electrons are accelerated in an orbit of fixed radius by a rapidly increasing magnetic field. The rising field is produced by discharging a large condenser bank through the magnet coils. Part of the field goes through the relatively small *flux bars* near the orbit center, and part through the pole faces and vacuum chamber.

As the electrons quickly approach the speed of light, their mass begins to increase rapidly; from about 2 Mev on, they move at almost constant speed (between 98 and 100% the speed of light). Increasing energy is added in this *second phase* by an alternating potential applied to the *sector dee* shown in the diagram. Instead of decreas-

ing the frequency, as in the synchro-cyclotron, the magnetic induction B is increased (see Eq. 74d) and, as the electron *mass* increases, the stronger field maintains the beam orbit constant.

Upon reaching a maximum energy of 300 Mev, for example, the electrons, with a mass some 600 times their *rest mass,* are caused to spiral inward to strike a tungsten target where they produce 300 Mev X rays.

74.7. The Linear Accelerator. Although linear accelerators were proposed as early as 1929, and several were constructed, they have never proved satisfactory until recently. Applying the principles of tubular wave guides and resonant cavities, L. Alvarez and his collaborators, immediately after World War II, constructed the first successful linear accelerator. Since a giant machine employing the same principles is soon to be built at Stanford University, the ideas involved are of considerable importance.

A cut-away diagram of part of the Alvarez lineac is given in Fig. 74I. Protons are initially produced and accelerated to 4 Mev by a pressure Van de Graaff generator (see Fig. 74D) and then injected at that energy into one end of a 40-ft tank, as shown at the upper left. Once inside they are further accelerated as they pass through a series of "drift tubes," and arrive at the other end with an energy of about 40 Mev.

The tank cavity within the copper lining, fed by 30 radar transmitting oscillators, is set resonating at its *dominant mode* at a frequency of 200 megacycles. The "standing-wave" conditions set up are such that the electric field E is parallel to the tube axis and is everywhere rising and falling together. The lengths of the drift tubes gradually increase so that the protons cross each gap when the field E is to the right, and are inside the tubes, in a field free space, when the field is to the left. It now seems possible that additional tank sections can be added end to end to this system to obtain almost any desired energy. Calculations indicate that more than 1 Mev per lineal foot can be expected from such a system.

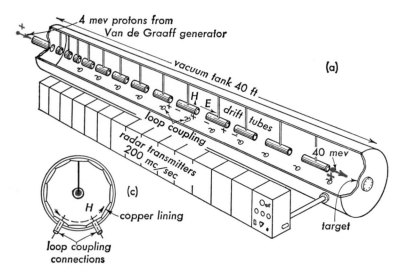

Fig. 74I *Diagrams showing the first section of a linear accelerator.*

74.8. Billion Electron Volt Accelerators.

The design and construction of an instrument capable of accelerating particles to energies of billions of electron volts (*Bev*) involve many problems. Not the least of these is the economic factor concerned primarily with the initial cost of such an instrument as well as its subsequent maintenance.

A number of accelerators producing particles of 1 Bev or more are now in operation and others of greater and greater energy are being planned.

In Operation (1960)

Pasadena, California	1.1 Bev (electrons)
Ithaca, New York	1.3 Bev (electrons)
Berkeley, California	6.2 Bev (protons)
Dubna, Russia	10 Bev (protons)
Geneva, Switzerland	28 Bev (protons)
Brookhaven, Long Island	31 Bev (protons)

Planned or Under Construction

Cambridge, Massachusetts	7.5 Bev (electrons)
Argonne, Illinois	12.5 Bev (protons)
Palo Alto, California	15-45 Bev (electrons)

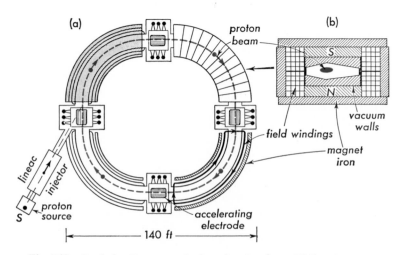

Fig. 74J *Berkeley Bevatron designed to produce 6.2 Bev protons.*

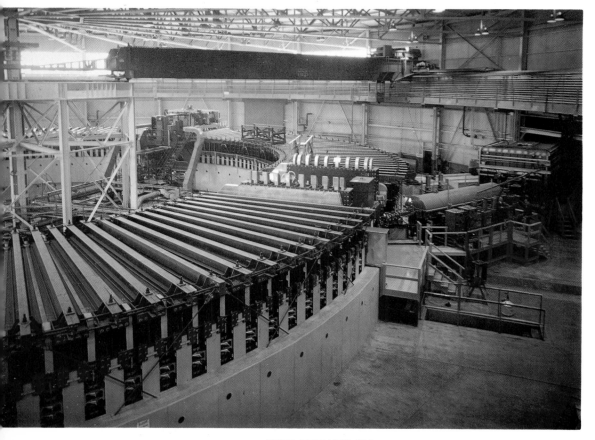

THE BEVATRON

Fig. 74K   *A six-billion volt accelerator of atomic particles, located at the University of California, Berkeley.* (Photographed by K. Hildebrand and G. Kagawa. Courtesy of E. Lofgren, D. Cooksey, the Radiation Laboratory at the University of California, and the Atomic Energy Commission.) *Just behind the two men on the platform, at the far right and center, can be seen the rectangular housing of the atomic source and the Cockroft-Walton accelerator. The cylindrical tank section containing the linear accelerator is clearly seen leading into the inflector assembly between quadrants 1 and 4. The main accelerating electrode assembly with the yellow colored ducts leading to it is seen farther back between quadrants 3 and 4. Note the overhead crane used for assembling, repairing, and the handling of massive apparatus and equipment.*

The basic design of one of these large instruments, the 6.3 Bev *bevatron,* is shown in Fig. 74J. The magnet arrangement consists of four quadrant segments spaced so that the particle orbits are quarter-circles connected by 20-ft straight sections. The electrical power supplied to the 10,000-ton magnet is provided by a motor generator with a large flywheel. During buildup of the magnetic field, a peak power of 100,000 kilowatts is drawn from the flywheel and stored in the magnet. As the field is reduced between beam pulses, the generator acts as a motor and returns energy to the flywheel.

The protons from a source S, as shown in Fig. 74J, are first accelerated to 10 Mev by a linear accelerator, and then injected into the 385-ft race track proper. As they pass through the accelerator electrode in one of the straight sections and are speeded up by the high-frequency potentials, the magnetic field increases at the proper rate to keep the beam in the same orbit. The output beam consists, as it does in all high-energy accelerators, of a series of pulses. From the time of injection, each pulse of protons takes about 2 sec to acquire its final speed, and in so doing makes about four million revolutions of the orbit and travels about 300,000 miles.

QUESTIONS AND PROBLEMS

1. What is a cyclotron? What is its purpose? What does it accelerate?

2. What is deuterium? Is deuterium the same as hydrogen?

3. What is a Van de Graaff generator? What is it frequently used for? Can it be used to accelerate protons and electrons?

4. What does the abbreviation "Mev" stand for? What does the abbreviation "Bev" stand for?

5. What is a betatron? Where do you think it got its name?

6. Approximately what is the highest energy to which atomic particles have been accelerated in the laboratory?

7. If the frequency of the potential applied to the dees of a cyclotron is 8×10^6 cycles/sec, what must be the magnetic induction B to accelerate α particles?

8. Calculate the frequency of the oscillating potential that must be applied to a cyclotron in which deuterons are accelerated. Assume the magnetic induction has a constant value of 25,000 gauss. (*Ans.* 19.0 Mc/sec.)

9. The frequency applied to the dees of a cyclotron is 9.4 megacycles/sec. What must be the magnetic induction if protons are to be accelerated?

10. What total accelerator voltage will give protons a velocity of 99% the speed of light? (*Ans.* 5.7 Bev.)

Chapter 75

Transmutation
of the Elements

75.1. Proton and Deuteron Disintegrations. When high-energy protons or deuterons are used to bombard different known elements, various disintegration products are formed. An experimental arrangement in which the cyclotron acts as the source of high-speed particles is shown in Fig. 75A.

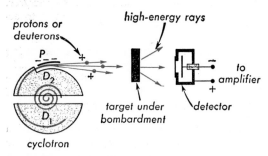

cyclotron

Fig. 75A *Experimental arrangement generally used for bombarding known substances with high-speed deuterons from the cyclotron and for detecting the disintegration products with an ionization chamber as a detector.*

To determine the nature of the disintegration taking place within the substance under bombardment, it is common practice to identify the penetrating rays emerging from the other side by the use of suitable detectors.

Numerous experiments have shown that the disintegration products to be looked for may be *protons, α particles, neutrons, γ rays,* or even *electrons* and *positrons.* For some of these penetrating rays, one kind of detector may be more suitable than another. The *scintillation counter,* for example (see Fig. 71O), is particularly useful in detecting γ rays and electrons, whereas the *Wilson cloud chamber* and *ionization chamber* are useful in detecting protons, α particles, or neutrons.

The detector shown at the right in Fig. 75A represents an ionization chamber. When a Wilson cloud chamber is used to identify disintegration products, charged particles can be identified by the density of their fog tracks, and their energy can be determined by the curvature of the tracks when a magnetic field is applied. This is illustrated in Fig. 75H for positrons. Once the nature of the emerging rays from a bombarded target is known, the recoil product of the disintegration also becomes known by writing down a reaction equation. Six examples of such reaction equations are given by the following:

$$\text{Q values}$$

$$\begin{array}{lll}
{}_1\text{H}^1 + {}_9\text{F}^{19} = {}_8\text{O}^{16} + {}_2\text{He}^4 & 8.1 \text{ Mev} & (75a) \\
{}_1\text{H}^1 + {}_5\text{B}^{11} = {}_6\text{C}^{12} + \gamma \text{ ray} & 15.8 \text{ Mev} & (75b) \\
{}_1\text{H}^2 + {}_7\text{N}^{14} = {}_6\text{C}^{12} + {}_2\text{He}^4 & 13.6 \text{ Mev} & (75c) \\
{}_1\text{H}^2 + {}_8\text{O}^{16} = {}_7\text{N}^{14} + {}_2\text{He}^4 & 3.1 \text{ Mev} & (75d) \\
{}_1\text{H}^2 + {}_3\text{Li}^6 = {}_3\text{Li}^7 + {}_1\text{H}^1 & 5.0 \text{ Mev} & (75e) \\
{}_1\text{H}^2 + {}_4\text{Be}^9 = {}_5\text{B}^{10} + {}_0\text{n}^1 & 4.4 \text{ Mev} & (75f)
\end{array}$$

It is customary to omit the *mass energy* of the bombarding particle from the left-hand side of all reaction equations and to designate the total energy liberated by the disintegration as shown at the right above. The values of Q given above therefore represent the experimentally determined values of the energy over and above that supplied by the incident projectile.

Consider the fifth reaction, which can be taken to represent an experiment in which

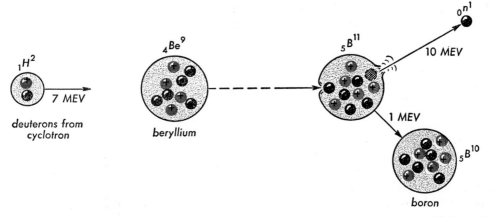

Fig. 75B *Deuteron disintegration of a beryllium nucleus to produce high-speed neutrons.*

a beam of two-million-volt deuterons from the cyclotron bombards a target of lithium metal. From the other side of the target a stream of high-energy protons would be detected. If they are sent through a Wilson cloud chamber in a magnetic field, for example, their tracks could be identified as proton tracks and their energy determined by the curvature of the tracks to be 6.0 Mev. The lithium atoms in the target would recoil with the remaining 1 Mev. When the accurate weights of the four nuclei involved are taken into acount, there is a total loss of 0.00540 atomic mass units. Multiplying by 931, this is equivalent to 5.0 Mev energy. This value plus the energy of the incident bombarding particle gives 7.0 Mev.

As a second example consider Eq.(75f) in which deuterons, bombarding beryllium metal, produce high-speed neutrons and recoiling boron nuclei. This particular disintegration is important experimentally because it is used as a means of obtaining intense beams of neutrons for use as projectiles in other disintegrations. The nuclear changes are illustrated schematically in Fig. 75B. The available energy from the loss in mass alone is equivalent to 4.4 Mev; so that, if deuterons with an energy of 7 Mev are used to bombard the beryllium target, the available energy becomes 11.4 Mev, 1 Mev going to the recoil boron nucleus and approximately 10.4 Mev to the neutron.

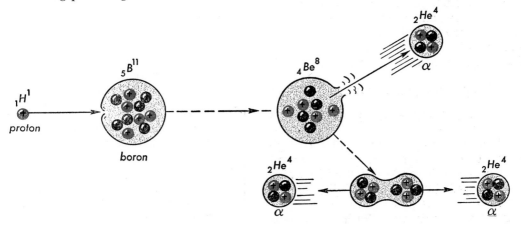

Fig. 75C *Diagram of the disintegration of a boron nucleus of mass 11 by a proton to produce three α particles.*

75.2. Multiple Disintegrations. A study of certain disintegration experiments shows that some of the unstable nuclei created by the capture of a proton or deuteron by a stable nucleus split up into more than two stable nuclei. Examples of this arise when boron is bombarded by protons and when nitrogen is bombarded by deuterons. In the case of boron (see Fig. 75C), the proton is first captured by a $_5B^{11}$ nucleus to form an unstable carbon nucleus, $_6C^{12}$. This composite structure disintegrates by the expulsion of an α particle with several million volts energy, leaving behind a beryllium nucleus, $_4Be^8$.

$$_1H^1 + _5B^{11} = _4Be^8 + _2He^4$$
$$= _2He^4 + _2He^4 + _2He^4 \qquad (75g)$$

This nuclear combination is still unstable and splits apart into two more α particles. When the phenomenon was first observed, it was thought that all three α particles came apart simultaneously, but further observations showed that first one and then two were ejected. The total energy liberated has been measured to be about 11 Mev, which checks almost exactly with the value obtained from the loss in mass.

75.3. Branch Disintegrations. It so happens that, when certain atoms are bombarded with high-speed particles, two or more disintegration processes may subsequently take place. As an illustration of this phenomenon of *branch disintegration,* consider the proton bombardment of beryllium in which the following two types of disintegration have been identified:

$$_1H^1 + _4Be^9 = _3Li^6 + _2He^4 \qquad (75h)$$

$$_1H^1 + _4Be^9 = _5B^{10} + \gamma \text{ ray} \qquad (75i)$$

When a proton is captured by a beryllium nucleus to form an unstable boron nucleus, $_5B^{10}$, there are two ways in which it may split up. The instability of the boron in the first place is due to the presence of too much mass. Such an atom is said to be in an *excited state,* for by the emission of a γ ray it gives up its surplus

energy and becomes a stable $_5B^{10}$ nucleus, or by splitting up into two particles it gives up its surplus in the form of kinetic energy to become $_2He^4$ and $_3Li^6$, two stable nuclei.

An abbreviated notation for nuclear reactions is illustrated by the following examples.

$$_1H^1 + _9F^{19} = _8O^{16} + _2He^4$$
$$_1H^2 + _7N^{14} = _6C^{12} + _2He^4$$
$$_1H^2 + _3Li^7 = _2He^4 + _2He^4 + _0n^1$$

Abbr. $\quad F^{19}(p, \alpha) O^{16}$
Abbr. $\quad N^{14}(d, \alpha) C^{12}$
Abbr. $\quad Li^7(d, 2\alpha n)$

75.4. Discovery of Induced Radioactivity. The discovery of induced radioactivity was made in 1934 by F. Joliot and I. Curie Joliot.*

For years the Curie-Joliots, as they are now often called, had been exposing various substances to the α rays from naturally radioactive elements and had been studying the various disintegrations that took place. In the specific instance referred to above, they bombarded aluminum with α *particles from polonium* and measured the energies of the ejected neutrons by the recoiling of protons from paraffin (see Fig. 75D). They observed that, even after the polonium source was taken away, the detector continued to respond to some kind of penetrating radiation. Upon investigating the nature of these rays, they found positively charged electrons coming from the aluminum.

Repeating the experiments to make certain of the results, they came to the conclusion that, under the bombardment of α particles, the aluminum had become radioactive in its own right. What was happening has since been verified: α particles striking aluminum nuclei are captured, and

* Irene Curie, daughter of the most famous woman physicist, Marie Curie, is the wife of Frederick Joliot. Because of the now famous name of Curie, the physicists of the world hyphenate the name and call them Mme. Curie-Joliot and M. J. F. Joliot, or for short the Curie-Joliots. It is not so strange a coincidence that induced radioactivity was discovered by these observers since for years they had worked with radioactive substances in the famous laboratory of the late Mme. Marie Curie at the Radium Institute in Paris.

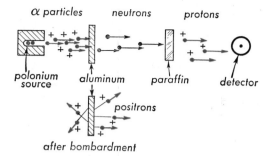

Fig. 75D Experimental arrangement used by the Curie-Joliots when they discovered induced radioactivity.

the resulting nuclei disintegrate with the violent ejection of neutrons.

$$_2He^4 + _{13}Al^{27} = _{15}P^{30} + _0n^1 \qquad (75j)$$

The newly created recoil particles, with a charge of +15 and mass 30 have been identified as phosphorus nuclei which are not stable but radioactive. Spontaneously disintegrating, these radioactive phosphorus nuclei $_{15}P^{30}$ shoot out positrons, leaving behind them stable silicon atoms of charge +14 and mass 30.

$$_{15}P^{30} = _{14}Si^{30} + _1e^0 + \nu \qquad (75k)$$

The *half-life* of this activity, which measures the rate of decay of the phosphorus into silicon (for the meaning of half-life see Sec. 70.2), is only 2.5 min. The emission of a positively charged electron is accompanied by a neutrino, just as in the case of β-emission. Often times, however, the neutrino is omitted from the reaction since it carries no charge and no rest mass.

Although the mass of the electron is not zero, it is so small compared with unit mass (the mass of one electron, it will be remembered, is 1/1836th of the mass of the proton) that e is written with a zero superscript. According to this notation a positron is written $_1e^0$ and an electron $_{-1}e^0$.

Because the phosphorus does not all disintegrate immediately, it has been possible to identify the activity as coming from the newly created phosphorus atoms in the following way. A piece of aluminum metal, immediately after being bombarded, is dissolved in hydrochloric acid together with

some ordinary inactive phosphorus, and then a standard chemical separation is made. Testing each part separately, the radioactivity is found to be present with the phosphorus residue, and not with the aluminum.

75.5. The Discovery of Radioactive Sodium.

Immediately after the discovery of induced radioactivity by the Curie-Joliots, Lawrence bombarded sodium with 2 Mev deuterons from the cyclotron and found that it too, like aluminum, became radioactive (see Fig. 75E). Upon testing for the

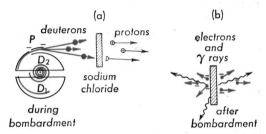

Fig. 75E Experimental arrangement used by Lawrence in discovering radioactive sodium.

nature of the rays given off during bombardment, Lawrence found protons with an energy of about 7 Mev. When the sodium target was removed from the deuteron beam, as shown in diagram (b), and then tested for activity, it was found to be emitting both electrons and γ rays. The bombarding reaction, therefore, is

$$_1H^2 + _{11}Na^{23} = _{11}Na^{24} + _1H^1 \qquad (75l)$$

followed by the radioactive decay of the unstable sodium nuclei,

$$_{11}Na^{24} = _{12}Mg^{24} + _{-1}e^0 + \gamma \text{ ray} \qquad (75m)$$

The first stage of the disintegration process is shown at the left in Fig. 75F, and the radioactive decay is shown at the right.

The residual nucleus $_{11}Na^{24}$ of the first disintegration is called *radio-sodium*. Having a charge of +11 and mass of 24, it must be an isotope of sodium not found in nature. Since measurements of the activity of radio-sodium give a *half-life* of only 15 hr, it is clear why such atoms are not found in nature. If they were formed some time in

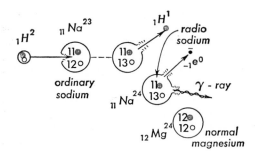

the ages past, they would all have disintegrated by this time.

An energy level diagram for the decay of radioactive sodium is shown in Fig. 75G. The left-hand energy scales are given equally well in *amu* or in *Mev.* After emitting an electron, the nuclear charge increases by unity, and we have a magnesium nucleus in an excited state or energy level. With two successive transitions in which 2.75 Mev and 1.37 Mev γ rays are emitted, the nucleus becomes a stable system, a normal isotope of magnesium $_{12}Mg^{24}$.

Up to the present time more than six hundred different kinds of radioactive atoms have been produced in the laboratory. Two examples, in addition to those already given, are illustrated by the following reactions:

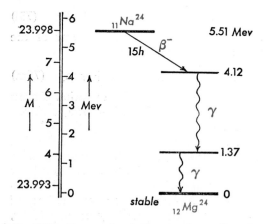

Fig. 75G   *Energy level diagram for radioactive decay of sodium-24.*

$$_1H^2 + {}_{15}P^{31} = {}_{15}P^{32} + {}_1H^1,$$
$$_{15}P^{32} = {}_{16}S^{32} + {}_{-1}e^0 \qquad (75n)$$

$$_1H^2 + {}_6C^{12} = {}_7N^{13} + {}_0n^1,$$
$$_7N^{13} = {}_6C^{13} + {}_1e^0 \qquad (75o)$$

The first of these reactions forms *radioactive phosphorus* $_{15}P^{32}$ which is *electron active* with a half-life of 15 days.

A cloud chamber photograph of the positrons emitted by radioactive nitrogen $_7N^{13}$ is reproduced in Fig. 75H. The magnetic

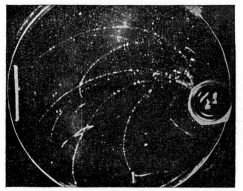

Fig. 75H   *Photograph of the Wilson cloud chamber tracks of positrons ejected by radio nitrogen,* $_7N^{13}$.

field bends all the rays in the same direction, indicating that all are positive charges. The low-density fogdrops forming the tracks indicate particles with the mass of an electron.

75.6. Electron Capture. Many radioactive nuclei, when created by some collision process, are unstable to the extent of one extra positive charge. Although many such nuclei disintegrate and become stable by the emission of a positron, others draw to them an orbital electron from the *K*-shell of the same atom. Inside the nucleus this negative charge neutralizes a positive charge, whereas outside an *L* or *M* electron jumps into the *K*-shell vacancy with the simultaneous emission of a characteristic X ray (see Fig. 75I). Beryllium 7 and gallium 65 are specific examples of unstable nuclei in which *K-capture* occurs. The reactions for these are

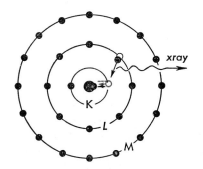

Fig. 75I *Unstable nucleus captures an electron from the K-shell of orbital electrons. As a consequence, an X ray is emitted.*

$$_4Be^7 + _{-1}e^0 = _3Li^7$$
$$_{31}Ga^{65} + _{-1}e^0 = _{30}Zn^{65} \qquad (75p)$$

An energy level diagram involving the radioactive decay of actinium-226 is shown in Fig. 75J. This nucleus is β-active; 80% of its atoms disintegrating by emitting β

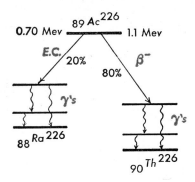

Fig. 75J *Energy level diagram of the two-way radioactive decay of actinium-226.*

particles with an end-point energy of approximately 1 Mev, each followed by the emission of one or two γ rays to become thorium-226. The other 20% of the atoms capture an electron from the K-shell, and immediately emit one or two γ rays to become radium-226.

Electron capture (*abbr.* E.C.) changes one of the nuclear protons into a neutron, and the atomic number drops by unity from 89 to 88. The emission of a β particle changes one of the neutrons into a proton, and the atomic number increases by unity from 89

to 90. In some few isotopes, E.C. is the only means of radioactive decay.

75.7. Nuclear Stability. We now know that, if we bombard targets with atomic particles of sufficiently high energy, every known stable element can be converted into radioactive isotopes of that element or of neighboring elements. Furthermore, a number of isotopes can be produced for any one element, some with masses smaller than any of its stable isotopes, and some with greater masses. In the case of copper, for example, the following isotopes have been produced.

	COPPER $Z = 29$		
Mass	*Activity*	*Half-life*	
58	β^+	3s	
59	β^+	81s	
60	β^+	24m	
61	β^+	3.3h	
62	β^+	10m	
63	Stable	—	70%
64	$\beta^-/\beta^+ = 2$	12.8h	42% E. C.
65	Stable	—	30%
66	β^-	5.1m	
67	β^-	58s	
68	β^-	32s	

The first five isotopes have too many protons to be stable nuclides, and by positron emission convert a proton into a neutron and become an isotope of nickel. The last three isotopes have too few protons, and by electron emission convert a neutron into a proton and become an isotope of zinc. Isotope $_{29}Cu^{64}$ lying between two stable isotopes is unstable several ways; this nuclide may emit a β^-, a β^+, or capture an electron (E. C.). The term *nuclide* is applied to any known assembly of nuclear particles called a nucleus.

A small section of a chart of the known nuclides of all the elements is shown in Fig. 75K.* Each hexagon represents one

* The complete chart of nuclides, prepared by William H. Sullivan, of the Oak Ridge National Laboratory, can be purchased at small cost from the Superintendent of Documents, U. S. Government Printing Office, Washington 25, D.C.

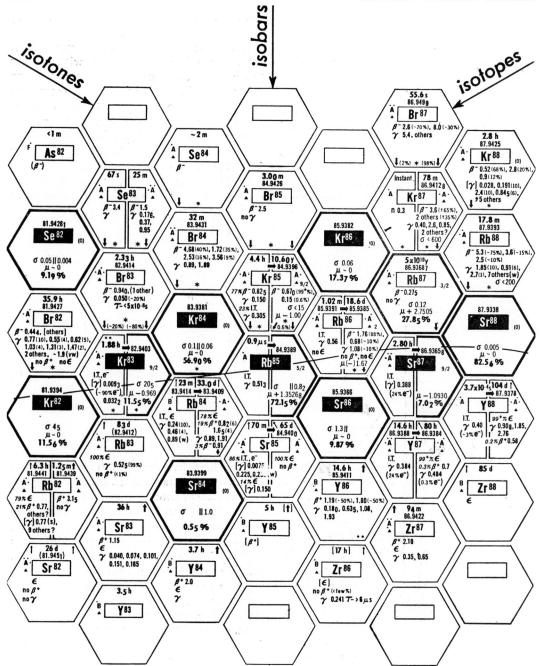

Fig. 75K *Section of the "Trilinear Chart of Nuclides," by W. H. Sullivan.*
(Complete chart obtainable from Supt. of Documents U.S. Gov't. Printing Office,
Washington 25, D.C.)

nuclide, and includes such information as relative abundance, atomic number, mass, half-life, activity, etc. *Isotopes,* nuclides having the same number of protons, lie along a line inclined at 30° with the horizontal. *Isotones,* nuclides having the same number of neutrons, lie along the other 30° line. *Isobars,* nuclides having the same number of nucleons, lie along vertical lines. The small black rectangles represent the stable nuclides; all others are radioactive.

The stability of every nucleus is associated with the relative numbers of neutrons shown in Fig. 75L. It will be noted that along any isobaric line, constant A, there is but one nuclide for *odd-A*. For *even-A*, there are usually two, and occasionally three, stable nuclides having the same A.

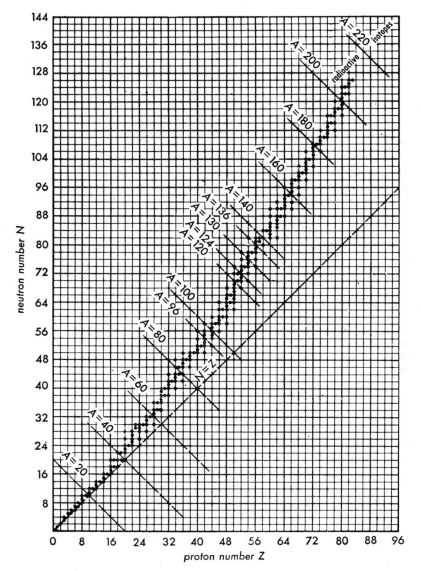

Fig. 75L *Neutron-proton diagram of stable nuclei.*

and protons bound together. If N represents the number of neutrons and Z the number of protons in any nucleus, and we plot a graph for all the known stable nuclides, we obtain a chart like the one

If we plotted vertically upward from the page in Fig. 75L the accurately known atomic masses M for all known stable as well as radioactive nuclides, we would obtain a kind of valley running diagonally up the chart, with the lowest points near the center of the stable nuclides. This is illustrated by a cross-section diagram in Fig. 75M, for $A = 87$. These are the isobars given in the second column from the right in Fig. 75K. Note that the only stable nuclide, $_{38}Sr^{87}$, lies deepest in the valley curve.

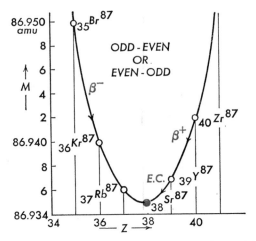

Fig. 75M *Atomic mass graph for nuclides with $A = 87$, and an odd number of protons and even number of neutrons, or vice versa.*

75.8. Medical Applications. Since the time of its discovery, radio-sodium has found numerous and important applications in many branches of science. It has, for example, been used as a means of tracing certain organic and inorganic chemicals passing through the human body, through plants, and through chemical experiments of one kind or another. To give a simple

example, one can show, by drinking water containing radio-sodium in the form of common table salt (NaCl), that within 2 min some of it has entered the blood stream and has been distributed to all parts of the body. The presence of the salt in the finger tips or the toes can be demonstrated by detecting the electrons and γ rays from the sodium with a scintillation counter. Similar experiments can be performed with trees and plants to see how rapidly their roots take up certain plant foods and distribute them to the leaves and branches. At the present time radio-phosphorus 32, because of its chemical properties and its comparatively long *half-life*, is being used in a number of medical researches as a possible cure for certain diseases, as well as for tracing the migration of phosphorus through the body.

One useful medical technique is the use of radioactive elements to obtain *radio-autographs*. A plant or animal is given a single dose of liquid containing the "tagged" atoms; at various times thereafter *thin sections of tissue* from the plant or animal are placed in direct contact against a photographic film. After several hours of exposure to any possible rays from "tagged" atoms in the section, the film is developed. Fig. 75N shows at the left a thin cross-section of the mouse, previously fed radio-phosphorus (see Eq. 75n), and at the right the resulting radio-autograph of this same section. The dark areas indicate the uptake of phosphorus by the *spleen* and *liver* sections, and nowhere else.

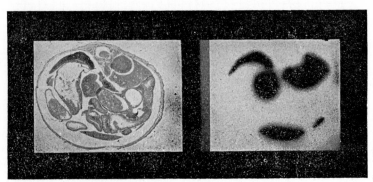

Fig. 75N   *Radio-autograph of the type used in medical studies, showing selective absorption of phosphorus by the liver and spleen.*

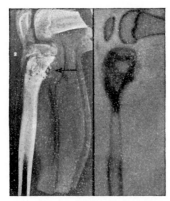

Fig. 75O *X-ray and radio-autograph of a human leg.* (Courtesy, Dr. J. G. Hamilton.)

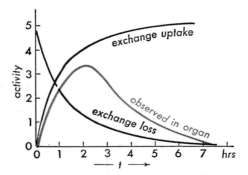

Fig. 75P *Typical exchange curves for radioactive molecules in living systems.*

Fig. 75O shows an X *ray* and *strontium radio-autograph* of a section of an amputated leg from a patient with osteogenic sarcoma (bone cancer). The patient received radio-strontium orally two days before removal of the extremity. The X ray shows the bone tumor at the upper end of the tibia, while the radio-autograph shows selective deposits of strontium in the tumor, with small amounts in the surrounding bone and relatively little in the soft tissues. These studies indicate that radio-strontium may prove useful in clinical therapy.

Since the process of life is one of continual change, there is a rapid turnover of elements in living systems. When common molecules are chemically formed with one or more of their atoms radioactive, they are said to be tagged. In living systems, such as the various organs of the body, these tagged molecules can change places with others of like kind. In time, however, these molecules disappear by natural elimination processes or by decay.

If $_{15}P^{32}$ is taken orally, for example, one finds that after four hours 44% is in the bones, 25% in the muscles, and 2.4% in the blood. When $_{53}I^{131}$ is taken orally, turnover studies show that 80 times as much iodine has been taken up by the thyroid as by any other per gram mass of the body.

A typical graph of the behavior of radioactive elements by living systems is shown in Fig. 75P.

75.9. Radiation Damage. Energy absorbed by the passage of radiation through matter gives rise to structural changes called *radiation damage*. The nature and amount of damage produced is closely related to the number of ion pairs created, and this in turn depends upon the absorbing material and the characteristics of the radiation.

Since biological effects vary widely between body tissues and different types of radiation, it is customary to measure radiation absorption by the number of ion pairs produced in air. The exposure of specimens to any and all kinds of radiation is measured in terms of a unit called the *roentgen*.

Roentgen. The roentgen unit, abbreviated 1r, is that quantity of x- or γ-radiation that produces one electrostatic unit of negative, or positive, charge in 0.001293 grams of dry air. Under standard conditions air has a density of 0.001293 gm/cm³, and one coulomb = 3×10^9 esu. Since the charge of a single electron, or ion, is 1.60×10^{-19} coulomb, the roentgen can also be defined as the quantity of x- or γ-radiation which, under standard conditions, produces in air.

$$\frac{1}{3 \times 10^9 \times 1.6 \times 10^{-19}} =$$

$$2.08 \times 10^9 \text{ ion pairs/cm}^3$$

Experimental measurements show that on the average it takes 32.5 electron volts to produce one ion pair. Consequently,

$$1r = 2.08 \times 10^9 \times 32.5 = 67.6 \text{ Bev}$$

This energy is equivalent to 0.108×10^{-7} joules, or 0.108 ergs. In one gram of air 1r would produce

$$\frac{0.108 \text{ ergs}}{0.001293} = 83.5 \text{ ergs}$$

This same radiation will produce 93 ergs per gram of water (the main constituent of tissue), approximately 40 ergs/gm in fat, and 900 ergs/gm in bone.

Roentgen Equivalent, Physical (rep). This is a unit applied to statements of dose of ionizing radiation not covered by the definition of the roentgen. One *rep* has been defined as the dose that produces an energy absorption of 93 ergs per gram of tissue for the particular radiations in question.

Roentgen Equivalent, Man (rem). A dose of any ionizing radiation producing the same biological effect in tissue as that produced by *one roentgen* of high-voltage, x-radiation is called 1 *rem*. The roentgen is frequently divided into one thousand equal parts called the *milliroentgen*.

1 roentgen = 1000 milliroentgens

1r = 1000 mr

Radiation Dose. The total radiation entering a specified area or volume is called the radiation dose and is measured in *roentgens per hour* or *milliroentgens per hour*.

One effect of penetrating radiation is to bring about gene mutation. Such mutations are of greatest concern to the individual from birth until he conceives no more children. In humans this is assumed to be about 30 years. Experiments show that a total of 50 r per person received during the reproduction period of 30 years doubles the number of mutations that occur naturally in the absence of radiation.

The amount of radiation to which an individual can be subjected with no adverse effects is called a *permissible dose*. This is generally accepted to be 250 mr per week, or 6.25 mr per hr based on a 40 hr working week.*

* See *Pile Neutron Research*, by D. J. Hughes, Addison Wesley Press.

References: Radioactivity and Nuclear Physics, by James Cork, D. Van Nostrand Co.; *Introduction to Atomic Physics*, by Henry Semat, Farrar and Rinehart. *The Atomic Nucleus*, by R. D. Evans, McGraw-Hill Co.

PROBLEMS

1. When 5 Mev α particles bombard Na^{23}, protons are observed being ejected. (a) Write down the disintegration equation, and (b) find the energy liberated.

2. If a 4-Mev deuteron on N^{14} produces a proton, what is the energy liberated? Assume that 94% of the energy goes into the proton. What will be (a) its maximum energy, and (b) its range in air? (See Fig. 70G.) (*Ans.* (a) 11.8 Mev, (b) 152 cm.)

3. When 10-Mev deuterons bombard B^{10}, protons, neutrons, and α particles are observed as disintegration products. Assuming these are branch disintegrations write down the three reactions and give the liberated energies.

4. If 6-Mev deuterons on N^{14} produce C^{12} and α particles, (a) how much energy is liberated? If the available energy is divided between the two particles in the inverse ratio of their respective masses, what is (b) the maximum energy of the α particles, and (c) their range in air? (*Ans.* (a) 19.6 Mev, (b) 14.7 Mev, (c) 20 cm.)

5. If 5-Mev protons are incident on Be^9, α particles are observed emitted as high-speed disintegration products. (a) Write down the reaction, and (b) find the energy liberated. If the liberated energy is divided between the disintegration products in the inverse ratio of their respective masses, what is (c) the energy of the α particles, and (d) their maximum range in air?

6. Copper-64 is a radioactive isotope with a half-life of 12.8 *h*, and decays in three different ways. About 39% of the nuclei decay by the emission of an electron, 19% by the emission of a positron, and 42% by electron capture followed by a γ ray. The electron end-point energy is 0.58 Mev, the positron end-point energy is 0.66 Mev, and the γ-ray energy is 1.34 Mev. Draw an energy level diagram for these changes. (See Fig. 75J.) Write down all three reactions.

7. Cesium-130 is a radioactive isotope with a half-life of 30 *m*. Some of them decay by positron emission with an end-point energy of 1.97 Mev, while the others decay by electron emission with an end-point energy of 0.44 Mev. Write down the reactions, and draw an energy level diagram. (See Fig. 75J.)

Chapter 76

Neutron and Gamma Ray Reactions

76.1. Neutron Reactions. The first disintegrations produced by high-speed neutrons as atomic projectiles were announced in 1932 by the English physicist, Feather. Immediately following Chadwick's discovery of these neutral particles, Feather allowed neutrons from beryllium (see Fig. 76A) to enter a Wilson cloud chamber containing pure nitrogen gas. Numerous expansions of the chamber and the simultaneous clicks of a camera shutter gave many photographs of the ion tracks left by recoiling nitrogen atoms.

Although most of the photographs indicated elastic collisions between nitrogen atoms and neutrons, an occasional photograph showed a forked track, indicating a disintegration of a nitrogen nucleus.

$$_0n^1 + _7N^{14} = _6C^{14} + _1H^1 \qquad (76a)$$

Two photographs of several such disintegrations are reproduced in Fig. 76A. Although hundreds of neutrons enter the cloud chamber every second, they do not ionize atoms as charged particles do, and hence leave no tracks. When a head-on nuclear collision occurs, however, the disintegrated nuclei, possessing as they do high

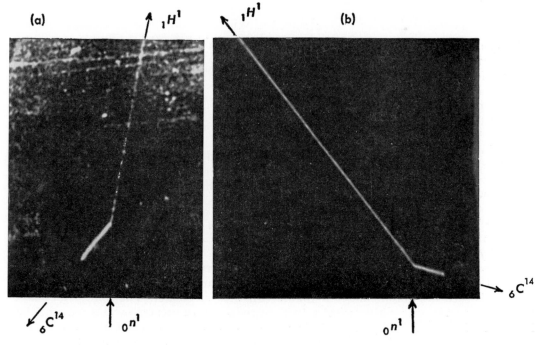

(a) $_1H^1$ $_1H^1$ (b)

$_6C^{14}$ $_0n^1$ $_0n^1$ $_6C^{14}$

Fig. 76A *Cloud-track photographs of neutron disintegrations of nitrogen.* (After Feather and Rasetti.)

659

speeds and positive charges, leave a trail of ions behind them. The fork in each photo shows a proton track of considerable length originating at the same point as the more dense, short-ranged track of the recoiling carbon nucleus.

Strong sources of neutrons are produced by inserting a thin plate of beryllium metal in the intense beam of deuterons coming from the cyclotron as shown in Fig. 76B. The disintegration process, giving rise to the neutrons, is the reaction Eq.(75f).

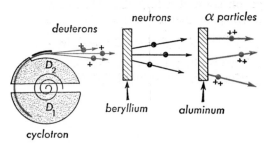

Fig. 76B *Experimental arrangement for producing intense beams of neutrons by bombarding beryllium with deuterons. The neutrons are then used as projectiles for further disintegrations, as illustrated here for aluminum.*

Into such a beam of chargeless particles, numerous substances of known chemical constitution have been inserted, and the disintegration products studied with suitable detectors. To illustrate by an example, suppose that a thin sheet of aluminum is inserted into the beam of neutrons as shown in the figure. In this particular instance, α particles are observed emerging from the aluminum, thus enabling one to write down the following neutron reaction:

$$_0n^1 + _{13}Al^{27} = _{11}Na^{24} + _2He^4 \quad (76b)$$

Thus *radioactive sodium*, produced originally by the deuteron bombardment of ordinary sodium, is here produced by a different reaction. As proof of the result, the bombarded aluminum target is found to be β-ray and γ-ray active with a half-life of 15 hr (see Eq.(75l). There are at least two other known disintegration processes by which radio-sodium is produced: one by the neutron bombardment of sili-

con, and the other by the α-particle bombardment of magnesium.

This is but one example of the many known radioactive elements that can be manufactured in four different ways. As a matter of fact, with sufficiently energetic atomic bullets, it is now possible to produce hundreds of atomic nuclei not found in nature. While most of them have short half-lives and do not last very long, there are many with long half-lives, some extending into thousands of years.

Examples of other neutron disintegrations are illustrated by the following reactions,

$$_0n^1 + _9F^{19} = _7N^{16} + _2He^4 \quad (76c)$$
$$_0n^1 + _{20}Ca^{42} = _{19}K^{42} + _1H^1 \quad (76d)$$
$$_{19}K^{42} = _{20}Ca^{42} + _{-1}e^0$$

Eq.(76d) represents a typical case of the capture of a neutron to form a radioactive isotope $_{19}K^{42}$ which, by the ejection of an electron, reverts back to the original stable element, $_{20}Ca^{42}$. Many such reactions are known, particularly among the heavier elements in the first half of the periodic table.

When 100- to 200-Mev deuterons from a large cyclotron strike almost any target, neutrons with energies of 100 Mev or more are produced. Fig. 76C is a Wilson cloud chamber photo showing the result of a 100-Mev neutron impact with an oxygen nucleus. The paths of the recoiling fragments, four α particles, are bent in the magnetic field.

Not all disintegration processes liberate more energy than that required to produce them. This is illustrated by the following example:

$$_0n^1 + _6C^{12} = _4Be^9 + _2He^4$$
$$Q = -5.7 \text{ Mev} \quad (76e)$$

To carry out this disintegration, the bombarding neutrons must have an energy of 5.7 Mev or greater. The sum of the masses produced are greater by this amount than those that went to make them. This is an example of what is called a fast neutron reaction. It is interesting to point out that this reaction is the reverse of the reaction

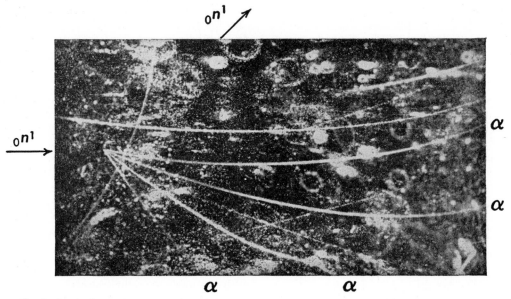

Fig. 76C *Wilson cloud chamber photo showing the result of a 100-Mev neutron impact on an oxygen nucleus. (Courtesy, W. Powell.)*

by which neutrons were first produced in large quantity. (See Sec. 72.5 and Eq.(72g).)

76.2. Slow Neutron Reactions. The fact that neutrons, slowed down to very low speeds, have the ability to disintegrate certain atoms was first discovered and investigated by the Italian physicist, Enrico Fermi, and his collaborators. A neutron approaching the nucleus of an atom does not experience a repulsive force, as does a proton, deuteron, or α particle, and consequently its chances of penetration into, and of being captured by, a nucleus are relatively large. It is for this reason that slowly moving neutrons are able to bring about disintegrations that slowly moving charged particles cannot.

The customary method of producing *slow neutrons* is to surround a source of fast neutrons with paraffin or some material containing large quantities of hydrogen or deuterium. As neutrons pass through this "moderator" material, elastic collisions with hydrogen nuclei continually slow them down, until at a distance of several centimeters from the source most of them have lost all of their original energy. What little energy they do have is picked up by

regular thermal collisions with other atoms.

Since their resultant motions become quite the same as the random motions of the atoms and molecules of the moderator, they are called *thermal neutrons*. Thermal neutrons are defined as neutrons in equilibrium with the substance in which they exist, commonly, neutrons of kinetic energy of 0.0253 electron volts. Compared with fast neutrons moving with almost the speed of light, like those from a target of beryllium bombarded by the beam from a cyclotron, thermal neutrons have a velocity of only 2200 m/sec. This is essentially the velocity of hydrogen molecules in a gas at normal temperature and pressure. See calculation below Eq.(30g).

One of the many known slow neutron reactions is one in which boron-10 captures a neutron and ejects an α particle.

$$_0n^1 + {}_5B^{10} \rightarrow {}_3Li^7 + {}_2He^4 \qquad (76f)$$

76.3. A Thermal Neutron Source. A very good laboratory source of thermal neutrons can be made with a small quantity of radium and beryllium. The radium sample is surrounded by a thin jacket of beryllium metal and an outer jacket of lead, and then this unit is imbedded at the center of several cubic feet of paraffin. (See Fig. 76D.) The α particles from radium produce neutrons by the reaction

$$_2\text{He}^4 + {}_4\text{Be}^9 \rightarrow {}_6\text{C}^{12} + {}_0\text{n}^1 \qquad Q = 5.6 \text{ Mev}$$

The fast neutrons given off by the beryllium metal bounce around in the paraffin, quickly slowing down to thermal velocities, while the unwanted β and γ rays from the radium are absorbed by the lead.

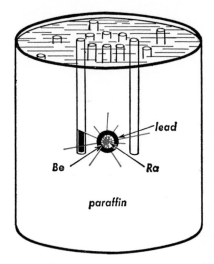

Fig. 76D   *Diagram of a Ra-Be source of thermal neutrons for laboratory experiments.*

Any source to be radiated by slow neutrons is placed in a holder and lowered through any one of several ports shown in the top surface.

An effective demonstration of slow neutron reactions can be made by rolling a thin sheet of silver metal into a hollow cylinder, about 1 in. in diameter and 4 in. long, and subjecting it to the Ra-Be source (Fig. 76D). After several minutes the cylinder is withdrawn and quickly placed around a geiger-counter tube, or near the fluor of a scintillation counter. The activity detected will be strong at first and then will slowly die out over a period of several minutes.

If a scaler counting system like the one shown in Fig. 71O is employed, and the number of counts registered on the tube faces are recorded at 10 sec intervals, a decay curve like the one shown in Fig. 76E can be plotted. Such a graph with two distinct straight sections is found to be a composite of two half-life curves, one for 24 sec and the other for 2.3 min. These two half-lives are attributed to the two stable isotopes of silver, one of mass 107 amu and one of 109 amu.

The capture of a neutron by each of these nuclides produces the radioactive isotopes, silver-108 and silver-110. Both of these are electron active, and produce stable cadmium nuclides as follows:

$$_{48}\text{Ag}^{108} \rightarrow {}_{49}\text{Cd}^{108} + {}_{-1}\text{e}^0 \qquad (2.3m)$$
$$_{48}\text{Ag}^{110} \rightarrow {}_{49}\text{Cd}^{110} + {}_{-1}\text{e}^0 \qquad (24.2s)$$

The procedure for finding the two half-lives from the graph in Fig. 76E is to start with the lower straight section and extrapolate back to zero time. This straight line is then subtracted from the upper curve at two points of time, such as $t = 0$ and $t = 100$ sec, and the other straight line drawn in as shown. The summation of these two straight lines should produce the observed curve. Note that the straight lines drop to half their initial values at $t = 24$ sec and $t = 138$ sec.

Another effective demonstration of slow neutron reactions is to roll a thin sheet of indium metal into a hollow cylinder, subject it to the slow neutron source (Fig. 76D) and then place it over a geiger-counter tube or scintillation counter. Like silver, it too will show a strong activity at first and then die out over a period of several minutes.

Indium has two stable isotopes, $_{49}\text{In}^{213}$ and $_{49}\text{In}^{215}$. Upon neutron capture they will become the radioactive isotopes, $_{49}\text{In}^{214}$ and $_{49}\text{In}^{216}$. Both of these nuclides decay by electron emission into stable tin isotopes.

$$_{49}\text{In}^{214} \rightarrow {}_{50}\text{Sn}^{214} + {}_{-1}\text{e}^0 \qquad (72 \text{ sec})$$
$$_{49}\text{In}^{216} \rightarrow {}_{50}\text{Sn}^{216} + {}_{-1}\text{e}^0 \qquad (13 \text{ sec})$$

76.4. Neutron Diffraction. We have seen in a preceding chapter that wave properties are associated with all moving bodies. The DeBroglie wavelength of any mass m is given by Eq.(68i) as

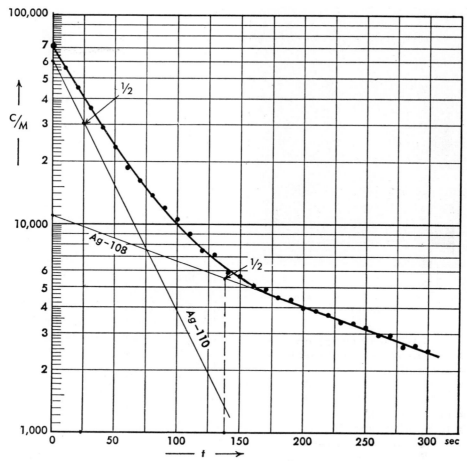

Fig. 76E *Semi-log graph of the β rays from the two silver isotopes, made active by thermal neutrons.*

$$\lambda = \frac{h}{mv} \qquad (76g)$$

which for thermal neutrons with a velocity of 2200 m/sec gives $\lambda = 1.8 \times 10^{-10}$ meters, or 1.8 A. This value is comparable to the spacings of atoms in solids and suggests the possibilities of diffraction, as in the case of X rays and Laue patterns. (See Figs. 62F and 62G.)

The diffraction of strong beams of neutrons by the atoms of a crystal has been studied by many people. Wollan and Shull, using a sodium chloride crystal and an experimental arrangement similar to that shown for X rays in Fig. 62F, obtained the picture reproduced in Fig. 76F. Since neu-

trons have little or no effect upon photographic films, the front face of the film was covered with a sheet of indium metal 0.5 mm thick.

Neutrons captured by the indium nuclei produce radioactive isotopes, as shown in the preceding section. These unstable isotopes disintegrate with the emission of electrons. Electrons do affect a photographic emulsion and upon development produce the spots shown. Neutrons, like X rays, therefore, become useful tools in the study of the atomic structure of matter.

76.5. Photon Interactions. The term "photon interaction" refers to the disintegration of atomic nuclei brought about by photons. In general, the photons to be used

Fig. 76F *Neutron diffraction pattern of sodium chloride.* (Courtesy E. O. Wollan and C. G. Shull.)

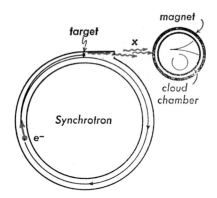

Fig. 76G *Photons produced by the electron beam from a synchrotron are used to study photon reactions in a cloud chamber.*

must have a very high energy $h\nu$, and this means their frequency ν must be high and their wavelength λ short. $(c = \nu\lambda)$.

X rays and γ rays are electromagnetic waves in character, and both are composed of photons. The terms X ray or γ ray only signify their origin and, in reactions with nuclei, are of no consequence.

Instead of specifying a photon by giving its frequency ν, it is customary in nuclear reactions to express its energy in electron volts. By the general energy equation, Eq. (70k), we have

$$Ve = h\nu \quad \text{or} \quad V = h\nu/e \quad (76h)$$

For reference purposes, only the following wavelengths and frequencies are calculated from this equation.

V (volts)	λ (m)	ν (1/sec)
1 Kev	1.24×10^{-9}	2.4×10^{17}
1 Mev	1.24×10^{-12}	2.4×10^{20}
1 Bev	1.24×10^{-15}	2.4×10^{23}

To obtain sources of high-energy photons, it is common practice to use γ rays from radioactive sources, or to produce

X rays with the high-energy electron beam of a betatron or synchrotron. Thorium C″, for example, produces 2.62 Mev γ rays that are useful for many kinds of experiments.

As an example of the production of high-energy photons with the beam from a large electron accelerator, consider the 1.3 Bev electrons of the Cornell synchrotron (see Fig. 76G). Each time the beam in this machine is allowed to strike the metal target inside the vacuum chamber, the 1.3— Bev electrons produce X rays of extreme penetrating power. Target composition is of little importance in this process, since the phenomenon called "Bremsstrahlung" is responsible for the high-

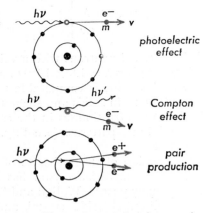

Fig. 76H *Illustration of the three major processes responsible for the absorption of high-energy photons in matter.*

energy X ray beam that emerges. (See Fig. 62M.) In such a beam one finds a continuous band of photons ranging in energy from practically 0 up to 1.3 Bev.

As such a beam is made to traverse any form of matter, there are several processes by which the rays are absorbed or scattered from the beam. These, as shown in Fig. 76H, are:

photoelectric effect
Compton effect
pair production

For photons of low energy the photoelectric effect is chiefly responsible for absorption. As the energy increases, the Compton effect becomes more and more important until, at energies of 1 Mev, pair production sets in and eventually becomes predominant.

A diffusion cloud chamber photograph of a Compton recoil electron, and an electron pair is shown in Fig. 76I. The hundreds of photons that passed through this gas-filled cloud chamber, from left to right, left no tracks since they were electrically neutral. One photon, however, collided with an atomic electron near the upper center of the field, and the forward recoiling electron, in the magnetic field applied to the chamber, made $1\frac{3}{4}$ turns around a circle. Another photon, coming close to a nucleus at the upper left, created an electron pair. From the curvatures of the

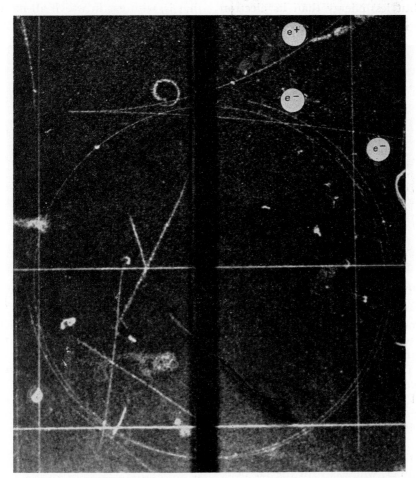

Fig. 76I *Cloud chamber photograph showing a Compton recoil electron (circle) and an electron pair (V-track) produced by photons.* (Courtesy, Cornell Laboratory.)

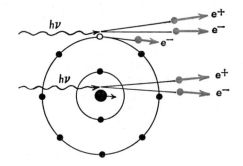

Fig. 76J *High-energy photons can produce electron pairs by collision with a nucleus or an orbital electron.*

tracks it is clear that the positron curving upward had more energy than the Compton electron, but less energy than its electron associate.

A cloud chamber photograph showing an electron triplet and an electron pair is reproduced in Fig. 76K.* Of the many photons traversing the chamber from left to right, one came extremely close to an atomic electron, and there in the strong electric field created a pair, the positron bending upward, the slower electron downward, and the still slower recoiling electron spiraling around in a small circle. The second photon coming close to the nucleus of a hydrogen atom produced another pair, the positron bending upward and the electron downward. Note the tiny recoil track of the nucleus.

76.6. Photon-Deuteron Interactions. If a cloud chamber is filled with deuterium, that is, with gas in which all molecules are composed of the heavy hydrogen atoms,

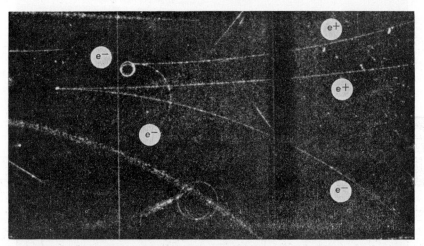

Fig. 76K *Cloud chamber photograph showing an electron triplet and an electron pair produced by high-energy photons. See Fig. 76J. (Courtesy, Cornell Laboratory.)*

The production of a pair of electrons by a photon passing close to an atomic nucleus can also occur in the region close to an electron. (See Fig. 76J.) In both of these processes, the force exerted by the photon on the charged particle during the pair creation causes that particle to recoil forward. Because of its relatively small mass, the electron recoil may be large enough to appear as a third track in a cloud chamber, whereas with the far heavier nucleus the recoil is so small that a track is seldom observed.

$_1H^2$, interesting photon interactions can be observed. One process is shown in Fig. 76L. A deuteron, the nucleus of a deuterium atom, is composed of one neutron and one proton.

If a photon collides with the neutron of a deuteron, it may produce a proton p and a pi-minus meson, π^-, as shown. Since the

* The photographs in Figs. 76I, 76K, 76M, 76O, and 76Q were supplied by the diffusion cloud chamber research group, B. Chasan, G. Cocconi, V. Cocconi, E. Hart, R. Schectman, and D. White, at Cornell University.

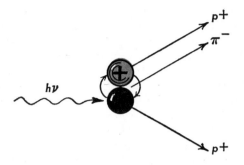

Fig. 76L *Diagram showing one type of reaction produced by photon collisions with deuterons. See Fig. 76M.*

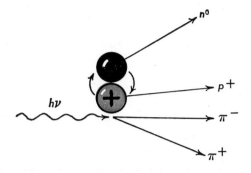

Fig. 76N *Diagram of a photon collision with the proton of a deuteron, producing a pair of π mesons. See Fig. 76O.*

two particles leave so quickly after the collision, the remaining "spectator proton" continues on with whatever momentum it had at the moment of impact. The reaction for this can be written

$$h\nu + d \rightarrow p + \pi^- + \underbrace{p}_{spectator} \qquad (76i)$$

Such an explanation accounts for the cloud chamber event shown in Fig. 76M. A photon entering from the left, collides with the neutron of a deuteron. The neutron is split into a proton, p and a π meson, π^-, with the low momentum "spectator proton" stopping in the chamber.

Since everyone knows that a proton or deuteron has unit positive charge, and neutrons and neutrinos have none, their charge exponents are usually omitted in reactions.

76.7. Photo Production of Meson Pairs. If a high-energy photon comes close enough to a proton in a nucleus, a π meson pair may be created in much the same way that an electron pair is produced with a photon

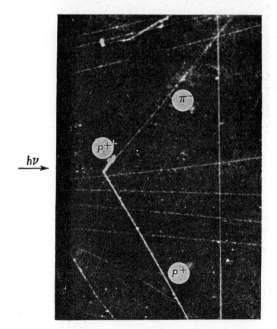

Fig. 76M *Cloud chamber photograph showing one type of photon reaction. (See Fig. 76L.) (Courtesy, Cornell Laboratories.)*

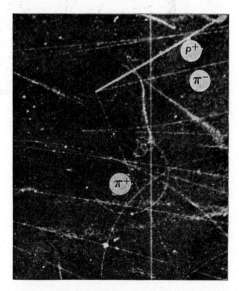

Fig. 76O *Photograph of a photon collision with the proton of a deuteron, producing a pair of π mesons. (Courtesy, Cornell Laboratories.)*

of lower energy. If the nucleus is a deuteron, as shown in Fig. 76N, the proton recoils from the impact while the neutron continues on with whatever momentum it had at the moment of impact.

As a reaction, we can write,

$$h\nu + d \rightarrow p + \pi^- + \pi^+ + \underbrace{n}_{spectator} \qquad (76j)$$

This reaction accounts for the cloud chamber event shown in Fig. 76O. A photon, entering from the left, comes close to the proton of a deuteron. A pair of π mesons is created, the proton recoils under the impact, and the neutron "spectator," not being able to form a track, goes on in some unknown direction.

In all such reactions the conservation laws of energy, momentum, and charge must hold. Measurements of track curvatures give velocities and momenta of particles, and calculations are made to see that the conservation of energy and momentum hold. We have seen previously that approximately 1 Mev is required to create an electron pair. Since a π meson has a mass 275 times that of an electron, an energy of approximately 275 Mev is required to create a pair of π mesons. This is the thresh-

hold energy for meson pair-production.

Another interesting reaction involving the impact of a high-energy photon with a deuteron is one in which the processes shown in Figs. 76L and 76O are combined. As shown schematically in Fig. 76P, a photon collides with the neutron, splits it apart into a proton, p, and a π meson, π^-, and simultaneously creates a π meson pair, while the proton "spectator" continues on with its relatively low energy. The reaction is written

$$h\nu + d \rightarrow p + p + \pi^- + \pi^+ + \pi^- \quad (76k)$$

All five of these particles have a charge and may be identified in the cloud chamber event reproduced in Fig. 76Q. The labora-

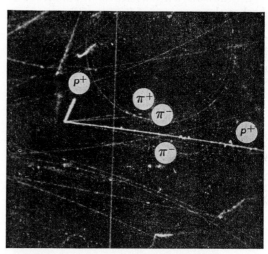

Fig. 76Q *Cloud chamber photograph of a photon collision with a deuteron, splitting the neutron and producing a pair of π mesons.* (Courtesy, Cornell Laboratories.)

tory-measured angles, the ionization along the tracks of the five particles, as well as the momentum calculations, readily verify the dynamics of this event.

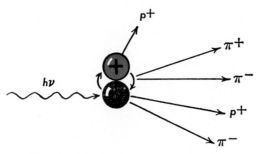

Fig. 76P *Diagram of a photon collision with a deuteron, splitting the neutron and producing a pair of π mesons. See Fig. 76Q.*

QUESTIONS AND PROBLEMS

1. Charged particles show their tracks in a Wilson cloud chamber. Neutrons and γ rays do not. Why?

2. How are strong beams of neutrons produced? Can neutrons be accelerated in a cyclotron?

3. When magnesium-24 is bombarded by neutrons, protons are found coming from the target. Write down the resultant reaction.

4. When neutrons collide with oxygen-16 nuclei, α particles are observed to be given off. Write down the reaction.

5. If radioactive sulfur-35 is produced by the neutron bombardment of chlorine-35, what is the reaction equation?

6. How are photons with an energy of 1 Bev produced in the laboratory? Make a diagram and explain the atomic process involved.

7. What are thermal neutrons? What are slow neutrons?

8. Make a diagram of a radium-beryllium source of thermal neutrons. Explain the function of each substance used.

9. When slow neutrons are captured by iodine-127, the resulting nuclei give off electrons with an end-point energy of 2.1 Mev. Write down the two reactions.

10. If the mass of iodine-127 is 126.9460 amu, find the masses of the two other nuclei resulting from slow neutron capture described in Prob. 9. (*Ans.* (a) $I^{128} = 127.9550$, (b) $Xe^{128} = 127.9532$.)

11. If indium metal is subjected to thermal neutrons for some time, and then placed close to a scintillation counter, the initial counting rate is found to be 60,000 counts per min. Plot a semi-log graph for the activity from this metal for the succeeding 2 min.

12. If a photon in coming close to a nucleus were to create a pair of protons, what would the threshhold energy be in electron volts? (*Note:* Proton mass is 1.00763 amu.) (*Ans.* 1.876 Bev.)

Chapter 77

The Atomic Nucleus

77.1. What Holds the Nucleus Together?
Although the disintegrations of different nuclei give rise to many different kinds of particles or units of energy, it would appear that we need assume only two kinds of particles existing within the nucleus—*neutrons* and *protons*. If this is correct, our task becomes the difficult one of explaining not only the disintegration mechanism of an unstable nucleus but the binding forces that hold a stable nucleus together. An answer to the latter question will serve as a starting point for the following presentations.

According to the *neutron-proton theory* of the atomic nucleus (see Fig. 77A), the

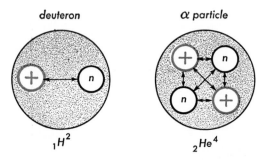

Fig. 77A *Schematic diagram of the nucleus for (a) a deuterium atom, and (b) a helium atom.*

deuteron nucleus contains but one neutron and one proton. Let us compare, therefore, the mass of one free proton and one free neutron with their mass when combined as a deuteron (for masses, see Appendix VII).

Neutron mass $_0n^1 = 1.00898$
Proton mass $_1H^1 = 1.00814$
Sum $= 2.01712$
Deuteron mass $_1H^2 = 2.01474$

The difference in mass of 0.00238 atomic mass unit (*abbr.* amu) is not due to inaccurate measurements of mass but is a real difference to be accounted for as the annihilation energy that binds the two particles together. When a neutron and proton come together to form a deuteron, a small part of their mass—namely 0.00238 amu (equivalent to 2.2 Mev energy)—is radiated from the newly formed nucleus. At close approach, in other words, the two particles attract each other so strongly that, once together, it takes the equivalent of a little more than two million electron volts of energy to pull them apart. This has been confirmed by a nuclear photoelectric effect, an experiment in which γ rays of 2.2 Mev energy or greater are found to break up deuterium nuclei into their constituent parts, while γ rays of lower energy have no effect. How neutrons and protons attract each other when very close together is a question of great importance, for we now realize that the stability of all the universe as we know it depends upon these forces.

Consider as a second example, the attractive forces between the four nucleons of a helium nucleus, i.e., the two neutrons and two protons of an α particle as shown in Fig. 77A. By combining the masses of the four free particles and comparing them with the mass of the helium atom, we obtain

$$2_0n^1 + 2_1H^1 = 4.03424 \text{ amu}$$
$$He^4 = 4.00387 \text{ amu}$$
$$\text{Mass difference} = 0.03037 \text{ amu}$$
$$E = 28 \text{ Mev}$$

This value of 28 Mev indicates a binding energy of 7 Mev per nucleon, a value considerably higher than 2.2 Mev for the deu-

670

teron. This is a measure of the energy that must be expended in breaking the attractive bonds shown in the diagram.

If we make similar calculations for other nuclides near the beginning of the periodic table, and plot a graph of the binding energy per nucleon, E/A, where A is the mass number, we obtain Fig. 77B. If this same

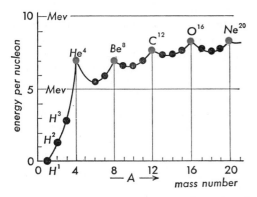

Fig. 77B *Binding energy per nucleon for the lightest elements in the periodic table.*

procedure is carried out for the entire periodic table, a graph like the one shown in Fig. 77C is obtained. By drawing a horizontal line across the upper part of the graph at 8 Mev, as shown by the red line, we obtain a kind of average binding energy per nucleon for nearly all the elements. This value is approximately the difference between unit atomic mass and the mass of a free neutron or proton.

Collisions between high-energy photons and nuclei, giving rise to several kinds of reactions, are given in the preceding chapter. One process not described there, and called the *nuclear photoelectric effect,* is shown in Fig. 77D. A photon of energy $h\nu$, passing close to a nucleus, is absorbed; part of the energy is used to remove a neutron or proton from the nucleus, and the remainder given to the particle as kinetic energy. See Eq.(61a).

$$h\nu = W + \tfrac{1}{2}mv^2 \qquad (77a)$$

The work function W, as we have seen above, is about 8 Mev and is essentially the energy required to create the extra mass needed by the nucleon to set it free.

77.2. The Packing Fraction. An informative method of displaying the mass differences and binding energies of stable nuclei is to plot a graph of all packing fractions. The *packing fraction P* of any nuclide is obtained from the relation

$$P = \frac{M - A}{A} \qquad (77b)$$

where $M - A$ for any nuclide is called its *mass defect.*

$$\begin{aligned} M &= \text{mass of nuclide} \\ A &= \text{mass number} \end{aligned} \qquad (77c)$$

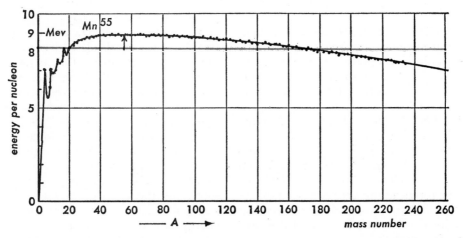

Fig. 77C *Binding energy per nucleon for the stable isotopes of the periodic table.*

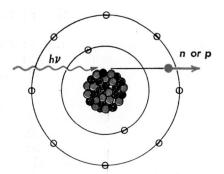

Fig. 77D *Diagram illustrating the nuclear photoelectric effect.*

Picture again a proton or an α particle, with its positive charge, approaching a positively charged nucleus. As the two charges come closer and closer together, they repel each other with greater and greater forces as given by Coulomb's law. This repulsion cannot continue to increase all the way to zero separation, however, for as the two charges come very close together we know, from what has been said in the preceding section, there must be an attraction. Gamow proposed, therefore, that at close approach there is another law of force that comes into play and that this force is one of attraction for neutrons as well as protons and is very strong.

In other words, P is the difference between the average nucleon mass for that nuclide and unit atomic mass. It will be seen in Fig. 77E that the very light and the

Since Coulomb's law is known to hold quite accurately at large distances, this

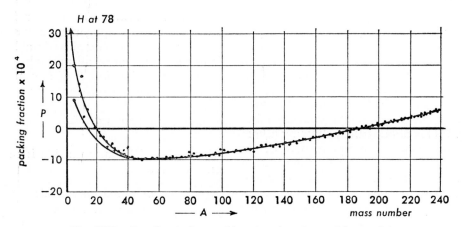

Fig. 77E *Graph of the packing fraction for stable nuclei.*

heavy nuclides have an average mass greater than unity, whereas those near the middle of the graph have a mass less than unity. In the next chapter we shall see that these differences are directly related to the availability of nuclear energy.

77.3. The Nuclear Potential Barrier. Early in the development of ideas concerning nuclear disintegration, Gamow proposed a model by which one might represent the atomic nucleus. This model is based upon the forces acting between two positive charges and is an extension of the nuclear model described in Sec. 72.2, and illustrated in Figs. 72D and 72E.

added factor is called a *short-range force.* Graphs of Coulomb's law for repulsion and the short-range force for attraction are shown in Fig. 77F. Note that when the particle is at the distance shown, 9×10^{-13} cm, Coulomb's law of repulsion is predominant, whereas, at a distance less than 2×10^{-13} cm, the short-range force of attraction predominates. Since both of these forces are effective for all distances, they should be combined into one graph as shown by the F curve in Fig. 77G. If instead of the force F we plot the potential energy stored between the two particles, we obtain the P.E. curve shown by the

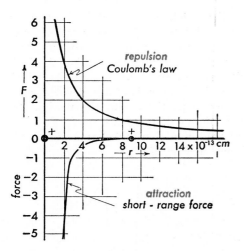

Fig. 77F *Diagram showing the two force laws for a positive charge close to a nucleus.*

dotted line. Such a curve represents what is called the *potential barrier* of the nucleus. The highest point of the barrier is frequently called the edge of the nucleus which, for heavy atoms in the periodic table, occurs at, and gives a nuclear radius of, from 1 to 6×10^{-13} cm.

A very good mechanical model of the nucleus, having the form of a *well* or the *crater of a volcano,* can be made by rotating the dotted line around the vertical axis (see Fig. 77H). The electrical potential energy,

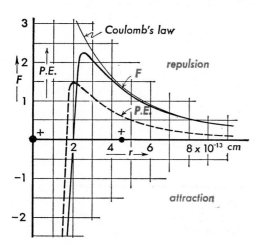

Fig. 77G *Graphs of the force and potential energy of a positively charged particle close to a nucleus.*

P.E., between the two positively charged particles, is analogous to the potential energy of a ball at any point on the hill, and the electrostatic force of repulsion is analogous to the force of gravity.

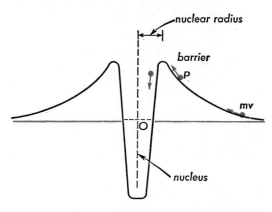

Fig. 77H *A graphical model of the atomic nucleus as proposed by Gamow. The potential barrier of a nucleus to an approaching positive charge is analogous to the crater of a volcano.*

If now a small marble, representing a proton or an α particle, approaches the nuclear barrier, it will roll up the hill as shown in the diagram. Experiencing a rapidly increasing force down the hill, the ball may be turned back, or off to one side, and we have elastic scattering of the kind observed by Rutherford (see Fig. 72C). If the initial velocity is high enough, however, the ball may go over the top of the barrier and drop down inside, representing a capture.

77.4. Bohr's Nuclear Model. In 1937 Niels Bohr, the famous Danish physicist, made another outstanding contribution to modern physics when he improved Gamow's model of the nucleus by extending what is sometimes called the *waterdrop model* of the nucleus. Bohr, and his collaborator Kalkar, imagines the many particles in a heavy nucleus as moving about within a spherical enclosure with motions analogous to the molecules in a drop of water. The surface of the spherical enclosure, which is the top of the potential barrier as represented in Fig. 77I, is analogous to

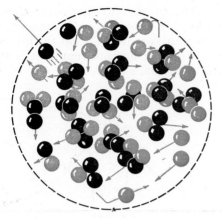

Fig. 77I   *Nucleus in the act of ejecting a neutron, based upon the Bohr-Gamow waterdrop model.*

the surface tension which holds a small waterdrop to its spherical form.

Just as the rapid motion of the molecules in water is a measure of the temperature, so Bohr speaks of the rapid motion of the neutrons and protons within the spherical boundary of the nucleus as a sort of *pseudo-temperature*. To explain disintegration, the analogy is drawn that the ejection of a particle from the nucleus is like the evaporation of a water molecule from a drop of water. Just as a rise in temperature brings about a more rapid evaporation of water, so an increase in the motions within the nucleus gives rise to a higher probability of disintegration.

In a stable nucleus, the particles within are moving about with very little kinetic energy, and are in the analogous state of a relatively low temperature. When a high-

speed particle from outside penetrates the potential barrier, it is accelerated toward the center of the nucleus and acquires a very high kinetic energy before it collides with one or more of the particles inside. Soon the energy becomes divided among the many particles, and the nucleus takes on a higher temperature state. The potential well model of this same condition is shown in Fig. 77J.

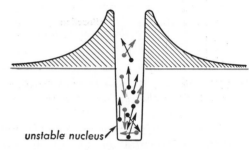

Fig. 77J   *Well-model diagram representing an unstable nucleus.*

Now, as the particles move about inside, there is a certain probability or chance that, within a given interval of time, some one particle will be hit by several particles, giving it a sufficiently high velocity in an outward direction to permit an escape through the potential barrier. The more rapid the internal motions, that is, the higher the temperature, the greater is this chance of escape.

A direct disintegration may be described in this way: If upon entering the nucleus a high-speed particle like a proton adds sufficient energy to give the nucleus a high

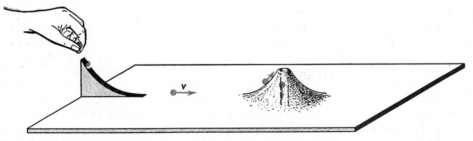

Fig. 77K   *Mechanical model of a nucleus for demonstrating the capture of a high-speed proton, deuteron, or α particle, prior to disintegration.*

temperature, another particle like a neutron or an α particle may be ejected immediately. Since such an ejected particle has to be supplied with a certain minimum energy to get free, the remaining particles will be slowed down, and the nucleus will have a lower temperature.

77.5. Nuclear Demonstration Models. A demonstration model illustrating the capture of a high-speed proton or an α particle by a nucleus, prior to disintegration, is shown in Fig. 77K. Marbles rolled down the incline represent the speeding-up of atomic projectiles by an accelerator like the cyclotron. Approaching the potential barrier, a marble may roll part way up and then be deflected off to one side, illustrating an elastic collision without capture; or it may roll up the side and drop into the crater opening at the top, representing a capture prior to disintegration.

A demonstration of what happens inside the nucleus is illustrated by another model as shown in Fig. 77L. In this case the ver-

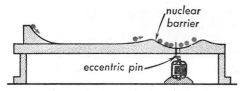

Fig. 77L *Mechanical model of a nucleus for demonstrating (a) the increased kinetic energy of nuclear particles after a capture, and (b) the chance probability of radioactive decay or disintegration by the ejection of a particle.*

tical scale of the barrier has, of necessity, been reduced, i.e., flattened out. When a marble is rolled down the incline and into the group of marbles at the center of the barrier, there may be several collisions before another particle usually goes bouncing out on the other side. This corresponds to a direct disintegration where one particle like a proton goes in and a neutron comes out.

If a single particle does not emerge, most of the particles inside take on random motions, colliding with each other much the same as do the molecules or atoms in a gas

or liquid. To prevent friction from stopping them (there is no friction in an atom), the marbles are continually agitated by a small pin protruding through from underneath the barrier. This pin is mounted slightly off center at the end of the shaft of a small electric motor. If the motor is left running for some time, a single marble will eventually be hit by several particles moving in the same direction and will recoil with sufficient speed to carry it over the barrier and out. This corresponds to a disintegration or radioactive decay, which takes place according to the *laws of chance,* and to the resultant drop in "temperature" of the nucleus.

The faster the motor runs, the greater is the internal agitation and chance of ejection, and the shorter is the so-called, half-life of the element.

77.6. Nuclear Model for Neutron Disintegrations. When a neutron approaches a nucleus prior to a disintegration, it does not encounter a potential barrier of the type already described for protons and α particles. A neutron has no charge, so that at large distances it is not repelled by the positively charged nucleus. It may, therefore, approach a nucleus with very little speed of its own and be captured when it comes too close. At very close range the short-range attractive force shown in Fig. 77F sets in, and draws the two together.

To an approaching neutron, the nucleus acts as though it were a pit into which the particle will fall. This is illustrated by the flat potential curve in Fig. 77M. The marble rolling along the horizontal plane to-

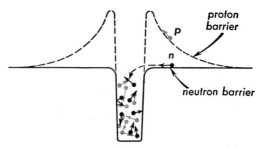

Fig. 77M *A graphical model of the nucleus as it is presented to an approaching neutron or proton.*

ward the pit represents the influence of the nucleus upon the neutron's motion, whereas the marble rolling up the hill (dotted line) represents the influence of the same nucleus upon the motion of a proton. A mechanical model patterned after Fig. 77H, and made with the neutron barrier shape, makes an excellent demonstration of neutron scattering and capture.

77.7. Nuclear Spin. Approximately $\frac{1}{3}$ of all known stable nuclei, and many of the radioactive nuclides, are known to have a mechanical moment p_I and a magnetic moment μ_I. The earliest evidence for a nuclear spin, as it is called, was found in atomic spectra. Many spectrum lines show a fine structure which in Sec. 66.4 was explained as being due to electron spin. Many of these fine structure lines show a still finer structure, now known to be due to a nuclear spin.

As an example of this *hyperfine structure,* as it is called, several of the spectrum lines of the element praseodymium are shown

tive experiments show that this *quantum number, I,* can take half-integral as well as whole-number values. (See Table 77A.)

TABLE 77A. TYPICAL NUCLEAR SPINS AND MAGNETIC MOMENTS

	I	g-factor		I	g-factor
$_1\text{H}^1$	$\frac{1}{2}$	$+2.792$	$_{23}\text{V}^{51}$	$\frac{7}{2}$	$+5.15$
$_1\text{H}^2$	1	$+0.857$	$_{25}\text{Mn}^{55}$	$\frac{5}{2}$	$+3.47$
$_3\text{Li}^6$	1	$+0.82$	$_{50}\text{Sn}^{119}$	$\frac{1}{2}$	-1.05
$_3\text{Li}^7$	$\frac{3}{2}$	$+3.26$	$_{55}\text{Cs}^{135}$	$\frac{7}{2}$	$+2.73$
$_4\text{Be}^9$	$\frac{3}{2}$	-1.18	$_{80}\text{Hg}^{198}$	0	0
$_5\text{B}^{10}$	3	$+1.80$	$_{80}\text{Hg}^{199}$	$\frac{1}{2}$	$+0.50$
$_8\text{O}^{16}$	0	0	$_{80}\text{Hg}^{200}$	0	0
$_8\text{O}^{17}$	$\frac{5}{2}$	-1.89	$_{80}\text{Hg}^{201}$	$\frac{3}{2}$	-0.56
$_8\text{O}^{18}$	0	0	$_{83}\text{Bi}^{209}$	$\frac{9}{2}$	$+4.08$

The magnetic moments of nuclei in general are extremely small as compared with those associated with electrons in the outer structures of atoms. For all nuclei the magnetic moment is given by the relation

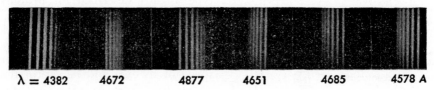

$$\lambda = 4382 \qquad 4672 \qquad 4877 \qquad 4651 \qquad 4685 \qquad 4578 \text{ A}$$

Fig. 77N *Photographs of the hyperfine structure of a few of the spectrum lines of the element praseodymium, Z = 59. Wavelengths are in Angstrom units. Structure produced by nuclear spin.*

in Fig. 77N. In a normal spectrogram these look like single lines, but, under the high dispersion and magnification shown here, each line reveals six hyperfine components. The six components signify that the nucleus of praseodymium has a spin angular momentum $p_I = \frac{5}{2}\hbar$ and a large magnetic moment.

The angular momenta of nuclei in general are given by

$$p_I = I\hbar \qquad (77\text{d})$$

where I is the nuclear spin quantum number, and $\hbar$ represents unit angular momentum given by $\dfrac{h}{2\pi}$. (See Eq.(66b).) Quantita-

$$\mu_I = g\hbar \frac{e}{2M} \qquad (77\text{e})$$

where the *g-factor* varies from nucleus to nucleus, $\hbar$ is unit angular momentum, and M is the mass of the proton. The last two factors involve fixed atomic constants, and combined are called the *nuclear magneton.* One nuclear magneton is given by

$$\mu_n = \hbar \frac{e}{2M} \qquad (77\text{f})$$

or $\mu_n = 5.050 \times 10^{-27}$ ampere meters^2

The g-factor therefore gives the nuclear magnetic moment in nuclear magnetons.

Note that one nuclear magneton is 1/1836 of one Bohr magneton. (See Eq.(66e).)

A list of a few nuclides in Table 77A shows typical values of the nuclear spin quantum number I, and the measured magnetic moments in nuclear magnetons.

77.8. Proton and Neutron Spin. Every proton, whether it is bound to an atom or is free, has a spin angular momentum of $\frac{1}{2}\hbar$. (See Fig. 77N.)

$$p_{proton} = \tfrac{1}{2}\hbar \qquad (77g)$$

Having a positive charge, the magnetic field around a proton is parallel to its mechanical moment, instead of oppositely directed as is the case with an electron. (See Fig. 66F.) Furthermore, since the mass of a proton is 1836 times the mass of an electron, it maintains the same angular momentum by spinning much slower, and this reduces its magnetic moment to a relatively small value. The magnetic moment of a proton is found by precision experimental measurements to be

$$\mu_{proton} = 2.792 \text{ nuclear magnetons} \qquad (77h)$$

The neutron, like the proton and electron, has a spin angular momentum of $\frac{1}{2}\hbar$.

$$p_{neutron} = \tfrac{1}{2}\hbar \qquad (77i)$$

Having no net charge, the neutron might well be expected to have zero magnetic moment. Experimentally, however, its spin does produce a magnetic field, and one that is oppositely directed to angular mo-

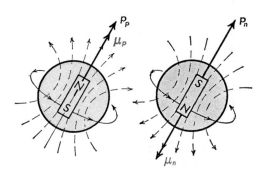

Fig. 77O *Schematic diagrams showing proton and neutron spins and associated magnetic moments.*

mentum. (See Fig. 77O.) The neutrons magnetic moment is

$$\mu_{neutron} = -1.913 \text{ nuclear magnetons} \qquad (77j)$$

A negative magnetic moment is a clear indication that the neutron is a complex particle containing negative and positive charges in equal amounts, and that the negative charge is, on the average, farther from its axis of rotation.

77.9. The Deuteron. The deuteron is a nuclear particle composed of one proton and one neutron. Its known spin of $I = 1$ (see Table 77A) indicates that the spins of the two particles are parallel to each other as shown in Fig. 77P. Since the two mag-

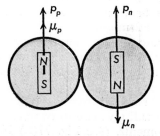

Fig. 77P *Schematic diagram of the deuteron, showing proton and neutron spins parallel and magnetic moments opposing.*

netic moments are oppositely directed, the resultant magnetic moment of the combination should be $2.792 - 1.913$, or 0.879 nuclear magnetons. Precision measurements, however, show that μ_d is slightly smaller than this, and is

$$\mu_{deuteron} = 0.857 \text{ nuclear magnetons} \qquad (77k)$$

77.10. Nuclear Shell Model. A reasonably successful theory of nuclear spins and magnetic moments is based upon the electron spin-orbit model so successful in explaining the outer structure of atoms. (See Sec. 66.5.) Experimental evidence for this idea stems in large measure from a classification of all stable nuclides as to their odd or even numbers of protons and neutrons. (See Table 77B.)

While all nucleons have a spin of $\frac{1}{2}\hbar$ neutrons and protons appear to pair off with opposing spins, thus canceling both the

TABLE 77B. CLASSIFICATION OF KNOWN
STABLE NUCLIDES

Z Protons	N Neutrons	Known Stable Nuclides	Nuclear Spin I
odd	odd	4	1, 2, 3, 4
odd	even	50	$\frac{1}{2}, \frac{3}{2}, \frac{5}{2}, \frac{7}{2}, \frac{9}{2}$
even	odd	55	$\frac{1}{2}, \frac{3}{2}, \frac{5}{2}, \frac{7}{2}, \frac{9}{2}$
even	even	165	0

mechanical moments and magnetic moments. While the positive magnetic moments (see Table 77A) are probably due to *odd protons*, and the negative magnetic moments to *odd neutrons*, the wide range in values and the half-integral values of I in the *odd-even* and *even-odd* nuclides suggests orbital motions.

By analogy with the electron structure of atoms, orbital quantum numbers $l = 0, 1, 2, 3 \ldots$, for $s, p, d, f, g, \ldots$, respectively, are assigned to all nucleons. If the odd orbital nucleon is a proton, its positive charge and spin will give rise to two positive magnetic moments. (See Fig. 77Q.) If l and s

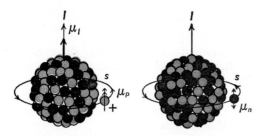

Fig. 77Q *Schematic diagrams of proton and neutron orbits around nuclei.*

are parallel as in the diagram, so that $j = l + s$, the magnetic moments will add; if l and s are oppositely directed, $j = l - s$, the magnetic moments will subtract.

For a proton the orbital angular momentum is given by

$$p_l = l\hbar$$

and the associated orbital magnetic moment by

$$\mu_l = l\hbar \, \frac{e}{2M}$$

By adding, or subtracting, the spin magnetic moment μ_{proton} (see Eq. 77h), we obtain the expected total nuclear magnetic moment μ_I. While experimentally determined values of μ_I do not agree exactly with the values calculated by this simple model they are in surprisingly good agreement.

If the orbital nucleon is a neutron, its orbital motion cannot give rise to an orbital magnetic moment. (See Fig. 77Q.) Neutron spin, however, does have a negative magnetic moment, and the magnitude of its contribution to the entire nucleus will depend upon its orientation with respect to the nuclear spin axis.

Some success with the application of the Pauli exclusion principle, applied to the filling of proton and neutron subshells, has been achieved. (See Sec. 66.7.) The experimental evidence that such closed subshells exist in nuclei is to be found in a number of nuclear properties. If the binding energy (Fig. 77C) angular momentum, or magnetic moment, are plotted against proton number Z or neutron number N, discontinuities occur when either Z or N has the value 2, 8, 14, 20, 28, 50, 82, and 126. While these so-called "magic numbers" seem to represent closed shells and subshells, much is yet to be learned about the structure of atomic nuclei.

77.11. Mesic Atoms. Because of the coulomb attractive forces between unlike charges, negatively charged mesons have a far greater probability of being captured by atomic nuclei than have their positively charged antiparticles. (See Table 80A.) There is a certain probability that as π^- and μ^- particles pass through matter they may be captured in any one of a number of outside orbits to form a kind of Bohr atom.

All equations derived for hydrogen can be applied to such mesic atoms by replacing the proton charge $+e$ by the nuclear charge $+Ze$, where Z is the atomic number. When this is done, Eq.(60c) for the radius of circular orbits becomes

$$r = \frac{n^2 h^2}{4\pi^2 m e^2 k Z} \tag{77l}$$

where m is the particle mass and n is the

principal quantum number. The inner-most orbit for hydrogen and its electron, where $n = 1$ and $Z = 1$, has a radius $r_1 = 5.28 \times 10^{-9}$ cm.

Since the radius varies inversely as the mass of the orbiting particle, the radius of the allowed orbits, $n = 1, 2, 3, 4$, etc., for π and μ mesic atoms will be about $\frac{1}{273} r_1 n^2$ for π^- and $\frac{1}{207} r_1 n^2$, respectively. Around a pro-ton, the π^- orbit, $n = 1$, would have a radius of 1.93×10^{-11} cm, and for $n = 2$ a radius four times this. In an atom like $_{35}Br^{79}$, the innermost π^- orbit would be only $\frac{1}{35 \times 273}$, or $\frac{1}{9555}$ th as large as the normal hydrogen atom, and the meson would be just skimming the surface of the nucleus with a radius of 5.53×10^{-13} cm. (See Fig. 77R.)

Since the orbital energy is proportional to the particle mass m (see Eq.(60k)), tran-sitions between orbits will have energies $h\nu$ comparable to X rays. X rays arising

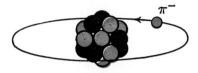

Fig. 77R *Schematic orbital diagram of a π mesonic atom—phosphorus, $_{15}P^{31}$—in the $n = 1$ circular orbit.*

from jumps from the $n = 2$ to $n = 1$ orbits of π^- mesic atoms were first observed in 1952 by Cemak, McGuire, Platt, and Schulte. These were produced by a beam of π^- mesons from the University of Roch-ester cyclotron traversing the beryllium, carbon, and oxygen target.

Similar observations were observed by Rainwater and Fitch in 1953 for μ^- par-ticles from a cyclotron. Confirmation of the origin of these X rays is attributed to the agreement between measured X-ray wave-lengths and those calculated from the Bohr formula.*

* For more details of nuclear structure, see *Intro-duction to Atomic and Nuclear Physics*, by H. Semat, Rinehart and Company.

QUESTIONS AND PROBLEMS

1. Using the atomic masses given in Appen-dix VI, calculate the binding energy per nu-cleon for (a) boron-10 and (b) carbon-12.

2. Using the atomic masses given in Appen-dix VI, calculate the binding energy per nu-cleon for (a) oxygen-16, and (b) silicon-29. (*Ans.* (a) 7.97 Mev, (b) 8.44 Mev.)

3. Calculate the packing fraction for (a) he-lium-4, and (b) argon-40. (See Appendix VI for atomic masses.)

4. Calculate the packing fraction for (a) bo-ron-10, and (b) chlorine-35. (*Ans.* (a) 0.00161 amu, (b) 0.00057 amu.)

5. Substitute the values of the atomic con-stants in Eq.(77f) and calculate the nuclear mag-neton.

6. Calculate the ratio between the angular velocity of electron spin and proton spin. As-sume uniform homogeneous spheres of equal size. (*Ans.* 1836.)

7. If the odd proton in a nucleus were in a d-orbit, with its spin parallel to l, what would you expect (a) the nuclear spin value I, and (b) the nuclear magnetic moment μ_I to be?

8. If the odd proton in a nucleus were in a g-orbit, $l = 4$, with its spin parallel to l, what would you expect (a) the nuclear spin value I, and (b) the nuclear magnetic moment μ_I, to be? (*Ans.* (a) $I = \frac{9}{2}$, (b) 6.792 nuclear magnetons.)

9. (a) Calculate the radius of the μ^- orbit, $n = 1$, for an aluminum atom. (b) Calculate nuclear radius using Eq.(79b).

10. (a) Calculate the radius of the π^- orbit, $n = 1$, for the nuclide $_{20}Ca^{40}$. (b) Calculate the nuclear radius using Eq.(79b). (*Ans.* (a) 9.7×10^{-13} cm, (b) 4.1×10^{-13} cm.)

11. Calculate (a) the radius of the π^- orbit, $n = 1$, and (b) the radius of the nucleus, for the nucleus shown in Fig. 77R. (*Note:* Use Eq.(79b) for part (b).)

Chapter 78

Fission and Fusion

78.1. A New Discovery. In 1937 Fermi, Segré, and their collaborators subjected uranium to the bombardment of neutrons. From the radioactivity produced they believed they had succeeded, for the first time, in producing a series of new elements, 93, 94, 95, etc., beyond uranium 92. The reason for their belief was that the uranium, after bombardment, gave off electrons with a number of different half-lives. If one attributed these different half-lives to the successive disintegrations of the same atoms, a single nucleus should emit several electrons, one after the other. With each emission the nuclear charge would increase by unity, thus producing an atom of higher and higher atomic number.

Although similar observations were later made by the Curie-Joliots, all observers seemed to have misinterpreted the phenomenon because, in 1939, Hahn made a new and important discovery. After bombarding uranium with neutrons, Hahn and his collaborators carefully performed a series of chemical separations of the uranium sample to determine the element to which the newly produced radioactivity belonged. To their amazement they found the radioactive atoms to be identical chemically to a number of different elements, nearly all of which are near the center of the periodic table. In other words, a uranium nucleus, after the capture of a single neutron, seemed to be splitting apart into two nearly equal fragments, as illustrated in Fig. 78A.

In the few weeks that followed this discovery, many observers in different laboratories the world over not only confirmed the results, but extended the observations by studying in detail the products of the disintegrations. To explain the phenomenon in simple words, consider the details of the process illustrated in Fig. 78A. An original uranium nucleus, $_{92}U^{235}$, with its 92 protons and 143 neutrons is shown at the left as it captures a slowly moving neutron.

In the center diagram (b), the newly

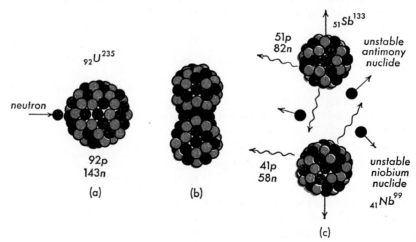

Fig. 78A *Diagrams of the fission of a uranium nucleus into two unstable nuclides.*

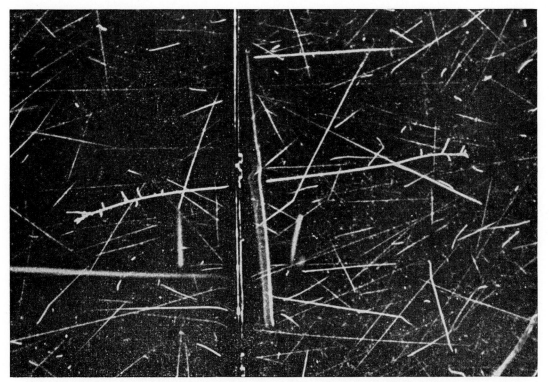

Fig. 78B *Wilson cloud chamber photograph showing a pair of fission fragments recoiling in opposite directions. Note the delta ray forks near the ends. Fission was produced by a neutron beam from a cyclotron. (Courtesy, I. K. Boggild.)*

formed nucleus is unstable and starts to separate into two nearly equal parts. Because this process resembles cell division in the science of biology, the phenomenon is called *fission*. In coming apart, the uranium nucleus, behaving like the analogous waterdrop, splashes out small drops, that is, neutrons and γ rays. So great is the energy liberated by this explosion of the nucleus that each of the two heavy nuclei fly apart in opposite directions with tremendous speeds. That they do so has been confirmed by many Wilson cloud chamber photographs, one of which is reproduced in Fig. 78B.

For the first photograph the cloud chamber contained a thin film of material coated with uranium. The fission of one uranium nucleus reveals two tracks of the same density, showing clearly that the particles traveled outward in opposite directions. The heavy forks near the ends of the tracks are characteristic of highly charged fission fragments that have made several collisions with other nuclei before coming to rest.

Not all of the uranium nuclei divide into antimony and niobium as shown in Fig. 78A, but into any one of many pairs of fragments corresponding to elements near the center of the periodic table. The experimental evidence seems to favor pairs of slightly unequal mass, accompanied by from one to five or more neutrons, as shown in diagram (c).

Numerous measurements of the masses of fission fragments have made it possible to construct the graph shown in Fig. 78C. The fission fragment yield is plotted vertically to a logarithmic scale, and the mass number A is plotted horizontally to a uniform scale. The curve is seen to rise sharply between $A = 75$ and 80 and to drop equally fast between $A = 155$ and 160. The most probable values for the mass numbers of

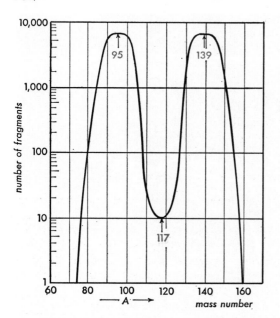

Fig. 78C *Semi-log graph showing the fission fragment yield for slow neutrons on uranium-235.*

the two fragments are 95 and 139 with a minimum of $\frac{1}{10}$th of 1% at $A = 117$.

In general, fission fragments are not stable nuclei but contain an excess number of neutrons. Typical ensuing events that occur to most fragments, like those shown in Fig. 78A(c), are detailed in Fig. 78D. After a

of four electrons raises the nuclear charge by four unit steps, ending with a stable cesium nuclide, $_{55}Cs^{133}$. The other fragment, $_{41}Nb^{99}$, in Fig. 78A(c), carries out a similar series of β-ray emissions, ending up with $_{44}Ru^{99}$.

As proof that the above series is produced by fission, previously bombarded uranium has been chemically analyzed for elements near the center of the periodic table. After each chemical separation is performed, a test of the β-ray activity is made by a measurement of the half-life. A comparison of this measured half-life with the values already known for the same element from other disintegration experiments has made it possible to identify some of the radioactive nuclei produced. Such tests, for example, have been made by Wu* for the series of four elements in Fig. 78D. Note the increasing half-lives she identified for this series, indicating increased stability as the stable nucleus cesium is approached.

Approximately 99% of the neutrons ejected as the result of the fission of uranium occur within an extremely short time interval and are called *prompt neutrons* or *secondary neutrons*. About one out of a hundred neutrons are emitted one or more seconds later, and these are called *delayed neutrons*. Delayed neutrons originate from

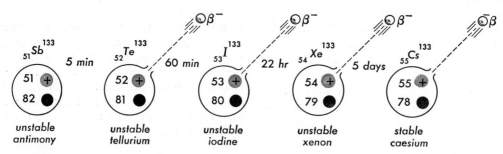

Fig. 78D *Disintegration series starting with unstable antimony, one of the fragments of the fission of a uranium-235 nucleus.*

series of β-emissions, in which neutrons are converted into protons in the nucleus, a stable nuclide results.

Starting at the left in the diagram with the unstable antimony nuclide of charge +51 and mass 133, the successive emissions

unstable fragments that decay by neutron emission on their way to becoming stable nuclei.

78.2. Fission Energy. The energy liberated in the fission of uranium is due largely

* C. S. Wu, *Physical Review,* Vol. 58, 1940, p. 925.

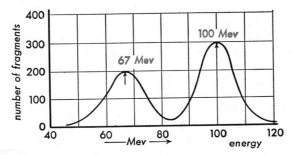

Fig. 78E *Graph of the energies of the fission fragments from uranium-235.*

to the U-235 isotope. Uranium found in the earth's crust has three principal isotopes with the following relative abundance.

U-238	99.280	4.51×10^9 y
U-235	0.714	7.10×10^8 y
U-234	0.006	2.48×10^5 y

All three of these nuclides are radioactive and decay by α-emission. (See Appendix VI.)

When a slow or fast neutron is captured by a U-235 nucleus, the two fission fragments as well as the neutrons fly apart with a tremendous amount of kinetic energy. This energy release can best be illustrated by graphs. In Fig. 78E the number of fission fragments is plotted vertically, and their kinetic energy in Mev is plotted horizontally. The result is a double peaked curve with maxima at 67 Mev and 100 Mev. While the greatest probability is for a particle of 100 Mev, the areas under the two peaks represent the total numbers of particles produced, and these are approximately equal.

When U-235 nuclei undergo fission as the result of slow neutron capture, the average number of neutrons liberated is found to be 2.5 neutrons per fission. Some may yield as many as five neutrons, but two or three are the most probable numbers. When the initial kinetic energies of prompt neutrons are measured, a graph of the kind shown in Fig. 78F is obtained. Although the maximum probability is for a neutron of 0.7 Mev, the median energy is approximately 2.0 Mev.

The average γ-ray energy emitted in the fission of U-235 is approximately 23 Mev.

A rough calculation of the average energy liberated in the fission of U-235 can be made from known atomic masses. For U-235, the atomic mass, $M = 235.117$ amu, gives a mass defect $M - A$ of 0.11704 amu. The incoming neutron with a mass of

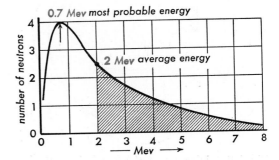

Fig. 78F *Graph of the prompt neutron energies from uranium-235 fission.*

1.00898 amu has a mass defect of 0.00898 amu. The average mass defect $M - A$ for isotopes near the middle of the periodic table is approximately -0.055 amu. If the fission products, for example, are the two masses 100 and 133, accompanied by three prompt neutrons, the mass balance gives the following.

	Before fission		*After fission*
U-235	235.11704 amu	2 frag.	232.89000 amu
n	1.00898 amu	3 n	3.02694 amu
	236.12602 amu		235.91694 amu

The total mass converted is the difference, $236.12602 - 235.91694 = 0.20908$ amu. After multiplying by 931 Mev/amu, we find the energy released to be 195 Mev. This value is consistent with the measured energies given in Figs. 78E and 78F. For the two fragments the average measured energy is 167 Mev. For the three neutrons the average measured energy is 6 Mev. These, added to the γ-ray energy release of 23 Mev, give a measured total of 196 Mev.

78.3. Bohr's Liquid Drop Model. It was Bohr who first proposed that heavy nuclei behave like a liquid drop, and that fission may be explained as the result of oscillations brought about by the impinging neutron. (See Fig. 78G.) Attractive forces be-

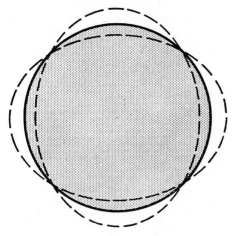

Fig. 78G *Diagram of the oscillations of a waterdrop, Bohr's model for the nuclei of heavy atoms.*

tween nucleons, like the attractive forces between liquid molecules, give rise to surface tension and the spheroidal state. As raindrops grow in size while falling through the air, their spherical stability decreases; they respond more readily to disruptive forces of the air stream and break up into smaller drops. A similar instability could be expected in heavy nuclei where the attractive forces give rise to a similar kind of surface tension.

Consider a nucleus like $_{92}U^{235}$, containing 92 protons and 143 neutrons, closely packed so that attractive forces between neighboring nucleons are all the same. This nucleus should be slightly larger than six nucleons in diameter, as shown in Fig. 78A (a). Each nucleon in the interior of such a

system will be in contact with, and therefore will be bound by, 12 others, as shown in Fig. 78H. Since the binding energy U between each pair of nucleons belongs

Fig. 78H *Diagram showing that, with a large number of closely packed spheres, each will be in contact with 12 others: six around, three above, and three below.*

equally to both, the total binding energy of each nucleon should be $6U$.

$$B_v = +6U \qquad (78a)$$

This quantity B_v applies only to the interior of the nucleus and is called the *volume binding energy*. Experimentally, B_v is about 14 Mev per nucleon for heavy nuclides.

Nucleons on the surface of the sphere are attracted by only half as many neighbors as those on the interior. For this reason the *surface binding energy* per nucleon should be approximately half as great as the volume binding energy. As more and more particles are added to build up larger and larger nuclides, the number inside and on the surface both increase, but the number inside increases more rapidly. The surface area of a sphere is proportional to the square of the radius, while the volume is proportional to the cube of the radius.

If, therefore, we assign the volume binding energy B_v to all nucleons, we must subtract some surface binding energy B_s to take care of surface nucleons. The relative amount to be subtracted will decrease as

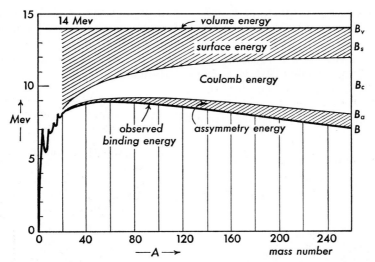

Fig. 78I *Graph of the binding energy factors for the liquid drop model of atomic nuclei.*

A, the total number of nucleons, increases. (See Fig. 78I.)

While the short range forces of attraction between nucleons account for nuclear stability, the weaker Coulomb forces between protons are also present. Since these Coulomb forces are repulsive, the binding energy per nucleon is further reduced. The amount by which it is reduced is called the *Coulomb energy.*

Finally, the total binding energy is also reduced in heavy nuclei by the preponderance of neutrons. If we tried to construct a heavy nucleus out of equal numbers of protons and neutrons, the repulsive Coulomb forces between protons would not be overcome by the attractive short-range forces between all nucleons, and the nucleus would be unstable. The excess number of neutrons provides the additional attractive forces necessary to ensure stability. However, since subshells of neutrons and protons are filled according to the Pauli exclusion principle (see Sec. 77.9) the excess neutrons must be placed in higher energy levels. Being in higher energy levels means they are less tightly bound to the nucleus, thus reducing the average binding energy per nucleon.

Hence there are four factors affecting the stability of nuclei:

$+B_v$ = volume binding energy
$-B_s$ = surface binding energy
$-B_c$ = Coulomb energy
$-B_a$ = assymometry energy

The curves and their shaded areas in Fig. 78I, show how, starting with the volume binding energy of 14 Mev for each nucleon, each of the other three factors reduces this value in going to heavier and heavier nuclides. This gives but a rough accounting of the experimentally determined curve shown by the heavy line, and reproduced from Fig. 77C.

78.4. The Transuranic Elements. The first transuranic element, neptunium, atomic number 93, was identified in 1939 by McMillan and Abelson. A beam of neutrons incident on a target of uranium metal gave rise to several known nuclear reactions. A neutron captured by one of the most abundant nuclei, U-238, forms U-239 and a γ ray, followed by β-emission, to give neptunium, element 93.

$$_0n^1 + {}_{92}U^{238} \rightarrow {}_{92}U^{239} + \gamma \text{ ray}$$
$$_{92}U^{239} \rightarrow {}_{93}Np^{239} + {}_{-1}e^0 + \gamma \text{ ray}$$

Ten different radioactive isotopes of neptunium are now known. Ranging in mass number from 231 to 240, isotope ${}_{93}Np^{237}$ emits α particles and has the longest half-life, 2.2 million years. While slow or fast neutron capture by U-238 is almost always followed by β-emission, about one out of a hundred fast neutrons will cause fission.

Plutonium (Pu), element 94, was first identified by Kennedy, McMillan, Seaborg, Segre, and Wahl, as arising from the spontaneous emission of β particles from $_{92}Np^{239}$.

$$_{92}Np^{239} \rightarrow {}_{94}Pu^{239} + {}_{-1}e^0 + \gamma \text{ ray}$$

Schematic diagrams of the above processes are given in Fig. 78J. Fifteen different

half-life of 8000 years and emits α particles.

Thirteen radioactive isotopes of curium are now known. Ranging in mass number from 239 to 250, several isotopes have long half-lives. These are

$_{96}Cm^{245}$ α-active 8000y

$_{96}Cm^{247}$ α-active 4 $\times$ 10^7 y

$_{96}Cm^{248}$ α-active 5 $\times$ 10^5 y

Berkelium (Bk), element 97, was discovered in 1949 by Thompson, Ghiorso, and Seaborg. $_{95}Am^{241}$ bombarded by 35 Mev α particles yields $_{97}Bk^{243}$. K-capture with a

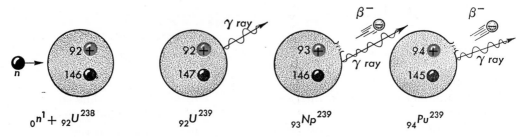

Fig. 78J *Neutron capture by uranium-238 produces, by radioactive β-decay, neptunium and plutonium.*

radioactive isotopes of plutonium are now known. Ranging in mass numbers from 232 to 246, several have long half-lives.

$_{94}Pu^{239}$ α-active 24,300 y

$_{94}Pu^{240}$ α-active 6,000 y

$_{94}Pu^{242}$ α-active 380,000 y

$_{94}Pu^{244}$ α-active 7.6 $\times$ 10^7 y

Americium (Am), element 95, and curium (Cm), element 96, were discovered in 1944 by Seaborg, James, Morgan, and Ghiorso, in collaboration with Hamilton. A sizable quantity of $_{94}Pu^{239}$ was bombarded in the Berkeley cyclotron by 40 Mev helium nuclei and two isotopes, $_{96}Cm^{240}$ and $_{96}Cm^{242}$, formed by (α,n) and $(\alpha,3n)$ reactions. These nuclei are α-emitters with half-lives of one month and five months, respectively. $_{95}Am^{241}$ was first discovered as arising from a relatively long-lived β-emitter, $_{94}Pu^{241}$, and emits α particles with a half-life of about 500 years.

Ten radioactive isotopes of americium are now known. Ranging in mass number from 237 to 246, $_{95}Am^{243}$ has the longest

half-life of 4.7 hours turns 99.9% of these nuclei into $_{96}Cm^{243}$, with 0.1% emitting α particles to become $_{95}Am^{239}$.

Eight radioactive isotopes of berkelium are known. Ranging in mass number from 243 to 250, $_{97}Bk^{247}$ has a half-life of 1000 years, and is α-active.

Californium (Cf), element 98, was discovered in 1950 by Thompson, Street, Ghiorso, and Seaborg. $_{96}Cm^{242}$ bombarded by 35 Mev α particles yields $_{98}Cf^{244}$. With a half-life of 45 min, $_{98}Cf^{244}$ ejects α particles with an energy of 7.1 Mev to produce $_{96}Cm^{240}$.

Eleven radioactive isotopes ranging in mass number from 244 to 254 are known. Isotope $_{98}Cf^{251}$ has the longest half-life, 800 years, and is α active.

Einsteinium (E), element 99, and fermium (Fm) element 100, were discovered as a joint project by 16 scientists.

In November, 1952, the first full-scale, thermonuclear explosion was detonated on an island in the Pacific ocean. The explosion produced a mile-wide crater in the coral island site, and the radioactive cloud rose ten miles and reached a diameter of approximately 100 miles. Drone planes, radio-controlled, flew though this cloud collecting samples for laboratory study. Among other things it was found that some of the uranium nuclei not undergoing fission had captured as many as 17 neutrons, and formed $_{92}U^{255}$. This very heavy isotope proceeds to give off electrons one after the other, each one raising the nuclear charge by one. Elements 99 and 100 were identified by their predicted chemical properties.

Ten radioactive isotopes of einsteinium are now known, and range in atomic mass number from 246 to 255. Isotope $_{99}E^{254}$ has the longest half-life, 480 days, and is α-active.

Seven radioactive isotopes of fermium are now known, and range in atomic mass number from 250-256. Isotope $_{100}Fm^{253}$ has the longest half-life, 7 days, and is α-active.

Mendelevium (Mv), element 101, was discovered by Ghiorso, Harvey, Chappin, Thompson, and Seaborg in 1955. One radioactive isotope, $_{101}Mv^{256}$, is known and its half-life is approximately one hour. This nuclide was produced by bombarding einsteinium-253 with helium nuclei from a cyclotron beam.

It is now known that all heavy nuclei starting approximately with Th-232 are fissionable, i.e., under proper excitation conditions they split apart with great violence into almost equal pair fragments. Some of them, like U-233, U-235, and Pu-239, fission by the capture of a slow neutron as well as a fast neutron, whereas others like U-238 and Pu-241 fission only by the capture of fast neutrons. The capture of a slow neutron by U-238 is followed by β-decay to produce Np and Pu, whereas fast neutron capture is followed by fission.

78.5. Photofission of Heavy Nuclei.
The fission of uranium and thorium initiated by γ rays was first discovered by Haxley, Schoupp, Stevens, and Wells in 1941. These experimenters bombarded a uranium target with 6.2 Mev γ rays and observed fission fragments. Later experiments by others have shown that photofission can be demonstrated with many of the heavy elements,

and that the threshhold energy for nuclides Th-230, U-233, U-235, U-238, and Pu-239 is just over 5 Mev.

The discovery that some nuclei undergo fission spontaneously was discovered by Petrzhak and Flerov in 1940. Many of the heavier isotopes of the transuranic elements show spontaneous fission.

78.6. The Meson Theory of the Nucleus.
The possible existence of mesons was first proposed by the Japanese mathematical physicist, Yukawa, in 1935. He proposed that the short-range forces between protons and neutrons inside the nucleus are to be attributed to relatively smaller particles.

According to Yukawa, nucleons emit and absorb mass-quanta, called *mesons,* just as electrons in the outer structure of the atom emit and absorb photons. The fact that the nuclear forces extend only over a short range can be shown to mean that the meson, unlike the massless photon, would have a finite rest mass. Furthermore, some mesons are charged, and some are neutral. (See Fig. 73O.)

The present concept of nucleons is that they consist of some sort of common core surrounded by a pulsating cloud of π mesons called *pions.*

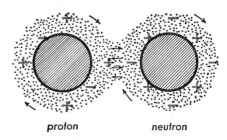

proton   neutron

Fig. 78K   *Schematic diagram of the π mesonic clouds around each of two nucleon cores, the charge exchange accounting for the strong attractive force U.*

Since pions are charged +, 0, or −, the rapid jumping back and forth between nucleons, changes the nucleon identity equally fast, and at the same time binds the two nucleons together. (See Fig. 78K.) This diagram might well represent a deuteron, with both spins in the same direction to give $I = 1$, and the negative pion charge at a greater distance from the center of the neutron to produce its negative magnetic moment. (See Fig. 76N.)

To liberate two pions as free particles, sufficient energy must be imparted to the nucleus to create their rest mass of 270 m_e each, or 276 Mev. (See Fig. 73O.)

78.7. Fusion. Measurements of solar radiation reaching the earth each day not only make it possible to calculate the surface temperature of the sun, but also to determine its total radiation. The fact that the sun, over a period of many years, shows no signs of cooling off, has long been an unsolved mystery. With the discovery of nuclear disintegration and the development of methods of producing many new types of atoms, this mystery has in a measure been recently solved.

Although there is no direct way known of observing the interior of a star like our sun, mathematical calculations based upon well-established physical laws show that down deep within such a mass the temperature is so extremely high that matter must be a conglomeration of atoms, electrons, and light waves, all moving about at tremendously high speeds.

Near the center of the sun where the temperature is about 20 million degrees, the atoms are stripped of their electrons and the light waves produced are of such high frequencies that they should be classified as γ rays and X rays. Here, where the average particle velocity is so high, nuclear reactions must be taking place on a large scale and the liberated energy must be filtering up through to cooler and cooler layers as light waves of lower and lower frequency. At the surface, most of the radiations escaping are of sufficiently low frequency to be classified as *visible, ultraviolet,* and *infrared.*

A careful study of all known nuclear reactions led Bethe, in 1938, to propose the following set of chain processes as those most probably responsible for the generation of energy at the sun's central core.

$$
\begin{array}{lll}
(1) & {}_1H^1 + {}_6C^{12} = {}_7N^{13} + \gamma \text{ ray} & \\
(2) & {}_7N^{13} \rightarrow {}_6C^{13} + {}_1e^0 & \\
(3) & {}_1H^1 + {}_6C^{13} = {}_7N^{14} + \gamma \text{ ray} & \\
(4) & {}_1H^1 + {}_7N^{14} = {}_8O^{15} + \gamma \text{ ray} & (78b) \\
(5) & {}_8O^{15} \rightarrow {}_7N^{15} + {}_1e^0 & \\
(6) & {}_1H^1 + {}_7N^{15} = {}_6C^{12} + {}_2He^4 &
\end{array}
$$

By summing up the equations it will be seen that four hydrogen atoms are consumed and that two positrons, three γ rays, and one helium nucleus, are created. The other nuclei cancel out since the original carbon atom in the first reaction is returned unaltered in the last reaction. Hence hydrogen is burned and helium is liberated. The loss in mass for each such cycle of reactions is, therefore, as follows:

$$4_1H^1 = 4.03256 \qquad {}_2He^4 = 4.00387$$
$$2_1e^0 = 0.00109$$

Subtracting gives $4.03256 - 4.00387 - 0.00109 = 0.02761$ amu. This is equivalent to 27.6 Mev energy.

More recent experiments and calculations[*] indicate that the proton-proton cycle given below is of even greater importance in the creation of solar and stellar energy than the above carbon cycle.

$$
\begin{array}{ll}
{}_1H^1 + {}_1H^1 \rightarrow {}_1H^2 + {}_1e^0 + 0.93 \text{ Mev} & (78c) \\
{}_1H^1 + {}_1H^2 \rightarrow {}_2He^3 + \gamma \text{ ray} & \\
\qquad\qquad\qquad\qquad + 5.5 \text{ Mev} & (78d) \\
{}_2He^3 + {}_2He^3 \rightarrow {}_2He^4 + 2_1H^1 & \\
\qquad\qquad\qquad\qquad + 12.8 \text{ Mev} & (78e)
\end{array}
$$

The net result is the same as before, four hydrogen atoms have been converted into one helium atom. Note that since two ${}_2He^3$ nuclei are involved in the reaction, Eq. (78e), two proton reactions of the type of Eqs.(78c) and (78d) are required to form one ${}_2He^4$ nucleus. Six protons are used and two are returned.

The rates at which these reactions should take place are not only consistent with the temperature of 20 million degrees, calculated from other considerations, but hydrogen and helium are known to be the

[*] See "Nuclear Reactions in Stars," by E. E. Salpeter, *Physical Review,* 88, 547 (1952).

most abundant elements of which stars are made.

In order for the sun to radiate 3.8×10^{33} ergs of energy per second, Einstein's equation $E = mc^2$ shows that mass must be annihilated at the rate of 4.2×10^{12} gm/sec (or 4,500,000 tons/sec). While this result indicates that the sun is losing mass at a tremendous rate, the amount is small when compared with the sun's total mass of 1.98×10^{33} gm. To illustrate, in one million years the sun should lose one ten-millionth of its total mass.*

* For a more complete treatment of nuclear energy, see *Atomic Energy*, by S. Glasstone, D. Van Nostrand, Princeton. For more details of the general subject of nuclear physics, see *The Atomic Nucleus*, by R. D. Evans, McGraw-Hill, New York.

QUESTIONS AND PROBLEMS

1. Make a diagram like Fig. 78A, showing a plutonium-239 nucleus, capturing a slow neutron and undergoing fission. Assume that three prompt neutrons are emitted, and that the fragments have initial charges of 142 and 98, respectively.

2. If one of the fission fragments of U-235 is the radioactive isotope iodine-139, what stable isotope will it become if a series of β particles ensues? Make a diagram like Fig. 78D. (*Ans.* $_{57}La^{139}$.)

3. If one of the fission fragments of U-235 is the radioactive isotope strontium-97, what stable isotope will it become if a series of β-decays takes place? Make a diagram like Fig. 78O.

4. If one of the fission fragments of U-235 is the radioactive isotope krypton-95, what stable isotope will it become if a series of β particles ensues? Make a diagram like Fig. 78D. (*Ans.* $_{42}Mo^{95}$.)

5. If a small quantity of curium-247 is bombarded by deuterons and β particles are emitted, what is the reaction?

6. When americium-243 is bombarded by deuterons from a cyclotron, α particles are emitted. What is the reaction? (*Ans.* $_1H^2 + {}_{95}Am^{243} \rightarrow {}_{94}Pu^{241} + {}_2He^4$.)

7. What are the reactions by which neptunium and plutonium were discovered.

8. If nuclei are composed of closely packed spherical shells of nucleons, how many nucleons are required to form a nucleus with three complete shells around one nucleon at the center? Assume nucleon centers to lie on the surface of a sphere. (*Ans.* 176.)

9. If nucleons have a diameter of 2.4×10^{-13} cm, what is the diameter of the nucleus described in Prob. 8?

10. (a) How many surface nucleons are there in Prob. 8? (b) How many interior nucleons are there? (*Ans.* (a) 113, (b) 63.)

Chapter 79

Nuclear Energy

79.1. A Chain Reaction. Not long after the discovery of fission it became evident to many scientific groups in America and in Europe that, if a sufficient quantity of pure uranium-235 (U-235) could be isolated from its more abundant isotope uranium 238 (U-238), it might have explosive powers many times greater than anything heretofore known. The reasons for believing this appeared at the time to be somewhat as follows.

Suppose that a given mass of uranium metal, all composed of U-235 atoms, was brought together into one lump. The first cosmic ray that penetrated this mass and produced a neutron might well set off the chain reaction shown schematically in Fig. 79A. A U-235 nucleus would capture the neutron and in splitting apart with great

violence would liberate one or more additional neutrons. These in turn would be quickly absorbed by other nearby atoms, which in turn would split up, at the same time liberating other neutrons. Hence a rapidly growing kind of avalanche might occur, a kind which, if fast enough, would have the characteristics of an explosion.

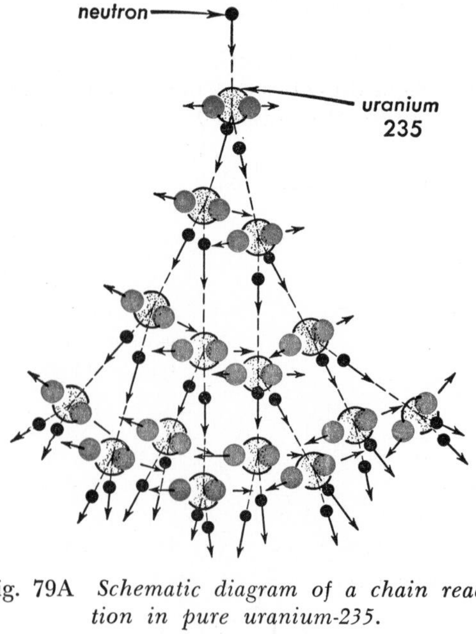

A graph showing the rate of growth of such a chain process is given in Fig. 79B.

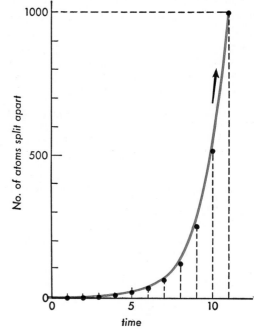

Fig. 79B   *Growth curve of fission in pure uranium-235.*

Since even the slowest of neutrons in solid matter will have average speeds of hundreds of thousands of centimeters per second, and since many neutron collisions will, on the average, occur within several centimeters,

Fig. 79A   *Schematic diagram of a chain reaction in pure uranium-235.*

the graph shows how quickly the growth reaches gigantic proportions. (The *time* scale is of the order of microseconds.)

The escape of neutrons from any quantity of uranium is a *surface effect* depending on the area of the surface, whereas fission capture occurs throughout the body and is therefore a *volume effect*. If the assembled mass of uranium is too small, the probability that most neutrons liberated by fission would escape through the surface before being captured might well be so large that a growing chain reaction cannot occur. Since the volume of a sphere increases with the cube of the radius while the surface area increases with the square of the radius, the *probability of escape* would decrease with increasing size. In other words, if the uranium mass were too small, the growth process shown in Figs. 79A and 79B would be cut off before it became very large, and only if the mass were greater than some critical value would an explosion take place.

Consider, therefore, a large quantity of U-235 in two or more units, each smaller than the critical size, and separated by a short distance. See Fig. 79C. Because of the relatively large surface area of each unit, neutrons readily escape and a chain reaction cannot develop. Suddenly, an explosive

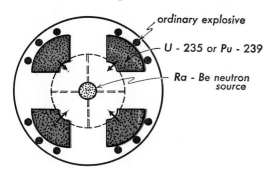

Fig. 79C *A schematic diagram of a hypothetical atomic explosion device, based upon a fast chain reaction in pure U-235 or Pu-239.*

like TNT is detonated behind the separated blocks, driving them together as indicated at the center of the diagram. Neutrons entering this greater-than-critical mass from a Ra-Be source will now initiate a

rapid chain reaction which results in a violent explosion. The tremendous energy release of such a device can only be fully realized by those who have actually seen and heard one detonated.

The first atomic bomb ever produced was assembled by scientists under the direction of the University of California, and was successfully detonated at Almagordo, New Mexico, on July 16, 1945. This device was composed of practically pure U-235. (See page one.) Many of the atomic devices exploded since that time have used plutonium-239 as the fission material, and peaceful uses of all kinds are now being studied by many.

One promising such development makes use of the tremendous amount of heat energy liberated. Repeated explosions underground can be confined to relatively small volumes of space, and the heat can be tapped off through some heat-transfer system, such as circulating steam pipes, etc.

79.2. Nuclear Radius and Geometrical Cross Section. Many experiments concerned with the collisions between atomic particles indicate that nuclei may be considered as a conglomerate of closely packed spheres of the same size. The average nucleon radius is now believed to be

$$r_0 = 1.2 \times 10^{-13} \text{ cm} \qquad (79a)$$

If spheres of this size are packed together into a ball-like structure as shown in Fig. 77D, the approximate radius of the combination will be given by

$$R = r_0 \sqrt[3]{A} \qquad (79b)$$

where the number of nucleons is given by the mass number A. For a uranium nucleus, U-238, for example, $A = 238$, and $R = 7.4 \times 10^{-13}$ cm, a value only six times that of the proton.

The concept of nuclear cross section is one of considerable importance in nuclear studies. If a nucleus is set up as a target for other atoms to hit, its *geometrical cross section* serves as a reasonably good measure of the target size, and is given by

$$\sigma_g = \pi R^2 \qquad (79c)$$

For U-238 this cross section is approximately

$$\sigma_g = 1.73 \times 10^{-24} \text{ cm}^2$$

The unit area for nuclei has been arbitrarily set at 1×10^{-24} cm^2, and is called the barn. The geometrical cross section for U-238, for example, would be written $\sigma_g = 1.73$ barns.

$$1 \text{ barn} = 1 \times 10^{-24} \text{ cm}^2 \qquad (79\text{d})$$

Calculated cross sections for a few nuclides are given in Table 79A, along with the heights of the nuclear barrier B for incident α particles. (See Fig. 77H.)

TABLE 79A. NUCLEAR RADII, GEOMETRICAL CROSS-SECTIONS AND POTENTIAL BARRIER HEIGHTS

Nuclide	R (10^{-13} cm)	σ_g (barns)	B (Mev)
$_2$He^4	1.9	.11	2.4
$_8$O^{16}	3.2	.32	6.0
$_{30}$Zn^{64}	4.8	.72	14.0
$_{48}$Cd^{113}	5.8	1.06	19.0
$_{100}$Fm^{252}	7.6	1.82	29.0

79.3. Cross Sections and Mean-Free-Path.

When neutrons are incident upon some material, each nucleus within the target area does not always behave as though its cross section is a constant. For example, in the capture of a neutron prior to radioactive decay, the nuclear size may appear to be quite different from its calculated geometric cross section. For fast neutrons, a nuclear cross section might be relatively small, while for slow neutrons it may be quite large.

With this explanation we see that cross section is not a target area in the literal sense, but is a figurative concept expressing the interaction probability.

The probability of interaction between a neutron and a nucleus is called the microscopic cross section σ, and is considered as the effective target area of a nucleus. If a beam of neutrons is incident on 1 cm^3 of material, as shown in Fig. 79D, the total effective target area will be $n\sigma$, where n is

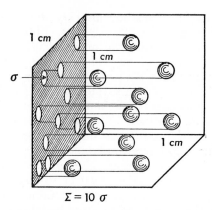

Fig. 79D Diagram showing the microscopic cross section and the meaning of the macroscopic cross section.

the total number of atoms per cm^3. This product is called the macroscopic cross section, and is designated Σ.

$$\Sigma = n\sigma \qquad (79\text{e})$$

The total cross section σ_t of a single nuclide is the sum of several cross sections, one for each different kind of process that alters the bombarding particles' energy or momentum.

$$\sigma_t = \sigma_s + \sigma_c \qquad (79\text{f})$$

where σ_s is the effective nuclear area that produces measurable scattering, and σ_c is the effective area for capture. The latter is sometimes called the radiative capture cross section since radioactivity usually follows capture. If fission is also one of the effects of capture, as it is with some of the heaviest nuclides like U-235 and Pn-239, we have

$$\sigma_t = \sigma_s + \sigma_c + \sigma_f \qquad (79\text{g})$$

As an illustration of these various σ's, the cross sections for U-235 for fast neutrons (2 Mev) and thermal neutrons (0.0253 ev) are given in Table 79B. U-235 is one of a number of exceptional nuclei, for most cross sections are small and comparable with geometrical cross sections. The whole subject of nuclear energy and the design of nuclear reactors and explosives are very dependent upon the smallness of the cross

TABLE 79B. CROSS-SECTIONS FOR PURE U-235

Cross-Sections in barns	Fast Neutrons 2 Mev $\left(\dfrac{2 \times 10^7}{\text{m/sec}}\right)$	Slow Neutrons 0.0253 ev $\left(\dfrac{2200}{\text{m/sec}}\right)$
Scattering $\sigma_s =$	5.0	10
Capture $\sigma_c =$	0.25	107
Fission $\sigma_f =$	1.27	580

sections of some elements and the largeness of others.

The average distance a neutron travels between nuclear events is given by the re-

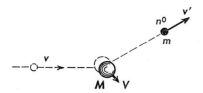

Fig. 79E *Elastic scattering of a neutron by a nucleus.*

ciprocal of the macroscopic cross section. This average distance is called the *mean-free-path.*

$$\text{mean-free-path } \lambda = \frac{1}{\Sigma} \qquad (79h)$$

Example 1. Find (a) the total macroscopic cross section, and (b) the mean-free-path for 2 Mev neutrons in pure U-235.

Solution. From Table 79B, and by Eq.(79g), we obtain

$$\sigma_t = 6.52 \text{ barns}$$

To find n for Eq.(79e), we take the density of uranium metal, $\rho = 18.7$ gm/cm³, and divide by the mass in grams of one uranium atom. Since unit atomic mass is 1.66×10^{-24} gm (see Appendix VIII), the mass of one U-235 atom is

$$M = 235 \times 1.66 \times 10^{-24} = 3.90 \times 10^{-22} \text{ gm}$$

Dividing ρ by M, gives

$$n = \frac{18.7}{3.9 \times 10^{-22}} = 4.79 \times 10^{22} \frac{\text{atoms}}{\text{cm}^3}$$

Substituting σ_t and n in Eq.(79e), we obtain

$$\Sigma_t = 4.79 \times 10^{22} \times 6.52 \times 10^{-24}$$

or $\qquad$ (a) $\quad \Sigma_t = 0.312$ cm⁻¹

To find the mean-free-path, Eq.(79h) gives

(b) $\quad \lambda_t = 3.21$ cm $\qquad$ (79i)

By using the separate value σ_s, σ_c, or σ_f alone, and the procedure given in Example 1, the mean-free-paths for scattering, radiative capture, or fission alone can be calculated. For the scattering and fission of U-235, by 2 Mev neutrons, for example,

$$\lambda_s = 4 \text{ cm} \qquad (79j)$$

and $\qquad \lambda_f = 16$ cm $\qquad$ (79k)

Since the scattering cross section of U-235 is four times the fission cross section, secondary neutrons will collide several times with U-235 nuclei before producing fission. A schematic diagram of this process is illustrated in Fig. 79E.

79.4. Neutron Scattering. There are, in general, two ways in which particles may be scattered by impacts with atomic nuclei, one is by *elastic scattering,* and the other is called *inelastic scattering.* In cases of elastic scattering, the total kinetic energy as well as the total momentum before impact is equal, respectively, to the total kinetic energy and the total momentum after impact. In mechanics this means that the coefficient of restitution $r = 1$. (See Eq.(23h).)

If a fast neutron collides elastically with a light particle like a proton, deuteron, or an α particle, considerable energy may be imparted to the recoiling nuclide. If the neutron collides with a heavy nucleus, on the other hand, conservation laws show that little kinetic energy can be imparted to the recoiling heavy nucleus and that the neutron will rebound in some new direction with most of its original energy. (See Fig. 79E.)

If, therefore, fast neutrons are to be slowed down to relatively low velocities by elastic scattering, materials composed of large quantities of atoms of low atomic weight, such as hydrogen, will be most effective. Any material used for this purpose is called a *moderator.*

Since the function of a moderator is to reduce the speeds of fast neutrons to low velocities by elastic collisions, the material used to do this will best serve its purpose if the nuclei scatter elastically and have small capture cross sections. Furthermore, the lighter the atoms the greater will be the recoil energy of the moderator nuclei when they do collide, and the fewer will be the impacts necessary to reduce the neutrons to thermal energies. (See Table 79C.)

TABLE 79C. NUMBER OF IMPACTS TO REDUCE 2 MEV NEUTRONS TO THERMAL ENERGIES, 0.0253 EV

Element	No. of Impacts
Hydrogen	18
Deuterium	25
Beryllium	87
Carbon	115
Uranium	2160

Capture cross sections of a few moderators are given in Table 79D.

TABLE 79D. NEUTRON CAPTURE CROSS SECTIONS OF MODERATORS AND STRUCTURAL MATERIALS

Element	σ_c (barns)
Hydrogen	0.33
Deuterium	0.00046
Carbon	0.0032
Beryllium	0.010
Aluminum	0.23
Zirconium	0.18
Molybdenum	2.4
Iron	2.5
Copper	3.6

Note the extremely low cross section and atomic mass of the first four elements.

When fast neutrons collide with uranium nuclei, either U-235 or U-238, some of them are scattered inelastically, while others are captured. The inelastic scattering process is illustrated in Fig. 79F. In passing close to one of these heavy nuclei, a considerable amount of energy is taken from the neutron, and the nucleus is raised to an excited state. The neutron leaves the nucleus in some new direction, with perhaps less than half its initial kinetic energy.

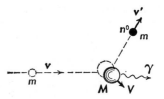

Fig. 79F *Inelastic scattering of a neutron by a uranium nucleus.*

The excited nuclei, in returning to their normal state, emit γ rays. While inelastic impacts always obey the law of conservation of momentum, thus giving rise to the heavy particle recoil shown, *conservation of kinetic energy does not hold.*

79.5. Explosive Chain Reactions. Uranium metal as it is usually refined is composed of three radioactive isotopes.

Uranium Isotope	Relative Abundance
$A = 238$	99.280%
235	0.714%
234	0.006%

Since both U-235 and U-238 undergo fission with fast neutrons, one might think ordinary uranium in a large-enough mass might explode. One good reason for believing this is that fission cross sections for both isotopes are about the same for fast neutrons. (σ_f for U-235 is 1.27 barns. See Table 79B.) Another reason is that fast neutrons might be expected to shorten the time between fission events.

The reason that ordinarily refined uranium in a mass of any size will not explode is that the scattering cross sections are larger than fission cross sections, thus making the mean-free-path between scattering events relatively small. After one or two inelastic impacts with uranium nuclei, the secondary neutrons have lost most of their initial energy of 2 Mev, and the fission capability of U-238 has dropped to an extremely low value. The fission cross section of U-238 for slow neutrons is practically zero.

Since the fission cross section for U-235 increases as the neutron velocity decreases, and becomes extremely large at thermal energies (see Table 79B), only relatively pure U-235 can develop an explosive chain reaction. Other nuclides capable of developing explosive chain reactions are given in Table 79E.

TABLE 79E. THERMAL NEUTRON CROSS SECTION FOR FISSIONABLE MATERIALS. (IN BARNS, AT 2200 METERS/SEC)

Nuclide	σ_s	σ_c	σ_f
U-235	10	107	580
Pu-239	9.6	315	750
U-233	—	52	533
U-238	8.3	3.50	0

79.6. Critical Mass Factors. For a mass of fissionable material like pure U-235 or Pu-239 to be explosive, the time between fission events must be very small, and relatively few neutrons must escape through the surface, or be lost somewhere by capture. A schematic diagram of possible paths of neutrons between two consecutive fission events is shown in Fig. 79G.

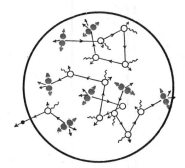

Fig. 79G *Schematic diagram of inelastic scattering between fission events in U-235 or Pu-239.*

Starting out as fast neutrons, the neutrons lose considerable energy with each inelastic impact. As the neutron velocity decreases, the U-235 fission cross section increases and fission capture becomes more and more probable.

To find the time T_f between fission events, we note that the velocity of 2 Mev neutrons is approximately 2×10^9 cm/sec,

while the average velocity of thermal neutrons (0.0253 ev) is 2.2×10^5 cm/sec. If we adopt a geometric average velocity of 2×10^7 cm/sec, and an average mean-free-path for scattering of 4 cm, as given by Eq.(79j), *the average time between scattering events will be*

$$T_s = \frac{4 \text{ cm}}{2 \times 10^7 \text{ cm/sec}} = 2 \times 10^{-7} \text{ sec} \quad (79l)$$

Allowing an average of five scattering events before fission capture, we obtain

$$T_f = 1 \times 10^{-6} \text{ sec} \quad (79m)$$

Owing to the random directions of the inelastic scattering (see Fig. 79G) the diffusion distance or *straight-line-distance* between fission events is from 5 to 8 cm. See Eqs.(79j) and (79k).

The critical mass for a nuclear explosive device should lie somewhere between the size of a marble (2 cm diameter) and the size of a basketball (24 cm diameter). Visualize, therefore, two spheres of pure U-235 or Pu-239, one large and one small, as shown in Fig. 79H. It is clear that if the

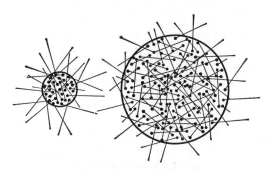

Fig. 79H *Schematic diagram of pure U-235, or Pu-239, showing escape of most of the neutrons for a subcritical size, and capture of most of the neutrons for greater than critical size.*

average straight-line-distance between fission events is 6 cm (see Fig. 79G) few neutrons will be captured in the small sphere, while many will be captured in a mass the size of a basketball.

Whether or not any mass will sustain a chain reaction at all is determined by what is called the *reproduction factor*. The reproduction factor k is given by the ratio,

$$k = \frac{\text{rate of neutron production}}{\text{rate of neutron disappearance}} \quad (79n)$$

If the rate of neutron production equals the rate at which neutrons disappear, the mass is said to be *critical*, and $k = 1$.

Curves showing the growth in an assembly where k is slightly greater, and slightly smaller, than unity are given in Fig. 79I. Since one generation of neutrons requires about one microsecond (see Eq.(79m)), the horizontal scale can represent time in microseconds.

In five generations the curve $k = 1.1$ rises to

$$1.1 \times 1.1 \times 1.1 \times 1.1 \times 1.1$$
$$= 1.61 \text{ neutrons}$$

In ten generations this same curve rises to $(1.1)^{10}$ or 2.59 neutrons, and in 100 generations to $(1.1)^{100}$ or 1×10^5 neutrons. In 1000 generations, or approximately $\frac{1}{1000}$

of a second, the number rises to approximately 1×10^{41} neutrons. Since this represents more atoms than would be available in any given assembly, 1000 generations would not materialize.

In pure U-235, or Pu-239 the size of a marble, the reproduction factor is approximately 0.1, while, for a sphere the size of a basketball, $k = 2.4$.

79.7. Nuclear Reactors. A nuclear reactor, sometimes called an atomic pile, is an apparatus in which nuclear fission can be maintained as a self-supporting, yet controlled, chain reaction. It is a kind of furnace in which uranium is the "fuel burned," and many useful products such as heat, neutrons, and radioactive isotopes are products.

Reactors, or piles, are of many kinds, sizes, and shapes, the two principal ingredients of them being a quantity of fissionable material, and a moderating substance for slowing down the neutrons to thermal ve-

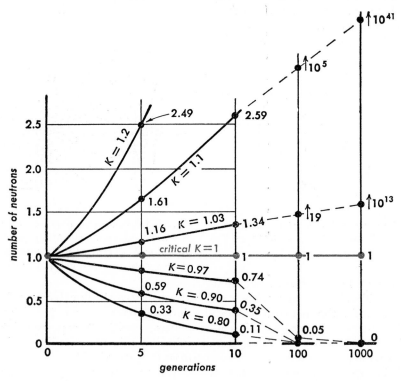

Fig. 79I *Growth curves for neutrons with reproduction factors barely above and below critical, K = 1.*

locities. A reactor is often designated according to the moderator, or coolant, used within it. Because of the immensity of the subject, only the simplest elements of these devices will be described here, and these as illustrations of the basic principles of many others.

A self-sustaining chain reaction cannot be maintained in pure uranium alone, no matter how large the mass. By properly combining or surrounding the metal with a moderator, however, the 2-Mev neutrons produced in the fission of U-235 can be slowed down by elastic scattering to thermal energies of 0.0253 ev. At these relatively low velocities of 2200 m/sec, the fission cross section of U-235 has the enormous value of 582 barns (see Table 79B).

The cross sections of a few nuclear fuels at thermal energy are given in Table 79D.

The first self-sustaining chain reaction ever created by man was put into operation at the University of Chicago on December 2, 1942. This device consisted of a huge "pile" of small carbon blocks, carefully laid together to form one solid mass about the size of a normal school room. During construction, lumps of pure uranium metal were inserted at regular intervals throughout the mass.

A schematic diagram of a pile constructed of large carbon blocks is shown in Fig. 79J.

Long cylindrical holes through the blocks provide for the insertion or removal of fuel elements, control rods, detecting devices, samples to be irradiated, etc. The fuel elements consist of pure uranium metal sealed in thin-walled aluminum cylinders.

The distance between uranium fuel elements in the moderator material is of importance in reactor design. The slowing-down distances for three commonly used moderators are as follows:

ordinary water,	H_2O	5.7 cm
heavy water,	D_2O	11.0 cm
carbon blocks,	C	19.0 cm

When, within the uranium metal, a few U-235 nuclei undergo fission, fast neutrons are liberated. Most of these enter the surrounding carbon (the moderator), where they collide elastically with carbon nuclei and slow down. Eventually, many of them enter the uranium metal as thermal neutrons and are captured by U-235 nuclei to cause fission. A diagram showing this process is given in Fig. 79K.

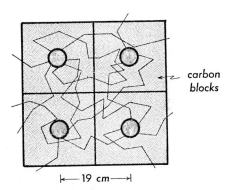

Fig. 79K *Diagram showing moderator action in an atomic reactor. Elastic collisions of neutrons with carbon nuclei slows the neutrons to thermal energies.*

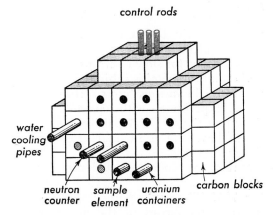

Fig. 79J *Uranium pile of carbon blocks used to produce plutonium-239 and many other radioactive atomic nuclei. (Concrete protective walls are not shown.)*

Not all neutrons produced within a reactor result in capture by U-235. Some are lost by escape through the surface, some by radiative capture by U-235 as well as U-238, and some by capture by structural materials and fission products.

The neutron balance in a natural uranium reactor, operating at the critical rate

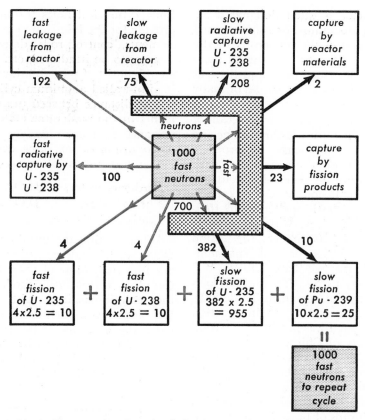

Fig. 79L   *A block diagram showing the balance of neutrons in a natural uranium reactor that is just critical.* (Calculated numbers by courtesy of Westinghouse Electric Corp.)

$k = 1$, is shown in Fig. 79L. Of the millions of fast neutrons produced in the reactor in each microsecond, the diagram starts with 1000 fast neutrons at the center, and shows what might reasonably happen to them in regenerating 1000 more fast neutrons. The average number of neutrons produced per fission is 2.5. This factor is directly involved in the bottom four squares where it is used in accounting for reproduction. It should be noted that 60% of the neutrons disappear by other than fission processes.

If the reproduction factor k of the reactor assembly is greater than unity, see Eq.(79n), the total number of neutrons will rise, and along with it the temperature. To prevent the temperature from rising too high, control rods, which are strong neu-

tron absorbers, are lowered into the central core.

The most widely used control rods, or plates, contain boron or cadmium. Both of these elements have enormous capture cross sections for slow neutrons. When *normal cadmium metal* is subjected to thermal neutrons, the *average cross section* is 2500 barns. Experiments with separated isotopes show that the six principal isotopes of cadmium have the individual cross sections shown in Table 79F.

Direct experimental evidence for the large cross section of Cd-113 is shown in Fig. 79M. The upper photograph is a mass spectrograph record of the five principal stable isotopes of cadmium made with the metal as normally refined. The lower repro-

TABLE 79F. THERMAL NEUTRON CAPTURE CROSS SECTIONS FOR CADMIUM ISOTOPES

Isotope (A)	Abundance (%)	Cross Section (barns)
110	12.4	.20
111	12.7	.26
112	24.1	.03
113	12.3	20,000
114	28.9	.14
116	7.6	1.5

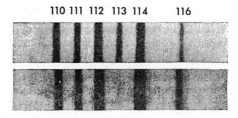

Fig. 79M *Normal cadmium mass spectrogram (above) and isotopes altered by neutron absorption (below). (After Dempster.)*

duction is a similar record made with cadmium metal after it had been subjected to intense neutron irradiation in a reactor. Note that the isotope 113 is missing and that isotope 114 is enhanced. The capture of a neutron by Cd-113 produces Cd-114.

An excellent demonstration can be made by placing a piece of metallic silver in a thin-walled box made of cadmium metal and subjecting it to a Ra-Be neutron source as shown in Fig. 76D. After some time the silver is removed from the cadmium box and placed near a geiger or scintillation counter. No counts will be recorded. If the silver metal is subjected to the neutrons without the cadmium shield, it will show considerable β-activity, as expected.

79.8. Power Reactors or Nuclear Power Plants. The idea that the natural heat developed in a uranium reactor might be utilized as a source of great power has long been recognized as a feasible enterprise. The basic principles of one type of "power reactor" are shown in Fig. 79N. A quantity of enriched uranium, in the form of a pure metal, or in the form of a solution of soluble salt in water, forms the center of the heat energy source.

The energy released by fission produces great quantities of heat, and the rising temperature is regulated to a predetermined value by cadmium rods. To reduce the fission rate, and thereby lower the temperature, the central rods are pushed in a little farther to absorb more neutrons, while to

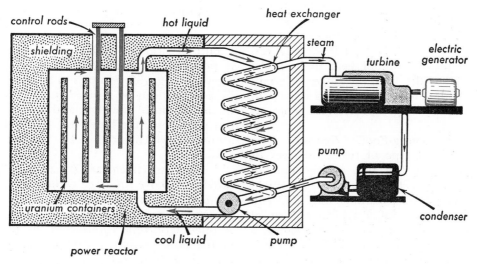

Fig. 79N *Schematic diagram of one type of nuclear power plant.*

raise the temperature they are pulled out a little farther.

Because of the harmful effects of the intense neutron radiation to men and equipment, it is not reasonable to vaporize a liquid directly as in a steam boiler; it is better to circulate a fluid through the shielded reactor and heat-exchanger, as shown in the diagram.

The hot liquid flowing through the heat-exchanger vaporizes a more volatile liquid like water; the resulting hot gas or steam under pressure drives a turbine of special design. The turbine in turn drives an electric generator, developing power that can be used to light our cities and factories, or to drive ships and submarines through the water and large planes through the air.

One of the problems connected with such power reactors is the effect of the intense neutron radiation on the metal structures. The neutrons change some atoms and permanently displace others from their normal positions in the crystal lattice of the solids, and as a result weaken certain crucial mechanical parts. Intensive studies of the properties of various materials under conditions likely to be encountered in power reactors are continually carried on in our research laboratories.

Another important problem concerns the nature of the coolant; it must be able to withstand high temperatures, not absorb neutrons and become radioactive to any appreciable extent, and yet it must be efficient in the transfer of heat in both the reactor and the heat-exchanger. Certain metals with low melting points appear to be most promising in these and other respects.

79.9. "Swimming-Pool" Reactor. The swimming-pool type of reactor derives its name from the fact that a large tank of ordinary water is used as a protective shield for the operating personnel. Fig. 79O is a cut-away diagram of a typical reactor of this kind, and one that is designed as a multipurpose instrument. The several fuel elements at the bottom of the tank are in the form of small cylindrical rods; each is composed of a solid homogeneous alloy of uranium and zirconium hydride moderator, clad in their aluminum cylinders. The uranium is enriched to 20% of U-235. The three control rods are of boron carbide.

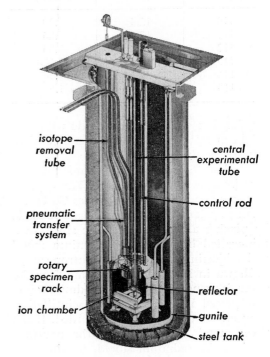

Fig. 79O *Cross-section diagram of a "swimming pool" type of reactor, showing fuel elements, carbon moderator, and access channels and equipment at the bottom. (Courtesy, General Atomics.)*

Full physical and visual access to the core is possible at all times from the top, as shown in Fig. 79P. Samples to be irradiated by neutrons can be lowered into the water in the region of the core, and an observer can readily see the blue glow of the water around it, which is caused by the Cerenkov radiation.

A rotary specimen rack ("lazy susan") located just above the large carbon or graphite moderator block, provides a water-tight facility for radioactive isotope production. A pneumatic tube running to the bottom of the tank permits a sample element, in a small container called a *rabbit,* to be subjected to neutrons and quickly removed for the measurement of very short half-lives.

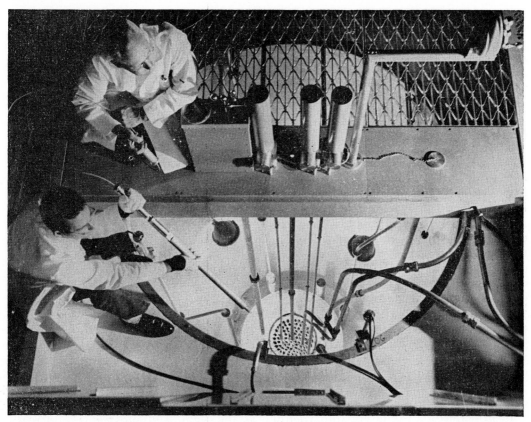

Fig. 79P *Photograph looking down through the water to the principal elements at the bottom of a "swimming pool" type of reactor.* (Courtesy, General Atomics.)

79.10. Uncontrolled Fusion. We have seen in Sec. 78.7 how the sun, and other stars, by means of certain nuclear reaction cycles and temperatures of millions of degrees, are able to fuse protons into α particles (hydrogen into helium), with the simultaneous emission of great quantities of energy. While all of the ingredients needed in these reactions are plentiful on the earth's surface, and can be purified and assembled in the research laboratory, the temperature of several million degrees required to cause them to fuse cannot be produced by any of the standard laboratory methods.

Here the atomic bomb employing the process of fission has come to our aid and made such temperatures possible. When an atomic bomb, containing U-235 or Pu-239, explodes, the temperature reached at the central core, although it may last only a small fraction of a second, is comparable to that reached at the center of the Sun.

While superatomic bombs containing hydrogen and other light elements have been highly successful, the exact materials used, their proportions, the physical size and shape of the devices, and the mechanical and electrical systems involved, are all classified by governments as secret military information. These same government agencies however, do conduct, through their civilian directed laboratories, scientific research projects on the peaceful uses of nuclear explosions.

In the interest of knowledge itself, it should be said that through the study of explosive reactions we can learn more of nature's fathomless mysteries. We can look, for example, at some of the lightest of nuclides and select several reactions that look promising from an energy standpoint. Five promising reactions involving the hydrogen and lithium isotopes are:

$$_1H^2 + _1H^2 \rightarrow _2He^3 + _0n^1 \quad + \quad 4.0 \text{ Mev}$$
$$_1H^2 + _1H^3 \rightarrow _2He^4 + _0n^1 \quad + 17.6 \text{ Mev}$$
$$_1H^2 + _3Li^6 \rightarrow _2He^4 + _2He^4 + 22.1 \text{ Mev}$$
$$_1H^1 + _3Li^7 \rightarrow _2He^4 + _2He^4 + 17.5 \text{ Mev}$$
$$_0n^1 + _3Li^6 \rightarrow _2He^4 + _1H^3 \quad + \quad 4.6 \text{ Mev}$$

Note the particularly large energies released with the fusion of deuterium with lithium-6 and tritium, and hydrogen with lithium-7.

Lithium is relatively abundant on the earth, and lithium-6 can be separated in reasonable quantities from its more abundant isotope, lithium-7. Tritium, on the other hand, is not found in nature, because of its relatively short half life of 31 years, and is only produced in quantities at considerable expense, in atomic reactors.

79.11. Controlled Fusion. The firm conviction on the part of many physicists that controlled fusion is possible has led, these past few years, to the expenditure of a great deal of scientific manpower and money.

In principle one would visualize a jet of fusible material, such as deuterium, being fed from a nozzle into a cavity where, upon fusion, great quantities of energy in the form of heat would be continuously generated and tapped off.

From the very start of all projects working on this problem, it has been realized that, owing to the temperature requirements of millions of degrees, no material walls can be close to the region in which fusion is to be consummated. This has led many to the use of a gaseous discharge called a *"plasma,"* held suspended in space by the magnetic lines of force of an electromagnet.

A plasma is an electrically neutral stream or mass of ionized atoms, molecules and electrons, and may be produced in various ways. A high current arc, such as that used in a search light, is a good plasma source. Plasma in many devices is confined by what has been termed a *magnetic bottle.* Visualize, as shown in Fig. 79Q, a stream of io-

nized atoms injected into the central region of a hollow solenoid. Moving with the high speeds of ions in a hot gas, these particles spiral around in the field with the lines of force acting as guides.

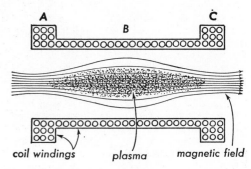

Fig. 79Q *Schematic diagram of a plasma held suspended in a magnetic field. A "magnetic bottle."*

As particles spiral into the stronger field at either end, the force components drive them back again toward the center. By increasing and decreasing the currents in the field coils *A, B,* and *C,* the field shape can be modified at will, and the plasma widened or narrowed. By decreasing the field at the right, and progressively increasing the field from left to right, the plasma can be transported lengthwise from one tube to another.

If all fields are increased, the plasma volume is compressed and the temperature rises. A rising temperature means higher ion velocities, and greater probability that impacts will produce fusion. If the field is decreased at one end and increased at the other, the plasma may be quickly moved along the cylinder axis, thus constituting a jet. Plasma jet studies by various aircraft and other research laboratories offer promising results for the near future. While much has been learned from the various controlled fusion study projects, there is still much to be discovered before successful power sources are realized. There are many who now believe that greater research effort should be placed on studies of the basic principles of the plasma itself, and that eventual rewards will be well worth the effort.

QUESTIONS AND PROBLEMS

1. Since the critical size for a uranium-235 explosion lies between a marble and a basketball, find (a) the ratio of these sphere diameters, (b) the ratio of their surface areas, (c) the ratio of their volumes, and (d) the ratio of volume to surface area.

2. Find (a) the radius, and (b) the geometrical cross section for the nucleus of silver-109. (*Ans.* (a) 5.73×10^{-13} cm, (b) 1.03 barns.)

3. Find (a) the radius, and (b) the geometrical cross section for the nucleus of tellurium-125.

4. If the reproduction factor for fission in a mass of U-235 is 1.20, how many secondary neutrons will be produced in (a) 5 generations, (b) 10 generations, (c) 100 generations, and (d) 1000 generations? (*Note:* Use logarithms.) (*Ans.* (a) 2.49, (b) 6.19, (c) 8.28×10^7, (d) 1.52×10^{79}.)

5. If the reproduction factor for fission in a mass of Pu-239 is 1.50, how many secondary neutrons will be produced in (a) 5 generations, (b) 10 generations, and (c) 100 generations? (*Note:* Use logarithms.)

6. The reproduction factor in a mass of U-235 is 1.05. (a) How many neutron generations will occur in 2 milliseconds, and (b) how many secondary neutrons will be released? (*Ans.* (a) 2000, (b) 2.39×10^{42}.)

7. The reproduction factor in a mass of Pu-239 is 1.20. (a) How many neutron generations will occur in $\frac{1}{10}$ of a millisecond, and (b) how many secondary neutrons will be released?

8. (a) Find the total macroscopic cross section for thermal neutrons in pure U-235. (b) Find the total mean-free-path. (*Ans.* (a) 33.4 cm^{-1}, (b) 0.299 mm.)

9. (a) Find the macroscopic fission cross section for thermal neutrons in pure U-235. (b) Find the corresponding mean-free-path.

10. (a) Find the macroscopic fission cross section for thermal neutrons in pure Pu-239. (b) Find the corresponding mean-free-path. (Assume the density of Pu to be 17 gm/cm^3.) (*Ans.* (a) 46.0 cm^{-1}, (b) 0.21 mm.)

11. (a) Find the macroscopic scattering cross section for thermal neutrons in pure Pu-239. (b) Find the corresponding mean-free-path. (Assume the density of Pu to be 17 gm/cm^3.)

12. Calculate the average cross section in barns for thermal neutrons on the six cadmium isotopes given in Table 79F. (*Ans.* 2460 barns.)

Chapter 80

Elementary Particles

For many decades now, physicists have been searching for the ultimate particles of which all matter is composed. From the atom and its electron structure, the search has extended into the nucleus, and from the nucleus to the structure of nucleons themselves.

The purpose behind the planning and building of atomic accelerators that will produce higher and higher energies, reaching into the Bev and hundreds of Bev ranges, has been, and continues to be, the hitting of nuclei harder and harder. When a nucleus is shattered by a very high energy particle, a variety of newly recognized particles are frequently produced.

The questions concerning the origin and nature of these particles present challenging problems to experimentalist and theorist alike. Do these particles exist in some strange form within the nucleus, or are they created from the release of mass and impact energy? If they are created, what is the mechanism involved, how long do they last, and what becomes of their energy?

In this last chapter we will take a brief look at some of the recent discoveries and observations in "high-energy physics," in the hopes that such glimpses may instill some interest and give you, the reader, some clue as to what new experiments might be performed that would shed new light on these "elementary particles."

80.1. Particle Classification. With the discovery of the neutron by Chadwick in 1932, the number of elementary particles became four in number: the *electron,* the *proton,* the *neutron,* and the *photon.* The first three are the atomic particles of which atoms are built, while the photon is the quantum unit of radiation emitted or absorbed by the electrons in the outer structure of atoms or by the particles within the nucleus.

The photon can only exist when traveling with the speed of light, and because of its motion possesses energy $h\nu$. By the mass-energy relation, $E = mc^2$, a photon also has mass $h\nu/c^2$. It possesses mass by virtue of its motion, for at rest it would have no energy and no mass.

The electron, proton, and neutron, on the other hand, have a definite rest mass and a rest energy. When they are set into motion, their mass increases.

80.2. Antiparticles. The positron, discovered by Anderson in 1932, is a positively charged electron. We have seen in Sec. 73.11 how electron pairs can be created, and how a free positron in coming together with an electron is annihilated and becomes two γ rays. It is this very property that gives the positron the name *antiparticle*—it destroys itself along with an electron and becomes another form of energy.

We have also seen in Fig. 76N that, when a high-energy photon comes close to the nucleus, mesons may be produced. If a pair of mesons is produced, one positive and one negative, one is the antiparticle of the other. These π-mesons may react with other nuclei or they may decay into muons as shown in Fig. 73P. The muons in turn may decay into electrons and positrons, or they may be captured by some other nucleus.

80.3. Particle Classification. A list of all the elementary particles known today leads to the colossal number of 30. Most of these particles have very short half-lives, and half of them are antiparticles.

The table given in Fig. 80A shows normal particles on the left in black, and anti-

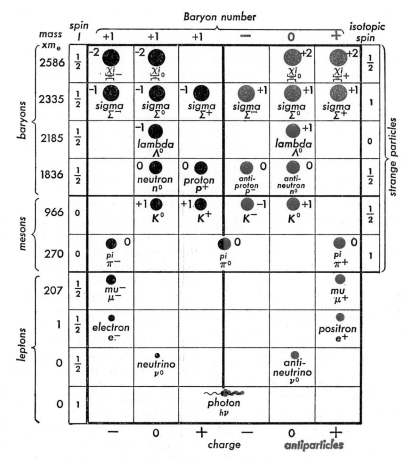

Fig. 80A *Table of elementary particles and antiparticles, showing their classification, mass, charge, symbol, and various quantum numbers.*

particles on the right in red. All are listed in the order of decreasing mass, with *baryon numbers* across the top as column heading (for baryons only), the *nuclear spin I* on the left, the *isotopic spin* on the right, and the *electric charge* across the bottom. The meanings of these numbers will be given in the following sections. Note that the left half of the table is practically a mirror image of the right half.

The photon $h\nu$ and the π^0 meson are placed on the center line because they differ from all the rest in one important respect: each of these particles acts as its own antiparticle.

The very interesting idea put forward that some distant galaxies in the heavens might be made up of antimatter might well be true. In such a galaxy, all hydrogen atoms would be made of antiprotons and positrons, and the protons and electrons would be their antiparticles. Thus Fig. 80A carries a double meaning, and *either half represents the antiparticles for the other half.*

80.4. Baryons and Strange Particles. The heavier particles in the top four rows of the table, Fig. 80A, are called *baryons,* and they with the *mesons* form a larger group called *strange particles.* While most of these particles were first discovered as rare events in cosmic rays, they can now be produced in the laboratory with the proton beam from a high-energy accelerator.

Working up from the bottom of the table, it will be seen that we have already studied *leptons* and their properties, as well as π mesons and nucleons. The others, briefly, are as follows:

K-Particles. These elementary particles belong to the meson class and have no spin angular momentum. Being heavier than the π mesons they have more possible modes for decay into other particles. K^+-particles have a mean-life of 0.85×10^{-8} sec and decay with the following modes. For a definition of mean-life, see end of Sec. 70.2.

$$K^+ \rightarrow \pi^+ + \pi^+ + \pi^- \quad (\tau \text{ mode})$$
$$K^+ \rightarrow \pi^+ + \pi^0 \qquad (\theta \text{ mode})$$
$$K^+ \rightarrow \pi^+ + \pi^0 + \pi^0$$
$$K^+ \rightarrow \mu^+ + \nu \qquad\qquad (80a)$$
$$K^+ \rightarrow \mu^+ + \nu + \pi^0$$
$$K^+ \rightarrow e^+ + \nu + \pi^0$$

The neutral K has similar decay modes and a very much shorter mean-life.

Λ-Particles. These neutral particles belong to the baryon class and, being heavier than nucleons, are also called *hyperons.* Their mass is about 70 electron masses greater than a proton plus a pion, and their principal decay modes are:

$$\Lambda^0 \rightarrow p + \pi^-$$
$$\Lambda^0 \rightarrow n + \pi^0 \qquad\qquad (80b)$$
$$\Lambda^0 \rightarrow p^- + \pi^+$$

Σ-Particles. These hyperons are of three kinds, Σ^+, Σ^0, and Σ^-, and belong to the baryon class. They have a spin of $\frac{1}{2}\hbar$, and decay principally by the following modes:

$$\Sigma^+ \rightarrow p + \pi^0$$
$$\Sigma^+ \rightarrow n + \pi^+$$
$$\Sigma^- \rightarrow n + \pi^- \qquad\qquad (80c)$$
$$\Sigma^0 \rightarrow \Lambda^0 + h\nu$$

Ξ-Particles. These hyperons are about 130 electron masses heavier than $\Lambda + \pi$, and belong to the baryon class. They also have a spin of $\frac{1}{2}\hbar$ and decay principally by the following modes

$$\Xi^- \rightarrow \Lambda^0 + \pi^-$$
$$\Xi^0 \rightarrow \Lambda^0 + \pi^0 \qquad\qquad (80d)$$

Most collision events requiring particles of high energy are called *strong interactions,* and are to be contrasted with natural decay processes, such as $\pi^+ \rightarrow \mu^+ + \nu \rightarrow e^+ + \nu + \bar{\nu}$, which are called *weak interactions.*

The strangeness numbers given in the upper left- or right-hand corner of each square in Fig. 80A, were introduced by Gell-Mann* to predict which new particles could be produced by impact, that is, by strong interactions. Strangeness numbers are conserved in strong interactions, but not in weak interactions. All interactions obey the ordinary conservation laws of *energy, momentum, angular momentum,* and *charge.*

80.5. Isotopic Spin. The concept of nuclear spin I was introduced in Chap. 77 to explain the hyperfine structure of spectrum lines, as well as the measured magnetic moments of neutrons and protons. The neutrino was then introduced into β-decay in order to maintain the conservation laws of energy, momentum, and angular momentum.

In writing down nuclear reactions as equations, the *law of conservation of electrical charge* is always imposed as part of the balancing process. Since elementary particles carry a charge of $+1e$, $0e$, or $-1e$, Heisenberg was the first to apply quantum numbers to charge and refer to the concept as *isotopic spin.*

While both words in this term are misnomers, they arose from the idea that pairs of particles like nucleons, and triplets like the π mesons, may be thought of as isotopes and that their charges, differing from each other by unity, suggest space quantization like electron spin and orbit in a magnetic field. (See Fig. 66N.)

Within the nucleus, short-range forces between neutrons and protons are exactly alike, but the ever-present coulomb forces between protons removes this symmetry and we are able to differentiate between the two different kinds of nucleons. In an effort to formulate a theory of these differences, particle charge has been likened to a vector, here called isotopic spin, and differences in charge have been compared with the space quantization of a spin vector in a field. (See Fig. 80B.)

* See *Scientific American,* pp. 72-88, July 1957.

By this analogy a nucleon may be thought of as a particle with an isotopic spin of $\frac{1}{2}$, and a *spin average* or center of $+\frac{1}{2}$. If the particle spin lines up with the

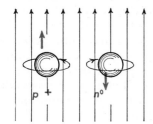

Fig. 80B *Schematic diagram of isotopic spin, a kind of charge quantization for elementary doublets like the neutron and proton.*

spin average, we have a proton with isotopic spin $+1$; if it lines up in the opposite direction we have a neutron with isotopic spin 0.

The isotopic spin of antinucleons is $-\frac{1}{2}$,

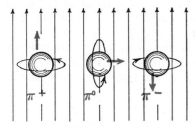

Fig. 80C *Schematic diagram of isotopic spin, a kind of charge quantization for elementary triplets like π mesons.*

and with a spin average or center of $-\frac{1}{2}$, gives 0 for the antineutron and -1 for the antiproton.

The π mesons form a triplet, with

charges $+1$, 0, -1. This particle is therefore assigned an isotopic spin of 1. Applying the concept of space quantization to this vector magnitude, we obtain three possible orientations as shown in Fig. 80C. These three positions, centered at charge zero, give $+1$, 0, and -1, corresponding to π^+, π^0, and π^-.

It would seem that this fiction of comparing electrical charge with spin orientation in a field might have some basic foundation and that additional experimental data will lead to a more acceptable theory of the basic concept we call electric charge.

80.6. Photographic Emulsions. When a photon or ionizing particle traverses the sensitive emulsion of a photographic film, the clear silver bromide crystal grains that are penetrated are turned into black silver upon development by regular film-developing processes.

Since the sensitive emulsion on most film is extremely thin, satisfactory emulsions up to 1 mm in thickness, containing about 80% silver bromide, were first developed by C. F. Powel in England. These can be stacked in layers to build up larger volumes, exposed to high-energy nuclear beams, or cosmic rays, and then developed. (See Fig. 80D.) By studying consecutively numbered films separately, under a suitable measuring microscope, one can observe nuclear collision events and make measurements of the different particles, their directions, ranges, track densities, etc.

Track densities vary widely with particle *charge* and *velocity*, as shown in Fig. 80E. The energies required of various particles to travel 1 mm in an average nuclear emulsion are:

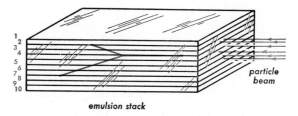

emulsion stack

Fig. 80D *Numbered stack of extra thick photographic emulsions used in photographing high-energy nuclear events.*

e	0.7 Mev	p	14.0 Mev
μ	5.5 Mev	d	20.0 Mev
π	6.1 Mev	α	55.0 Mev

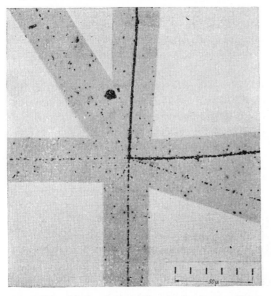

Fig. 80E *Charged particle tracks in a photographic emulsion showing differences in track density.* (Courtesy of C. F. Powell, P. H. Fowler, and D. H. Perkins, *from* The Study of Elementary Particles, *Pergamon Press Ltd.*)

Because emulsion densities are far greater than the gas in a cloud chamber, the track ranges are extremely small. This high-density and short-range feature is particularly useful, therefore, to the study of nuclear events involving very high-speed particles.

The procedure used for displaying emulsion tracks is to make microscopic enlargements of neighboring sections, and to piece the photographic prints together as shown in Fig. 80F. These print assemblies were made from a stack of 46 emulsions, 15 cm × 15 cm, exposed at high altitude over England in 1952.

The first assembly (a) shows a "star" of tracks in emulsion 17, one track being that of a K^+-meson as indicated. Six cm along this track (this corresponds to 60 ft on the enlarged scale shown here), assembly (b) from emulsion 6, the K^+-meson disintegrated by the τ-mode into π mesons. (See Eq.(80a).) Two cm along the π^- track, in assembly (c), the meson was captured by a heavy nucleus, resulting in a nuclear explosion. Among the secondary products were four singly charged particles and a $_3Li^8$ nucleus. The latter, on reaching the end of its range, emitted a β particle forming $_4Be^8$ which spontaneously splits up into

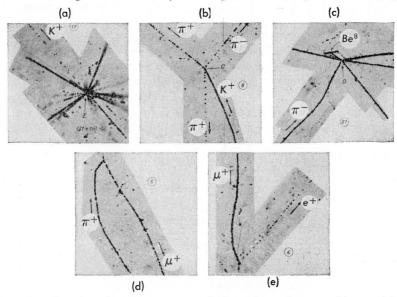

Fig. 80F *Five directly related events traced through a photographic emulsion stack.* (Courtesy of C. F. Powell, P. H. Fowler, and D. H. Perkins, *from* The Study of Elementary Particles, *Pergamon Press Ltd.*)

two α particles to produce the "hammer-track" shown.

About 3 cm along the π^+ track, in assembly (d), the meson decays into a μ^+ and a neutrino. A short distance along this track, in assembly (e), the μ^+ decays into a positron e^+, a neutrino ν, and an antineutrino $\bar{\nu}$.

The nuclear emulsion photograph in Fig. 80G shows a "star" of 22 tracks. A

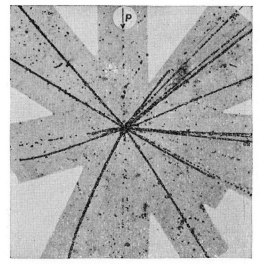

Fig. 80G *Photographic emulsion star produced by a cosmic-ray proton. (Courtesy of C. F. Powell, P. H. Fowler, and D. H. Perkins, from The Study of Elementary Particles, Pergamon Press Ltd.)*

primary cosmic ray, a proton, enters from the top, and collides with a silver or bromine nucleus in the emulsion, causing an explosion. Most of the tracks were made by π mesons, and the others probably by K-mesons and protons.

80.7. The Bubble Chamber. The bubble chamber, invented in 1952 by D. H. Glaser, has become one of the most valuable instruments for studying the minute details of high-energy nuclear events. In a cloud chamber, fogdrops form on the ions produced by charged atomic particles that have just previously traversed the gas-filled chamber. In the bubble chamber, the ions, formed by charged particles traversing the liquid, form local heat centers in which

tiny gas bubbles develop and grow.

The basic principles of the bubble chamber involve the superheating of a liquid and the bubbles that form in the process of boiling. Water, for example, boils at 100°C at standard atmospheric pressure. If the pressure is increased as in a geyser (Fig. 29H), boiling will not begin until a higher temperature is reached. If the pressure is then suddenly reduced, boiling begins with the sudden formation of tiny bubbles that grow quickly in size.

A simplified diagram of a bubble chamber is shown in Fig. 80H. A box with thick glass walls, filled with a liquid, is connected to a pressure system and then heated to some predetermined temperature. High-

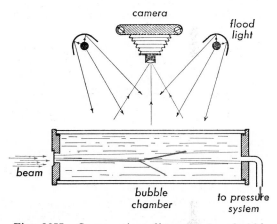

Fig. 80H *Cross-section diagram of a bubble chamber showing track illumination, camera, and incident particle beam.*

energy particles enter the liquid through a thin window, W. A sudden release of a valve in the pressure system is quickly followed by the flash of floodlights and the snap of a camera shutter. If the chamber is operating properly, and events are correctly timed, sharply defined trails of bubbles that have formed on the paths of ions made by the traversing particles will be photographed. (See Figs. 80K, 80L, 80N, and 80P.)

The extensive use of liquid hydrogen in bubble chambers has been particularly effective in the study of elementary and strange particle events. The difficulties of handling liquid hydrogen at −253°C in large bubble chambers has been developed by L. Alvarez and his colleagues at the University of California over a period of several years. Liquid hydrogen is particularly useful in that it provides a high concentration of "target protons," the simplest of atomic nuclei, and at the same time greatly shortens the distance between events that would be required in the gas-filled space of a cloud chamber. See Figs. 80I and 80J.

It is customary to locate a bubble chamber at the center of a large electromagnet so that particle charge and momentum relations can be obtained from track curvature. (See Figs. 80K and 80L.)

80.8. Antiprotons. The existence of antiprotons was discovered in 1955 by Chamberlain, Segre, Wiegand, and Ypsilantis at the University of California. This discovery came as the result of long-range plans laid for the purpose of answering the question, "Is there in nature, or can there be created by a strong interaction, a negatively charged particle with the mass of a proton?" One of the principal objectives in building the 6.2-Bev proton accelerator in 1953 was to find an answer to this question. Protons accelerated to a high-enough energy should, in colliding with heavier nuclei, impart sufficient energy to create, if such were possible, a pair of protons, one plus, the other minus.

The first antiprotons were discovered as high-energy negatively charged particles emerging from a copper target in the proton beam of the bevatron, and having all of the anticipated properties. By means of

Fig. 80I *Cutaway model of the 72-inch liquid hydrogen bubble chamber at the Lawrence Radiation Laboratory.*

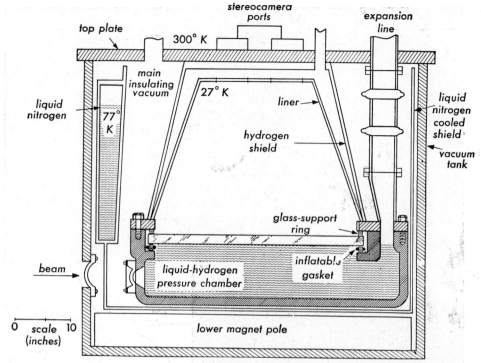

Fig. 80J *Cross-section diagram of the 72-inch liquid hydrogen bubble chamber.*

a strong magnet the antiprotons were bent away from the protons and into a scintillation counter. Today antiproton events are commonly observed and studied by means of a bubble chamber.

Fig. 80K is a photograph in which an antiproton entered the liquid hydrogen bubble chamber from the left. Near the center of the picture it interacted with a proton, and both particles were annihilated in the production of four pairs of π mesons. Since the bubble chamber operated in the uniform field of a strong electromagnet, the π^- tracks curve clockwise, and the π^+ tracks curve counterclockwise. The π^+ that curved back to the left and down decayed into a μ^+ and an e^+ as shown in the accompanying legend diagram.

The reactions for this event are written as follows:

$$p^- + p \rightarrow 4\pi^- + 4\pi^+$$
$$\pi^+ \rightarrow \mu^+ + \nu \quad \text{(80e)}$$
$$\mu^+ \rightarrow e^+ + \nu + \bar{\nu}$$

80.9. Baryon Reactions. An antiproton event involving the production of a baryon-antibaryon pair is reproduced in Fig. 80L. As shown in the legend diagram of Fig. 80M, an antiproton from the bevatron target enters the bubble chamber at the left and interacts with a proton.

The track disappears at this point because the interaction with a proton in the liquid hydrogen produces a neutral lambda-antilambda pair. With but a short life-time of about 10^{-10} seconds, each of these Λ^0 particles disintegrate, one into π^- and $p+$, and the other into p^- and π^+. The antiproton is captured by another proton at the upper right, and is immediately annihilated in the production of two pion pairs. The reactions for these events are:

$$p^- + p \rightarrow \bar{\Lambda} + \Lambda$$
$$\Lambda \rightarrow p + \pi^-$$
$$\bar{\Lambda} \rightarrow p^- + \pi^+ \quad \text{(80f)}$$
$$p^- + p \rightarrow 2\pi^+ + 2\pi^-$$

As high-energy protons from a large accelerator traverse any target material whatever, a considerable number of π mesons are produced along with other particles.

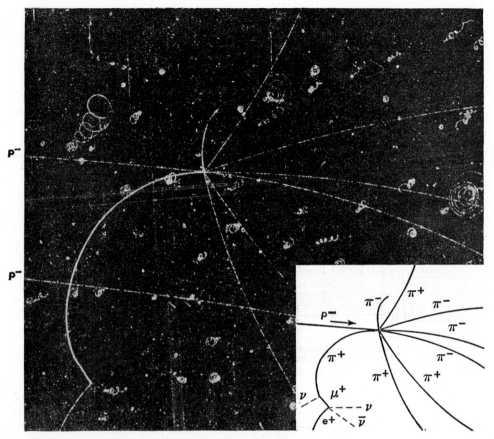

Fig. 80K *Pi-meson star produced by the proton capture of an antiproton in a liquid hydrogen bubble chamber.* (Courtesy, L. Alvarez and colleagues.)

These charged mesons, π^+ or π^-, can be channeled, by bending in a magnetic field, to any other area for experimentation. Directed into a bubble chamber, for example, their reactions with protons can be studied.

Fig. 80N is a photograph in which a π^--meson enters a liquid hydrogen bubble chamber from the left. As shown in the legend diagram of Fig. 80O, interaction with a proton cancels the charges, and ends the track by creating two neutral particles.

These two recoiling particles K^0 and Λ^0 do not produce tracks in the chamber but, having short life-times, quickly disintegrate. The neutral K-particle decays into a pair of pions, π^+ and π^-, while the Λ-particle decays into a proton and a π^-. As reactions

$$\pi^- + p \rightarrow K^0 + \Lambda^0$$
$$K^0 \rightarrow \pi^+ + \pi^- \qquad (80g)$$
$$\Lambda \rightarrow p + \pi^-$$

The bubble chamber photograph in Fig. 80P shows a series of related events involving 14 particles: π^+, $2\pi^0$, $2\pi^-$, p, n, K^+, Σ^+, μ^+, e^+, $\bar{\nu}$ and 2ν. As shown by the labeled diagram in Fig. 80Q, one of the high energy π^--particles enters from the left and interacts with a proton. This strong interaction produces Σ^- and K^+ particles. The Σ^- decays into a π^- and a neutron, while the K^+ decays into a π^+ and two (not showing) π^0.s. The π^+ decays into a μ^+ and then e^+ in the customary way.

The reactions involved may be written

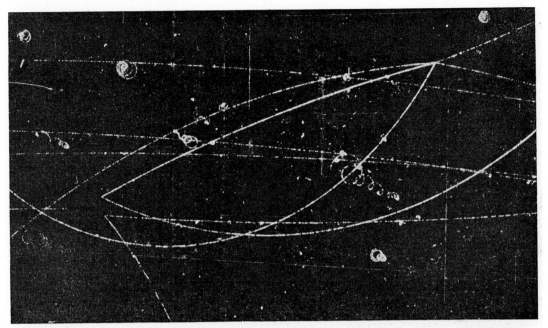

Fig. 80L *Bubble chamber photograph of correlated events involving two antiprotons, two Λ^0 particles, and seven π mesons. (See diagram, Fig. 80M.) (Courtesy, L. Alvarez and colleagues.)*

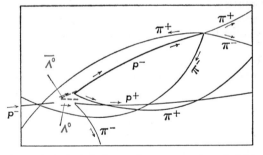

Fig. 80M *Labeled track pattern for bubble chamber photograph, Fig. 80L.*

$$\pi^- + p \rightarrow \Sigma^- + K^+$$
$$\Sigma^- \rightarrow \pi^- + n$$
$$K^+ \rightarrow \pi^+ + \pi^0 + \pi^0 \quad \text{(80h)}$$
$$\pi^+ \rightarrow \mu^+ + \nu$$
$$\mu^+ \rightarrow e^+ + \nu + \bar{\nu}$$

The photograph reproduced in Fig. 80R shows K^- meson tracks entering from the left. In the upper left, one of these particles collides with a carbon nucleus and produces three charged particles, as shown by the three-pronged fork. Energy and momentum calculations from the measured tracks show that the reaction is

$$K^- + {}_6C^{12} \rightarrow K^+ + \Xi^- + p + {}_4Be^{10}$$

The lower prong of the fork is the K^+ particle, which decays into a neutrino, and a μ^+ recoiling down to the left.

$$K^+ \rightarrow \mu^+ + \nu$$

The middle prong of the fork is the Ξ^- particle which at the bend in the middle of the picture decays into a π^- and a Λ^0.

$$\Xi^- \rightarrow \pi^- + \Lambda^0$$

The neutral Λ-particle, recoiling to the left, creates no track but quickly decays into a π^- and a p to form the V-shaped track at the right.

$$\Lambda^0 \rightarrow \pi^- + p$$

The making of a diagram of this event is left as an exercise for the student.

80.10. Parity. Parity is a mathematical treatment of what is best described as a

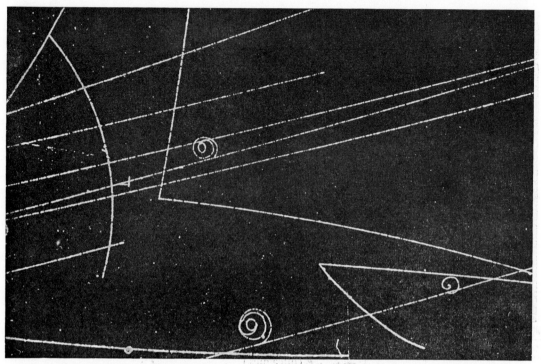

Fig. 80N *Bubble chamber photograph with π^-, p, K^o, Λ^o, π^+ and π^- tracks, all in one related event. For legend, see Fig. 80O. (Courtesy, L. Alvarez and Colleagues.)*

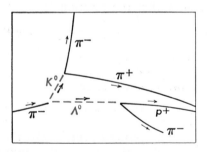

Fig. 80O *Labeled track pattern for bubble chamber photograph, Fig. 80N.*

mirror symmetry of many natural phenomena. Up until recently it was believed that the mirror image of any physical phenomenon, or laboratory experiment, is just as true to nature as the direct image itself. This is consistent with the principle called *conservation of parity.*

According to the conservation of parity, it was believed that if one observed an experiment by looking in a mirror and was not told he was looking in a mirror, there

would be no way in which he would know it. As an example of parity, many crystalline structures show mirror symmetry. With many cubic crystals (for example, see Fig. 22G), there is no question, since the image and mirror image have identical structures.

Diagrams of two kinds of quartz crystals found in nature are shown in Fig. 80S. One, called right-handed quartz, has its silicon and oxygen atoms lined up in clockwise spirals around the axis, while the left-handed quartz is a mirror image of the other and has its molecules lined up in a counterclockwise direction. One will rotate plane-polarized light clockwise as it traverses the crystal along the optic axis, while the other will rotate it counterclockwise. The existence of both of these crystals is consistent with the conservation of parity.

The first serious question regarding the conservation of parity arose in the minds of two young theoretical physicists, Yang and Lee, when they pointed out, in 1956,

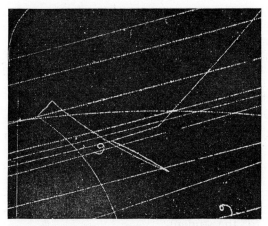

Fig. 80P *Bubble chamber photograph (in liquid hydrogen) of correlated events involving, Σ^- and K^+ particles. See diagram Fig. 80O. (Courtesy, L. Alvarez and colleagues.)*

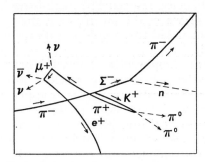

Fig. 80Q *Labeled track pattern for bubble chamber photograph in Fig. 80P.*

Fig. 80R *Propane bubble chamber photograph of an event involving K-mesons and a Xi-particle. (Courtesy, Wilson Powell and colleagues.)*

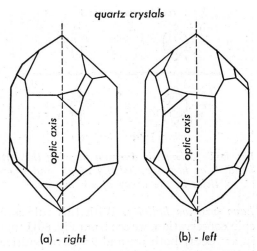

quartz crystals

(a) - right   (b) - left

Fig. 80S *Diagrams of right- and left-handed quartz crystals. Each is a mirror image of the other.*

that K^+ mesons can decay into two pions (θ-mode) or three pions (τ-mode). (See Eq. (80a).) An experiment suggested by Yang and Lee to test for parity was carried out by C. S. Wu, W. E. Ambler, R. W. Hayward, D. D. Hoppes, and R. P. Hudson. This experiment showed that, when radioactive cobalt-60 nuclei were lined up with their spin axes parallel to each other, more β particles were emitted along this axis in one direction than in the other.

To realize the significance of this result, consider the common decay of a π^+ meson into a μ^+ and a ν. The π^+ has zero spin, while the μ^+ and ν have spins of $\frac{1}{2}$. To conserve angular momentum, the two particles must fly apart spinning in opposite directions as shown (p. 716) in Fig. 80T. Moving in the direction of the arrows, both are advancing, as would left-handed screws. The mirror image in (b), which is apparently forbidden by nature, shows both particles advancing as right-handed screws. *A spinning particle advancing as a right-handed screw is said to have positive helicity; advancing as a left-handed screw it is said to have negative helicity.*

From the observed spin directions of β particles, it is now known that all *neutrinos have negative helicity* while *antineutrinos*

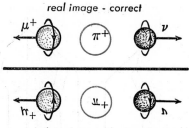

real image - correct

mirror image - incorrect

Fig. 80T *Schematic diagram showing the left-handed, or negative, helicity of μ^+ and ν-particles in the decay of π^+ mesons.*

have positive helicity. With this rule and spin conservation, we see from Fig. 80U that in π^- decay both μ^- and $\bar{\nu}^-$ have positive helicity.

It should be pointed out that helicity has meaning for neutrinos only, since they move with the speed of light. To an observer moving faster than a muon, for example, the spin direction would appear to be the reverse of that seen by an observer moving slower than the muon.

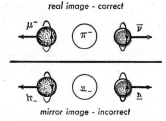

real image - correct

mirror image - incorrect

Fig. 80U *Schematic diagram showing the right-handed, or positive, helicity of a μ^- and $\bar{\nu}$ particles in the decay of π^- mesons.*

If all the particles in one or the other of the two mirror images of Figs. 80T and 80U are changed to their ·corresponding antiparticles, the resulting interaction becomes the real interaction of the other. Thus there is an over-all symmetry between both decay reactions.

When a μ^+ decays in the customary way into a positron, a neutrino, and an antineutrino, helicity for the neutrinos as well as the μ^+ are already fixed. What helicity is imparted to the electron and the μ^+ will depend on the relative directions of all recoiling particles. If the neutrinos go off

Fig. 80V *Schematic diagram of μ^+ decay showing the helicity of particles where the two neutrinos move off in the same direction.*

together as shown in Fig. 80V, the positron must recoil with negative helicity. If the antiprotons recoil in opposite directions, the positron, to conserve spin, can have either positive or negative helicity. Drawings for these cases will be left as exercises for the student.

If a distant world is made of antimatter, there is no known way whereby we on the earth can determine this. Furthermore, though μ^- and μ^+ have positive and negative helicity, respectively, there is no information we could impart to a man on a distant world that would tell him which is which.

80.11. Conservation Laws. We have seen in earlier chapters on nuclear processes that certain conservation laws apply to all reactions. These laws relate measurable quantities existing just before impact with those existing immediately after impact. For convenience we can state them as follows:

Law 1. The total energy, including rest mass, remains constant.

Law 2. The total linear momentum remains constant.

Law 3. The total angular momentum remains constant.

Law 4. The total charge remains constant.

To these four laws we add four more to apply to elementary particle reactions.

Law 5. The total lepton number remains constant.

This fifth law has greater implications when it is stated another way. "The total number of baryons in the world remains constant." Here we count an antibaryon as minus one baryon. This law is not pertinent for reactions involving only mesons and leptons. All mesons and leptons have baryon number zero.

Law 6 .The total lepton number remains constant.

The leptons ν, e^- and μ^- have lepton number $+1$ and their antiparticles have lepton number -1. These particles are involved in the decay of the muons.

Law 7. The total strangeness number remains constant.

This last law does not apply to weak reactions as in the decay of unstable particles, but does apply to strong interactions.

Law 8. The over-all symmetry of anti-particle-parity is preserved.

This is represented by Figs. 80P and 80R.

Example. Apply the rules of conservation of baryons and conservation of strangeness to the strong reaction involved in Fig. 80P.

Solution. From the first reaction in Eq.(80h), and the baryon and strangeness numbers in Fig. 80A, we can write

$$\pi^- + p \rightarrow \Sigma^- + K^+$$

Baryon number $\quad 0 + 1 = 1 + 0$

Strangeness number $\quad 0 + 0 = -1 + 1$

80.12. Omega Meson. The identification of the ω meson, an atomic particle composed of three π mesons, was first detected by L. W. Alvarez, B. C. Maglic, A. H. Rosenfeld, and M. L. Stevenson in 1961. Antiproton reactions in a hydrogen bubble chamber frequently give rise to four pronged tracks of the kind shown in Fig. 80W. Momentum and energy measurements of many such events clearly show that two pairs of oppositely charged π mesons are responsible for the four emergent tracks. Frequently, however, one pair of π mesons is produced and the remaining mass quickly decays (in about 10^{-22} sec) into three π mesons, $\pi^+ + \pi^0 + \pi^-$. Before decaying, this uncharged particle, with a mass of 1540 m_e, is called an ω *meson*. The alternate reactions for this event are

$$p^- + p \rightarrow 2\pi^+ + 2\pi^-$$

or

$$p^- + p \rightarrow \pi^+ + \pi^- + \omega$$

followed by

$$\omega \rightarrow \pi^+ + \pi^0 + \pi^-$$

An excellent illustration of the decay of a π^+ meson into a μ^+ and e^+ is shown at the lower right in Fig. 80U. (See Fig. 73P.)

In the upper right in Fig. 80X, a π^- meson is captured by a proton to produce a neutron and a π^0. Normally a π^0 decays into γ rays, but about one out of eighty such neutral particles converts one of the γ rays into an electron pair. Such a *Dalitz pair*, as it is called, is shown by the oppositely directed spirals. The reactions for this event are

$$\pi^- + p \rightarrow \pi^0 + n$$

$$\pi^0 \rightarrow e^+ + e^- \; \gamma \; \text{ray}$$

At the present state of development, in trying to unravel the many mysteries concerning elementary particles, some important questions stand out. Are all of the particles listed in Fig. 80A really elementary, or are some of them just composites of others? Could it be that some of the stars in the universe, or entire galaxies, are made of antimatter, with hydrogen atoms composed of antiprotons and positrons, etc.? Why are elementary charges limited to values of $+1$, 0, and -1.

Every physicist believes that some day we will know the answers to these and many other questions about the nature of elementary particles, the building blocks of the universe.

QUESTIONS AND PROBLEMS

1. Calculate the threshold energy for the production of a proton pair.

2. If, ignoring the time dilation attributed to relativity, the actual measured distance the K-particle travels in Fig. 80N is 2.5 cm, and the speed is very nearly the speed of light, what is its life-time? (*Ans.* 0.83×10^{-10} sec.)

3. If the actual measured distance the Λ-particle traveled in Fig. 80N is 7.5 cm, and the speed is very nearly the speed of light, what is its life-time?

4. If the measured distance the Λ-particles traveled in Fig. 80L is 1.0 cm, and the speed is very nearly the speed of light, what was their life-time? (*Ans.* 0.33×10^{-10} sec.)

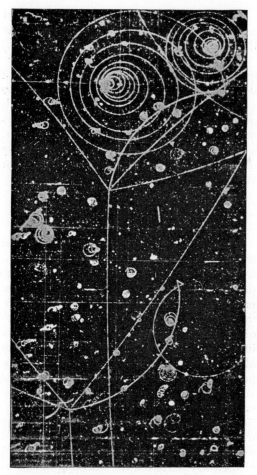

Fig. 80W *Photograph of anti-proton reactions in a hydrogen bubble chamber showing meson pairs in the kind of reaction that first led to the identification of the ω meson.* (Courtesy of the Lawrence Radiation Laboratory, and L. W. Alvarez and associates.)

5. Make a list of all hyperons, and another list of all strange-particles.

6. In Fig. 80N, a π^- meson and proton come together and create a K^0 and Λ°. (a) Show that strangeness-numbers are conserved by writing numbers under the reaction symbols. (b) Could the same two original particles have created a Σ^+ and K^-? (*Ans.* (a) $0 + 0 = 1 - 1$, (b) No.)

7. Write down the first reaction in Eq.(80g), and then replace each particle by its antiparticle. Does this law (a) obey the baryon law #5, and (b) the strangeness law #7?

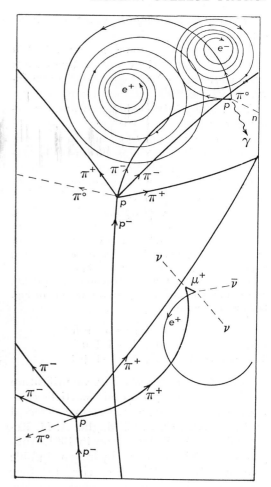

Fig. 80X *Legend diagram for Fig. 80W showing the uncharged trackless particles as dotted lines.*

8. Write down the first reaction in Eq.(80h), and then replace each particle by its antiparticle. Does this law (a) obey the baryon law #5, and (b) the strangeness law #7? (*Ans.* (a) yes, (b) yes.)

9. Apply the law of conservation of baryons and conservation of strangeness number to show why the strongly reacting particles in Fig. 80N could not have resulted in the reaction $\pi^- + p \rightarrow \Sigma^0 + \Lambda^\circ$.

10. Apply the laws of conservation of baryon number and strangeness number, and show why the strong reaction in Fig. 80N could not have been $p^- + p \rightarrow \Lambda^\circ + K^0$. (*Ans.* Baryons not conserved.)

Appendix 1

A LIST OF THE NOBEL PRIZE WINNERS IN PHYSICS

1901   Roentgen, Wilhelm Conrad (1845-1923), German. *Discovery of X-rays.*

1902   Lorentz, Hendrik Antoon (1853-1928), Dutch, and
Zeeman, Pieter (1865-1943), Dutch. *Zeeman Effect.*

1903   Becquerel, Henri Antoine (1852-1908), French. *Discovery of Radioactivity.*
Curie, Pierre (1859-1906), French, and
Curie, Marie Sklodowska (1867-1934), Polish chemist in France. *Studies of Radioactivity.*

1904   Lord Rayleigh (John William Strutt) (1842-1919), English. *Studies of Gases.*

1905   Lenard, Philipp (1862-1947), German. *Studies of Cathode Rays.*

1906   Thomson, Sir Joseph John (1856-1940), English. *Discharges through Gases.*

1907   Michelson, Albert A. (1852-1931), American. *Precision Optical Instruments.*

1908   Lippmann, Gabriel (1845-1921), French. *Interference Color Photography.*

1909   Marconi, Guglielmo (1874-1937), Italian, and
Braun, Ferdinand (1850-1918), German. *Development of Wireless.*

1910   Van der Waals, Johannes D. (1837-1923), Dutch. *Gas Laws.*

1911   Wien, Wilhelm (1864-1928), German. *Heat Radiation Laws.*

1912   Dalen, Gustaf (1869-1937), Swedish. *Automatic Lighting of Lighthouses.*

1913   Kamerlingh-Onnes, Heike (1853-1926), Dutch. *Liquid Helium and Low Temperatures.*

1914   Von Laue, Max Theodor Felix (1879-1960), German. *Diffraction of X-rays.*

1915   Bragg, Sir W. H. (1862-1942), English, and his son
Bragg, W. L. (1890-   ), English. *Crystal Structure.*

1917   Barkla, Charles G. (1877-1944), English. *Characteristic X-rays of the Elements.*

1918   Planck, Max (1858-1947), German. *Quantum Theory of Radiation.*

1919   Stark, Johannes (1874-1957), German. *The Stark Effect of Spectrum Lines.*

1920   Guillaume, Charles E. (1861-1938), Spanish. *Study of Nickel-Steel Alloys.*

1921   Einstein, Albert (1879-1955), German. *Theory of Relativity and the Photoelectric Effect.*

1922   Bohr, Niels (1885-   ), Danish. *Theory of Atomic Structure.*

1923   Millikan, Robert A. (1868-1953), American. *Charge on Electron and Photoelectric Effect.*

1924   Siegbahn, Karl M. (1886-   ), Swedish. *X-ray Spectroscopy.*

1925   Franck, James (1882-   ), German, and
Hertz, Gustav (1887-   ), German. *Electron Impact on Atoms.*

1926   Perrin, Jean B. (1870-1942), French. *Discovery of the Equilibrium of Sedimentation.*

1927   Compton, Arthur H. (1892-1962), American. *Compton Effect.*
Wilson, Charles T. R. (1869-1959), English. *Wilson Cloud Chamber.*

1928   Richardson, Owen Willans (1879-1959), English. *Studies of Thermal Ions.*

719

1929 De Broglie, Louis V. (1892-   ), French. *Wave Character of Electrons.*

1930 Raman, Sir Chandrasekhara V. (1888-   ), Hindu. *Raman Effect.*

1932 Heisenberg, Werner (1901-   ), German. *Creation of Quantum Mechanics.*

1933 Schroedinger, Edwin (1887-   ), German, and
      Dirac, P. A. M. (1902-   ), English. *Atomic Theory.*

1935 Chadwick, James (1891-   ), English. *Discovery of the Neutron.*

1936 Hess, Victor F. (1883-   ), Austrian. *Discovery of Cosmic Rays.*
      Anderson, Carl D. (1905-   ), American. *Discovery of Positron.*

1937 Davisson, Clinton J. (1881-   ), American, and
      Thompson, George P. (1892-   ), English. *Electron Diffraction by Crystals.*

1938 Fermi, Enrico (1901-1954), Italian. *Slow Neutron Reactions.*

1939 Lawrence, Ernest O. (1901-1958), American. *Development of Cyclotron.*

1940, 1941, 1942, not awarded

1943 Stern, O. (1888-   ), German. *Magnetic Moment of Proton.*

1944 Rabi, I. I. (1898-   ), American. *Magnetic Moments of Nuclei.*

1945 Pauli, W. (1900-1958), German. *Pauli Exclusion Principle.*

1946 Bridgman, P. W. (1882-1961), American. *Physical Effects of High Pressures.*

1947 Appleton, Sir Ed. V. (1892-   ), English. *Exploration of the Ionosphere.*

1948 Blackett, P. M. S. (1897-   ), English. *Discoveries in Cosmic Radiation.*

1949 Yukawa, H. (1907-   ), Japanese. *Theoretical Prediction of Mesons.*

1950 Powell, C. F. (1903-   ), English. *Photographic Cosmic Ray Studies.*

1951 Cockcroft, Sir J. D. (1897-   ), English, and
      Walton, E. T. S. (1903-   ), English. *First Transmutation of Atomic Nuclei.*

1952 Bloch, Felix (1905-   ), American. *Nuclear Magnetic Moments.*
      Purcell, Ed. M. (1912-   ), American. *Radio Astronomy.*

1953 Zernike, Frits (1888-   ), Dutch. *Phase Contrast Microscope.*

1954 Born, Max (1882-   ), German. *Quantum mechanics, and wave functions.*
      Bothe, Walther (1891-1957), German. *Quantum mechanics, and wave functions.*

1955 Kusch, P. (1911-   ), American, and
      Lamb, W. E. (1913-   ), American. *Microwave Spectroscopy and Atomic Structure.*

1956 Shockley, W. (1910-   ), American,
      Brattain, W. H. (1902-   ), American, and
      Bardeen, J. (1908-   ), American. *Semi-conductors, and Their Application to Transistors.*

1957 Yang, C. N. (1922-   ), Chinese, and
      Lee, T. D. (1926-   ), Chinese. *Studies of the Concept of Parity in Atomic Physics.*

1958 Cerenkov, P. A. (1904-   ), Russian,
      Tamm, I. E. (1895-   ), Russian, and
      Frank, I. M. (1908-   ), Russian. *Discovery and Study of Cerenkov Radiation.*

1959 Segre, E. (1905-   ), American, and
      Chamberlain, O. (1920-   ), American. *Discovery of the Anti-proton.*

1960 Glaser, D. A. (1926-   ), American. *The Bubble Chamber.*

1961 Hofstadter, Robt. (1916-   ), American, and
      Mossbauer, R. L. (1930-   ), German. *Nuclear Radiation and Absorption.*

THE GREEK ALPHABET

A	α	*Alpha*	H	η	*Eta*	N	ν	*Nu*	T	τ	*Tau*
B	β	*Beta*	Θ	θ	*Theta*	Ξ	ξ	*Xi*	Υ	υ	*Upsilon*
Γ	γ	*Gamma*	I	ι	*Iota*	O	o	*Omicron*	Φ	ϕ	*Phi*
Δ	δ	*Delta*	K	κ	*Kappa*	Π	π	*Pi*	X	χ	*Chi*
E	ϵ	*Epsilon*	Λ	λ	*Lambda*	P	ρ	*Rho*	Ψ	ψ	*Psi*
Z	ζ	*Zeta*	M	μ	*Mu*	Σ	σ	*Sigma*	Ω	ω	*Omega*

Appendix II

ELEMENTS OF TRIGONOMETRY

USEFUL IN SOLVING PHYSICS PROBLEMS

Trigonometry of the Right Triangle. Of the mathematics to be encountered in this book none involves more than the simplest equations in algebra and the three most common functions in trigonometry, *sine, cosine,* and *tangent.* These, however, are quite generally used and a brief review of the trigonometric functions is not out of place here. The principal use of the sin, cos, and tan occurs in problems where the solution requires the solving of a right triangle.

As shown in Fig. 1 the small letters *a, b,* and *c* represent the lengths of the sides of the triangle and the capital letters *A, B,* and *C* represent their corresponding opposite angles. Angle $C = 90°$.

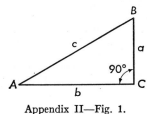

Appendix II—Fig. 1.

By definition

$$\sin = \frac{\text{side opposite}}{\text{hypotenuse}}, \qquad \cos = \frac{\text{side adjacent}}{\text{hypotenuse}},$$

$$\tan = \frac{\text{side opposite}}{\text{side adjacent}}.$$

(It would be well to memorize these definitions and from them and Fig. 1 practice writing down the following equations:)

(1) $\quad \sin A = \dfrac{a}{c}$ (2) $\quad \cos A = \dfrac{b}{c}$ (3) $\quad \tan A = \dfrac{a}{b}$

(4) $\quad \sin B = \dfrac{b}{c}$ (5) $\quad \cos B = \dfrac{a}{c}$ (6) $\quad \tan B = \dfrac{b}{a}$.

Each of these equations is a relation between one angle and two sides of the triangle. By transposing they take on another useful form. Eqs. (1) and (2), for example, become

(7) $\quad a = c \sin A$ (8) $\quad b = c \cos A$.

If two of the sides of any right triangle are known, the other side and the two acute angles can be calculated from the above equations. This is done by making use of trigonometric tables of sin, cos, and tan given in the following table for all angles between 0° and 90°.

Example: For a given right triangle, angle $C = 90°$, the side $a = 6$ cm, and side $c = 12$ cm. Find angle A, angle B, and side b.

Solution: Using Eq.(1) and substituting, $\sin A = 6/12 = 0.5$. Looking up 0.500 in the sin column of Appendix III, the angle 30° is read. Since the sum of the three angles in any triangle is 180°,

(9) $\quad A + B + C = 180°$.

Subtraction gives angle $B = 60°$. Applying Eq.(8), $b = c \cos A$, we look up the cos of $30°$ in the tables and find 0.866, which substituted for $\cos A$ gives $b = 12 \times 0.866 = 10.39$ cm.

When two of the sides of a right triangle are known, the other side can also be calculated from the theorem that the square on the hypotenuse equals the sum of the squares on the other two sides.

$$(10) \quad c^2 = a^2 + b^2.$$

When in a right triangle, one of the acute angles is known, only the length of one side need be known to calculate the lengths of the other two sides.

From the definitions of the sin, cos, and tan in Eqs. (1), (2), and (3) it will be noted that the tan is equal to the sin divided by the cos.

$$(11) \quad \tan \theta = \frac{\sin \theta}{\cos \theta}.$$

$c^2 = a^2 + b^2 - 2\,ab\,\cos\theta$ Appendix II—Fig. 2. $c^2 = a^2 + b^2 + 2\,ab\,\cos\phi$

Solution of Any Triangle. Many times in the solving of a physics problem it becomes necessary to solve an oblique triangle (see Fig. 2). Where two sides and the included angle of such a triangle are known, the **Law of Cosines** may be used to calculate the other side.

$$(12) \quad c^2 = a^2 + b^2 - 2ab \cos \theta.$$

If the included angle is less than $90°$ as shown in diagram (a), the values of a and b and $\cos \theta$ are substituted directly into Eq.(12) and the value of the side c calculated. If the angle θ is greater than $90°$, as in diagram (b), the supplementary angle ϕ is found and Eq.(13) used.

$$(13) \quad c^2 = a^2 + b^2 + 2ab \cos \phi.$$

In reality Eqs. (12) and (13) are one and the same equation since $\phi = 180° - \theta$. In the special case $\theta = 90°$, the cosine term becomes zero, since $\cos 90° = 0$, and both formulas reduce to Eq.(10), as they should.

In words, the *Law of Cosines* states: *the square of any side of a triangle is equal to the sum of the squares on the other two sides minus twice their product multiplied by the cosine of the included angle.*

When three sides of a triangle are known, the angles can all be determined from Eq.(12). Transposing all but $\cos \theta$ to the same side of the equation,

$$(14) \quad \cos \theta = \frac{a^2 + b^2 - c^2}{2ab}.$$

With this as a general formula for angle θ, similar equations for all three angles of any triangle may be written,

$$(15) \quad \cos A = \frac{b^2 + c^2 - a^2}{2bc}, \quad \cos B = \frac{c^2 + a^2 - b^2}{2ca},$$

$$\cos C = \frac{a^2 + b^2 - c^2}{2ab}.$$

A negative value for the cosine calculated from these equations means that the angle is greater than 90°. Its value can be found by looking in the tables for the angle whose sine has the same positive value, and then add 90°. For example, suppose $\cos A$ equals —0.5. Looking up the angle whose sine is +0.500 we find 30°. Angle A is therefore 30° + 90° or 120°.

If two angles and the included side of an oblique triangle are known, the other two sides are readily calculated from the well-known **Law of Sines.**

$$(16) \quad \frac{a}{\sin A} = \frac{b}{\sin B} = \frac{c}{\sin C}.$$

Any two terms from these equalities give an equation with only one unknown.

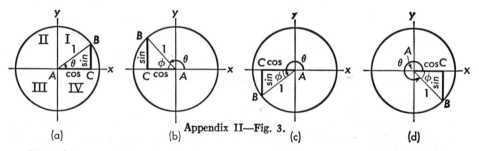

Appendix II—Fig. 3.

(a)   (b)   (c)   (d)

The trigonometric functions sin, cos, and tan apply not only to angles between 0° and 90° but to larger angles as well. How they apply is illustrated in Fig. 3 where four circles of unit radius are drawn. Diagram (a) shows a right triangle ABC with angle θ in the first quadrant. It follows from the definitions of the sin and cos given by Eqs. (1) and (2) that

$$\sin \theta = BC/AB, \quad \text{and} \quad \cos \theta = AC/AB.$$

Since $AB = 1$, the sin θ becomes just the length of the line BC. From Eq.(11), the tan $\theta = BC/AC$.

All angles between 90° and 180° lie in the second quadrant, and are represented by θ in diagram (b). Similarly, angles between 180° and 270° lie in the third quadrant as illustrated in diagram (c), and angles between 270° and 360° lie in the fourth quadrant as illustrated in diagram (d). In all quadrants the length of the line $BC = \sin \theta$, the length of the line $AC = \cos \theta$, and the ratio $BC/AC = \tan \theta$.

To find the numerical values of the functions for all angles greater than 90°, the angle ϕ is first determined by finding the difference between θ and 180° and/or 360°, as the case may be. The values of sin ϕ, cos ϕ, and tan ϕ are then read from the Tables in Appendix III. In the second quadrant the sin, being in the + direction, is positive, whereas the cos, being in the —x direction, is negative. In the third quadrant the sine and cosine are both negative, whereas in the fourth quadrant the sine is negative and the cosine positive.

Examples: let $\theta = 150°$. Find sin θ, cos θ, and tan θ. Subtracting from 180° gives $\phi = 30°$. From the Tables in Appendix III sin 30° = 0.500, cos 30° = 0.866, and tan 30° = 0.577, giving sin 150° = 0.500, cos 150° = −0.866 and tan 150° = −0.577.

Problems in Trigonometry

1. Find the number of degrees in the following angles: (a) sin $\theta = 0.342$, (b) sin $\theta = 0.809$, (c) cos $\theta = 0.530$, (d) cos $\theta = 0.454$, (e) tan $\theta = 0.520$, and (f) tan $\theta = 1.881$.

2. Find the sin, cos, and tan for the following angles: (a) 32.6°, and (b) 84.3°. (*Ans.* (a) 0.539, 0.842, 0.639; (b) 0.995, 0.0993, 10.02.)

3. Find the sin, cos, and tan for the following angles: (a) 118°, (b) 205°, and (c) 325°.

4. Find the angle θ for each of the following: (a) cos $\theta = -0.249$, (b) sin $\theta = -0.618$, and (c) tan $\theta = -2.023$. (*Ans.* (a) 104.4° or 255.6°, (b) 116.3° or 306.3°, (c) 218.2° or 321.8°.)

5. One of the acute angles of a right triangle is 33° and the shortest side is 5 m long. Find the lengths of the other two sides and the remaining angle.

6. One of the acute angles of a right triangle is 48° and the hypotenuse is 6 m long. Find the other angle and the lengths of the other two sides. (*Ans.* 42°, 4.01 m, 4.46 m.)

7. A right triangle has sides of length: 3 ft, 4 ft, and 5 ft. Make a diagram to scale and measure the angles. Calculate the angles and compare them with those measured.

8. If the hypotenuse of a right triangle is 16 m long and one side is 10 m long, what is the length of the remaining side and the size of the two acute angles? (*Ans.* 12.5 m, 38.7°, and 51.3°.)

9. From a point on the level ground 180 ft from the base of a flag pole, an observer sights the top at an angle of 48° 24'. How high is the flag pole?

10. A base line 160 m long is measured along the beach; from its ends a rock can be seen some distance off shore. If the angles of sight from the ends make with the base line are 90° and 72.5°, how far from shore is the rock? (*Ans.* 508 m.)

11. A base line 20 m long is measured along the bank of a river, and from its ends a tree on the opposite bank is sighted. If the angles that these lines make with the base line are 65.5° and 72.6°, what is the width of the river? Make a diagram to scale.

12. To find the distance to a mountain peak, a base line 2 mi long is measured out on level ground in the valley below. From each end of this line the peak is sighted through a surveyor's telescope, and the lines of sight are found to make angles of 74.5° and 67.2° with the base line. Find the distance to the peak from the ends of the base line. Make a diagram to scale. (*Ans.* (a) 2.97 mi, (b) 3.11 mi.)

13. A ship in distress is sighted from two lighthouses 10 mi apart. From the first lighthouse the line of sight to the ship is found to make an angle of 125° with the line of sight to the second lighthouse, while from the second the line of sight is found to make 48° with the line of sight to the first lighthouse. How far is the ship from the nearest lighthouse? Make a diagram to scale.

14. When the sun is 35.4° above the horizon, the shadow of a tall tree is found to be 260 ft long, as measured along level ground from the base of the tree. How high is the tree? (*Ans.* 185 ft.)

15. Two sides of a triangle are 24.8 m and 32.6 m, respectively, and the included angle is 35.5°. Find the length of the other side, and the values of the other two angles.

16. Two sides of a triangle are 5.7 m and 8.4 m, respectively, and the included angle is 115°. Find the length of the other side, and the values of the other two angles. (*Ans.* 12.0 m, 39.4°, and 35.6°.)

17. From a point on level ground 150 ft from the base of a flag pole, an observer sights the top at an elevation angle of 35°. How high is the flag pole? (*Ans.* 105 ft.)

18. A base line 400 ft long is measured along the ocean shore, and from the end a rock can be seen offshore. If the angles that the lines of sight make with the base line are 90° and 75°, how far off shore is the rock? (*Ans.* 1490 ft.)

TRIGONOMETRIC FUNCTIONS (*Natural*)

Angle	Sine	Cosine	Tangent	Angle	Sine	Cosine	Tangent
0°	0.000	1.000	0.000				
1°	.018	1.000	.018	46°	.719	.695	1.036
2°	.035	0.999	.035	47°	.731	.682	1.072
3°	.052	.999	.052	48°	.743	.669	1.111
4°	.070	.998	.070	49°	.755	.656	1.150
5°	.087	.996	.088	50°	.766	.643	1.192
6°	.105	.995	.105	51°	.777	.629	1.235
7°	.122	.993	.123	52°	.788	.616	1.280
8°	.139	.990	.141	53°	.799	.602	1.327
9°	.156	.988	.158	54°	.809	.588	1.376
10°	.174	.985	.176	55°	.819	.574	1.428
11°	.191	.982	.194	56°	.829	.559	1.483
12°	.208	.978	.213	57°	.839	.545	1.540
13°	.225	.974	.231	58°	.848	.530	1.600
14°	.242	.970	.249	59°	.857	.515	1.664
15°	.259	.966	.268	60°	.866	.500	1.732
16°	.276	.961	.287	61°	.875	.485	1.804
17°	.292	.956	.306	62°	.883	.470	1.881
18°	.309	.951	.325	63°	.891	.454	1.963
19°	.326	.946	.344	64°	.899	.438	2.050
20°	.342	.940	.364	65°	.906	.423	2.145
21°	.358	.934	.384	66°	.914	.407	2.246
22°	.375	.927	.404	67°	.921	.391	2.356
23°	.391	.921	.425	68°	.927	.375	2.475
24°	.407	.914	.445	69°	.934	.358	2.605
25°	.423	.906	.466	70°	.940	.342	2.747
26°	.438	.899	.488	71°	.946	.326	2.904
27°	.454	.891	.510	72°	.951	.309	3.078
28°	.470	.883	.532	73°	.956	.292	3.271
29°	.485	.875	.554	74°	.961	.276	3.487
30°	.500	.866	.577	75°	.966	.259	3.732
31°	.515	.857	.601	76°	.970	.242	4.011
32°	.530	.848	.625	77°	.974	.225	4.331
33°	.545	.839	.649	78°	.978	.208	4.705
34°	.559	.829	.675	79°	.982	.191	5.145
35°	.574	.819	.700	80°	.985	.174	5.671
36°	.588	.809	.727	81°	.988	.156	6.314
37°	.602	.799	.754	82°	.990	.139	7.115
38°	.616	.788	.781	83°	.993	.122	8.144
39°	.629	.777	.810	84°	.995	.105	9.514
40°	.643	.766	.839	85°	.996	.087	11.43
41°	.656	.755	.869	86°	.998	.070	14.30
42°	.669	.743	.900	87°	.999	.052	19.08
43°	.682	.731	.933	88°	.999	.035	28.64
44°	.695	.719	.966	89°	1.000	.018	57.29
45°	.707	.707	1.000	90°	1.000	.000	∞

Appendix IV

COMMON LOGARITHMS

(To obtain Naperian logarithm of a number multiply these logarithms by 2.3026.)

N	0	1	2	3	4	5	6	7	8	9
0	....	0000	3010	4771	6021	6990	7782	8451	9031	9542
1	0000	0414	0792	1139	1461	1761	2041	2304	2553	2788
2	3010	3222	3424	3617	3802	3979	4150	4314	4472	4624
3	4771	4914	5051	5185	5315	5441	5563	5682	5798	5911
4	6021	6128	6232	6335	6435	6532	6628	6721	6812	6902
5	6990	7076	7160	7243	7324	7404	7482	7559	7634	7709
6	7782	7853	7924	7993	8062	8129	8195	8261	8325	8388
7	8451	8513	8573	8633	8692	8751	8808	8865	8921	8976
8	9031	9085	9138	9191	9243	9294	9345	9395	9445	9494
9	9542	9590	9638	9685	9731	9777	9823	9868	9912	9956
10	0000	0043	0086	0128	0170	0212	0253	0294	0334	0374
11	0414	0453	0492	0531	0569	0607	0645	0682	0719	0755
12	0792	0828	0864	0899	0934	0969	1004	1038	1072	1106
13	1139	1173	1206	1239	1271	1303	1335	1367	1399	1430
14	1461	1492	1523	1553	1584	1614	1644	1673	1703	1732
15	1761	1790	1818	1847	1875	1903	1931	1959	1987	2014
16	2041	2068	2095	2122	2148	2175	2201	2227	2253	2279
17	2304	2330	2355	2380	2405	2430	2455	2480	2504	2529
18	2553	2577	2601	2625	2648	2672	2695	2718	2742	2765
19	2788	2810	2833	2856	2878	2900	2923	2945	2967	2989
20	3010	3032	3054	3075	3096	3118	3139	3160	3181	3201
21	3222	3243	3263	3284	3304	3324	3345	3365	3385	3404
22	3424	3444	3464	3483	3502	3522	3541	3560	3579	3598
23	3617	3636	3655	3674	3692	3711	3729	3747	3766	3784
24	3802	3820	3838	3856	3874	3892	3909	3927	3945	3962
25	3979	3997	4014	4031	4048	4065	4082	4099	4116	4133
26	4150	4166	4183	4200	4216	4232	4249	4265	4281	4298
27	4314	4330	4346	4362	4378	4393	4409	4425	4440	4456
28	4472	4487	4502	4518	4533	4548	4564	4579	4594	4609
29	4624	4639	4654	4669	4683	4698	4713	4728	4742	4757
30	4771	4786	4800	4814	4829	4843	4857	4871	4886	4900
31	4914	4928	4942	4955	4969	4983	4997	5011	5024	5038
32	5051	5065	5079	5092	5105	5119	5132	5145	5159	5172
33	5185	5198	5211	5224	5237	5250	5263	5276	5289	5302
34	5315	5328	5340	5353	5366	5378	5391	5403	5416	5428
35	5441	5453	5465	5478	5490	5502	5514	5527	5539	5551
36	5563	5575	5587	5599	5611	5623	5635	5647	5658	5670
37	5682	5694	5705	5717	5729	5740	5752	5763	5775	5786
38	5798	5809	5821	5832	5843	5855	5866	5877	5888	5899
39	5911	5922	5933	5944	5955	5966	5977	5988	5999	6010
40	6021	6031	6042	6053	6064	6075	6085	6096	6107	6117
41	6128	6138	6149	6160	6170	6180	6191	6201	6212	6222
42	6232	6243	6253	6263	6274	6284	6294	6304	6314	6325
43	6335	6345	6355	6365	6375	6385	6395	6405	6415	6425
44	6435	6444	6454	6464	6474	6484	6493	6503	6513	6522
45	6532	6542	6551	6561	6571	6580	6590	6599	6609	6618
46	6628	6637	6646	6656	6665	6675	6684	6693	6702	6712
47	6721	6730	6739	6749	6758	6767	6776	6785	6794	6803
48	6812	6821	6830	6839	6848	6857	6866	6875	6884	6893
49	6902	6911	6920	6928	6937	6946	6955	6964	6972	6981
50	6990	6998	7007	7016	7024	7033	7042	7050	7059	7067
N	0	1	2	3	4	5	6	7	8	9

COMMON LOGARITHMS (*Cont.*)

N	0	1	2	3	4	5	6	7	8	9
50	6990	6998	7007	7016	7024	7033	7042	7050	7059	7067
51	7076	7084	7093	7101	7110	7118	7126	7135	7143	7152
52	7160	7168	7177	7185	7193	7202	7210	7218	7226	7235
53	7243	7251	7259	7267	7275	7284	7292	7300	7308	7316
54	7324	7332	7340	7348	7356	7364	7372	7380	7388	7396
55	7404	7412	7419	7427	7435	7443	7451	7459	7466	7474
56	7482	7490	7497	7505	7513	7520	7528	7536	7543	7551
57	7559	7566	7574	7582	7589	7597	7604	7612	7619	7627
58	7634	7642	7649	7657	7664	7672	7679	7686	7694	7701
59	7709	7716	7723	7731	7738	7745	7752	7760	7767	7774
60	7782	7789	7796	7803	7810	7818	7825	7832	7839	7846
61	7853	7860	7868	7875	7882	7889	7896	7903	7910	7917
62	7924	7931	7938	7945	7952	7959	7966	7973	7980	7987
63	7993	8000	8007	8014	8021	8028	8035	8041	8048	8055
64	8062	8069	8075	8082	8089	8096	8102	8109	8116	8122
65	8129	8136	8142	8149	8156	8162	8169	8176	8182	8189
66	8195	8202	8209	8215	8222	8228	8235	8241	8248	8254
67	8261	8267	8274	8280	8287	8293	8299	8306	8312	8319
68	8325	8331	8338	8344	8351	8357	8363	8370	8376	8382
69	8388	8395	8401	8407	8414	8420	8426	8432	8439	8445
70	8451	8457	8463	8470	8476	8482	8488	8494	8500	8506
71	8513	8519	8525	8531	8537	8543	8549	8555	8561	8567
72	8573	8579	8585	8591	8597	8603	8609	8615	8621	8627
73	8633	8639	8645	8651	8657	8663	8669	8675	8681	8686
74	8692	8698	8704	8710	8716	8722	8727	8733	8739	8745
75	8751	8756	8762	8768	8774	8779	8785	8791	8797	8802
76	8808	8814	8820	8825	8831	8837	8842	8848	8854	8859
77	8865	8871	8876	8882	8887	8893	8899	8904	8910	8915
78	8921	8927	8932	8938	8943	8949	8954	8960	8965	8971
79	8976	8982	8987	8993	8998	9004	9009	9015	9020	9025
80	9031	9036	9042	9047	9053	9058	9063	9069	9074	9079
81	9085	9090	9096	9101	9106	9112	9117	9122	9128	9133
82	9138	9143	9149	9154	9159	9165	9170	9175	9180	9186
83	9191	9196	9201	9206	9212	9217	9222	9227	9232	9238
84	9243	9248	9253	9258	9263	9269	9274	9279	9284	9289
85	9294	9299	9304	9309	9315	9320	9325	9330	9335	9340
86	9345	9350	9355	9360	9365	9370	9375	9380	9385	9390
87	9395	9400	9405	9410	9415	9420	9425	9430	9435	9440
88	9445	9450	9455	9460	9465	9469	9474	9479	9484	9489
89	9494	9499	9504	9509	9513	9518	9523	9528	9533	9538
90	9542	9547	9552	9557	9562	9566	9571	9576	9581	9586
91	9590	9595	9600	9605	9609	9614	9619	9624	9628	9633
92	9638	9643	9647	9652	9657	9661	9666	9671	9675	9680
93	9685	8689	9694	9699	9703	9708	9713	9717	9722	9727
94	9731	9736	9741	9745	9750	9754	9759	9763	9768	9773
95	9777	9782	9786	9791	9795	9800	9805	9809	9814	9818
96	9823	9827	9832	9836	9841	9845	9850	9854	9859	9863
97	9868	9872	9877	9881	9886	9890	9894	9899	9903	9908
98	9912	9917	9921	9926	9930	9934	9939	9943	9948	9952
99	9956	9961	9965	9969	9974	9978	9983	9987	9991	9996
100	0000	0004	0009	0013	0017	0022	0026	0030	0035	0039
N	0	1	2	3	4	5	6	7	8	9

Fig. A.

Appendix V—The Slide Rule

A slide rule is a simple mechanical device used for carrying out the arithmetic processes of *multiplication* and *division*. Since slide rules are easy to use, and inexpensive ones are quite adequate for most purposes, every physics student should acquire a slide rule and learn how to use it.

The beginner should select a straight inexpensive rule about ten inches in length and one that contains four and not more than six scales. The scales most commonly used are the *A, B, C,* and *D* scales as shown in Fig. A. Note that the slide rule consists of the slide rule *body,* and two movable parts we will call the *slipstick* and the *slider*.

Significant Figures. Before learning to use a slide rule we should clearly understand the meaning of the term *significant figures*. The three lists of numbers in the columns below will help to illustrate its meaning.

The first significant figure of a number is the first numeral that is not zero. The last significant figure is the last numeral that is not zero.

Most slide rules are capable of handling the multiplication and division of numbers to three significant figures only. Furthermore, the answers are correct to three significant figures only.

A Two significant figures	B Three significant figures	C Four significant figures
24	374	5279
6.9	21.5	63.08
0.37	6.05	0.1062
0.053	0.00328	0.04503
4600	546000	692700

If numbers like those in column C are to be used in any slide rule calculation, they should be reduced to three significant figures. These particular numbers would, therefore, be assumed to have the values 5280, 63.1, 0.106, 0.0450, and 693000, respectively. Since many of the measurements made in the science laboratory are accurate to only three significant figures, the use of a slide rule is usually, but not always, sufficient and justified.

The C and D Scales. In making your first critical examination of your slide rule, note that there are four fundamental scales, and that they are marked at the left

728

end of the rule by *A, B, C,* and *D.* (See Fig. A.) Since multiplication and division are usually carried out with the two identical *C* and *D* scales, we shall examine the entire length of these scales in three sections and see how to determine any position of the slider hairline.

Consider the left-hand section of the *C* and *D* scales from the left index 1 to the principal number 2, as shown in Fig. B. Note that the interval is divided into ten divisions representing tenths, and each of these into ten divisions representing hundredths.

C
D

1.14   1.37   1.535   1.950

Fig. B.

If the slider hairline were located in the position shown by the arrow at the left, its position would be written down as 1.14. Similarly, the second arrow position represents the reading 1.37. The third arrow position appears to be halfway between 1.53 and 1.54; hence we do what is called *interpolate* and write 1.535. Interpolation is a process of inserting or finding intermediate values by making a reasonable estimate as to an exact value. Since interpolation is nothing more than a good guess, the reading 1.535 is hardly better than three significant figures would indicate. Applying the interpolation process to the fourth arrow position, we could write 1.950, with the understanding that the last figure 0 may not be correct.

Although a decimal point has been inserted after the first digit of each arrow position in Fig. B, it could just as readily be placed before the first digit, after the second digit, or after the third digit, etc. In other words the left index 1 can represent any of the numbers 1, 10, 100, 1000, etc. If we let this index represent 10, the right-hand number 2 will represent 20, and the arrow positions would be read as 11.4, 13.7, 15.35, and 19.50. If we let the left index represent 100, the right-hand number 2 will represent 200, and the arrow positions would read as 114, 137, 153.5, and 195.0.

Set the slider of your rule at random between the principal numbers 1 and 2, and then practice reading its position until you feel confident you are reading it correctly.

We are now ready to examine the center section of the *C* and *D* scales between the index numbers 2, 3, and 4. Note in Fig. C, and on your own rule, that each of the

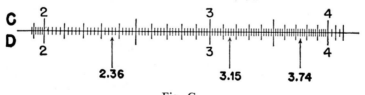

2.36   3.15   3.74

Fig. C.

two intervals are divided into tenths, and each subdivision into fifths. In other words, the smallest intervals, as marked, each represent 2/10 of a subdivision. Suppose we wanted to locate the position 2.36 on these scales. The first significant figure indicates that the position lies between 2 and 3. Set the hairline of your rule on 2. The second significant figure 3 indicates that the position is between the third and fourth subdivision, while the third significant figure 6 shows it is ⁶⁄₁₀ or ³⁄₅ of the distance between these two subdivisions. Hence the left arrow is properly located at 2.36.

Since the index numbers 3, 4, and 5 can also represent the numbers 30, 40, and 50, or 300, 400, and 500, the arrow positions could represent 23.6, 31.5, and 37.4, or 236, 315, and 374, respectively.

Finally we can examine the right-hand section of the *C* and *D* scales between the index numbers 4, 5, 6, 7, 8, 9, and 1. (See Fig. D.) Between each pair of numbers are ten subdivisions and each subdivision is divided into halves or ⁵⁄₁₀. Note carefully the positions of the arrows and be sure you can read any position of your slider hairline when it is located any place on the *C* and *D* scales.

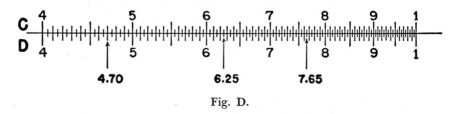

Fig. D.

Multiplication. To multiply two factors, carry out the four following steps: (1) Set the slider hairline on your first number on the *D* scale. (2) Move the slipstick so the left-hand index 1 of the C scale is exactly under the hairline. (3) Move the slider hairline to your second number on the *C* scale. (4) Read your answer on the *D* scale under the hairline.

Suppose for example you want to find the product 3 × 2. While you don't need the slide rule to find the answer, the performance of such a simple operation will clarify the method. (See Fig. E.) (1) Set the slider hairline on 3 of the *D* scale. (2) Move the slipstick and bring the left index 1 of the C scale to the hairline. (3) Move the slider to the second number 2 on the *C* scale. (4) Read the answer as 6 on the *D* scale.

A little study will show the slide rule settings for the products 30 × 20, 3 × 20, 30 × 2300 × 20, etc., would all be the same as the above. The numeral 6 is the correct

Fig. E.

first numeral for all answers, but the number of zeros to be added must be determined by inspection.

Consider the procedure for obtaining the product of 24.0 × 1.5. (1) Set the slider hairline exactly on the fourth subdivision line beyond the 2 of the *D* scale. This position represents 24.0. (2) Move the left-hand index 1 of the *C* scale to the hairline. (3) Move the slider to the fifth subdivision between 1 and 2 on the *C* scale. (4) The answer is under the hairline on the *D* scale and appears exactly at the sixth subdivision beyond 3 or 360. To locate the decimal point, inspect the two original numbers. One-and-a-half times 24 cannot be as small as 3.60 nor as large as 360. Therefore it must be 36.0. Similarly the product 24.0 × 2 is 48.0 as shown by the hairline position at the right in Fig. F.

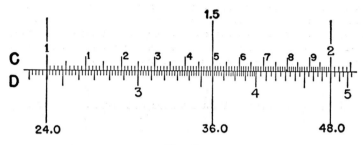

Fig. F.

Find the product 3.8 × 56.5. When the above steps are carried out for this product, the answer will be found to lie beyond the right-hand end of the *D* scale. In such cases one moves the right-hand index 1 of the *C* scale to the first number 3.8 on the *D* scale. (See Fig. G.) Moving the slider to the left, until the hairline is on the second number 56.5 on the *C* scale, the answer is read off the *D* scale as 215.

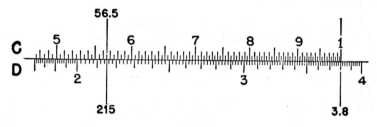

Fig. G.

The Decimal Point. To find the decimal point in any problem, substitute round numbers for those appearing in the problem and determine the position of the decimal point by approximation. For example, in the last problem round off the number 3.8 to 4, and the number 56.5 to 60. The product 4 × 60 by mental arithmetic is 240, so the answer is 215 and not 21.5 or 2150.

Division. Division on the slide rule is just the reverse of multiplication.

Rule. To divide one number by the other, carry out the following steps: (1) Set the slider hairline on the dividend, or numerator, on the D *scale. (2) Move the slipstick until the divisor, or denominator, on the* C *scale lines up with the hairline. (3) The quotient, or answer, is under the* C *index at one end of the slipstick or the other.* In simple terms, line up the numerator on the *D* scale with the denominator on the *C* scale, and the answer is under the *C* scale index.

For example, find the quotient for ⁶⁄₂. (1) Set the slider hairline on 6 of the *D* scale. (See Fig. E.) (2) Bring the 2 of the *C* scale to the hairline. (3) The answer 2 is now under the *C* index on the *D* scale. Note that the fraction ⅔ is just upside down on the rule.

As a second example find the quotient of 215/56.5. (See Fig. G.) Set the hairline on 215 of the *D* scale and then line up 56.5 of the *C* scale. The answer 3.8 is on the *D* scale under the *C* index at the right. Note again that the fraction is lined up but inverted at the hairline position.

To find the decimal point in the last problem, round off the numbers and use mental arithmetic. For the number 215 write 200 and for 3.8 write 4. The quotient for 200/4 is 50. The answer, therefore, is 56.5 and not 5.65 or 565.

Square and Square Roots. To find the square of a number, one multiplies that number by itself. To find the square root of a number requires the carrying out of a complicated arithmetic process. With the slide rule these operations are relatively simple.

To find the square of a number, use the following rules: (1) Set the slider hairline to the number on the D *scale. (2) Read the answer under the hairline on the* A *scale.*

Inspection of Fig. A shows that directly above 2 on the *D* scale we find its square,

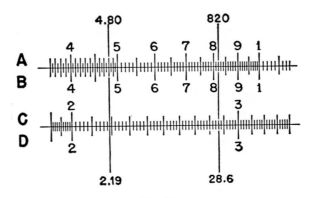

Fig. H.

or 4, on the *A* scale. Directly above 3 on the *D* scale is its square, or 9, on the *A* scale. Directly above 4 on the *D* scale (the position of the slider hairline shown) we find its square, or 16, on the *A* scale.

To find the square root of a number, the reverse process is used: (1) Set the hairline at the number on the A *scale. (2) Read the square root on the* D *scale under the hairline.* Always use the left half of the *A* scale for numbers with an odd number of figures in front of the decimal point, and the right half for those with an even number of figures before the decimal point.

In Fig. H the hairline settings are shown for finding the square roots of 4.80 and 820. The two answers are shown on the *D* scale as 2.19 and 28.6.

Summary

The slide rule is most frequently and conveniently used for multiplication, division, squares, and square roots. A ten-in. rule is capable of an accuracy to three significant figures. The first significant figure of a number is the first numeral that is not zero. The last significant figure is the last numeral that is not zero.

Multiplication and division are most accurately performed on the longer C and D scales, whereas squares and square roots are found by using the A and D scales.

Problems

1. Express each of the following numbers to three significant figures only: (a) 6497, (b) 38.27, (c) 0.43927, (d) 0.06008, (e) 349.8.

2. Express each of the following numbers to three significant figures only: (a) 2359, (b) 64.32, (c) 0.4953, (d) 0.007647, (e) 987.7.

3. Find the product of each of the following: (a) 2.5 × 3, (b) 2.5 × 3.7, (c) 1.6 × 5.0, (d) 6 × 3.5, (e) 4.7 × 5.8.

4. Find the product of each of the following: (a) 2.7 × 3, (b) 3.4 × 2.1, (c) 2.3 × 2.9, (d) 5.6 × 3.4, (e) 4.3 × 8.7.

5. Find the product of each of the following: (a) 3 × 26.4, (b) 28 × 35, (c) 29 × 17, (d) 13.5 × 6. (e) 17.2 × 21.6.

6. Find the product of each of the following: (a) 2.5 × 17, (b) 32 × 1.7, (c) 19 × 14, (d) 26.2 × 1.75, (e) 23.2 × 9.4.

7. Find the quotient of each of the following: (a) 6/5, (b) 25/4, (c) 38/7, (d) 64/3, (e) 72/2.7.

8. Find the quotient of each of the following: (a) 7/2, (b) 32/5, (c) 56/4.2, (d) 26/3.4, (e) 8.5/4.6.

9. Find the quotient of each of the following: (a) 35/6.2, (b) 67/5.9, (c) 325/28, (d) 430/270, (e) 675/780.

Appendix VI

At. No.	Element	Sym.	Isotopes, Mass. No.	At. Wt.
1	hydrogen	H	**1**, (2)	1.0078
2	helium	He	**4**, (3)	4.002
3	lithium	Li	6, **7**	6.940
4	beryllium	Be	**9**	9.02
5	boron	B	10, **11**	10.82
6	carbon	C	**12**, (13)	12.01
7	nitrogen	N	**14**, (15)	14.008
8	oxygen	O	**16**, (18), (17)	16.000
9	fluorine	F	**19**	19.000
10	neon	Ne	**20**, (21), 22	20.183
11	sodium	Na	**23**	22.997
12	magnesium	Mg	**24**, 25, 26	24.32
13	aluminum	Al	**27**	26:97
14	silicon	Si	**28**, 29, 30	28.06
15	phosphorus	P	**31**	31.02
16	sulfur	S	**32**, 33, 34	32.06
17	chlorine	Cl	**35**, 37	35.457
18	argon	A	(36), (38), **40**	39.944
19	potassium	K	**39**, (40), 41	39.096
20	calcium	Ca	**40**, (42), (43), 44	40.08
21	scandium	Sc	**45**	45.10
22	titanium	Ti	46, 47, **48**, 49, 50	47.90
23	vanadium	V	**51**	50.95
24	chromium	Cr	50, **52**, 53, 54	52.01
25	manganese	Mn	**55**	54.93
26	iron	Fe	54, **56**, 57, (58)	55.84
27	cobalt	Co	**59**	58.94
28	nickel	Ni	**58**, 60, 61, 62, **(64)**	58.69
29	copper	Cu	**63**, 65	63.57
30	zinc	Zn	**64**, 66, 67, 68, (70)	65.38
31	gallium	Ga	**69**, 71	69.72
32	germanium	Ge	70, 72, 73, **74**, 76	72.60
33	arsenic	As	**75**	74.91
34	selenium	Se	(74), 76, 77, 78, **80**, 82	78.96
35	bromine	Br	**79**, 81	79.916
36	krypton	Kr	(78), 80, 82, 83, **84**, 86	83.7
37	rubidium	Rb	**85**, *87*	85.48
38	strontium	Sr	(84), 86, 87, **88**	87.63

734

COMPLETE LIST OF THE STABLE ISOTOPES OF THE CHEMICAL ELEMENTS

At. No.	Element	Sym.	Isotopes, Mass. No.	At. Wt.
39	yttrium	Yt	89	88.92
40	zirconium	Zr	90, 91, 92, 94, 96	91.22
41	columbium	Cb	93	92.91
42	molybdenum	Mo	92, 94, 95, 96, 97, **98**, 100, 102	96.0
43	technetium	Tc	*99*	97.8
44	ruthenium	Ru	96, 98, 99, 100, 101, **102**, 104	101.7
45	rhodium	Rh	103	102.91
46	palladium	Pd	(102), 104, 105, **106**, 108, 110	106.7
47	silver	Ag	**107**, 109	107.88
48	cadmium	Cd	106, (108), 110, 111, **112**, 113, 114, 116	112.41
49	indium	In	113, **115**	114.76
50	tin	Sn	112, (114), (115), 116, 117, 118, 119, 120, 122, 124	118.70
51	antimony	Sb	**121**, 123	121.76
52	tellurium	Te	(120), 122, 123, 124, 125, 126, **128**, 130	127.61
53	iodine	I	127	126.92
54	xenon	Xe	(124), (126), 128, **129**, 130, 131, 132, 134, 136	131.3
55	caesium	Cs	133	132.91
56	barium	Ba	(130), (132), 134, 135, 136, 137, **138**	137.36
57	lanthanum	La	139	138.92
58	cerium	Ce	(136), (138), **140**, 142	140.13
59	praseodymium ...	Pr	141	140.92
60	neodymium	Nd	**142**, 143, **144**, 145, 146, (148), (150)	144.27
61	prometeum........	Pm		146.0?
62	samarium	Sa	144, 147, 148, 149, 150, **152**, 154	150.43
63	europium	Eu	**151**, **153**	152.0
64	gadolinium	Gd	155, **156**, 157, **158**, 160	156.9
65	terbium	Tn	159	159.2
66	dysprosium	Dy	161, 162, 163, **164**	162.46
67	holmium	Ho	165	163.5
68	erbium	Er	**166**, 167, 168, 170	167.64
69	thulium	Tm	169	169.4
70	ytterbium	Yb	171, 172, 173, **174**, 176	173.04
71	lutecium	Lu	175	175.0
72	hafnium	Hf	176, 177, 178, 179, **180**	178.6
73	tantalum	Ta	181	180.88
74	tungsten	W	182, 183, **184**, **186**	184.0
75	rhenium	Re	185, **187**	186.31
76	osmium	Os	186, (187), 188, 189, 190, **192**	191.5
77	iridium	Ir	191, **193**	193.1
78	platinum	Pt	(192), 194, **195**, 196, 198	195.23
79	gold	Au	197	197.2
80	mercury	Hg	(196), 198, 199, 200, 201, **202**, 204	200.61

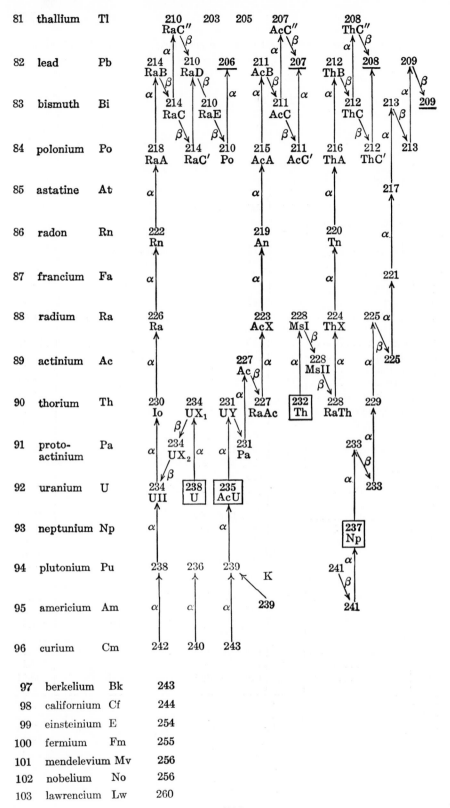

81	thallium	Tl	210 RaC″	203	205	207 AcC″	208 ThC″	
82	lead	Pb	214 RaB	210 RaD	206	211 AcB	207	212 ThB	208	209
83	bismuth	Bi		214 RaC	210 RaE	211 AcC	212 ThC	213	209
84	polonium	Po	218 RaA	214 RaC′	210 Po	215 AcA	211 AcC′	216 ThA	212 ThC′	213
85	astatine	At							217
86	radon	Rn	222 Rn			219 An	220 Tn	
87	francium	Fa							221
88	radium	Ra	226 Ra			223 AcX	228 MsI	224 ThX	225
89	actinium	Ac				227 Ac	228 MsII	225
90	thorium	Th	230 Io	234 UX₁	231 UY	227 RaAc	232 Th	228 RaTh	229
91	proto-actinium	Pa		234 UX₂	231 Pa		233
92	uranium	U	234 UII	238 U	235 AcU		233
93	neptunium	Np					237 Np
94	plutonium	Pu	238	236	239	241
95	americium	Am					241
96	curium	Cm	242	240	243

97	berkelium	Bk	243
98	californium	Cf	244
99	einsteinium	E	254
100	fermium	Fm	255
101	mendelevium	Mv	256
102	nobelium	No	256
103	lawrencium	Lw	260

TABLE OF ATOMIC WEIGHTS FOR ISOTOPES OF THE LIGHT ELEMENTS

s = seconds. m = minutes. hr = hours. d = days. y = years.

Isotope Symbol	Relative Abundance and Half-life		Atomic Weight	Isotope Symbol	Relative Abundance and Half-life		Atomic Weight
$_0n^1$	β^-	10^{-6}s	1.00898	$_9F^{17}$	β^+	70s	17.00749
				$_9F^{18}$	β^+	112m	18.00667
$_1H^1$	99.98		1.00814	$_9F^{19}$		100	19.00446
$_1H^2$	0.02		2.01474	$_9F^{20}$	β^-	12s	20.00635
$_1H^3$	β^-	31y	3.01700				
				$_{10}Ne^{19}$	β^+		19.00792
$_2He^3$			3.01698	$_{10}Ne^{20}$		90	19.99886
$_2He^4$	100		4.00387	$_{10}Ne^{21}$		0.27	21.00059
$_2He^6$	β^-	0.8s	6.02047	$_{10}Ne^{22}$		9.73	21.99827
$_3Li^6$	7.5		6.01702	$_{10}Ne^{23}$	β^-	43s	23.00168
$_3Li^7$	92.5		7.01822	$_{11}Na^{21}$	β^+	23s	. . . .
$_3Li^8$	β^-	0.88s	8.02502	$_{11}Na^{22}$	β^+, γ	3y	22.00132
$_4Be^7$	K, γ	43d	7.01915	$_{11}Na^{23}$		100	22.99714
$_4Be^8$	2α		8.00785	$_{11}Na^{24}$	β^-, γ	14.8h	23.99865
$_4Be^9$	100		9.01504	$_{11}Na^{25}$	β^-, γ	62s	24.99779
$_4Be^{10}$	β^-, γ	10^3y	10.01671	$_{12}Mg^{23}$	β^+	11.6s	23.00111
$_5B^{10}$	18.4		10.01611	$_{12}Mg^{24}$	77.4		23.99270
$_5B^{11}$	81.6		11.01279	$_{12}Mg^{25}$	11.5		24.99381
$_5B^{12}$	β^-	0.02s	12.01816	$_{12}Mg^{26}$	11.1		25.99087
				$_{12}Mg^{27}$	β^-, γ	10.2m	26.99295
$_6C^{10}$	β^+	8.8s	10.02060	$_{13}Al^{26}$	β^+	7s	25.99619
$_6C^{11}$	β^+	20m	11.01492	$_{13}Al^{27}$		100	26.99014
$_6C^{12}$	98.9		12.00380	$_{13}Al^{28}$	B$^-, \gamma$	2.4m	27.99083
$_6C^{13}$	1.1		13.00747	$_{13}Al^{29}$	β^-	6.7m	28.98975
$_6C^{14}$	β^-	10^3y	14.00768				
				$_{14}Si^{27}$	β^+	4.9s	26.99525
$_7N^{13}$	β^+, γ	9.9m	13.00986	$_{14}Si^{28}$	89.6		27.98584
$_7N^{14}$	99.62		14.00751	$_{14}Si^{29}$	6.2		28.98572
$_7N^{15}$	0.38		15.00486	$_{14}Si^{30}$	4.2		29.98331
$_7N^{16}$	β^-	8s	16.01074	$_{14}Si^{31}$	β^-	170m	30.98521
$_8O^{15}$	β^+	126s	15.00777	$_{15}P^{29}$	β^+	4.6s	28.98962
$_8O^{16}$	99.76		16.00000	$_{15}P^{30}$	β^+	2.5m	29.98817
$_8O^{17}$	0.04		17.00453	$_{15}P^{31}$		100	30.98362
$_8O^{18}$	0.20		18.00487	$_{15}P^{32}$	β^-	14.3d	31.98409
$_8O^{19}$	β^-	31s	19.00948				

Isotope Symbol	Relative Abundance and Half-life		Atomic Weight	Isotope Symbol	Relative Abundance and Half-life	Atomic Weight
$_{16}S^{31}$	β^+	3.2s	30.98886	$_{82}Pb^{208}$		208.04140
$_{16}S^{32}$	95.1		31.98226			
$_{16}S^{33}$	0.74		32.98196	$_{83}Bi^{209}$		209.04550
$_{16}S^{34}$	4.2		33.97877			
$_{16}S^{35}$	β^-	87d	34.98035	$_{84}Po^{218}$		218.07676
$_{16}S^{36}$	0.016		....			
				$_{86}Rn^{222}$		222.08663
$_{17}Cl^{33}$	β^+	2.4s	....			
$_{17}Cl^{34}$	β^+	33m	33.98100	$_{88}Ra^{226}$		226.09574
$_{17}Cl^{35}$	75.4		34.98018			
$_{17}Cl^{36}$	β^+, K, β^-		35.97996	$_{90}Th^{232}$		232.11034
$_{17}Cl^{37}$	24.6		36.97762	$_{92}U^{234}$		234.11379
$_{17}Cl^{38}$	β^-, γ	33m	37.98004	$_{92}U^{235}$		235.11704
				$_{92}U^{238}$		238.12869
$_{18}A^{35}$	β^+	1.9s	....			
$_{18}A^{36}$	0.31		35.97893	$_{93}Np^{237}$		237.12158
$_{18}A^{37}$			36.97850			
$_{18}A^{38}$	0.06		37.97488	$_{94}Pu^{239}$		239.12653
$_{18}A^{39}$	β^-	4m	....			
$_{18}A^{40}$	91.63		39.97510	$_{98}Cf^{244}$		244.14211
$_{18}A^{41}$	β^-, γ	110m	40.97776			

Appendix VIII

VALUES OF THE GENERAL PHYSICAL CONSTANTS (AFTER DU MOND)

Planck's constant of action.................... $h = 6.6238 \times 10^{-34}$ joule sec

Electronic charge............................. $e = 1.6019 \times 10^{-19}$ coulombs

Electronic charge............................. $e = 4.8022 \times 10^{-10}$ e.s.u.

Specific electronic charge..................... $e/m = 1.7589 \times 10^{11}$ coulombs/Kg

Specific proton charge........................ $e/M_p = 9.5795 \times 10^7$ coulombs/Kg

Electronic mass............................... $m = 9.1072 \times 10^{-31}$ Kg

Mass of atom of unit atomic weight............. $M = 1.6600 \times 10^{-27}$ Kg

Mass of proton................................ $M_p = 1.6722 \times 10^{-27}$ Kg

Ratio mass proton to mass electron............. $M_p/m = 1836.1$

Wien's displacement-law constant............... $C = 0.28976$ cm deg

Velocity of light............................. $c = 299,790$ Km/sec

Square of velocity of light.................... $c^2 = 8.9874 \times 10^{10}$ Km²/sec²

Unit atomic angular momentum................. $\hbar = 1.0544 \times 10^{-34}$ joule sec

PERIODIC TABLE OF THE ELEMENTS																
$\frac{n}{+1}$	Sub-Shells	1	2	3	4	5	6	7	8	9	10	11	12	13	14
1	1s	1.0080 H 1	4.003 He 2												
2	2s	6.940 Li 3	9.013 Be 4												
	2p	10.82 B 5	12.011 C 6	14.008 N 7	16 O 8	19.00 F 9	20.183 Ne 10								
3	3s	22.991 Na 11	24.32 Mg 12												
	3p	26.98 Al 13	28.09 Si 14	30.975 P 15	32.066 S 16	35.457 Cl 17	39.944 A 18								
4	4s	39.100 K 19	40.08 Ca 20												
	3d	44.96 Sc 21	47.90 Ti 22	50.95 V 23	52.01 Cr 24	54.94 Mn 25	55.85 Fe 26	58.94 Co 27	58.69 Ni 28	63.54 Cu 29	65.38 Zn 30				
5	4p	69.72 Ga 31	72.60 Ge 32	74.91 As 33	78.96 Se 34	79.916 Br 35	83.80 Kr 36								
	5s	85.48 Rb 37	87.63 Sr 38												
	4d	88.92 Y 39	91.22 Zr 40	92.91 Nb 41	95.95 Mo 42	(99) Tc 43	101.1 Ru 44	102.91 Rh 45	106.7 Pd 46	107.880 Ag 47	112.41 Cd 48				
6	5p	114.76 In 49	118.70 Sn 50	121.76 Sb 51	127.61 Te 52	126.91 I 53	131.3 Xe 54								
	6s	132.91 Cs 55	137.36 Ba 56												
	4f	138.92 La 57	140.13 Ce 58	140.92 Pr 59	144.27 Nd 60	(145) Pm 61	150.43 Sm 62	152.0 Eu 63	156.9 Gd 64	158.93 Tb 65	162.46 Dy 66	164.94 Ho 67	167.2 Er 68	168.94 Tm 69	173.04 Yb 70
7	5d	174.99 Lu 71	178.6 Hf 72	180.95 Ta 73	183.92 W 74	186.31 Re 75	190.2 Os 76	192.2 Ir 77	195.23 Pt 78	197.0 Au 79	200.61 Hg 80				
	6p	204.39 Tl 81	207.21 Pb 82	209.00 Bi 83	210 Po 84	(210) At 85	222 Rn 86								
	7s	(223) Fr 87	226.05 Ra 88												
8	5f	227 Ac 89	232.05 Th 90	231 Pa 91	238.07 U 92	(237) Np 93	(242) Pu 94	(243) Am 95	(245) Cm 96	(245) Bk 97	(248) Cf 98	(253) E 99	(254) Fm 100	(256) Mv 101	102
	6d	103	104	105	106	107	108	109	110	111	112				

739

THE PERIODIC TABLE OF CHEMICAL ELEMENTS

I	II	III	IV	V	VI	VII	VIII
1 H 1.0078							2 He 4.002
3 Li 6.940	4 Be 9.02	5 B 10.82	6 C 12.01	7 N 14.008	8 O 16.000	9 F 19.000	10 Ne 20.183
11 Na 22.997	12 Mg 24.32	13 Al 26.97	14 Si 28.06	15 P 31.02	16 S 32.06	17 Cl 35.57	18 A 39.944
19 K 39.096	20 Ca 40.08	21 Sc 45.10	22 Ti 47.90	23 V 50.95	24 Cr 52.01	25 Mn 54.93	26 Fe 55.84 — 27 Co 58.94 — 28 Ni 58.69
29 Cu 63.57	30 Zn 65.38	31 Ga 69.72	32 Ge 72.60	33 As 74.91	34 Se 78.96	35 Br 79.916	36 K 83.7
37 Rb 85.48	38 Sr 87.63	39 Yt 88.92	40 Zr 91.22	41 Cb 92.91	42 Mo 96.0	43 Tc	44 Ru 101.7 — 45 Rh 102.91 — 46 Pd 106.7
47 Ag 107.9	48 Cd 112.41	49 In 114.8	50 Sn 118.7	51 Sb 121.8	52 Te 127.6	53 I 126.9	54 Xe 131.3
55 Cs 132.9	56 Ba 137.4	57 La 138.9	72 Hf 178.6	73 Ta 180.88	74 W 184.0	75 Re 186.3	76 Os 191.5 — 77 Ir 193.1 — 78 Pt 195.2
79 Au 179.2	80 Hg 200.6	81 Tl 204.39	82 Pb 207.18	83 Bi 209.00	84 Po 210.	85 At	86 Rn 222.
87 Fa	88 Ra 225.95	89 Ac 227	90 Th 232.15	91 Pa 234	92 U 238.17	93 Np	94 Pu — 95 Am — 96 Cm

58 Ce 140.2	59 Pr 140.9	60 Nd 144.3	61 Il 146.0	62 Sa 150.4	63 Eu 152.0	64 Gd 156.9	65 Tn 159.2	66 Ds 162.5	67 Ho 163.5	68 Er 167.6	69 Tm 169.4	70 Yb 173.0	71 Lu 175.0
90 Th	91 Pa	92 U	93 Np	94 Pu	95 Am	96 Cm	97 Bk	98 Cf	99 E	100 Fm	101 Mv	102 No	103 Lw

Index